Volume 1
Southern Connecticut State University

CHEMISTRY
The Molecular Nature of Matter

Sixth Edition

Jespersen • Brady • Hyslop

WILEY *Custom*
LEARNING SOLUTIONS

To order books or for customer service, please call 1(800)-CALL-WILEY (225-5945).

Printed in the United States of America.

ISBN 978-1-118-11809-2
Printed and bound by IPAK.

10 9 8 7 6 5 4 3 2 1

Brief Contents

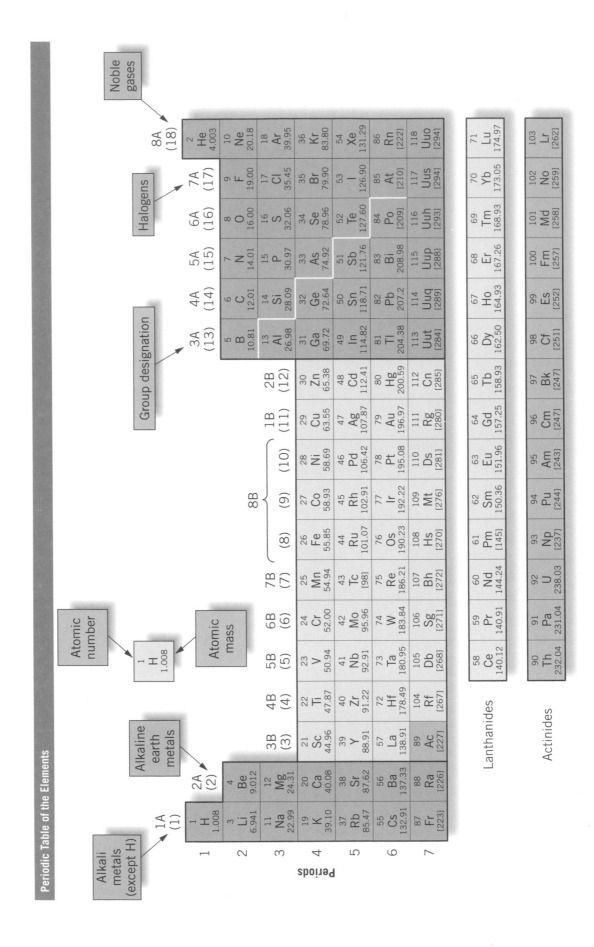

Periodic Table of the Elements

ATOMIC MASSES OF THE ELEMENTS

This table is based on the 2007 table at *Pure Appl. Chem.*, **81**, 2131–2156 (2009) with changes to the values for lutetium, molybdenum, nickel, ytterbium and zinc from the 2005 table. Mass number of the longest-lived isotope of hassium from *Phys. Rev. Lett.*, **97** 242501 (2006). For the name of element 112 see *Pure Appl. Chem.* 2010, **82**, 753–755. http://www.chem.qmul.ac.uk/iupac/AtWt/. The number in parentheses following the atomic mass is the estimated uncertainty in the last digit.

At No	Symbol	Name	Atomic Mass	Notes	At No	Symbol	Name	Atomic Mass	Notes
89	Ac	Actinium	[227]	5	42	Mo	Molybdenum	95.96(2)	1
13	Al	Aluminium	26.9815386(8)		60	Nd	Neodymium	144.242(3)	1
95	Am	Americium	[243]	5	10	Ne	Neon	20.1797(6)	1, 3
51	Sb	Antimony	121.760(1)	1	93	Np	Neptunium	[237]	5
18	Ar	Argon	39.948(1)	1, 2	28	Ni	Nickel	58.6934(4)	
33	As	Arsenic	74.92160(2)		41	Nb	Niobium	92.90638(2)	
85	At	Astatine	[210]	5	7	N	Nitrogen	14.0067(2)	1, 2
56	Ba	Barium	137.327(7)		102	No	Nobelium	[259]	5
97	Bk	Berkelium	[247]	5	76	Os	Osmium	190.23(3)	1
4	Be	Beryllium	9.012182(3)		8	O	Oxygen	15.9994(3)	1, 2
83	Bi	Bismuth	208.98040(1)		46	Pd	Palladium	106.42(1)	1
107	Bh	Bohrium	[272]	5	15	P	Phosphorus	30.973762(2)	
5	B	Boron	10.811(7)	1, 2, 3	78	Pt	Platinum	195.084(9)	
35	Br	Bromine	79.904(1)		94	Pu	Plutonium	[244]	5
48	Cd	Cadmium	112.411(8)	1	84	Po	Polonium	[209]	5
55	Cs	Cesium	132.9054519(2)		19	K	Potassium	39.0983(1)	1
20	Ca	Calcium	40.078(4)	1	59	Pr	Praseodymium	140.90765(2)	
98	Cf	Californium	[251]	5	61	Pm	Promethium	[145]	5
6	C	Carbon	12.0107(8)	1, 2	91	Pa	Protactinium	231.03588(2)	5
58	Ce	Cerium	140.116(1)	1	88	Ra	Radium	[226]	5
17	Cl	Chlorine	35.453(2)	3	86	Rn	Radon	[222]	5
24	Cr	Chromium	51.9961(6)		75	Re	Rhenium	186.207(1)	
27	Co	Cobalt	58.933195(5)		45	Rh	Rhodium	102.90550(2)	
112	Cn	Copernicium	[285]	5	111	Rg	Roentgenium	[280]	5
29	Cu	Copper	63.546(3)	2	37	Rb	Rubidium	85.4678(3)	1
96	Cm	Curium	[247]	5	44	Ru	Ruthenium	101.07(2)	1
110	Ds	Darmstadtium	[281]	5	104	Rf	Rutherfordium	[265]	5
105	Db	Dubnium	[268]	5	62	Sm	Samarium	150.36(2)	1
66	Dy	Dysprosium	162.500(1)	1	21	Sc	Scandium	44.955912(6)	
99	Es	Einsteinium	[252]	5	106	Sg	Seaborgium	[271]	5
68	Er	Erbium	167.259(3)	1	34	Se	Selenium	78.96(3)	
63	Eu	Europium	151.964(1)	1	14	Si	Silicon	28.0855(3)	2
100	Fm	Fermium	[257]	5	47	Ag	Silver	107.8682(2)	1
9	F	Fluorine	18.9984032(5)		11	Na	Sodium	22.98976928(2)	
87	Fr	Francium	[223]	5	38	Sr	Strontium	87.62(1)	1, 2
64	Gd	Gadolinium	157.25(3)	1	16	S	Sulfur	32.065(5)	1, 2
31	Ga	Gallium	69.723(1)		73	Ta	Tantalum	180.94788(2)	
32	Ge	Germanium	72.64(1)		43	Tc	Technetium	[98]	5
79	Au	Gold	196.966569(4)		52	Te	Tellurium	127.60(3)	1
72	Hf	Hafnium	178.49(2)		65	Tb	Terbium	158.92535(2)	
108	Hs	Hassium	[270]	5	81	Tl	Thallium	204.3833(2)	
2	He	Helium	4.002602(2)	1, 2	90	Th	Thorium	232.03806(2)	1, 5
67	Ho	Holmium	164.93032(2)		69	Tm	Thulium	168.93421(2)	
1	H	Hydrogen	1.00794(7)	1, 2, 3	50	Sn	Tin	118.710(7)	1
49	In	Indium	114.818(3)		22	Ti	Titanium	47.867(1)	
53	I	Iodine	126.90447(3)		74	W	Tungsten	183.84(1)	
77	Ir	Iridium	192.217(3)		116	Uuh	Ununhexium	[293]	5
26	Fe	Iron	55.845(2)		118	Uuo	Ununoctium	[294]	5
36	Kr	Krypton	83.798(2)	1, 3	117	Uus	Ununseptium	[294]	5
57	La	Lanthanum	138.90547(7)	1	115	Uup	Ununpentium	[288]	5
103	Lr	Lawrencium	[262]	5	114	Uuq	Ununquadium	[289]	5
82	Pb	Lead	207.2(1)	1, 2	113	Uut	Ununtrium	[284]	5
3	Li	Lithium	6.941(2)	1, 2, 3, 4	92	U	Uranium	238.02891(3)	1, 3, 5
71	Lu	Lutetium	174.9668(1)	1	23	V	Vanadium	50.9415(1)	
12	Mg	Magnesium	24.3050(6)		54	Xe	Xenon	131.293(6)	1, 3
25	Mn	Manganese	54.938045(5)		70	Yb	Ytterbium	173.054(5)	1
109	Mt	Meitnerium	[276]	5	39	Y	Yttrium	88.90585(2)	
101	Md	Mendelevium	[258]	5	30	Zn	Zinc	65.38(2)	
80	Hg	Mercury	200.59(2)		40	Zr	Zirconium	91.224(2)	1

Geological specimens are known in which the element has an isotopic composition outside the limits for normal material. The difference between the atomic mass of the element in such specimens and that given in the Table may exceed the stated uncertainty.

Range in isotopic composition of normal terrestrial material prevents a more precise value being given; the tabulated value should be applicable to any normal material.

Modified isotopic compositions may be found in commercially available material because it has been subject to an undisclosed or inadvertent isotopic fractionation. Substantial deviations in atomic mass of the element from that given in the Table can occur.

4. Commercially available Li materials have atomic masses that range between 6.939 and 6.996; if a more accurate value is required, it must be determined for the specific material [range quoted for 1995 tables 6.94 and 6.99].

5. Element has no stable nuclides. The value enclosed in brackets, e.g. [209], indicates the mass number of the longest-lived isotope of the element. However three such elements (Th, Pa, and U) do have a characteristic terrestrial isotopic composition, and for these an atomic mass is tabulated.

The names and symbols for elements 113–118 are under review. The temporary system recommended by J Chatt, *Pure Appl. Chem.*, **51**, 381–384 (1979) is used above.

Chemistry

The Molecular Nature of Matter

Sixth Edition

Chemistry

The Molecular Nature of Matter

Neil D. Jespersen
St. John's University, New York

James E. Brady
St. John's University, New York

In collaboration with **Alison Hyslop**
St. John's University, New York

WILEY

John Wiley and Sons, Inc.

VICE PRESIDENT, EXECUTIVE PUBLISHER	Kaye Pace
ASSOCIATE PUBLISHER	Petra Recter
ACQUISITION EDITOR	Nicholas Ferrari
PROJECT EDITOR	Jennifer Yee
MARKETING MANAGER	Kristine Ruff
SENIOR DESIGNER	Jim O'Shea
INTERIOR DESIGNER	Brian Salisbury
SENIOR ILLUSTRATION EDITOR	Anna Melhorn
SENIOR PHOTO EDITOR	Jennifer MacMillan
PHOTO RESEARCHER	Susan Kaprov
EXECUTIVE MEDIA EDITOR	Thomas Kulesa
MEDIA EDITOR	Marc Wezdecki
MEDIA PRODUCTION EDITOR	Evelyn Levich
CONTENT MANAGER	Lucille Buonocore
COVER PHOTO	Ken Lucas/Visuals Unlimited

This book was set in 10.5 Adobe Garamond by Prepare and printed and bound by Courier Kendallville. The cover was printed by Courier Kendallville.

This book is printed on acid free paper. ∞

Founded in 1807, John Wiley & Sons, Inc. has been a valued source of knowledge and understanding for more than 200 years, helping people around the world meet their needs and fulfill their aspirations. Our company is built on a foundation of principles that include responsibility to the communities we serve and where we live and work. In 2008, we launched a Corporate Citizenship Initiative, a global effort to address the environmental, social, economic, and ethical challenges we face in our business. Among the issues we are addressing are carbon impact, paper specifications and procurement, ethical conduct within our business and among our vendors, and community and charitable support. For more information, please visit our website: www.wiley.com/go/citizenship.

Evaluation copies are provided to qualified academics and professionals for review purposes only, for use in their courses during the next academic year. These copies are licensed and may not be sold or transferred to a third party. Upon completion of the review period, please return the evaluation copy to Wiley. Return instructions and a free of charge return shipping label are available at www.wiley.com/go/returnlabel. Outside of the United States, please contact your local representative.

Library of Congress Cataloging-in-Publication Data
Jespersen, Neil D.
   Chemistry: the molecular nature of matter/Neil D. Jespersen, James E. Brady; In collaboration with
   Alison Hyslop. – 6th ed.
      p. cm.
   Previous edition: Chemistry/James E. Brady, Fred Senese; in collaboration with Neil D. Jespersen.
   Includes index.

   ISBN 978-0-470-57771-4 (cloth)
   Binder-Ready Version ISBN 978-0-470-91770-1

   1. Chemistry. I. Jespersen, Neil D. II. Brady, James E. III. Hyslop, Alison
   IV. Title.
QD33.2.B73 2012
540–dc22   2010043302

Printed in the United States of America
10 9 8 7 6 5 4

About the Authors

Neil D. Jespersen is a Professor of Chemistry at St. John's University in New York. He earned a B.S. with Special Attainments in Chemistry at Washington and Lee University (VA) and his Ph.D. in Analytical Chemistry with Joseph Jordan at The Pennsylvania State University. He has received awards for excellence in teaching and research from St. John's University and the E. Emmit Reid Award in college teaching from the American Chemical Society's Middle Atlantic Region. He chaired the Department of Chemistry for 6 years and has mentored the St. John's student ACS club for over 30 years while continuing to enjoy teaching Quantitative and Instrumental Analysis courses, along with General Chemistry. He has been an active contributor to the Eastern Analytical Symposium, chairing it in 1991. Neil has authored the Barrons AP Chemistry Study Guide; has edited 2 books on Instrumental Analysis and Thermal Analysis; and has 4 chapters in research monographs, 50 refereed publications, and 150 abstracts and presentations.

He is active at the local, regional and national levels of the American Chemical Society, and was recently elected to the ACS Board of Directors. When there is free time you can find him playing tennis, baseball with four grandchildren, or traveling with his wife Marilyn.

James E. Brady received his BA degree from Hofstra College in 1959 and his Ph.D. from Penn State University under the direction of C. David Schmulbach in 1963. He is Professor Emeritus at St. John's University, New York, where he taught graduate and undergraduate courses for 35 years. His first textbook, *General Chemistry: Principles and Structure*, coauthored with Gerard Humiston, was published in 1975. An innovative feature of the text was 3D illustrations of molecules and crystal structures that could be studied with a stereo viewer that came tucked into a pocket inside the rear cover of the book. The popularity of his approach to teaching general chemistry is evident in the way his books have shaped the evolution of textbooks over the last 35 years. His useful *chemical tools* approach toward teaching problem solving was introduced by him at the 12th Biennial Conference on Chemical Education at UC Davis in 1992 and continues to evolve. He has been the principal coauthor of various versions of this text, along with John Holum, Joel Russell, Fred Senese, and Neil Jespersen. He is particularly pleased to be a member of the current author team.

In 1999, Jim retired from St. John's University to devote more time to writing, and since then he has coauthored three editions of this text. He and his wife, June, enjoy their current home in Jacksonville, Florida. Jim is an avid photographer and many of his photos of surfers have been published in the local newspaper.

Alison Hyslop received her BA degree from Macalester College in 1986 and her Ph.D. from the University of Pennsylvania under the direction of Michael J. Therien in 1998. She is an Associate Professor at St. John's University, New York, where she has been teaching graduate and undergraduate courses since 2000. She was a visiting Assistant Professor at Trinity College (CT) from 1998 to 1999. She was a visiting scholar at Columbia University (NY) in 2005 and in 2007 and at Brooklyn College in 2009, where she worked on research projects in the laboratory of Brian Gibney. Her research focuses on the synthesis and study of porphyrin-based light harvesting compounds.

When not in the laboratory, she likes to hike in upstate New York, and practice tae kwon do.

Brief Contents

Table of Contents

5 | Molecular View of Reactions in Aqueous Solutions   155

6 | Oxidation–Reduction Reactions   213

7 | Energy and Chemical Change   253

8 | The Quantum Mechanical Atom   305

9 | The Basics of Chemical Bonding   357

13 | Mixtures at the Molecular Level: Properties of Solutions   585

14 | Chemical Kinetics   636

15 | Chemical Equilibrium 695

16 | Acids and Bases, A Molecular Look 740

Bringing It Together: Chapters 14–16 771

17 | Acid–Base Equilibria in Aqueous Solutions 773

21 | Nuclear Reactions and Their Role in Chemistry 976

22 | Metal Complexes 1016

23 | Organic Compounds, Polymers, and Biochemicals 1047

Appendices | A-1

Special Topics

Preface

This textbook represents a significant revision of the fifth edition of *Chemistry: Matter and Its Changes* by James E. Brady, Frederick Senese, and Neil D. Jespersen. A new title was chosen to more closely reflect the increased emphasis that we have placed on the intimate relationship that exists between structure at the submicroscopic molecular level and the observable macroscopic properties of matter.

In this edition, it is our pleasure to have **Neil Jespersen** take on the role of lead author. Neil is a respected educator and an award-winning teacher who has more than proven himself in his role as a contributing author on the previous edition. We are fortunate to have him take the helm, and we are confident in his ability to carry the text forward into future editions. It is also our pleasure to welcome **Alison Hyslop** to the author team. Alison is an inorganic chemist with more than 10 years of experience teaching graduate and undergraduate inorganic chemistry as well as general chemistry. She brings to the team a commitment to excellence in teaching and an understanding of issues that stand in the way of student learning. We are excited about her contributions to this new edition.

Philosophy and Goals

The philosophy of the text is based on our conviction that a general chemistry course serves a variety of goals in the education of a student. First, of course, it must provide a sound foundation in the basic facts and concepts of chemistry upon which theoretical models can be constructed. The general chemistry course should also give the student an appreciation of the central role that chemistry plays among the sciences, as well as the importance of chemistry in society and day-to-day living. In addition, it should enable the student to develop skills in analytical thinking and problem solving. With these thoughts in mind, our aim in structuring the text was to provide a logical progression of topics arranged to provide the maximum flexibility for the teacher in organizing his or her course.

In revising this text, we were **guided by three principal goals**. The **first** was to strengthen the connection between observations on the macroscopic scale and the behavior of atoms, molecules, and ions at the atomic level. The **second** was to further enhance our already robust approach to teaching problem-solving skills. The **third** goal was to provide a seamless, total solution to the General Chemistry course by fully integrating the textbook content with the online assessment and resources delivered within *WileyPLUS.*

Emphasizing the Molecular View of Matter

The value of the molecular approach in teaching chemistry is well accepted and has always been a cornerstone in the approach taken by Professor Brady and his co-authors in presenting chemistry to students. From his first text, in which novel three-dimensional computer-drawn representations of molecules and crystal structures were presented and observed using stereoscopic viewers, up through the 5th edition of this text, the atomic/molecular view has dominated the pedagogy. This new edition builds on that tradition by employing the "molecular basis of chemistry" as a powerful central theme of the text. Through this approach, the student will gain a sound appreciation of the nature of matter and how structure determines properties. Some actions we have taken to accomplish this are as follows:

■ **Chapter One: Chemistry and the Atomic/Molecular View of Matter** The new edition begins with a new chapter (chapter one) that sets the tone for the entire book. It lays the groundwork for the atomic and molecular view of matter and outlines how these concepts are used throughout the text. Included is a discussion of what chemistry is and the kinds of activities that chemists participate in. We provide a brief introduction to atomic structure and introduce students to the way we visualize molecules and chemical reactions.

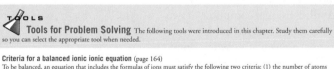

Figure 5.1 | **Formation of a solution of iodine molecules in alcohol.** *(a)* A crystal of iodine, I₂, on its way to the bottom of the beaker is already beginning to dissolve, the purplish iodine crystal forming a reddish brown solution. In the hugely enlarged view beneath the photo, we see the iodine molecules still bound in a crystal. For simplicity, the solute and solvent particles are shown as spheres. *(b)* Stirring the mixture helps the iodine molecules to disperse in the solvent, as illustrated in the molecular view below the photo. The solution is commonly called "tincture of iodine." *(Richard Megna/Fundamental Photographs)*

● Solvent molecule   ○ Solute molecule

Crystal of solute placed in the solvent.

A solution. Solute molecules are dispersed throughout the solvent.

■ **Macro-to-Micro Illustrations** To help students make the connection between the macroscopic world we see and events that take place at the molecular level, we have a substantial number of illustrations that combine both views. A photograph, for example, will show a chemical reaction as well as an artist's rendition of the chemical interpretation of what is taking place between the atoms, molecules, or ions involved. We have also increased the number of illustrations that visualize reactions at the molecular level. The goal is to show how models of nature enable chemists to better understand their observations and to get students to visualize events at the molecular level.

■ **Molecular Interpretations** Significant use is made of molecular interpretations, and substantial rewriting of the chapter material has taken place. Where required, new figures have been drawn to provide visual meaning to accompanying discussions.

■ **New Visual Exercises** In the end-of-chapter Questions and Problems, we include exercises that have a visual component requiring students to apply molecular concepts developed in the chapter discussions.

Developing Problem-solving Skills

We strongly believe that problem solving reinforces the learning of concepts and that assisting students in improving their skills in this area is one of the critical aspects of teaching chemistry. We also believe that it is possible to accommodate students who come into the course with a wide range of problem-solving skills. This is reflected in the attention paid to problem solving in the 6th Edition. In this new edition we have expanded and further refined the tools that students have available to develop their ability to analyze and solve problems.

■ We continue to use a **"chemical tools"** model and approach to aid in teaching problem analysis. This approach encourages students to think of basic skills, such as converting between grams and moles, as tools that can be combined in various ways to solve more complex problems. Students and instructors have responded positively to this concept in earlier editions and we continue to employ this strategy in problem analysis. Tools are identified by an icon in the margin when they are introduced in a chapter and the tools are summarized at the end of each chapter.

TOOLS

TOOLS
Tools for Problem Solving The following tools were introduced in this chapter. Study them carefully so you can select the appropriate tool when needed.

Criteria for a balanced ionic ionic equation (page 164)
To be balanced, an equation that includes the formulas of ions must satisfy the following two criteria: (1) the number of atoms of each kind must be the same on both sides of the equation, and (2) the net electrical charge shown on each side of the equation must be the same.

Ionization of an acid in water (page 165)
Equation 5.2 describes how an acid reacts with water to form hydronium ion plus an anion.
$$HA + H_2O \longrightarrow H_3O^+ + A^-$$
Use this tool to write equations for the ionizations of acids and to determine the formulas of the anions formed when the acid molecules lose H⁺. The equation also applies to acid anions such as HSO₄⁻, which gives SO₄²⁻ when it loses an H⁺. Often H₂O is omitted from the equation and the hydronium ion is abbreviated as H⁺.

Ionization of a molecular base in water (page 165)
Equation 5.3 describes how molecules of a molecular base acquire H⁺ from H₂O to form a cation plus a hydroxide ion.
$$B + H_2O \longrightarrow BH^+ + OH^-$$
Use this tool to write equations for the ionizations of bases and to determine the formula of the cation formed when a base molecule gains an H⁺. *Molecular bases are weak and are not completely ionized.*

List of strong acids (page 170)
Formulas of the most common strong acids are given here. If you learn this list and encounter an acid that's *not* on the list, you can assume it is a weak acid. The most common strong acids are HCl, HNO₃, and H₂SO₄. *Remember that strong acids are completely ionized in water.*

■ A significant strength of the 5th edition was the three-step process of ***Analysis, Solution,*** and asking ***Is the Answer Reasonable?,*** which was applied to all worked examples. We have now expanded this to include a fourth step called ***Assembling the Tools,*** which appears just following the *Analysis* step. Now, after analyzing the problem and defining the approach to obtain an answer, we describe specifically the tools that will be used in the *Solution* step that comes next. This reinforces the notion that tools can be combined in various ways to solve more complex problems

---

Example 5.3
Writing Equations for Ionization Reactions of Acids

Phosphoric acid, H_3PO_4, is a triprotic acid found in some soft drinks such as Coca-Cola (shown in the photo at the start of this chapter) where it adds a touch of tartness to the beverage. Write equations for its stepwise ionization in water.

■**Analysis:** We are told that H_3PO_4 is a triprotic acid, which is also indicated by the three hydrogens at the beginning of the formula. Because there are three hydrogens to come off the molecule, we expect there to be three steps in the ionization. Each step removes one H^+, and we can use that knowledge to deduce the formulas of the products. Let's line them up so we can see the progression.

$$H_3PO_4 \xrightarrow{-H^+} H_2PO_4^- \xrightarrow{-H^+} HPO_4^{2-} \xrightarrow{-H^+} PO_4^{3-}$$

Notice that the loss of H^+ decreases the number of hydrogens by one and increases the negative charge by one unit. Also, the product of one step serves as the reactant in the next step.

■**Assembling the Tools:** We'll use Equation 5.2 for the ionization of an acid as a tool in writing the chemical equation for each step.

■**Solution:** The first step is the reaction of H_3PO_4 with water to give H_3O^+ and $H_2PO_4^-$.

$$H_3PO_4(aq) + H_2O \longrightarrow H_3O^+(aq) + H_2PO_4^-(aq)$$

The second and third steps are similar to the first.

$$H_2PO_4^-(aq) + H_2O \longrightarrow H_3O^+(aq) + HPO_4^{2-}(aq)$$
$$HPO_4^{2-}(aq) + H_2O \longrightarrow H_3O^+(aq) + PO_4^{3-}(aq)$$

■**Is the Answer Reasonable?** Check to see whether the equations are balanced in terms of atoms and charge. If any mistakes were made, something would be out of balance and we would discover the error. In this case, all of the equations are balanced, so we can feel confident we've written them correctly.

■ We continue to provide **Practice Exercises** following the worked examples that give the student an opportunity to apply the principles used to solve the preceding example. These have been thoroughly reviewed and in some cases expanded. The answers to all of the Practice Exercises are available to the student in Appendix B at the back of the book.

Practice Exercises

5.3 | When solutions of $(NH_4)_2SO_4$ and $Ba(NO_3)_2$ are mixed, a precipitate of $BaSO_4$ forms, leaving soluble NH_4NO_3 in the solution. Write the molecular, ionic, and net ionic equations for the reaction. (*Hint:* Remember that polyatomic ions do not break apart when ionic compounds dissolve in water.)

5.4 | Write molecular, ionic, and net ionic equations for the reaction of aqueous solutions of cadmium chloride and sodium sulfide to give a precipitate of cadmium sulfide and a solution of sodium chloride.

■ The **end-of-chapter Questions and Problems** have undergone a reworking to ensure that they provide a range of difficulty, from routine drill-type problems to significantly more difficult ones. We have added a significant number of "visual" problems that include graphs or molecular structures that need to be explained or manipulated. Many problems require students to draw on knowledge acquired in earlier chapters. For example, in many of the problems in Chapter 4 and beyond, the chemical name of a compound in question is given rather than the formula, so students must apply (and review if necessary) the rules of nomenclature presented in Chapter 3.

On the basis of what you have learned so far in this course, sketch the molecular structures of CH_3NH_2 and $CH_3NH_3^+$ (the methylammonium ion).

5.23 A student was shown the structure of a molecule of propanoic acid (an organic acid similar to acetic acid) and was asked to draw the structure of the ion formed when the acid underwent ionization in water. Below is the structure the student drew. What is wrong with the structure, and what would you do to correct it?

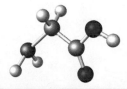

5.24 Would the molecule shown below be acidic or basic in water? What would you do to the structure to show what happens when the substance reacts with water? Write an equation for the ionization of this compound in water. (The compound is a weak electrolyte.)

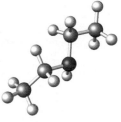

...ture of Acids and Bases

...e the following: (a) $H_2Se(g)$, (b) $H_2Se(aq)$

...ne, like chlorine, forms several acids. What are the ...es of the following? (a) HIO_4, (b) HIO_3, (c) HIO_2 ...HIO, (e) HI

■ One of the main goals of chemistry instruction is to help students develop the ability to solve problems that are more thought-provoking than typical review problems. Recognizing that students often have difficulty with solving problems that require application of several different concepts, we have introduced a new feature in our teaching arsenal called *Analyzing and Solving Multi-Concept Problems.* These problems are more difficult than those in a typical Worked Example and frequently require the use of concepts presented in more than one chapter. Students must combine two or more concepts before reaching a solution, and they must reduce a complex problem into a sum of simpler parts. Problems of this type first appear in Chapter 5 after students have had a chance to work on basic problem skills and after sufficient concepts have been introduced in earlier chapters to make such problems meaningful. *Analyzing and Solving Multi-Concept Problems* addresses instructor frustration and students' deficiencies in problem solving by teaching students how to de-construct problemsand **emphasize the thinking** that goes into solving problems.

■ The end-of-chapter Problems are categorized to assist instructors in selecting homework. They range in difficulty and include critical thinking and multi-concept problems.

■ Following groups of approximately three or four chapters we include problem sets titled *Bringing it Together* that consist mostly of problems that require students to apply concepts developed in two or more of the preceding chapters. Problems have been selected to provide a range of difficulties so as to challenge students of varying levels of achievement.

Analyzing and Solving Multi-Concept Problems

Milk of magnesia is a suspension of $Mg(OH)_2$ in water. It can be made by adding a base to a solution containing Mg^{2+}. Suppose that 40.0 mL of 0.200 M NaOH solution is added to 25.0 mL of 0.300 M $MgCl_2$ solution. What mass of $Mg(OH)_2$ will be formed, and what will be the concentrations of the ions in the solution after the reaction is complete?

■ **Analysis:** Our goal here is to break the problem down into parts that we already know how to solve. The approach is to read the problem carefully and extract from it the various pieces to the puzzle.

First, we're dealing with the stoichiometry of a chemical reaction, so we know we're going to need a balanced chemical equation. We will also need to determine the concentrations of ions, so we will have to be prepared to write an ionic equation, or at least to take into account the dissociation of each solute. These are things you know how to do, so we have that figured out.

Notice that we've been given the volume and molarity for *both* solutions. By now, you should realize that volume and molarity give us moles, so in effect *we have been given the number of moles of two reactants.* This means we have a limiting reactant problem. You learned how

Creamy milk of magnesia is an aqueous suspension of magnesium hydroxide. *(Robert Capece)*

to solve this kind of problem in Chapter 4, so working this part of the problem isn't anything new.

The problem also asks for the concentrations of the ions in the final mixture. The easiest way to find the answers here is to determine the number of moles of each of the ions present before and after the reaction, and then divide the latter by the total final volume of solution to calculate the molar concentrations. Because this is an ionic reaction, two of the ions will be reactants. One will be completely used up, but some of the other will be left over, and we will have to calculate how much. The other two ions are spectator ions and their amounts will not change.

At this point, we have a broad outline of what we have to do. To further clarify our thinking, let's refine and summarize each part so we can select appropriate tools to accomplish our tasks.

Part 1: Write a balanced molecular equation and then convert it to an ionic equation. (This comes first because all the rest of the reasoning is based on the equation.)

Part 2: Calculate the number of moles of each ion present before reaction, determine the limiting reactant, and then use it to calculate the moles and grams of $Mg(OH)_2$ formed.

Part 3: We already know the moles of the spectator ions from Part 2, but we have to calculate the moles of unreacted Mg^{2+} or OH^-. We also need to determine the total volume of the mixture and then calculate the molarities of the ions.

PART 1

■ **Assembling the Tools** We need to set up a metathesis equation and balance it. We follow the procedure developed earlier, making use of the solubility rules.

■ **Solution**
The balanced molecular equation for the reaction is

$$MgCl_2(aq) + 2NaOH(aq) \longrightarrow Mg(OH)_2(s) + 2NaCl(aq)$$

from which we construct the ionic and net ionic equations.

$$Mg^{2+}(aq) + 2Cl^-(aq) + 2Na^+(aq) + 2OH^-(aq) \longrightarrow Mg(OH)_2(s) + 2Na^+(aq) + 2Cl^-(aq)$$
$$Mg^{2+}(aq) + 2OH^-(aq) \longrightarrow Mg(OH)_2(s)$$

These are the equations we will use in Part 2.

PART 2

■ **Assembling the Tools** For each reactant solution,

$$molarity \times volume(L) = moles\ of\ solute$$

The chemical formulas of the reactants will be used to find the number of moles of each ion prior to reaction. The method of finding the limiting reactant developed in Chapter 4 will be applied. A tool we will use is the set of coefficients in the equation, which relates moles of the reactants and product. The molar mass tool will be used to convert moles of $Mg(OH)_2$ to grams.

$$58.31\ g\ Mg(OH)_2 = 1\ mol\ Mg(OH)_2$$

■ **Solution** Let's begin by determining the number of moles of NaOH and $MgCl_2$ supplied by the volumes of their solutions. The conversion factors are taken from their molarities: 0.200 M NaOH and 0.300 M $MgCl_2$.

$$0.0400\ \text{L NaOH soln} \times \frac{0.200\ \text{mol NaOH}}{1.00\ \text{L NaOH soln}} = 8.00 \times 10^{-3}\ mol\ NaOH$$

$$0.0250\ \text{L MgCl}_2\ \text{soln} \times \frac{0.300\ \text{mol MgCl}_2}{1.00\ \text{L MgCl}_2\ \text{soln}} = 7.50 \times 10^{-3}\ mol\ MgCl_2$$

From this information, we obtain the number of moles of each ion present before any reaction occurs. In doing this, notice that we take into

---

■ **Are the Answers Reasonable?** All the reasoning we've done seems to be correct, which is reassuring. For the amount of $Mg(OH)_2$ that forms, 0.001 mol would weigh approximately 0.06 g, so 0.004 mol would weigh 0.24 g. Our answer, 0.233 g $Mg(OH)_2$, is reasonable. The final concentrations of the spectator ions are lower than the initial concentrations, so that makes sense, too, because of the dilution effect.

Reinforcing Problem-solving Skills and Student Comprehension with *WileyPLUS*

We have strived to provide a seamless, total solution to the challenges of the general chemistry course with this edition, fully combining the development of the textbook content with the media and resources delivered within *WileyPLUS*, an innovative, research-based online environment designed for both effective teaching and learning. *WileyPLUS* for ***Chemistry: The Molecular Nature of Matter, Sixth Edition*** provides depth and breadth of assessment that is fully *integrated* with the learning content. The author team has carefully crafted the assessment content in *WileyPLUS* to directly correlate to the printed text … creating a synergy between text and online resources in *WileyPLUS*.

WileyPLUS was designed to facilitate dynamic learning and retention of learned concepts by promoting conceptual understanding and visualization of chemical phenomena at the undergraduate level. Assessment in *WileyPLUS* is offered in four unique question banks: practice questions, end-of-chapter questions, test bank, and concept mastery assignments. All assessment questions offer immediate feedback and online grading along with varying levels of question assistance.

Research-Based Design

WileyPLUS provides an online environment that integrates relevant resources, including the entire digital textbook, in an easy-to-navigate framework. The design of *WileyPLUS* makes it easy for students to know **what** it is they need to do, boosting their confidence and preparing them for greater engagement in class and lab. Concept Modules, Activities, Self Study and Progress Checks in *WileyPLUS* will ensure that students know **how** to study effectively so they will remain engaged and stay on task.

■ In *WileyPLUS*, all **Analyzing Multiple Concept Problems** are complemented by an Office Hours video, which is a video in which an instructor narrates the problem solving steps as the student watches those steps executed in a white board environment, and a Guided Online Tutorial, which is an interactive version of the problem presented. In the Guided Online Tutorial, the student has an opportunity to work through a version of the problem themselves, and is provided with feedback on each part of the answer they submit.

Student Assessment and Concept Mastery

An important part of teaching is student assessment. The prebuilt **Concept Mastery** assignments in *WileyPLUS* http://www.wiley.com/college/sc/jespersen facilitate dynamic learning and retention of learned concepts by promoting conceptual understanding and visualization of chemical phenomena. **Concept Mastery** assignments have multiple levels of parameterization and test key concepts from multiple points of view (visual, symbolic, graphical, quantitative). Each student receives a unique assignment and must achieve a default mastery threshold to receive full points for the assignment.

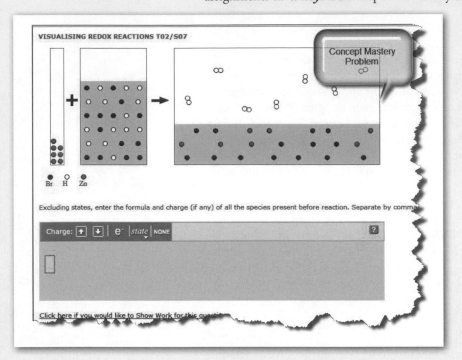

Instructor Resources

WileyPLUS provides reliable, customizable resources that reinforce course goals inside and outside the classroom as well as visibility into individual student progress. Pre-created materials and activities help instructors optimize their time:

Customizable Course Plan: *WileyPLUS* comes with a pre-created Course Plan designed by a subject matter expert uniquely for this course. Simple drag-and-drop tools make it easy to assign the course plan as is or modify it to reflect your course syllabus.

Pre-created Activity Types Include:
- Questions
- Readings and resources
- Concept Mastery

Course Materials and Assessment Content:
- PowerPoint Slides
- Classroom Response System (Clicker) Questions
- Instructor's Manuals
- Assessment consisting of Gradable Practice Questions (embedded with online text)
- Question Assignments
- End-of-chapter problems coded algorithmically with hints
- Links to text
- Instructor-controlled problem-solving help
- Prebuilt Concept Mastery Assignments
- Test Bank

For more information about *WileyPLUS* go to www.wileyplus.com.

Significant Changes in the 6th Edition

As noted earlier, our mission in developing this revision was to sharpen the focus of the text as it relates to the relationship between behavior at the molecular level and properties observed at the macroscopic level.

As much as possible, chapters are written to stand alone as instructional units, enabling instructors to modify the chapter sequence to suit the specific needs of their students. For example, if an instructor wishes to cover the chapter dealing with the properties of gases (Chapter 11) early in the course, they can easily do so. While we believe this chapter fits best in sequence with the chapters dealing with the other states of matter, we realize that there are other valid organizational preferences and the chapter has been written to accommodate them.

Some of the more significant changes to the organization are the following:

■ Special topics consisting of short essays are spread throughout the book. Those titled *Chemistry Outside the Classroom* and *Chemistry and Current Affairs* provide descriptions of real-world, practical applications of chemistry to industry, medicine, and the environment. Essays titled *On the Cutting Edge* serve to highlight chemical phenomena that are of current research interest and that have potential practical applications in the future. A list of these special topics appears at the end of the Table of Contents.

CHEMISTRY OUTSIDE THE CLASSROOM 5.1

Painful Precipitates Kidney Stones

Each year, more than a million people in the United States are hospitalized because of very painful kidney stone attacks. Kidney stone is a hard mass developed from crystals that separate from the urine and build up on the inner surfaces of the kidney. The formation of the stones is caused primarily by the buildup of Ca^{2+}, $C_2O_4^{2-}$, and PO_4^{3-} ions in the urine. When the concentrations of these ions become large enough, the urine becomes supersaturated with respect to calcium oxalate and/or calcium phosphate and precipitates begin to form (70% to 80% of all kidney stones are made up of calcium oxalate and phosphate). If the crystals remain tiny enough, they can travel through the urinary tract and pass out of the body in the urine without being noticed. Sometimes, however, they continue to grow without being passed and can cause intense pain if they become stuck in the urinary tract.

Kidney stones don't all look alike. Their color depends on what substances are mixed with the inorganic precipitates (e.g., proteins or blood). Most are yellow or brown, as seen in the accompanying photo, but they can be tan, gold, or even black. Stones can be round, jagged, or even have branches. They vary in size from mere specks to pebbles to stones as big as golf balls!

A calcium oxalate kidney stone. Kidney stones such as this can be extremely painful. *(Custom Medical Stock Photo, Inc.)*

■ **Chapter 1** is entirely new and sets the tone for the rest of the text. It provides an introduction to the atomic theory and the concepts of atoms, molecules, elements, and compounds. A clear connection is made between observations at the macroscopic level and their interpretation at the molecular level. We introduce chemical symbols and their use in representing atoms of elements. Ball-and-stick and space-filling representations of molecules are introduced, and students are taught to associate molecular structures with chemical formulas. The concepts of chemical reactions and chemical equations are presented and described by drawings of molecules and through the use of chemical symbols. The laws of definite proportions, conservation of mass, and multiple proportions are described and interpreted in molecular terms. All of this is done clearly and prepares students for the more in-depth treatments of these subjects in the chapters that follow. End-of-chapter exercises include concept questions that ask students to describe and interpret molecular structures and chemical changes.

■ **Chapter 2** is devoted to measurements and their units. The importance of quantitative measurements with respect to physical properties is introduced along with the concepts of intensive and extensive properties. The uncertainty of measurements is described. Significant figures are developed to provide the student with a logical method for assessing data. Finally, the method of dimensional analysis is discussed and applied to familiar calculations to develop confidence at an early stage. Color-coded cancellations are used to help the student understand the process.

■ **Chapter 3** provides students with their first exploration of the internal structures of atoms. We now include the history of the discovery of subatomic particles within the body of the chapter. We continue to divide chemical nomenclature into sections that deal separately with molecular and ionic compounds. From experience, we have found that students are able to digest these topics more easily when presented in manageable chunks. To drive home the importance of chemical nomenclature, students are required to construct formulas from names in homework problems in later chapters.

- **Chapter 4** covers the mole concept and stoichiometry. The discussions have been carefully revised where necessary, with molecular diagrams being used to relate stoichiometric principles on the molecular level to mole-sized quantities. Dimensional analysis with color-coded cancel marks is used rigorously for all examples.

- **Chapter 5** focuses on ionic reactions in aqueous solutions and includes additional molecular diagrams depicting solution formation and solution concentration as well as in exercises. Molarity is introduced and used in stoichiometry calculations involving solutions. In this chapter we introduce students to our new feature, *Analyzing and Solving Multi-Concept Problems*.

- **Chapter 6** deals with redox reactions and includes a revised set of rules for assigning oxidation numbers. The change is aimed at making it easier for the student to apply the rules. Illustrations for a variety of oxidation-reduction processes have changed to include molecular diagrams illustrating the changes that take place at the atomic scale.

- **Chapter 7** covers thermochemistry and has been carefully revised with the addition of more illustrations. The manner in which potential energy changes are illustrated has been modified to increase clarity.

- **Chapter 8** is a logical extension of Chapter 3 in our discussion of how our understanding of the atom has developed. The fundamentals of the quantum mechanical atom are introduced to the extent that the material is relevant to the remainder of the text. The discussion has been updated with some tweaking to improve clarity along with some additional illustrations.

- **Chapter 9,** the first of two chapters dealing with chemical bonding, now includes a more thorough discussion of lattice energy and its influence on the formation of ionic compounds. After the introduction of covalent bonding, we now include a separate *brief* section devoted to some common kinds of organic compounds. These are substances students encounter in discussions of physical and chemical properties in later chapters. The section also serves as a brief introduction to organic chemistry for students whose major requires only one semester of chemistry. For instructors who do not wish to discuss organic compounds at this point in the course, the section is easily skipped. Section 9.7 provides a discussion of the reducing properties of elements in Groups 1A and 2A, and the oxidizing power of the nonmetallic elements. This permits a timely discussion of the influence of electronegativity on chemical reactivity.

- **Chapter 10,** the second bonding chapter, now includes a discussion of the way the algebraic signs of atomic orbitals determine the formation of bonding and antibonding molecular orbitals. We also include a section on the bonding in solids as well as a section that discusses the influence of atomic size on the ability of atoms to form pi bonds. For the latter, we examine how multiple bond formation influences the molecular structures of the elemental nonmetals.

- **Chapter 11,** which deals with the properties of gases, now includes a brief section on the chemistry of the atmosphere and the concepts behind global energy transfer. A section on modern pressure sensors and transducers has also been added.

- **Chapter 12** covers intermolecular forces and their effects on physical properties of liquids and solids. Some topics have been rearranged to give a more logical topic flow. Calculations involving the Clausius-Clapeyron equation now appear in the main body of the text, rather than as a special topic.

■ **Chapter 13** discusses the physical properties of solutions. Diagrams showing Raoult's law for non-ideal solutions have been added. We've also added a section on heterogeneous mixtures that includes a discussion of colloids. The issue of potable water provided by reverse osmosis has been added. The concept of incremental heats of solution is introduced.

■ **Chapter 14** covers the kinetics of chemical reactions, including mechanisms, and catalysis. The section on instantaneous rates of reactions has been expanded, and the integrated zero order rate law has been added.

■ **Chapter 15** is the first of several chapters devoted to chemical equilibria. Changes to this chapter have been relatively minor. We have concentrated on developing the equilibrium concept at the molecular level and on polishing the worked examples to make them more accessible to the student.

■ **Chapter 16,** which examines acid-base chemistry theories, concludes with a treatment of modern ceramic materials prepared by the sol-gel process. This discussion illustrates how simple acid-base chemistry can be applied to the production of modern materials.

■ **Chapter 17** treats acid-base equilibria and calculations of pH in detail. Included are detailed examples of pH calculations involving strong and weak acids and bases, buffers and polyprotic acids. Interrelationships based on the Brønsted-Lowry theory are developed. Titration curves, including polyprotic acid titrations, are discussed. Use of simplifying assumptions is based on fundamental principles.

■ **Chapter 18,** the final chapter on equilibria, deals with solubility and simultaneous equilibria. This chapter continues the strong emphasis on solving equilibrium problems developed in the previous chapters. We have included a section on qualitative analysis of metal ions, and we continue to introduce complex ions in this chapter because they participate in equilibria.

■ **Chapter 19** presents the fundamentals of thermodynamics and includes discussions of the first, second, and third laws. Entropy and Gibbs free energy are introduced, and examples using the concept of state functions are presented with detailed solutions. New special topics on entropy and thermodynamics of sustainability are introduced.

■ **Chapter 20** discusses the two fundamental electrochemical processes: electrolysis, and the use of galvanic (voltaic) cells to produce external electron flow. Unambiguous electrochemical cells are always presented. Details of the relationships between $\Delta G°$, $E°_{cell}$ and K_{eq} are presented with detailed examples.

■ **Chapter 21** discusses nuclear reactions and their applications. In this chapter, we have incorporated current research on carbon-14 dating and included a new table that summarizes the nuclear reactions.

■ **Chapter 22** is devoted entirely to the study of metal complexes. We have removed from this chapter the material devoted to the nonmetals and metalloids that was present in Chapter 21 of the 5th edition. Some of the topics have been distributed into earlier chapters where it seemed to be appropriate.

■ **Chapter 23** provides an expanded discussion of organic chemistry. It has undergone significant restructuring and rewriting, both to shorten the chapter and to take into account the introduction to organic chemistry provided in Chapter 9.

|Teaching and Learning Resources

A comprehensive package of supplements has been created to assist both the teacher and the student and includes the following:

For Students

Study Guide by Neil Jespersen of St. John's University. This guide has been written to further enhance the understanding of concepts. It is an invaluable tool for students and contains chapter overviews, additional worked-out problems giving detailed steps involved in solving them, alternate problem-solving approaches, as well as extensive review exercises. (ISBN: 978-0-470-57772-1)

Solutions Manual by Duane Swank, of Pacific Lutheran University, with contributions by Alison Hyslop of St. John's University. The manual contains worked-out solutions for text problems whose answers appear in Appendix B. (ISBN: 978-0-470-57773-8)

Laboratory Manual for Principles of General Chemistry, 9th Edition, by Jo Beran of Texas A&M University, Kingsville. This comprehensive laboratory manual is for use in the general chemistry course. This manual is known for its broad selection of topics and experiments, and for its clear, user-friendly layout and design. Containing enough material for two or three terms, this lab manual emphasizes techniques, helping students learn the appropriate time and situation for their correct use. The accompanying Instructor's Manual presents the details of each experiment, including overviews, an instructor's lecture outline, and teaching hints. The Instructor's Manual also contains answers to the pre-laboratory assignment and laboratory questions. (ISBN: 978-0-470-64789-9)

For Instructors

Instructor's Manual by Scott Kirkby of East Tennessee State University. In addition to lecture outlines, alternate syllabi, and chapter overviews, this manual contains suggestions for small group active-learning projects, class discussions, tips for first-time instructors, class demonstrations, short writing projects, and contains relevant web links for each chapter.

Test Bank by Donovan Dixon of the University of Central Florida and Justin Meyer of South Dakota School of Mines and Technology. The Test Bank contains over 2000 questions including: multiple-choice, true-false, short answer questions, fill in the blank questions, and critical thinking problems. PC- and Macintosh-compatible versions of the entire test bank are available with full editing features to help the instructor customize tests.

Instructor's Solutions Manual by Duane Swank, of Pacific Lutheran University, with contributions by Alison Hyslop, of St. John's University, contains worked-out solutions to all end of chapter problems.

Digital Image Archive—Text web site includes downloadable files of text images in JPEG format. Instructors may use these images to customize their presentations and to provide additional visual support for quizzes and exams.

PowerPoint Lecture Slides by Elise Megehee, of St. John's University, feature images from the text on slides that are customizable to fit your course.

PowerPoint Slides with Text Images—PPT slides containing images, tables, and figures from the text.

Personal Response Systems/"Clicker" Questions—A bank of questions is available for anyone using personal response systems technology in their classroom.

All instructor supplements can be requested from your local Wiley sales representative.

| Acknowledgments

In this edition, it is our pleasure to see Neil Jespersen take on the role of lead author. He has more than proven himself in his role as a contributing author on the last edition and we are confident in his ability to carry the text forward into future editions. It is also our pleasure to welcome Alison Hyslop to the author team. Her expertise in physical inorganic chemistry and her dedication to teaching and to her students has been a significant asset toward the development of this book.

We express our fond thanks to our spouses, June Brady, Marilyn Jespersen, and Peter de Rege, and our children, Mark and Karen Brady, Lisa Fico and Kristen Pierce, and Nora, Alexander, and Joseph de Rege, for their constant support, understanding, and patience. They have been, and continue to be, a constant source of inspiration for us all.

We deeply appreciate the contributions of others who have helped in preparing materials for this edition. In particular, Duane Swank, of Pacific Lutheran University, for his help in preparing the Answer Appendix and Solutions Manuals, and Conrad Bergo of East Stroudsburg University, for reviewing the answers and solutions for accuracy. We thank John Murdzek for his thoughtful suggestions regarding various aspects of the text. We would also like to thank the following colleagues for helpful discussions: Gina Florio, Elise Megehee, Richard Rosso, Joseph Serafin, and Enju Wang.

Is it with particular pleasure that we thank the staff at Wiley for their careful work, encouragement, and sense of humor, particularly our editors, Nicholas Ferrari and Jennifer Yee. We are also grateful for the efforts of Marketing Manager Kristine Ruff, Editorial Program Assistant, Catherine Donovan, Editorial Assistant, Lauren Stauber, Senior Media Editor, Thomas Kulesa, Media Editors Marc Wezdecki and Evelyn Levich, our Photo Editor, Jennifer MacMillan, our Designer, James O'Shea, our Illustration Editor, Anna Melhorn, the entire production team, and especially Elizabeth Swain for her tireless attention to getting things right. Our thanks also go to Pietro Paolo Adinolfi and others at Preparé (the compositor) for their unflagging efforts towards changing a manuscript into a book.

We express gratitude to the colleagues whose careful reviews, helpful suggestions, and thoughtful criticism of previous editions as well as the current edition manuscript have been so important in the development of this book. Additional thanks go to those who participated in the media development by creating content and reviewing extensively. Our thanks go out to the reviewers of previous editions, your comments and suggestions have been invaluable to us over the years. Thank you to the reviewers of the current edition, and to the authors and reviewers of the supporting media package:

Sara L. Alvaro *Rensselaer Polytechnic Institute*
Rebecca Barlag *Ohio University*
Laurance Beauvais *San Diego State University*
Jonathan Breitzer *Fayetteville State University*
Bryan E. Breyfogle *Missouri State University*
Tara Carpenter *University of Maryland – Baltimore County*
Warren Chan *University of Toronto*
Andrew Craft *University of Hartford*
Patrick Crawford *Augustana College*
Cabot-Ann Christofferson *South Dakota School of Mines and Technology*
Mark S. Cybulski *Miami University*
Donovan Dixon *University of Central Florida*
Bill Durham *University of Arkansas*
Amina K. El-Ashmawy *Collin County Community College*
Eric Goll *Brookdale Community College*
Denise J. Gregory *Samford University*
John Hardee *Henderson State University*
Brian Hogan *University of North Carolina – Chapel Hill*
Paul A. Horton *Indian River State College*

Byron Howell *Tyler Junior College*
Carl Hultman *Gannon University*
Dell Jensen *Augustana College*
David W. Johnson *University of Dayton*
Kevin E. Johnson *Pacific University*
Jesudoss Kingston *Iowa State University*
Gary Long *Virginia Tech*
Michael Lufaso *University of North Florida*
Cora E. MacBeth *Emory University*
Kal Mahadev *University of Calgary*
Keith Marek *Bemidji State University*
Brian McClain *California State University – Long Beach*
Scott McIndoe *University of Victoria*
David H. Metcalf *University of Virginia*
Justin Meyer *South Dakota School of Mines and Technology*
John R. Miecznikowski *Fairfield University*
Troy Milliken *Jackson State University*
Ray Mohseni *East Tennessee State University*
Nancy J. Mullins *Florida State College – Jacksonville*
Alexander Y. Nazarenko *SUNY College at Buffalo*
Marie L. Nguyen *Indiana University Purdue University Indianapolis*
Anne-Marie Nickel *Milwaukee School of Engineering*
Fotis Nifiatis *SUNY – Plattsburgh*
Jodi O'Donnell *Siena College*
Maria Pacheco *Buffalo State College*
Cynthia N. Peck *Delta College*
Lydia Martinez Rivera *The University of Texas – San Antonio*
Niina J. Ronkainen *Benedictine University*
Christopher Roy *Duke University*
Raymond E. Schaak *Pennsylvania State University*
Mark W. Schraf *West Virginia University*
Aislinn Sirk *University of Victoria*
Richard Spinney *The Ohio State University*
Duane Swank *Pacific Lutheran University*
Colleen Taylor *Virginia State University*
Edmund L. Tisko *University of Nebraska – Omaha*
Kimberly Woznack *California University of Pennsylvania*
Mingming Xu *West Virginia University*
Ningfeng Zhao *East Tennessee State University*

1 Chemistry and the Atomic/Molecular View of Matter

Chapter Outline

The girl listening to music on her iPod probably isn't thinking much about chemistry, but if it were not for the inventions made possible by chemical discoveries there would be no music to fill her spare time. In this chapter you begin your study of a science that affects your life every single day. As you progress through your chemistry course, we hope you enjoy learning about how the properties of atoms and molecules affects the world in which you live. Granger Wootz/Getty Images, Inc.

This Chapter in Context

Clothing in a dazzling array of colors is possible because of synthetic dyes discovered by chemists.
(Getty Images, Inc.)

It's quite likely that you have an iPod, just like the young woman shown in the photo on the preceding page. This wonderful device is only one of a multitude of gadgets that enrich our lives. But if it were not for the science of chemistry, almost none of the materials used to make them, such as their plastic cases and electronic components, would exist. Even clothing made from "natural" fibers such as cotton or wool may be colored with synthetic dyes and sewn together with thread made of synthetic fibers. Chemistry affects our lives every day in countless ways, and one of our goals in this book is to give you an appreciation for the significant role that chemistry plays in modern society.

In this first chapter we present some fundamental concepts and definitions that we will use throughout the book. We also discuss how the theory of atoms came about, how the concept of atoms is used to describe chemical substances and chemical change, and how we will represent atoms and their combinations visually in later discussions. If you've had a prior course in chemistry, you're probably familiar with most of the topics that we cover here. Nevertheless, it is important to be sure that you have a mastery of these subjects, because we will use them frequently in the chapters ahead.

1.1 | Chemistry and Its Place among the Sciences

■ In our discussions, we do not assume that you have had a prior course in chemistry. However, even if some of the subjects discussed here are familiar, we urge you to study this chapter thoroughly, because the concepts developed here will be used in later chapters.

Chemistry[1] can be defined as *the study of the composition, properties, and transformations of matter.* This includes all of the chemicals that make up the tangible things in our world. In their studies, chemists seek answers to fundamental questions about how the composition of a substance affects its properties. With such knowledge comes the possibility of designing materials with specifically intended characteristics. Underlying all of this is a search for knowledge about the way the structure of matter at the atomic level is related to the behavior of substances that we observe through our senses.

Chemistry is particularly concerned with the way substances change, often dramatically, when they interact with each other in *chemical reactions.* By understanding such changes at a fundamental level, chemists have been able to create materials never before found on earth—materials with especially desirable properties that fulfill specific needs of society. For example, synthetic plastics, ceramics, and metal alloys now permit engineers and architects to build structures that would never have been possible using only naturally occurring materials. Knowledge of fundamental aspects of chemical reactions has also enabled biologists to develop a fundamental understanding of many of the processes taking place in living organisms.

Because of its broad scope, chemistry touches all of the sciences, which is why some have called it the central science. In fact, the involvement of chemistry among the various branches of science is reflected in the names of some of the divisions of the American Chemical Society, the largest scientific organization in the world (see Table 1.1). Although you may not plan to be a chemist, some knowledge of chemistry will surely be valuable to you.

---

[1] Important terms are set in bold type to call them to your attention. Be sure you learn their meanings. If you need to review them, they are also in the Glossary at the back of the book.

Table 1.1	Names of Some of the Divisions of the American Chemical Society	
Agricultural & Food Chemistry	Environmental Chemistry
Agrochemicals	Fertilizer & Soil Chemistry
Biochemical Technology	Fuel Chemistry
Biological Chemistry	Geochemistry
Business Development & Management	Industrial & Engineering Chemistry
Carbohydrate Chemistry	Medicinal Chemistry
Cellulose, Paper & Textile	Nuclear Chemistry & Technology
Chemical Health & Safety	Petroleum Chemistry
Chemical Toxicology	Polymer Chemistry
Chemistry & the Law	Polymeric Materials: Science & Engineering
Colloid & Surface Chemistry	Rubber
Computers in Chemistry	

1.2 | Laws and Theories: The Scientific Method

You've probably spent some time playing video games, so you know that you learn a game by trial and error. You try one thing and get shot down, so next time you try something else. Gradually you get to know how to get through all the traps and can fight your way to the finish. Your actions in game playing are not far removed from the way scientists approach the study of the world around them.

Scientists are curious creatures who want to know what makes the world "tick." The approach they take to their work is generally known as the **scientific method.** Basically it boils down to gathering information and formulating explanations.

In the sciences, we usually gather information by performing experiments in laboratories under controlled conditions so the observations we make are reproducible (Figure 1.1). An **observation** is a statement that accurately describes something we see, hear, taste, feel, or smell. The observations we make while performing experiments are referred to as **data**.

Data gathered during an experiment often lead us to draw conclusions. A **conclusion** is a statement that's based on what we think about a series of observations. For example, consider the following statements about the fermentation of grape juice to make wine:

1. Before fermentation, grape juice is very sweet and contains no alcohol.
2. After fermentation, the grape juice is no longer as sweet and it contains a great deal of alcohol.
3. In fermentation, sugar is converted into alcohol.

Statements 1 and 2 are observations because they describe properties of the grape juice that can be tasted and smelled. Statement 3 is a conclusion because it *interprets* the observations that are available.

■ Roger Bacon, a thirteenth century philosopher, is credited as the first to suggest that experimental observations must be the basis of modern science.

Figure 1.1 | **A research chemist working in a modern laboratory.** Reproducible conditions in a laboratory permit experiments to yield reliable results. *(©AP/Wide World Photos)*

Experimental Observations and Scientific Laws

One of the goals of science is to organize facts so that relationships or generalizations among the data can be established. For example, if we study the behavior of gases, such as the air we breathe, we soon discover that the volume of a gas depends on a number of factors, including the amount of the gas, its temperature, and its pressure. The observations we record relating these factors are our data.

■ The pressure of the gas is *inversely proportional* to its volume, so the smaller the volume, the larger the pressure.

One generalization we could make by studying data obtained from many experiments performed using different temperatures and pressures is that when the temperature of the gas is held constant, squeezing the gas into half of its original volume causes the pressure of the gas to double. If we were to repeat our experiments many times with numerous *different* gases, we would find that this generalization is uniformly applicable to all of them. Such a broad generalization, based on the results of many experiments, is called a **law** or **scientific law**.

We often express laws in the form of mathematical equations. For example, if we represent the pressure of a gas by the symbol P and its volume by V, the inverse relationship between pressure and volume can be written as

$$P = \frac{C}{V}$$

where C is a proportionality constant. (We will discuss gases and the laws relating to them in greater detail in Chapter 11.)

Hypotheses and Theories: Models of Nature

As useful as they may be, laws only state what happens; they do not provide explanations. *Why*, for example, *are gases so easily compressed to a smaller volume?* More specifically, *what must gases be like at the most basic, elementary level for them to behave as they do?* Answering such questions when they first arise is no simple task and requires much speculation. But over time scientists build mental pictures, called **theoretical models**, that enable them to explain observed laws.

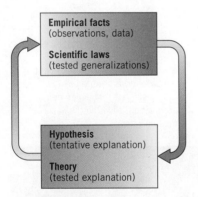

Figure 1.2 | **The scientific method is cyclical.** Observations suggest explanations, which suggest new experiments, which suggest new explanations, and so on.

In the development of a theoretical model, researchers form tentative explanations called **hypotheses** (Figure 1.2). They then perform experiments that test predictions derived from the model. Sometimes the results show that the model is wrong. When this happens, the model must be abandoned or modified to account for the new data. Eventually, if the model survives repeated testing, it achieves the status of a theory. *A* **theory** *is a tested explanation of the behavior of nature.* Keep in mind, however, that it is impossible to perform every test that might show a theory to be wrong, so we can never prove *absolutely* that a theory is correct.

Science doesn't always proceed in the orderly stepwise fashion described above. Luck sometimes plays an important role. For example, in 1828 Frederick Wöhler, a German chemist, was testing one of his theories and obtained an unexpected material when he heated a substance called ammonium cyanate. Out of curiosity he analyzed it and found it to be urea (a component of urine). This was exciting because it was the first time anyone had knowingly made a substance produced only by living creatures from a chemical not having a life origin. The fact that this could be done led to a whole new branch of chemistry called *organic chemistry*. Yet, had it not been for Wöhler's curiosity and his application of the scientific method to his unexpected results, the importance of his experiment might have gone unnoticed.

■ Many breakthrough discoveries in science have come about by accident.

As a final note, it is significant that the most spectacular and dramatic changes in science occur when major theories are proved to be wrong. Although this happens only rarely, when it does occur, scientists are sent scrambling to develop new theories, and exciting new frontiers are opened.

The Atomic Theory as a Model of Nature

Virtually every scientist would agree that the most significant theoretical model of nature ever formulated is the atomic theory, discussed in some detail in Section 1.4. According to this theory, all chemical substances are composed of tiny submicroscopic particles that we call **atoms,** which combine in various ways to form all the complex materials we find in the **macroscopic,** visible world around us. This concept forms the foundation for the way scientists think about nature. The atomic theory and how it enables us to explain chemical facts forms the central theme of this chapter, and much of the rest of this book as well.

■ *Macroscopic* commonly refers to physical objects that are measurable and observable by the naked eye.

1.3 | Matter and Its Classifications

We mentioned above that one of our goals is to be able to relate things we observe around us and in the laboratory to the way individual atoms and their combinations behave at the submicroscopic level. To begin this discussion we need to study how chemistry views the macroscopic world.

Matter Defined

In Section 1.1 we described chemistry as being concerned with the properties and transformations of matter. **Matter** is defined as anything that occupies space and has mass. It is the stuff our universe is made of. All of the objects around us, from rocks to pizza to people, are examples of matter.

Notice that our definition of matter uses the term *mass* rather than *weight*. The words mass and weight are often used interchangeably even though they refer to different things. **Mass** *refers to how much matter there is in a given object[2], whereas* **weight** *refers to the force with which the object is attracted by gravity.* For example, a golf ball contains a certain amount of matter and has a certain mass, which is the same regardless of the golf ball's location. However, the *weight* of a golf ball on earth is about six times greater than it would be on the moon because the gravitational attraction of the earth is six times that of the moon. Because mass does not vary from place to place, we use mass rather than weight when we specify the amount of matter in an object. Mass is measured with an instrument called a balance, which we will discuss in Chapter 2.

Elements

Chemistry is especially concerned with **chemical reactions,** which are transformations that alter the chemical compositions of substances. An important type of chemical reaction is **decomposition,** in which one substance is changed into two or more others. For example, if we pass electricity through molten (melted) sodium chloride (salt), the silvery metal sodium and the pale green gas, chlorine, are formed. This change has decomposed sodium chloride into two simpler substances. No matter how we try, however, sodium and chlorine cannot be decomposed further by chemical reactions into still simpler substances that can be stored and studied.

---

[2]Mass is a measure of an object's momentum, or resistance to a change in motion. Something with a large mass, such as a truck, contains a lot of matter and is difficult to stop once it's moving. An object with less mass, such as a baseball, is much easier to stop.

Figure 1.3 | **Some elements that occur naturally.** (*a*) Carbon in the form of diamonds. (Coal is also made up mostly of carbon.) (*b*) Gold. (*c*) Sulfur. (*Peter/Stef Lamberti/GettyImages, Inc.; Ken Lucas/VisualsUnlimited; Manfred Kage/PeterArnold, Inc.*)

In chemistry, *substances that cannot be decomposed into simpler materials by chemical reactions are called* **elements**. Sodium and chlorine are two examples. Others you may be familiar with include iron, aluminum, sulfur, and carbon (as in charcoal and diamonds). Some elements are gases at room temperature. Examples include chlorine, oxygen, hydrogen, nitrogen, and helium. Elements are the simplest forms of matter that chemists work with directly. All more complex substances are composed of elements in various combinations. Figure 1.3 shows some samples of elements that occur uncombined with other elements in nature.

Mountains of the bright yellow element sulfur await shipment on a dock in Vancouver, BC, Canada. The sulfur is extracted from crude oil where it is present as a contaminant that can cause serious air pollution if not removed. (*Courtesy of James Brady*)

Table 1.2	Elements That Have Symbols Derived from Their Latin Names	
Element	**Symbol**	**Latin Name**
Sodium	Na	Natrium
Potassium	K	Kalium
Iron	Fe	Ferrum
Copper	Cu	Cuprum
Silver	Ag	Argentum
Gold	Au	Aurum
Mercury	Hg	Hydrargyrum
Antimony	Sb	Stibium
Tin	Sn	Stannum
Lead	Pb	Plumbum

Chemical Symbols for Elements

So far, scientists have discovered 90 naturally occurring elements and have made 28 more, for a total of 118. Each element is assigned a unique **chemical symbol,** which can be used as an abbreviation for the name of the element. Chemical symbols are also used to stand for atoms of elements when we write *chemical formulas* such as H_2O (water) and CO_2 (carbon dioxide). We will have a lot more to say about formulas later.

The names and chemical symbols of the elements are given on the inside front cover of the book. In most cases, an element's chemical symbol is formed from one or two letters of its English name. For instance, the symbol for carbon is C, for bromine it is Br, and for silicon it is Si. For some elements, the symbols are derived from their non-English names. Those that come from their Latin names, given to them long ago, are listed in Table 1.2. The symbol for tungsten (W) comes from *wolfram*, the German name of the element. Regardless of the origin of the symbol, the first letter is always capitalized and the second letter, if there is one, is always lowercase.

Figure 1.4 | **Mixtures can have variable compositions.** Orange juice, Coca-Cola, and pancake syrup are mixtures that contain sugar. The amount of sugar varies from one to another because the composition can vary from one mixture to another. *(Thomas Brase/Stone/Getty Images; Andy Washnik; Andy Washnik)*

Compounds

By means of chemical reactions, elements combine in various *specific proportions* to give all of the more complex substances in nature. Thus, hydrogen and oxygen combine to form water (H_2O), and sodium and chlorine combine to form sodium chloride (NaCl, common table salt). Water and sodium chloride are examples of compounds. A **compound** is a substance formed from two or more *different elements* in which the elements are always combined in the same, fixed (i.e., constant) proportions by mass. For example, if any sample of pure water is decomposed, the mass of oxygen obtained is *always* eight times the mass of hydrogen. Similarly, when hydrogen and oxygen react to form water, the mass of oxygen consumed is always eight times the mass of hydrogen, never more and never less.

Mixtures

Elements and compounds are examples of **pure substances.**[3] The composition of a pure substance is always the same, regardless of its source. Pure substances are rare, however. Usually, we encounter mixtures of compounds or elements. Unlike elements and compounds, **mixtures** *can have variable compositions.* For example, Figure 1.4 shows three mixtures that contain sugar. They have different degrees of sweetness because the amount of sugar in a given size sample varies from one to the other.

Mixtures can be either homogeneous or heterogeneous. A **homogeneous mixture** has the same properties throughout the sample. An example is a thoroughly stirred mixture of sugar in water. We call such a homogeneous mixture a **solution.** Solutions need not be liquids, just homogeneous. For example, the alloy used in the U.S. 5 cent coin is a solid solution of copper and nickel, and clean air is a gaseous solution of oxygen, nitrogen, and a number of other gases.

A **heterogeneous mixture** consists of two or more regions, called **phases**, that differ in properties. A mixture of olive oil and vinegar in a salad dressing, for example, is a two-phase mixture in which the oil floats on the vinegar as a separate layer (Figure 1.5). The phases in a mixture don't have to be chemically different substances like oil and vinegar, however. A mixture of ice and liquid water is a two-phase heterogeneous mixture in which the phases have the same chemical composition but occur in different *physical states* (a term we discuss further in Chapter 2).

Figure 1.5 | **A heterogeneous mixture.** The salad dressing shown here contains vinegar and vegetable oil (plus assorted other flavorings). Vinegar and oil do not dissolve in each other, and they form two layers. The mixture is heterogeneous because each of the separate phases (oil, vinegar, and other solids) has its own set of properties that differ from the properties of the other phases. *(Andy Washnik)*

---

[3]We have used the term *substance* rather loosely until now. Strictly speaking, **substance** really means *pure substance*. Each unique chemical element and compound is a *substance*; a mixture consists of two or more substances.

Figure 1.6 | **Formation of a mixture of iron and sulfur.** (*a*) Samples of powdered sulfur and powdered iron. (*b*) A mixture of sulfur and iron is made by stirring the two powders together. (*Michael Watson*)

Figure 1.7 | **Formation of a mixture does not change chemical composition.** Here we see that forming the mixture has not changed the iron and sulfur into a compound of these two elements. The mixture can be separated by pulling the iron out with a magnet. Making a mixture involves a physical change. (*Michael Watson*)

Physical and Chemical Changes

Figure 1.8 | **"Fools gold."** The mineral pyrite (also called iron pyrite) is a compound of iron and sulfur. When the compound forms, the properties of iron and sulfur disappear and are replaced by the properties of the compound. Pyrite has an appearance that caused some miners to mistake it for real gold. (*WILDLIFE/Peter Arnold, Inc.*)

The process we use to create a mixture involves a **physical change,** because no new chemical substances form. This is illustrated in Figure 1.6 for powdered samples of the elements iron and sulfur. By simply dumping them together and stirring, the mixture forms, but both elements retain their original properties. To separate the mixture, we could similarly use just physical changes. For example, we could remove the iron by stirring the mixture with a magnet — a physical operation. The iron powder sticks to the magnet as we pull it out, leaving the sulfur behind (Figure 1.7). The mixture also could be separated by treating it with a liquid called carbon disulfide, which is able to dissolve the sulfur but not the iron. Filtering the sulfur solution from the solid iron, followed by evaporation of the liquid carbon disulfide from the sulfur solution, gives the original components, iron and sulfur, separated from each other.

The formation of a compound involves a **chemical change** (a chemical reaction) because the chemical makeup of the substances involved are changed. Iron and sulfur, for example, combine to form a compound often called "fool's gold" because it looks so much like real gold (Figure 1.8). In this compound the elements no longer have the same properties they had before they combined, and they cannot be separated by physical means. The decomposition of fool's gold into iron and sulfur is also a chemical reaction.

The relationships among elements, compounds, and mixtures are shown in Figure 1.9.

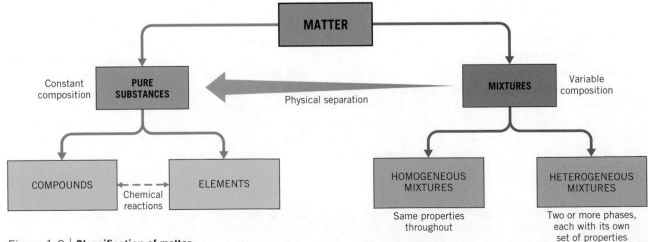

Figure 1.9 | **Classification of matter.**

1.4 | Dalton and the Atomic Theory

In our definition of an element in Section 1.3, no reference was made to the atomic nature of matter. In fact, the distinction between elements and compounds had been made even before the atomic theory of matter was formulated. In this section we examine how the atomic theory began. This will enable us to take a closer look at elements, compounds, and mixtures in terms of our modern view of atomic structure.

The concept of atoms began nearly 2500 years ago when certain Greek philosophers expressed the belief that matter is ultimately composed of tiny indivisible particles, and it is from the Greek word *atomos*, meaning "not cut," that the word *atom* is derived. The philosophers' conclusions, however, were not supported by any evidence; they were derived simply from philosophical reasoning. Scientific support for the existence of atoms awaited the establishment of the *law of definite proportions* and the *law of conservation of mass*—two important general observations about the nature of compounds and chemical reactions.

Laws of Chemical Combination

Prior to the nineteenth century, progress in science was slow because there was little understanding of the need for accurate measurements. Over the course of time, however, scientists gradually accumulated data that revealed some truths that apply to all chemical compounds and chemical reactions.

The first, which we've actually used in our definition of a compound, is that when a compound is formed, elements always combine in the same proportion by mass. For example, we noted that when hydrogen and oxygen combine to form water, the mass of oxygen that reacts is *always* eight times the mass of hydrogen—never more and never less. In forming water, we cannot alter this ratio no matter how hard we try. Similar observations apply to every compound we study. Such observations led to a generalization known as the **law of definite proportions** (or **law of definite composition**): *In any chemical compound the elements are always combined in a definite proportion by mass.*

The second observation is that when a reaction is carried out in a sealed vessel, so that nothing can escape or enter the reaction mixture, the total mass after the reaction is over is exactly the same as before the reaction began. For instance, if we place a certain mass of hydrogen, plus eight times that mass of oxygen, into a sealed container and initiate the reaction to form water, the mass of water after the reaction is over is the same as the masses of hydrogen and oxygen we started with. Such observations, repeated over and over for large numbers of chemical reactions, led to another generalization known as the **law of conservation of mass:** *Mass is neither lost nor created during a chemical reaction.*

> **Law of Definite Proportions**
>
> In a given chemical compound, the elements are always combined in the same proportions by mass.
>
> **Law of Conservation of Mass**
>
> No detectable gain or loss of mass occurs in chemical reactions. Mass is *conserved.*

In Chapter 2 you will see how these laws can be used to perform calculations related to chemical composition.

The Atomic Theory

The laws of definite proportions and conservation of mass served as the *experimental foundation* for the atomic theory. They prompted the question: "What must be true about the nature of matter, given the truth of these laws?" In other words, what is matter made of?

TOOLS

Laws of definite proportions and conservation of mass

■ Important relationships that we will use in solving chemistry problems are identified by this Tools icon in the margin. In this case, the tools are two important chemical laws that affect how we write chemical formulas and chemical equations. How the tools are used is summarized on page 24.

At the beginning of the nineteenth century, John Dalton (1766–1844), an English scientist, used the Greek concept of atoms to make sense out of the laws of definite proportions and conservation of mass. Dalton reasoned that if atoms really exist, they must have certain properties to account for these laws. He described what those properties must be, and the list constitutes what we now call **Dalton's atomic theory.**

Dalton's Atomic Theory

1. *Matter consists of tiny particles called atoms.*
2. *In any sample of a pure element, all the atoms are identical in mass and other properties.*
3. *The atoms of different elements differ in mass and other properties.*
4. *When atoms of different elements combine to form compounds, new and more complex particles form. However, in a given compound the constituent atoms are always present in the same fixed **numerical** ratio.*
5. *Atoms are indestructible. In chemical reactions, the atoms rearrange but they do not themselves break apart.*

Modern Experimental Evidence for Atoms

■ The Nobel Prize, consisting of a gold medal, a citation, and a sum of money, was established in 1895 by the Swedish chemist Alfred Bernhard Nobel, the inventor of dynamite. It was first awarded for physics, chemistry, physiology or medicine, literature, and peace in 1901.

In Section 1.5 we will study how Dalton's theory accounted for the laws of definite proportions and conservation of mass. Before we get to this, however, you might wonder whether there is any additional proof today that atoms actually exist. Although atoms and most molecules are so incredibly tiny that even the most powerful optical microscopes are unable to detect them, experiments have been performed that provide pretty convincing evidence that atoms are real.

In recent times, scientists have developed very sensitive instruments that are able to map the surfaces of solids with remarkable resolution. One such instrument is called a **scanning tunneling microscope.** It was invented in the early 1980s by Gerd Binnig and Heinrich Rohrer and earned them the 1986 Nobel Prize in physics. With this instrument, the tip of a sharp metal probe is brought very close to an electrically conducting surface and an electric current bridging the gap is begun. The flow of current is extremely sensitive to the distance between the tip of the probe and the sample. As the tip is moved across the surface, the height of the tip is continually adjusted to keep the current flow constant. By accurately recording the height fluctuations of the tip, a map of the hills and valleys on the surface is obtained. The data are processed using a computer to reveal an image of atoms on the surface. (See Figure 1.10.)

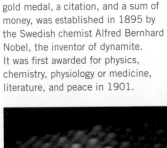

Figure 1.10 | **Individual atoms can be imaged using a scanning tunneling microscope.**
This STM micrograph reveals the pattern of individual atoms of palladium deposited on a graphite surface. Palladium is a silvery white metal used in alloys such as white gold and dental crowns. (*P. Plailly/Phototake*)

Colors used to represent atoms

1.5 | Atoms and Molecules and Chemical Formulas

In describing substances at the atomic level, it is frequently useful to use mental or graphic images of the way the individual atoms combine. Because we live in a three-dimensional world, atoms are represented as spheres (circles if you're drawing them by hand). Different colors are used to differentiate atoms of one element from those of another. In most of the artwork in this book, the standard color scheme shown in Figure 1.11 will be followed. Scientists are not locked into this color scheme, however, and sometimes colors are chosen to emphasize some particular aspect of a substance. In such cases, the legend for the figure will identify which colors are associated with which elements. You should learn to recognize atoms in drawings according to their colors.

Atoms of different elements have different sizes, so often the size of the sphere used to represent an atom will be large for larger atoms and small for smaller atoms. This is done when we particularly wish to emphasize size difference among atoms. The sizes of the different spheres in Figure 1.11 roughly indicate the relative sizes of the atoms. The following illustrate the relative sizes of atoms of oxygen and chlorine. As suggested by these drawings, a chlorine atom is larger than an oxygen atom.

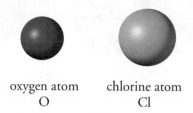

oxygen atom   chlorine atom
O   Cl

Earlier we mentioned that each element is assigned its own unique chemical symbol, which can be used as shorthand for the name of the element or to represent a single atom of the element. Thus an atom of oxygen is represented by the symbol O and an atom of chlorine by the symbol Cl.

Molecules

Atoms combine in a variety of ways to form all of the more complex substances we find in nature. One type of substance consists of discrete particles called **molecules**, each of which is made up of two or more atoms. Enormous numbers of different compounds as well as many elements exist in nature as molecules.[4] Another type of compound (called an *ionic compound*) consists of electrically charged atoms and will be discussed in Chapter 3.

Chemical Formulas

To describe chemical substances, both elements and compounds, we commonly use **chemical formulas**, in which chemical symbols are used to represent atoms of the elements that are present. For a **free element** (one that is not combined with another element in a compound) we often simply use the chemical symbol. Thus, the element sodium is represented by its symbol, Na, which is interpreted to mean one atom of sodium.

Many of the elements we encounter frequently are found in nature as **diatomic molecules** (molecules composed of two atoms each). Among them are the gases hydrogen, oxygen, nitrogen, and chlorine. A **subscript** following the chemical symbol is used to indicate the number of atoms of an element in a molecule. Thus, the formula for molecular hydrogen is H_2, and those for oxygen, nitrogen, and chlorine are O_2, N_2, and Cl_2, respectively. Drawings of these molecules are shown in Figure 1.12. A more complete list of such elements is found in Table 1.3. This would be a good time to learn the formulas of these elements because you will come upon them often throughout the course.

Just as chemical symbols can be used as shorthand notations for the names of elements, a chemical formula is a shorthand way of writing the name for a compound. However, *the most important characteristic of a compound's formula is that it specifies the atomic composition of the substance.*

In the formula of a compound, each element present is identified by its chemical symbol. Water, H_2O, is probably the best known example and consists of two atoms of hydrogen and one of oxygen. The lack of a subscript after the symbol O means that the formula specifies just one atom of oxygen. Another example is methane, CH_4, the combustible compound found in "natural gas," which is used for cooking in the kitchen and Bunsen burners in the lab. The formula tells us that methane molecules are composed of one atom of carbon and four atoms of hydrogen.

[4]CAS REGISTRY, the most comprehensive and high-quality compendium of publicly disclosed chemical information, now includes 50 million compounds!

Carbon	C
Hydrogen	H
Nitrogen	N
Oxygen	O
Phosphorus	P
Sulfur	S
Fluorine	F
Chlorine	Cl
Bromine	Br
Iodine	I
Silicon	Si
Boron	B

Figure 1.11 | **Colors used to represent atoms of different elements.** The sizes of the spheres roughly illustrate the relative sizes of the different atoms. The atomic symbols of the elements are shown next to their names.

Symbols and subscripts in a chemical formula

Table 1.3	Elements That Occur Naturally as Diatomic Molecules		
Hydrogen	H_2	Fluorine	F_2
Nitrogen	N_2	Chlorine	Cl_2
Oxygen	O_2	Bromine	Br_2
		Iodine	I_2

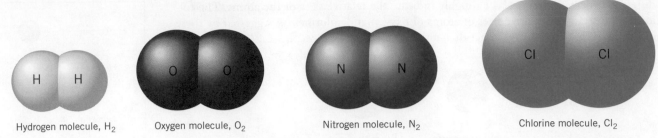

Figure 1.12 | **Models that depict the diatomic molecules of hydrogen, oxygen, nitrogen, and chlorine.** Each contains two atoms per molecule; their different sizes reflect differences in the sizes of the atoms that make up the molecules. The atoms are shaded by color to indicate the element (hydrogen, white; oxygen, red; nitrogen, blue; and chlorine, green).

■ Knowing the arrangement of atoms in a molecule is not something that is obvious from its chemical formula. We discuss some of this in later chapters.

When sufficient information is available it is possible to represent how the atoms in a molecule are connected to each other and even the three-dimensional shape of a molecule. To show how the atoms are connected, we can use chemical symbols to represent the atoms and dashes to indicate the *chemical bonds* that bind the atoms to each other. This kind of formula is often called a *structural formula*.

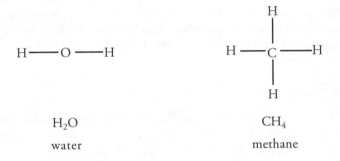

■ Molecular model kits can be purchased that consist of balls with different colors corresponding to the different elements. Also supplied are sticks that can be used to connect the balls to form models of different molecules. The balls have holes drilled at specific angles to give the "molecules" their correct shapes.

Later we will explore in depth the concept of chemical bonds, but for now we can just think of them as "connections" between atoms.

Three-dimensional representations of molecules can take several forms. One is called a **"ball-and-stick" model,** in which spheres representing atoms are connected by sticks that indicate the connections between the atoms. Ball-and-stick models of methane, CH_4 (natural gas), and chloroform, $CHCl_3$ (a compound once used as an anesthetic) are shown in Figure 1.13. Notice that the formula $CHCl_3$ describes a molecule in which there is one atom each of carbon and hydrogen as well as three atoms of chlorine.

■ *WileyPLUS*, found on the Web site for the text, has a number of interactive molecular visualizations that allow you to view and rotate molecules in three dimensions.

Another type of representation is called a **"space-filling" model,** which shows the relative sizes of the atoms and how they take up space with the molecule. The drawings of the diatomic molecules in Figure 1.12 are examples. Space-filling models for water, methane, and chloroform molecules are shown in Figure 1.14.

Figure 1.13 | **Ball-and-stick models.** (*a*) Methane, CH_4. (*b*) Chloroform, $CHCl_3$.

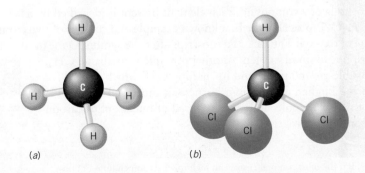

(*a*)   (*b*)

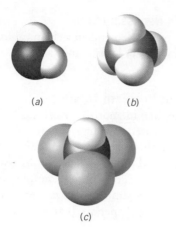

Figure 1.14 | **Space-filling models.** (*a*) Water, H_2O. (*b*) Methane, CH_4. (*c*) Chloroform, $CHCl_3$.

For more complicated compounds, we sometimes find formulas that contain parentheses. An example is the formula for urea, $CO(NH_2)_2$, which tells us that the group of atoms within the parentheses, NH_2, occurs twice. (The formula for urea could also be written as CON_2H_4, but there are good reasons for writing certain formulas with parentheses, as you will see later.) Ball-and-stick and space-filling models of urea are shown in Figure 1.15.

Hydrates: Crystals That Contain Water in Fixed Proportions

Certain compounds form crystals that contain water molecules. An example is ordinary plaster — the material often used to coat the interior walls of buildings. Plaster consists of crystals of a compound called calcium sulfate, $CaSO_4$, which contain two molecules of water for each $CaSO_4$. These water molecules are not held very tightly and can be driven off by heating the crystals. The dried crystals absorb water again if exposed to moisture, and the amount of water absorbed always gives crystals in which the H_2O-to-$CaSO_4$ ratio is 2 to 1. Compounds whose crystals contain water molecules in fixed ratios are called **hydrates,** and they are quite common. The formula for this hydrate of calcium sulfate is written $CaSO_4 \cdot 2H_2O$ to show that there are two molecules of water per $CaSO_4$. The raised dot is used to indicate that the water molecules are not bound very tightly in the crystal and can be removed.

Sometimes the *dehydration* (removal of water) of hydrate crystals produces changes in color. An example is copper sulfate, which is sometimes used as an agricultural fungicide. Copper sulfate forms blue crystals with the formula $CuSO_4 \cdot 5H_2O$ in which there are five water molecules for each $CuSO_4$. When the blue crystals are heated, most of the water is driven off and the solid that remains, now nearly pure $CuSO_4$, is almost white (Figure 1.16). If left exposed to the air, the $CuSO_4$ will absorb moisture and form blue $CuSO_4 \cdot 5H_2O$ again.

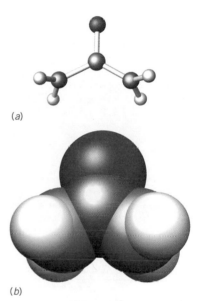

Figure 1.15 | **Models of the urea molecule, $CO(NH_2)_2$.** (*a*) Ball-and-stick model. (*b*) Space filling model.

■ When all the water is removed, the solid is said to be **anhydrous**, meaning without water.

 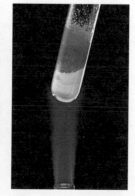

Figure 1.16 | **Water can be driven from hydrates by heating.** (*a*) Blue crystals of copper sulfate pentahydrate, $CuSO_4 \cdot 5H_2O$, about to be heated. (*b*) The hydrate readily loses water when heated. The light-colored solid observed in the lower half of the test tube is pure $CuSO_4$. (*Richard Megna/ Fundamental Photographs; Michael Watson*)

Counting Atoms in Formulas: A Necessary Skill

Counting the number of atoms of the elements in a chemical formula is an operation you will have to perform many times, so let's look at an example.

■ An Important Word about Problem Solving

Learning chemistry is far more than memorizing facts and formulas. To a large degree, your success in this course will be tied to your ability to solve problems, both numerical and non-numerical. Because this is so important, one of the principal goals of this textbook is to help you develop and improve your problem-solving skills. Toward this end we include a large number of detailed worked examples throughout the book. You should study these and then work the similar practice exercises that follow. The answers to all of the practice exercises are in Appendix B at the back of the book, so you can check your work as you proceed.

You will find each of the examples divided into four steps intended to guide you through the thought processes followed by good problem solvers. We encourage you to practice this approach when you tackle problems on your own. As you gain experience, these steps will merge into a seamless, effective way to solve problems, not only in chemistry but in other subjects as well. Let's take a brief look at these four steps and the purpose of each.

■ **Analysis:** If you intend to drive from your home to someplace you haven't been before, you don't just jump in the car and start driving. You first give some thought to where you're going and the route you have to take. Solving chemistry problems begins the same way. In the *Analysis* section, we identify exactly what is being asked and then plan what we have to do to arrive at the solution. Sometimes the analysis will be relatively simple, but with more complex problems, you may have to spend some time thinking about how to solve the problem. You may find it necessary to review a concept to be certain you're on the right track.

■ **Assembling the Tools:** After we've determined how to proceed, the next step is to assemble the various *chemical tools* that apply to the particular problem at hand. These are the tools that have been developed in the text and are identified by the "Tool" icon in the margin. Each tool is chosen because it accomplishes a task required to solve the problem.

■ **Solution:** At last we're ready to work out the answer by applying the appropriate tool to each step of the plan we developed in the *Analysis* section. This is really the simplest part of the problem, because we've already figured out what we have to do and which tools we need to do the job.

■ **Is the Answer Reasonable?** The preceding step has given us an answer, but is it the right answer? Does the answer make sense? It is always prudent to conclude your problem-solving experience with a quick check to see whether the answer is reasonable. As we progress, you will learn some techniques to help you check your answer.

In solving a problem, you have to be flexible. There may be times when you're able to figure out part of a problem in the *Analysis* step, but the full solution isn't apparent. If this happens, proceed with the next two steps and then come back to the *Analysis* again to try to plan the rest of the solution.

The most important thing to remember in working problems in this book is that all of the concepts and tools necessary to solve them have been given to you. If you're struggling, don't despair. Take a break and come back with a fresh perspective. You can be successful.

Example 1.1
Counting Atoms in Formulas

How many atoms of each element are represented by the formulas (a) $(CH_3)_3COH$ and (b) $CoCl_2 \cdot 6H_2O$? In each case, identify the elements in the compound by name.

■ **Analysis:** This is not a difficult problem, but let's proceed methodically just for practice. To answer both parts of this question requires that we understand the meaning of subscripts and parentheses in formulas. We also have to make a connection between the chemical symbol and name of the element, so we need to know where to find this information if we don't already know it.

■ **Assembling the Tools:** Here are the three tools we will use: (1) The subscript following a symbol indicates how many of that element are part of the formula; a subscript of 1 is implied if there is no subscript. (2) A quantity within parentheses is repeated a number of times equal to the subscript that follows. (3) A raised dot in a formula indicates the substance is a hydrate in which the number preceding H_2O specifies how many water molecules are present.

You will gradually learn the names and symbols for many elements. If you forget, you can refer to the table inside the front cover of the book.

■ **Solution:** (a) Here we must recognize that all the atoms within the parentheses occur three times.

Subscript 3 indicates three CH_3 units

↓

$(CH_3)_3COH$

Each CH_3 contains one C and three H atoms, so three of them contain three C and nine H atoms. In the COH unit, there is one additional C and one additional H, which gives a total of four C atoms and 10 H atoms. The molecule also contains one O atom. Therefore, the formula $(CH_3)_3COH$ shows

4 C   10 H   1 O

The elements in the compound are carbon (C), hydrogen (H), and oxygen (O).

(b) This is a formula for a hydrate, as indicated by the raised dot. It contains six water molecules, each with two H and one O, for every $CoCl_2$.

The 6 indicates there are 6 molecules of H_2O.

↓

$CoCl_2 \cdot 6H_2O$

↗

The dot indicates the compound is a hydrate.

Therefore, the formula $CoCl_2 \cdot 6H_2O$ represents

1 Co   2 Cl   12 H   6 O

Checking the table inside the front cover of the book, we see that the elements here are cobalt (Co), chlorine (Cl), hydrogen (H), and oxygen (O).

■ **Are the Answers Reasonable?** The only way to check the answer here is to perform a recount.

Practice Exercises[5]

1.1 | How many atoms of each element are expressed by the following formulas? (*Hint:* Pay special attention to counting elements within parentheses.)

(a) SF_6 (b) $(C_2H_5)_2N_2H_2$ (c) $Ca_3(PO_4)_2$ (d) $Co(NO_3)_2 \cdot 6H_2O$

1.2 | How many atoms of each element are present in each of the formulas below? Consult the table inside the front cover to write the full name of each element as well as its symbol.

(a) NH_4NO_3 (b) $FeNH_4(SO_4)_2$ (c) $Mo(NO_3)_2 \cdot 5H_2O$ (d) $C_6H_4ClNO_2$

1.3 | Write the chemical formula for the fishy-smelling compound with the molecular structure shown in the margin. (See Figure 1.11.) There are groups of atoms that can be written as CH_3 in this molecule. Rewrite the chemical formula for the compound to show the presence of these CH_3 groups.

Atoms, Molecules, and the Law of Definite Proportions

Let's now use our methods of representing atoms and molecules to understand how Dalton's atomic theory accounts for the law of definite proportions. According to the theory, all of the molecules of a compound are alike and contain atoms in the same numerical ratio. Thus all water molecules have the formula H_2O and contain two atoms of hydrogen and one of oxygen.

Today we know that oxygen atoms are much heavier than hydrogen atoms. In fact, one oxygen atom weighs 16 times as much as a hydrogen atom. We haven't said how much mass this is, so let's say that one hydrogen atom has a mass of one unit. On this scale an oxygen atom would then weigh 16 times as much, or 16 mass units.

1 H atom	1 mass unit
1 O atom	16 mass units

In Figure 1.17*a* we see one water molecule with two hydrogen atoms and one oxygen atom. The mass of oxygen in that molecule (16 mass units) is eight times the total mass of hydrogen (2 mass units). In Figure 1.17*b* we have five water molecules containing a total of 10 hydrogen atoms and 5 oxygen atoms. Notice that the total mass of oxygen in the five molecules is, once again, eight times the total mass of hydrogen. Regardless of the number of water molecules in the sample, the total mass of oxygen is eight times the total mass of hydrogen.

Recall from Section 1.3 that in any sample of pure water, the mass of oxygen present is always found experimentally to be eight times the mass of hydrogen—an example of how the law of definite proportions applies to water. Figure 1.17 explains *why* the law works in terms of the atomic theory.

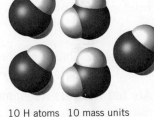

Figure 1.17 | **Law of Definite Proportions.** Regardless of the number of water molecules, the mass of oxygen is always eight times the mass of hydrogen.

2 H atoms	2 mass units		10 H atoms	10 mass units
1 O atom	16 mass units		5 O atoms	80 mass units
(a)			(b)	

---

[5]Answers to the Practice Exercises are found in Appendix B at the back of the book.

The Law of Multiple Proportions

One of the real successes of Dalton's atomic theory was that it predicted another chemical law—one that had not been discovered yet. This law is called the law of multiple proportions and applies to atoms that are able to form two or more different compounds with each other.

Law of Multiple Proportions

Whenever two elements form more than one compound, the different masses of one element that combine with the same mass of the other element are in the ratio of small whole numbers.

To see what this means, consider the two compounds sulfur dioxide, SO_2, and sulfur trioxide, SO_3, which are illustrated in Figure 1.18. In one molecule of each of these compounds there is one atom of sulfur, so both molecules must have the *same mass of sulfur*. Now let's focus on the oxygen. The SO_2 molecule has two O atoms; the SO_3 molecule has three O atoms. This means that the ratio of the atoms of O in the two compounds is 2-to-3.

$$\frac{\text{atoms of O in } SO_2}{\text{atoms of O in } SO_3} = \frac{2 \text{ atoms O}}{3 \text{ atoms O}} = \frac{2}{3}$$

Because all O atoms have the same mass, the *ratio* of the masses of O in the two molecules *must* be the same as the ratio of the atoms, and this ratio (2/3) is a ratio of small whole numbers.

Molecules Small and Large

All of the molecules we've discussed so far are considered to be small molecules because there are so few atoms in each of them. Most of the molecules you will encounter in this book would generally be considered to be small. However, nature does present us with some very large molecules as well, particularly in living organisms. For example, DNA, which is the molecule that differentiates humans from all other species of living things on the planet, consists of millions of atoms woven into a very complex structure. A short segment of a DNA molecule is illustrated in Figure 1.19. We will say more about DNA in Chapter 23.

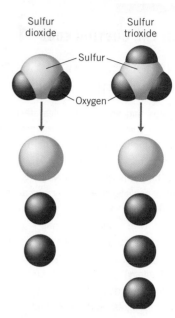

Figure 1.18 | **Oxygen compounds of sulfur demonstrate the law of multiple proportions.** Illustrated here are molecules of sulfur trioxide and sulfur dioxide. Each has one sulfur atom, and therefore the same mass of sulfur. The oxygen ratio is 2-to-3, both by atoms and by mass.

■ DNA, which stands for *deoxyribonucleic acid*, carries the instructions a cell uses to manufacture molecules needed for it to function.

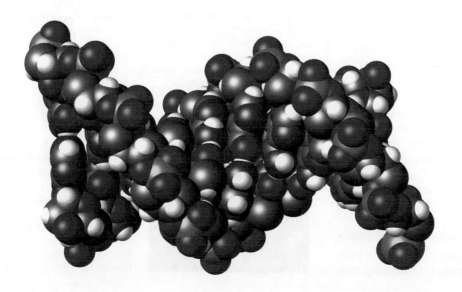

Figure 1.19 | **Some molecules are extremely large.** Shown here is a short segment of a DNA molecule, the structure of which is responsible for the diffences between the various species of living things on earth. An entire DNA molecule contains millions of atoms.

Nanotechnology: Controlling Structure at the Molecular Level

Atoms and small molecules are incredibly tiny. Experiments have shown that they have diameters of the order of several billionths of an inch. For example, the diameter of a carbon atom is about 6 billionths of an inch (6×10^{-9} in.). As you will learn in Chapter 2, the prefix *nano* implies 10^{-9}, so when we examine matter at the *nano-scale* level, we are looking at very small structures, usually with dimensions of perhaps tens to hundreds of atoms. **Nanotechnology** deals with using such small-scale objects and the special properties that accompany them to develop useful applications. Ultimately, the goal of nanotechnology (also sometimes called **molecular nanotechnology**) is to be able to build materials from the atom up. Such technology doesn't quite exist yet, but scientists are beginning to make progress in that direction. This discussion, therefore, is kind of a progress report that will give you some feeling of where science is now and where it's heading—sort of a glimpse at the future.

There are several reasons why there is so much interest in nanotechnology. For one, the properties of materials are related to their structures. By controlling structures at the atomic and molecular level, we can (in principle) tailor materials to have specific properties. Driving much of the research in this area is the continuing efforts by computer and electronics designers to produce ever smaller circuits. The reductions in size achieved through traditional methods are near their limit, so new ways to achieve smaller circuits and smaller electrical devices are being sought.

Molecular Self-Assembly

An area of research that is of great interest today is the field of molecular self-assembly, in which certain molecules, when brought together, spontaneously arrange themselves into desirable structures. Biological systems employ this strategy in constructing structures such as cellular membranes. The goal of scientists is to mimic biology by designing molecules that will self-assemble into specific arrangements.

Visualizing and Manipulating Very Tiny Structures

What has enabled scientists to begin the exploration of the nanoworld is the development of tools that allow them to see and sometimes manipulate individual atoms and molecules. We've already discussed one of these important devices, the scanning tunneling microscope (STM), when we discussed experimental evidence for atoms (see page 10). This instrument, which can only be used with electrically conducting samples, makes it possible to image individual atoms. What is very interesting is that it can also be used to move atoms around on a surface. To illustrate this, scientists have arranged atoms to spell out words (Figure 1). Although writing words with atoms doesn't have much practical use, it demonstrates that one of the required capabilities for working with substances at the molecular level is achievable.

To study nonconducting samples, a device called an **atomic force microscope (AFM)** can be used. Figure 2 illustrates its basic principles. A very sharp stylus (sort of like an old fashioned phono-

Figure 1   **Atoms of iron on copper.** Scientists at IBM used an STM instrument to manipulate iron atoms into the Kanji letters for "atom." The literal translation is something like "original child." *(Courtesy IBM Research Division)*

graph needle) is moved across the surface of the sample under study. Forces between the tip of the probe and the surface molecules cause the probe to flex as it follows the ups and downs of the bumps that are the individual molecules and atoms. A mirrored surface attached to the probe reflects a laser beam at angles proportional to the amount of deflection of the probe. A sensor picks up the signal from the laser and translates it into data that can be analyzed by a computer to give three-dimensional images of the sample's surface. A typical image produced by an AFM is shown in Figure 3.

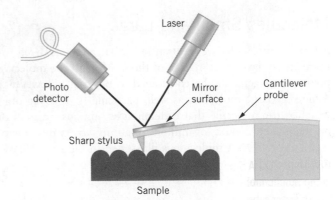

Figure 2   **An Atomic Force Microscope (AFM).** A sharp stylus attached to the end of a cantilever probe rides up and down over the surface features of the sample. A laser beam, reflected off a mirrored surface at the end of the probe, changes angle as the probe moves up and down. A photo detector reads these changes and sends the information to a computer, which translates the data into an image.

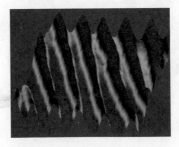

Figure 3   **Silver nanowires imaged using an atomic force microscope.** Colored micrograph of thin silver nanowires spaced about 0.8 millionth of an inch apart on a calcium fluoride crystal surface. Such wires could be used for miniature electronics. *(Science/Photo Library/Photo Researchers)*

The Relationship between Atoms, Molecules, and the World We See

At this point you may begin to think that the formulas and shapes of molecules come to chemists mysteriously "out of the blue." This is hardly the case. When a chemical is first prepared or isolated from nature, its formula is unknown. The compound, for example, might be produced from an experiment in the form of a white powder, and there's nothing about its formula or the arrangement of the atoms within it that come from the outward appearance of the substance. To acquire such knowledge chemists perform experiments, some of which will be described later in this book, that enable them to calculate what the formula of the substance is. Once a formula is known, we might speculate on the shape of the molecule, but a lot of work and very expensive and sophisticated instruments are required to know for sure. (If you take advanced courses in chemistry, it is likely you will get hands-on experience using such instruments.) It is important for you to understand that when we describe the formulas of compounds and the structures of molecules, such information is the culmination of the work of many scientists over many years.

Mixtures at the Atomic/Molecular Level

Earlier we noted that mixtures differ from elements and compounds in that mixtures can have variable compositions. Figure 1.20 illustrates this at the atomic/molecular level, where we have used different-color spheres to stand for two substances in a homogeneous mixture (also called a solution). Notice that the two substances are quite uniformly mixed. The difference between homogeneous and heterogeneous mixtures on the molecular level can be seen by comparing Figure 1.20 and 1.21.

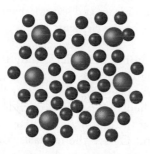

Figure 1.20 | **A portion of a homogeneous mixture viewed at the atomic/molecular level.** Red and blue spheres represent two different substances (not two different elements). One substance is uniformly distributed throughout the other.

Figure 1.21 | **A portion of a heterogeneous mixture viewed at the atomic/molecular level.** Two substances exist in separate phases in a heterogeneous mixture.

1.6 | Chemical Reactions and Chemical Equations

Chemical reactions are at the heart of chemistry. When they occur, dramatic changes often occur among the chemicals involved. While chemical reactions are interesting to observe in the laboratory, they have an enormous number of applications in industry and ordinary everyday living. Some reactions occur rapidly and violently, such as the reaction between hydrogen and oxygen in the main engine of the space shuttle, which is used to help lift the vehicle from its launch pad (Figure 1.22). In this case, the reaction forms harmless water vapor. Other reactions are less violent. For example, you may use Clorox as a bleach because its active ingredients react with stains in clothing and also destroy bacteria. These are just two examples; many others lie in the pages ahead.

Figure 1.22 | **Reaction of hydrogen with oxygen.** This photo shows the three main engines of the space shuttle at full power an instant before the booster rockets fire and lift the space craft from its launch pad. The violent reaction of hydrogen with oxygen provides the thrust produced by the main engines. *(Courtesy NASA)*

Figure 1.23 | **The combustion of methane.** Gas-burning stoves that use natural gas (methane) as a fuel are common in many parts of the United States. The reaction consumes oxygen and produces carbon dioxide and water vapor. *(photocuisine/© Corbis)*

Coefficients in an equation

■ The coefficients of CH_4 and CO_2 are each equal to 1.

To understand chemical reactions, we need to observe how they lead to changes among the properties of chemical substances. Consider, for example, the mixture of elements iron and sulfur shown in Figure 1.6 on page 8. The sulfur has a bright yellow color, and the iron appears in this mixture as a black powder with magnetic properties. If these elements react, they can form a compound called iron sulfide (also known as "fools gold"), and as shown in Figure 1.8, it doesn't look like either sulfur or iron, and it is not magnetic. When iron and sulfur combine chemically, the properties of the elements give way to the new properties of the compound.

To see how a chemical change occurs at the atomic level, let's study the combustion of methane, CH_4, the chief component in natural gas used in typical gas-burning kitchen stoves (Figure 1.23). The reaction consumes CH_4 and oxygen (O_2, which is how oxygen occurs in nature) and forms in their place carbon dioxide, CO_2, and water, H_2O. Figure 1.24 illustrates the reaction at the atomic/molecular level. For the reaction between methane and oxygen, CH_4 and O_2 are the **reactants**; these are the substances present before the reaction begins and are shown on the left in Figure 1.24. On the right we see the **products** of the reaction, which are the molecules present after the reaction is complete. The arrow indicates that the reactants undergo the change to form the products.

Drawing pictures to describe a chemical change can be awkward. Instead, chemists normally use chemical symbols to describe reactions by writing chemical equations. A **chemical equation** uses chemical formulas to describe what happens when a chemical reaction occurs. As also shown in Figure 1.24, it describes the before-and-after picture of the chemical substances involved.

$$CH_4 + 2O_2 \longrightarrow CO_2 + 2H_2O \tag{1}$$

The symbols stand for atoms of the elements involved. The numbers that precede O_2 and H_2O are called **coefficients**. In this equation, the coefficients tell us how many CH_4 and O_2 molecules react and how many CO_2 and H_2O molecules are formed. Note that when no coefficient is written in front of a formula, it is assumed to be equal to 1. The arrow in a chemical equation is read as "reacts to yield." Thus, this chemical equation would be read as *methane and oxygen react to yield carbon dioxide and water.*

Chemical Reactions and Conservation of Mass

The law of conservation of mass says that mass is neither created nor destroyed in a chemical reaction. In Figure 1.24, observe that before the reaction begins there are four H atoms, four O atoms, and one C atom among the reactants. They are found in one CH_4 molecule and two O_2 molecules. After the reaction is over, we still have the same number of atoms of each kind, but they have become rearranged into one CO_2 molecule and two H_2O molecules. Because atoms are neither lost nor created during the reaction, the total mass must remain the same. Thus, by applying the concept of atoms and the postulate of Dalton's atomic theory that says atoms simply rearrange during a chemical reaction, we've accounted for the law of conservation of mass.

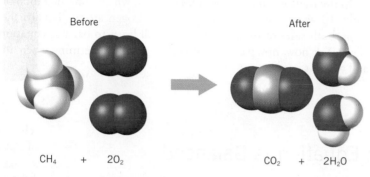

Before   After

CH_4 + $2O_2$ CO_2 + $2H_2O$

Figure 1.24 | **The reaction of methane, CH$_4$, with oxygen, O$_2$ to give carbon dioxide, CO$_2$, and water, viewed at the atomic-molecular level.** On the left are methane and oxygen molecules before reaction, and on the right are the carbon dioxide and water molecules that are present after the reaction is complete. Below the drawings is the chemical equation for the reaction.

Coefficients in Equations and the Law of Conservation of Mass

All chemical reactions obey the law of conservation of mass, which means that in any reaction the total number of atoms of each kind before and after are the same. When we write chemical equations we adjust the numbers of molecules on each side of the arrow to make the equation conform to this principle. We say we *balance* the equation, and we accomplish this by adjusting the coefficients in front of reactant and product molecules. In the equation for the combustion of methane, the coefficients in front of O_2 on the left and H_2O on the right make this a **balanced equation**.

Let's look at another example, the combustion of butane, C_4H_{10}, the fuel in disposable cigarette lighters (Figure 1.25).

Figure 1.25 | **The combustion of butane, C$_4$H$_{10}$.** The products are carbon dioxide and water vapor. *(Robert Capece)*

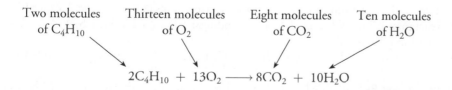

Two molecules of C_4H_{10} Thirteen molecules of O_2 Eight molecules of CO_2 Ten molecules of H_2O

$$2C_4H_{10} + 13O_2 \longrightarrow 8CO_2 + 10H_2O$$

The 2 before the C_4H_{10} tells us that two molecules of butane react. This involves a total of 8 carbon atoms and 20 hydrogen atoms, as we see in Figure 1.26. Notice that we

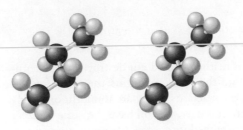

Figure 1.26 | **Understanding coefficients in an equation.** The expression $2C_4H_{10}$ describes two molecules of butane, each of which contains 4 carbon and 10 hydrogen atoms. This gives a total of 8 carbon and 20 hydrogen atoms.

Two molecules of butane contain 8 atoms of C and 20 atoms of H.

have multiplied the numbers of atoms of C and H in one molecule of C_4H_{10} by the coefficient 2. On the right we find 8 molecules of CO_2, which contain a total of 8 carbon atoms. Similarly, 10 water molecules contain 20 hydrogen atoms. Finally, there are 26 oxygen atoms on both sides of the equation. You will learn to balance equations such as this in Chapter 4. For now, however, you should be able to determine when an equation is balanced and when it is not.

Example 1.2
Determining Whether an Equation Is Balanced

Determine whether or not the following chemical equations are balanced. Support your conclusions by writing how many of each element is on either side of the arrow.

(a) $Fe(OH)_3 + 2HNO_3 \longrightarrow Fe(NO_3)_3 + 2H_2O$

(b) $BaCl_2 + H_2SO_4 \longrightarrow BaSO_4 + 2HCl$

(c) $C_6H_{12}O_6 + 6O_2 \longrightarrow 6CO_2 + 6H_2O$

■ **Analysis:** The statement of the problem asks whether the equations are balanced. You can prove an equation is balanced if each element has the same number of atoms on either side of the arrow.

■ **Assembling the Tools:** The meaning of subscripts and parentheses in formulas as well as the meaning of coefficients in front of formulas are the tools we will use to count atoms. Note that in two of the equations, oxygen appears in both reactants and both products. We must be sure to count all of the atoms.

■ **Solution:**

(a) Reactants: 1 Fe, 9 O, 5 H, 2 N; Products: 1 Fe, 11 O, 4 H, 3 N   Only Fe has the same number of atoms on either side of the arrow. This equation is *not* balanced.

(b) Reactants: 1 Ba, 2 Cl, 2 H, 1 S, 4 O; Products: 1 Ba, 2 Cl, 2 H, 1 S, 4 O.   This equation *is* balanced.

(c) Reactants: 6 C, 12 H, 18 O; Products: 6 C, 12 H, 18 O.   This equation *is* balanced.

■ **Is the Answer Reasonable?** The appropriate way to check this is to recount the atoms. Try counting the atoms in the reverse direction this time.

1.4 | How many atoms of each element appear on each side of the arrow in the following equation? (*Hint*: Recall that coefficients multiply the elements in the entire formula.)

$$4NH_3 + 3O_2 \longrightarrow 2N_2 + 6H_2O$$

1.5 | Count the number of atoms of each element on both sides of the arrow to determine whether the following equation is balanced.

$$2(NH_4)_3PO_4 + 3Ba(C_2H_3O_2)_2 \longrightarrow Ba_3(PO_4)_2 + 6NH_4C_2H_3O_2$$

1.6 | The gas ethane, C_2H_6, burns in oxygen (O_2) to give carbon dioxide (CO_2) and water. Use drawings to construct a balanced equation showing C_2H_6 and O_2 on the left and CO_2 and H_2O on the right. The ethane molecule can be represented as shown in the margin.

Practice Exercises

| Summary

Chemistry and the Scientific Method. **Chemistry** is a science that studies the properties and composition of **matter**, which is defined as anything that has **mass** and occupies space. Chemistry employs the **scientific method** in which **observations** are used to collect **empirical facts**, or **data**, that can be summarized in **scientific laws**. **Models** of nature begin as **hypotheses** that mature into **theories** when they survive repeated testing.

Elements, Compounds, and Mixtures. An **element**, which is identified by its **chemical symbol**, cannot be decomposed into something simpler by a **chemical reaction**. Elements combine in fixed proportions to form **compounds**. Elements and compounds are **pure substances** that may be combined in *varying* proportions to give **mixtures**. If a mixture has two or more **phases**, it is **heterogeneous**. A one-phase **homogeneous** mixture is called a **solution**. Formation or separation of a mixture into its components can be accomplished by a **physical change**, which doesn't alter the chemical composition of the substances involved. Formation or decomposition of a compound takes place by a **chemical change** that changes the chemical makeup of the substances involved.

Atomic Theory. Dalton based his **atomic theory** on two laws of chemical combination, the **law of definite proportions** (in a compound, the elements are combined in fixed proportions by mass) and the **law of conservation of mass** (no change in mass occurs during a chemical reaction). Dalton's theory proposed that matter consists of indestructible **atoms** with masses that do not change during chemical reactions. During a chemical reaction, atoms may change partners, but they are neither created nor destroyed. After Dalton had proposed his theory, it was discovered that whenever two elements form more than one compound, the different masses of one element that combine with a fixed mass of the other are in a ratio of small whole numbers (the **law of multiple proportions**). Using modern instruments such as the **scanning tunneling microscope**, scientists are able to "see" atoms on the surfaces of solids.

Atoms, Molecules, and Chemical Formulas. In drawing atoms, spheres of different sizes and colors are used, each standing for a particular element. Each element has its own unique **chemical symbol**. Atoms combine to form more complex substances, many of which consist of **molecules** composed of two or more atoms.

Chemical formulas are used to describe chemical substances. **Subscripts** are used to indicate the number of atoms of each type in a molecule. Many common **free elements** occur as **diatomic molecules**. Chemical symbols can be used in drawings to indicate how atoms are attached to each other in compounds. Three-dimensional representations of molecules can be **ball-and-stick** or **space-filling models**. Some compounds form solids called **hydrates**, which contain water molecules in definite proportions.

Using atoms we can account for the law of definite proportions. The atomic theory also led to the discovery of the **law of multiple proportions.**

Chemical Reactions and Chemical Equations. Significant changes in the properties of substances are observed when **chemical reactions** occur, and **chemical equations** are used to show how the **reactants** change to **products**. **Coefficients** in front of formulas indicate the number of molecules that react or are formed and are used to balance an equation, making the total numbers of atoms of each kind the same on both sides of the arrow. A **balanced equation** conforms to the law of conservation of mass.

Tools for Problem Solving

In this chapter you learned a variety of concepts that are useful as tools for solving problems. Study each one carefully so that you know what each is used for. When faced with solving a problem, recall what each tool does and consider whether it will be helpful in finding a solution. This will aid you in selecting the tools you need.

Law of definite proportions (page 9)

When dealing with a chemical compound, we can rely on its formula to accurately describe its atomic composition in all samples of the substance. A given compound will *always* have the same atomic composition and the elements will always be present in the same proportions by mass.

Law of conservation of mass (page 9)

We use this law whenever we balance a chemical equation. When dealing with any chemical reaction, all of a given element in the reactants must also be present in the products. You will use this principle in chemical calculations in later chapters.

Colors used to represent different elements in a model of a molecule (page 11)

Use the color code in Figure 1.11 to recognize elements in a drawing of a model of a molecule.

Chemical symbols and subscripts in a chemical formula (page 11)

In a chemical formula, the chemical symbol stands for an atom of an element. Subscripts show the number of atoms of each kind represented in a chemical formula. When a subscript follows parentheses, it multiplies everything within the parentheses.

Coefficients in an equation (page 20)

Coefficients indicate the number of chemical units of each type that are present in reactants and products. They are used to balance an equation.

Review Questions

Introduction; the Scientific Method

1.1 After some thought, give two reasons why a course in chemistry will benefit *you* in the pursuit of your particular major.

1.2 What steps are involved in the scientific method?

1.3 What is the difference between (a) a law and a theory, (b) an observation and a conclusion, (c) an observation and data?

1.4 Can a theory be proved to be correct? Can a theory be proved to be wrong?

Properties of Substances

OH **1.5** Define *matter.* Which of the following are examples of matter? (a) air, (b) a pencil, (c) a cheese sandwich, (d) a squirrel, (e) your mother

1.6 What is *a physical change*? What is *a chemical change*? What is the chief distinction between physical and chemical changes?

1.7 "A sample of calcium (an electrically conducting white metal that is shiny, relatively soft, melts at 850 °C, and boils at 1440 °C) was placed into liquid water that was at 25 °C. The calcium reacted slowly with the water to give bubbles of gaseous hydrogen and a solution of the substance calcium hydroxide." Based on this description, what physical changes and what chemical changes occurred?

OH **1.8** In places like Saudi Arabia, freshwater is scarce and is recovered from seawater. When seawater is boiled, the water evaporates and the steam can be condensed to give pure water that people can drink. If all the water is evaporated, solid salt is left behind. Are the changes described here chemical or physical?

Elements, Compounds, and Mixtures

1.9 Define (a) element, (b) compound, (c) mixture, (d) homogeneous, (e) heterogeneous, (f) phase, (g) solution.

1.10 Which kind of change, chemical or physical, is needed to change a compound into its elements?

1.11 What is the chemical symbol for each of the following elements? (a) chlorine, (b) sulfur, (c) iron, (d) silver, (e) sodium, (f) phosphorus, (g) iodine, (h) copper, (i) mercury, (j) calcium

1.12 What is the name of each of the following elements? (a) K, (b) Zn, (c) Si, (d) Sn, (e) Mn, (f) Mg, (g) Ni, (h) Al, (i) C, (j) N

1.13 For each of the following molecular pictures, state whether it represents a pure substance or a mixture. For pure substances, state whether it represents an element or a compound. For mixtures, state whether it is homogeneous or heterogeneous.

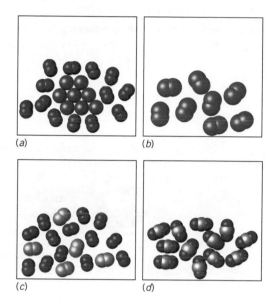

(a)   (b)

(c)   (d)

1.14 Consider the following four samples of matter.

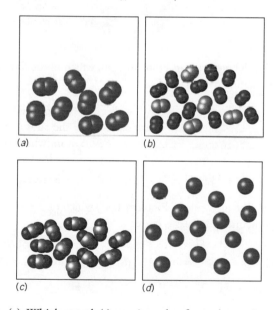

(a)   (b)

(c)   (d)

(a) Which sample(s) consist only of one element?

(b) Which sample(s) consist only of a compound?

(c) Which sample(s) consist of diatomic molecules?

Laws of Chemical Combination and Dalton's Theory

1.15 Name and state the two laws of chemical combination discussed in this chapter.

1.16 In your own words, describe how Dalton's atomic theory explains the law of conservation of mass and the law of definite proportions.

1.17   Which of the laws of chemical combination is used to define the term *compound*?

1.18 Describe the law of multiple proportions. Use the molecules illustrated below to demonstrate the law.

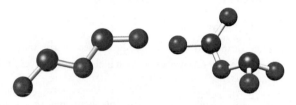

1.19 Explain how the following molecules demonstrate the law of multiple proportions.

1.20 Do samples containing the following molecules demonstrate the law of multiple proportions? Explain.

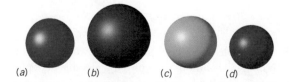

Chemical Formulas

1.21 What are two ways to interpret a chemical symbol?

1.22 What is the difference between an atom and a molecule?

1.23 Write the formulas and names of the elements that exist in nature as diatomic molecules.

1.24 Atoms of which elements are usually represented by the following drawings? Give their names and chemical symbols.

(a)   (b)   (c)   (d)

1.25 Atoms of which elements are usually represented by the following drawings? Give their names and chemical symbols.

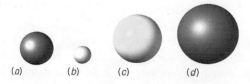

(a)   (b)   (c)   (d)

1.26 A DNA molecule is small in actual size but contains an enormous number of atoms. Surprisingly, the molecule is made up of atoms of just five different elements. Study Figure 1.19 and identify which elements those are.

Chemical Equations

1.27 What do we mean when we say a chemical equation is *balanced*? Why do we balance chemical equations?

1.28 For a chemical reaction, what do we mean by the term *reactants*? What do we mean by the term *products*?

1.29 The combustion of a thin wire of magnesium metal (Mg) in an atmosphere of pure oxygen produces the brilliant light of a flashbulb, once commonly used in photography. After the reaction, a thin film of magnesium oxide is seen on the inside of the bulb. The equation for the reaction is

$$2Mg + O_2 \longrightarrow 2MgO$$

(a) State in words how this equation is read.

(b) Give the formula(s) of the reactants.

(c) Give the formula(s) of the products.

| Review Problems

Chemical Formulas

1.30 The compound $Cr(C_2H_3O_2)_3$ is used in the tanning of leather. How many atoms of each element are given in this formula?

1.31 Asbestos, a known cancer-causing agent, has a typical formula of $Ca_3Mg_5(Si_4O_{11})_2(OH)_2$. How many atoms of each element are given in this formula?

1.32 Epsom salts is a hydrate of magnesium sulfate, $MgSO_4 \cdot 7H_2O$. What is the formula of the substance that remains when Epsom salts is completely dehydrated?

1.33 Rochelle salt is the tetrahydrate of $KNaC_4H_4O_6$, which means there are four molecules of water per $KNaC_4H_4O_6$. Write the formula for Rochelle salt.

1.34 A molecule of acetic acid, formed when wine spoils and becomes sour, is shown below. Write the chemical formula for the molecule.

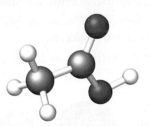

1.35 A molecule of dimethyl sulfide is shown below. The compound is a sulfurous gas with a disagreeable odor produced from breakdown products of phytoplankton through biological interactions. Write the chemical formula for the molecule. Is there a way you can write this formula using parentheses?

1.36 Write the chemical formula for the molecule illustrated below.

1.37 Write the chemical formula for the molecule illustrated below.

1.38 For the molecule in Problem 1.36, which of the following structural formulas is correct?

(a)
$$\overset{\displaystyle N}{\overset{\displaystyle |}{H-H-H}}$$

(b)
$$\overset{\displaystyle H}{\overset{\displaystyle |}{H-N-H}}$$

(c) $H-H-H-N$

(d)
$$\overset{\displaystyle H}{\overset{\displaystyle |}{N-H-H}}$$

1.39 For the molecule in Problem 1.37, which of the following structural formulas is correct?

(a)
$$H-O-\overset{\displaystyle H}{\underset{\displaystyle H}{\overset{\displaystyle |}{\underset{\displaystyle |}{C}}}}-\overset{\displaystyle H}{\underset{\displaystyle H}{\overset{\displaystyle |}{\underset{\displaystyle |}{C}}}}-O-H$$

(b)
$$H-\overset{\displaystyle H}{\underset{\displaystyle H}{\overset{\displaystyle |}{\underset{\displaystyle |}{C}}}}-O-\overset{\displaystyle H}{\underset{\displaystyle H}{\overset{\displaystyle |}{\underset{\displaystyle |}{C}}}}-O-H$$

(c)
$$H-\overset{\displaystyle H}{\underset{\displaystyle H}{\overset{\displaystyle |}{\underset{\displaystyle |}{C}}}}-O-\overset{\displaystyle H}{\underset{\displaystyle H}{\overset{\displaystyle |}{\underset{\displaystyle |}{O}}}}-C-H$$

(d)
$$H-O-\overset{\displaystyle H}{\underset{\displaystyle H}{\overset{\displaystyle |}{\underset{\displaystyle |}{C}}}}-\overset{\displaystyle H}{\underset{\displaystyle H}{\overset{\displaystyle |}{\underset{\displaystyle |}{C}}}}-O-H$$

1.40 How many atoms of each element are represented in each of the following formulas? For each, name the elements present. (a) $K_2C_2O_4$, (b) H_2SO_3, (c) $C_{12}H_{26}$, (d) $HC_2H_3O_2$, (e) $(NH_4)_2HPO_4$

1.41 How many atoms of each kind are represented in the following formulas? For each, name the elements present. (a) H_3PO_4, (b) $Ca(H_2PO_4)_2$, (c) C_4H_9Br, (d) $Fe_3(AsO_4)_2$, (e) $C_3H_5(OH)_3$

1.42 How many atoms of each kind are represented in the following formulas? For each, name the elements present. (a) $Ni(ClO_4)_2$, (b) $COCl_2$, (c) $K_2Cr_2O_7$, (d) CH_3CO_2H, (e) $(NH_4)_2HPO_4$

1.43 How many atoms of each kind are represented in the following formulas? For each, name the elements present. (a) $CH_3CH_2CO_2C_3H_7$, (b) $MgSO_4 \cdot 7H_2O$, (c) $KAl(SO_4)_2 \cdot 12H_2O$, (d) $Cu(NO_3)_2$, (e) $(CH_3)_3COH$

1.44 How many atoms of each element are represented in each of the following expressions?

(a) $3N_2O$,   (b) $4(CH_3)_2S$,   (c) $2CuSO_4 \cdot 5H_2O$

OH **1.45** How many atoms of each element are represented in each of the following expressions?

(a) $7CH_3CO_2H$,   (b) $2(NH_2)_2CO$,   (c) $5C_3H_5(OH)_3$

Law of Multiple Proportions

1.46 Write chemical formulas for the following molecules and explain how samples containing them can be chosen to demonstrate the law of multiple proportions.

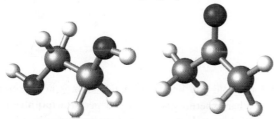

1.47 Write chemical formulas for the following molecules and explain how samples containing them can be chosen to demonstrate the law of multiple proportions.

Chemical Equations

1.48 Consider the balanced equation

$$2Fe(NO_3)_3 + 3Na_2CO_3 \longrightarrow Fe_2(CO_3)_3 + 6NaNO_3$$

(a) How many atoms of Na are on each side of the equation?
(b) How many atoms of C are on each side of the equation?
(c) How many atoms of O are on each side of the equation?
(d) How many atoms of Fe are on each side of the equation?

1.49 Consider the balanced equation for the combustion of hexane, a component of gasoline:

$$2C_6H_{14} + 19O_2 \longrightarrow 12CO_2 + 14H_2O$$

(a) How many atoms of C are on each side of the equation?
(b) How many atoms of H are on each side of the equation?
(c) How many atoms of O are on each side of the equation?

1.50 When sulfur impurities in fuels burn, they produce pollutants such as sulfur dioxide, a major contributor to acid rain. The following is a typical reaction.

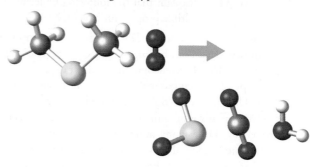

On the left are reactant molecules and on the right are product molecules in a chemical reaction. How many molecules of each kind are necessary to have a balanced equation containing the smallest total number of molecules? Write the balanced chemical equation using chemical formulas.

1.51 Race car drivers can get extra power by burning methyl alcohol with nitrous oxide. Below on the left are the reactant molecules and on the right are product molecules of the chemical reaction. How many molecules of each kind are necessary to have a balanced equation containing the smallest total number of molecules? Write the balanced chemical equation using chemical formulas.

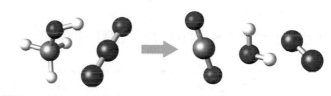

1.52 Is the following chemical equation for the combustion of octane (C_8H_{18}), a component of gasoline, balanced?

$$C_8H_{18} + 12O_2 \longrightarrow 8CO_2 + 9H_2O$$

If not, what is the smallest set of coefficients that would make the equation balanced?

1.53 Is the following chemical equation balanced? This reaction is used for the production of nitric acid, HNO_3, and is one of the reactions responsible for acid rain.

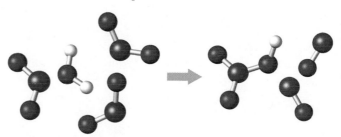

$$3NO_2 + H_2O \longrightarrow HNO_3 + 2NO$$

If the equation is not balanced, find coefficients that would make it balanced.

| Additional Exercises

1.54 How would you explain that the following molecules follow the law of multiple proportions? N_2O, NO_2

1.55 The following are models of molecules of two compounds composed of carbon, hydrogen, and oxygen. The one on the left is ethanol, the alcohol that's added to gasoline with the hope of reducing our dependence on foreign oil supplies. The one on the right is dimethyl ether, a compound that is a gas at room temperature and is used as an aerosol propellant. How many atoms of carbon, hydrogen, and oxygen are in each of these molecules? Find a way to write the formula of one of them using parentheses so that the two compounds can be distinguished one from the other.

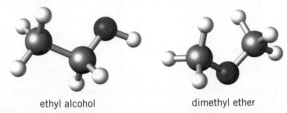

ethyl alcohol   dimethyl ether

1.56 A student obtained a sample from an experiment that had the following composition:

If the experiment were repeated and another sample were obtained, would it have to have the exact same composition? Would the results of these experiments illustrate the law of definite proportions? Explain.

1.57 Suppose you wanted to separate the sample illustrated in the preceding question into its constituent chemical elements. (a) Would a physical change be sufficient? (b) If not, what could be accomplished by a physical change? (c) Would a chemical change be required? (d) If so, on which substance would a chemical change have to be applied? (e) Would the elements isolated by these changes necessarily be composed of individual atoms, or would at least one be composed of molecules?

| Exercises in Critical Thinking

1.58 A solution is defined as a uniform mixture consisting of a single phase. With our vastly improved abilities to "see" smaller and smaller particles, down to the atomic level, present an argument for the proposition that all mixtures are heterogeneous. Present the argument that the ability to observe objects as small as an atom has no effect on the definitions of heterogeneous and homogeneous.

1.59 How do you know that Coca Cola is not a compound? What experiments could you perform to prove it? What would you do to prove that the rusting of iron is a chemical change rather than a physical change?

2 Scientific Measurements

Chapter Outline

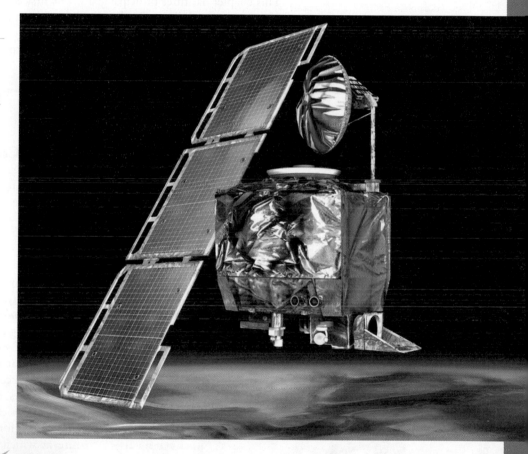

The grand photos and artist's renderings of spacecraft reaching the moon, planets, and outer reaches of the solar system are familiar to all. The achievement is remarkable because it has been a little over one hundred years since powered flight was achieved. Along with the grandeur come the details. On September 23, 1999, the Mars Climate Orbiter crashed into the surface of Mars. On September 30, NASA announced that the cause of the accident was a mix-up in measurement units. Although computers can transfer numbers easily, units are more difficult. Without the units, scientists were unaware that their calculations were in error, and the spacecraft was given incorrect instructions. This incident simply highlights the central theme of this chapter, which emphasizes the use of units along with numbers in all calculations.   (NASA/JPL)

This Chapter in Context

In Chapter 1 we saw that chemistry is an atomic and molecular science. One of the basic tenets of chemistry is that if we understand the nature of our atoms and molecules on the microscopic scale, we will be able to understand the properties of chemicals on the macroscopic scale. We obtain this understanding by making precise observations and numerical measurements.

At this point in time, scientists have become very systematic in making and reporting measurements. As we will see in this chapter, we need to understand which physical and chemical properties are important to measure. Then we will find that of all the many measurements we can make, there are only seven basic units, in various combinations, that describe all of them. Finally, we will see that once we make our measurements there are certain rules to follow so that the answers to our calculations will be reported correctly.

This chapter has three principal goals. The first is to provide you with an appreciation of the nature of and distinction between physical and chemical properties. The second is to explain the way scientists approach the process of making quantitative experimental observations of these properties. The third goal is to describe the accepted methods for treating experimental data.

2.1 | Physical and Chemical Properties

■ As in Chapter 1, some material may be familiar from a past science course. This chapter emphasizes that mathematics is an important tool for success in chemistry. A very good working knowledge of algebra will be important as we progress.

In chemistry we use **properties** (characteristics) of materials to identify them and to distinguish one substance from another. To help organize our thinking, we classify properties into two different types, physical and chemical.

Physical Properties

One way to classify properties is based on whether or not the chemical composition of an object is changed by the act of observing the property. *A* **physical property** *is one that can be observed without changing the chemical makeup of a substance.* For example, a physical property of gold is that it is yellow. The act of observing this property (color) doesn't change the chemical makeup of the gold. Neither does observing that gold conducts electricity, so color and electrical conductivity are physical properties.

Sometimes, observing a physical property does lead to a physical change. To measure the melting point of ice, for example, we observe the temperature at which the solid begins to melt (Figure 2.1). This is a physical change because it does not lead to a change in chemical composition; both ice and liquid water are composed of water molecules.

States of Matter

When we observe ice melting, we see two states of matter, liquid and solid. Water can also exist as a gas that we call water vapor or steam. Although ice, liquid water, and steam have quite different appearances and physical properties, they are just different forms of the same substance, water. **Solid, liquid,** and **gas** are the most common **states of matter.** As with water, most substances are able to exist in all

Figure 2.1 | **Liquid water and ice are both composed of water molecules.** Melting the ice cube does not change the chemical composition of the molecules. *(Daniel Smith/Corbis)*

three of these states, and the state we observe generally depends on the temperature. The obvious properties of solids, liquids, and gases can be interpreted at a submicroscopic level according to the different ways the individual atomic-size particles are organized (Figure 2.2). For a given substance, a change from one state to another is a physical change.

In Chapter 1 we discussed chemical equations. We saw that they must obey the law of conservation of mass by being balanced. We also saw that these equations represented the actual interaction of atoms and molecules. An additional refinement of the chemical equation that we can make is to specify the state of each substance. For instance, we can rewrite the combustion reaction for butane and include the states of each substance.

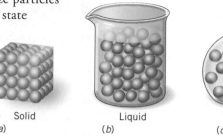

Solid (a)   Liquid (b)   Gas (c)

$$2C_4H_{10}(g) + 13O_2(g) \longrightarrow 8CO_2(g) + 10H_2O(g)$$

Each of the substances is followed by (g) to show it is in the gas state, since butane burns at a temperature above the boiling point of water. In a similar way we can indicate that a substance is a solid with (s) or a liquid with (l).

Figure 2.2 | Solid, liquid, and gaseous states viewed using the atomic model of matter.
(*a*) In a solid, the particles are tightly packed and cannot move easily. (*b*) In a liquid, the particles are still close together but can readily move past one another. (*c*) In a gas, particles are far apart with much empty space between them.

Chemical Properties

A **chemical property** *describes a chemical change (chemical reaction) that a substance undergoes.* When a chemical reaction takes place, chemicals interact to form entirely *different* substances with different chemical and physical properties. An example is the rusting of iron, which involves a chemical reaction between iron, oxygen, and water. When these three react, the product, rust, no longer looks like iron, oxygen, or water. It's a brown solid that isn't at all like a metal, and it is not attracted by a magnet (Figure 2.3).

The ability of iron to form rust in the presence of oxygen and moisture is a chemical property of iron. When we observe this property, the reaction changes the iron, oxygen, and water into rust, so after we've made the observation we no longer have the same substances as before. In describing a chemical property, we usually refer to a chemical reaction.

In modern science, we often want to know whether a substance presents a health hazard before we use it. Health hazards of materials are usually a type of chemical property whereby a substance will have an adverse effect on one or more of the many chemical reactions within our bodies. Toxicology is a field of science that depends heavily on chemical principles to assess the effects of poisons and toxins on living organisms.

Intensive and Extensive Properties

Another way of classifying a property is according to whether or not it depends on the size of the sample. For example, two different pieces of gold can have different volumes, but both have the same characteristic shiny yellow color and both will begin to melt at the same temperature. Color and melting point (and boiling point, too) are examples of **intensive properties**—*properties that are independent of sample size.* Volume, on the other hand, is an **extensive property**—*a property that depends on sample size.* Mass is another extensive property.

A job chemists often perform is *chemical analysis.* They're asked, "What is a particular sample composed of?" To answer such a question, the chemist relies on the properties of the chemicals that make up the sample. For identification purposes, intensive properties are more useful than extensive ones because every sample of a given substance exhibits the same set of intensive properties.

Color, freezing point, and boiling point are examples of intensive physical properties that can help us identify substances. Chemical properties are also intensive properties and also can be used for identification. For example, gold miners were able to distinguish between real gold and fool's gold, a mineral also called pyrite (Figure 1.8, page 8), by heating the material in a flame. Nothing happens to the gold, but the pyrite sputters, smokes, and releases bad-smelling fumes because of its ability, when heated, to react chemically with oxygen in the air.

Figure 2.3 | Chemical reactions cause changes in composition.
Here we see a coating of rust that has formed on an iron object. The properties and chemical composition of the rust are entirely different from those of the iron. *(George B. Diebold/Corbis Images)*

2.2 | Measurement of Physical and Chemical Properties

Qualitative and Quantitative Observations

Earlier you learned that an important step in the scientific method is observation. In general, observations fall into two categories, qualitative and quantitative. **Qualitative observations**, such as the color of a chemical or that a mixture becomes hot when a reaction occurs, do not involve numerical information. **Quantitative observations** are those **measurements** that do yield numerical data. You make such observations in everyday life, for example, when you glance at your watch or step onto a bathroom scale. In chemistry, we make various measurements that aid us in describing both chemical and physical properties.

Measurements Include Units

Measurements involve numbers, but they differ from the numbers used in mathematics in two crucial ways.

First, measurements always involve a comparison. When you say that a person is six feet tall, you're really saying that the person is six times taller than a reference object that is 1 foot high, where *foot* is an example of a **unit of measurement**. *Both the number and the unit are essential parts of the measurement,* because the unit gives the reported value a sense of size. For example, if you were told that the distance between two points is 25, you would naturally ask "25 what?" The distance could be 25 inches, 25 feet, 25 miles, or 25 of any other unit that's used to express distance. A number without a unit is really meaningless. *Writing down a measurement without a unit is a common and serious mistake, and one you should avoid.*

The second important difference is that measurements always involve uncertainty; they are *inexact*. The act of measurement involves an estimation of one sort or another, and both the observer and the instruments used to make the measurement have inherent physical limitations. As a result, measurements always include some uncertainty, which can be minimized but never entirely eliminated. We will say more about this topic in Section 2.3.

International System of Units (SI Units)

A standard system of units is essential if measurements are to be made consistently. In the sciences, and in virtually every nation on Earth, except the United States, metric-based units are used. The advantage of working with metric units is that converting to larger or smaller values can be done simply by moving a decimal point, because metric units are related to each other by simple multiples of ten.

In 1960, a simplification of the original metric system was adopted by the General Conference on Weights and Measures (an international body). It is called the **International System of Units**, abbreviated **SI** from the French name, *Le Système International d'Unités*. The SI is now the dominant system of units in science and engineering, although there is still some usage of older metric units.

The SI has as its foundation a set of **base units** (Table 2.1) for seven measured quantities. For now, we will focus on the base units for length, mass, time, and temperature. We will discuss the unit for amount of substance, the mole, at length in Chapter 4. The unit for electrical current, the ampere, will be discussed briefly when we study electrochemistry in Chapter 20. The unit for luminous intensity, the candela, will not be discussed in this book.

Most of the base units are defined in terms of reproducible physical phenomena. For instance, the meter is defined as exactly the distance light travels in a vacuum in 1/299,792,458 of a second. Everyone has access to this standard because light and a vacuum

Table 2.1	The SI Base Units		
Measurement		**Unit**	**Symbol**
Length		meter	m
Mass		kilogram	kg
Time		second	s
Electric current		ampere	A
Temperature		kelvin	K
Amount of substance		mole	mol
Luminous intensity		candela	cd

TOOLS

Base SI units

Figure 2.4 | **The international standard kilogram.** The SI standard for mass is made of a platinum–iridium alloy and is protected under two bell jars, as shown, at the International Bureau of Weights and Measures in France. Precise copies, called secondary standards, are maintained by many countries. *(NIST)*

are available to all. Only the base unit for mass is defined by an object made by human hands. It is a carefully preserved platinum–iridium alloy block stored at the International Bureau of Weights and Measures in France (Figure 2.4). This block serves indirectly as the calibrating standard for all "weights" used for scales and balances throughout the world.[1]

In scientific measurements, *all* physical quantities will have units that are combinations of the seven base SI units. For example, there is no SI base unit for area, but we know that to calculate the area of a rectangular room we multiply its length by its width. Therefore, the *unit* for area is derived by multiplying the *unit* for length by the *unit* for width. Length and width are each a measurement that have the SI base unit of the **meter (m)**.

$$\text{length} \times \text{width} = \text{area}$$
$$(\text{meter}) \times (\text{meter}) = (\text{meter})^2$$
$$\text{m} \times \text{m} = \text{m}^2$$

The SI **derived unit** for area is therefore m^2 (read as *meters squared*, or *square meter*).

In deriving SI units, we employ a very important concept that we will use repeatedly throughout this book when we perform calculations: *Units undergo the same kinds of mathematical operations that numbers do.* We will see how this fact can be used to convert from one unit to another in Section 2.4.

Example 2.1
Deriving SI Units

Linear momentum is a measure of the "push" a moving object has, equal to the object's mass times its velocity. What is the SI derived unit for linear momentum?

■ **Analysis:** To derive a unit for a quantity we must first express it in terms of simpler quantities. We're told that linear momentum is mass times velocity. Therefore, the SI unit for linear momentum will be the SI unit for mass times the SI unit for velocity. Since velocity is not one of the base SI units, we will need to find the SI units for velocity.

■ **Assembling the Tools:** The only tool we need for this question is the list of SI base units in Table 2.1. We will also have to recall that velocity is distance traveled (length) per unit time. The tools are:

SI unit for mass is the kg

SI units for velocity (length/time) are m/s

---

[1]Scientists are working on a method of accurately counting atoms whose masses are accurately known. Their goal is to develop a new definition of the kilogram that doesn't depend on an object that can be stolen, lost, or destroyed.

■ **Solution:** We start by expressing the given information as an equation:

$$\text{mass} \times \text{velocity} = \text{linear momentum}$$

Next we write the same equation with units because units undergo the same mathematical operations as the numbers.

$$\text{kg} \times \text{m/s} = \text{kg m/s} \quad \text{or} \quad \text{kg m s}^{-1}$$

Our result is that linear momentum has units of kg m/s or kg m s^{-1}.

■ **Is the Answer Reasonable?** *Before leaving a problem, it is always wise to examine the answer to see whether it makes sense.* For numerical calculations, ask yourself, "Is the answer too large or too small?" Judging the answers to such questions serves as a check on the arithmetic as well as on the method of obtaining the answer. It can help you find obvious errors. In this problem, the check is simple. The derived unit for linear momentum should be the product of units for mass and velocity, and this is obviously true. Therefore, our answer is correct.

Practice Exercises

2.1 | The volume of a sphere is given by the formula $V = \frac{4}{3}\pi r^3$, where r is the radius of the sphere. From this equation, determine the SI units for volume. (*Hint: r* is a length, so it must have a length unit.)

2.2 | When you "step hard on the gas" in a car you feel an invisible force pushing you back in your seat. This force, F, equals the product of your mass, m, times the acceleration, a, of the car. In equation form, this is $F = ma$. Acceleration is the change in velocity, v, with time, t:

$$a = \frac{\text{change in } v}{\text{change in } t}$$

Therefore, the units of acceleration are those of velocity divided by time. What is the SI derived unit for force expressed SI base units?

Non-SI Units

Some older metric units that are not part of the SI system are still used in the laboratory and in the scientific literature. Some of these units are listed in Table 2.2; others will be introduced as needed in upcoming chapters.

The United States is the only large nation still using the **English system** of units, which measures distance in inches, feet, and miles; volume in ounces, quarts, and gallons; and mass in ounces and pounds. However, a gradual transition to metric units is occurring and, in fact, many of the English units are defined with reference to base SI units. Beverages,

■ Many of the "English" measurements are now defined based on the SI base units.

Table 2.2	Some Non-SI Metric Units Commonly Used in Chemistry		
Measurement	**Name**	**Symbol**	**Value in SI Units**
Length	angstrom	Å	$1\,\text{Å} = 0.1\,\text{nm} = 10^{-10}\,\text{m}$
Mass	atomic mass unit	u (amu)	$1\,\text{u} = 1.66054 \times 10^{-27}\,\text{kg}$, approximately
	metric ton	t	$1\,\text{t} = 10^3\,\text{kg}$
Time	minute	min.	$1\,\text{min.} = 60\,\text{s}$
	hour	h (hr)	$1\,\text{h} = 60\,\text{min.} = 3600\,\text{s}$
Temperature	degree Celsius	°C	$T_K = t_{°C} + 273.15$
Volume	liter	L	$1\,\text{L} = 1000\,\text{cm}^3$

Table 2.3	Some Useful Conversions	
Measurement	**English Unit**	**English/SI Equality[a]**
Length	inch	1 in. = 2.54 cm
	yard	1 yd = 0.9144 m
	mile	1 mi = 1.609 km
Mass	pound	1 lb = 453.6 g
	ounce (mass)	1 oz = 28.35 g
Volume	gallon	1 gal = 3.785 L
	quart	1 qt = 946.4 mL
	ounce (fluid)	1 oz = 29.6 mL

[a]These equalities allow us to convert English to metric or metric to English units.

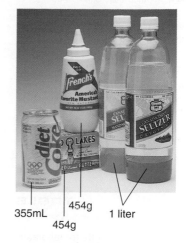

355mL   454g   1 liter
454g

food packages, tools, and machine parts are often labeled in metric units (Figure 2.5). Common conversions between the English system and the SI are given in Table 2.3 and inside the back cover of this book.[2]

Figure 2.5 | **Metric units are becoming commonplace on most consumer products.**
(Michael Watson)

Decimal Multipliers

Sometimes the basic units are either too large or too small to be used conveniently. For example, the meter is inconvenient for expressing the size of very small things such as bacteria. The SI solves this problem by forming larger or smaller units by applying **decimal multipliers** to the base units. Table 2.4 lists the most commonly used decimal multipliers and the prefixes used to identify them.

Table 2.4	SI Prefixes—Their meanings and values[a]			
Prefix	**Meaning**	**Symbol**	**Prefix Value[b]** (numerical)	**Prefix Value[b]** (power of ten)
exa		E		10^{18}
peta		P		10^{15}
tera		T		10^{12}
giga	**billions of**	**G**	**1000000000**	**10^{9}**
mega	**millions of**	**M**	**1000000**	**10^{6}**
kilo	**thousands of**	**k**	**1000**	**10^{3}**
hecto		h		10^{2}
deka		da		10^{1}
deci	**tenths of**	**d**	**0.1**	**10^{-1}**
centi	**hundredths of**	**c**	**0.01**	**10^{-2}**
milli	**thousandths of**	**m**	**0.001**	**10^{-3}**
micro	**millionths of**	**μ**	**0.000001**	**10^{-6}**
nano	**billionths of**	**n**	**0.000000001**	**10^{-9}**
pico	**trillionths of**	**p**	**0.000000000001**	**10^{-12}**
femto		f		10^{-15}
atto		a		10^{-18}

[a]Prefixes in bold type are used most often.

[b]Numbers in these columns can be interchanged with the corresponding prefix.

T**OO**LS

SI prefixes

[2]Originally, these conversions were established by measurement. For example, if a metric ruler is used to measure the length of an inch, it is found that 1 in. equals 2.54 cm. Later, to avoid confusion about the accuracy of such measurements, it was agreed that these relationships would be taken to be exact. For instance, 1 in. is now defined as *exactly* 2.54 cm. Exact relationships also exist for the other quantities, but for simplicity many have been rounded off. For example, 1 lb = 453.59237 g, *exactly*.

■ A modified base unit can be conveniently converted to the base unit by removing the prefix and inserting $\times 10^x$.

$$25.2 \text{ pm} = 25.2 \times 10^{-12} \text{ m}$$

A prefix can be inserted by adjusting the exponential part of a number to match the definition of a prefix. Then the exponent is removed and replaced by the prefix.

$$2.34 \times 10^{10} \text{ g} = 23.4 \times 10^9 \text{ g}$$
$$= 23.4 \text{ Gg}$$

TOOLS

Units for laboratory measurements

■ An older, non-SI unit called the angstrom (Å) is often used to describe dimensions of atomic- and molecular-sized particles.

$$1 \text{ Å} = 0.1 \text{ nm} = 10^{-10} \text{ m}$$

When the name of a unit is preceded by one of these prefixes, the size of the unit is modified by the corresponding decimal multiplier. For instance, the prefix *kilo* indicates a multiplying factor of 10^3, or 1000. Therefore, a *kilo*meter is a unit of length equal to 1000 meters.[3] The symbol for kilometer (km) is formed by applying the symbol meaning kilo (k) as a prefix to the symbol for meter (m). Thus 1 km = 1000 m (or alternatively, 1 km = 10^3 m). Similarly a decimeter (dm) is 1/10th of a meter, so 1 dm = 0.1 m (1 dm = 10^{-1} m).

The symbols and multipliers are listed in Table 2.4. Those listed in boldface type are the ones most commonly encountered in chemistry.

Laboratory Measurements

The most common measurements you will make in the laboratory will be those of length, volume, mass, and temperature.

Length

The SI base unit for length, the **meter (m)**, is too large for most laboratory purposes. More convenient units are the **centimeter (cm)** and the **millimeter (mm)**. Using Table 2.4 we see that they are related to the meter as follows.

$$1 \text{ cm} = 10^{-2} \text{ m} = 0.01 \text{ m}$$
$$1 \text{ mm} = 10^{-3} \text{ m} = 0.001 \text{ m}$$

It is also useful to know the relationships

$$1 \text{ m} = 100 \text{ cm} = 1000 \text{ mm}$$
$$1 \text{ cm} = 10 \text{ mm}$$

Volume

Volume is a derived unit with dimensions of (length)³. With these dimensions expressed in meters, the derived SI unit for volume is the **cubic meter, m³**.

In chemistry, measurements of volume usually arise when we measure amounts of liquids. The traditional metric unit of volume used for this is the **liter (L)**. In SI terms, a liter is defined as exactly 1 cubic decimeter.

$$1 \text{ L} = 1 \text{ dm}^3 \text{ (exactly)} \tag{2.1}$$

However, even the liter is too large to conveniently express most volumes measured in the lab. The glassware we normally use, as illustrated in Figure 2.6, is marked in **milliliters (mL)**.[4]

$$1 \text{ L} = 1000 \text{ mL}$$

Because 1 dm = 10 cm, then 1 dm³ = 1000 cm³. Therefore, 1 mL is exactly the same as 1 cm³.

$$1 \text{ cm}^3 = 1 \text{ mL}$$
$$1 \text{ L} = 1000 \text{ cm}^3 = 1000 \text{ mL}$$

Sometimes you may see cm³ abbreviated cc (especially in medical applications), although the SI frowns on this symbol. Figure 2.7 compares the cubic meter, liter, and milliliter.

---

[3]In the sciences, powers of 10 are often used to express large and small numbers. The quantity 10^3 means $10 \times 10 \times 10 = 1000$. Similarly, the quantity $6.5 \times 10^2 = 6.5 \times 100 = 650$. Numbers less than 1 have negative exponents when expressed as powers of 10. Thus, the fraction $\frac{1}{10}$ is expressed as 10^{-1}, so the quantity 10^{-3} means $\frac{1}{10} \times \frac{1}{10} \times \frac{1}{10} = \frac{1}{1000}$. A value of $6.5 \times 10^{-3} = 6.5 \times 0.001 = 0.0065$. Numbers written as 6.5×10^2 and 6.5×10^{-3}, with the decimal point between the first and second digit, are said to be expressed in **scientific notation**.

[4]Use of the abbreviations L for liter and mL for milliliter is rather recent. Confusion between the printed letter l and the number 1 prompted the change from l to L and ml to mL. You may encounter the abbreviation ml in other books or on older laboratory glassware.

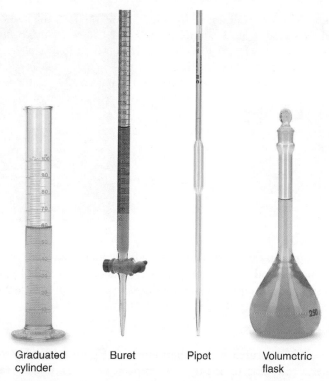

Figure 2.6 | **Common laboratory glassware used for measuring volumes.** Graduated cylinders are used for measuring volumes to the nearest milliliter. Precise measurements of volumes are made using burets, pipets, and volumetric flasks. *(Andy Washnik)*

Figure 2.7 | **Comparing volume units.** A cubic meter (m^3) is approximately equal to a cubic yard. 1000 cm^3 is approximately a quart, and approximately 30 cm^3 is equal to one fluid ounce.

Mass

In the SI, the base unit for mass is the **kilogram (kg)**, although the **gram (g)** is a more conveniently sized unit for most laboratory measurements. One gram, of course, is $\frac{1}{1000}$ of a kilogram (1 kilogram = 1000 g, so 1 g must equal 0.001 kg).

Mass is measured by comparing the weight of a sample with the weights of known standard masses. (Recall from Chapter 1 that mass and weight are not the same thing.) The instrument used is called a **balance** (Figure 2.8). For the balance in Figure 2.8*a*, we

Figure 2.8 | **Typical laboratory balances.** (*a*) A traditional two-pan analytical balance capable of measurements to the nearest 0.0001 g. (*b*) A modern top-loading balance capable of mass measurements to the nearest 0.1 g. (*c*) A modern analytical balance capable of measurements to the nearest 0.0001 g. *(Michael Watson; © 2005 Richard Megna/Fundamental Photographs; Charles D. Winters/Photo Researchers)*

Figure 2.9 | **Masses of several common objects.** *(1Stockphoto; 1Stockphoto; Andy Washnik; Jim Cummins/Taxi/ Getty Images, Inc.)*

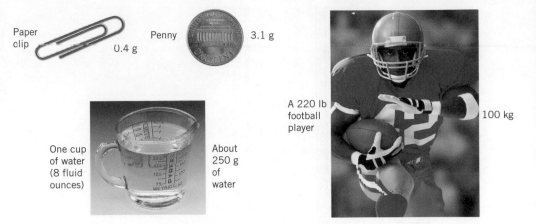

Figure 2.9 | **Masses of several common objects.** *(1Stockphoto; 1Stockphoto; Andy Washnik; Jim Cummins/Taxi/ Getty Images, Inc.)*

Paper clip 0.4 g

Penny 3.1 g

A 220 lb football player 100 kg

One cup of water (8 fluid ounces)

About 250 g of water

would place our sample on the left pan and then add standard masses to the other. When the weight of the sample and the total weight of the standards are in balance (when they match), their masses are then equal. Figure 2.9 shows the masses of some common objects in SI units.

Temperature

■ In chemistry, reference data are commonly tabulated at 25 °C, which is close to room temperature. Biologists often carry out their experiments at 37 °C because that is our normal body temperature.

Temperature is usually measured with a thermometer (Figure 2.10). Thermometers are graduated in *degrees* according to one of two temperature scales. On the **Fahrenheit scale** water freezes at 32 °F and boils at 212 °F. If you've been raised in the United States, this is probably the scale you're most familiar with. In recent times, however, you have probably noticed an increased use of the **Celsius scale**, especially in weather broadcasts. This is the scale we use most often in the sciences. On the Celsius scale water freezes at 0 °C and boils at 100 °C. (See Figure 2.11.)

As you can see in Figure 2.11, on the Celsius scale there are 100 degree units between the freezing and boiling points of water, while on the Fahrenheit scale this same temperature range is spanned by 180 degree units. Consequently, 5 Celsius degrees are the same as 9 Fahrenheit degrees. We can use the following equation as a tool to convert between these temperature scales.

TOOLS

Celsius to Fahrenheit conversion

$$t_F = \left(\frac{9\,°F}{5\,°C} \right) t_C + 32\,°F \tag{2.2}$$

In this equation, t_F is the Fahrenheit temperature and t_C is the Celsius temperature. As noted earlier, units behave like numbers in calculations, and we see in Equation 2.2 that

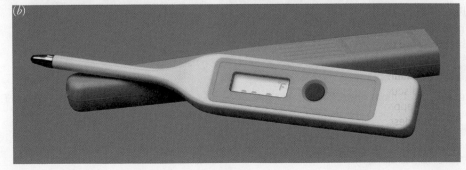

Figure 2.10 | **Typical laboratory thermometers.** (*a*) A traditional mercury thermometer. (*b*) An electronic thermometer. *(Michael Watson; Corbis Images)*

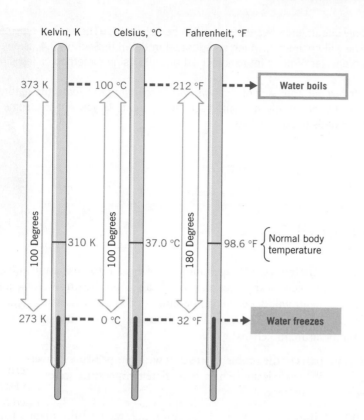

°C "cancels out" to leave only °F. The 32 °F is added to account for the fact that the freezing point of water (0 °C) occurs at 32 °F on the Fahrenheit scale. Equation 2.2 can easily be rearranged to permit calculating the Celsius temperature from the Fahrenheit temperature.

The SI unit of temperature is the **kelvin (K)**, which is the degree unit on the **Kelvin temperature scale**. Notice that the temperature unit is K, not °K (the degree symbol, °, is omitted). Also notice that the name of the unit, kelvin, is not capitalized. Equations that include temperature as a variable sometimes take on a simpler form when Kelvin temperatures are used. We will encounter this situation many times throughout the book.

Figure 2.11 shows how the Kelvin, Celsius, and Fahrenheit temperature scales relate to each other. Notice that the kelvin is *exactly* the same size as the Celsius degree. *The only difference between these two temperature scales is the zero point.* The zero point on the Kelvin scale is called **absolute zero** and corresponds to nature's lowest temperature. It is 273.15 degree units below the zero point on the Celsius scale, which means that 0 °C equals 273.15 K, and 0 K equals −273.15 °C. Common laboratory thermometers are never marked with the Kelvin scale, so to convert from Celsius to Kelvin temperatures the following equation applies.

$$T_{\mathrm{K}} = (t_{\mathrm{C}} + 273.15)\; {°\!\!\!\!C}\; \frac{1\,\mathrm{K}}{1\,°\!\!\!\!C}$$ (2.3)

This amounts to simply adding 273.15 to the Celsius temperature to obtain the Kelvin temperature. Often we are given Celsius temperatures rounded to the nearest degree, in which case we round 273.15 to 273. Thus, 25 °C equals $(25 + 273)$ K or 298 K.

Types of Mathematical Calculations

We will discuss many problems throughout the book that require mathematical calculations. In approaching them you will see that they can be divided into two general types. The type described in Example 2.2 involves applying a mathematical equation in which we have numerical values for all but one of the variables in the equation. To perform the calculation, we solve the equation by substituting known values for the variables until

■ The name of the temperature scale, the Kelvin scale, is capitalized, but the name of the unit, the kelvin, is not. However, the symbol for the kelvin is a capital K.

Celsius to Kelvin conversion

■ We will use a capital *T* to stand for the Kelvin temperature and a lowercase *t* (as in t_{C}) to stand for the Celsius temperature. This conforms to the usage described by the International Bureau of Weights and Measures in Sevres, France, and the National Institute of Standards and Technology in Gaithersburg, Maryland.

there is only one unknown variable that can be calculated. The second type of calculation that we will encounter, which is described in detail in Section 2.4, is one where we convert one set of units into another set of units using a method called dimensional analysis.

If you follow our approach of *Analysis and Assembling the Tools*, the nature of the types of calculations involved should become apparent. As you will see, some problems involve both kinds of calculations.

Example 2.2
Converting among Temperature Scales

Thermal pollution, the release of large amounts of heat into rivers and other bodies of water, is a serious problem near power plants and can affect the survival of some species of fish. For example, trout will die if the temperature of the water rises above approximately 25 °C. (a) What is this temperature in °F? (b) Rounded to the nearest whole degree unit, what is this temperature in kelvins?

■ **Analysis:** Both parts of the problem here deal with temperature conversions. Therefore, we ask ourselves, "What tools do we have that relate temperature scales to each other?" We have just seen two of these tools.

■ **Assembling the Tools:** The first tool, Equation 2.2, relates Fahrenheit temperatures to Celsius temperatures, so this is the tool we need to answer part (a).

$$t_F = \left(\frac{9 \,°F}{5 \,°C}\right) t_C + 32 \,°F$$

Equation 2.3 relates Kelvin temperatures to Celsius temperatures, so this is the tool we need for part (b).

$$T_K = (t_C + 273.15) \,°C \left(\frac{1 \,K}{1 \,°C}\right)$$

■ **Solution:**
Part (a): We substitute the value of the Celsius temperature (25 °C) for t_C and calculate the answer

$$t_F = \left(\frac{9 \,°F}{5 \,°C}\right)(25 \,°C) + 32 \,°F$$

$$= 45 \,°F + 32 \,°F = 77 \,°F$$

Therefore, 25 °C = 77 °F. (Notice that we have canceled the unit °C in the equation above.)
Part (b): Once again, we have a simple substitution. Since $t_C = 25$ °C, the Kelvin temperature (rounded) is calculated as

$$T_K = (25 \,°C + 273 \,°C)\left(\frac{1 \,K}{1 \,°C}\right)$$

$$= 298 \,°C\left(\frac{1 \,K}{1 \,°C}\right) = 298 \,K$$

Thus, 25 °C = 298 K.

■ **Are the Answers Reasonable?** For part (a), we know that a Fahrenheit degree is about half the size of a Celsius degree, so 25 Celsius degrees should be about 50 Fahrenheit degrees. The positive value for the Celsius temperature tells us we have a temperature *above* the freezing point of water. Since water freezes at 32 °F, the Fahrenheit temperature should be approximately 32 °F + 50 °F = 82 °F. The answer of 77 °F is quite close.

For part (b), we recall that 0 °C = 273 K. A temperature above 0 °C must be higher than 273 K. Our calculation, therefore, appears to be correct.

2.3 | What Fahrenheit temperature corresponds to a Celsius temperature of 86 °C? (*Hint:* What tool relates these two temperature scales?)

2.4 | What Celsius temperature corresponds to 50 °F? What Kelvin temperature corresponds to 68 °F (expressed to the nearest whole kelvin unit)?

Practice Exercises

2.3 | The Uncertainty of Measurements

We noted in the preceding section that measurements are inexact; they contain **uncertainties** (also called **errors**). One source of uncertainty is associated with limitations in our ability to read the scale of the measuring instrument. Uncontrollably changing conditions at the time of the measurement can also cause errors that are more important than scale-reading errors. For example, if you are measuring a length of wire with a ruler, you may not be holding the wire perfectly straight every time.

If we were to take an enormous number of measurements using appropriately adjusted instruments, statistically half of the measurements should be larger and half smaller than the true value of the measured quantity. In fact, we do observe that a repetitive series of measurements tends to give results that cluster around a central value, which we generally assume is close to the true value. We can estimate the central value quite simply by reporting the **average**, or **mean**, of the series of measurements. This is done by summing the measurements and then dividing by the number of measurements we made. Although making repeated measurements is tedious, the more measurements we make, the more confident we can be that the average is close to the true value.

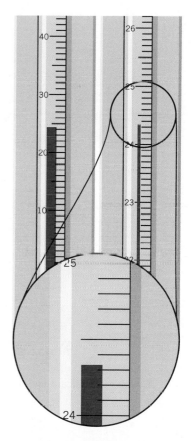

Uncertainties in Measurements

One kind of error that cannot be eliminated arises when we attempt to obtain a measurement by reading the scale on an instrument. Consider, for example, reading the same temperature from each of the two thermometers in Figure 2.12.

The marks on the left thermometer are one degree apart, and we can see that the temperature lies between 24 °C and 25 °C. When reading a scale, we always record the last digit to the nearest tenth of the smallest scale division. Looking closely, therefore, we might estimate that the fluid column falls about 3/10 of the way between the marks for 24 and 25 degrees, so we can report the temperature to be 24.3 °C. However, it would be foolish to say that the temperature is *exactly* 24.3 °C. The last digit is only an estimate, and the left thermometer might be read as 24.2 °C by one observer or 24.4 °C by another. Because different observers might obtain values that differ by 0.1 °C, there is an uncertainty of ±0.1 °C in the measured temperature. We can express this by writing the temperature as 24.3 ± 0.1 °C.

The thermometer on the right has marks that are 1/10 of a degree apart, which allows us to estimate the temperature as 24.32 °C. In this case, we are estimating the hundredths place and the uncertainty is ±0.01 °C. We could write the temperature as 24.32 ± 0.01 °C. Notice that because the thermometer on the right is more finely graduated, we are able to obtain measurements with smaller uncertainties. We would have more confidence in temperatures read from the thermometer on the right in Figure 2.12 because it has more digits and a smaller amount of uncertainty. *The reliability of a measurement is indicated by the number of digits used to represent it.*

Figure 2.12 | **Thermometers with different scales give readings with different precision.** The thermometer on the left has marks that are one degree apart, allowing the temperature to be estimated to the nearest tenth of a degree. The thermometer on the right has marks every 0.1 °C. This scale permits estimation of the hundredths place.

By convention in science, *all digits in a measurement up to and including the first estimated digit are recorded.* If a reading measured with the thermometer on the right seemed exactly on the 24 °C mark, we would record the temperature as 24.00 °C, not 24 °C, to show that the thermometer can be read to the nearest 1/100 of a degree.

Modern laboratory instruments such as balances and meters often have digital displays. If you read the mass of a beaker on a digital balance as 65.23 grams, everyone else observing the same beaker will see the same display and obtain exactly the same reading. There seems to be no uncertainty, or estimation, in reading this type of scale. However, scientists agree that the uncertainty is $\pm 1/2$ of the last readable digit. Using this definition our digital reading may be written as 65.230 ± 0.005 grams.[5]

Significant Figures

The concepts discussed above are so important that we have special terminology to describe numbers that come from measurements.

| *Digits that result from a measurement such that only the digit farthest to the right is not known with certainty are called* **significant figures** (*or* **significant digits**).

The number of significant figures in a measurement is equal to the number of digits known for sure *plus* one that is estimated. Let's look at our two temperature measurements:

<table>
<tr>
<td align="center">This digit has some
uncertainty
\
24.3 °C
⌞⌟
These two digits
are known for sure</td>
<td align="center">This digit has some
uncertainty
\
24.32 °C
⌞⌟
These three digits
are known for sure</td>
</tr>
</table>

The first measurement, 24.3 °C, has three significant figures; the second, 24.32 °C, has four significant figures.

When Are Zeros Significant?

Usually, it is simple to determine the number of significant figures in a measurement; we just count the digits. Thus 3.25 has three significant figures and 56.205 has five of them. When zeros are in the middle of a number, imbedded zeros, they are always significant, but when they come at the beginning or the end of a number they sometimes cause confusion.

Trailing zeros are always counted as significant if the number has a decimal point. Thus, 4.500 m and 630.0 g have four significant figures each because the zeros would not be written unless those digits were known to be zeros.

Zeros to the left of the first nonzero digit, called leading zeros, are never counted as significant. For instance, a length of 2.3 mm is the same as 0.0023 m. Since we are dealing with the same measured value, its number of significant figures cannot change when we change the units. Both quantities have two significant figures.

Zeros on the end of a number that does not have a decimal point are assumed not to be significant. For example, suppose you were told that a protest march was attended by 45,000 people. If this was just a rough estimate, it might be uncertain by as much as several thousand, in which case the value 45,000 represents just two significant figures, since the "5" is the uncertain digit. None of the zeros would then count as significant figures. On the other hand, suppose the protesters were carefully counted using an aerial photograph, so that the count could be reported to be 45,000—give or take about 100 people. In this

TOOLS

Counting significant figures

---

[5]Some instructors may wish to maintain a uniform procedure of assigning an uncertainty of ± 1 in the last readable digit for both analog and digital scale readings.

case, the value represents $45,000 \pm 100$ protesters and contains three significant figures, with the uncertain digit being the zero in the hundreds place. Thus, a simple statement such as "there were 45,000 people attending the march" is ambiguous. We can't tell how many significant digits the number has from the number alone. We can be sure that the nonzero digits are significant, though. The best we can do is to say "45,000 has *at least* two significant figures."

We can avoid this confusion by using **scientific notation** when we report a measurement. For example, if we want to report the number of protesters as 45,000 give or take a thousand, we can write the rough estimate as 4.5×10^4. The 4.5 shows the number of significant figures and the 10^4 tells us the location of the decimal. The value obtained from the aerial photograph count, on the other hand, can be expressed as 4.50×10^4. This time the 4.50 shows three significant figures and an uncertainty of $\pm 0.01 \times 10^4$ or ± 100 people.

Accuracy and Precision

Two words often used in reference to measurements are accuracy and precision. **Accuracy** *refers to how close a measurement is to the true or the accepted true value.* **Precision** *refers to how close repeated measurements come to their average.* Notice that the two terms are not synonyms, because the average doesn't always correspond to the true or correct value. A practical example of how accuracy and precision differ is illustrated in Figure 2.13.

For measurements to be **accurate**, the measuring device must be carefully calibrated (adjusted) with a standard reference so it gives correct readings. For example, to calibrate an electronic balance, a known reference mass is placed on the balance and a calibration routine within the balance is initiated. Once calibrated, the balance will give accurate readings, the accuracy of which is determined by the quality of the standard mass used. Standard reference masses, often "traceable" to the international prototype kilogram in Paris, can be purchased from scientific supply companies.

Precision refers to how closely repeated measurements of the same quantity come to each other. In general, the smaller the uncertainty (i.e., the "plus or minus" part of the measurement), the more precise the measurement. This translates as: *The more significant figures in a measured quantity, the more precise the measurement.*

We usually assume that a very precise measurement is also of high accuracy. We can be wrong, however, if our instruments are improperly calibrated. For example, the improperly marked ruler in Figure 2.14 might yield measurements that vary by a hundredth of a centimeter (± 0.01 cm), but all the measurements would be too large by 1 cm—a case of good precision but poor accuracy.

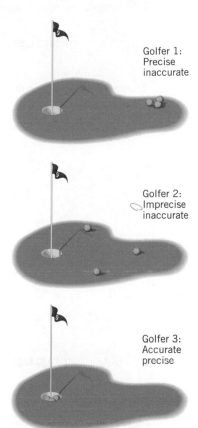

Golfer 1: Precise inaccurate

Golfer 2: Imprecise inaccurate

Golfer 3: Accurate precise

Figure 2.13 | **The difference between precision and accuracy in the game of golf.** Golfer 1 hits shots that are precise (because they are tightly grouped), but the accuracy is poor because the balls are not near the target (the "true" value). Golfer 2 needs help. His shots are neither precise nor accurate. Golfer 3 wins the prize with shots that are precise (tightly grouped) and accurate (in the hole).

How accurate would measurements be with this ruler?

Figure 2.14 | **An improperly marked ruler.** This improperly marked ruler will yield measurements that are each wrong by one whole unit. The measurements might be precise, but the accuracy would be very poor.

Significant Figures in Calculations

When several measurements are obtained in an experiment they are usually combined in some way to calculate a desired quantity. For example, to determine the area of a rectangular carpet we require two measurements, length and width, which are then multiplied to give the answer we want. To get some idea of how precise the area really is, we need a way to take into account the precision of the various values used in the calculation. To make sure this happens, we follow certain rules according to the kinds of arithmetic being performed.

Multiplication and Division

For multiplication and division, the number of significant figures in the answer should not be greater than the number of significant figures in the least precise measurement. The least precise measurement is the number with the fewest significant figures. Let's look at a typical problem involving some measured quantities.

$$\frac{\overset{\text{3 sig. figures}}{3.14} \times \overset{\text{4 sig. figures}}{2.751}}{\underset{\text{2 sig. figures}}{0.64}} = 13$$

The result displayed on a calculator[6] is 13.49709375. However, the least precise factor, 0.64, has only two significant figures, so the answer should have only two. The correct answer, 13, is obtained by rounding off the calculator answer.[7] When we multiply and divide measurements, the units of those measurements are multiplied and divided in the same way as the numbers.

Addition and Subtraction

For addition and subtraction, the answer should have the same number of decimal places as the quantity with the fewest number of decimal places. As an example, consider the following addition of measured quantities.

$$\begin{array}{r} 3.247 \\ 41.36 \\ +125.2 \\ \hline 169.8 \end{array}$$

← (This number has only 1 decimal place.)

← (This answer has been rounded to 1 decimal place.)

In this calculation, the digits beneath the 6 and the 7 are unknown; they could be anything. (They're not necessarily zeros because if we *knew* they were zeros, then zeros would have been written there.) Adding an unknown digit to the 6 or 7 will give an answer that's also unknown, so for this sum we are not justified in writing digits in the second and third places after the decimal point. Therefore, we round the answer to the nearest tenth. We must also recall that we can only add and subtract numbers that have identical units, and the answer will have the same units.

Exact Numbers

Numbers that come from definitions, such as 12 in. = 1 ft, and those that come from a direct count, such as the number of people in a small room, have no uncertainty, and we can assume that they have an infinite number of significant figures. Therefore, exact numbers do not affect the number of significant figures in multiplication or division calculations.

---

[6]Calculators usually give too many significant figures. An exception is when the answer has zeros at the right that are significant figures. For example, an answer of 1.200 is displayed on most calculators as 1.2. If the zeros belong in the answer, be sure to write them down.

[7]When we wish to round off a number at a certain point, we simply drop the digits that follow if the first of them is less than 5. Thus, 8.1634 rounds to 8.16 if we wish to have only two decimal places. If the first digit after the point of round off is larger than 5, or if it is 5 followed by other nonzero digits, then we add 1 to the preceding digit. Thus 8.167 and 8.1653 both round to 8.17. Finally, when the digit after the point of round off is a 5 and no nonzero digits follow the 5, then we drop the 5 if the preceding digit is even and add 1 if it is odd. Thus, 8.165 rounds to 8.16 and 8.17500 rounds to 8.18.

2.5 | Perform the following calculations involving measurements and round the results so they have the correct number of significant figures and proper units. (*Hint:* Apply the rules for significant figures described in this section, and keep in mind that units behave as numbers do in calculations.)

(a) 21.0233 g + 21.0 g

(b) 10.0324 g ÷ 11.7 mL

(c) $\dfrac{14.25\text{ cm} \times 12.334\text{ cm}}{(2.223\text{ cm} - 1.04\text{ cm})}$

2.6 | Perform the following calculations involving measurements and round the results so that they are written to the correct number of significant figures and have the correct units.

(a) 32.02 mL − 2.0 mL

(b) 54.183 g − 0.0278 g

(c) 10.0 g + 1.03 g + 0.243 g

(d) 43.4 in. × $\dfrac{1\text{ ft}}{12\text{ in.}}$

(e) $\dfrac{1.03\text{ m} \times 2.074\text{ m} \times 3.9\text{ m}}{12.46\text{ m} + 4.778\text{ m}}$

2.4 | Dimensional Analysis

Earlier we mentioned that for numerical problems we often do not have a specific equation to solve; instead, all we need to do is convert one set of units to another. After analyzing the problem and assembling the necessary information to solve it, scientists usually use a technique commonly called **dimensional analysis** (also called the **factor-label method**) to help them perform the correct arithmetic. As you will see, often this method also helps in analyzing the problem and selecting the tools needed to solve it.

Conversion Factors

In dimensional analysis we treat a numerical problem as one involving a conversion of units (the dimensions) from one kind to another. To do this we use one or more *conversion factors* to change the units of the given quantity to the units of the answer.

$$(\text{given quantity}) \times (\text{conversion factor}) = (\text{desired quantity})$$

A **conversion factor** *is a fraction formed from a* valid *equality or equivalence between units and is used to switch from one system of measurement and units to another.* To illustrate, suppose we want to express a person's height of 72.0 inches in centimeters. To do this we need the relationship between the inch and the centimeter. We can obtain this from Table 2.3:

$$2.54\text{ cm} = 1\text{ in. (exactly)} \qquad (2.4)$$

If we divide both sides of this equation by 1 in., we obtain a conversion factor.

$$\frac{2.54\text{ cm}}{1\text{ in.}} = \frac{1\text{ in.}}{1\text{ in.}} = 1$$

Notice that we have canceled the units from both the numerator and denominator of the center fraction, leaving the first fraction equaling 1. As mentioned earlier, *units behave*

■ To construct a valid conversion factor, the relationship between the units must be true. For example, the statement 3 ft = 41 in. is false. Although you might make a conversion factor out of it, any answers you would calculate are sure to be wrong. Correct answers require correct relationships between units.

just as numbers do in mathematical operations; this is a key part of dimensional analysis. Let's see what happens if we multiply 72.0 inches, the height that we mentioned, by this fraction.

$$72.0 \text{ in.} \times \frac{2.54 \text{ cm}}{1 \text{ in.}} = 183 \text{ cm}$$

(given quantity) × (conversion factor) = (desired quantity)

■ The relationship between the inch and the centimeter is exact, so that the numbers in 1 in. = 2.54 cm have an infinite number of significant figures.

Because we have multiplied 72.0 in. by something that is equal to 1, we know we haven't changed the magnitude of the person's height. We have, however, changed the units. Notice that we have canceled the unit inches. The only unit left is centimeters, which is the unit we want for the answer. The result, therefore, is the person's height in centimeters.

One of the benefits of dimensional analysis is that it often lets you know when you have done the *wrong* arithmetic. From the relationship in Equation 2.4, we can actually construct two conversion factors:

$$\frac{2.54 \text{ cm}}{1 \text{ in.}} \quad \text{and} \quad \frac{1 \text{ in.}}{2.54 \text{ cm}}$$

We used the first one correctly, but what would have happened if we had used the second by mistake?

$$72.0 \text{ in.} \times \frac{1 \text{ in.}}{2.54 \text{ cm}} = 28.3 \text{ in.}^2/\text{cm}$$

In this case, none of the units cancel. We get units of in.²/cm because inches times inches is inches squared. Even though our calculator may be very good at arithmetic, we've got the wrong answer. *Dimensional analysis lets us know we have the wrong answer because the units are wrong!*

We will use dimensional analysis extensively throughout this book to aid us in setting up the proper arithmetic in problems. In fact, we will see that in many cases this approach also helps us assemble the information we need to solve a problem.

There is a general strategy for all problems that involve a conversion. We always start with a given piece of data along with its units. Then we write down the desired units that we want the answer to have. This gives us the start and end points of our calculation. Then, all we need to do is find the correct conversion factors that will lead us from one set of units to the next. Sometimes this will require one conversion factor, other times it may take two or three (or more!) to complete the conversion. The next examples illustrate this process.

Example 2.3
Dimensional Analysis Applied to Metric Prefixes

Convert 3.25 m to millimeters (mm).

■ **Analysis:** We are asked to convert a number with meter units to another number that has millimeter units. This is a problem that involves conversion of metric prefixes.

■ **Assembling the Tools:** To solve this problem, our tool will be a conversion factor that relates the unit meter to the unit millimeter. From Table 2.4, the table of decimal multipliers, the prefix "milli" means "× 10^{-3}," so we can write

$$1 \text{ mm} = 10^{-3} \text{ m}$$

Notice that this relationship connects the units given to the units desired.

We now have all the information we need to solve the problem.

■ **Solution:** Based on the general strategy for conversion problems, let's write the given quantity (with its units) on the left and the *units* of the desired answer on the right.

$$3.25 \text{ m} = ? \text{ mm}$$

From the relationship above, we can form two conversion factors.

$$\frac{1 \text{ mm}}{10^{-3} \text{ m}} \quad \text{and} \quad \frac{10^{-3} \text{ m}}{1 \text{ mm}}$$

We know we have to cancel the unit meter, so we need to multiply by a conversion factor with this unit in the denominator. Therefore, we select the one on the left as our tool. This gives

$$3.25 \text{ m} \times \frac{1 \text{ mm}}{10^{-3} \text{ m}} = 3.25 \times 10^3 \text{ mm}$$

Notice that we have expressed the answer to three significant figures because that is how many there are in the given quantity, 3.25 m. The equality that relates meters and millimeters involves exact numbers because it is a definition.

■ **Is the Answer Reasonable?** We know that millimeters are much smaller than meters, so 3.25 m must represent a lot of millimeters. We also know that conversions between prefixes will not change the 3.25 part of our number, just the power of 10. Our answer, therefore, makes sense.

Example 2.4
Using Dimensional Analysis

A liter, which is slightly larger than a quart, is defined as 1 cubic decimeter (1 dm³). How many liters are there in exactly 1 cubic meter (1 m³)?

■ **Analysis:** Let's begin once again by stating the problem in equation form.

$$1 \text{ m}^3 = ? \text{ L}$$

Now we will use this to identify what relationships we will need to solve the problem. We don't have any direct conversions between cubic meters and liters. There was, however, a definition of the liter in terms of base metric units that we can combine with metric prefixes to do the job.

■ **Assembling the Tools:** The relationship between liters and cubic decimeters was given in Equation 2.1,

$$1 \text{ L} = 1 \text{ dm}^3$$

From the table of decimal multipliers, we also know the relationship between decimeters and meters,

$$1 \text{ dm} = 0.1 \text{ m}$$

but we need a relationship between cubic units. Since units undergo the same kinds of operations numbers do, we simply cube each side of this equation (being careful to cube *both* the numbers and the units).

$$(1 \text{ dm})^3 = (0.1 \text{ m})^3$$
$$1 \text{ dm}^3 = 0.001 \text{ m}^3 \qquad\qquad \textbf{(2.5)}$$

Notice how Equations 2.5 and 2.1 provide a path from the given units to those we seek. Such a path is always a necessary condition when we work with dimensional analysis.

$$\text{m}^3 \xrightarrow[\text{Equation 2.5}]{} \text{dm}^3 \xrightarrow{\text{Equation 2.1}} \text{L}$$

Now we are ready to solve the problem.

■ **Solution:** The first step is to eliminate the units m³. We use Equation 2.5.

$$1\ \cancel{\text{m}^3} \times \frac{1\ \text{dm}^3}{0.001\ \cancel{\text{m}^3}} = 1000\ \text{dm}^3$$

Then we use Equation 2.1 to take us from dm³ to L.

$$1000\ \cancel{\text{dm}^3} \times \frac{1\ \text{L}}{1\ \cancel{\text{dm}^3}} = 1000\ \text{L}$$

Thus, 1 m³ = 1000 L.

Usually, when a problem involves the use of two or more conversion factors, they can be "strung together" in a "chain calculation" to avoid having to compute intermediate results. For example, this problem can be set up as follows.

$$1\ \cancel{\text{m}^3} \times \frac{1\ \cancel{\text{dm}^3}}{0.001\ \cancel{\text{m}^3}} \times \frac{1\ \text{L}}{1\ \cancel{\text{dm}^3}} = 1000\ \text{L}$$

Since all of our conversion factors involve exact numbers and we were given exactly one cubic meter, our answer is an exact number also.

■ **Is the Answer Reasonable?** One liter is about a quart. A cubic meter is about a cubic yard. Therefore, we expect a large number of liters in a cubic meter, so our answer seems reasonable. (Notice here that in our analysis we have approximated the quantities in the calculation in units of quarts and cubic yards, which may be more familiar than liters and m³ if you've been raised in the United States. We get a feel for the approximate magnitude of the answer using our familiar units and then relate this to the actual units of the problem.)

Example 2.5
Applying Dimensional Analysis to Non-SI Units

Some mountain climbers are susceptible to high altitude pulmonary edema (HAPE), a life-threatening condition that causes fluid retention in the lungs. It can develop when a person climbs rapidly to heights greater than 2.5×10^3 meters (2,500 m). What is this distance expressed in feet?

■ **Analysis:** The problem can be stated as

$$2.5 \times 10^3\ \text{m} = ?\ \text{ft}$$

We are converting a metric unit of length (the meter) into an English unit of length (the foot). Since Table 2.3 does not have a relationship between feet and meters this is obviously not a one-step conversion, let's develop a sequence of conversions by looking at the units we can convert. One sequence may be:

$$2.5 \times 10^3\ \text{m} \longrightarrow \text{centimeters} \longrightarrow \text{inches} \longrightarrow \text{feet}$$

and if we consult the inside back cover of this book we find the conversion factor 1 yard = 0.9144 meters, so another multistep sequence could be

$$2.5 \times 10^3\ \text{m} \longrightarrow \text{yards} \longrightarrow \text{feet}$$

We will choose the first sequence for this example.

■**Assembling the Tools:** The tools we will need can be found by looking in the appropriate tables as shown.

$$1 \text{ cm} = 10^{-2} \text{ m} \quad \text{(from Table 2.4)}$$
$$1 \text{ in.} = 2.54 \text{ cm} \quad \text{(from Table 2.3)}$$
$$1 \text{ ft} = 12. \text{ in.}$$

■**Solution:** Now we apply dimensional analysis by following our planned sequence of eliminating unwanted units to bring us to the units of the answer.

$$2.5 \times 10^3 \text{ m} \times \frac{1 \text{ cm}}{10^{-2} \text{ m}} \times \frac{1 \text{ in.}}{2.54 \text{ cm}} \times \frac{1 \text{ ft}}{12 \text{ in.}} = 8.2 \times 10^3 \text{ ft}$$

Notice that if we were to stop after the first conversion factor, the units of the answer would be centimeters. If we stop after the second, the units would be inches, and after the third we get feet—the units we want. This time the answer has been rounded to two significant figures because that's how many there were in the measured distance. Notice that the numbers 12 and 2.54 do not affect the number of significant figures in the answer because they are exact numbers derived from definitions.

As suggested in the analysis, this is not the only way we could have solved this problem. Other sets of conversion factors could have been chosen. For example, we could have followed the second sequence of conversions and used: 1 yd = 0.9144 m and 3 ft = 1 yd. Then the problem would have been set up as follows:

$$2500 \text{ m} \times \frac{1 \text{ yd}}{0.9144 \text{ m}} \times \frac{3 \text{ ft}}{1 \text{ yd}} = 8200 \text{ ft} \quad \text{(rounded correctly)}$$

Many problems that you meet, just like this one, have more than one path to the answer. There isn't necessarily any *one* correct way to set up the solution. *The important thing is for you to be able to reason your way through a problem and find some set of relationships that can take you from the given information to the answer.* Dimensional analysis can help you search for these relationships if you keep in mind the units that must be eliminated by cancellation.

■**Is the Answer Reasonable?** Let's do some approximate arithmetic to get a feel for the size of the answer. A meter is slightly longer than a yard, so let's approximate the given distance, 2500 m, as 2500 yd. In 2500 yd, there are 3 × 2500 = 7500 ft. Since the meter is a bit longer than a yard, our answer should be a bit longer than 7500 ft, so the answer of 8200 ft seems to be reasonable.

2.7 | Use dimensional analysis to convert an area of 124 ft² to square meters. (*Hint:* What relationships would be required to convert feet to meters?)

2.8 | Use dimensional analysis to perform the following conversions: (a) 3.00 yd to inches, (b) 1.25 km to centimeters, (c) 3.27 mm to feet, (d) 20.2 miles/gallon to kilometers/liter.

Practice Exercises

Equivalencies

Up to now we've constructed conversion factors from relationships that are literally equalities. We can also make conversion factors from expressions that show how one thing is *equivalent* to another. For instance, if you buy a pair of sneakers for $75, we can say you converted $75 into a pair of sneakers or $75 is equivalent to a pair of sneakers. We would write this as

$$\$75 \Leftrightarrow 1 \text{ pair of sneakers}$$

where the symbol ⇔ is read as "is equivalent to." Mathematically, this equivalence sign works the same as an equal sign and we can construct two conversion factors as

$$\frac{\$75}{1 \text{ pair of sneakers}} \quad \text{or} \quad \frac{1 \text{ pair of sneakers}}{\$75}$$

that allow us to convert from sneakers to dollars or from dollars to sneakers.

Let's now look at a problem that has a direct relationship to the chemistry we are studying. In Chapter 1 we learned that Dalton's atomic theory predicted the **law of multiple proportions**. The basic idea of this law is that two elements often can form two different compounds. If we take samples of the two compounds so that the mass of one of the elements in those samples is the same, then the mass ratio of the other element in the two samples will be a ratio of small whole numbers. It is experimentally difficult, or very inconvenient, to obtain sample masses suggested above. However, if we analyze each sample for the elemental composition, we can perform a calculation that will illustrate the law of multiple proportions. Let's see how this works by working through Example 2.6.

Example 2.6
Applying the Law of Multiple Proportions

Titanium forms two different compounds with bromine. In compound A we find that 4.787 g of Ti are combined with 15.98 g of bromine. In compound B we find that 6.000 g of Ti are combined with 40.06 g of bromine. Determine whether these data support the law of multiple proportions.

■ **Analysis:** We need to set up a situation where we have the same mass of one of the elements in samples of the two compounds, and then take the corresponding ratio of the masses of the other element. For this example, let's assume that we select samples so that we have 6.000 g of Ti in compound A and 6.000 g of Ti in compound B.

■ **Assembling the Tools:** We will need to use the law of definite proportions to relate the amounts in the two compounds. We set up the two equivalencies we may need using the composition of each substance:

In compound A: 4.787 g Ti $\Leftrightarrow$ 15.98 g Br

In compound B: 6.000 g Ti $\Leftrightarrow$ 40.06 g Br

■ **Solution:** We decided in the Analysis to compare the two compounds when samples of them each had 6.000 g of titanium. Our initial data shows that compound B was given to us with 6.000 g of Ti. However, the sample of compound A had only 4.787 g of Ti. We need to determine how much bromine will be present if a sample of compound A has 6.000 g of Ti. To do this we convert 6.000 g of Ti in compound A to the equivalent mass of Br using the conversion factor from the compound A data. We start by writing this question as an equation,

■ The equivalence symbol, $\Leftrightarrow$, acts just like an equal sign.

6.000 g Ti $\Leftrightarrow$? g Br   (in compound A)

then we apply the conversion factor for compound A to get the solution,

$$6.000 \ \cancel{g \, Ti} \times \frac{15.98 \ g \, Br}{4.787 \ \cancel{g \, Ti}} = 20.03 \ g \, Br$$

We now know that 6.000 g of Ti combine with 20.03 g of Br in compound A, and we were given information that 6.000 g of Ti combine with 40.06 g of Br in compound B. Taking the ratio of bromine in the two compounds, we get

■ A mathematically equivalent method is to take the ratio of the masses of the elements in the two compounds, ratio$_a$ and ratio$_b$. Then take the ratio of those ratios, $\frac{ratio_a}{ratio_b}$, to obtain the ratio of small whole numbers.

$$\frac{20.03}{40.06} = \frac{1}{2} \quad \text{or} \quad \frac{40.06}{20.03} = \frac{2}{1}$$

Either of these is a ratio of small whole numbers. This verifies the law of multiple proportions.

■ **Is the Answer Reasonable?** The fact that our ratio gave us whole numbers is usually sufficient to consider the answer reasonable.

2.5 | Density and Specific Gravity

In our earlier discussion of properties we noted that intensive properties are useful for identifying substances. One of the interesting things about extensive properties is that if you take the ratio of two of them, the resulting quantity is usually independent of sample size. In effect, the sample size cancels out and the calculated quantity becomes an intensive property. A useful property obtained this way is **density**, *which is defined as the ratio of an object's mass to its volume.* Using the symbols d for density, m for mass, and V for volume, we can express this mathematically as

$$d = \frac{m}{V} \qquad \text{IS unit of } d \quad kg/m^3 \qquad \textbf{(2.6)}$$

TOOLS

Density

Notice that to determine an object's density we make two measurements, mass and volume.

Example 2.7
Calculating Density

A sample of blood completely fills an 8.20 cm³ vial. The empty vial has a mass of 10.30 g. The vial has a mass of 18.91 g after being filled with blood. What is the density of blood in units of g/cm³?

■**Analysis:** This problem asks you to connect the mass and volume of blood with its density. We are given the volume of the blood but not its mass. However, we are given information that allows us to calculate the mass. Once we have the mass and volume, we can use the definition of density to solve the problem.

■**Assembling the Tools:** The law of conservation of mass is one tool we need. It can be stated as follows:

$$\text{mass of full vial} = \text{mass of empty vial} + \text{mass of blood}$$

The other tool needed is the definition of density, given by Equation 2.6.

■**Solution:** The mass of the blood is the difference between the masses of the full and empty vials:

$$\text{mass of blood} = 18.91 \text{ g} - 10.30 \text{ g} = 8.61 \text{ g}$$

To determine the density we simply take the ratio of mass to volume.

$$\text{density} = \frac{m}{V} = \frac{8.61 \text{ g}}{8.20 \text{ cm}^3} = 1.05 \text{ g cm}^{-3}$$

This could also be written as density = 1.05 g/mL, because 1 cm³ = 1 mL.

■**Is the Answer Reasonable?** First, the answer has the correct units, so that's encouraging. In the calculation we are dividing 8.61 by a number that is slightly smaller, 8.20. The answer should be slightly larger than one, which it is, so a density of 1.05 g/cm³ seems reasonable.

Each pure substance has its own characteristic density (Table 2.5). Gold, for instance, is much more dense than iron. Each cubic centimeter of gold has a mass of 19.3 g, so its density is 19.3 g/cm³. The same volume of iron will weigh 7.86 g and have a density of 7.86 g/cm³. By comparison, the density of water is 1.00 g/cm³, and the density of air at room temperature is about 0.0012 g/cm³.

■ There is more mass in 1 cm³ of gold than in 1 cm³ of iron.

Table 2.5	Densities of Some Common Substances in g/cm³ at Room Temperature
Water	1.00
Aluminum	2.70
Iron	7.86
Silver	10.5
Gold	19.3
Glass	2.2
Air	0.0012

Table 2.6	Density of Water as a Function of Temperature
Temperature (°C)	**Density (g/cm³)**
10	0.999700
15	0.999099
20	0.998203
25	0.997044
30	0.995646
50	0.988036
100	0.958364

■ Although the density of water varies slightly with temperature, it is very close to 1.00 g/cm³ when the temperature is close to room temperature, 25 °C.

Most substances, such as the fluid in the bulb of a thermometer, expand slightly when they are heated, so the amount of matter packed into each cubic centimeter is less. Therefore, density usually decreases slightly with increasing temperature.[8] For solids and liquids the size of this change is small, as you can see from the data for water in Table 2.6. When only two or three significant figures are required, we can often ignore the variation of density with temperature.

Density as a Conversion Factor

A useful property of density is that it provides a way to convert between the mass and volume of a substance. It defines a relationship, which we previously called an equivalence, between the amount of mass and its volume. For instance, the density of gold (19.3 g/cm³) tells us that 19.3 g of the metal is equivalent to a volume of 1.00 cm³. We express this relationship symbolically as

$$19.3 \text{ g gold} \Leftrightarrow 1.00 \text{ cm}^3 \text{ gold}$$

where we have used the symbol $\Leftrightarrow$ to mean "is equivalent to." In setting up calculations for dimensional analysis, an equivalence can be used to construct conversion factors just as equalities can. From the equivalence we have just written, we can form two conversion factors:

$$\frac{19.3 \text{ g gold}}{1.00 \text{ cm}^3 \text{ gold}} \quad \text{and} \quad \frac{1.00 \text{ cm}^3 \text{ gold}}{19.3 \text{ g gold}}$$

The following example illustrates how we use density in calculations.

Example 2.8
Calculations Using Density

Seawater has a density of about 1.03 g/mL. (a) What mass of seawater would fill a sampling vessel to a volume of 225 mL? (b) What is the volume, in milliliters, of 45.0 g of seawater?

■ **Analysis:** For both parts of this problem, we are relating the mass of a material to its volume. We have recently found that density provides a direct relationship between mass and volume, so this should be a one-step conversion.

[8]Liquid water behaves oddly. Its maximum density is at 4 °C, so when water at 0 °C is warmed, its density increases until the temperature reaches 4 °C. As the temperature is increased further, the density of water gradually decreases.

■**Assembling the Tools:** Density, Equation 2.6, is the only tool that we need to convert between these two quantities. We write the equivalence for this problem as

$$1.03 \text{ g seawater} \Leftrightarrow 1.00 \text{ mL seawater}$$

From this relationship we can construct two conversion factors. These will be the tools we use to obtain the answers.

$$\frac{1.03 \text{ g seawater}}{1.00 \text{ mL seawater}} \quad \text{and} \quad \frac{1.00 \text{ mL seawater}}{1.03 \text{ g seawater}}$$

■**Solution to (a):** The question can be restated as:

$$225 \text{ mL seawater} \Leftrightarrow ? \text{ g seawater}$$

We need to eliminate the unit *mL seawater*, so we choose the conversion factor on the left as our tool.

$$225 \text{ mL seawater} \times \frac{1.03 \text{ g seawater}}{1.00 \text{ mL seawater}} = 232 \text{ g seawater}$$

Thus, 225 mL of seawater has a mass of 232 g.

■**Solution to (b):** The question is: 45.0 g seawater ⇔ ? mL seawater. This time we need to eliminate the unit *g seawater*, so we use the conversion factor on the right as our tool.

$$45.0 \text{ g seawater} \times \frac{1.00 \text{ mL seawater}}{1.03 \text{ g seawater}} = 43.7 \text{ mL seawater}$$

Thus, 45.0 g of seawater has a volume of 43.7 mL.

■**Are the Answers Reasonable?** Notice that the density tells us that 1 mL of seawater has a mass of slightly more than 1 g. Thus, for part (a), we might expect that 225 mL of seawater should have a mass slightly more than 225 g. Our answer, 232 g, is reasonable. For part (b), 45 g of seawater should have a volume not too far from 45 mL, so our answer of 43.7 mL is the right size.

Practice Exercises

2.9 | A gold-colored metal object has a mass of 365 g and a volume of 22.12 cm³. Is the object composed of pure gold? (*Hint:* How does the density of the object compare with that of pure gold?)

2.10 | A certain metal alloy has a density of 12.6 g/cm³. How many pounds would 0.822 ft³ of this alloy weigh? (*Hint:* What is the density of this alloy in units of lb/ft³?)

2.11 | An ocean-dwelling dinosaur was estimated to have had a body volume of 1.38×10^6 cm³. The animal's mass when alive was estimated at 1.24×10^3 kg. What was its density?

2.12 | The density of diamond is 3.52 g/cm³. What is the volume in cubic centimeters of a 1.125 carat diamond, which has a mass of 225 mg?

Specific Gravity

Density is the ratio of mass to volume of a substance. We used units of grams for the mass and cubic centimeters for the volume in our examples. This is entirely reasonable since most liquids and solids have densities between 0.5 and 20 g/cm³. There are many different units for mass. Kilograms, grams, micrograms, pounds, ounces, and drams come to mind, and there are undoubtedly more. Volume also has many possible units: cm³, liters, ounces, gallons, and so on. From those listed, there are 30 different possible ratios of mass and volume units for density. Many professions have their own preferred units for density and

CHEMISTRY OUTSIDE THE CLASSROOM | 2.1

Density and Wine

Density, or specific gravity, is one of the basic measurements in the wine making process. The essential chemical reaction is that yeast cells feed on the sugars in the grape juice and one of the products is ethanol (ethyl alcohol) and the other product is carbon dioxide. This is the fermentation process. The two main sugars in grapes are glucose and fructose. The fermentation reaction for these sugars are

(Steve Hyde/Flicker/Getty Images, Inc)

$$C_6H_{12}O_6(aq) \longrightarrow 2CH_3CH_2OH \ (aq) + 2CO_2(g)$$

If there is too little sugar the amount of alcohol in the product will be low. Too much sugar will result in a maximum amount of alcohol, about 13%, but there will be leftover sugar. Wines that are sweet with leftover sugars or low in alcohol are not highly regarded.

To make high quality wines the natural sugar content of the grapes is monitored carefully, toward the end of the growing season. When the sugar content reaches the optimum level the grapes are harvested, crushed and pressed to start the fermentation process.

A very quick way to determine the sugar content of the grapes is to determine the density of the juice. The higher the density, the higher the sugar content. Vintners use a simple device called a hydrometer. The hydrometer is a weighted glass bulb with a graduated stem. Placed in a liquid and given a slight spin the hydrometer will stay centered in the graduated cylinder and sink to a level that is proportional to the density. After the density is read from the hydrometer scale, the vintner consults a calibration chart to find the corresponding sugar content.

Once the fermentation ends, the alcohol content must also be determined. Again, this is done by measuring the density. To do this, a sample of wine is distilled by heating it to boiling and condensing the alcohol and water that are vaporized. When the required amount of liquid has been condensed, its density is determined using another hydrometer. Using calibration tables, the density reading is converted into the percentage alcohol.

Hydrometer used for measuring sugar content in crushed grapes before fermentation. *(WarrenMcConnaughie/Alamy)*

Hydrometer used for measuring alcohol content in a distilled wine sample after fermentation. *(Paul Silverman/Fundamental Photographs)*

would like to see them tabulated in reference books. This would result in each substance having 30 different densities listed in tables. Imagine the confusion, and the possibility of repeating the Mars Orbiter mistake becomes very probable.

The concept of *specific gravity solves this problem.* The **specific gravity** for a substance is simply the density of that substance divided by the density of water. The units for the two densities must be the <u>same</u> so that specific gravity will be a *dimensionless number*. In addition other experimental conditions, such as temperature, for determining the two densities must be the same.

Specific gravity

$$\text{specific gravity} = \frac{\text{density of substance}}{\text{density of water}} \tag{2.7}$$

To use the specific gravity, the scientist simply selects the specific gravity of the desired substance and then multiplies it by the density of water that has the units desired. Now we can have a relatively compact table that lists the specific gravity for our chemical substances and then a second short table of the density of water, perhaps in the 30 different units suggested above.

Example 2.9
Using Specific Gravity

Concentrated sulfuric acid is sold in bottles with a label that states that the specific gravity at 25 °C is 1.84. The density of water at 25 °C is 62.4 pounds per cubic foot. How many cubic feet of sulfuric acid will weigh 55.5 pounds?

■ **Analysis:** We rewrite the question as an equation,

$$55.5 \text{ lb sulfuric acid} = ? \text{ ft}^3 \text{ sulfuric acid}$$

We saw how to use density to convert mass to volume. The specific gravity needs to be converted to density units, preferably pounds and cubic feet so that this can be a one-step conversion.

■ **Assembling the Tools:** We have Equation 2.7 defining specific gravity. We know two of the variables, and simple algebra will allow us to calculate the density of sulfuric acid. We will then use the density as a conversion factor as we did in Example 2.7.

■ **Solution:** Rearranging the specific gravity equation we get

density sulfuric acid = (specific gravity) × (density of water) = 1.84×62.4 lb/ft^3

density sulfuric acid = 114.8 lb/ft^3

We now perform the conversion with the conversion factor from the density,

$$55.5 \text{ lb sulfuric acid} \times \frac{1 \text{ ft}^3}{114.8 \text{ lb}} = 0.483 \text{ ft}^3$$

■ **Is the Answer Reasonable?** We can do some quick estimations. The density seems correct: since the specific gravity is approximately 2 and the density of water is approximately 60, an answer near 120 is expected. For the second part, we see that 114 is about twice the size of 55.5 so we expect an answer of about 0.5. Our answer is very close to that, suggesting that our answers are reasonable.

Importance of Reliable Measurements

We saw earlier that substances can be identified by their properties. If we are to rely on properties such as density for identification of substances, it is very important that our measurements be reliable. We must have some idea of what the measurements' accuracy and precision are.

The importance of accuracy is obvious. If we have no confidence that our measured values are close to the true values, we certainly cannot trust any conclusions that are based on the data we have collected.

Precision of measurements can be equally important. For example, suppose we had a gold wedding ring and we wanted to determine whether or not the gold was 24 carat. We could determine the mass of the ring, and then its volume, and compute the density of the ring. We could then compare our experimental density with the density of 24 carat gold (which is 19.3 g/mL). Suppose the ring had a volume of 1.0 mL and the ring had a mass of 18 g, as measured using a graduated cup measure and a kitchen scale. The density of the ring would then be 18 g/mL, to the correct number of significant figures. Could we conclude that the ring was made of 24 carat gold? We know the density to only two significant figures, and we compare it to the tabulated densities, also rounded to two significant figures. The experimental density could be as low as 17 g/mL or as high as 19 g/mL, which means the ring could be 24 carat gold—or it could be 22 carat gold (which has a density of around 17.7 to 17.8 g/mL) or maybe even 18 carat gold (which has a density up to 16.9 g/mL).

■ The carat system for gold states that pure gold is referred to as 24 carat gold. Gold that is 50% gold by mass will be 12 carat. Gold that is less than 24 carats is usually alloyed with cheaper metals such as silver and copper.

Suppose we now measure the mass of the ring with a laboratory balance capable of measurements to the nearest ± 0.001 g and obtain a mass of 18.153 g. We measure the volume using volumetric glassware and find a volume of 1.03 mL. The density is 17.6 g/mL to the correct number of significant figures. The difference between this density and the density of 24 carat gold is 19.3 g/mL − 17.6 g/mL = 1.7 g/mL. This is considerably larger than the uncertainty in the experimental density (which is about ± 0.1 g/mL). We can be reasonably confident that the ring is not 24 carat gold, and in fact the measurements point toward the ring being composed of 22 carat gold.

To trust conclusions drawn from measurements, we must be sure the measurements are accurate and that they are of sufficient precision to be meaningful. This is a key consideration in designing experiments.

| Summary

Properties of Materials. **Physical properties** are measured without changing the chemical composition of a sample. A physical change doesn't alter the chemical composition of the substances involved. **Solid, liquid,** and **gas** are the most common **states of matter.** The properties of the states of matter can be related to the different ways the individual atomic-size particles are organized. A **chemical property** describes a chemical reaction a substance undergoes. Formation or decomposition of a compound takes place by a chemical change that changes the chemical makeup of the substances involved. **Intensive properties** are independent of sample size; **extensive properties** depend on sample size.

Units of Measurement. **Qualitative observations** lack numerical information, whereas **quantitative observations** require numerical measurements. The units used for scientific measurements are based on the set of seven **SI base units**, which can be combined to give various **derived units.** These all can be scaled to larger or smaller sized units by applying **decimal multiplying factors.** In the laboratory we routinely measure length, volume, mass, and temperature. Convenient units for length and volume are, respectively, **centimeters** or **millimeters**, and **liters** or **milliliters. Mass** is a measure of the amount of matter in an object and differs from weight. Mass is measured with a **balance** and is expressed in units of **kilograms** or **grams**. Temperature is measured in units of **degrees Celsius** (or **Fahrenheit**) using a thermometer. For many calculations, temperature must be expressed in **kelvins (K)**. The zero point on the **Kelvin temperature scale** is called **absolute zero.**

Significant Figures. The **precision** of a measured quantity is expressed by the number of **significant figures** that it contains, which equals the number of digits known for sure plus the first one that possesses some uncertainty. Measured values are **precise** if they contain many significant figures and therefore differ from each other by small amounts. A measurement is **accurate** if its value lies very close to the true value. When measurements are combined in calculations, rules help us determine the correct number of significant figures in the answer (see below). **Exact numbers** are considered to have an infinite number of significant figures.

Dimensional Analysis. **Dimensional analysis (the factor-label method)** is based on the ability of units to undergo the same mathematical operations as numbers. **Conversion factors** are constructed from *valid relationships* between units. These relationships can be either equalities or **equivalencies** (indicated by the symbol ⇔) between units. Unit cancellation serves as a guide to the use of conversion factors and aids us in correctly setting up the arithmetic for a problem.

Density and Specific Gravity. **Density** is an intensive property equal to the ratio of a sample's mass to its volume. Besides serving as a means for identifying substances, density provides a conversion factor that relates mass to volume. **Specific gravity** is the ratio of the density of a substance to the density of water and is a **dimensionless** quantity. This serves as a convenient way to have density data available in a large number of mass and volume units.

TOOLS

Tools for Problem Solving
The following tools were introduced in this chapter. Study them carefully so you can select the appropriate tool when needed.

Base SI units (Table 2.1, page 32)
The eight basic units of the SI system are used to derive the units for all scientific measurements.

SI prefixes (Table 2.4, page 35)

We use the prefixes to create larger and smaller units. They are also used as conversion factors for converting between differently sized units. Be sure you are familiar with the ones in bold type in Table 2.4.

Units in laboratory measurements (page 36)

Often we must convert among units commonly used for laboratory measurements.

Length: 1 m = 100 cm = 1000 mm

Volume: 1 L = 1000 mL = 1000 cm³

Temperature conversions (pages 38 and 39)

Use these equations to convert between temperature scales.

$$t_F = \left(\frac{9\,°F}{5\,°C}\right)t_C + 32\,°F \qquad T_K = (t_C + 273.15)°C\left(\frac{1\,K}{1\,°C}\right)$$

Counting significant figures (page 42)

To gauge the quality of a measurement, we must know the number of significant figures it contains:

- All nonzero digits are significant.
- Zeros between significant digits, imbedded zeros, are significant.
- Zeros to the *left* of the first nonzero digit are never significant.
- Zeros on the end of a number (a) with a decimal point are significant; (b) those without a decimal point are assumed not to be significant. (To avoid confusion, scientific notation should be used.)

Significant figures: multiplication and division (page 44)

In these operations we round the answer to the same number of significant figures as the least precise factor (i.e. the factor with the fewest significant figures).

Significant figures: addition and subtraction (page 44)

We round the answer to match the same number of decimal places as the quantity with the fewest number of decimal places.

Significant figures: exact numbers (page 44)

Numbers such as those that arise from definitions do not affect the number of significant figures in the result of a calculation.

Density (page 51)

The density, d, relates mass, m, and volume, V, for a substance.

$$d = \frac{m}{V}$$

Density provides an equivalence between mass and volume, from which we can construct conversion factors to convert between mass and volume for a substance.

Specific gravity (page 54)

The specific gravity relates the density of a substance to the density of water,

$$\text{Specific gravity} = \frac{d_{\text{substance}}}{d_{\text{water}}}$$

Specific gravity is dimensionless, and when multiplied by the density of water, in the desired units, will give the density of the substance in those units.

Review Questions

Physical and Chemical Properties

2.1 Give five examples of physical properties.

2.2 How does a chemical property differ from a physical property?

2.3 Determine whether each of the following is a physical or chemical change, and explain your reasoning.

(a) Copper conducts electricity.

(b) Gallium metal will melt in your hand.

(c) Bread turns brown in a toaster.

(d) Wine turns to vinegar.

(e) Cement hardens.

2.4 Determine whether each of the following is a physical or chemical change, and explain your reasoning.

(a) Kernels of corn are heated to make popcorn.

(b) Molten copper is mixed with molten gold to make an alloy.

(c) Heavy cream is mixed vigorously to whipped cream.

(d) Heavy cream is churned to make butter.

(e) Aluminum soda cans are recycled.

Intensive and Extensive Properties

2.5 Distinguish between an extensive and an intensive property.

2.6 Determine whether each of the following is an intensive or extensive property, and justify your reasoning:

(a) mass

(b) boiling point

(c) color

(d) physical state

2.7 Determine whether each of the following is an intensive or extensive property, and justify your reasoning:

(a) melting point

(b) density

(c) volume

(d) surface area

States of Matter

2.8 Describe one or more physical properties of each state of matter that distinguishes it from the other states of matter:

(a) gas   (b) liquid   (c) solid

2.9 At room temperature, what is the state of each of the following? If necessary, look up the information in a reference source.

(a) hydrogen

(b) aluminum

(c) nitrogen

(d) mercury

2.10 At room temperature, determine the appropriate phase for each of the following substances. (Look up the substance in data tables if needed.)

(a) potassium chloride

(b) carbon dioxide

(c) ethyl alcohol

(d) methane

(e) sucrose

2.11 At room temperature, determine the appropriate phase for each of the following substances. (Look up the substance in data tables if needed.)

(a) sodium chloride

(b) ozone

(c) Teflon

(d) cholesterol

(e) silicon dioxide

SI Units

2.12 Why must measurements always be written with a unit?

2.13 What is the only SI base unit that includes a prefix?

2.14 What is the meaning of each of the following prefixes?

(a) centi   (c) kilo   (e) nano   (g) mega

(b) milli   (d) micro   (f) pico

2.15 What abbreviation is used for each of the prefixes named in Question 2.14?

2.16 What reference points do we use in calibrating the scale of a thermometer? What temperature on the Celsius scale do we assign to each of these reference points?

OH **2.17** In each pair, which is larger: (a) A Fahrenheit degree or a Celsius degree? (b) A Celsius degree or a kelvin? (c) A Fahrenheit degree or a kelvin?

Significant Figures; Dimensional Analysis

2.18 Define the term *significant figures*.

2.19 What is the difference between *accuracy* and *precision*?

2.20 Suppose a length had been reported to be 31.24 cm. What is the minimum uncertainty implied in this measurement?

2.21 Suppose someone suggested using the fraction 3 yd/1 ft as a conversion factor to change a length expressed in feet to its equivalent in yards. What is wrong with this conversion factor? Can we construct a valid conversion factor relating centimeters to meters from the equation 1 cm = 1000 m? Explain your answer.

2.22 In 1 hour there are 3600 seconds. By what conversion factor would you multiply 250 seconds to convert it to hours? By what conversion factor would you multiply 3.84 hours to convert it to seconds?

2.23 If you were to convert the measured length 4.165 ft to yards by multiplying by the conversion factor (1 yd/3 ft), how many significant figures should the answer contain? Why?

Density

2.24 Write the equation that defines density. Identify the symbols in the equation.

2.25 Silver has a density of 10.5 g cm^{-3}. Express this as an equivalence between mass and volume for silver. Write two conversion factors that can be formed from this equivalence for use in calculations.

Review Problems

SI Prefixes

2.26 What number should replace the question mark in each of the following?

(a) 1 cm = ? m   (d) 1 dm = ? m

(b) 1 km = ? m   (e) 1 g = ? kg

(c) 1 m = ? pm   (f) 1 cg = ? g

2.27 What numbers should replace the question marks below?

(a) 1 nm = ? m   (d) 1 Mg = ? g

(b) 1 μg = ? g   (e) 1 mg = ? g

(c) 1 kg = ? g   (f) 1 dg = ? g

Temperature Conversions

2.28 Perform the following conversions.

(a) 57 °C to °F   (d) 49 °F to °C

(b) 16 °C to °F   (e) 62 °C to K

(c) 25.5 °F to °C   (f) −31 °C to K

2.29 Perform the following conversions.

(a) 96 °F to °C   (d) 273 K to °C

(b) −6 °F to °C   (e) 299 K to °C

(c) −55 °C to °F   (f) 40.0 °C to K

2.30 A healthy dog has a temperature ranging from 37.2 °C to 39.2 °C. Is a dog with a temperature of 103.5 °F within the normal range?

2.31 The coldest permanently inhabited place on earth is the Siberian village of Oymyakon in Russia. In 1964 the temperature reached a shivering −96 °F! What is this temperature in °C?

2.32 Estimates of the temperature at the core of the sun range from 10 megakelvins to 25 megakelvins. What is this range in °C and °F?

2.33 Natural gas is mostly methane, a substance that boils at a temperature of 111 K. What is its boiling point in °C and °F?

2.34 Helium has the lowest boiling point of any liquid. It boils at 4 K. What is its boiling point in °C?

2.35 The atomic bomb detonated over Hiroshima, Japan, at the end of World War II raised the temperature on the ground below to about 6100 K. Is this hot enough to melt concrete? (Concrete melts at 2050 °C.)

Significant Figures

2.36 How many significant figures do the following measured quantities have?

(a) 37.53 cm   (d) 0.00024 kg

(b) 37.240 cm   (e) 0.07080 m

(c) 202.0 g   (f) 2400 mL

2.37 How many significant figures do the following measured quantities have?

(a) 0.0230 g   (d) 614.00 mg

(b) 105.303 m   (e) 10 L

(c) 0.007 kg   (f) 3.8105 mm

OH **2.38** Perform the following arithmetic and round off the answers to the correct number of significant figures. Include the correct units with the answers.

(a) 0.0023 m × 315 m

(b) 84.25 kg − 0.01075 kg

(c) (184.45 g − 94.45 g)/(31.4 mL − 9.9 mL)

(d) (23.4 g + 102.4 g + 0.003 g)/(6.478 mL)

(e) (313.44 cm − 209.1 cm) × 8.2234 cm

2.39 Perform the following arithmetic and round off the answers to the correct number of significant figures. Include the correct units with the answers.

(a) 3.58 g/1.739 mL

(b) 4.02 mL + 0.001 mL

(c) (22.4 g − 8.3 g)/(1.142 mL − 0.002 mL)

(d) (1.345 g + 0.022 g)/(13.36 mL − 8.4115 mL)

(e) (74.335 m − 74.332 m)/(4.75 s × 1.114 s)

Unit Conversions Using Dimensional Analysis

OH **2.40** Perform the following conversions.

(a) 32.0 dm/s to km/hr   (d) 137.5 mL to L

(b) 8.2 mg/mL to μg/L   (e) 0.025 L to mL

(c) 75.3 mg to kg   (f) 342 pm^2 to dm^2

2.41 Perform the following conversions.

(a) 92 dL to μm^3 (d) 230 km^3 to m^3

(b) 22 ng to μg   (e) 87.3 cm s^{-2} to km hr^{-2}

(c) 83 pL to nL   (f) 238 mm^2 to nm^2

2.42 Perform the following conversions. If necessary, refer to Tables 2.3 and 2.4.

(a) 36 in. to cm   (d) 1 cup (8 oz) to mL

(b) 5.0 lb to kg   (e) 55 mi/hr to km/hr

(c) 3.0 qt to mL   (f) 50.0 mi to km

2.43 Perform the following conversions. If necessary, refer to Tables 2.3 and 2.4.

(a) 250 mL to qt   (d) 1.75 L to fluid oz

(b) 3.0 ft to m   (e) 35 km/hr to mi/hr

(c) 1.62 kg to lb   (f) 80.0 km to mi

2.44 Perform the following conversions.

(a) 8.4 ft^2 to cm^2 (b) 223 mi^2 to km^2 (c) 231 ft^3 to cm^3

2.45 Perform the following conversions.

(a) 2.4 yd^2 to m^2 (b) 8.3 in.^{2} to mm^2 (c) 9.1 ft^3 to L

2.46 The human stomach can expand to hold up to 4.2 quarts of food. A pistachio nut has a volume of about 0.9 mL. Use this information to estimate the maximum number of pistachios that can be eaten in one sitting.

2.47 In the movie *Cool Hand Luke* (1967), Luke wagers that he can eat 50 eggs in one hour. The prisoners and guards bet against him, saying, "Fifty eggs gotta weigh a good six pounds. A man's gut can't hold that." A peeled, chewed chicken egg has a volume of approximately 53 mL. If Luke's stomach has a volume of 4.2 quarts, does he have any chance of winning the bet?

ILW 2.48 The winds in a hurricane can reach almost 200 miles per hour. What is this speed in meters per second? (Assume three significant figures.)

2.49 A bullet is fired at a speed of 2435 ft/s. What is this speed expressed in kilometers per hour?

2.50 A bullet leaving the muzzle of a pistol was traveling at a speed of 2230 feet per second. What is this speed in miles per hour?

2.51 On average, water flows over Niagara Falls at a rate of 2.05×10^5 cubic feet per second. One cubic foot of water weighs 62.4 lb. Calculate the rate of water flow in tons of water per day. (1 ton = 2000 lb)

2.52 The brightest star in the night sky in the northern hemisphere is Sirius. Its distance from earth is estimated to be 8.7 light years. A light year is the distance light travels in one year. Light travels at a speed of 3.00×10^8 m/s. Calculate the distance from earth to Sirius in miles. (1 mi = 5280 ft).

2.53 One degree of latitude on the earth's surface equals 60.0 nautical miles. One nautical mile equals 1.151 statute miles. (A *statute mile* is the distance over land that we normally associate with the unit mile). Calculate the circumference of the earth in statute miles.

2.54 The deepest point in the earth's oceans is found in the Mariana Trench, a deep crevasse located about 1000 miles southeast of Japan beneath the Pacific Ocean. Its maximum depth is 6033.5 fathoms. One fathom is defined as 6 feet. Calculate the depth of the Mariana Trench in meters.

2.55 At sea level, our atmosphere exerts a pressure of about 14.7 lb/in^2, which means that each square inch of your body experiences a force of 14.7 lb from the air that surrounds you. As you descend below the surface of the ocean, the pressure produced by the seawater increases by about 14.7 lb/in^2 for every 10 meters of depth. In the preceding problem you calculated the maximum depth of the Mariana Trench, located in the Pacific Ocean. What is the approximate pressure in pounds per square inch and in tons per square inch exerted by the sea at the deepest point of the trench? (1 ton = 2000 lb)

Density and Specific Gravity

2.56 A sample of kerosene weighs 36.4 g. Its volume was measured to be 45.6 mL. What is the density of the kerosene in g mL^{-1}?

2.57 A block of magnesium has a mass of 14.3 g and a volume of 8.46 cm^3. What is the density of magnesium in g/cm^3?

OH 2.58 Acetone, the solvent in some nail polish removers, has a density of 0.791 g/mL. What is the volume, in mL, of 25.0 g of acetone?

2.59 A glass apparatus contains 26.223 g of water when filled at 25 °C. At this temperature, water has a density of 0.99704 g/mL. What is the volume, in mL, of the apparatus?

2.60 Chloroform, a chemical once used as an anesthetic, has a density of 1.492 g/mL. What is the mass in grams of 185 mL of chloroform?

2.61 Gasoline has a density of about 0.65 g/mL. How much does 34 L (approximately 18 gallons) weigh in kilograms? In pounds?

ILW 2.62 A graduated cylinder was filled with water to the 15.0 mL mark and weighed on a balance. Its mass was 27.35 g. An object made of silver was placed in the cylinder and completely submerged in the water. The water level rose to 18.3 mL. When reweighed, the cylinder, water, and silver object had a total mass of 62.00 g. Calculate the density of silver in g cm^{-3}.

2.63 Titanium is a metal used to make golf clubs. A rectangular bar of this metal measuring 1.84 cm × 2.24 cm × 2.44 cm was found to have a mass of 45.7 g. What is the density of titanium in g mL^{-1}?

2.64 The space shuttle uses liquid hydrogen as its fuel. The external fuel tank used during takeoff carries 227,641 lb of hydrogen with a volume of 385,265 gallons. Calculate the density of liquid hydrogen in units of lb/gal and g/mL. (Express your answer to three significant figures.) What is the specific gravity of liquid hydrogen?

2.65 You are planning to make a cement driveway that has to be 10.1 feet wide, 32.3 feet long, and 4.00 inches deep on average. The specific gravity of concrete is 0.686. How many kilograms of concrete are needed for the job?

Additional Exercises

2.66 Some time ago, a U.S. citizen traveling in Canada observed that the price of regular gasoline was 0.959 Canadian dollars per liter. The exchange rate at the time was 1.142 Canadian dollars per one U.S. dollar. Calculate the price of the Canadian gasoline in units of U.S. dollars per gallon. (Just the week before, the traveler had paid $2.249 per gallon in the United States.)

OH 2.67 You are the science reporter for a daily newspaper, and your editor has asked you to write a story based on a report in the scientific literature. The report states that analysis of the sediments in Hausberg Tarn (elevation 4350 m) on the side of Mount Kenya (elevation 4600–4700 m) shows that the average temperature of the water rose by 4.0 °C between 350 BC and 450 AD. Your editor wants all the data expressed in the English system of units. Make the appropriate conversions.

2.68 An astronomy Web site states that neutron stars have a density of 1.00×10^8 tons per cubic centimeter. The site does not specify whether "tons" means metric tons (1 metric ton = 1000 kg) or English tons (1 English ton = 2000 pounds). How many grams would one teaspoon of a neutron star weigh, if the density were in metric tons per cm^3? How many grams would the teaspoon weigh if the density were in English tons per cm^3? (One teaspoon is approximately 4.93 mL.)

2.69 The star Arcturus is 3.50×10^{14} km from the earth. How many days does it take for light to travel from Arcturus to earth? What is the distance to Arcturus in light years? One light year is the distance light travels in one year (365 days); light travels at a speed of 3.00×10^8 m/s.

*2.70 A pycnometer is a glass apparatus used for accurately determining the density of a liquid. When dry and empty, a certain pycnometer had a mass of 27.314 g. When filled with distilled water at 25.0 °C, it weighed 36.842 g. When filled with chloroform (a liquid once used as an anesthetic before its toxic properties were known), the apparatus weighed 41.428 g. At 25.0 °C, the density of water is 0.99704 g/mL. **(a)** What is the volume of the pycnometer? **(b)** What is the density of chloroform?

2.71 Radio waves travel at the speed of light, 3.00×10^8 m/s. If you were to broadcast a question to an astronaut on the moon, which is 239,000 miles from earth, what is the minimum time that you would have to wait to receive a reply?

2.72 Suppose you have a job in which you earn $4.50 for each 30 minutes that you work.

(a) Express this information in the form of an equivalence between dollars earned and minutes worked.

(b) Use the equivalence defined in (a) to calculate the number of dollars earned in 1 hr 45 min.

(c) Use the equivalence defined in (a) to calculate the number of minutes you would have to work to earn $17.35.

2.73 When an object floats in water, it displaces a volume of water that has a weight equal to the weight of the object. If a ship has a weight of 4255 tons, how many cubic feet of seawater will it displace? Seawater has a density of 1.025 g cm^{-3}; 1 ton = 2000 lb.

2.74 Aerogel or "solid smoke" is a novel material that is made of silicon dioxide, like glass, but is a thousand times less dense than glass because it is extremely porous. Material scientists at NASA's Jet Propulsion Laboratory created the lightest aerogel ever in 2002, with a density of 0.00011 pounds per cubic inch. The material was used for thermal insulation in the 2003 Mars Exploration Rover. If the maximum space for insulation in the spacecraft's hull was 2510 cm^3, what mass (in grams) did the aerogel insulation add to the spacecraft?

Aerogel *(NASA/JPL)*

2.75 A liquid known to be either ethanol (ethyl alcohol) or methanol (methyl alcohol) was found to have a density of 0.798 ± 0.001 g/mL. Consult tabulated data to determine which liquid it is. What other measurements could help to confirm the identity of the liquid?

2.76 An unknown liquid was found to have a density of 69.22 lb/ft^3. The density of ethylene glycol (the liquid used in antifreeze) is 1.1088 g/mL. Could the unknown liquid be ethylene glycol?

2.77 When an object is heated to a high temperature, it glows and gives off light. The color balance of this light depends on the temperature of the glowing object. Photographic lighting is described, in terms of its color balance, as a temperature in kelvins. For example, a certain electronic flash gives a color balance (called color temperature) rated at 5800 K. What is this temperature expressed in °C?

OH 2.78 There exists a single temperature at which the value reported in °F is numerically the same as the value reported in °C. What is this temperature?

*2.79 In the text, the Kelvin scale of temperature is defined as an absolute scale in which one Kelvin degree unit is the same size as one Celsius degree unit. A second absolute temperature scale exists called the Rankine scale. On this scale, one Rankine degree unit (°R) is the same size as one Fahrenheit degree unit. **(a)** What is the only temperature at which the Kelvin and Rankine scales possess the same numerical value? Explain your answer. **(b)** What is the boiling point of water expressed in °R?

*2.80 Density measurements can be used to analyze mixtures. For example, the density of solid sand (without air spaces) is about 2.84 g/mL. The density of gold is 19.3 g/mL. If a 1.00 kg sample of sand containing some gold has a density of 3.10 g/mL (without air spaces), what is the percentage of gold in the sample?

*2.81 An artist's statue has a surface area of 14.6 ft². The artist plans to apply gold leaf to the statue and wants the coating to be 2.50 μm thick. If the price of gold were $1,125.10 per troy ounce, how much would it cost to give the statue its gold coating? (1 troy ounce = 31.1035 g; the density of gold is 19.3 g/mL.)

*2.82 A cylindrical metal bar has a diameter of 0.753 cm and a length of 2.33 cm. It has a mass of 8.423 g. Calculate the density of the metal in the units lb/ft³.

2.83 What is the volume in cubic millimeters of a 3.54 carat diamond, given that the density of diamond is 3.51 g/mL? (1 carat = 200 mg)

*2.84 Because of the serious consequences of lead poisoning, the Federal Centers for Disease Control in Atlanta has set a threshold of concern for lead levels in children's blood. This threshold was based on a study that suggested that lead levels in blood as low as *10 micrograms of lead per deciliter of blood* can result in subtle effects of lead toxicity. Suppose a child had a lead level in her blood of 2.5×10^{-4} grams of lead per liter of blood. Is this person in danger of exhibiting the effects of lead poisoning?

*2.85 Gold has a density of 19.31 g cm⁻³. How many grams of gold are required to provide a gold coating 0.500 mm thick on a ball bearing having a diameter of 2.000 mm?

*2.86 A Boeing 747 jet airliner carrying 568 people burns about 5.0 gallons of jet fuel per mile. What is the rate of fuel consumption in units of gallons per person per mile? Is this better or worse than the rate of fuel consumption in an automobile carrying two people that gets 21.5 miles per gallon? If the airliner were making the 3470 mile trip from New York to London, how many pounds of jet fuel would be consumed? (Jet fuel has a density of 0.803 g/mL.)

Exercises in Critical Thinking

2.87 Find two or more Web sites that give the values for each of the seven base SI units. Keeping in mind that not all Web sites provide reliable information, which Web site do you believe provides the most reliable values? Justify your answer.

2.88 Reference books such as the *Handbook of Chemistry and Physics* report the specific gravities of substances instead of their densities. Find the definition of specific gravity, and discuss the relative merits of specific gravity and density in terms of their usefulness as a physical property.

*2.89 A student used a 250 mL graduated cylinder having volume markings every 2 mL to carefully measure 100 mL of water for an experiment. A fellow student said that by reporting the volume as "100 mL" in her lab notebook, she was only entitled to one significant figure. The first student disagreed. Why did her fellow student say the reported volume had only one significant figure?

Considering the circumstances, how many significant figures are in her measured volume? Justify your answer.

*2.90 Download a table of data for the density of water between its freezing and boiling points. Use a spreadsheet program to plot (a) the density of water versus temperature and (b) the volume of a kilogram of water versus temperature. Interpret the significance of these plots.

2.91 List the physical and chemical properties mentioned in this chapter. What additional physical and chemical properties can you think of to extend this list?

*2.92 A barge pulled by a tugboat can be described as a rectangular box that is open on the top. A certain barge is 30.2 feet wide and 12.50 feet high, with the base of each side being 116 feet long. If the barge itself weighs 6.58×10^4 pounds, what will be the draft (depth in the water) if the cargo weighs 1.12×10^6 pounds in (a) seawater with a density of 1.025 g/mL and (b) freshwater with a density of 0.997 g/mL?

3 Elements, Compounds, and the Periodic Table

Chapter Outline

A supernova, such as the one whose remnants are shown in the photograph taken by the Hubble space telescope, occurs when a large star collapses and explodes. It is in such explosions that particles of matter with names such as electrons, protons, and neutrons are forced together to form atoms of the elements that make up our universe. As you will learn in this chapter, these atomic particles are important in understanding the make-up of elements and the kinds of compounds elements form when they undergo chemical reactions.   NASA, ESA, and M. Livio and the Hubble 20th Anniversary Team (STScI)

This Chapter in Context

Students sometimes say that "chemistry is a foreign language." This statement is not far from the truth. We can consider the elements in the periodic table to be our new alphabet; the formulas for compounds are the words of chemistry; and the balanced equations that show how those compounds react with each other are the sentences of this new language. Learning the language of chemistry will help you succeed because you will be able to concentrate on new concepts that depend on your being fluent in your new language.

In Chapter 1 we introduced the broad scope and nature of the subject of chemistry, elements, classification of matter, the atomic theory, formulas, and reactions. In Chapter 2, we discussed the ways that precise and accurate measurements and calculations are central to all sciences, especially chemistry. Now we turn our attention to atoms, the periodic table, chemical compounds, and naming these compounds. We will take a closer look at the particles that make up the atoms, and how these particles define the identity of the elements. Then, we will use this information to arrange the elements into a table that is a storehouse of relationships, trends, and similarities among the elements. These elements combine to form compounds, and the type of compound formed can be determined by the makeup of the atoms. Finally, we will introduce you to *chemical nomenclature*—the system used to name chemical compounds.

3.1 | Internal Structure of the Atom

The earliest theories about atoms imagined them to be indestructible and totally unable to be broken into smaller pieces. However, as you probably know, atoms are not quite as indestructible as Dalton and other early philosophers had thought. During the late 1800s and early 1900s, experiments were performed that demonstrated that atoms are composed of **subatomic particles**. From this work the current theoretical model of atomic structure evolved. We will examine it in general terms in this chapter. A more detailed discussion of the electronic structure of the atom will follow in Chapter 8.

Discovery of the Electron, Proton, and Neutron

Our current knowledge of atomic structure was pieced together from facts obtained from experiments by scientists that began in the nineteenth century. In 1834, Michael Faraday discovered that the passage of electricity through aqueous solutions could cause chemical changes. This was the first hint that matter was electrical in nature. Later in that century, scientists began to experiment with *gas discharge tubes* in which a high-voltage electric current was passed through a gas at low pressure in a glass tube (Figure 3.1). Such a tube is fitted with a pair of metal *electrodes*, and when the electricity begins to flow between them, the gas in the tube glows. This flow of electricity is called an *electric discharge*, which is how the tubes got their name.

The physicists who first studied this phenomenon did not know what caused the tube to glow, but tests soon revealed that negatively charged particles were moving from the negative electrode (the **cathode**) to the positive electrode (the **anode**). The physicists called these emissions *rays,* and because the rays came from the cathode, they were called **cathode rays.**

In 1897, the British physicist J. J. Thomson modified a *cathode ray tube,* a special gas discharge tube, to make quantitative measurements of the properties of cathode rays, Figure 3.2. In Thomson's tube, a beam of cathode rays was focused on a glass surface coated with a phosphor, a substance that

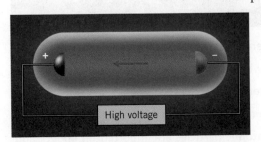

High voltage

Figure 3.1 | **A gas discharge tube.** Cathode rays flow from the negatively charged cathode to the positively charged anode.

glows when the cathode rays strike it (point 1). The cathode ray beam passed between the poles of a magnet and between a pair of metal electrodes that could be given electrical charges. The magnetic field tends to bend the beam in one direction (toward point 2), while the charged electrodes bend the beam in the opposite direction (toward point 3). By adjusting the charge on the electrodes, the two effects can be made to cancel, and from the amount of charge on the electrodes required to balance the effect of the magnetic field, Thomson was able to calculate the first bit of quantitative information about a cathode ray particle—the ratio of its charge to its mass (often expressed as e/m, where e stands for charge and m stands for mass). The charge-to-mass ratio has a value of -1.76×10^8 coulombs/gram, where the coulomb (C) is a standard unit of electrical charge and the negative sign reflects the negative charge on the particle.

Many experiments were performed using the cathode ray tube, and they demonstrated that cathode ray particles are in all matter. They are, in fact, *electrons*.

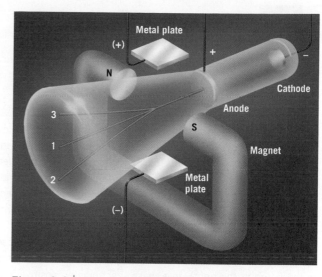

Figure 3.2 | **Thomson's cathode ray tube,** which was used to measure the charge-to-mass ratio for the electron.

Measuring the Charge and Mass of the Electron

In 1909, a researcher at the University of Chicago, Robert Millikan, designed an experiment that enabled him to measure the electron's charge (Figure 3.3). During the experiment he sprayed a fine mist of oil droplets above a pair of parallel metal plates, the top one of which had a small hole in it. As the oil drops settled, some would pass through this hole into the space between the plates, where he would irradiate them briefly with X rays. The X rays knocked electrons off molecules in the air, and the electrons became attached to the oil drops, which thereby were given an electrical charge. By observing the rate of fall of the charged drops both when the metal plates were electrically charged and when they were not, Millikan was able to calculate the amount of charge carried by each drop. When he examined his results, he found that all the values he obtained were whole-number multiples of -1.60×10^{-19} C. He reasoned that since a drop could only pick up whole numbers of electrons, this value must be the charge carried by each individual electron.

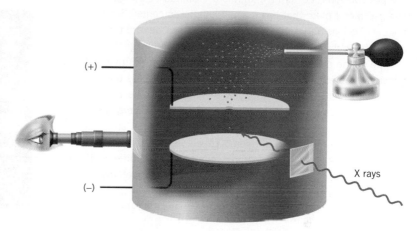

Figure 3.3 | **Millikan's oil drop experiment.** Electrons, which are ejected from molecules in the air by the X rays, are picked up by very small drops of oil falling through the tiny hole in the upper metal plate. By observing the rate of fall of the charged oil drops, with and without electrical charges on the metal plates, Millikan was able to calculate the charge carried by an electron.

Once Millikan had measured the electron's charge, its mass could then be calculated from Thomson's charge-to-mass ratio. This mass was calculated to be 9.09×10^{-28} g. More precise measurements have since been made, and the mass of the electron is currently reported to be $9.1093897 \times 10^{-28}$ g. Thomson's early measurements are in good agreement with today's more precise measurements.

Discovery of the Proton

The removal of electrons from an atom gives a positively charged particle (called an *ion*). To study these particles, a modification was made in the construction of the cathode ray tube to produce a new device called a *mass spectrometer*. This apparatus is described in *On the Cutting Edge 3.1* and was used to measure the charge-to-mass ratios of positive ions. These ratios were found to vary, depending on the chemical nature of the gas in the discharge tube, showing that their masses also varied. The lightest positive particle observed was produced when hydrogen was in the tube, and its mass was about 1800 times as heavy as an electron. When other gases

ON THE CUTTING EDGE | 3.1

The Mass Spectrometer and the Experimental Measurement of Atomic Masses

When a spark is passed through a gas, electrons are knocked off the gas molecules. Because electrons are negatively charged, the particles left behind carry positive charges; they are called *positive ions.* These positive ions have different masses, depending on the masses of the molecules from which they are formed. Thus, some molecules have large masses and give heavy ions, while others have small masses and give light ions.

The device that is used to study the positive ions produced from gas molecules is called a *mass spectrometer* (illustrated in the figure at the right). In a mass spectrometer, positive ions are created by passing an electrical spark (called an *electric discharge*) through a sample of the particular gas being studied. As the positive ions are formed, they are attracted to a negatively charged metal plate that has a small hole in its center. Some of the positive ions pass through this hole and travel onward through a tube that passes between the poles of a powerful magnet.

One of the properties of charged particles, both positive and negative, is that their paths become curved as they pass through a magnetic field. This is exactly what happens to the positive ions in the mass spectrometer as they pass between the poles of the magnet. However, the extent to which their paths are bent depends on the masses of the ions. This is because the path of a heavy ion, like that of a speeding cement truck, is difficult to change, but the path of a light ion, like that of a motorcycle, is influenced more easily. As a result, heavy ions emerge from between the magnet's poles along different lines than the lighter ions. In effect, an entering beam containing ions of different masses is sorted by the magnet into a number of beams, each containing ions of the same mass. This spreading out of the ion beam thus produces an array of different beams called a *mass spectrum.* There are many types of mass spectrometers. Here the array of beams can be detected by exposing photographic film.

In another type of mass spectrometer, the strength of the magnetic field is gradually changed, which sweeps the beams of ions across a detector located at the end of the tube. As a beam of ions strikes the detector, its intensity is measured and the masses of the particles in the beam are computed based on the strength of the magnetic field, the speed of the particles, and the geometry of the apparatus.

Among the benefits derived from measurements using the mass spectrometer are very accurate isotopic masses and relative isotopic abundances. These serve as the basis for the very precise values of the atomic masses that you find in the periodic table. (Isotopes are atoms of the same element with slightly different masses. They are discussed on page 68.)

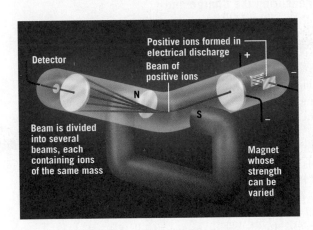

were used, their masses always seemed to be whole-number multiples of the mass observed for hydrogen ions. This suggested the possibility that clusters of the positively charged particles made from hydrogen atoms made up the positively charged particles of other gases. The hydrogen atom, minus an electron, thus seemed to be a fundamental particle in all matter and was named the *proton,* after the Greek word *proteios,* meaning "of first importance."

Discovery of the Atomic Nucleus

Early in the twentieth century, Hans Geiger and Ernest Marsden, working under Ernest Rutherford at Great Britain's Manchester University, studied what happened when *alpha rays* hit thin gold foils. Alpha rays are composed of particles having masses four times those of the proton and bearing two positive charges; they are emitted by certain unstable atoms in a phenomenon called *radioactive decay.* Most of the alpha particles sailed right on through as if the foils were virtually empty space (Figure 3.4). A significant number of alpha particles, however, were deflected at very large angles. Some were even deflected backward, as if they had hit a stone wall. Rutherford was so astounded that he compared the effect to that of firing a 15 inch artillery shell at a piece of tissue paper and having it come back and hit the gunner! From studying the angles of deflection of the particles, Rutherford reasoned that only something extraordinarily massive and positively charged

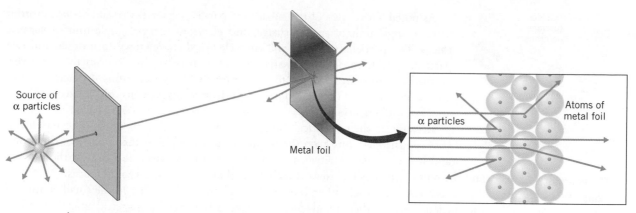

Figure 3.4 | **Some alpha particles are deflected by a thin gold foil.** Some hit something very massive head-on and are deflected backward. Many sail through. Some, making near misses with the massive "cores" (nuclei), are still deflected, because alpha particles have the same kind of charge (+) as these cores.

could cause such an occurrence. Since most of the alpha particles went straight through, he further reasoned that the metal atoms in the foils must be mostly empty space. Rutherford's ultimate conclusion was that virtually all of the mass of an atom must be concentrated in a particle having a very small volume located in the center of the atom. He called this massive particle the atom's *nucleus*.

Discovery of the Neutron

From the way alpha particles were scattered by a metal foil, Rutherford and his students were able to estimate the number of positive charges on the nucleus of an atom of the metal. This had to be equal to the number of protons in the nucleus. When they computed the nuclear mass based on this number of protons, however, the value always fell short of the actual mass. In fact, Rutherford found that only about half of the nuclear mass could be accounted for by protons. This led him to suggest that there were other particles in the nucleus that had a mass close to or equal to that of a proton, but with no electrical charge. This suggestion initiated a search that finally ended in 1932 with the discovery of the *neutron* by Sir James Chadwick, a British physicist.

■ For his work, Sir Chadwick earned the Nobel Prize in physics in 1935.

Subatomic Particles

The experiments described above showed that atoms are composed of three principal kinds of subatomic particles: **protons, neutrons,** and **electrons.** Experiments also revealed that at the center of an atom there exists a very tiny, extremely dense core called the *nucleus,* which is where an atom's protons and neutrons are found. Because they are found in nuclei, protons and neutrons are sometimes called **nucleons.** The electrons in an atom surround the nucleus and fill the remaining volume of the atom. (*How* the electrons are distributed around the nucleus is the subject of Chapter 8.) The properties of the subatomic particles are summarized in Table 3.1, and the general structure of the atom is illustrated in Figure 3.5.

■ Physicists have discovered a large number of subatomic particles, but protons, neutrons, and electrons are the only ones that will concern us at this time.

■ Protons are in all nuclei. Except for ordinary hydrogen, all nuclei also contain neutrons.

Table 3.1	Properties of Subatomic Particles		
Particle	**Mass (g)**	**Electrical Charge**	**Symbol**
Electron	$9.1093897 \times 10^{-28}$	$1-$	$_{-1}^{0}e$
Proton	$1.6726231 \times 10^{-24}$	$1+$	$_{1}^{1}H^{+}, _{1}^{1}p$
Neutron	$1.6749286 \times 10^{-24}$	0	$_{0}^{1}n$

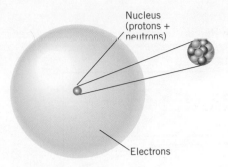

Nucleus
(protons +
neutrons)

Electrons

Figure 3.5 | **The internal structure of a atom.** An atom is composed of a tiny nucleus that holds all of the protons (red) and neutrons (grey). The electrons are in the space outside the nucleus.

■ The binding energy of nucleons is discussed in Chapter 21. This binding energy is what allowed for the easy formation of the elements up to iron.

As noted above, two of the subatomic particles carry electrical charges. Protons carry a single unit of **positive charge,** and electrons carry a single unit of **negative charge.** Two particles that have the same electrical charge repel each other, and two particles that have opposite charges attract each other. In an atom the negatively charged electrons are attracted to the positively charged protons. In fact, it is this attraction that holds the electrons around the nucleus. Neutrons have no charge and are electrically neutral.

Because of their identical charges, electrons repel each other. The repulsions between the electrons keep them spread out throughout the volume of the atom, and it is the *balance* between the attractions the electrons feel toward the nucleus and the repulsions they feel toward each other that controls the sizes of atoms.

Protons also repel each other, but they are able to stay together in the small volume of the nucleus because their repulsions are apparently offset by powerful nuclear binding forces that involve other subatomic particles that are studied in particle physics.

Matter as we generally find it in nature appears to be electrically neutral, which means that it contains equal numbers of positive and negative charges. Therefore, *in a neutral atom, the number of electrons must equal the number of protons.*

The proton and neutron are much more massive than the electron, about 1800 times heavier, so in any atom almost all of the atomic mass is contributed by the particles found in the nucleus. It is also interesting to note, however, that the diameter of the atom is approximately 10,000 times the diameter of its nucleus, so almost all of the *volume* of an atom is occupied by its electrons, which fill the space around the nucleus. (To place this on a more meaningful scale, if the nucleus was 1 ft in diameter, it would lie at the center of an atom with a diameter of approximately 1.9 miles or 10,000 feet!)

Atomic Numbers and Mass Numbers

TOOLS

Number of subatomic particles in atoms

What distinguishes one element from another is the number of protons in the nuclei of its atoms, because *all of the atoms of a particular element have an identical number of protons.* In fact, this allows us to redefine an **element** as *a substance whose atoms all contain the identical number of protons.* Thus, each element has associated with it a unique number, which we call its **atomic number** *(Z)*, that equals the number of protons in the nucleus of each of its atoms.

$$\text{Atomic number } (Z) = \text{number of protons}$$

Most elements exist in nature as mixtures of similar atoms called *isotopes* that differ only in mass. What makes isotopes of the same element different are the numbers of neutrons in their nuclei. *The **isotopes** of a given element have atoms with the same number of protons but different numbers of neutrons.* The numerical sum of the protons and neutrons in the atoms of a particular isotope is called the **mass number** *(A)* of the isotope.

$$\text{Isotope mass number } (A) = (\text{number of protons}) + (\text{number of neutrons})$$

Therefore, every isotope is fully defined by two numbers, its atomic number and its mass number. Sometimes these numbers are added to the left of the chemical symbol as a subscript and a superscript, respectively. Thus, if X stands for the chemical symbol for the element, an isotope of X is represented as

$$^{A}_{Z}X$$

TOOLS

Atomic symbols for isotopes

The isotope of uranium used in nuclear reactors, for example, can be symbolized as follows:

Mass number (number of protons and number of neutrons) $\longrightarrow$ $^{235}_{92}\text{U}$

Atomic number (number of protons) $\longrightarrow$

Uranium-235

As indicated, the name of this isotope is uranium-235 or U-235. Each neutral atom contains 92 protons and $(235 - 92) = 143$ neutrons as well as 92 electrons. In writing the symbol for the isotope, the atomic number is often omitted because it is redundant. Every atom of uranium has 92 protons, and every atom that has 92 protons is an atom of uranium. Therefore, this uranium isotope can be represented simply as ^{235}U.

In naturally occurring uranium, a more abundant isotope is ^{238}U. Atoms of this isotope also have 92 protons, but the number of neutrons is 146. Thus, atoms of ^{235}U and ^{238}U have the identical number of protons but differ in the numbers of neutrons.

■ For a neutral atom, the atomic number equals both the number of protons and the number of electrons.

Example 3.1
Counting Protons, Neutrons, and Electrons

How many electrons, protons, and neutrons does the isotope Cr-52 have?

■ **Analysis:** This problem asks for all three of the major subatomic particles in the Cr-52 isotope that has a mass of 52.

■ **Assembling the Tools:** First, we have to determine the identity of the element from the symbol using the table inside the front cover. All three of the tools for subatomic particles must be used:

$$\text{Number of protons} = \text{atomic number} = Z$$
$$\text{Number of electrons} = \text{atomic number} = Z$$
$$\text{Number of neutrons} = \text{mass number} - \text{atomic number} = A - Z$$

■ **Solution:** We find that Cr is the symbol for chromium, so $Z = 24$ and $A = 52$, and we conclude

$$\text{Protons} = 24; \qquad \text{Electrons} = 24; \qquad \text{Neutrons} = 52 - 24 = 28$$

■ **Is the Answer Reasonable?** One check is to be sure that the sum of the number of protons and neutrons is the isotope mass number. A second check is that the number of any of the particles is not larger than the isotope mass number (the largest number given in the problem), and in most cases the number of electrons, protons, or neutrons is usually close to half of the mass number. A final check is that the number of protons equals the number of electrons because it is a neutral atom. Our answers fulfill these conditions.

Practice Exercises

3.1 | Write the symbol for the isotope of plutonium (Pu) that contains 146 neutrons. How many electrons does it have? (*Hint:* Review the tools for writing isotope symbols and counting electrons.)

3.2 | How many protons, neutrons, and electrons are in each atom of $^{35}_{17}Cl$?

3.3 | In Practice Exercise 3.2, can we discard the 35 or the 17 or both from the symbol without losing the ability to solve the problem? Explain your reasoning.

Relative Atomic Masses of Elements

Before subatomic particles were discovered, a significant body of data had already been developed that showed that atoms of different elements had different distinctive masses. In fact, one of the most useful concepts to come from Dalton's atomic theory is that atoms of an element have a constant, characteristic **atomic mass** (or **atomic weight**). This concept opened the door to the determination of chemical formulas and ultimately to one of the most useful devices chemists have for organizing chemical information, the *periodic table of the elements*. But how could the masses of atoms be measured without a knowledge of atomic structure?

Individual atoms are much too small to weigh in the traditional manner. However, the *relative masses* of the atoms of elements can be determined *provided we know the ratio in which the atoms occur in a compound.* Let's look at an example to see how this could work.

Hydrogen (H) combines with the element fluorine (F) to form the compound hydrogen fluoride. Each molecule of this compound contains one atom of hydrogen and one atom of fluorine, which means that in *any* sample of this substance the fluorine-to-hydrogen *atom ratio* is always 1 to 1. It is also found that when a sample of hydrogen fluoride is decomposed, the mass of fluorine obtained is always 19.0 times larger than the mass of hydrogen, so the fluorine-to-hydrogen *mass ratio* is always 19.0 to 1.00.

F-to-H atom ratio: 1 to 1

F-to-H mass ratio: 19.0 to 1.00

Relative atomic masses

How could a 1-to-1 atom ratio give a 19.0-to-1.00 mass ratio? *It could do this only if each fluorine atom is 19.0 times heavier than each H atom.*

Notice that even though we haven't found the actual masses of F and H atoms, we now know how their masses compare (i.e., we know their *relative masses*). Similar procedures, with other elements in other compounds, are able to establish relative mass relationships among the other elements as well. What we need next is a way to place all of these masses on the same mass scale.

Carbon-12: Standard for the Atomic Mass Scale

To establish a uniform mass scale for atoms it is necessary to select a standard against which the relative masses can be compared. Currently, the agreed-upon reference uses the most abundant isotope of carbon, carbon-12, ^{12}C. From this reference, one atom of this isotope is *exactly* 12 units of mass, which are called **atomic mass units.** Some prefer to use the symbol **amu** for the atomic mass unit. The internationally accepted symbol is **u,** which is the symbol we will use throughout the rest of the book. By assigning 12 u to the mass of one atom of ^{12}C, the size of the atomic mass unit is established to be $\frac{1}{12}$ of the mass of a single carbon-12 atom:

■ In biology, the atomic-mass unit is sometimes called a dalton. 1 u = 1 dalton.

> 1 atom of ^{12}C has a mass of 12 u (exactly)
>
> 1 u equals $\frac{1}{12}$ the mass of 1 atom of ^{12}C (exactly)

In modern terms, the atomic mass of an element is the average mass of the element's atoms (as they occur in nature) relative to an atom of carbon-12, which is assigned a mass of 12 units. Thus, if an average atom of an element has a mass twice that of a ^{12}C atom, its atomic mass would be 24 u.

The definition of the size of the atomic mass unit is really quite arbitrary. It could just as easily have been selected to be $\frac{1}{24}$ of the mass of a carbon atom, or $\frac{1}{10}$ of the mass of an iron atom, or any other value. Why $\frac{1}{12}$ of the mass of a ^{12}C atom? First, carbon is a very common element, available to any scientist. Second, and most important, by choosing the atomic mass unit of this size, the atomic masses of nearly all of the other elements are almost whole numbers, with the lightest atom (hydrogen) having a mass of approximately 1 u.

■ Even the smallest laboratory sample of an element has so many atoms that the relative proportions of the isotopes is constant.

■ Tritium, ^{3}H, is a third isotope of hydrogen, but the naturally occurring amount is so small that we need not consider it.

Chemists generally work with whatever *mixture* of isotopes that occur naturally for a given element. Because the composition of this isotopic mixture is very nearly constant regardless of the source of the element, we can speak of an *average mass of an atom* of the element—average in terms of mass. For example, naturally occurring hydrogen is almost entirely a mixture of two isotopes in the relative proportions given in Table 3.2 on page 71. The "average mass of an atom" of the element hydrogen, as it occurs in nature, has a mass that is 0.083992 times that of a ^{12}C atom. Since 0.083992×12.000 u = 1.0079 u, the average atomic mass of hydrogen is 1.0079 u. Notice that this average value is only a little larger than the atomic mass of ^{1}H because naturally occurring hydrogen contains mostly ^{1}H and only a little ^{2}H, as shown in Table 3.2.

In general, the mass number of an isotope differs slightly from the atomic mass of the isotope. For instance, the isotope ^{35}Cl has an atomic mass of 34.968852 u. In fact, the *only* isotope that has an atomic mass equal to its mass number is ^{12}C, since *by definition* the mass of this atom is exactly 12 u.

Table 3.2	Abundance of Hydrogen Isotopes	
Hydrogen Isotope	Mass	Percentage Abundance
^1H	1.007825 u	99.985
^2H	2.0140 u	0.015

Average Atomic Masses from Isotopic Abundances

Originally, the relative atomic masses of the elements were determined in a way similar to that described for hydrogen and fluorine in our earlier discussion. A sample of a compound was analyzed and from the formula of the substance the relative atomic masses were calculated. These were then adjusted to place them on the unified atomic mass scale. In modern times, methods, such as mass spectrometry discussed in On the Cutting Edge 3.1, have been developed to measure very precisely both the relative abundances of the isotopes of the elements and their atomic masses. This kind of information has made it possible to calculate more precise values of the average atomic masses, which are found in the table on the inside front cover of the book. The average atomic mass for any element can be calculated by (multiplying the percentage of each isotope by its mass and adding the values together.) Example 3.2 illustrates how this calculation is done.

■ Weighted averages allow you to calculate how much each isotope contributes to the overall atomic mass of the element.

Example 3.2
Calculating Average Atomic Masses from Isotopic Abundances

Naturally occurring chlorine is a mixture of two isotopes. In every sample of this element, 75.77% of the atoms are ^{35}Cl and 24.23% are atoms of ^{37}Cl. The accurately measured atomic mass of ^{35}Cl is 34.9689 u and that of ^{37}Cl is 36.9659 u. From these data, calculate the average atomic mass of chlorine.

■ **Analysis:** In a sample of chlorine, 75.77% of the mass is contributed by atoms of ^{35}Cl and 24.23% comes from atoms of ^{37}Cl. Thus, when we calculate the mass of the "average atom" we have to take into account both the masses of the isotopes and their relative abundances.

■ **Assembling the Tools:** If a sample is made up of more than one substance, then the mass contribution of one of the substances, *x*, in the sample is calculated using the equation

$$\text{Mass contribution of } x = (\text{total mass of } x) \times \frac{\text{percentage of } x}{100\%}$$

This is the tool we will use to calculate the mass contribution from each isotope toward the total mass of an average atom of Cl. For "percentage of *x*" we substitute the percent abundance of the isotope in question, and for "total mass of *x*" we substitute the mass of that isotope.

■ **Solution:** We will calculate the contribution of the 75.77% of the mass of an atom of ^{35}Cl to the total mass

$$\text{Mass contribution of } ^{35}Cl = 34.9689 \text{ u} \times \frac{75.77\% \ ^{35}Cl}{100\%} = 26.496 \text{ u}$$

and for the ^{37}Cl, its contribution is

$$\text{Mass contribution of } ^{37}Cl = 36.9659 \text{ u} \times \frac{24.23\% \ ^{37}Cl}{100\%} = 8.9568 \text{ u}$$

Now we add these contributions to give us the total mass of the "average atom."

$$26.496 \text{ u} + 8.957 \text{ u} = 35.453 \text{ u rounded to } 35.45 \text{ u}$$

Notice that in this two-step problem we kept one extra significant figure until the final rounding to four significant figures.

■ **Is the Answer Reasonable?** Once again, the final step is a check to see whether the answer makes sense. Here is how we might do such a check: First, from the masses of the isotopes, we know the average atomic mass is somewhere between approximately 35 and 37. If the abundances of the two isotopes were equal, the average would be nearly 36. However, there is more ^{35}Cl than ^{37}Cl, so a value closer to 35 than 37 seems reasonable; therefore, we can feel pretty confident our answer is correct.

Practice Exercises

3.4 | Aluminum atoms have a mass that is 2.24845 times that of an atom of ^{12}C. What is the atomic mass of aluminum? (*Hint:* Recall that we have a tool that gives the relationship between the atomic mass unit and ^{12}C.)

3.5 | How much heavier is the average atom of naturally occurring copper than an atom of ^{12}C? Refer to the table inside the front cover of the book for the necessary data.

3.6 | Naturally occurring boron is composed of 19.9% of ^{10}B and 80.1% of ^{11}B. Atoms of ^{10}B have a mass of 10.0129 u and those of ^{11}B have a mass of 11.0093 u. Calculate the average atomic mass of boron.

3.7 | Neon, the gas used in neon lamps, is composed of 90.483% of ^{20}Ne, 0.271% of ^{21}Ne, and 9.253% of ^{22}Ne. The ^{20}Ne atoms have a mass of 19.992 u, ^{21}Ne atoms have a mass of 20.994, and those of ^{22}Ne have a mass of 21.991 u. Calculate the average atomic mass of neon.

3.2 | The Periodic Table

When we study different kinds of substances, we find that some are elements and others are compounds. Among compounds, some are composed of discrete molecules. Others are *ionic compounds*, made up of atoms that have acquired electrical charges. Some elements, such as sodium, have properties we associate with metals, whereas others, such as chlorine, do not have metallic properties and are said to be nonmetallic. If we were to continue on this way, without attempting to build our subject around some central organizing structure, it would not be long before we became buried beneath a mountain of information of seemingly unconnected facts.

Mendeleev's Periodic Table

The need for organization was recognized by many early chemists, and there were numerous attempts to discover relationships among the chemical and physical properties of the elements. The periodic table we use today is based primarily on the efforts of a Russian chemist, Dmitri Ivanovich Mendeleev (1834–1907) and a German physicist, Julius Lothar Meyer (1830–1895). Working independently, these scientists developed similar periodic tables only a few months apart in 1869. Mendeleev is usually given the credit, however, because he had the good fortune to publish first.

Mendeleev was preparing a chemistry textbook for his students at the University of St. Petersburg. Looking for some pattern among the properties of the elements, he found that when he arranged them in order of increasing atomic mass, similar chemical properties were repeated over and over again at regular intervals. For instance, the elements lithium (Li), sodium (Na), potassium (K), rubidium (Rb), and cesium (Cs) are soft metals that are very reactive toward water. They form compounds with chlorine that have a 1-to-1 ratio of metal to chlorine. Similarly, the elements that immediately follow each of these also constitute a set with similar chemical properties. Thus, beryllium (Be) follows lithium, magnesium (Mg) follows sodium, calcium (Ca) follows potassium, strontium

(Sr) follows rubidium, and barium (Ba) follows cesium. All of these elements form a water-soluble chlorine compound with a 1-to-2 metal to chlorine atom ratio. Mendeleev used such observations to construct his **periodic table.**

The elements in Mendeleev's table are arranged in order of increasing atomic mass. When the sequence is broken at the right places, the elements fall naturally into columns in which the elements in a given column have similar chemical properties. Mendeleev's genius rested on his placing elements with similar properties in the same column even when this left occasional gaps in the table. Mendeleev reasoned, correctly, that the elements that belonged in these gaps had simply not yet been discovered. In fact, on the basis of the location of these gaps, Mendeleev was able to predict with remarkable accuracy the properties of these yet-to-be-found substances. His predictions helped serve as a guide in the search for the missing elements.

■ Periodic refers to the recurrence of properties at regular intervals.

Arrangement of the Modern Periodic Table

When the concept of atomic numbers was developed, it was soon realized that the elements in Mendeleev's table were arranged in precisely the order of increasing atomic number. The fact that it is the atomic number—the number of protons in the nucleus of an atom—that determines the order of elements in the table is very significant. We will see later that this has important implications with regard to the relationship between the number of electrons in an atom and the atom's chemical properties.

The modern periodic table is shown in Figure 3.6 and also appears on the inside front cover of the book. We will refer to the table frequently, so it is important for you to become familiar with it and with some of the terminology applied to it.

TOOLS

Periodic table

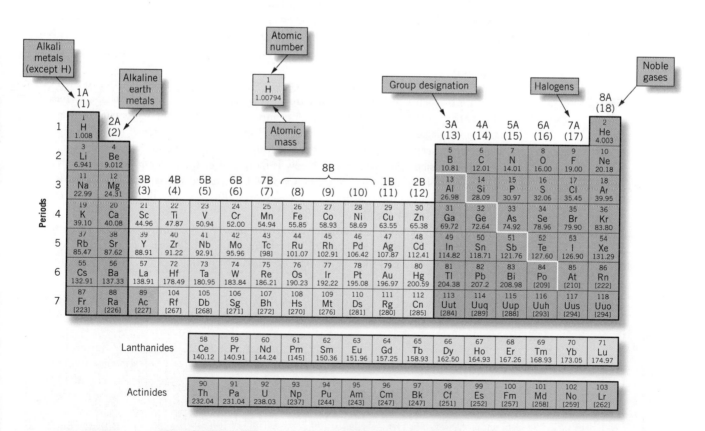

Figure 3.6 | **The modern periodic table.** At room temperature, mercury and bromine are liquids. Eleven elements are gases, including the noble gases and the diatomic gases of hydrogen, oxygen, nitrogen, fluorine, and chlorine. The remaining elements are solids.

Special Terminology of the Periodic Table

In the modern periodic table the elements are arranged in order of increasing atomic number. The rows in the table are called **periods,** and for identification purposes the periods are numbered. Below the main body of the table are two long rows of 14 elements each. These actually belong in the main body of the table following La ($Z = 57$) and Ac ($Z = 89$), as shown in Figure 3.7. They are almost always placed below the table simply to conserve space. If the fully spread-out table is printed on one page, the type is so small that it's difficult to read. Notice that in the fully extended form of the table, with all the elements arranged in their proper locations, there is a great deal of empty space. An important requirement of a detailed atomic theory, which we will get to in Chapter 8, is that it must explain not only the repetition of properties, but also why there is so much empty space in the table.

■ Recall that the symbol Z stands for atomic number.

The vertical columns in the periodic table are called **groups,** also identified by numbers. However, there is not uniform agreement among chemists on the numbering system. In an attempt to standardize the table, the International Union of Pure and Applied Chemistry (the IUPAC), an international body of scientists responsible for setting standards in chemistry, officially adopted a system in which the groups are simply numbered sequentially, 1 through 18, from left to right using Arabic numerals. Chemists in North America favor the system where the longer groups are labeled 1A to 8A and the shorter groups are labeled 1B to 8B in the sequence depicted in Figure 3.6. (In some texts, groups are identified with Roman numerals; Group 3A appears as Group IIIA, for example.) Note that Group 8B actually encompasses three short columns. The sequence of the B-group elements is unique and will make sense when we learn more about the structure of the atom in Chapter 8. Additionally, European chemists favor a third numbering system with the designation of A and B groups but with a different sequence from the North American table.

In Figure 3.6 and on the inside front cover of the book, we have used both the North American labels as well as those preferred by the IUPAC. Because of the lack of uniform agreement among chemists on how the groups should be specified, we will use the North American A-group/B-group designations in Figure 3.6 when we wish to specify a particular group.

As we have already noted, the elements in a given group bear similarities to each other. Because of such similarities, groups are sometimes referred to as **families of elements.** The elements in the longer columns (the A groups) are known as the **representative elements** or **main group elements.** Those that fall into the B groups in the center of the table are called **transition elements.** The elements in the two long rows below the main body of the table are the **inner transition elements,** and each row is named after the element that it follows in the main body of the table. Thus, elements 58–71 are called the **lanthanide elements** because they follow lanthanum ($Z = 57$), and elements 90–103 are called the **actinide elements** because they follow actinium ($Z = 89$).

Some of the groups have acquired common names. For example, except for hydrogen, the Group 1A elements are metals. They form compounds with oxygen that dissolve in water to give solutions that are strongly alkaline, or caustic. As a result, they are called the

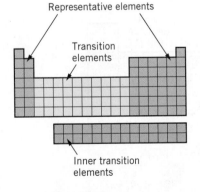

Representative elements

Transition elements

Inner transition elements

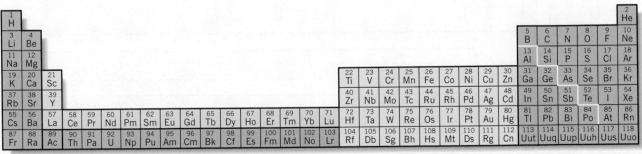

Figure 3.7 | **Extended form of the periodic table.** The two long rows of elements below the main body of the table in Figure 3.6 are placed in their proper places in this table.

alkali metals or simply the *alkalis*. The Group 2A elements are also metals. Their oxygen compounds are alkaline, too, but many compounds of the Group 2A elements are unable to dissolve in water and are found in deposits in the ground. Because of their properties and where they occur in nature, the Group 2A elements became known as the **alkaline earth metals.**

On the right side of the table, in Group 8A, are the **noble gases.** They used to be called the inert gases until it was discovered that the heavier members of the group show a small degree of chemical reactivity. The term *noble* is used when we wish to suggest a very limited degree of chemical reactivity. Gold, for instance, is often referred to as a noble metal because so few chemicals are capable of reacting with it.

Finally, the elements of Group 7A are called the **halogens,** derived from the Greek word meaning "sea" or "salt." Chlorine (Cl), for example, is found in familiar table salt, a compound that accounts in large measure for the salty taste of seawater. The other groups of the representative elements have less frequently used names, and we will name those groups based on the first element in the family. For example, Group 5A is the **nitrogen family**.

■ The Group 6A elements are also called the *chalcogens*, and the Group 5A elements are also called the *pnictogens*.

3.3 | Metals, Nonmetals, and Metalloids

The periodic table organizes all sorts of chemical and physical information about the elements and their compounds. It allows us to study systematically the way properties vary with an element's position within the table and, in turn, makes the similarities and differences among the elements easier to understand and remember.

Even a casual inspection of samples of the elements reveals that some are familiar metals and that others, equally well known, are not metals. Most of us recognize metals such as lead, iron, or gold and nonmetals such as oxygen or nitrogen. A closer look at the nonmetallic elements, though, reveals that some of them, silicon and arsenic to name two, have properties that lie between those of true metals and true nonmetals. These elements are called **metalloids**. The elements are not evenly divided into the categories of metals, nonmetals, and metalloids. (See Figure 3.8.) Most elements are metals, slightly over a dozen are nonmetals, and only a handful are metalloids.

TOOLS

Periodic table: metals, nonmetals, and metalloids

■ The metalloids are grouped around the bold stair-step line that is drawn diagonally from boron (B) down to astatine (At).

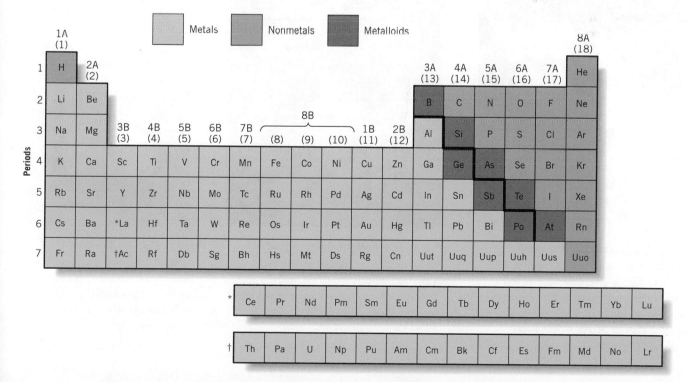

Figure 3.8 | **Distribution of metals, nonmetals, and metalloids among the elements in the periodic table.**

Metals

Properties of metals

You probably know a **metal** when you see one, and you are familiar with their physical properties. Metals tend to have a shine so unique that it's called a *metallic luster*. For example, the silvery sheen of the surface of potassium in Figure 3.9 would most likely lead you to identify potassium as a metal even if you had never seen or heard of it before. We also know that metals conduct electricity. Few of us would hold an iron nail in our hand and poke it into an electrical outlet. In addition, we know that metals conduct heat very well. On a cool day, metals always feel colder to the touch than do neighboring nonmetallic objects because metals conduct heat away from your hand very rapidly. Nonmetals seem less cold because they can't conduct heat away as quickly and therefore their surfaces warm up faster.

Other properties that metals possess, to varying degrees, are **malleability**—the ability to be hammered or rolled into thin sheets—and **ductility**—the ability to be drawn into wire. The ability of gold to be hammered into foils a few atoms thick depends on the malleability of gold (Figure 3.10), and the manufacture of electrical wire is based on the ductility of copper.

■ Thin lead sheets are used for sound deadening because the easily deformed lead absorbs the sound vibrations.

Hardness is another physical property that we usually think of for metals. Some, such as chromium or iron, are indeed quite hard; but others, including copper and lead, are rather soft. The alkali metals such as potassium (Figure 3.9) are so soft they can be cut with a knife, but they are also so chemically reactive that we rarely get to see them as free elements.

All the metallic elements, except mercury, are solids at room temperature (Figure 3.11). Mercury's low freezing point (−39 °C) and fairly high boiling point (357 °C) make it useful as a fluid in thermometers. Most of the other metals have much higher melting points. Tungsten, for example, has the highest melting point of any metal (3400 °C, or 6150 °F), which explains its use as filaments that glow white-hot in electric lightbulbs.

Figure 3.9 | **Potassium is a metal.** Potassium reacts quickly with moisture and oxygen to form a white coating. Due to its high reactivity, it is stored under oil to prevent water and oxygen from reacting with it. *(© 1995 Richard Megna/Fundamental Photographs)*

Figure 3.10 | **Malleability of gold.** Pure gold is not usually used in jewelry because it is too malleable. It is used decoratively to cover domes since it can be hammered into very thin sheets called gold leaf. *(Joseph Sohm; Visions of America/©Corbis)*

Figure 3.11 | **Mercury droplet.** The metal mercury (once known as quicksilver) is a liquid at room temperature, unlike other metals, which are solids. *(OPC, Inc.)*

The chemical properties of metals vary tremendously. Some, such as gold and platinum, are very unreactive toward almost all chemical agents. This property, plus their natural beauty and rarity, makes them highly prized for use in jewelry. Other metals, however, are so reactive that few people except chemists and chemistry students ever get to see them in their "free" states. For instance, the metal sodium reacts very quickly with oxygen or moisture in the air, and its bright metallic surface tarnishes almost immediately.

■ We use the term "free element" to mean an element that is not chemically combined with any other element.

Nonmetals

Substances such as plastics, wood, and glass that lack the properties of metals are said to be *nonmetallic*, and an element that has nonmetallic properties is called a **nonmetal**. Most often, we encounter the nonmetals in the form of compounds or mixtures of compounds. There are some nonmetals, however, that are very important to us in their elemental forms. The air we breathe, for instance, contains mostly nitrogen and oxygen. Both are gaseous, colorless, and odorless nonmetals. Since we can't see, taste, or smell them, however, it's difficult to experience their existence. (Although if you step into an atmosphere without oxygen, your body will soon tell you that something is missing!) Probably the most commonly *observed* nonmetallic element is carbon. We find it as the graphite in pencils, as coal, and as the charcoal used for barbecues. It also occurs in a more valuable form as diamond (Figure 3.12). Although diamond and graphite differ in appearance, each is a form of elemental carbon.

Many of the nonmetals are solids at room temperature and atmospheric pressure, while many others are gases. Photographs of some of the nonmetallic elements appear in Figure 3.13. Their properties are almost completely opposite those of metals. Each of these elements lacks the characteristic appearance of a metal. They are poor conductors of heat and, with the exception of the graphite form of carbon, are also poor conductors of electricity. The electrical conductivity of graphite appears to be an accident of molecular structure, since the structures of metals and graphite are completely different.

Figure 3.12 | **Diamonds.** Gems such as these are simply another form of the element carbon. *(Charles D. Winters/Photo Researchers, Inc.)*

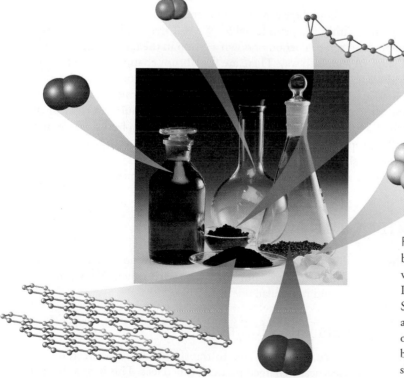

Figure 3.13 | **Some nonmetallic elements.** In the bottle on the left is dark-red liquid bromine, which vaporizes easily to give a deeply colored orange vapor. Pale green chlorine fills the round flask in the center. Solid iodine lines the bottom of the flask on the right and gives off a violet vapor. Powdered red phosphorus occupies the dish in front of the flask of chlorine, and black powdered graphite is in the watch glass. Also shown are lumps of yellow sulfur. *(Michael Watson)*

The nonmetallic elements lack the malleability and ductility of metals. A lump of sulfur crumbles when hammered and breaks apart when pulled on. Diamond cutters rely on the brittle nature of carbon when they split a gem-quality stone by carefully striking a quick blow with a sharp blade.

As with metals, nonmetals exhibit a broad range of chemical reactivities. Fluorine, for instance, is extremely reactive. It reacts readily with almost all of the other elements. At the other extreme is helium, the gas used to inflate children's balloons and the blimps seen at major sporting events. This element does not react with anything, a fact that chemists find useful when they want to provide a totally *inert* (unreactive) atmosphere inside some apparatus.

Metalloids

The properties of metalloids lie between those of metals and nonmetals. This shouldn't surprise us since the metalloids are located between the metals and the nonmetals in the periodic table. In most respects, metalloids behave as nonmetals, both chemically and physically. However, in their most important physical property, electrical conductivity, they somewhat resemble metals. Metalloids tend to be **semiconductors**; they conduct electricity, but not nearly as well as metals. This property, particularly as found in silicon and germanium, is responsible for the remarkable progress made during the last five decades in the field of solid-state electronics. The operation of every computer, audio system, TV receiver, DVD or CD player, and AM-FM radio relies on transistors made from semiconductors. Perhaps the most amazing advance of all has been the fantastic reduction in the size of electronic components that semiconductors have allowed (Figure 3.14). To it, we owe the development of small and versatile cell phones, cameras, flash drives, MP3 players, calculators, and computers. The heart of these devices is an integrated circuit that begins as a wafer of extremely pure silicon (or germanium) that is etched and chemically modified into specialized arrays of thousands of transistors.

Metallic and Nonmetallic Character

The occurrence of the metalloids between the metals and the nonmetals is our first example of trends in properties within the periodic table. We will frequently see that as we move from position to position across a period or down a group in the table, chemical and physical properties change in a gradual way. There are few abrupt changes in the characteristics of the elements as we scan across a period or down a group. The location of the metalloids can be seen, then, as an example of the gradual transition between metallic and nonmetallic properties. From left to right across Period 3, we go from aluminum, an element that has every appearance of a metal; to silicon, a semiconductor; to phosphorus, an element with clearly nonmetallic properties. A similar gradual change is seen going down Group 4A. Carbon is a nonmetal, silicon and germanium are metalloids, and tin and lead are metals. Trends such as these are useful to spot because they help us remember properties.

3.4 | Ionic Compounds

Most of the substances that we encounter on a daily basis are not free elements but are compounds in which the elements are combined with each other. We will discuss two types of compounds: ionic and molecular.

Reactions of Metals with Nonmetals

Under appropriate conditions, atoms are able to transfer electrons between one another when they react to yield electrically charged particles called **ions**. This is what happens, for example, when the metal sodium combines with the nonmetal chlorine. As shown in Figure 3.15, when sodium, a typical shiny metal, and chlorine, a pale green gas, are mixed,

Figure 3.14 | **Modern electronic circuits rely on the semiconductor properties of silicon.** The silicon wafer shown here contains more electronic components (10 billion) than there are people on our entire planet (about 6.5 billion)! *(Courtesy NASA)*

a vigorous reaction takes place yielding a white powder, sodium chloride. The equation for the reaction is

$$2Na(s) + Cl_2(g) \longrightarrow 2NaCl(s)$$

The changes that take place at the atomic level are also illustrated in Figure 3.15.

The formation of the ions in sodium chloride results from the transfer of electrons between the reacting atoms. Specifically, each sodium atom gives up one electron to a chlorine atom. We can diagram the changes in equation form by using the symbol e^- to stand for an electron.

$$\overset{e^-}{\overbrace{Na + Cl}} \longrightarrow Na^+ + Cl^-$$

The electrically charged particles formed in this reaction are a sodium ion (Na^+) and a chloride ion (Cl^-). The sodium ion has a positive 1+ charge, indicated by the superscript plus sign, because the loss of an electron leaves it with one more proton in its nucleus than there are electrons outside. Similarly, by gaining one electron the chlorine atom has added one more negative charge, so the chloride ion has a single negative charge indicated by the minus sign. Solid sodium chloride is composed of these charged sodium and chloride ions and is said to be an **ionic compound**.

■ Here we are concentrating on what happens to the individual atoms, so we have not shown chlorine as diatomic Cl_2 molecules.

■ A neutral sodium atom has 11 protons and 11 electrons; a sodium ion has 11 protons and 10 electrons, so it carries a unit positive charge. A neutral chlorine atom has 17 protons and 17 electrons; a chloride ion has 17 protons and 18 electrons, so it carries a unit negative charge.

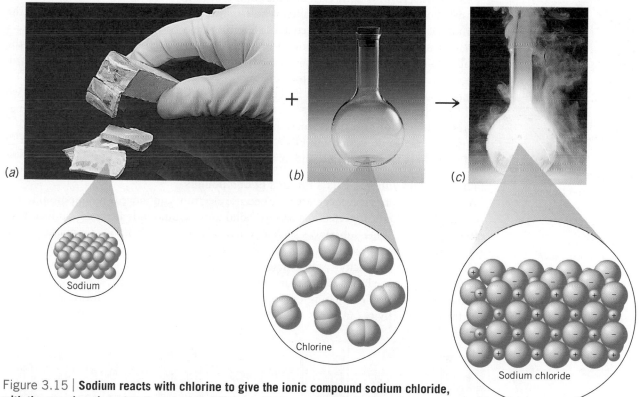

Figure 3.15 | **Sodium reacts with chlorine to give the ionic compound sodium chloride, with the reaction viewed at the atomic level.** *(a)* Freshly cut sodium has a shiny metallic surface. The metal reacts with oxygen and moisture, so it cannot be touched with bare fingers. *(b)* Chlorine is a pale green gas. *(c)* When a small piece of sodium is melted in a metal spoon and thrust into the flask of chlorine, it burns brightly as the two elements react to form sodium chloride. The smoke coming from the flask is composed of fine crystals of salt. The electrically neutral atoms and molecules react to yield positive and negative ions, which are held to each other by electrostatic attractions (attractions between opposite electrical charges). *(Michael Watson; Richard Megna/Fundamental Photographs; Richard Megna/Fundamental Photographs)*

Ionic compounds

As a general rule, *ionic compounds are formed when metals react with nonmetals*. In the electron transfer, however, not all atoms gain or lose just one electron; some gain or lose more. For example, when calcium atoms react they lose two electrons to form Ca^{2+} ions, and when oxygen atoms form ions they each gain two electrons to give O^{2-} ions. Notice that in writing the formulas for ions, the number of positive or negative charges is indicated by a superscript before the positive or negative charge. (We will have to wait until a later chapter to study the reasons why certain atoms gain or lose one electron each, whereas other atoms gain or lose two or more electrons.)

Practice Exercises

3.8 | For each of the following atoms or ions, give the number of protons and the number of electrons in one particle: (a) an Fe atom, (b) an Fe^{3+} ion, (c) an N^{3-} ion, (d) an N atom. (*Hint:* Recall that electrons have a negative charge and ions that have a negative charge must have gained electrons.)

3.9 | For each of the following atoms or ions, give the number of protons and the number of electrons in one particle: (a) an O atom, (b) an O^{2-} ion, (c) an Al^{3+} ion, (d) an Al atom.

Looking at the structure of sodium chloride in Figure 3.15, it is impossible to say that a particular Na^+ ion belongs to a particular Cl^- ion. The ions in a crystal of NaCl are simply packed in the most efficient way, so that positive ions and negative ions can be as close to each other as possible. In this way, the attractions between oppositely charged ions, which are responsible for holding the compound together, can be as strong as possible.

Since discrete units don't exist in ionic compounds, the subscripts in their formulas are always chosen to specify the smallest whole-number ratio of the ions. This is why the formula of sodium chloride is given as NaCl rather than Na_2Cl_2 or Na_3Cl_3. The idea of a "smallest unit" of an ionic compound is still quite often useful. Therefore, we take the smallest unit of an ionic compound to be whatever is represented in its formula and call this unit a **formula unit**. Thus, one formula unit of NaCl consists of one Na^+ and one Cl^-, whereas one formula unit of the ionic compound $CaCl_2$ consists of one Ca^{2+} and two Cl^- ions. (In a broader sense, we can use the term *formula unit* to refer to whatever is represented by a formula. Sometimes the formula specifies a set of ions, as in NaCl; sometimes it is a molecule, as in O_2 or H_2O; sometimes it can be just an ion, as in Cl^- or Ca^{2+}; and sometimes it might be just an atom, as in Na.)

■ The charges on the ions are omitted when writing formulas for compounds because compounds are electrically neutral overall.

Experimental Evidence Exists for Ions in Compounds

We know that metals conduct electricity because electrons can move from one atom to the next in a wire when connected to a battery. Solid ionic compounds are poor conductors of electricity as are other substances such as water. However, if an ionic compound is dissolved in water or is heated to a high temperature so that it melts, the resulting liquids are able to conduct electricity easily. These observations suggest that ionic compounds are composed of charged ions rather than neutral molecules and that these ions when made mobile by dissolving or melting can conduct electricity. Figure 3.16 illustrates how the electrical conductivity can be tested.

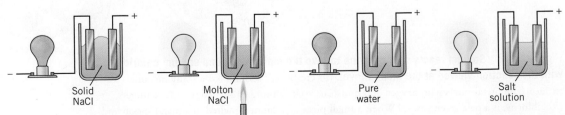

Solid NaCl   Molton NaCl   Pure water   Salt solution

Figure 3.16 | **An apparatus to test for electrical conductivity.** The electrodes are dipped into the substance to be tested. If the lightbulb glows when electricity is applied, the sample is an electrical conductor. Here we see that solid sodium chloride does not conduct electricity, but when the solid is melted it does conduct. Liquid water, a molecular compound, is not a conductor of electricity because it does not contain electrically charged particles.

Formulas of Ionic Compounds

We have noted that metals combine with nonmetals to form ionic compounds. In such reactions, metal atoms lose one or more electrons to become positively charged ions and nonmetal atoms gain one or more electrons to become negatively charged ions. In referring to these particles, a positively charged ion is called a **cation** (pronounced *CAT-i-on*) and a negatively charged ion is called an **anion** (pronounced *AN-i-on*).[1] Thus, solid NaCl is composed of sodium cations and chloride anions.

Ions of Representative Metals and Nonmetals

The periodic table can help us remember the kinds of ions formed by many of the representative elements (elements in the A-groups of the periodic table). For example, except for hydrogen, the neutral atoms of the Group 1A elements always lose one electron each when they react, thereby becoming ions with a charge of 1+. Similarly, atoms of the Group 2A elements always lose two electrons when they react, so these elements always form ions with a charge of 2+. In Group 3A, the only important positive ion we need consider now is that of aluminum, Al^{3+}; an aluminum atom loses three electrons when it reacts to form this ion.

All these ions are listed in Table 3.3. *Notice that the number of positive charges on each of the cations is the same as the group number when we use the North American numbering of the groups in the periodic table.* Thus, sodium is in Group 1A and forms an ion with a 1+ charge, barium (Ba) is in Group 2A and forms an ion with a 2+ charge, and aluminum is in Group 3A and forms an ion with a 3+ charge. Although this generalization doesn't work for all the metallic elements (for example, the transition elements), it does help us remember what happens to the metallic elements of Groups 1A and 2A and aluminum when they react.

Among the nonmetals on the right side of the periodic table we also find some useful generalizations. For example, when they combine with metals, the halogens (Group 7A) form ions with one negative charge (written as 1−) and the nonmetals in Group 6A form ions with two negative charges (written as 2−). Notice that *the number of negative charges on the anion is equal to the number of spaces to the right that we have to move in the periodic table to get to a noble gas.*

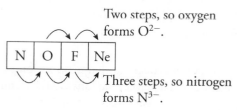

TOOLS

Predicting cation charge

TOOLS

Predicting anion charge

Table 3.3	Some Ions Formed from the Representative Elements						
Group Number						
1A	**2A**	**3A**	**4A**	**5A**	**6A**	**7A**
H^+						
Li^+	Be^{2+}		C^{4-}	N^{3-}	O^{2-}	F^-
Na^+	Mg^{2+}	Al^{3+}	Si^{4-}	P^{3-}	S^{2-}	Cl^-
K^+	Ca^{2+}				Se^{2-}	Br^-
Rb^+	Sr^{2+}				Te^{2-}	I^-
Cs^+	Ba^{2+}					

[1] The names *cation* and *anion* come from the way the ions behave when electrically charged metal plates called electrodes are dipped into a solution that contains them. We will discuss this in detail in Chapter 20.

■ A substance is electrically neutral, with a net charge of zero, if the total positive charge equals the total negative charge.

Writing Formulas for Ionic Compounds

All chemical compounds are electrically neutral, so the ions in an ionic compound always occur in a ratio such that the total positive charge is equal to the total negative charge. This is why the formula for sodium chloride is NaCl; the l-to-l ratio of Na^+ to Cl^- gives electrical neutrality. In addition, as we've already mentioned, discrete molecules do not exist in ionic compounds, so we always use the smallest set of subscripts that specify the correct ratio of the ions. The following, therefore, are the rules we use in writing the formulas of ionic compounds.

Formulas for ionic compounds

Rules for Writing Formulas of Ionic Compounds

1. The positive ion is given first in the formula. (This isn't required by nature, but it is a custom we always follow.)
2. The subscripts in the formula must produce an electrically neutral formula unit. (Nature *does* require electrical neutrality.)
3. The subscripts should be the smallest set of whole numbers possible. For instance, if all subscripts are even, divide them by 2. (You may have to repeat this simplification step several times.)
4. The charges on the ions are not included in the finished formula for the substance. When a subscript is 1 it is left off; no subscript implies a subscript of 1.

Example 3.3
Writing Formulas for Ionic Compounds

Write the formulas for the ionic compounds formed from (a) Ba and S, (b) Al and Cl, and (c) Al and O.

■ **Analysis:** To correctly write the formula, determine the charges on the anion and the cation and then follow the rules for writing ionic compounds listed above.

■ **Assembling the Tools:** First, we need the tool to figure out the charges of the ions from the periodic table. Then we apply the tool that summarizes the rules for writing the formula of ionic compounds.

■ **Solution:**

(a) The element Ba is in Group 2A, so the charge on its ion is 2+. Sulfur is in Group 6A, so its ion has a charge of 2−. Therefore, the ions are Ba^{2+} and S^{2-}. Since the charges are equal but opposite, a 1-to-1 ratio will give a neutral formula unit. Therefore, the formula is BaS. Notice that we have *not* included the charges on the ions in the finished formula.

(b) By using the periodic table, the ions of these elements are Al^{3+} and Cl^-. We can obtain a neutral formula unit by combining one Al^{3+} with three Cl^-. (The charge on Cl is 1−; the 1 is understood.)

$$1(3+) + 3(1-) = 0$$

The formula is $AlCl_3$.

(c) For these elements, the ions are Al^{3+} and O^{2-}. In the formula we seek there must be the same number of positive charges as negative charges. This number must be a whole-number multiple of both 3 and 2. The smallest number that satisfies this condition is 6, so there must be two Al^{3+} and three O^{2-} in the formula.

$$
\begin{aligned}
2Al^{3+} \quad & 2(3+) = 6+ \\
3O^{2-} \quad & \underline{3(2-) = 6-} \\
& \text{sum} = 0
\end{aligned}
$$

The formula is Al_2O_3.

A "trick" you may have seen before is to use the *number* of positive charges for the subscript of the anion and the *number* of negative charges as the subscript for the cation as shown in the diagram.

When using this method, always be sure to check that the subscripts cannot be reduced to smaller numbers.

■ **Are the Answers Reasonable?** In writing a formula, there are two things to check. First, be sure you've correctly written the formulas of the ions. (This is often the main reason for a lot of mistakes.) Then check that you've combined them in a ratio that gives electrical neutrality. Performing these checks assures us we've got the right answers.

Practice Exercises

3.10 | Write formulas for ionic compounds formed from (a) Na and F, (b) Na and O, (c) Mg and F, and (d) Al and C. (*Hint:* One element must form a cation, and the other will form an anion based on its position in the periodic table.)

3.11 | Write the formulas for the compounds made from (a) Ca and N, (b) Al and Br, (c) K and S, (d) Cs and Cl.

Many of our most important chemicals are ionic compounds. We have mentioned NaCl, common table salt, and $CaCl_2$, which is a substance often used to melt ice on walkways in the winter. Other examples are sodium fluoride, NaF, used by dentists to give fluoride treatments to teeth, and calcium oxide, CaO, an important ingredient in cement.

Cations of Transition and Post-transition Metals

The transition elements are located in the center of the periodic table, from Group 3B on the left to Group 2B on the right (Groups 3 to 12 if using the IUPAC system). All of them lie to the left of the metalloids, and they all are metals. Included here are some of our most familiar metals, including iron, chromium, copper, silver, and gold.

Most of the transition metals are much less reactive than the metals of Groups 1A and 2A, but when they react they also transfer electrons to nonmetal atoms to form ionic compounds. However, the charges on the ions of the transition metals do not follow as straightforward a pattern as do those of the alkali and alkaline earth metals. One of the characteristic features of the transition metals is the ability of many of them to form more than one positive ion. Iron, for example, can form two different ions, Fe^{2+} and Fe^{3+}. This means that iron can form more than one compound with a given nonmetal. For example, with chloride ion, Cl^-, iron forms two compounds, with the formulas $FeCl_2$ and $FeCl_3$. With oxygen, we find the compounds FeO and Fe_2O_3. As usual, we see that the formulas contain the ions in a ratio that gives electrical neutrality. Some of the most common ions of the transition metals are given in Table 3.4. Notice that one of the ions of mercury is diatomic Hg_2^{2+}. It consists of two Hg^+ ions joined by the same kind of bond found in molecular substances. The simple Hg^+ ion does not exist.

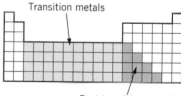

Distribution of transition and post-transition metals in the periodic table.

Practice Exercises

3.12 | Write formulas for the chlorides and oxides formed by (a) chromium and (b) copper. (*Hint:* There are more than one chloride and one oxide for each of these transition metals.)

3.13 | Write the formulas for the sulfides and nitrides of (a) gold and (b) titanium.

The **post-transition metals** are those metals that occur in the periodic table immediately following a row of transition metals. The two most common and important ones are tin (Sn) and lead (Pb). Except for bismuth, post-transition metals have the ability to form two

■ The prefix *post* means "after."

different ions and therefore two different compounds with a given nonmetal. For example, tin forms two oxides, SnO and SnO_2. Lead also forms two oxides that have similar formulas (PbO and PbO_2). The ions that these metals form are also included in Table 3.4.

Compounds Containing Polyatomic Ions

Polyatomic ions

The ionic compounds that we have discussed so far have been **binary compounds**—compounds formed from *two* different elements. There are many other ionic compounds that contain more than two elements. These substances usually contain **polyatomic ions,** which are ions that are themselves composed of two or more atoms linked by the same kinds of bonds that hold molecules together. Polyatomic ions differ from molecules, however, in that they contain either too many or too few electrons to make them electrically neutral. Table 3.5 lists some important polyatomic ions. It is very important that you learn the formulas, charges, and names of all of these ions.

The formulas of compounds formed from polyatomic ions are determined in the same way as are those of binary ionic compounds: the ratio of the ions must be such that the formula unit is electrically neutral, and the smallest set of whole-number subscripts is used. One difference in writing formulas with polyatomic ions is that parentheses are needed around the polyatomic ion if a subscript is required.

■ A substance is **diatomic** if it is composed of molecules that contain only two atoms. It is a **binary compound** if it contains two different elements, regardless of the number of each. Thus, BrCl is a binary compound and is also diatomic; CH_4 is a binary compound but is not diatomic.

■ In general, polyatomic ions are not formed by the direct combination of elements. They are the products of reactions between compounds.

Table 3.4	Ions of Some Transition Metals and Post-transition Metals
Transition Metals	
Titanium	$Ti^{2+}, Ti^{3+}, Ti^{4+}$
Chromium	Cr^{2+}, Cr^{3+}
Manganese	Mn^{2+}, Mn^{3+}
Iron	Fe^{2+}, Fe^{3+}
Cobalt	Co^{2+}, Co^{3+}
Nickel	Ni^{2+}
Copper	Cu^+, Cu^{2+}
Zinc	Zn^{2+}
Silver	Ag^+
Cadmium	Cd^{2+}
Gold	Au^+, Au^{3+}
Mercury	Hg_2^{2+}, Hg^{2+}
Post-transition Metals	
Tin	Sn^{2+}, Sn^{4+}
Lead	Pb^{2+}, Pb^{4+}
Bismuth	Bi^{3+}

Table 3.5 Formulas and Names of Some Polyatomic Ions	
Ion	**Name (Alternate Name in Parentheses)**
NH_4^+	Ammonium ion
H_3O^+	Hydronium ion[a]
OH^-	Hydroxide ion
CN^-	Cyanide ion
NO_2^-	Nitrite ion
NO_3^-	Nitrate ion
ClO^- or OCl^-	Hypochlorite ion
ClO_2^-	Chlorite ion
ClO_3^-	Chlorate ion
ClO_4^-	Perchlorate ion
MnO_4^-	Permanganate ion
$C_2H_3O_2^-$	Acetate ion
$C_2O_4^{2-}$	Oxalate ion
CO_3^{2-}	Carbonate ion
HCO_3^-	Hydrogen carbonate ion (bicarbonate ion)[b]
SO_3^{2-}	Sulfite ion
HSO_3^-	Hydrogen sulfite ion (bisulfite ion)[b]
SO_4^{2-}	Sulfate ion
HSO_4^-	Hydrogen sulfate ion (bisulfate ion)[b]
SCN^-	Thiocyanate ion
$S_2O_3^{2-}$	Thiosulfate ion
CrO_4^{2-}	Chromate ion
$Cr_2O_7^{2-}$	Dichromate ion
PO_4^{3-}	Phosphate ion
HPO_4^{2-}	Monohydrogen phosphate ion
$H_2PO_4^-$	Dihydrogen phosphate ion

[a]You will only encounter this ion in aqueous solutions.

[b]You will often see and hear the alternate names for these ions.

Example 3.4
Formulas That Contain Polyatomic Ions

One of the minerals responsible for the strength of bones is the ionic compound calcium phosphate, which is formed from Ca^{2+} and PO_4^{3-}. Write the formula for this compound.

■ **Analysis:** The problem is asking for the formula of an ionic compound that contains a polyatomic ion. While much information about ions relates to the periodic table, the names and formula for the polyatomic ions must be memorized.

■ **Assembling the Tools:** The essential tool for solving this problem is to follow the rules for writing formulas, paying special attention to the requirement that the compound be electrically neutral, which means that we have to balance the positive and negative charges.

■ **Solution:** Since the formula must be neutral, and the number of positive charges on the cation does not equal the number of negative charges on the anion, we use the number of positive charges as the subscript for the anion and the number of negative charges as the subscript for the cation. We will need three calcium ions to give a total charge of 6+ and two phosphate ions to give a charge of 6− so that the total charge is $(6+) + (6-) = 0$. The formula is written with parentheses to show that the PO_4^{3-} ion occurs two times in the formula unit.

$$Ca_3(PO_4)_2$$

■ **Is the Answer Reasonable?** We double-check to see that electrical neutrality is achieved for the compound. We have six positive charges from the three Ca^{2+} ions and six negative charges from the two PO_4^{3-} ions. The sum is zero and our compound is electrically neutral as required.

Practice Exercises

3.14 | Write the formula for the ionic compound formed from (a) potassium ion and acetate ion, (b) strontium ion and nitrate ion, and (c) Fe^{3+} and acetate ion. (*Hint:* See whether you remember these polyatomic ions before looking at the table.)

3.15 | Write the formula for the ionic compound formed from (a) Na^+ and CO_3^{2-} and (b) NH_4^+ and SO_4^{2-}.

Polyatomic ions are found in a large number of very important compounds. Examples include $CaSO_4$ (calcium sulfate, found in plaster of Paris or gypsum), $NaHCO_3$ (sodium bicarbonate, also called baking soda), $NaOCl$ (sodium hypochlorite, in liquid laundry bleach), $NaNO_2$ (sodium nitrite, a meat preservative), $MgSO_4$ (magnesium sulfate, also known as Epsom salts), and $NH_4H_2PO_4$ (ammonium dihydrogen phosphate, a fertilizer).

3.5 | Nomenclature of Ionic Compounds

In conversation, chemists rarely use formulas to describe compounds. Instead, names are used. For example, you already know that water is the name for the compound having the formula H_2O and that sodium chloride is the name of $NaCl$.

At one time there was no uniform procedure for assigning names to compounds, and those who discovered compounds used whatever method they wished. Today, we know of more than 50 million different chemical compounds, so it is necessary to have a logical system for naming them. Chemists around the world now agree on a systematic method for naming substances that is overseen by the **IUPAC**. By using basic methods we are able to write the correct formula given the name for the many compounds we will encounter. Additionally, we will be able to take a formula and correctly name it, since up to this point we have used common names for substances. In addition, when we first name a compound in this book, we will give the IUPAC name first, followed by the common name, if there is one, in parentheses. We will subsequently use the common name.

Naming Ionic Compounds of Representative Elements

Naming ionic compounds

In this section we discuss the **nomenclature** (naming) of simple inorganic ionic compounds. In general, **inorganic compounds** are substances that would *not* be considered to be derived from hydrocarbons such as methane (CH_4), ethane (C_2H_6), and other carbon–hydrogen compounds. In naming ionic compounds, our goal is that we want a name that someone else could use to reconstruct the formula.

For ionic compounds, the name of the cation is given first, followed by the name of the anion. This is the same as the sequence in which the ions appear in the formula. If the metal in the compound forms only one cation, such as Na^+ or Ca^{2+}, the cation is specified by just giving the English name of the metal. The anion in a binary compound is formed from a nonmetal and its name is created by adding the suffix *-ide* to the stem of the name for the nonmetal. An example is KBr, potassium bromide. Table 3.6 lists some common **monatomic** (one-atom) negative ions and their names. It is also useful to know that the *-ide* suffix is usually used only for monatomic ions, with just two common exceptions— *hydroxide ion* (OH^-) and *cyanide ion* (CN^-).[2]

■ To keep the name as simple as possible, we give the minimum amount of information necessary to be able to reconstruct the formula. To write the formula of an ionic compound, we only need the formulas of the ions.

To form the name of an ionic compound, we simply specify the names of the cation and anion. We do not need to state how many cations or anions are present, since once we know what the ions are we can assemble the formula correctly just by taking them in a ratio that gives electrical neutrality.

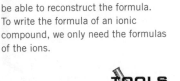

Monatomic anion names

Table 3.6	Monatomic Negative Ions							
H^-	Hydride	N^{3-}	Nitride	O^{2-}	Oxide	F^-	Fluoride
C^{4-}	Carbide	P^{3-}	Phosphide	S^{2-}	Sulfide	Cl^-	Chloride
Si^{4-}	Silicide	As^{3-}	Arsenide	Se^{2-}	Selenide	Br^-	Bromide
				Te^{2-}	Telluride	I^-	Iodide

Example 3.5
Naming Compounds and Writing Formulas

(a) What is the name of $SrBr_2$? (b) What is the formula for aluminum selenide?

■ **Analysis:** Both compounds are ionic, and we will name the first one using the names of the elements with the appropriate endings for the anion. For the second compound, we will write the formula using the concept of electrical neutrality.

■ **Assembling the Tools:** The tools that we will use will be the ones for naming ionic compounds and the concept that ionic compounds must be electrically neutral. In naming ionic compounds, we follow the sequence of the ions in the formula and we add the suffix *-ide* to the stem of the anion. In writing the formula for an ionic compound, we write the symbols in the order of the names and we make sure that the number of each element makes the compound electrically neutral.

■ **Solution:** (a) The compound $SrBr_2$ is composed of the elements Sr and Br. Sr is a metal from Group 2A, and Br is a nonmetal from Group 7A. Compounds of a metal and nonmetal are ionic, so we use the rules for naming ionic compounds. The cation simply takes the name of the metal, which is strontium. The anion's name is derived from bromine by replacing *-ine* with *-ide*; it is the bromide ion. The name of the compound is strontium bromide.

---

[2]If the name of a compound ends in *-ide* and it isn't either a hydroxide or a cyanide, you can feel confident the substance is a binary compound.

(b) Aluminum is a metal from Group 3A and forms the cation Al^{3+}. The *-ide* ending of selenide suggests the anion is composed of a single atom of a nonmetal. The only one that begins with the letters "selen-" is selenium, Se. (See the table inside the front cover.) The anion that is formed from selenium (Group 6A), is Se^{2-}. Since the correct formula must represent an electrically neutral formula unit, we use the number of charges on one ion as the subscript of the other—the formula is Al_2Se_3.

■ **Are the Answers Reasonable?** First, we review the analysis and check to be sure we've applied the correct rules, which we have. Next we can reverse the process to be sure our name, strontium bromide does mean $SrBr_2$, and that it is reasonable to call Al_2Se_3 aluminum selenide.

Practice Exercises

3.16 | Give the correct formulas for (a) potassium sulfide, (b) barium bromide, (c) sodium cyanide, (d) aluminum hydroxide, and (e) calcium phosphide. (*Hint:* Recall what the ending *-ide* means.)

3.17 | Give the correct names for (a) $AlCl_3$, (b) $Ba(OH)_2$, (c) NaBr, (d) CaF_2, and (e) K_3P.

Naming Cations of Transition Metals

Earlier we learned that many of the transition metals and post-transition metals are able to form more than one positive ion. Compounds that contain these different ions have different formulas, so in their names it is necessary to specify which ion is present.

The currently preferred method for naming ions of metals that can have more than one (only the cation) charge in compounds is called the **Stock system**. Here we use the English name followed, *without a space*, by the numerical value of the charge written as a Roman numeral in parentheses.[3] Examples using the Stock system are shown below.

■ Alfred Stock (1876–1946), a German inorganic chemist, was one of the first scientists to warn the public of the dangers of mercury poisoning.

Fe^{2+}	iron(II)	$FeCl_2$	iron(II) chloride
Fe^{3+}	iron(III)	$FeCl_3$	iron(III) chloride
Cr^{2+}	chromium(II)	CrS	chromium(II) sulfide
Cr^{3+}	chromium(III)	Cr_2S_3	chromium(III) sulfide

Remember that *the Roman numeral equals the positive charge on the metal ion*; it is not necessarily a subscript in the formula. For example, copper forms two oxides, one containing the Cu^+ ion and the other containing the Cu^{2+} ion. Their formulas are Cu_2O and CuO and their names are as follows:[4]

TOOLS

Using the Stock system

Cu^+	copper(I)	Cu_2O	copper(I) oxide
Cu^{2+}	copper(II)	CuO	copper(II) oxide

These copper compounds illustrate that in deriving the formula from the name, you must figure out the formula from the ionic charges, as previously discussed in this section and illustrated in Example 3.5.

Example 3.6
Naming Compounds and Writing Formulas

The compound $MnCl_2$ has a number of commercial uses, including as a disinfectant, in the manufacture of batteries, and for purifying natural gas. What is the name of the compound?

---

[3]Silver and nickel are almost always found in compounds as Ag^+ and Ni^{2+}, respectively. Therefore, AgCl and $NiCl_2$ are almost always called simply silver chloride and nickel chloride.

[4]For some metals, such as copper and lead, one of their ions is much more commonly found in compounds than any of their others. For example, most common copper compounds contain Cu^{2+} and most common lead compounds contain Pb^{2+}. For compounds of these metals, if the charge is not indicated by a Roman numeral, we assume the ion present has a 2+ charge. Thus, it is not unusual to find $PbCl_2$ called lead chloride or for $CuCl_2$ to be called copper chloride.

■**Analysis:** We can see that the compound is an ionic compound since it is made up of a metal and a nonmetal, so we use the rules for naming ionic compounds.

Manganese (Mn) is a transition element, and transition elements often form more than one cation, so we apply the Stock method. We also need to determine the charge on the manganese cation. We can figure this out because the sum of the charges on the manganese and chlorine ions must equal zero, and because the only ion chlorine forms has a single negative charge.

■**Assembling the Tools:** The tool we will use to find the charge on the metal ion is the requirement that the compound be electrically neutral. Also, because the cation is that of a transition metal, the Stock system will be the tool used to specify the charge on the cation.

■**Solution:** The anion of chlorine (the chloride ion) is Cl^-, so a total of two negative charges are supplied by the two Cl^- ions. Therefore, for $MnCl_2$ to be electrically neutral, the Mn ion must carry two positive charges, 2+. The cation is named as manganese(II), and the name of the compound is *manganese(II) chloride*.

■**Is the Answer Reasonable?** Performing a quick check of the arithmetic assures us we've got the correct charges on the ions. Everything appears to be okay.

Example 3.7
Naming Compounds and Writing Formulas

What is the formula for cobalt(III) fluoride?

■**Analysis:** To answer this question, we first need to determine the charges on the two ions. Then we assemble the ions into a chemical formula being sure to achieve an electrically neutral formula unit.

■**Assembling the Tools:** We will use the same tools as in Example 3.6.

■**Solution:** Cobalt(III) corresponds to Co^{3+}. The fluoride ion is F^-. To obtain an electrically neutral substance, we must have three F^- ions for each Co^{3+} ion, so the formula is CoF_3.

■**Is the Answer Reasonable?** We can check to see that we have the correct formulas of the ions and that we've combined them to achieve an electrically neutral formula unit. This will tell us we've obtained the correct answer.

Practice Exercises

3.18 | Name the compounds Li_2S, Mg_3P_2, $NiCl_2$, $TiCl_2$, and Fe_2O_3. Use the Stock system where appropriate. (*Hint:* Determine which metals can have more than one charge.)

3.19 | Write formulas for (a) aluminum sulfide, (b) strontium fluoride, (c) titanium(IV) oxide, (d) cobalt(II) oxide, and (e) gold(III) oxide.

Naming Ionic Compounds Containing Polyatomic Ions

TOOLS

Naming with polyatomic ions

■ It is important that you learn the formulas (including charges) and the names of the polyatomic ions in Table 3.5. You will encounter them frequently throughout your chemistry course.

The extension of the nomenclature system to include ionic compounds containing polyatomic ions is straightforward. Most of the polyatomic ions listed in Table 3.5 are anions and their names are used without modification as the second word in the name of the compound. For example, Na_2SO_4 contains the sulfate ion, SO_4^{2-}, and is called sodium sulfate. Similarly, $Cr(NO_3)_3$ contains the nitrate ion, NO_3^-. Chromium is a transition element, and in this compound its charge must be 3+ to balance the negative charges of three NO_3^- ions. Therefore, $Cr(NO_3)_3$ is called chromium(III) nitrate.

Among the ions in Table 3.5, the only cation that forms compounds that can be isolated is ammonium ion, NH_4^+. It forms ionic compounds such as NH_4Cl (ammonium chloride) and $(NH_4)_2SO_4$ (ammonium sulfate) even though NH_4^+ is not a metal cation. Notice that $(NH_4)_2SO_4$ is composed of two polyatomic ions.

Example 3.8
Naming Compounds and Writing Formulas

What is the name of $Mg(ClO_4)_2$, a compound used commercially for removing moisture from gases?

■ **Analysis:** To answer this question, it is essential that you recognize that the compound contains a polyatomic ion since ClO_4 is in parentheses. If you've learned the contents of Table 3.5, you know that "ClO_4" is the formula (without the charge) of the perchlorate ion. With the charge, the ion's formula is ClO_4^-. We also have to decide whether we need to apply the Stock system in naming the metal Mg.

■ **Assembling the Tools:** We will use the names of polyatomic ions in Table 3.5 and the tools about deciding whether or not to use the Stock system.

■ **Solution:** Magnesium is in Group 2A, and it only forms the ion Mg^{2+}. Therefore, we don't need to use the Stock system in naming the cation; it is named simply as "magnesium." The anion is perchlorate, so the name of $Mg(ClO_4)_2$ is *magnesium perchlorate*.

■ **Is the Answer Reasonable?** We can check to be sure we've named the anion correctly, and we have. The metal is magnesium, which only forms Mg^{2+}. Therefore, the answer seems to be correct.

3.20 | What are the names of (a) Li_2CO_3, (b) $KMnO_4$, and (c) $Fe(OH)_3$? (*Hint:* Recall the names of the polyatomic ions and the positions of Li, K, and Fe in the periodic table.)

3.21 | Write the formulas for (a) potassium chlorate, (b) sodium hypochlorite, and (c) nickel(II) phosphate.

Practice Exercises

Naming Hydrates

In Chapter 1 we discussed compounds called hydrates, such as $CuSO_4 \cdot 5H_2O$. Usually, hydrates are ionic compounds whose crystals contain water molecules in fixed proportions relative to the ionic substance. To name them, we provide two pieces of information: the name of the ionic compound and the number of water molecules in the formula. The number of water molecules is specified using the following Greek prefixes:

mono-	= 1		hexa-	= 6
di-	= 2		hepta-	= 7
tri-	= 3		octa-	= 8
tetra-	= 4		nona-	= 9
penta-	= 5		deca-	= 10

TOOLS

Greek prefixes

These prefixes precede the word "hydrate." Thus, $CuSO_4 \cdot 5H_2O$ is named as "copper sulfate *pentahydrate*." Similarly, $CaSO_4 \cdot 2H_2O$ is named calcium sulfate dihydrate, and $FeCl_3 \cdot 6H_2O$ is iron(III) chloride hexahydrate.[5]

---

[5]Chemical suppliers (who do not always follow current rules of nomenclature) sometimes indicate the number of water molecules using a number and a dash. For example, one supplier lists $Ca(NO_3)_2 \cdot 4H_2O$ as "Calcium nitrate, 4-hydrate."

3.6 | Molecular Compounds

The concept of molecules dates to the time of Dalton's atomic theory, where a part of his theory was that atoms of elements combine in fixed numerical ratios to form "molecules" of a compound. By our modern definition *a **molecule** is an electrically neutral particle consisting of two or more atoms*. Accordingly, the term molecule applies to many elements such as H_2 and O_2 as well as to compounds.

Experimental Evidence for Molecules

One phenomenon that points to the existence of molecules is called **Brownian motion**, named after Robert Brown (1773–1858), the Scottish botanist who first observed it. When very small particles such as tiny grains of pollen are suspended in a liquid and observed under a microscope, the tiny particles are seen to be constantly jumping and jiggling about. It appears as though they are continually being knocked back and forth by collisions with something. One explanation is that this "something" is *molecules* of the liquid. The microscopic particles are constantly bombarded by molecules of the liquid, but because the suspended particles are so small, the collisions are not occurring equally on all sides. The unequal numbers of collisions cause the lightweight particles to jerk about. There is additional evidence for molecules, and today scientists accept the existence of molecules as fact.

Looking more closely, within molecules the atoms are held to each other by attractions called **chemical bonds**, which are electrical in nature. In molecular compounds chemical bonds arise from the sharing of electrons between one atom and another. We will discuss such bonds at considerable length in Chapters 9 and 10. What is important to know about molecules now is that *the group of atoms that make up a molecule move about together and behave as a single particle*, just as the various parts that make up a car move about as one unit. The chemical formulas that we write to describe the compositions of molecules are called **molecular formulas,** which specify the actual numbers of atoms of each kind that make up a single molecule.

Compare the structures of water and sodium chloride in Figure 3.17. Water is a discrete unit with the two hydrogen atoms bonded to the oxygen atom. In contrast, in sodium chloride, the ions are packed as close as possible to each other; each cation has six anions next to it, and each anion has six cations next to it. It cannot be said that one sodium ion "belongs" to one chloride ion. Instead, there is an attraction between each ion and its nearest neighbors of the opposite charge.

Molecular Compounds Made from Nonmetals

■ Carbon monoxide is a poisonous gas found in the exhaust of automobiles, and we exhale carbon dioxide.

As a general rule, *molecular compounds are formed when nonmetallic elements combine*. For example, you learned that H_2 and O_2 combine to form molecules of water. Similarly, carbon and oxygen combine to form either carbon monoxide, CO, or carbon dioxide, CO_2. (Both are gases that are formed in various amounts as products in the combustion of fuels such as gasoline and charcoal.) Although molecular compounds can be formed by the direct combination of elements, often they are the products of reactions between compounds. You will encounter many such reactions in your study of chemistry.

Although there are relatively few nonmetals, the number of molecular substances formed by them is huge. This is because of the variety of ways in which nonmetals combine as well as the varying degrees of complexity of their molecules. Variety and complexity reach a maximum with compounds in which carbon is combined with a handful of other elements such as hydrogen, oxygen, and nitrogen. There are so many of these compounds, in fact, that their study encompasses the chemical specialties called **organic chemistry** and **biochemistry.**

Molecules vary in size from small to very large. Some contain as few as two atoms (diatomic molecules). Most molecules are more complex, however, and contain more

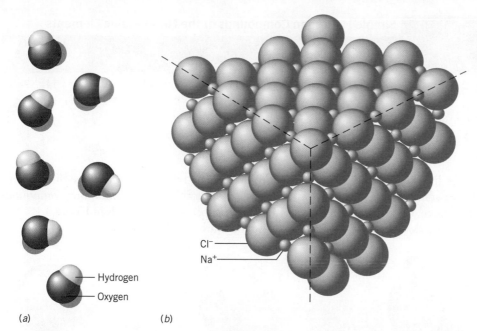

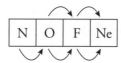

(a) (b)

Figure 3.17 | **Molecular and ionic substances.** *(a)* In water there are discrete molecules that each consist of one atom of oxygen and two atoms of hydrogen. Each particle has the formula H_2O. *(b)* In sodium chloride, ions are packed in the most efficient way. Each Na^+ is surrounded by six Cl^-, and each Cl^- is surrounded by six Na^+. Because individual molecules do not exist, we simply specify the ratio of ions as NaCl.

atoms. Molecules of water (H_2O), for example, have three atoms and those of ordinary table sugar ($C_{12}H_{22}O_{11}$) have 45. There also are molecules that are very large, such as those that occur in plastics and in living organisms, some of which contain millions of atoms.

At this early stage we can only begin to look for signs of order among the vast number of nonmetal–nonmetal compounds. To give you a taste of the subject, we will look briefly at some simple compounds that the nonmetals form with hydrogen, as well as some simple compounds of carbon.

Hydrogen-containing Compounds

Hydrogen forms a variety of compounds with other elements, and the formulas of the simple hydrogen compounds of the nonmetals (called **nonmetal hydrides**) are given in Table 3.7.[6] These compounds provide an opportunity to observe how we can use the periodic table as an aid in remembering factual information, in this case, the formulas of the hydrogen compounds of the nonmetals. Notice that the number of hydrogen atoms combined with the nonmetal atom equals *the number of spaces to the right that we have to move in the periodic table to get to a noble gas.* (You will learn *why* this is so in Chapter 9, but for now we can just use the periodic table to help us remember the formulas.)

Two steps, so oxygen combines with two hydrogens to give H_2O.

Three steps, so nitrogen combines with three hydrogens to give NH_3.

Also note in Table 3.7 that the formulas of the hydrogen compounds within a given group of the periodic table are similar for nonmetals. If you know the formula for the hydrogen compound of the top member of the group, then you know the formulas of all of them in that group.

TOOLS

Predicting formulas of nonmetal hydrogen compounds

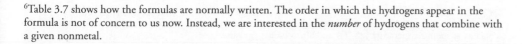

[6]Table 3.7 shows how the formulas are normally written. The order in which the hydrogens appear in the formula is not of concern to us now. Instead, we are interested in the *number* of hydrogens that combine with a given nonmetal.

Table 3.7	Simple Hydrogen Compounds of the Nonmetallic Elements			
	Group			
Period	4A	5A	6A	7A
2	CH_4	NH_3	H_2O	HF
3	SiH_4	PH_3	H_2S	HCl
4	GeH_4	AsH_3	H_2Se	HBr
5		SbH_3	H_2Te	HI

■ Many of the nonmetals form more complex compounds with hydrogen, but we will not discuss them here.

We live in a three-dimensional world, and this is reflected in the three-dimensional shapes of molecules. The shapes of the simple nonmetal hydrogen containing compounds of nitrogen, oxygen, and fluorine are illustrated as space-filling models in Figure 3.18. The geometric shapes of molecules will be described futher in Chapter 10.

Ammonia, NH_3 Water, H_2O Hydrogen fluoride, HF

Figure 3.18 | Nonmetal hydrides of nitrogen, oxygen, and fluorine.

Carbon Compounds: The Basis of Organic Chemistry

Among all the elements, carbon is unique in the variety of compounds it forms with elements such as hydrogen, oxygen, and nitrogen, and their study constitutes the major specialty, organic chemistry. The term "organic" here comes from an early belief that these compounds could only be made by living organisms. We now know this isn't true, but the name organic chemistry persists nonetheless.

■ Our goal at this time is to acquaint you with some of the important kinds of organic compounds we encounter regularly, so our discussion here is brief.

Organic compounds are around us everywhere and we will frequently use such substances as examples in our discussions. Therefore, it will be helpful if you can begin to learn some of them now.

The study of organic chemistry begins with **hydrocarbons** (compounds of hydrogen and carbon). The simplest hydrocarbon is methane, CH_4, which is a member of a series of hydrocarbons with the general formula C_nH_{2n+2}, where n is an integer (i.e., a whole number). The first six members of this series, called the **alkane** series, are listed in Table 3.8 along with their boiling points. Notice that as the molecules become larger, their boiling points increase. Molecules of methane, ethane, and propane are illustrated as space-filling models in Figure 3.19.

The alkanes are common substances. They are the principal constituents of petroleum from which most of our useful fuels are produced. Methane itself is the major component of natural gas that is often used for home heating and cooking. Gas-fired barbecues and

Table 3.8	Hydrocarbons Belonging to the Alkane Series		
Compound	Name	Boiling Point (°C)	Structural Formula
CH_4	Methane[a]	−161.5	CH_4
C_2H_6	Ethane[a]	−88.6	CH_3CH_3
C_3H_8	Propane[a]	−42.1	$CH_3CH_2CH_3$
C_4H_{10}	Butane[a]	−0.5	$CH_3CH_2CH_2CH_3$
C_5H_{12}	Pentane	36.1	$CH_3CH_2CH_2CH_2CH_3$
C_6H_{14}	Hexane	68.7	$CH_3CH_2CH_2CH_2CH_2CH_3$

[a]Gases at room temperature (25 °C) and atmospheric pressure.

Methane, CH₄   Ethane, C₂H₆   Propane, C₃H₈

Methane

Methanol

Figure 3.19 | **The first three members of the alkane series of hydrocarbons.**

■ Methanol is also known as wood alcohol because it was originally made by distilling wood. It is quite poisonous. Ethanol in high doses is also a poison.

Figure 3.20 | **Relationship between an alkane and an alcohol.** The alcohol methanol is derived from methane by replacing one H by OH.

some homes use propane as a fuel, and butane is the fuel in inexpensive cigarette lighters.[7] Hydrocarbons with higher boiling points are found in gasoline, kerosene, paint thinners, diesel fuel, and even candle wax.

Alkanes are not the only class of hydrocarbons. For example, there are three two-carbon hydrocarbons. In addition to ethane, C_2H_6, there are ethene (ethylene), C_2H_4, which has two fewer hydrogens in the molecule than ethane, and ethyne (acetylene), C_2H_2 (which is the fuel used in *acetylene* welding torches).

The hydrocarbons serve as the foundation for organic chemistry. Derived from them are various other classes of organic compounds. An example is the class of compounds called **alcohols**, in which the atoms OH replace a hydrogen in the hydrocarbon. Thus, *methanol*, CH_3OH (also called *methyl alcohol*), is related to methane, CH_4, by removing one H and replacing it with OH (Figure 3.20). Methanol is used as a fuel and as a raw material for making other organic chemicals. Another familiar alcohol is *ethanol* (also called *ethyl alcohol*), C_2H_5OH. Ethanol, known as grain alcohol because it is obtained from the fermentation of grains, is in alcoholic beverages. It is also mixed with gasoline to reduce petroleum consumption. A 10% ethanol/90% gasoline mixture is known as gasohol, and an 85% mixture of ethanol and gasoline is called E85.

Alcohols constitute just one class of compound derived from hydrocarbons. We will discuss some others after you've learned more about how atoms bond to each other and about the structures of molecules.

Writing Formulas for Organic Compounds

Organic formulas can be written in different ways, depending on what information is needed. A molecular formula such as C_2H_6 for ethane or C_3H_8 for propane simply indicates the number of each type of atom in the molecule. The order of the elements in the molecular formula starts with carbon since it is the basis for organic compounds. This is followed by hydrogen, and then the rest of the elements are written in alphabetical order. For example, sucrose is $C_{12}H_{22}O_{11}$. There are exceptions; for example, if we wish to emphasize an alcohol, the OH is separated and listed last, as in ethanol, C_2H_5OH. Condensed structural formulas indicate how the carbon atoms are connected. Ethane is written as CH_3CH_3, and propane is $CH_3CH_2CH_3$ in the condensed structural formula format.

3.22 | Gasoline used in modern cars is a complex mixture of hundreds of different organic compounds. Less than 1% of gasoline is actually octane. Write the formula for octane using the molecular and condensed structural formats. (*Hint:* To figure out the number of carbon atoms, recall the meaning of the Greek prefix "octa.")

3.23 | What is the formula of the alkane hydrocarbon having 10 carbon atoms, decane? Write both the molecular formula and the condensed structural formula.

3.24 | On the basis of the discussions in this section, what are the formulas of (a) propanol and (b) butanol? Write both the molecular formula and the condensed structural formula.

Practice Exercises

---

[7]Propane and butane are gases when they're at the pressure of the air around us, but become liquids when compressed. When you purchase these substances, they are liquids with pressurized gas above them. The gas can be drawn off and used by opening a valve to the container.

3.7 | Nomenclature of Molecular Compounds

Binary Molecular Compounds

Just as in naming the ionic compound, we want to be able to translate a chemical formula into a name that anyone with a background in chemistry can understand. For a binary molecular compound, therefore, we must indicate which two elements are present and the number of atoms of each in a molecule of the substance.

To identify the first element in a formula, we just specify its English name. Thus, for HCl the first word in the name is "hydrogen" and for PCl_5 the first word is "phosphorus." To identify the second element, we append the suffix *-ide* to the stem of the element's English name just as we did for the monoatomic anions in ionic compounds.

To form the name of the compound, we place the two parts of the name one after another. Therefore, the name of HCl is hydrogen chloride. However, to name PCl_5, we need a way to specify the number of Cl atoms bound to the phosphorus in the molecule. This is done using the Greek prefixes listed in the hydrates section on page 89; the main difference is that the prefix mono- is often omitted.

To name PCl_5, therefore, we add the prefix penta- to chloride to give the name phosphorus pentachloride. Notice how easily this allows us to translate the name back into the formula.

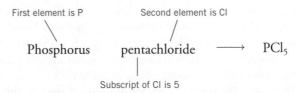

Naming binary molecular compounds

The prefix mono- is used when we want to emphasize that only one atom of a particular element is present. For instance, carbon forms two compounds with oxygen, CO and CO_2. To clearly distinguish between them, the first is called carbon monoxide (one of the "o"s is omitted to make the name easier to pronounce) and the second is carbon dioxide.

As indicated above, the prefix mono- is often omitted from a name. Therefore, in general, if there is no prefix before the name of an element, we take it to mean there is only one atom of that element in the molecule. An exception to this is in the names of binary compounds of nonmetals with hydrogen. An example is hydrogen sulfide. The name tells us the compound contains the two elements hydrogen and sulfur. We don't have to be told how many hydrogens are in the molecule because, as you learned earlier, we can use the periodic table to determine the number of hydrogen atoms in molecules of the simple nonmetal, hydrogen-containing compounds. Sulfur is in Group 6A, so to get to the noble gas column (Group 8A) we have to move two steps to the right; the number of hydrogens combined with the atom of sulfur is two. The formula for hydrogen sulfide is therefore H_2S.

Example 3.9
Naming Compounds and Writing Formulas

(a) What is the name of $AsCl_3$? (b) What is the formula for dinitrogen tetraoxide?

■ **Analysis:** (a) In naming compounds, the first step is to determine the type of compound involved. Looking at the periodic table, we see that $AsCl_3$ is made up of two nonmetals, so we conclude that it is a molecular compound.

(b) To write the formula from the name, we convert the prefixes to numbers.

■ **Assembling the Tools:** (a) We apply the tool for naming molecular compounds from the molecule's formula described previously.

■ Now that we've discussed both ionic and molecular compounds, this first step in the analysis will be particularly important, because different rules apply depending on the type of compound being named.

(b) The meanings of the Greek prefixes will be our tool to convert the prefixes to numbers that we apply as subscripts for the chemical symbols in the formula.

■**Solution:** (a) In $AsCl_3$, As is the symbol for arsenic and Cl is the symbol for chlorine. The first word in the name is just arsenic and the second will contain chloride with an appropriate prefix to indicate number. There are three Cl atoms, so the prefix is tri. Therefore, the name of the compound is *arsenic trichloride*.

(b) As we did earlier for phosphorus pentachloride, we convert the prefixes to numbers and apply them as subscripts.

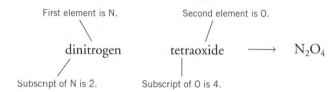

First element is N.

Second element is O.

dinitrogen   tetraoxide $\longrightarrow$ N_2O_4

Subscript of N is 2.   Subscript of O is 4.

■ Sometimes we drop the *a* before an *o* for ease of pronunciation. N_2O_4 would then be named dinitrogen tetroxide.

■**Are the Answers Reasonable?** To feel comfortable with the answers, be sure to double-check for careless errors. Next, take your answers and reverse the process. Does arsenic trichloride result in the original formula, $AsCl_3$? Does N_2O_4 have the name of dinitrogen tetraoxide? We can say yes to both and have confidence in our work.

3.25 | Name the following compounds using Greek prefixes when needed: (a) PCl_3, (b) SO_2, (c) Cl_2O_7, and (d) H_2S. (*Hint:* See the list of prefixes above.)

3.26 | Write formulas for the following compounds: (a) arsenic pentachloride, (b) sulfur hexachloride, (c) disulfur dichloride, and (d) hydrogen telluride.

Practice Exercises

Common Names for Molecular Compounds

Not every compound is named according to the systematic procedure we have described so far. Many familiar substances were discovered long before a systematic method for naming them had been developed, and they acquired common names that are so well known that no attempt has been made to rename them. For example, following the scheme described above we might expect that H_2O would have the name hydrogen oxide (or even dihydrogen monoxide). Although this isn't wrong, the common name water is so well known that it is always used. Another example is ammonia, NH_3, whose odor you have no doubt experienced while using household ammonia solutions or the glass cleaner Windex®. Common names are used for the other hydrogen-containing compounds of the nonmetals in Group 5A as well. The compound PH_3 is called phosphine and AsH_3 is called arsine.

Common names are also used for very complex substances. An example is sucrose, which is the chemical name for table sugar, $C_{12}H_{22}O_{11}$. The structure of this compound is pretty complex, and its name assigned following the systematic method is equally complex. It is much easier to say the simple name sucrose, and be understood, than to struggle with the cumbersome systematic name for this common compound.

Naming Molecular and Ionic Compounds

In this chapter we've discussed how to name two classes of compounds, molecular and ionic, and you saw that slightly different rules apply to each. To name chemical compounds successfully we need to make a series of decisions based on the rules we just covered. We can summarize this decision process in a flow chart such as the one shown in Figure 3.21. The next example illustrates how to use the flow chart, and when working on the Review Questions, you may want to refer to Figure 3.21 until you are able to develop the skills that will enable you to work without it.

Figure 3.21 | Flowchart for naming molecular and ionic compounds.

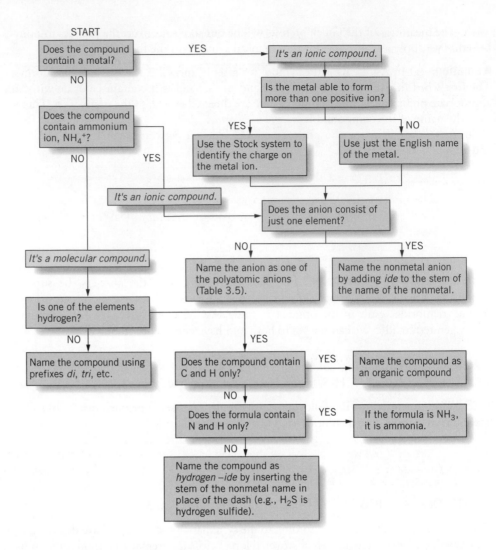

Example 3.10
Applying the Rules for Naming Compounds

What is the name of (a) $CrCl_3$, (b) P_4S_3, and (c) NH_4NO_3?

■ **Analysis:** We need to start by determining whether or not the compounds are ionic or molecular, and then follow the rules given for naming the appropriate type of compound.

■ **Assembling the Tools:** For each compound, we use the tools summarized in Figure 3.21 and proceed through the decision processes to arrive at the name of the compound.

■ **Solution:** (a) Starting at the top of Figure 3.21, we first determine that the compound contains a metal (Cr), so it's an ionic compound. Next, we see that the metal is a transition element, and chromium is one of those that forms more than one cation, so we have to apply the Stock method. To do this, we need to know the charge on the metal ion. We can figure this out using the charge on the anion and the fact that the compound must be electrically neutral overall. The anion is formed from chlorine, so its charge is 1− (the anion is Cl^-). Since there are three chlorine ions, the metal ion must be Cr^{3+}; we name the metal *chromium(III)*. Next, we see that there is only one nonmetallic element in the compound, Cl, so the name of the anion ends in -ide; it's the *chloride* ion. The compound $CrCl_3$ is therefore named *chromium(III) chloride*.

(b) Once again, we start at the top of Figure 3.21. First, we determine that the compound doesn't contain a metal or NH_4^+, so the compound is molecular. It doesn't contain hydrogen, so we are led to the decision that we must use Greek prefixes to specify the numbers of atoms of each element. Applying the procedure on page 94, the name of the compound P_4S_3 is *tetraphosphorus trisulfide*.

(c) We begin at the top of Figure 3.21. Studying the formula, we see that it does not contain the symbol for a metal, so we proceed down the left side of the figure. The formula does contain NH_4^+, which indicates that the compound contains the *ammonium* ion, NH_4^+ (it's an ionic compound). The rest of the formula is NO_3, which consists of more than one atom. This suggests the polyatomic anion, NO_3^- (*nitrate* ion). The name of the compound NH_4NO_3 is *ammonium nitrate*.

■ **Are the Answers Reasonable?** To check the answers in a problem of this kind, review the decision processes that led you to the names. In Part (a), you can check to be sure you've calculated the charge on the chromium ion correctly. Also, check to be sure you've used the correct names of any polyatomic ions. Doing these things will show that you've named the compounds correctly.

Practice Exercises

3.27 | The compound I_2O_5 is used in respirators where it serves to react with highly toxic carbon monoxide to give the much less toxic gas, carbon dioxide. What is the name of I_2O_5? (*Hint:* Is this a molecular or an ionic compound?)

3.28 | The compound $Cr(C_2H_3O_2)_3$ is used in the tanning of leather. What is the name for this compound?

3.29 | The compound $KClO_4$ is used in fireworks. What is the name for this compound?

| Summary

Atomic Structure. Atoms can be split into **subatomic particles,** such as **electrons, protons,** and **neutrons. Nucleons** are particles that make up the atomic **nucleus** and include the protons, each of which carries one unit of **positive charge** (charge = 1+) and the neutrons that have no charge. The number of protons is called the **atomic number** (*Z*) of the element. Each element has a different atomic number. The electrons, each with one unit of **negative charge** (charge = 1−), are found outside the nucleus; their number equals the atomic number in a neutral atom. Isotopes of an element have identical atomic numbers but different numbers of neutrons. In more modern terms, an **element** can be defined as a substance whose atoms all have the same number of protons in their nuclei.

Atomic Mass. An element's **atomic mass (atomic weight)** is the relative mass of its atoms on a scale in which atoms of carbon-12 have a mass of exactly 12 u (**atomic mass units**). Most elements occur in nature as uniform mixtures of a small number of **isotopes,** whose masses differ slightly. However, all isotopes of an element have very nearly identical chemical properties, and the percentages of the isotopes that make up an element are generally so constant throughout the world that we can say that the average mass of their atoms is a constant.

The Periodic Table. In the modern **periodic table** the elements are arranged in rows, called **periods,** in order of increasing atomic number. The rows are stacked so that elements in the columns, called **groups** or **families,** have similar chemical and physical properties. The A-group elements (IUPAC Groups 1, 2, and 13–18) are called **representative elements;** the B-group elements (IUPAC Groups 3–12) are called **transition elements.** The two long rows of **inner transition elements** located below the main body of the table consist of the **lanthanides,** which follow La ($Z = 57$), and the **actinides,** which follow Ac ($Z = 89$). Certain groups are given family names: Group 1A (Group 1), except for hydrogen, are the **alkali metals** (the alkalis); Group 2A (Group 2) are the **alkaline earth metals;** Group 7A (Group 17) are the **halogens;** and Group 8A (Group 18) are the **noble gases.**

Metals, Nonmetals, and Metalloids. Most elements are **metals;** they occupy the lower left-hand region of the periodic table (to the left of a line drawn approximately from boron, B, to astatine, At). **Nonmetals** are found in the upper right-hand region of the table. **Metalloids** occupy a narrow band between the metals and nonmetals.

Metals exhibit a **metallic luster,** tend to be **ductile** and **malleable,** and conduct heat and electricity. Nonmetals tend to be brittle, lack metallic luster, and are nonconductors of electricity. Many nonmetals are gases. **Metalloids** have properties intermediate between those of metals and nonmetals and are **semiconductors** of electricity.

Ions and Ionic Compounds. Binary ionic compounds are formed when metals react with nonmetals. In the reaction, electrons are transferred from a metal to a nonmetal. The metal atom becomes a positive ion (a **cation**); the nonmetal atom becomes a negative ion (an **anion**). The formula of an ionic compound specifies the smallest whole-number ratio of the ions. The smallest unit of an ionic compound is called a **formula unit,** which specifies the smallest whole-number ratio of the ions that produces electrical neutrality. Many ionic compounds also contain **polyatomic ions**—ions that are composed of two or more atoms.

Naming Ionic Compounds. In naming an ionic compound, the cation is specified first, followed by the anion. Metal cations take the English name of the element, and when more than one positive ion can be formed by the metal, the **Stock system** is used to identify the amount of positive charge on the cation. This is done by placing a Roman numeral equal to the positive charge in parentheses following the name of the metal. Simple **monatomic** anions are formed by nonmetals, and their names are formed by adding the suffix -ide to the stem of the nonmetal's name. Only two common polyatomic anions (cyanide and hydroxide) end in the suffix -ide.

Molecules and Molecular Compounds. **Molecules** are electrically neutral particles consisting of two or more atoms. The erratic movements of microscopic particles suspended in a liquid (**Brownian motion**) can be interpreted as the result of collisions with molecules of the liquid. Molecules are held together by **chemical bonds** that arise from the sharing of electrons between atoms. The formulas we write for molecules are **molecular formulas**. Molecular compounds are formed when nonmetals combine with each other. The simple **nonmetal hydrides** have formulas that can be remembered by the position of the nonmetal in the periodic table. **Organic compounds** are **hydrocarbons,** or compounds considered to be derived from hydrocarbons by replacing H atoms with other atoms.

Properties of Molecular and Ionic Compounds. We found that it is often possible to distinguish ionic compounds from molecular compounds by their ability to **conduct electricity**. Molecular compounds are generally poor electrical conductors, whereas ionic compounds when melted into the liquid state or dissolved in water will conduct electricity readily.

Naming Molecular Compounds. The system of **nomenclature** for **binary** molecular **inorganic compounds** uses a set of **Greek prefixes** to specify the numbers of atoms of each kind in the formula of the compound. The first element in the formula is specified by its English name; the second element takes the suffix -ide, which is added to the stem of the English name. For simple nonmetal hydrogen compounds, it is not necessary to specify the number of hydrogens in the formula. Many familiar substances, as well as very complex molecules, are usually identified by **common names**. The decision tree in Figure 3.21 is a helpful tool in naming ionic and molecular compounds.

Tools for Problem Solving The following tools were introduced in this chapter. Study them carefully so you can select the appropriate tool when needed.

Number of subatomic particles in atoms (page 68)

There are three important relationships between the numbers of **protons, neutrons (the nucleons),** and **electrons.** These relationships are:

Number of electrons = number of protons

Atomic number (Z) = number of protons

Mass number (A) = number of protons + number of neutrons

Atomic symbols for isotopes (page 68)

The mass number (A) comes before the element symbol as a superscript and the atomic number (Z) also comes before the element as a subscript.

$$^A_Z X$$

Relative atomic masses (page 70)

Atomic masses are relative to the mass of a ^{12}C atom that has a mass of exactly 12 atomic mass units (u). Therefore, the atomic mass of ^{12}C is exactly 12 u.

Periodic table (page 73)

The periodic table has several tool icons in this chapter illustrating its use in a variety of different ways. For example, we can obtain atomic numbers and average masses of the elements from the periodic table. The periodic table lists the atoms by atomic number and organizes them by their properties in periods and groups. We can also tell if a element is a metal, nonmetal, or metalloid from it position in the periodic table (page 75).

Properties of metals (page 76)

Metals have specific properties such as luster, electrical and heat conductivity, malleability, and ductility, which help distinguish them from nonmetals and metalloids.

Ionic compounds (page 80)

The rules permit us to write correct chemical formulas for ionic compounds. You will need to learn to use the periodic table to remember the charges on the cations and anions of the representative metals and nonmetals.

Predicting cation charge (page 81)

For the metals in Groups 1A and 2A, we can use the elements' positions in the periodic table to obtain the charges on their ions.

Predicting anion charge (page 81)

From a nonmetal's position in the periodic table, we can determine the charge of the monatomic anions.

Formulas for ionic compounds (page 82)

Following the rules gives us the correct formulas for ionic compounds with electrically neutral formula units and with subscripts in the smallest set of whole numbers.

Polyatomic ions (page 84)

Certain groups of atoms arrange themselves into stable, electrically charged particles that we call polyatomic ions. It is very important that you commit to memory the names, formulas, and charges of these ions which are listed in Table 3.5. You will need them to write formulas and name compounds.

Naming ionic compounds (page 86)

These rules give us a systematic method for naming ionic compounds. The name of the cation is combined with the name of a monatomic anion. These rules are used with slight modification for cations that can have more than one possible charge (see the **Stock system**) and for situations in which a polyatomic ion is involved (see naming with **polyatomic ions**).

Monatomic anion names (page 86)

The list on this page gives the common names of anions that must be remembered so you can use them to name ionic compounds.

Using the Stock system (page 87)

The Stock system specifies the charge of a cation by placing a Roman numeral in parentheses just after the name of the cation. The Stock system and its Roman numerals are only used for cations that can have more than one possible charge.

Naming with polyatomic ions (page 88)

Naming compounds that contain polyatomic anions is done by specifying the cation name, using the Stock system if needed, and then specifying the polyatomic anion name as given in Table 3.5. The one polyatomic cation, the ammonium ion (NH_4^+), uses its name and then the appropriate name of the anion.

Greek prefixes (page 89)

This page has a list of the Greek prefixes from one to ten that you should know for naming molecular compounds and hydrates.

Predicting formulas of nonmetal hydrogen compounds (page 91)

From a nonmetal's position in the periodic table we can write the formula of its simple hydrogen compound. These are given in Table 3.7.

Naming binary molecular compounds (page 94)

These rules give us a logical system for naming binary molecular compounds by specifying the number of each type of atom using Greek prefixes.

Review Questions

Atomic Masses and Atomic Structure

3.1 What are the names, symbols, and electrical charges of the three subatomic particles introduced in this chapter?

3.2 Where in an atom is nearly all of its mass concentrated? Explain your answer in terms of the particles that contribute to this mass.

3.3 What is a *nucleon*? Which ones have we studied?

3.4 How was the charge-to-mass ratio of the electron determined?

3.5 How did Robert Millikan determine the charge of an electron, and how did this allow the mass of the electron to be determined?

3.6 How was the proton discovered?

3.7 What experiment did Rutherford carry out to determine the existence of the nucleus?

3.8 Define the terms *atomic number* and *mass number*. What symbols are used to designate these terms?

3.9 Consider the symbol $_b^aX$, where X stands for the chemical symbol for an element. What information is given in locations **(a)** a and **(b)** b?

3.10 Write the symbols of the isotopes that contain the following. (Use the table of atomic masses and numbers printed inside the front cover for additional information, as needed.)

(a) An isotope of iodine whose atoms have 78 neutrons

(b) An isotope of strontium whose atoms have 52 neutrons

(c) An isotope of cesium whose atoms have 82 neutrons

(d) An isotope of fluorine whose atoms have 9 neutrons

3.11 What is wrong with the following statement? "The atomic mass of an atom of chlorine is 35.453 u."

The Periodic Table

3.12 In the compounds formed by Li, Na, K, Rb, and Cs with chlorine, how many atoms of Cl are there per atom of each metal? In the compounds formed by Be, Mg, Ca, Sr, and Ba with chlorine, how many atoms of Cl are there per atom of each metal? How did this kind of information lead Mendeleev to develop his periodic table?

3.13 On what basis did Mendeleev construct his periodic table? On what basis are the elements arranged in the modern periodic table?

3.14 On the basis of their positions in the periodic table, why is it not surprising that strontium-90, a dangerous radioactive isotope of strontium, replaces calcium in newly formed bones?

3.15 In the refining of copper, sizable amounts of silver and gold are recovered. Why is this not surprising?

3.16 Why would you reasonably expect cadmium to be a contaminant in zinc but not in silver?

3.17 Using the symbol for nitrogen, $_7^{14}N_2^0$, indicate what information is conveyed by the two superscripts, and what information is conveyed by the two subscripts.

3.18 Make a rough sketch of the periodic table and mark off those areas where you would find **(a)** the representative elements, **(b)** the transition elements, and **(c)** the inner transition elements.

3.19 Which of the following is

(a) an alkali metal? Ca, Cu, In, Li, S

(b) a halogen? Ce, Hg, Si, O, I

(c) a transition element? Pb, W, Ca, Cs, P

(d) a noble gas? Xe, Se, H, Sr, Zr

(e) a lanthanide element? Th, Sm, Ba, F, Sb

(f) an actinide element? Ho, Mn, Pu, At, Na

(g) an alkaline earth metal? Mg, Fe, K, Cl, Ni

Metals, Nonmetals, and Metalloids

3.20 Name five physical properties that we usually observe for metals.

3.21 Why is mercury used in thermometers? Why is tungsten used in lightbulbs?

3.22 Which nonmetals occur as monatomic gases (i.e., gases whose particles consist of single atoms)?

3.23 Which two elements exist as liquids at room temperature and pressure?

3.24 Which physical property of metalloids distinguishes them from metals and nonmetals?

3.25 Sketch the shape of the periodic table and mark off those areas where we find **(a)** metals, **(b)** nonmetals, and **(c)** metalloids.

3.26 Most periodic tables have a heavy line that looks like a staircase starting from boron down to polonium. What information does this line convey?

3.27 Which metals can you think of that are commonly used to make jewelry? Why isn't iron used to make jewelry? Why isn't potassium used?

3.28 What trends—regular changes in physical or chemical properties—in the periodic table have been mentioned in this chapter?

3.29 Find a periodic table on the Internet that lists physical properties of the elements. Can you distinguish trends in the periodic table based on (a) melting point, (b) boiling point, or (c) density?

Ionic Compounds

3.30 Describe what kind of event must occur (involving electrons) if the atoms of two different elements are to react to form an ionic compound.

3.31 With what kind of elements do metals react?

3.32 What is an ion? How does it differ from an atom or a molecule?

3.33 Why do we use the term *formula unit* for ionic compounds instead of the term *molecule*?

3.34 Consider the sodium atom and the sodium ion.
  (a) Write the chemical symbol of each.
  (b) Do these particles have the same number of nuclei?
  (c) Do they have the same number of protons?
  (d) Could they have different numbers of neutrons?
  (e) Do they have the same number of electrons?

3.35 Define *cation, anion,* and *polyatomic ion.*

3.36 How many electrons has a titanium atom lost if it has formed the ion Ti^{4+}? What are the total numbers of protons and electrons in a Ti^{4+} ion?

3.37 If an atom gains an electron to become an ion, what kind of electrical charge does the ion have?

3.38 How many electrons has a nitrogen atom gained if it has formed the ion N^{3-}? How many protons and electrons are in an N^{3-} ion?

3.39 What is wrong with the formula $RbCl_3$? What is wrong with the formula SNa_2?

3.40 A student wrote the formula for an ionic compound of titanium as Ti_2O_4. What is wrong with this formula? What should the formula be?

3.41 What are the formulas of the ions formed by (a) iron, (b) cobalt, (c) mercury, (d) chromium, (e) tin, and (f) manganese?

3.42 Which of the following formulas are incorrect? Write the formulas for the compounds correctly. (a) NaO_2, (b) $RbCl$, (c) K_2S, (d) Al_2Cl_3, (e) MgP_2

3.43 What are the formulas (including charges) for (a) cyanide ion, (b) ammonium ion, (c) nitrate ion, (d) sulfite ion, (e) chlorate ion, and (f) sulfate ion?

3.44 What are the formulas (including charges) for (a) hypochlorite ion, (b) bisulfate ion, (c) phosphate ion, (d) dihydrogen phosphate ion, (e) permanganate ion, and (f) oxalate ion?

3.45 What are the names of the following ions? (a) $Cr_2O_7^{2-}$, (b) OH^-, (c) $C_2H_3O_2^-$, (d) CO_3^{2-}, (e) CN^-, (f) ClO_4^-

3.46 Write correct balanced equations for the reactions between (a) calcium and chlorine, (b) magnesium and oxygen, (c) aluminum and oxygen, and (d) sodium and sulfur.

3.47 Write the balanced equations for the following reactions:
  (a) Iron(III) hydroxide reacts with hydrogen chloride forming water and iron(III) chloride.
  (b) Silver nitrate is reacted with barium chloride to form silver chloride and barium nitrate.

3.48 Write the balanced equations for the following reactions:
  (a) Propane reacts with oxygen to form carbon dioxide and water.
  (b) Sodium metal is added to water and the products are sodium hydroxide and hydrogen gas.

Molecular Compounds

3.49 With what kind of elements do nonmetals react?

3.50 Which are the only elements that exist as free, individual atoms when not chemically combined with other elements?

3.51 Write chemical formulas for the elements that normally exist in nature as diatomic molecules.

3.52 Which kind of elements normally combine to form molecular compounds?

3.53 Why are nonmetals found in more compounds than are metals, even though there are fewer nonmetals than metals?

3.54 Most compounds of aluminum are ionic, but a few are molecular. How do we know that Al_2Cl_6 is molecular?

3.55 Without referring to Table 3.7 but using the periodic table, write chemical formulas for the simplest hydrogen compounds of (a) carbon, (b) nitrogen, (c) tellurium, and (d) iodine.

3.56 The simplest hydrogen compound of phosphorus is phosphine, a highly flammable and poisonous compound with an odor of decaying fish. What is the formula for phosphine?

3.57 Astatine, a member of the halogen family, forms a compound with hydrogen. Predict its chemical formula.

3.58 Under appropriate conditions, tin can be made to form a simple molecular compound with hydrogen. Predict its formula.

3.59 Write the chemical formulas for (a) methane, (b) ethane, (c) propane, and (d) butane. Give one practical use for each of these hydrocarbons.

3.60 What are the formulas for (a) methanol and (b) ethanol?

3.61 What is the formula for the alkane, decane, that has 10 carbon atoms?

3.62 Candle wax is a mixture of hydrocarbons, one of which is an alkane with 23 carbon atoms. What is the formula for this hydrocarbon?

3.63 The formula for a compound is correctly given as $C_6H_{12}O_6$. State two reasons why we expect this to be a molecular compound, rather than an ionic compound.

3.64 Explore the Internet and find a reliable source of structures for molecular compounds. For Problems 3.59 to 3.63, print out the ball-and-stick and space-filling models of the compounds mentioned.

Nomenclature of Ionic and Molecular Compounds

3.65 What is the difference between a binary compound and one that is diatomic? Give examples that illustrate this difference.

3.66 In naming the compounds discussed in this chapter, why is it important to know whether a compound is molecular or ionic?

3.67 In naming ionic compounds of the transition elements, why is it essential to give the charge on the anion?

3.68 Describe (**a**) the three situations in which Greek prefixes are used and (**b**) when Roman numerals are used.

| Review Problems

Atomic Masses and Isotopes

3.69 The chemical substance in natural gas is a compound called methane. Its molecules are composed of carbon and hydrogen, and each molecule contains four atoms of hydrogen and one atom of carbon. In this compound, 0.33597 g of hydrogen is combined with 1.0000 g of carbon-12. Use this information to calculate the atomic mass of the element hydrogen.

3.70 Carbon tetrachloride contains one carbon and four chlorine atoms. For this compound 11.818 g of chlorine combine with 1.000 g of C-12. Using this information, calculate the atomic mass of chlorine.

OH 3.71 A certain element X forms a compound with oxygen in which there are two atoms of X for every three atoms of O. In this compound, 1.125 g of X are combined with 1.000 g of oxygen. Use the average atomic mass of oxygen to calculate the average atomic mass of X. Use your calculated atomic mass to identify the element X.

3.72 Nitrogen reacts with a metal to form a compound in which there are three atoms of the metal for each atom of nitrogen. If 1.486 g of the metal reacts with 1.000 g of nitrogen, what is the calculated atomic mass of the metal? Use your calculated atomic mass to identify the metal.

3.73 If an atom of carbon-12 had been assigned a relative mass of 24.0000 u, what would be the average atomic mass of hydrogen relative to this mass?

3.74 One atom of ^{109}Ag has a mass that is 9.0754 times that of a ^{12}C atom. What is the atomic mass of this isotope of silver expressed in atomic mass units?

Atomic Structure

ILW 3.75 Naturally occurring copper is composed of 69.17% of ^{63}Cu, with an atomic mass of 62.9396 u, and 30.83% of ^{65}Cu, with an atomic mass of 64.9278 u. Use these data to calculate the average atomic mass of copper.

3.76 Naturally occurring magnesium (one of the elements in milk of magnesia) is composed of 78.99% of ^{24}Mg (atomic mass = 23.9850 u), 10.00% of ^{25}Mg (atomic mass = 24.9858 u), and 11.01% of ^{26}Mg (atomic mass = 25.9826 u). Use these data to calculate the average atomic mass of magnesium.

ILW 3.77 Give the numbers of neutrons, protons, and electrons in the atoms of each of the following isotopes. (**a**) radium-226, (**b**) ^{206}Pb, (**c**) carbon-14, (**d**) ^{23}Na (Use the table of atomic masses and numbers printed inside the front cover for additional information, as needed.)

3.78 Give the numbers of electrons, protons, and neutrons in the atoms of each of the following isotopes. (**a**) cesium-137, (**b**) ^{238}U, (**c**) iodine-131, (**d**) ^{285}Cn (As necessary, consult the table of atomic masses and numbers printed inside the front cover.)

3.79 Iodine-131 is used to treat overactive thyroids; it has a mass of 130.9061 u. Give the number of protons, neutrons, and electrons in the atom.

3.80 In the polyatomic ion TcO_4^-, Tc has a hypothetical charge of 7+. The ^{99}Tc isotope is used in medicine for imaging purposes. It has a mass of 98.90625 u. Give the number of protons, neutrons, and electrons for a Tc^{7+} ion.

Ionic Compounds

3.81 Use the periodic table, but not Table 3.3, to write the symbols for the ions of (**a**) K, (**b**) Br, (**c**) Mg, (**d**) S, and (**e**) Al.

3.82 Use the periodic table, but not Table 3.3, to write the symbols for ions of (**a**) barium, (**b**) oxygen, (**c**) fluorine, (**d**) strontium, and (**e**) rubidium.

OH 3.83 Write formulas for ionic compounds formed between (**a**) Na and Br, (**b**) K and I, (**c**) Ba and O, (**d**) Mg and Br, and (**e**) Ba and F.

3.84 Write the formulas for the ionic compounds formed by the following transition metals with the chloride ion, Cl^-: (**a**) chromium, (**b**) iron, (**c**) manganese, (**d**) copper, and (**e**) zinc.

3.85 Write formulas for the ionic compounds formed from (**a**) K^+ and nitrate ion, (**b**) Ca^{2+} and acetate ion, (**c**) ammonium ion and Cl^-, (**d**) Fe^{3+} and carbonate ion, and (**e**) Mg^{2+} and phosphate ion.

3.86 Write formulas for the ionic compounds formed from (**a**) Zn^{2+} and hydroxide ion, (**b**) Ag^+ and chromate ion, (**c**) Ba^{2+} and sulfite ion, (**d**) Rb^+ and sulfate ion, and (**e**) Li^+ and bicarbonate ion.

3.87 Each of the following metals can form two compounds with oxygen. Write their formulas. (a) lead, (b) tin, (c) manganese, (d) iron, and (e) copper.

3.88 Write formulas for the ionic compounds formed from Cl^- and (a) cadmium ion, (b) silver ion, (c) zinc ion, and (d) nickel ion.

Nomenclature

3.89 Name the following ionic compounds: (a) CaS, (b) $AlBr_3$, (c) Na_3P, (d) Ba_3As_2, (e) Rb_2S.

3.90 Name the following ionic compounds: (a) NaF, (b) Mg_2C, (c) Li_3N, (d) Al_2O_3, (e) K_2Se.

3.91 Name the following molecular compounds: (a) SiO_2, (b) XeF_4, (c) P_4O_{10}, (d) Cl_2O_7.

3.92 Name the following molecular compounds: (a) ClF_3, (b) S_2Cl_2, (c) N_2O_5, (d) $AsCl_5$.

3.93 Name the following ionic compounds using the Stock system: (a) FeS, (b) CuO, (c) SnO_2, (d) $CoCl_2 \cdot 6H_2O$.

3.94 Name the following ionic compounds using the Stock system: (a) Mn_2O_3, (b) Hg_2Cl_2, (c) PbS, (d) $CrCl_3 \cdot 4H_2O$.

3.95 Name the following. If necessary, refer to Table 3.5 on page 84. (a) $NaNO_2$, (b) $KMnO_4$, (c) $MgSO_4 \cdot 7H_2O$, (d) KSCN

3.96 Name the following. If necessary, refer to Table 3.5 on page page 84. (a) K_3PO_4, (b) $NH_4C_2H_3O_2$, (c) $Fe_2(CO_3)_3$, (d) $Na_2S_2O_3 \cdot 5H_2O$

3.97 Identify each of the following as molecular or ionic and give its name:

(a) $CrCl_2$ (e) KIO_3 (h) AgCN

(b) S_2Cl_2 (f) P_4O_6 (i) $ZnBr_2$

(c) $NH_4C_2H_3O_2$ (g) $CaSO_3$ (j) H_2Se

(d) SO_3

3.98 Identify each of the following as molecular or ionic and give its name:

(a) $V(NO_3)_3$ (e) $GeBr_4$ (h) I_2O_4

(b) $Co(C_2H_3O_2)_2$ (f) K_2CrO_4 (i) I_4O_9

(c) Au_2S_3 (g) $Fe(OH)_2$ (j) P_4Se_3

(d) Au_2S

OH 3.99 Write formulas for the following.

(a) sodium monohydrogen phosphate

(b) lithium selenide

(c) chromium(III) acetate

(d) disulfur decafluoride

(e) nickel(II) cyanide

(f) iron(III) oxide

(g) antimony pentafluoride

3.100 Write formulas for the following.

(a) dialuminum hexachloride

(b) tetraarsenic decaoxide

(c) magnesium hydroxide

(d) copper(II) bisulfate

(e) ammonium thiocyanate

(f) potassium thiosulfate

(g) diiodine pentaoxide

3.101 Write formulas for the following.

(a) ammonium sulfide

(b) chromium(III) sulfate hexahydrate

(c) silicon tetrafluoride

(d) molybdenum(IV) sulfide

(e) tin(IV) chloride

(f) hydrogen selenide

(g) tetraphosphorus heptasulfide

3.102 Write formulas for the following.

(a) mercury(II) acetate

(b) barium hydrogen sulfite

(c) boron trichloride

(d) calcium phosphide

(e) magnesium dihydrogen phosphate

(f) calcium oxalate

(g) xenon tetrafluoride

3.103 The compounds Se_2S_6 and Se_2S_4 have been shown to be antidandruff agents. What are their names?

3.104 The compound P_2S_5 is used to manufacture safety matches. What is the name of this compound?

|Additional Exercises

3.105 An element has 24 protons in its nucleus.

   (a) Is the element a metal, a nonmetal, or a metalloid?

   (b) On the basis of the average atomic mass, write the symbol for the element's most abundant isotope.

   (c) How many neutrons are in the isotope you described in part (b)?

   (d) How many electrons are in atoms of this element?

   (e) How many times heavier than ^{12}C is the average atom of this element?

3.106 The elements in Group 1A and Group 7A of the periodic table are some of the most reactive elements. What is the difference in reactivity between these two groups?

3.107 Iron is composed of four isotopes with the percentage abundances and atomic masses given in the following table. Calculate the average atomic mass of iron.

Isotope	Percentage Abundance	Atomic Mass (u)
^{54}Fe	5.80	53.9396
^{56}Fe	91.72	55.9349
^{57}Fe	2.20	56.9354
^{58}Fe	0.28	57.9333

OH ***3.108** Bromine (shown in Figure 3.13, page 77) is a dark red liquid that vaporizes easily and is very corrosive to the skin. It is used commercially as a bleach for fibers and silk. Naturally occurring bromine is composed of two isotopes: ^{79}Br, with a mass of 78.9183 u, and ^{81}Br, with a mass of 80.9163 u. Use this information and the average atomic mass of bromine given in the table on the inside front cover of the book to calculate the percentage abundances of these two isotopes.

3.109 One atomic mass unit has a mass of $1.6605402 \times 10^{-24}$ g. Calculate the mass, in grams, of one "average" atom of magnesium. What is the mass of one "average" atom of iron, expressed in grams? Use these two answers to determine how many atoms of Mg are in 24.305 g of magnesium and how many atoms of Fe are in 55.847 g of iron. Compare your answers. What conclusions can you draw from the results of these calculations? Without actually performing any calculations, how many atoms do you think would be in 40.078 g of calcium?

OH **3.110** What are the formulas for mercury(I) nitrate dihydrate and mercury(II) nitrate monohydrate?

3.111 Consider the following substances: Cl_2, CaO, HBr, $CuCl_2$, AsH_3, $NaNO_3$, and NO_2.

   (a) Which are binary substances?

   (b) Which is a triatomic molecule?

   (c) In which do we find only electron sharing?

   (d) Which are diatomic?

   (e) In which do we find only attractions between ions?

   (f) Which are molecular?

   (g) Which are ionic?

OH **3.112** Write the balanced chemical equation for the reaction between elements with atomic numbers of **(a)** 20 and 35, **(b)** 6 and 17, **(c)** 13 and 16. For each of these, determine the ratio of the mass of the heavier element to the lighter element in the compound.

3.113 Write the balanced gas phase chemical equation for the reaction of dinitrogen pentoxide with sulfur dioxide to form sulfur trioxide and nitrogen oxide. What small, whole-number ratios are expected for oxygen in the nitrogen oxides and the sulfur oxides?

3.114 Bromine is a diatomic molecule, and it has two isotopes, ^{79}Br and ^{81}Br, with a natural abundance of about 50% for each isotope. How many different molecules can be formed for Br_2? What instrument would you use to distinguish between the different molecules?

3.115 Using the figures below, match the image with the correct molecular formula: CH_3CH_2OH, NaCl, $SnCl_4$, and H_2O. Write the names of the compounds.

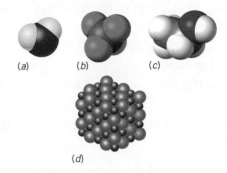

(a)   *(b)*   *(c)*

(d)

3.116 What color are the protons, neutrons, and electrons in the following figure? What element is it? What is the mass number of the atom? Write the symbol for the atom using the $_b^a X$ notation.

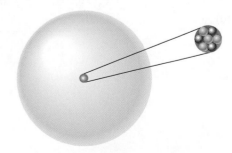

Exercises in Critical Thinking

3.117 Imagine a world where, for some reason, hydrogen and helium have not been discovered. Would Mendeleev have had enough information to predict their existence?

3.118 Around 1750 Benjamin Franklin knew of two opposite types of electric charge, produced by rubbing a glass rod or amber rod with fur. He decided that the charge developed on the glass rod should be the "positive" charge, and from there on charges were defined. What would have changed if Franklin had decided the amber rod was the positive charge?

3.119 Explore the Internet and find a reliable source of physical properties of elements and compounds. Justify how you decided the site was reliable.

3.120 Spreadsheet applications such as Microsoft Excel can display data in a variety of ways, some of which are shown throughout this book. What method of displaying periodic trends (for example, line graphs, tables, bar graphs, 3-D views, etc.) is most effective for your learning style? Explain your answer by stating why your chosen display is better than the others.

3.121 Scientists often validate measurements, such as measuring the circumference of the earth, by using two independent methods to measure the same value. Describe two independent methods for determining the atomic mass of an element. Explain how these methods are truly independent.

3.122 Immediately after the Big Bang, helium and other very light elements were formed. Later, more elements were formed up to about magnesium. It was not until stars were formed that heavier atoms up to iron were created. The heaviest naturally occurring elements did not form until the explosion of massive stars in supernovas. Look at the periodic table and divide it up by these masses. Is there any trend or information about these elements that you can determine from this information?

3.123 Sir James Chadwick discovered the neutron. The Web site for the Nobel Prize committee contains his acceptance speech for the Nobel Prize he won in physics in 1935. Read the speech and draw a diagram that summarizes the experiment.

4 The Mole and Stoichiometry

Chapter Outline

Billions of hamburgers are served each year in restaurants and fast-food establishments. Typically the hamburger will have one beef patty, one sliced bun, several pickles, and a tablespoon of sauce. At the start, restaurants order their food supplies by the pound. In preparing an order for 1,000 hamburgers, the purchasing agent needs to know that one hamburger requires 1/4 pound of beef, there are about 200 pickle slices in a pound, a tablespoon of ketchup weighs 0.25 ounces, and each hamburger bun weighs 1.5 ounces. From this information the purchasing agent can order 250 pounds of ground beef, 5 pounds of pickles, 16 pounds of ketchup, and 95 pounds of hamburger buns. Instead of counting out individual items, the agent converts them to the mass that is required. This chapter illustrates that chemists count their atoms and molecules the same way, by weighing them. Figure 4.1 illustrates the difference between making a single hamburger and 1,000 hamburgers. © Michael Sofronski/The Image Works

[This Chapter in Context

In this chapter we use the tools from Chapters 2 and 3 to learn the fundamentals of chemical calculations called **stoichiometry** (stoy-kee-AH-meh-tree), which loosely translates as "the measure of the elements." You will find that these calculations are very important for success in the chemistry laboratory. You will also find this chapter to be important for future courses in organic chemistry, biochemistry, and almost any other advanced laboratory course in the sciences.

Stoichiometry involves converting chemical formulas and equations that represent individual atoms, molecules, and formula units to the laboratory scale that uses milligrams, grams, and even kilograms of these substances. To do this we introduce the concept of the *mole*. The mole allows the chemist to scale up from the atomic/molecular level to the laboratory scale much as the purchasing agent in Figure 4.1 scales up the amount of ingredients from a single hamburger to a mass-production scale. Our stoichiometric calculations are usually conversions from one set of units to another using dimensional analysis. To be successful using dimensional analysis calculations we need two things: a knowledge of the equalities that can be made into conversion factors and a logical sequence of steps to guide us from the starting set of units to the desired units. Figure 4.6, at the end of this chapter, is a flowchart that organizes the sequence of conversion steps and the conversion factors used in stoichiometric calculations in this chapter. In the following chapters, as we learn new concepts, they will be added to this flowchart to illustrate how many of our chemical ideas are interrelated.

4.1 | The Molecular Scale versus the Laboratory Scale

We can tell from the fundamental measurements of the mass of the proton, neutron, and electron in Chapter 3 that even the largest of the atoms must have extremely small masses and correspondingly small sizes. Consequently, any sample of matter that is observable by the naked eye must have very large numbers of atoms or molecules. The methods of calculation developed in Chapter 2, along with the mole concept, allow us to count by weighing and then use that information to solve some very interesting problems.

Counting by weighing is familiar to everyone even if we are not aware of it. Our introductory example of mass-produced hamburgers illustrated one use of counting by weighing.

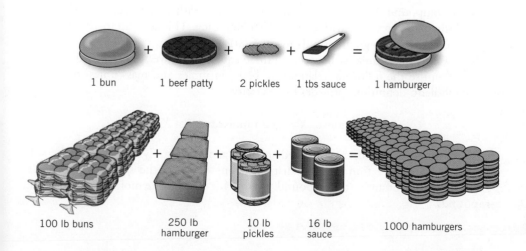

| 1 bun | 1 beef patty | 2 pickles | 1 tbs sauce | 1 hamburger |

| 100 lb buns | 250 lb hamburger | 10 lb pickles | 16 lb sauce | 1000 hamburgers |

Figure 4.1 | **Hamburgers on the small and large scale.** Making a single hamburger requires one bun, one hamburger patty, two pickles, and a tablespoon of sauce. To make a thousand hamburgers we need 100 lb of rolls, 250 lb of hamburger meat, 10 lb of pickles, and 16 lb of sauce.

A pound of chocolate chips counts out the needed number of chocolate chips for your cookies. A quarter pound of rice counts out the correct number of rice grains to accompany a family meal. Weighing a bag of dimes, knowing that each dime weighs 2.27 grams, will allow you to calculate the number of coins. Similarly, the mass of a chemical substance can be used to determine the number of atoms or molecules in the sample. This last conversion is possible because of the mole concept.

Defining the Mole

In Chapter 2 we noted that the mole is the SI unit for the amount of substance. The amount of substance does not refer to the mass or volume of your sample but it does refer to the number of atoms, molecules, or formula units, etc. in your sample. Exactly **one mole (mol) is defined as a number equal to the number of atoms in exactly 12 grams of ^{12}C atoms.** Based on this definition and the fact that the average atomic masses in the periodic table are relative values, we can deduce that we will have a mole of atoms of any element if we weigh an amount equal to the atomic mass in gram units (this is often called the gram atomic mass).

Figure 4.2 | **Moles of elements.** Each sample of these elements—iron, mercury, copper, and sulfur—contains the same number of atoms. *(Michael Watson)*

Atomic mass

■ Mole is a Latin word with several meanings, including a shapeless mass, a large number, or trouble or difficulty.

■ Many chemists still use terms like molecular weight and atomic weight for molecular mass and atomic mass.

$$1 \text{ mole of element } X = \text{gram atomic mass of } X$$

For example, the atomic mass of sulfur is 32.06 u and one mole of sulfur will weigh 32.06 g and it will have as many atoms as exactly 12 g of carbon-12. Figure 4.2 is a photo showing one mole of some common elements—iron, mercury, copper, and sulfur.

The Mole Concept Applied to Compounds

Molecules and ionic compounds discussed in Chapter 3 have definite formulas. For molecular compounds and elements, adding the atomic masses of all atoms in the formula results in the **molecular mass** (sometimes called the **molecular weight**). The gram molecular mass of a molecular substance (the mass in grams equal to the molecular mass) is also equal to one mole of those molecules.

Molecular mass or formula mass

$$1 \text{ mole of molecule } X = \text{gram molecular mass of } X$$

For example, the molecular mass of water is 18.02 u, the sum of the atomic masses of two H atoms and one O atom. Similarly, the gram **formula mass** of an ionic compound is the sum of the atomic masses of all the atoms in the formula of an ionic compound expressed with units of grams.

$$1 \text{ mole of ionic compound } X = \text{gram formula mass of } X$$

The ionic compound Al_2O_3 has two aluminum atoms with an atomic mass of 26.98 u each and three oxygen atoms with a mass of 16.00 u each. This adds up to 101.96 u, and one mole of Al_2O_3 has a gram formula mass of 101.96 g.

There is a distinct similarity between all three equations above. To simplify discussions we will often use the following relationship between moles and mass unless one of the other, equivalent, definitions provides more clarity.

Molar mass

$$1 \text{ mole of } X = \text{gram molar mass of } X$$

The gram molar mass (often shortened to **molar mass**) is simply the mass of the substance under consideration without distinguishing whether the substance is an element, a molecule, or an ionic compound. Figure 4.3 depicts one mole of four different compounds.

Figure 4.3 | **Moles of compounds.** One mole of four different compounds: water, sodium chloride, copper sulfate pentahydrate, and sodium chromate. Each sample contains the same number of formula units or molecules. *(Michael Watson)*

Converting between Mass and Moles

At this point we recognize the above relationships or equalities as the necessary information for conversion problems similar to those in Chapter 2. Now, however, the problems will be couched in chemical terms.

Example 4.1
Converting from Grams to Moles

Titanium(IV) oxide is one of the best sunscreens because it completely blocks ultraviolet radiation from reaching the skin. In an experiment to prepare TiO_2, we start with a 23.5 g sample of titanium. How many moles of Ti do we have?

■ **Analysis:** We see that the problem starts with a certain mass of titanium and asks us to convert it to moles. This uses the tool we just described that equates moles and grams of an element.

■ **Assembling the Tools:** We have a tool for converting the mass into moles that states 1 mol X is equal to the atomic mass of X with gram units. Now we make it specific for titanium by replacing X with the symbol for titanium and entering the atomic mass of Ti to get

$$1 \text{ mol Ti} = 47.867 \text{ g Ti}$$

(When we work problems that include tabulated data, such as the atomic mass of Ti, we will always *keep at least one more significant figure* than the given information.)

■ **Solution:** Start by setting up the problem in the form of an equation showing the number and its units that we start with and the units we want when we're finished.

$$\underset{\text{start}}{23.5 \text{ g Ti}} = \underset{\text{end}}{? \text{ mol Ti}}$$

Now use the equality between mass and moles to set up the ratio that will cancel the grams of titanium as shown below

$$23.5 \text{ g Ti} \times \left(\frac{1 \text{ mol Ti}}{47.867 \text{ g Ti}} \right) = 0.491 \text{ mol Ti}$$

■ Solving stoichiometry problems is much like giving directions from your house to your college. You need both the starting and ending points. Stating the problem as an equation gives you these reference points, and the conversion factors get us from the start to the end.

■ **Is the Answer Reasonable?** First, be sure that the units cancel properly. Second, round all numbers to one or two significant figures and calculate an estimated answer. One way to round the numbers gives us 25/50, and that is equal to 1/2. Our answer is not very different (very different would be a factor of 10 or more) from 1/2, so our answer is reasonable.

Example 4.2
Converting from Moles to Grams

We need 0.254 moles of $FeCl_3$ for a certain experiment. How many grams do we need to weigh?

■ **Analysis:** As in the last problem the conversion is between moles and mass, but now we also need an additional step to calculate the molar mass of $FeCl_3$.

■ **Assembling the Tools:** We need the tool for calculating the molar mass of $FeCl_3$. That is the sum of masses of one mole of iron atoms and three moles of chlorine atoms.

$$\text{Molar mass } FeCl_3 = 55.845 \text{ g/mol} + (3 \times 35.453 \text{ g/mol}) = 162.204 \text{ g/mol}$$

Now the tool that represents the equality between mass and moles can be written as

$$1 \text{ mol } FeCl_3 = 162.204 \text{ g } FeCl_3$$

■ **Solution:** The problem is set up by translating the question into equation form:

$$0.254 \text{ mol } FeCl_3 = ? \text{ g } FeCl_3$$

Then we construct the conversion factor from the equality between mass and moles to perform the conversion:

$$0.254 \text{ mol } FeCl_3 \times \left(\frac{162.204 \text{ g } FeCl_3}{1 \text{ mol } FeCl_3} \right) = 41.2 \text{ g } FeCl_3$$

■ **Is the Answer Reasonable?** First, we verify that the units cancel properly. Next we do an approximate calculation. If we round 0.254 to 0.25 and 162.204 to 160, the arithmetic becomes $0.25 \times 160 = 40$, which gives a result that is very close to the calculated value. Alternately we can round to one significant figure, which gives $0.3 \times 200 = 60$ and still conclude that the answer is reasonable. Remember that this is just an estimate, but it tells us that our more precise answer, 41.2 g $FeCl_3$, is in the right ballpark.

Practice Exercises

4.1 | How many moles of aluminum are there in a 3.47 gram sheet of aluminum foil used to wrap your sandwich for lunch today? (*Hint:* Recall the tool that relates the mass of an element to moles of that element.)

4.2 | Your laboratory balance can weigh samples to three decimal places. If the uncertainty in your weighing is ±0.002 g, what is the uncertainty expressed in terms of moles, if the sample being weighed is pure potassium sulfate?

Avogadro's Number

■ Avogadro's number was named for Amedeo Avogadro (1776–1876), an Italian chemist who was one of the pioneers of stoichiometry.

Avogadro's number

The SI definition of the mole refers to a number equal to the number of atoms in exactly 12 g of ^{12}C. Just what is that number? After much experimentation the scientific community agrees that the value, to four significant figures, is 6.022×10^{23}. This value has been named **Avogadro's number**. Now we can write a very important relationship between the atomic scale and the laboratory scale as

$$1 \text{ mole of } X = 6.022 \times 10^{23} \text{ units of } X$$

The units of our chemicals can be atoms, molecules, formula units, and so on. This means that one mole of xenon atoms is the same as 6.022×10^{23} atoms of Xe. Similarly, 6.022×10^{23} molecules of NO_2 represents one mole of nitrogen dioxide molecules.

Using Avogadro's Number

The relationships developed above allow us to connect the laboratory scale with the atomic scale using our standard dimensional analysis calculations as shown in the next two examples.

> ■ Avogadro's number is the link between the moles of a substance and its elementary units. If a problem is on the laboratory scale (atoms or molecules are not mentioned) then Avogadro's number is not needed in the calculation.

Example 4.3
Converting from the Laboratory Scale to the Atomic Scale

Tungsten wire is the filament inside most incandescent lightbulbs. In a typical lightbulb, the tungsten filament weighs 0.635 grams. How many atoms of tungsten are there in such a lightbulb filament?

■ **Analysis:** Let's first translate the question into an equation:

$$0.635 \text{ g tungsten} = ? \text{ atoms tungsten}$$

Here we do not have any tool that directly relates grams of tungsten to atoms of tungsten. However, we can start with the grams of tungsten and make the following *sequence of conversions.*

$$\text{grams tungsten} \longrightarrow \text{moles tungsten} \longrightarrow \text{atoms tungsten}$$

■ **Assembling the Tools:** The first tool we need is the mass-to-moles tool,

$$183.84 \text{ g W} = 1 \text{ mol W}$$

which lets us construct conversion factors between grams of tungsten and moles of tungsten. Next we need the tool for Avogadro's number that allows us to construct conversion factors between the moles of tungsten atoms and the number of tungsten atoms,

$$1 \text{ mol W} = 6.022 \times 10^{23} \text{ atoms W}$$

■ **Solution:** Having expressed the question as an equation, we can use it along with the two tools for the conversions to construct the two conversion factors. The first is

$$\frac{1 \text{ mol W}}{183.84 \text{ g W}}$$

and the second conversion factor is

$$\frac{6.022 \times 10^{23} \text{ atoms W}}{1 \text{ mol W}}$$

We multiply the original 0.635 grams of tungsten by the conversion factors to get

$$0.635 \text{ g W} \times \left(\frac{1 \text{ mol W}}{183.84 \text{ g W}} \right) \times \left(\frac{6.022 \times 10^{23} \text{ atoms W}}{1 \text{ mol W}} \right)$$

$$= 2.08 \times 10^{21} \text{ atoms W}$$

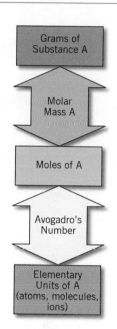

General sequence of calculations to convert between mass and elementary units of a substance. Arrows indicate which tools apply to each conversion.

■ **Is the Answer Reasonable?** The most important check in this type of question involves the magnitude of the numbers. We know that even the smallest measurable sample of a chemical must contain a very large number of atoms. Our answer is a very large number, and therefore the answer seems reasonable.

> ■ Review Table 2.4 to see that positive exponents indicate large numbers and negative exponents indicate small numbers.

Example 4.4
Calculating the Mass of a Molecule

Carbon tetrachloride was used as a dry-cleaning fluid until it was found to be carcinogenic. What is the average mass of one molecule of carbon tetrachloride?[1]

■ **Analysis:** First, we can set up the question as an equation:

$$1 \text{ molecule carbon tetrachloride} = ? \text{ g carbon tetrachloride}$$

We can see that this problem has many steps that need to be combined to obtain the complete solution. First, we need to identify the chemical formula from its name; then we need to use that formula to calculate the molar mass of the compound. Finally, we need to construct the appropriate conversion factors to first convert one molecule to moles and then convert those moles into the mass of the carbon tetrachloride molecule.

■ **Assembling the Tools:** We first use the nomenclature tools in Chapter 3 to determine that the formula for carbon tetrachloride is CCl_4. Next, we need the tool that uses Avogadro's number,

$$6.022 \times 10^{23} \text{ molecules } CCl_4 = 1 \text{ mol } CCl_4$$

After that we need the tool to calculate the molar mass of CCl_4 as the sum of the masses of one mole of carbon and four moles of chlorine atoms, 153.823 g/mol. The molar mass is used as our tool to express the equality

$$1 \text{ mol } CCl_4 = 153.823 \text{ g } CCl_4$$

■ **Solution:** We now follow the sequence of calculations in our analysis, and will do the calculation in two steps. First, we construct a conversion factor using Avogadro's number and use it to calculate the moles of CCl_4.

$$1 \text{ molecule } CCl_4 \times \left(\frac{1 \text{ mol } CCl_4}{6.022 \times 10^{23} \text{ molecules } CCl_4} \right) = 1.661 \times 10^{-24} \text{ mol } CCl_4$$

A second conversion factor is made from the molar mass equality to convert mol CCl_4 to g CCl_4.

$$1.661 \times 10^{-24} \text{ mol } CCl_4 \times \left(\frac{153.823 \text{ g } CCl_4}{1 \text{ mol } CCl_4} \right) = 2.555 \times 10^{-22} \text{ g } CCl_4$$

One molecule can be considered to be an exact number. The result is that the number of significant figures to keep in the answer depends upon the number of significant figures taken from the tabulated data. Four significant figures were used for Avogadro's number and four significant figures were kept in the answer.

■ **Is the Answer Reasonable?** We expect that a single molecule, even a very large molecule, would have a very small mass. Since our answer is very small, it seems reasonable.

Practice Exercises

4.3 | Most chemistry laboratories have balances that can weigh to the nearest milligram. Would it be possible to weigh 5.64×10^{18} molecules of octadecane, $C_{18}H_{38}$, on such a balance?

4.4 | If the uncertainty in weighing a sample in the lab is ±0.002 grams, what is this uncertainty expressed in terms of molecules of sucrose, $C_{12}H_{22}O_{11}$?

---

[1]Since atomic masses given in the periodic table are weighted averages of naturally occurring isotopes, we cannot determine the exact mass of a molecule unless we know the isotope of each atom. We can, however, calculate an average mass as requested in this question.

4.2 | Chemical Formulas and Stoichiometry

Mole-to-Mole Conversion Factors

The mole ratio concept that we develop here is a very powerful and important chemical tool. It allows the chemist to start with the amount of one substance and then find the chemically equivalent amount of another substance without doing the actual experiments. The relationships implied by the chemical formula allow this to happen.

Consider the chemical formula for water, H_2O:

- One molecule of water contains 2 H atoms and 1 O atom.
- Two molecules of water contain 4 H atoms and 2 O atoms.
- A dozen molecules of water contain 2 dozen H atoms and 1 dozen O atoms.
- A mole of molecules of water contains 2 moles of H atoms and 1 mole of O atoms.

Whether we're dealing with atoms, dozens of atoms, or moles of atoms, the chemical formula tells us that the ratio of H atoms to O atoms is always 2 to 1. In addition, we can write the following equivalencies concerning water molecules and moles of water molecules:

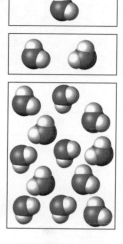

One water molecule	**One mole of water molecules**
1 molecule H_2O ⇔ 2 atoms H	1 mol H_2O ⇔ 2 mol H
1 molecule H_2O ⇔ 1 atom O	1 mol H_2O ⇔ 1 mol O
1 atom O ⇔ 2 atoms H	1 mol O ⇔ 2 mol H

Recall that the symbol ⇔ means "is chemically equivalent to" and that it is treated mathematically as an equal sign (see page 49 in Chapter 2).

> Within chemical compounds, moles of atoms always combine in the same ratio as the individual atoms themselves.

TOOLS

Mole ratios

This tool allows us to use the atom-to-atom ratios in a chemical formula to easily prepare mole-to-mole conversion factors for calculations on the laboratory scale. For example, in the formula P_4O_{10}, the subscripts mean that there are 4 atoms of P for every 10 atoms of O in the molecule. On the laboratory scale, this also means that there are 4 moles of P for every 10 moles of O in 1 mole of this compound. We can relate P and O within the compound using the following conversion factors.

$$4 \text{ mol P} \Leftrightarrow 10 \text{ mol O} \qquad \text{from which we write} \qquad \frac{4 \text{ mol P}}{10 \text{ mol O}} \quad \text{or} \quad \frac{10 \text{ mol O}}{4 \text{ mol P}}$$

The formula P_4O_{10} also implies other equivalencies, each with its two associated conversion factors.

$$1 \text{ mol } P_4O_{10} \Leftrightarrow 4 \text{ mol P} \quad \text{or} \quad \frac{1 \text{ mol } P_4O_{10}}{4 \text{ mol P}} \quad \text{and} \quad \frac{4 \text{ mol P}}{1 \text{ mol } P_4O_{10}}$$

$$1 \text{ mol } P_4O_{10} \Leftrightarrow 10 \text{ mol O} \quad \text{or} \quad \frac{1 \text{ mol } P_4O_{10}}{10 \text{ mol O}} \quad \text{and} \quad \frac{10 \text{ mol O}}{1 \text{ mol } P_4O_{10}}$$

The following example illustrates how we use chemical formulas to develop mole ratios for calculations.

Example 4.5
Calculating the Amount of a Compound by Analyzing One Element

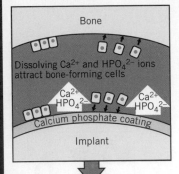

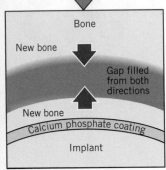

Some surfaces on bone implants are coated with calcium phosphate to permit the bone to actually bond to the surface.

Calcium phosphate is widely found in nature in the form of natural minerals. It is also found in bones and some kidney stones. In one case a sample is found to contain 0.864 moles of phosphorus. How many moles of $Ca_3(PO_4)_2$ are in that sample?

■ **Analysis:** Let's state the question in equation form first:

$$0.864 \text{ mol P} = ? \text{ mol } Ca_3(PO_4)_2$$

Since we start with moles of one substance and end with moles of a second, this is the appropriate place to use the mole ratio conversion factor.

■ **Assembling the Tools:** All we need is the mole ratio tool that relates P to the chemical formula $Ca_3(PO_4)_2$. We write it as

$$2 \text{ mol P} \Leftrightarrow 1 \text{ mol } Ca_3(PO_4)_2$$

■ **Solution:** Starting with the equation we expressed above, our tool is rearranged into a conversion factor so that the mol P cancels and we are left with the mol $Ca_3(PO_4)_2$. Applying that ratio we get

$$0.864 \text{ mol P} \times \left(\frac{1 \text{ mol } Ca_3(PO_4)_2}{2 \text{ mol P}} \right) = 0.432 \text{ mol } Ca_3(PO_4)_2$$

■ **Is the Answer Reasonable?** For a quick check, you can round 0.864 to 1 and divide by 2 to get 0.5. There is little difference between our estimate 0.5 and the calculated answer 0.432, and we conclude our answer is reasonable.

Practice Exercises

4.5 | Aluminum sulfate is analyzed, and the sample contains 0.0774 moles of sulfate ions. How many moles of aluminum are in the sample? (*Hint:* Recall the tool for writing the correct formula for aluminum sulfate.)

4.6 | How many moles of nitrogen atoms are combined with 8.60 mol of oxygen atoms in dinitrogen pentoxide?

Mass-to-Mass Calculations

One common use of stoichiometry in the lab occurs when we need to determine the mass of one reactant, B, needed to combine with a given mass of second reactant, A, to make a compound. These calculations are summarized by the following sequence of steps to convert the given mass of compound A to the mass of compound B.

Mass-to-mass conversions using formulas

$$\text{mass of A} \longrightarrow \text{moles of A} \longrightarrow \text{moles of B} \longrightarrow \text{mass of B}$$

In the following example we see how this is applied.

Example 4.6
Calculating the Amount of One Element from the Amount of Another in a Compound

Chlorophyll, the green pigment in leaves, has the formula $C_{55}H_{72}MgN_4O_5$. If 0.0011 g of Mg is available to a plant for chlorophyll synthesis, how many grams of carbon will be required to completely use up the magnesium?

■ **Analysis:** Let's begin, as usual, by restating the problem as follows.

$$0.0011 \text{ g Mg} \Leftrightarrow ? \text{ g C}$$

The tool on the preceding page shows the sequence of steps we use to relate the mass of one substance to the mass of another. Our first step is to convert the mass of Mg to moles of Mg. Once we know the moles of Mg, we can convert that to the moles of C using the formula of the compound. Finally, we can calculate the mass of the second substance, C, from the moles using the molar mass again. The sequence of calculations can be summarized as

$$0.0011 \text{ g Mg} \longrightarrow \text{mol Mg} \longrightarrow \text{mol C} \longrightarrow \text{g C}$$

■ **Assembling the Tools:** From the sequence of steps above we see that we will need the mass-to-moles tool to convert the mass of Mg to moles of Mg. The tool states that

$$24.3050 \text{ g Mg} = 1 \text{ mol Mg}$$

Next we need a mole ratio to convert moles of Mg to moles of C. This is

$$1 \text{ mol Mg} \Leftrightarrow 55 \text{ mol C} \quad \text{(these are exact numbers)}$$

Finally, the mass-to-moles tool for carbon is

$$1 \text{ mol C} = 12.011 \text{ g C}$$

Our complete sequence for the problem, with numbers rounded to three significant figures, is

$$\boxed{1 \text{ mol Mg} \Leftrightarrow 24.3 \text{ g Mg}} \quad \boxed{1 \text{ mol Mg} \Leftrightarrow 55 \text{ mol C}} \quad \boxed{1 \text{ mol C} \Leftrightarrow 12.0 \text{ g C}}$$
$$0.0011 \text{ g Mg} \longrightarrow \text{mol Mg} \longrightarrow \text{mol C} \longrightarrow \text{g C}$$

The general sequence for dealing with problems like the one we're solving here is illustrated below. The arrows indicate which tools are used for each conversion.

■ In a problem that asks to convert the amount (grams, moles, or atomic scale units) of one substance into the amount of a different substance, the most important conversion factor is the mole-to-mole relationship between the two substances.

■ **Solution:** We now set up the solution by forming conversion factors so the units cancel.

$$0.0011 \ \text{g Mg} \times \left(\frac{1 \ \text{mol Mg}}{24.3 \ \text{g Mg}} \right) \times \left(\frac{55 \ \text{mol C}}{1 \ \text{mol Mg}} \right) \times \left(\frac{12.0 \ \text{g C}}{1 \ \text{mol C}} \right) = 0.030 \ \text{g C}$$

A plant cell must supply 0.030 g C for every 0.0011 g Mg to completely use up the magnesium in the synthesis of chlorophyll.

■ **Is the Answer Reasonable?** After checking that our units cancel properly, a quick estimate can be made by rounding all numbers to one significant figure. One way to do this results in the following expression (without units):

$$\frac{0.001 \times 1 \times 50 \times 10}{20 \times 1 \times 1} = \frac{0.5}{20} = \frac{0.05}{2} = 0.025$$

This value is close to the answer we got and gives us confidence that it is reasonable. (Note that if we rounded the 55 up to 60 our estimate would have been 0.030, which would still confirm our conclusion.)

Practice Exercises

4.7 | How many grams of iron are needed to combine with 25.6 g of O to make Fe_2O_3? (*Hint:* Recall the mole ratios that the formula represents.)

4.8 | An important iron ore called hematite contains iron(III) oxide. How many grams of iron are in a 15.0 g sample of hematite?

4.9 | Titanium(IV) oxide is the main pigment in white and other light-colored paints. How many grams of titanium will combine with 12.0 g of oxygen to form titanium(IV) oxide?

Percentage Composition

The usual form for describing the relative masses of the elements in a compound is a list of *percentages by mass* called the compound's **percentage composition.** The **percentage by mass** of an element is the number of grams of the element present in 100 g of the compound. In general, a percentage by mass is found by using the following equation.

Percentage composition

$$\text{Percentage by mass of element} = \frac{\text{mass of element}}{\text{mass of whole sample}} \times 100\% \qquad (4.1)$$

We can determine the percentage composition based on chemical analysis of a substance as shown in the next Example.

Example 4.7
Calculating a Percentage Composition from Chemical Analysis

A sample of a liquid with a mass of 8.657 g was decomposed into its elements and gave 5.217 g of carbon, 0.9620 g of hydrogen, and 2.478 g of oxygen. What is the percentage composition of this compound?

■ **Analysis:** Solving problems often requires that we know the meaning of key terms, in this case *percentage composition*. We have just discussed this term and now we can apply it in answering the question.

■ **Assembling the Tools:** The tool we need is expressed by Equation 4.1. We are given the mass of each element in the sample, and the sum of those masses gives us the mass of the whole sample. The total mass is 8.657 g and the individual masses are given.

■ **Solution:** Using Equation 4.1 for each of the elements in sequence gives three equations that we use to compute the needed percentages:

$$\text{For C:} \quad \frac{5.217 \text{ g}}{8.657 \text{ g}} \times 100\% = 60.26\% \text{ C}$$

$$\text{For H:} \quad \frac{0.9620 \text{ g}}{8.657 \text{ g}} \times 100\% = 11.11\% \text{ H}$$

$$\text{For O:} \quad \frac{2.478 \text{ g}}{8.657 \text{ g}} \times 100\% = 28.62\% \text{ O}$$

Sum of percentages: 99.99%

One of the useful things about a percentage composition is that it tells us the mass of each of the elements in 100 g of the substance. For example, the results in this problem tell us that in 100.00 g of the liquid there are 60.26 g of carbon, 11.11 g of hydrogen, and 28.62 g of oxygen.

■ **Is the Answer Reasonable?** The "check" is that the percentages must add up to 100%, allowing for small differences caused by rounding. We can also check the individual results by rounding all the numbers to one significant figure to estimate the results. For example, the percentage C would be estimated as $5/9 \times 100$, which is a little over 50% and agrees with our answer.

Practice Exercises

4.10 | An organic compound weighing 0.6672 g is decomposed, giving 0.3481 g carbon and 0.0870 g hydrogen. What are the percentages of hydrogen and carbon in this compound? Is it likely that this compound contains another element? (*Hint:* Recall the tool concerning the conservation of mass.)

4.11 | When 0.5462 g of a compound was decomposed, 0.2012 g of nitrogen and 0.3450 g of oxygen were isolated. What is the percentage composition of this compound? Explain how you can determine if there are any other elements present in this compound.

We can also determine the percentage composition of a compound from its chemical formula. If we consider one mole of a substance, its molar mass will be the mass of the whole sample in Equation 4.1. The numerator in Equation 4.1 will be the mass associated with one of the elements in the formula. In the next section we see how this calculated percentage can be used as a physical property that is useful for identifying a substance.

Percentage Composition and Chemical Identity

We can use Equation 4.1 to determine the percentage composition of any chemical compound when we know its formula. Nitrogen and oxygen, for example, form all of the following compounds: N_2O, NO, NO_2, N_2O_3, N_2O_4, and N_2O_5. To identify an unknown sample of a compound of nitrogen and oxygen, one might compare the percentage composition found by experiment with the calculated, or theoretical, percentages for each possible formula. Which formula, for example, fits the percentage composition calculated in Practice Exercise 4.11? A strategy for matching formulas with mass percentages is outlined in the following example.

Example 4.8
Identifying a Compound Based on Percentage Composition

Do the mass percentages of 25.94% N and 74.06% O match the formula N_2O_5?

■**Analysis:** To calculate the mass percentages we need to use Equation 4.1. Looking at the equation, we will need the masses of N, O, and N_2O_5 in a sample of the compound. *If we choose 1 mol of the given compound to be this sample, it will be easy to determine the mass of the oxygen, nitrogen, and dinitrogen pentoxide that make up one mole of N_2O_5.*

■**Assembling the Tools:** We need Equation 4.1 to calculate the percent composition. We will need the tool for calculating the molar mass of N_2O_5 and the mole ratios we can obtain from that formula. We need to perform a mass-to-moles conversion for nitrogen and oxygen atoms.

The required relationships are:

$$2 \text{ mol N} \Leftrightarrow 1 \text{ mol } N_2O_5$$
$$5 \text{ mol O} \Leftrightarrow 1 \text{ mol } N_2O_5$$
$$1 \text{ mol N} = 14.01 \text{ g N}$$
$$1 \text{ mol O} = 16.00 \text{ g O}$$

■**Solution:** We know that 1 mol of N_2O_5 must contain 2 mol N and 5 mol O from the mol ratio tool. The corresponding number of grams of N and O are found as follows.

$$1 \text{ mol } N_2O_5 \times \frac{2 \text{ mol N}}{1 \text{ mol } N_2O_5} \times \frac{14.01 \text{ g N}}{1 \text{ mol N}} = 28.02 \text{ g N}$$

$$1 \text{ mol } N_2O_5 \times \frac{5 \text{ mol O}}{1 \text{ mol } N_2O_5} \times \frac{16.00 \text{ g O}}{1 \text{ mol O}} = 80.00 \text{ g O}$$

$$1 \text{ mol } N_2O_5 = 108.02 \text{ g } N_2O_5$$

Now we can calculate the percentages.

For % N: $\quad \dfrac{28.02 \text{ g}}{108.02 \text{ g}} \times 100\% = 25.94\% \text{ N in } N_2O_5$

For % O: $\quad \dfrac{80.00 \text{ g}}{108.02 \text{ g}} \times 100\% = 74.06\% \text{ O in } N_2O_5$

Thus the experimental values do match the theoretical percentages for the formula N_2O_5.

■**Is the Answer Reasonable?** The easiest check for this problem is to be sure that all percentages add up to 100%. They do add to 100% and so the calculated result is reasonable.

Practice Exercises

4.12 | Calculate the theoretical percentage composition of N_2O_4. (*Hint:* Recall the definition of percentage composition.)

4.13 | Calculate the theoretical percentage compositions for N_2O, NO, NO_2, N_2O_3, N_2O_4, and N_2O_5. Which of these compounds produced the data in Practice Exercise 4.11?

In working Practice Exercise 4.13, you may have noticed that the percentage composition of NO_2 was the same as that of N_2O_4. This is because both compounds have the same mole ratio. All compounds with the same mole ratios will have the same percentage compositions.

4.3 | Determining Empirical and Molecular Formulas

One of the major activities of chemists is to synthesize compounds that have never existed before. In pharmaceutical research, chemists often synthesize entirely new compounds, or isolate new compounds from plant and animal tissues. They must then determine the formula and structure of the new compound. Modern chemists use mass spectroscopy and other moderrn instruments for structure analysis. However, they still rely upon elemental analysis, where the compound is decomposed chemically to find the masses of elements within a given amount of compound to determine *empirical formulas*. Let's see how such experimental mass measurements, expressed in a variety of ways, can be used to determine these formulas.

A form of the element phosphorus known as "white phosphorus" is *pyrophoric*—that is, it spontaneously burns when exposed to air. The compound that forms when phosphorus burns in oxygen consists of molecules with the formula P_4O_{10}. When a formula gives the composition of one *molecule*, it is called a **molecular formula**. Notice, however, that both the subscripts 4 and 10 are divisible by 2, so the *smallest* numbers that tell us the *ratio* of P to O are 2 and 5. We can write a simpler (but less informative) formula that expresses this ratio, P_2O_5. This is called the **empirical formula** because it can also be obtained from an experimental analysis of the compound.

> The empirical formula expresses the simplest ratio of the atoms of each element in a compound.

TOOLS

Empirical formulas

We already know that the ratio of atoms in a compound is the same as a ratio of the moles of those atoms in the compound. We will determine the simplest ratio of moles from experimental data. The experimental data we need is any information that allows us to determine the moles of each element in a sample of the compound. We will investigate three types of data that can be used to determine empirical formulas. They are (a) masses of the elements, (b) percentage composition, and (c) combustion data. In all three, the goal is to obtain the simplest ratio of moles of each element in the formula.

Empirical Formulas from Mass Data

If we determine the mass of each element in a pure sample of a compound we can calculate the moles of each element. From that we can find the simplest ratio of moles, which by definition is the empirical formula. In many instances, we can analyze a sample for all but one element and then use the law of conservation of mass to calculate the missing mass, as shown in the next example.

1.4 g of Cl

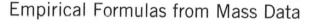

Example 4.9
Calculating an Empirical Formula from Mass Data

A 2.57 g sample of a compound composed of only tin and chlorine was found to contain 1.17 g of tin. What is the compound's empirical formula?

■ **Analysis:** The subscripts in an empirical formula can be interpreted as the relative number of moles of the elements in a compound. If we can find the *mole* ratio of Sn to Cl, we will have the empirical formula. The first step, therefore, is to convert the numbers of grams of Sn and Cl to the numbers of moles of Sn and Cl. Then we convert these numbers into their simplest positive *whole-number*, or *integer*, ratio.

■ The word integer is synonymous with whole number. Integers are never fractions or decimal numbers. Exact numbers are often integers.

The problem did not give the mass of chlorine in the 2.57 g sample. However, we can calculate it using the tool that expresses the law of conservation of mass.

■ **Assembling the Tools:** The law of conservation of mass, one of our tools from Chapter 1, requires that the mass of compound equal the sum of the mass of Cl and the mass of Sn.

$$2.57 \text{ g compound} = \text{mass of Cl} + 1.17 \text{ g Sn}$$

The molar mass is the tool that allows us to calculate the moles of each element.

$$118.7 \text{ g Sn} = 1 \text{ mol Sn}$$
$$35.45 \text{ g Cl} = 1 \text{ mol Cl}$$

■ **Solution:** First, we find the mass of Cl in 2.57 g of compound:

$$\text{Mass of Cl} = 2.57 \text{ g compound} - 1.17 \text{ g Sn} = 1.40 \text{ g Cl}$$

Now we use the molar mass equalities to create ratios to convert the mass data for tin and chlorine into moles.

$$1.17 \text{ g Sn} \times \frac{1 \text{ mol Sn}}{118.7 \text{ g Sn}} = 0.00986 \text{ mol Sn}$$

$$1.40 \text{ g Cl} \times \frac{1 \text{ mol Cl}}{35.45 \text{ g Cl}} = 0.0395 \text{ mol Cl}$$

We could now write a formula: $Sn_{0.00986}Cl_{0.0395}$, which does express the mole ratio, but subscripts also represent atom ratios and need to be integers. To convert the decimal subscripts to integers, we begin by dividing each by the smallest number in the set. *This is always the way to begin the search for whole-number subscripts; pick the smallest number of the set as the divisor.* It's guaranteed to make at least one subscript a whole number—namely, 1. Here, we divide both numbers by 0.00986.

$$Sn_{\frac{0.00986}{0.00986}}Cl_{\frac{0.0395}{0.00986}} = Sn_{1.00}Cl_{4.01}$$

In most cases if, after this step, a calculated subscript differs from a whole number by less than 0.1, we can safely round to the nearest whole number. We may round 4.01 to 4, so the empirical formula is $SnCl_4$.

■ **Is the Answer Reasonable?** In addition to the fact that whole-number subscripts were easily found, you should also recall from Chapter 3 that tin forms either the Sn^{2+} or the Sn^{4+} ion and that chlorine forms only the Cl^- ion. Therefore either $SnCl_2$ or $SnCl_4$ is a reasonable compound, and one of them was our answer.

Practice Exercises

4.14 | A 1.525 g sample of a compound between nitrogen and oxygen contains 0.712 g of nitrogen. Calculate its empirical formula. (*Hint:* How many grams of oxygen are there?)

4.15 | A 1.525 g sample of a compound between sulfur and oxygen was prepared by burning 0.7625 g of sulfur in air and collecting the product. What is the empirical formula for the compound formed?

Sometimes our strategy of using the lowest common divisor does not give whole numbers. If a decimal value corresponding to a rational fraction results, we can obtain integers by multiplying by the denominator of the rational fraction. Let's see how to handle such a situation.

Example 4.10
Calculating an Empirical Formula from Mass Composition

One of the compounds of iron and oxygen, "black iron oxide," occurs naturally in the mineral magnetite. When a 2.448 g sample was analyzed it was found to have 1.771 g of Fe and 0.677 g of O. Calculate the empirical formula of this compound.

■**Analysis:** We are given the masses of both iron and oxygen and we need to convert these masses into moles using their atomic masses. Finally, we need to obtain the simplest whole-number ratio of the moles of the elements to use as subscripts in the empirical formula.

■**Assembling the Tools:** The moles of each element are obtained from a mass-to-moles conversion using the equalities:

$$1 \text{ mol Fe} = 55.845 \text{ g Fe} \quad \text{and} \quad 1 \text{ mol O} = 16.00 \text{ g O}$$

We then follow the procedure above for obtaining integer subscripts. If we do not get integers (within $\pm$ 0.1) we will need to find the rational fraction that corresponds to the decimal portion of the number and multiply by its denominator.

■**Solution:** The moles of Fe and O in the sample are calculated.

$$1.771 \text{ g Fe} \times \frac{1 \text{ mol Fe}}{55.845 \text{ g Fe}} = 0.03171 \text{ mol Fe}$$

$$0.677 \text{ g O} \times \frac{1 \text{ mol O}}{16.00 \text{ g O}} = 0.0423 \text{ mol O}$$

These results let us write the formula as $Fe_{0.03171}O_{0.0423}$.

Our first effort to change the ratio of 0.03171 to 0.0423 into whole numbers is to divide both by the smallest number, 0.03171.

$$Fe_{\frac{0.03171}{0.03171}}O_{\frac{0.0423}{0.03171}} = Fe_{1.000}O_{1.33}$$

This time we cannot round 1.33 to 1.0 because the decimal we want to round, 0.33, is larger than the 0.1 criterion established previously. The subscript for O, 1.33, is much too far from a whole number to round off. In a *mole* sense, the ratio of 1 to 1.33 is correct; we just need a way to re-state this ratio in whole numbers. To do this, we need to recognize that the decimal 0.33 represents 1/3 (one-third). The denominator is 3, and if we multiply both subscripts by 3 we will get

$$Fe_{(1.000 \times 3)}O_{(1.33 \times 3)} = Fe_{3.000}O_{3.99}$$

or a formula of Fe_3O_4. Table 4.1 in the margin lists some common decimals and their related fractions.

A less mathematical method that works is to use trial and error. First, multiply all subscripts by 2; if that does not give integer subscripts, go back and try 3, then 4, 5, and so on. In this example you would have found integer subscripts after multiplying by 3.

■**Is the Answer Reasonable?** One way to check our answer is to estimate the percentage of iron from the given data and from our result. The given data for iron is 1.771 g Fe and the whole sample weighs 2.448 g. The percentage iron is estimated as:

$$\frac{1.771 \text{ g}}{2.448 \text{ g}} \times 100 \approx \frac{\mathbf{1.8 \text{ g}}}{\mathbf{2.4 \text{ g}}} \times \mathbf{100} = \frac{3}{4} \times 100 = \text{approximately } 75\%$$

The mineral magnitite like any magnet, is able to affect the orientation of a compass needle.
(Visuals Unlimited)

Table 4.1	Decimal and Rational Fractions	
Decimal		**Fraction[a]**
0.20		1/5
0.25		1/4
0.33		1/3
0.40		2/5
0.50		1/2
0.60		3/5
0.66		2/3
0.75		3/4
0.80		4/5

[a]Use the denominator of the fraction as a multiplier to create whole-number subscripts in empirical formulas.

TOOLS

Determination of integer subscripts

In one mole of the compound Fe_3O_4, the mass of iron is $3 \times 55.8 = 167.4$ and the molar mass is 231.4. The percentage of iron is estimated as:

$$\frac{167.4 \text{ g}}{231.4 \text{ g}} \times 100 \approx \frac{170 \text{ g}}{230 \text{ g}} \times 100 = \frac{\textbf{1.7 g}}{\textbf{2.3 g}} \times \textbf{100} = \text{approximately 75\%}$$

We don't have to do any calculations because we can see that mathematical expressions from both calculations are almost the same, and the answers will be very close to each other. Let's compare the bold term from each equation:

$$\frac{1.8 \text{ g}}{2.4 \text{ g}} \times 100 \approx \frac{1.7 \text{ g}}{2.3 \text{ g}} \times 100$$

We are able to conclude that our percentages of iron are the same and our empirical formula is reasonable.

Practice Exercises

4.16 | When aluminum is produced by electrolysis we get 5.68 tons of aluminum and 5.04 tons of oxygen. What is the empirical formula of the compound that is being electrolyzed? (*Hint:* 1 ton = 2000 lb and 1 lb = 454 g.)

4.17 | A 2.012 g sample of a compound of nitrogen and oxygen has 0.522 g of nitrogen. Calculate its empirical formula.

Empirical Formulas from Experimental Mass Percentages

Only rarely is it possible to obtain the masses of every element in a compound by the use of just one weighed sample. Two or more analyses carried out on different samples are often needed. For example, suppose an analyst is given a compound known to consist exclusively of calcium, chlorine, and oxygen. The mass of calcium in one weighed sample and the mass of chlorine in another sample would be determined in separate experiments. Then the mass data for calcium and chlorine would be converted to percentages by mass *so that the data from different samples relate to the same sample size, namely, 100 g of the compound.* The percentage of oxygen would be calculated by difference because % Ca + % Cl + % O = 100%. If we consider a 100 g sample of our compound, each mass percentage of an element would represent the number of grams of that element in the sample. From here, the masses are next converted into the corresponding number of moles of each element. Finally, mole proportions are converted to integers in the way we just studied, giving us the subscripts for the empirical formula. Let's see how this works.

TOOLS

Empirical formulas from percentage composition

Example 4.11
Calculating an Empirical Formula from Percentage Composition

A white powder used in paints, enamels, and ceramics has the following percentage composition: Ba, 69.6%; C, 6.09%; and O, 24.3%. What is its empirical formula? What is the name of this compound?

■ **Analysis:** Consider having 100 grams of this compound. The percentages of the elements given in the problem are numerically the same as the masses of these elements in a 100 g sample.

Now that we have the masses of the elements we can calculate the moles of each element and then the integer values for the subscripts as we did in the previous examples.

■ We see a general principle that by assuming a 100 g sample, all percent signs can be easily changed to gram units for our calculations.

■ **Assembling the Tools:** We will need the molar mass as our tool to determine the moles of each element. We will also need the procedures for finding integer subscripts.

■ **Solution:** Assuming a 100 g sample of the compound, we quickly convert 69.6% Ba to 69.6 g Ba, 6.09% C to 6.09 g C, and 24.3% O to 24.3 g O. Now these masses are converted to moles.

$$\text{Ba:} \qquad 69.6 \text{ g Ba} \times \frac{1 \text{ mol Ba}}{137.3 \text{ g Ba}} = 0.507 \text{ mol Ba}$$

$$\text{C:} \qquad 6.09 \text{ g C} \times \frac{1 \text{ mol C}}{12.01 \text{ g C}} = 0.507 \text{ mol C}$$

$$\text{O:} \qquad 24.3 \text{ g O} \times \frac{1 \text{ mol O}}{16.00 \text{ g O}} = 1.52 \text{ mol O}$$

Our preliminary empirical formula is then

$$Ba_{0.507}C_{0.507}O_{1.52}$$

We next divide each subscript by the smallest value, 0.507.

$$Ba_{\frac{0.507}{0.507}}C_{\frac{0.507}{0.507}}O_{\frac{1.52}{0.507}} = Ba_{1.00}C_{1.00}O_{3.00}$$

The subscripts are whole numbers, so the empirical formula is $BaCO_3$, representing barium carbonate.

■ **Is the Answer Reasonable?** First of all, we found simple, whole-number, subscripts, which strongly suggest that the answer is right. In addition, our knowledge of ionic compounds and the polyatomic ions from Chapter 3 tells us that the combination of a barium ion, Ba^{2+}, and the carbonate ion, CO_3^{2-}, yields the same formula, $BaCO_3$. We can conclude that our answer is reasonable.

Practice Exercises

4.18 | A white solid used to whiten paper has the following percentage composition: Na, 32.4%; S, 22.6%. The unanalyzed element is oxygen. What is the compound's empirical formula? (*Hint:* What law allows you to calculate the % oxygen?)

4.19 | Cinnamon gets some of its flavor from cinnamaldehyde that is 81.79% C; 6.10% H and the rest is oxygen. Determine the empirical formula for this compound.

The law of conservation of mass and its use with percentage composition is important because it allowed us to determine the amount of three substances using only two experiments. This in itself is a considerable saving in time and effort. Additionally, it is often difficult to analyze a sample for certain elements, oxygen for example, and using percentage measurements helps avoid this problem.

Empirical Formulas from Indirect Analysis

In practice, a compound is seldom broken down completely to its *elements* in a quantitative analysis. Instead, the compound is changed into other *compounds*. The reactions separate the elements by capturing each one entirely (quantitatively) in a *separate* compound *whose formula is known.*

In Example 4.12, we illustrate the indirect analysis of a compound made entirely of carbon, hydrogen, and oxygen. Such compounds burn completely in pure oxygen—it is called a *combustion reaction*—and the sole products are carbon dioxide and water. (This particular kind of indirect analysis is sometimes called a **combustion analysis.**) The complete

ON THE CUTTING EDGE | 4.1

Combustion Analysis

Determining the mass of carbon and hydrogen in a compound can be done by burning the compound in pure oxygen in the presence of substances called catalysts that ensure complete conversion of carbon to CO_2 and hydrogen to H_2O. The stream of gases passes through a pre-weighed tube containing anhydrous calcium sulfate and then through a second pre-weighed tube containing sodium hydroxide. The first tube absorbs the water and the second absorbs the carbon dioxide, as seen in Figure 1.

The increase in masses of these tubes represents the masses of CO_2 and H_2O from which the masses of carbon and hydrogen can be calculated. If a compound contains oxygen, it would be determined by subtracting the mass of hydrogen and carbon from the total mass burned. Compounds containing nitrogen, sulfur, or a halogen are more difficult to analyze and often require additional time-consuming experiments.

Modern instruments automate the process of analyzing the combustion products using a technique called gas chromatography. After burning a weighed sample, advanced catalysts make sure that all the carbon, nitrogen, and sulfur atoms are converted to CO_2, N_2, and SO_2. One instrument automatically takes a small sample of the gases and injects it into a gas chromatograph. Within the instrument the gases travel through a tubular column packed with absorbents that cause each gas to travel at a different rate. At the end of the column a thermal conductivity detector, which measures the ability of a gas to dissipate heat, senses each component of the mixture. The result is a chromatogram with a peak for each separate substance, as shown in Figure 2.

The area of each peak is proportional to the amount of each gas, and the internal computer computes the percentage composition. Very pure compounds, called standards, with known percentages of each element are burned to calibrate the instrument.

All instruments require standard samples of high purity and known composition to calibrate the readout. Typically, the classical method takes about 30 minutes per sample, and the instruments, once calibrated, take between 2 and 5 minutes per sample.

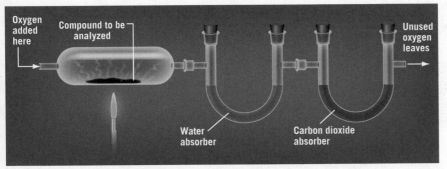

Figure 1 Classic CH analysis. This experimental setup shows pure oxygen added to the compound. Combustion products are absorbed by reaction with chemicals in the U-tubes. Calcium sulfate absorbs water and sodium hydroxide absorbs carbon dioxide.

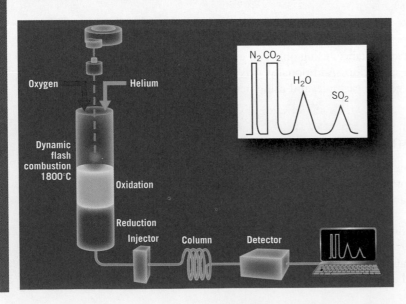

Figure 2 Diagram of an automated CHNS elemental analysis system. The diagram illustrates the combustion chamber, the chromatography column, a thermal conductivity detector, and a sample of a chromatogram with peaks for N_2, CO_2, H_2O, and SO_2.

combustion of methyl alcohol (CH_3OH), for example, occurs according to the following equation.

$$2CH_3OH + 3O_2 \longrightarrow 2CO_2 + 4H_2O$$

The carbon dioxide and water can be separated and are individually weighed. Notice that all of the carbon atoms in the original compound end up among the CO_2 molecules, and all of the hydrogen atoms are in H_2O molecules. In this way at least two of the original elements, C and H, are quantitatively measured.

We will calculate the mass of carbon in the CO_2 collected, which equals the mass of carbon in the original sample. Similarly, we will calculate the mass of hydrogen in the H_2O collected, which equals the mass of hydrogen in the original sample. When added together, the mass of C and mass of H are less than the total mass of the sample because part of the sample is composed of oxygen. The law of conservation of mass allows us to subtract the sum of the C and H masses from the original sample mass to obtain the mass of oxygen in the sample of the compound.

Example 4.12
Empirical Formula from Indirect Analysis

A 0.5438 g sample of a pure liquid consisting of only C, H, and O was burned in 100% oxygen, and 1.039 g of CO_2 and 0.6369 g of H_2O were obtained. What is the empirical formula of the compound?

■ **Analysis:** There are several parts to this problem; let's look at a logical sequence of what we have to do. First, we need to calculate the mass of the elements, C and H, by determining the number of grams of C in the CO_2 and the number of grams of H in the H_2O. Then the mass of oxygen is determined by difference. Next, we use the masses of C, H, and O to calculate the moles of each. Finally, we use our procedures to convert the moles of each element into integer subscripts in the empirical formula.

■ **Assembling the Tools:** To convert the masses of CO_2 and H_2O to grams of C and H we will need our tools for converting between mass and moles. In this problem we start with the equalities:

$$1 \text{ mol C} = 12.011 \text{ g C}$$
$$1 \text{ mol CO}_2 = 44.010 \text{ g CO}_2$$
$$1 \text{ mol O} = 15.999 \text{ g O}$$
$$1 \text{ mol H}_2O = 18.015 \text{ g H}_2O$$

Next we need the mole ratio equivalencies that we derive from the formulas.

$$1 \text{ mol C} \Leftrightarrow 1 \text{ mol CO}_2$$

$$2 \text{ mol H} \Leftrightarrow 1 \text{ mol H}_2\text{O}$$

This is similar to the calculations in Example 4.6, where we use the normal conversion sequence from grams of compound to grams of an element in the compound. We then need the law of conservation of mass,

$$\text{Mass of compound} = \text{mass of C} + \text{mass of H} + \text{mass of O}$$

to determine the oxygen content.

After we have the mass of each element, we will convert all the masses to moles. The final step is to convert the calculated moles of each element into an integer subscript for our formula.

■ **Solution:** First, we find the number of grams of C in the CO_2 as

$$1.039 \text{ g CO}_2 \times \frac{1 \text{ mol CO}_2}{44.009 \text{ g CO}_2} \times \frac{1 \text{ mol C}}{1 \text{ mol CO}_2} \times \frac{12.011 \text{ g C}}{1 \text{ mol C}} = 0.2836 \text{ g C}$$

For the number of grams of H in 0.6369 g of H_2O we calculate

$$0.6369 \text{ g H}_2\text{O} \times \frac{1 \text{ mol H}_2\text{O}}{18.015 \text{ g H}_2\text{O}} \times \frac{2 \text{ mol H}}{1 \text{ mol H}_2\text{O}} \times \frac{1.0079 \text{ g}}{1 \text{ mol H}} = 0.07127 \text{ g H}$$

The total mass of C and H is therefore the sum of these two quantities.

$$\text{Total mass of C and H} = 0.2836 \text{ g C} + 0.07127 \text{ g H} = 0.3549 \text{ g}$$

The difference between this total and the 0.5438 g mass of the original sample is the mass of oxygen (the only other element present).

$$\text{Mass of O} = 0.5438 \text{ g} - 0.3549 \text{ g} = 0.1889 \text{ g O}$$

Now we can convert the masses of the elements to an empirical formula.

For C: $$0.2836 \text{ g C} \times \frac{1 \text{ mol C}}{12.011 \text{ g C}} = 0.02361 \text{ mol C}$$

For H: $$0.07127 \text{ g H} \times \frac{1 \text{ mol H}}{1.0079 \text{ g H}} = 0.07071 \text{ mol H}$$

For O: $$0.1889 \text{ g O} \times \frac{1 \text{ mol O}}{15.999 \text{ g O}} = 0.01181 \text{ mol O}$$

Our preliminary empirical formula is thus $C_{0.02361}H_{0.070701}O_{0.01181}$. We divide all of these subscripts by the smallest number, 0.01181.

$$C_{\frac{0.02361}{0.01181}}H_{\frac{0.070701}{0.01181}}O_{\frac{0.01181}{0.01181}} = C_{1.999}H_{5.987}O_1$$

The results are acceptably close to integers, to conclude that the empirical formula is C_2H_6O.

■ **Is the Answer Reasonable?** Our checks on problems need to be quick and efficient. The fact that the integer subscripts were found easily suggests that the answer is correct and we can usually stop here. If more confirmation is needed, we can estimate the answers to the individual steps.

4.20 | A sample containing only sulfur and carbon is completely burned in air. The analysis produced 0.640 g of SO_2 and 0.220 g of CO_2. What is the empirical formula? (*Hint:* Use the tools for relating grams of a compound to grams of an element.)

4.21 | The combustion of a 5.048 g sample of a compound of C, H, and O gave 7.406 g of CO_2 and 3.027 g of H_2O. Calculate the empirical formula of the compound.

Molecular Formulas from Empirical Formulas and Molecular Masses

The empirical formula is the accepted formula unit for ionic compounds. For molecular compounds, however, chemists prefer *molecular* formulas because they give the number of atoms of each type in a molecule, rather than just the simplest ratio of moles of elements in a compound as the empirical formula does.

Sometimes an empirical and molecular formula are the same. Two examples are H_2O and NH_3. When they are different, the subscripts of the molecular formula are integer multiples of those in the empirical formula. The subscripts of the molecular formula P_4O_{10}, for example, are each two times those in the empirical formula, P_2O_5, as you saw earlier. The molecular mass of P_4O_{10} is likewise two times the empirical formula mass of P_2O_5. This observation provides us with a way to find out the molecular formula for a compound provided we have a way of determining experimentally the molecular mass of the compound. If the experimental molecular mass *equals* the calculated empirical formula mass, the empirical formula is the same as the molecular formula. Otherwise, the molecular mass will be a whole-number multiple of the empirical formula mass. Whatever the integer is, it's a common multiplier for the subscripts of the empirical formula.

■ There are many simple methods for determining molecular masses. They are discussed in Chapters 11 and 13. Instruments such as the mass spectrometers discussed in Chapter 3 can also be used.

Example 4.13
Determining a Molecular Formula from an Empirical Formula and a Molecular Mass

Styrene, the raw material for polystyrene foam plastics, has an empirical formula of CH. Its molecular mass is 104. What is its molecular formula?

■ **Analysis:** Since we know the empirical formula and the molar mass of the compound, styrene, we need to find out how many empirical formula units make up one molecule. Then the molecular formula will have subscripts that are an integer multiple of the empirical formula subscripts.

■ **Assembling the Tools:** The relationship between empirical and molecular formulas tells us that the molecular mass of styrene, 104, divided by the formula mass of the empirical formula, CH, will result in an integer that represents the number of empirical formula units in the molecule itself.

$$\frac{\text{Molecular mass of styrene}}{\text{Empirical formula mass of CH}} = \text{integer}$$

To obtain the molecular formula, all subscripts of the empirical formula are multiplied by that integer.

■ **Solution:** For the empirical formula, CH, the formula mass is

$$12.01 + 1.008 = 13.02$$

To find how many CH units weighing 13.02 are in a mass of 104, we divide.

$$\frac{104}{13.02} = 7.99$$

Rounding this to 8, we find that eight CH units make up the molecular formula of styrene, and styrene must have subscripts 8 times those in CH. Styrene, therefore, is C_8H_8.

■ **Is the Answer Reasonable?** The molecular mass of C_8H_8 is approximately $(8 \times 12) + (8 \times 1) = 104$, which is consistent with the molecular mass we started with.

Practice Exercises

4.22 | After determining that the empirical formulas of two different compounds were CH_2Cl and $CHCl$, a student mixed up the data for the molecular masses. However, the student knew that one compound had a molecular mass of 100 and the other had a molecular mass of 289. What are the likely molecular formulas of the two compounds? (*Hint:* Recall the relationship between the molecular and empirical formula.)

4.23 | The empirical formula of hydrazine is NH_2 and its molecular mass is 32.0. What is its molecular formula?

4.4 | The Mole and Chemical Reactions

Writing and Balancing Chemical Equations

Here we will see that a *balanced* chemical equation is a very useful tool for problem solving. We learned in Chapters 1 and 3 that a *chemical equation* is a shorthand, quantitative description of a chemical reaction. An equation is balanced when all atoms present among the reactants (written to the left of the arrow) are also somewhere among the products (written to the right of the arrow). Coefficients, numbers placed in front of formulas, are multiplier numbers for their respective formulas that are used to balance an equation.

Always approach the balancing of an equation as a two-step process.

Step 1. *Write the unbalanced "equation."* Organize the formulas in the pattern of an equation with plus signs and an arrow (think of the arrow as an equal sign because we need to end up with the same number of each atom on both sides). Use *correct* formulas. (You learned to write many of them in Chapter 3, but until we have studied more chemistry, you will usually be given formulas.)

Step 2. *Adjust the coefficients to get equal numbers of each kind of atom on both sides of the arrow.* When doing Step 2, make no changes in the formulas, either in the atomic symbols or their subscripts. If you do, the equation will involve different substances from those intended. It often helps to start the process with the most complex formula, leaving elements and simple compounds to the end.

We'll begin with simple equations that can be balanced easily by inspection. An example is the reaction of zinc metal with hydrochloric acid (see the margin photo). First, we need the correct formulas, and this time we'll include the physical states because they may not be obvious. The reactants are zinc, $Zn(s)$, and hydrochloric acid, an aqueous solution of the gas hydrogen chloride, HCl, symbolized as $HCl(aq)$. We also need formulas for the products. Zn changes to a water-soluble compound, zinc chloride, $ZnCl_2(aq)$, and hydrogen gas, $H_2(g)$, bubbles out as the other product. (Recall that hydrogen is one of the elements that occurs naturally as a *diatomic molecule*, not as an atom.)

Step 1. Write an unbalanced equation.

$$Zn(s) + HCl(aq) \longrightarrow ZnCl_2(aq) + H_2(g) \qquad \text{(unbalanced)}$$

Step 2. Adjust the coefficients to get equal numbers of each kind of atom on both sides of the arrow.

Zinc metal reacts with hydrochloric acid. (*Richard Megna/Fundamental Photographs*)

There is no simple set of rules for adjusting coefficients—as you may have discovered, experience is the greatest help. Experience has taught chemists that the following guidelines often get to the solution most directly when they are applied in the order given.

Some Guidelines for Balancing Equations

1. Start balancing with the most complicated formula first. Elements, particularly H_2 and O_2, should be left until the end.
2. Balance atoms that appear in only two formulas: one as a reactant and the other as a product. (Leave elements that appear in three or more formulas until later.)
3. Balance as a group those polyatomic ions that appear unchanged on both sides of the arrow.

TOOLS

Balancing chemical equations

Using the guidelines given here, we'll leave the $Zn(s)$ and $H_2(g)$ until later. The two remaining formulas have chlorine in common. Because there are two Cl to the right of the arrow but only one to the left, we put a 2 in front of the HCl on the left side. Remember that this also sets the coefficient of $ZnCl_2$ as 1, which by custom is not written. The result is

$$Zn(s) + 2HCl(aq) \longrightarrow ZnCl_2(aq) + H_2(g)$$

We then balance the hydrogen and zinc and find that no additional coefficient changes are needed. Everything is now balanced. On each side we find 1 Zn, 2 H, and 2 Cl. One complication is that an infinite number of *balanced* equations can be written for any given reaction! We might, for example, have adjusted the coefficients so that our equation came out as follows.

$$2Zn(s) + 4HCl(aq) \longrightarrow 2ZnCl_2(aq) + 2H_2(g)$$

This equation is also balanced. For simplicity, chemists prefer the *smallest* whole-number coefficients when writing balanced equations.

■ Although the smallest whole-number coefficients are preferred, stoichiometric calculations still work as long as the equation is balanced.

Example 4.14
Writing a Balanced Equation

Sodium hydroxide and phosphoric acid, H_3PO_4, react as aqueous solutions to give sodium phosphate and water. The sodium phosphate remains in solution. Write the balanced equation for this reaction.

■ **Analysis:** First, we need to write an unbalanced equation that includes the reactant formulas on the left-hand side and the product formulas on the right. Then we need to use the above procedures for balancing the equation.

■ **Assembling the Tools:** We are given the formula only for phosphoric acid. We need to use the nomenclature tools in Chapter 3 to determine that the formula of sodium hydroxide is $NaOH$; water is H_2O, and sodium phosphate has a formula of Na_3PO_4. Finally, we use our guidelines for balancing equations.

■ **Solution:** We write the unbalanced equation by placing all the reactants to the left of the arrow and all products to the right. The designation (*aq*) is added for all substances dissolved in water (except H_2O itself; we'll not give it any designation when it is in its liquid state).

$$NaOH(aq) + H_3PO_4(aq) \longrightarrow Na_3PO_4(aq) + H_2O \qquad \text{(unbalanced)}$$

We will focus on balancing the Na and P atoms first, since H and O atoms appear in more than two formulas. Focusing on the Na first, there are 3 Na on the right side, so we put a 3 in front of NaOH on the left, as a trial. Remember that this step also places an unwritten 1 in front of the Na_3PO_4 formula.

$$3NaOH(aq) + H_3PO_4(aq) \longrightarrow Na_3PO_4(aq) + H_2O \qquad \text{(unbalanced)}$$

Now that the Na are in balance we can focus on the P. Since all of the phosphorus is found in the PO_4 units, we will balance the phosphate units as a group of atoms rather

■ When a reaction occurs in aqueous solution, water is not pure water and the (*l*) is inappropriate. Also, the term (*aq*) is meaningless since we would be saying "an aqueous solution of water." In solution chemistry, therefore the state of water is not specified.

than individually. We see that the PO_4 unit is already balanced and that means that the H_3PO_4 has a coefficient of 1. Only the coefficient for water has not been assigned. We can see that the reactant side has 6 H and 3 O atoms (notice that we don't count the oxygen atoms in the PO_4 units since they have already been balanced), which will produce 3 H_2O molecules. Thus the coefficient of water should be three.

$$3NaOH(aq) + H_3PO_4(aq) \longrightarrow Na_3PO_4(aq) + 3H_2O \qquad \text{(balanced)}$$

We now have a balanced equation.

■ **Is the Answer Reasonable?** On each side we have 3 Na, 1 PO_4, 6 H, and 3 O besides those in PO_4, and since the coefficients for $H_3PO_4(aq)$ and $Na_3PO_4(aq)$ are 1 our coefficients cannot be reduced to smaller whole numbers.

Practice Exercises

4.24 | Write the balanced chemical equation that describes what happens when a solution containing calcium chloride is mixed with a solution containing potassium phosphate and the product of the reaction is solid calcium phosphate and a solution of potassium chloride. (*Hint:* Write the correct formulas based on information in Chapter 3.)

4.25 | When aqueous solutions of calcium nitrate, $Ca(NO_3)_2$, and ammonium phosphate, $(NH_4)_3PO_4$, are mixed, a reaction occurs in which solid calcium phosphate, $Ca_3(PO_4)_2$, separates from the solution. The other product is $NH_4NO_3(aq)$. Write the balanced equation.

The strategy of balancing whole units of polyatomic ions, like PO_4, as a group is extremely useful. Using this method, we have less atom counting to do and balancing equations is often easier.

Calculations that Use Balanced Chemical Equations

So far we have focused on mole ratios between elements within a single compound. We have seen that the essential conversion factor between substances within a compound is the mole ratio obtained from the compound's formula. In this section, we'll see that the same techniques can be used to relate substances involved in a chemical reaction. The tool that relates substances involved in a reaction is the mole ratio obtained from the coefficients of the balanced chemical equation.

Establishing Mole-to-Mole Ratios

To see how chemical equations can be used to obtain mole-to-mole relationships, consider the equation that describes the burning of octane (C_8H_{18}) in oxygen (O_2) to give carbon dioxide and water vapor:

$$2C_8H_{18}(l) + 25O_2(g) \longrightarrow 16CO_2(g) + 18H_2O(g)$$

This equation can be interpreted on the molecular scale as follows:

When two molecules of liquid octane react with twenty-five molecules of oxygen gas, sixteen molecules of carbon dioxide gas and eighteen molecules of water vapor are produced.

This statement immediately suggests many equivalence relationships that can be used to build conversion factors for stoichiometry problems:

$$2 \text{ molecules } C_8H_{18} \Leftrightarrow 25 \text{ molecules } O_2$$
$$2 \text{ molecules } C_8H_{18} \Leftrightarrow 16 \text{ molecules } CO_2$$
$$2 \text{ molecules } C_8H_{18} \Leftrightarrow 18 \text{ molecules } H_2O$$
$$25 \text{ molecules } O_2 \Leftrightarrow 16 \text{ molecules } CO_2$$
$$25 \text{ molecules } O_2 \Leftrightarrow 18 \text{ molecules } H_2O$$
$$16 \text{ molecules } CO_2 \Leftrightarrow 18 \text{ molecules } H_2O$$

■ The chemical equation gives the relative amounts of each of the molecules that participate in a reaction. It does not mean that 2 octane molecules actually collide with 25 O_2 molecules. The actual reaction occurs in many steps that the chemical equation does not show.

 TOOLS

Equivalencies from balanced chemical equations

Any of these *microscopic* relationships can be scaled up to the *macroscopic* laboratory scale by multiplying both sides of the equivalency by Avogadro's number, which effectively allows us to replace "molecules" with "moles" or "mol":

$$2 \text{ mol } C_8H_{18} \Leftrightarrow 25 \text{ mol } O_2$$

$$2 \text{ mol } C_8H_{18} \Leftrightarrow 16 \text{ mol } CO_2$$

$$2 \text{ mol } C_8H_{18} \Leftrightarrow 18 \text{ mol } H_2O$$

$$25 \text{ mol } O_2 \Leftrightarrow 16 \text{ mol } CO_2$$

$$25 \text{ mol } O_2 \Leftrightarrow 18 \text{ mol } H_2O$$

$$16 \text{ mol } CO_2 \Leftrightarrow 18 \text{ mol } H_2O$$

We can interpret the equation on a macroscopic (mole) scale as follows:

Two moles of liquid octane react with twenty-five moles of oxygen gas to produce sixteen moles of carbon dioxide gas and eighteen moles of water vapor.

To use these equivalencies in a stoichiometry problem, the equation must be **balanced**. That means that every atom found in the reactants must also be found somewhere in the products. You must always check to see whether this is true for a given equation before you can use the coefficients to build equivalencies and conversion factors.

First, let's see how mole-to-mole relationships obtained from a chemical equation can be used to convert moles of one substance to moles of another when both substances are involved in a chemical reaction.

Example 4.15
Stoichiometry of Chemical Reactions

How many moles of sodium phosphate can be made from 0.240 mol of sodium hydroxide by the following unbalanced equation?

$$3NaOH(aq) + H_3PO_4(aq) \longrightarrow Na_3PO_4(aq) + H_2O$$

■ **Analysis:** We are given an unbalanced equation and will have to balance it first before we can find an appropriate mole ratio. Then the question asks us to relate amounts, in moles, of two different substances. As in Example 4.5, all we need for this conversion is a mole ratio.

■ **Assembling the Tools:** We first balance the equation as we did previously,

$$3NaOH(aq) + H_3PO_4(aq) \longrightarrow Na_3PO_4(aq) + 3H_2O$$

Now an equivalence derived from the coefficients of the balanced equation is written as

$$3 \text{ mol NaOH} \Leftrightarrow 1 \text{ mol } Na_3PO_4$$

This enables us to prepare the mole ratio conversion factor that we need.

■ **Solution:** We start by writing the question in equation form as

$$0.240 \text{ mol NaOH} \Leftrightarrow ? \text{ mol } Na_3PO_4$$

Using the mole ratio $\dfrac{1 \text{ mol } Na_3PO_4}{3 \text{ mol NaOH}}$, we convert 0.240 mol NaOH to the number of moles of Na_3PO_4:

$$0.240 \text{ mol NaOH} \times \frac{1 \text{ mol } Na_3PO_4}{3 \text{ mol NaOH}} = 0.0800 \text{ mol } Na_3PO_4$$

The result states that we can make 0.0800 mol Na$_3$PO$_4$ from 0.240 mol NaOH. Recall that the coefficients, 1 and 3, in the conversion factor are exact numbers, so our answer has three significant figures.

■ **Is the Answer Reasonable?** The balanced equation tells us that 3 mol NaOH ⇔ 1 mol Na$_3$PO$_4$, so the actual number of moles of Na$_3$PO$_4$ (0.0800 mol) should be one-third the actual number of moles of NaOH (0.240 mol), and it is. We can also check that the units cancel correctly.

Practice Exercises

4.26 | In the reaction $2SO_2(g) + O_2(g) \longrightarrow 2SO_3(g)$, how many moles of O$_2$ are needed to produce 6.76 moles of SO$_3$? (*Hint:* Write the equality that relates O$_2$ to SO$_3$.)

4.27 | How many moles of sulfuric acid, H$_2$SO$_4$, are needed to react with 0.366 mol of NaOH by the following balanced chemical equation?

$$2NaOH(aq) + H_2SO_4(aq) \longrightarrow Na_2SO_4(aq) + 2H_2O$$

Mass-to-Mass Calculations

The most common stoichiometric calculation the chemist does is to relate grams of one substance with grams of another in a chemical reaction. For example, consider glucose, C$_6$H$_{12}$O$_6$, one of the body's primary energy sources. The body combines glucose and oxygen, in a process called metabolism, to give carbon dioxide and water. The balanced equation for the overall reaction is

$$C_6H_{12}O_6(aq) + 6\ O_2(aq) \longrightarrow 6\ CO_2(aq) + 6\ H_2O(l)$$

How many grams of oxygen must the body take in to completely process 1.00 g of glucose? The problem can be expressed as

$$1.00\ g\ C_6H_{12}O_6 \Leftrightarrow ?\ g\ O_2$$

The first thing we should notice about this problem is that we're relating *two different substances* in a reaction. The equality that relates the substances is the mole-to-mole relationship between glucose and O$_2$ given by the chemical equation. In this case, the equation tells us that 1 mol C$_6$H$_{12}$O$_6$ ⇔ 6 mol O$_2$. It is very important to realize that there is no direct conversion between the mass of C$_6$H$_{12}$O$_6$ and the mass of O$_2$. We need to convert the mass of glucose to moles of glucose, then we use the mole ratio to convert moles of glucose to moles of oxygen, and finally we convert moles of oxygen to mass of oxygen. This sequence, indicating where we use the mole-to-mole equivalence, is shown below

TOOLS

Mass-to-mass calculations using balanced chemical equations

$$\boxed{1\ mol\ C_6H_{12}O_6 \Leftrightarrow 6\ mol\ O_2}$$
$$1.00\ g\ C_6H_{12}O_6 \longrightarrow mol\ C_6H_{12}O_6 \longrightarrow mol\ O_2 \longrightarrow g\ O_2$$

The molar mass is used twice as a tool, once for converting 1.00 g of glucose to moles and again for converting moles of O$_2$ to grams of O$_2$.

Figure 4.4 outlines this flow for *any* stoichiometry problem that relates reactant or product masses. If we know the *balanced equation* for a reaction and the *mass of any*

Figure 4.4 | **The sequence of calculations for solving stoichiometry problems.** This sequence applies to all calculations that start with the mass of one substance *A* and require the mass of a second substance *B* as the answer. Each box represents a measured or calculated quantity. Each arrow represents one of our chemical tools.

reactant or product, we can calculate the required or expected mass of *any* other substance in the equation. Example 4.16 shows how it works.

Example 4.16
Stoichiometric Mass Calculations

Portland cement is a mixture of the oxides of calcium, aluminum, and silicon. The raw material for its calcium oxide is calcium carbonate, which occurs as the chief component of a natural rock, limestone. When calcium carbonate is strongly heated it decomposes. One product, carbon dioxide, is driven off to leave the desired calcium oxide as the only other product.

A chemistry student is to prepare 1.50×10^2 g of calcium oxide in order to test a particular "recipe" for Portland cement. How many grams of calcium carbonate should be used, assuming 100% conversion to product?

■ **Analysis:** As usual, this is a multi-part problem. First, we need to determine the formulas of the compounds and then write a balanced chemical reaction. Then we will perform the conversions from the given 1.50×10^2 grams of calcium oxide to moles of calcium oxide, then to moles of calcium carbonate, and then to grams of calcium carbonate.

■ **Assembling the Tools:** We need the nomenclature tools in Chapter 3 to translate the names of the compounds to formulas and then write the balanced chemical equation, which is

$$CaCO_3(s) \xrightarrow{\text{heat}} CaO(s) + CO_2(g)$$

> ■ Special reaction conditions are often shown with words or symbols above the arrow. In this reaction, temperatures above 2000 °C are needed and this is indicated with the word, heat, above the arrow.

Now we can write our sequence of conversions using formulas,

$$1.50 \times 10^2 \text{ g CaO} \longrightarrow \text{mol CaO} \longrightarrow \text{mol CaCO}_3 \longrightarrow \text{g CaCO}_3$$

We need tools for converting the mass to moles for CaO in the first step and the mass to moles for $CaCO_3$ in the last step. They are

$$56.08 \text{ g CaO} = 1 \text{ mol CaO} \quad \text{and} \quad 1 \text{ mol CaCO}_3 = 100.09 \text{ g CaCO}_3$$

Finally, we need a tool for the mole-to-mole conversion. Using our balanced chemical equation, the equivalence is

$$1 \text{ mol CaO} \Leftrightarrow 1 \text{ mol CaCO}_3$$

■ **Solution:** We start by writing the question as an equation.

$$1.50 \times 10^2 \text{ g CaO} \Leftrightarrow ? \text{ g CaCO}_3$$

Reviewing our sequence of calculation we can write the sequence of steps indicating where we use each of our tools.

1 mol CaO ⇔ 1 mol CaCO₃

1.50×10^2 g CaO ⟶ mol CaO ⟶ mol CaCO₃ ⟶ g CaCO₃

56.08 g CaO = 1 mol CaO   1 mol CaCO₃ = 100.09 g CaCO₃

Starting from the left, we assemble conversion factors so the units cancel correctly:

$$1.50 \times 10^2 \text{ g CaO} \times \left(\frac{1 \text{ mol CaO}}{56.08 \text{ g CaO}} \right) \times \left(\frac{1 \text{ mol CaCO}_3}{1 \text{ mol CaO}} \right) \times \left(\frac{100.09 \text{ g CaCO}_3}{1 \text{ mol CaCO}_3} \right) = 268 \text{ g CaCO}_3$$

Notice how the calculation flows from grams of CaO to moles of CaO, then to moles of $CaCO_3$ (using the equation), and finally to grams of $CaCO_3$. We cannot emphasize too much that *the key step in all calculations of reaction stoichiometry is the use of the balanced equation.*

■ **Is the Answer Reasonable?** In a mass-to-mass calculation like this, the first check is the magnitude of the answer compared to the starting mass. In the majority of reactions the calculated mass is not less than $\frac{1}{5}$ of the starting mass nor is it larger than five times the starting mass. Our result is reasonable based on this criteria. We can make a more detailed check by first checking that the units cancel properly. We can also round to one or two significant figures and estimate the answer. We would estimate $\frac{150 \times 100}{50} = 300$, and this value is close to our answer of 268, giving us confidence that the answer is reasonable.

■ This 5 to 1/5 range for conversions of the mass of A to a mass of B holds true for most (maybe 90–95%) calculations. If your answer is outside this range, do a very careful check for errors.

Example 4.17
Stoichiometric Mass Calculations

Figure 4.5 | The thermite reaction. Pictured here is a device for making white-hot iron by the reaction of aluminum with iron oxide and letting the molten iron run down into a mold between ends of two steel railroad rails. This welds the rails together. *(Wikimedia Commons)*

The thermite reaction is one of the most spectacular reactions with flames, sparks and glowing molten iron. Here aluminum reacts with iron(III) oxide to produce aluminum oxide and metallic iron. So much heat is generated that the iron forms in the liquid state (Figure 4.5).

A certain welding operation requires at least 86.0 g of iron each time a weld is made. What is the minimum mass, in grams, of iron(III) oxide that must be used for each weld? Also calculate how many grams of aluminum are needed.

■ **Analysis:** First, we need to determine the formulas of the compounds so we can write a balanced chemical equation. Next, we need to convert the 86.0 g Fe to the needed mass of iron(III) oxide. Remember that all problems in reaction stoichiometry must be solved at the mole level because an equation's coefficients disclose *mole* ratios, not mass ratios. The sequence of conversions to use is

86.0 g iron ⟶ mol iron ⟶ mol iron(III) oxide ⟶ g iron(III) oxide

For the second calculation we calculate the number of grams of Al needed, but we know that we must first find the number of *moles* of Al required. For this second calculation the sequence is

86.0 g iron ⟶ mol iron ⟶ mol aluminum ⟶ g aluminum

■ **Assembling the Tools:** We use our nomenclature tools from Chapter 3 to determine that Al and Fe_2O_3 are the reactants and that Fe and Al_2O_3 are the products. The balanced equation is:

$$2Al(s) + Fe_2O_3(s) \longrightarrow Al_2O_3(s) + 2Fe(l)$$

The following conversion equalities are needed to calculate the mass of Fe_2O_3

$$55.85 \text{ g Fe} = 1 \text{ mol Fe}$$
$$1 \text{ mol Fe}_2O_3 \Leftrightarrow 2 \text{ mol Fe}$$
$$159.70 \text{ g Fe}_2O_3 = 1 \text{ mol Fe}_2O_3$$

Next, we need the following conversion equalities to calculate the mass of aluminum:

$$55.85 \text{ g Fe} = 1 \text{ mol Fe}$$
$$2 \text{ mol Al} \Leftrightarrow 2 \text{ mol Fe}$$
$$26.98 \text{ g Al} = 1 \text{ mol Al}$$

■ **Solution:** Now we state the first part of the problem in mathematical form:

$$86.0 \text{ g Fe} \Leftrightarrow ? \text{ g Fe}_2O_3$$

We'll set up the first calculation as a chain. The steps are summarized below each conversion factor.

$$86.0 \text{ g Fe} \times \frac{1 \text{ mol Fe}}{55.85 \text{ g Fe}} \times \frac{1 \text{ mol Fe}_2O_3}{2 \text{ mol Fe}} \times \frac{159.70 \text{ g Fe}_2O_3}{1 \text{ mol Fe}_2O_3} = 123 \text{ g Fe}_2O_3$$

grams Fe $\longrightarrow$ moles Fe $\longrightarrow$ moles Fe_2O_3 $\longrightarrow$ grams Fe_2O_3

A minimum of 123 g of Fe_2O_3 is required to make 86.0 g of Fe.

To calculate the mass of aluminum, we follow a similar sequence, using the conversion factors in order so that the units cancel as shown. We employ another chain calculation to find the mass of Al needed to make 86.0 g of Fe.

$$86.0 \text{ g Fe} \times \frac{1 \text{ mol Fe}}{55.85 \text{ g Fe}} \times \frac{2 \text{ mol Al}}{2 \text{ mol Fe}} \times \frac{26.98 \text{ g Al}}{1 \text{ mol Al}} = 41.5 \text{ g Al}$$

grams Fe $\longrightarrow$ moles Fe $\longrightarrow$ moles Al $\longrightarrow$ grams Al

■ **Are the Answers Reasonable?** The estimate that our answers in a mass-to-mass calculation should be within 1/5 to 5 times the initial mass is true for both Al and Fe_2O_3. Rounding the numbers to one significant figure and estimating the answer (after rechecking that the units cancel properly) results in

$$\frac{90 \times 200}{60 \times 2} = 150 \text{ g Fe}_2O_3 \quad \text{and} \quad \frac{90 \times 30}{60} = 45 \text{ g Al}$$

Both estimates are close to our calculated values and give confidence that our answers are reasonable.

■ We could simplify the mole ratio to 1 mol Al ⇔ 1 mol Fe. Leaving the 2-to-2 ratio maintains the connection to the coefficients in the balanced equation.

Practice Exercises

4.28 | Using the information in Example 4.17, calculate the mass of Al_2O_3 formed under the conditions specified. (*Hint:* Recall the law of conservation of mass.)

4.29 | How many grams of carbon dioxide are also produced by the reaction described in Example 4.16?

4.5 | Limiting Reactants

Limiting Reactants Viewed at the Molecular Level

We've seen that balanced chemical equations can tell us how to mix reactants together in just the right proportions to get a certain amount of product. For example, ethanol, C_2H_5OH, is prepared industrially as follows:

$$\underset{\text{ethylene}}{C_2H_4} + H_2O \longrightarrow \underset{\text{ethanol}}{C_2H_5OH}$$

We often interpret the equation on a laboratory scale using moles. Every mole of ethylene that reacts requires one mole of water to produce one mole of ethanol. Let's look at this reaction at the molecular level. Now the equation tells us that one molecule of ethylene will react with one molecule of water to give one molecule of ethanol.

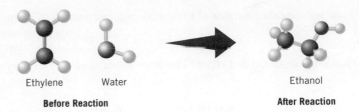

Ethylene   Water   Ethanol

Before Reaction   **After Reaction**

If we have three molecules of ethylene reacting with three molecules of water, then three ethanol molecules are produced:

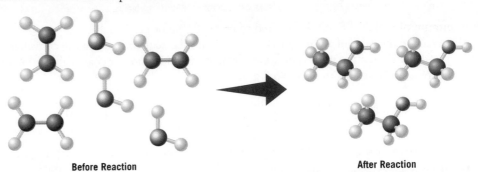

Before Reaction   **After Reaction**

What happens if we mix three molecules of ethylene with five molecules of water? The ethylene will be completely used up before all the water is, and the product will contain two unreacted water molecules:

■ Notice that in both the "before" and "after" views of the reaction, the numbers of carbon, hydrogen, and oxygen atoms are the same.

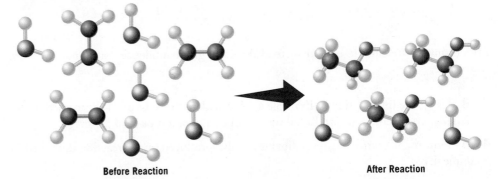

Before Reaction   **After Reaction**

We don't have enough ethylene to use up all the water. The excess water remains after the reaction stops. This situation can be a problem in the manufacture of chemicals because not only do we waste one of our reactants (water, in this case), but we also obtain a product that is contaminated with unused reactant.

In this reaction mixture, ethylene is called the **limiting reactant** because it limits the amount of product (ethanol) that forms. The water is called an **excess reactant,** because we have more of it than is needed to completely consume all the ethylene.

To predict the amount of product we'll actually obtain in a reaction, we need to know which of the reactants is the limiting reactant. In the example above, we saw that we needed only 3 H_2O molecules to react with 3 C_2H_4 molecules, but we had 5 H_2O molecules, so H_2O is present in excess and C_2H_4 is the limiting reactant. We could also have reasoned that 5 molecules of H_2O would require 5 molecules of C_2H_4, and since we have only 3 molecules of C_2H_4, it must be the limiting reactant.

A Strategy for Solving Limiting Reactant Problems

At the start of this chapter we referred to the billions of hamburger buns produced each year to reflect the large number of atoms and molecules we work with. Construction of hamburgers can also be a limiting reactant problem. For instance, how many quarter-pound hamburgers can be made from a package of eight hamburger rolls, a pound of hamburger meat, a bottle of ketchup, and a bottle of pickles? We can quickly see that one pound of hamburger meat will make four quarter-pound hamburgers. We obviously have an excess of buns, catsup, and pickles. The hamburger meat is our limiting reactant, and four hamburgers is the most we can prepare.

As we saw above, there are several steps involved in solving limiting reactant problems. First, we identify a limiting reactant problem by the fact that the amount of more than one reactant is given. Next, we need to identify the limiting reactant, and finally we solve the problem based on the amount of limiting reactant at hand. The first step is easy. Next, when finding the limiting reactant, we arbitrarily pick one of the reactants and calculate how much of the second reactant is needed. If the amount calculated for the second reactant is less than what is given, there is an excess of the second reactant and therefore the first reactant is limiting. If the calculated amount of the second reactant is more than what was given, then it will be consumed first and the second reactant is limiting.

Once we have identified the limiting reactant, it is possible to compute the amount of product that will actually form and the amount of excess reactant that will be left over after the reaction stops. For the final calculations we must use the amount of the limiting reactant given in the statement of the problem.

Example 4.18 shows how to solve a typical limiting reactant problem when the amounts of the reactants are given in mass units.

TOOLS

Limiting reactant calculations

Example 4.18
Limiting Reactant Calculation

Gold(III) hydroxide is used for electroplating gold onto other metals. It can be made by the following reaction.

$$2KAuCl_4(aq) + 3Na_2CO_3(aq) + 3H_2O \longrightarrow$$

$$2Au(OH)_3(aq) + 6NaCl(aq) + 2KCl(aq) + 3CO_2(g)$$

To prepare a fresh supply of $Au(OH)_3$, a chemist at an electroplating plant has mixed 20.00 g of $KAuCl_4$ with 25.00 g of Na_2CO_3 (both dissolved in a large excess of water). What is the maximum number of grams of $Au(OH)_3$ that can form?

■ **Analysis:** The clue that tells us this is a limiting reactant question is that *the quantities of two reactants are given.* Now we will break this question into two separate steps, identifying the limiting reactant and then calculating the grams of $Au(OH)_3$ produced.

Step I: To identify the limiting reactant, we arbitrarily pick one of the reactants ($KAuCl_4$ or Na_2CO_3; we were told that water is in excess, so we know that it does not limit the reaction) and calculate how much of the second reactant is needed. Based on the result we will be able to decide which reactant is limiting. We will need to use a combination of our stoichiometry tools to solve this problem.

Step II: Once we've identified the limiting reactant we can use it to calculate the amount of $Au(OH)_3$ produced using the following sequence of conversions. Notice that this sequence is essentially the same as the one we used in Figure 4.4.

g limiting reactant $\longrightarrow$ mol limiting reactant $\longrightarrow$ mol $Au(OH)_3$ $\longrightarrow$ g $Au(OH)_3$

■ **Assembling the Tools—Step I:** Our tool for limiting reactant calculations outlines the process for identifying the limiting reactant. First, we calculate the amount of reactant 1 that will react with reactant 2. To do this we use the following sequence of calculations:

mass of reactant 1 $\longrightarrow$ mol reactant 1 $\longrightarrow$ mol reactant 2 $\longrightarrow$ mass reactant 2

This is our typical mass-to-mass calculation that requires the following relationships

$$1 \text{ mol KAuCl}_4 = 377.88 \text{ g KAuCl}_4$$

$$2 \text{ mol KAuCl}_4 \Leftrightarrow 3 \text{ mol Na}_2\text{CO}_3$$

$$1 \text{ mol Na}_2\text{CO}_3 = 105.99 \text{ g Na}_2\text{CO}_3$$

■ **Solution—Step I:** We will show, in the two calculations that follow, the process used to identify the limiting reactant. In solving a limiting reactant problem you will need to do only one of these calculations.

We start with $KAuCl_4$ as the reactant to work with and calculate how many grams of Na_2CO_3 *should* be provided to react with 20.00 g of $KAuCl_4$. We'll set up a chain calculation as follows.

grams $KAuCl_4$ ⟶ moles $KAuCl_4$ ⟶ moles Na_2CO_3 ⟶ grams Na_2CO_3

$$20.00 \text{ g KAuCl}_4 \times \frac{1 \text{ mol KAuCl}_4}{377.88 \text{ g KAuCl}_4} \times \frac{3 \text{ mol Na}_2\text{CO}_3}{2 \text{ mol KAuCl}_4} \times \frac{105.99 \text{ g Na}_2\text{CO}_3}{1 \text{ mol Na}_2\text{CO}_3}$$
$$= 8.415 \text{ g Na}_2\text{CO}_3$$

We find that 20.00 g of $KAuCl_4$ needs 8.415 g of Na_2CO_3. The given amount of 25.00 g of Na_2CO_3 is more than enough to let the $KAuCl_4$ react completely. *We conclude that $KAuCl_4$ is the limiting reactant and that Na_2CO_3 is present in excess.*

We start with Na_2CO_3 as the reactant to work with and calculate how many grams of $KAuCl_4$ *should* be provided to react with 25.00 g of Na_2CO_3. Again we perform a chain calculation using the appropriate conversion factors

grams Na_2CO_3 ⟶ moles Na_2CO_3 ⟶ moles $KAuCl_4$ ⟶ grams $KAuCl_4$

$$25.00 \text{ g Na}_2\text{CO}_3 \times \frac{1 \text{ mol Na}_2\text{CO}_3}{105.99 \text{ g Na}_2\text{CO}_3} \times \frac{2 \text{ mol KAuCl}_4}{3 \text{ mol Na}_2\text{CO}_3} \times \frac{377.88 \text{ g KAuCl}_4}{1 \text{ mol KAuCl}_4}$$
$$= 59.42 \text{ g KAuCl}_4$$

We find that 25.00 g Na_2CO_3 would require almost three times the mass of $KAuCl_4$ provided, so *we again conclude that $KAuCl_4$ is the limiting reactant.*

The result from either calculation above is sufficient to designate $KAuCl_4$ as the limiting reactant. Now we proceed to Step II.

■ After identifying the limiting reactant, return to the statement of the problem and use the amount of the limiting reactant given in the problem to perform further calculations.

■ **Assembling the Tools—Step II:** Since $KAuCl_4$ is the limiting reactant, we can calculate the mass of $Au(OH)_3$ using the sequence of steps

mass of $KAuCl_4$ ⟶ moles of $KAuCl_4$ ⟶ moles of $Au(OH)_3$ ⟶ mass of $Au(OH)_3$

Now we write the equalities we need to finish the problem:

$$1 \text{ mol KAuCl}_4 = 377.88 \text{ g KAuCl}_4$$

$$2 \text{ mol KAuCl}_4 \Leftrightarrow 2 \text{ mol Au(OH)}_3$$

$$1 \text{ mol Au(OH)}_3 = 247.99 \text{ g Au(OH)}_3$$

■ **Solution—Step II:** From here on, we have a routine calculation converting the mass of the limiting reactant, $KAuCl_4$, to the mass of product, $Au(OH)_3$. We set up the following chain calculation.

grams $KAuCl_4$ $\longrightarrow$ moles $KAuCl_4$ $\longrightarrow$ moles $Au(OH)_3$ $\longrightarrow$ grams $Au(OH)_3$

$$20.00 \text{ g } \cancel{KAuCl_4} \times \left(\frac{1 \text{ mol } \cancel{KAuCl_4}}{377.88 \text{ g } \cancel{KAuCl_4}} \right) \times \left(\frac{2 \text{ mol } \cancel{Au(OH)_3}}{2 \text{ mol } \cancel{KAuCl_4}} \right) \times \left(\frac{247.99 \text{ g } Au(OH)_3}{1 \text{ mol } \cancel{Au(OH)_3}} \right) = 13.13 \text{ g } Au(OH)_3$$

Thus from 20.00 g of $KAuCl_4$ we can make a maximum of 13.13 g of $Au(OH)_3$.

In this synthesis, some of the initial 25.00 g of Na_2CO_3 is left over. Since one of our calculations showed that 20.00 g of $KAuCl_4$ requires only 8.415 g of Na_2CO_3 out of 25.00 g Na_2CO_3, the difference, (25.00 g − 8.415 g) = 16.58 g of Na_2CO_3, remains unreacted. It is possible that the chemist used an excess to ensure that every last bit of the very expensive $KAuCl_4$ would be changed to $Au(OH)_3$.

Notice that by breaking this problem into two parts, we were able to solve two mass-to-mass calculations to get the answer we needed.

■ **Are the Answers Reasonable?** First, the resulting masses are within the range of $\frac{1}{5}$ to 5 times the starting mass and are not unreasonable. Again, we check that our units cancel properly and then we estimate the answer as $\dfrac{20 \times 200}{400} = 10 \text{ g } Au(OH)_3$, which is close enough to our answer to give confidence that the calculation was done correctly.

Practice Exercises

4.30 | The reaction between the limestone and hydrochloric acid produces carbon dioxide as shown in the reaction.

$$CaCO_3(s) + 2HCl \ (aq) \longrightarrow CO_2(g) + CaCl_2(aq) + H_2O$$

How many grams of CO_2 can be made by reacting 125 g of $CaCO_3$ with 125 g of HCl? How many grams of which reactant are left over? (*Hint:* Find the limiting reactant.)

4.31 | In an industrial process for making nitric acid, the first step is the reaction of ammonia with oxygen at high temperature in the presence of a platinum gauze. Nitrogen monoxide forms as follows.

$$4NH_3 + 5O_2 \longrightarrow 4NO + 6H_2O$$

How many grams of nitrogen monoxide can form if a mixture initially contains 30.00 g of NH_3 and 40.00 g of O_2?

4.6 | Theoretical Yield and Percentage Yield

In most experiments designed for chemical synthesis, the amount of a product actually isolated falls short of the calculated maximum amount. Losses occur for several reasons. Some are mechanical, such as materials sticking to glassware. In some reactions, losses occur by the evaporation of a volatile product. In others, a product is a solid that separates from the solution as it forms because it is largely insoluble. The solid is removed by filtration. What stays in solution, although relatively small, contributes to some loss of product.

One of the common causes of obtaining less than the stoichiometric amount of a product is the occurrence of a **competing reaction**. It produces a **by product**, a substance made by a reaction that competes with the **main reaction**. The synthesis of phosphorus trichloride, for example, gives some phosphorus pentachloride as well, because PCl_3 can react further with Cl_2.

Main reaction: $2P(s) + 3Cl_2(g) \longrightarrow 2PCl_3(l)$

Competing reaction: $PCl_3(l) + Cl_2(g) \longrightarrow PCl_5(s)$

The competition is between newly formed PCl_3 and still unreacted phosphorus for still unchanged chlorine.

■ When determining the percentage yield, you must be given the actual yield of the experiment; it cannot be calculated.

Theoretical, actual, and percentage yields

The **actual yield** of desired product is simply how much is isolated, stated in either mass units or moles. The **theoretical yield** of the product is what must be obtained if no losses occur. When less than the theoretical yield of product is obtained, chemists generally calculate the *percentage yield* of product to describe how well the preparation went. The **percentage yield** is the actual yield calculated as a percentage of the theoretical yield.

$$\text{Percentage yield} = \frac{\text{actual yield}}{\text{theoretical yield}} \times 100\% \qquad (4.2)$$

Both the actual and theoretical yields must be in the same units.

It is important to realize that the actual yield is an experimentally determined quantity. It cannot be calculated. The theoretical yield is always a calculated quantity based on a chemical equation and the amounts of the reactants available.

Let's now work an example that combines the determination of the limiting reactant with a calculation of percentage yield.

Example 4.19
Calculating a Percentage Yield

A chemist set up a synthesis of phosphorus trichloride by mixing 12.0 g of phosphorus with 35.0 g chlorine gas and obtained 42.4 g of solid phosphorus trichloride. Calculate the percentage yield of this compound.

■**Analysis:** We start by determining the formulas for the reactants and products and then balancing the chemical equation. Phosphorus is represented as P(*s*) and chlorine gas is $Cl_2(g)$ and the product is $PCl_3(s)$. The balanced equation is

$$2P(s) + 3Cl_2(g) \longrightarrow 2PCl_3(s)$$

Now we notice that the masses of *both* reactants are given, so this must be a limiting reactant problem. The first step is to figure out which reactant, P or Cl_2, is the limiting reactant, because we must base all calculations on the limiting reactant. When we know the limiting reactant, we can calculate the theoretical yield of product, $PCl_3(s)$. Finally we calculate the percentage yield. The three main steps are summarized as,

$$\boxed{\text{Determine the limiting reactant}} \longrightarrow \boxed{\text{Determine the theoretical yield}} \longrightarrow \boxed{\text{Calculate the percentage yield}}$$

■**Assembling the Tools:** To solve the first two steps, our basic tools are the relationships

$$1 \text{ mol P} = 30.97 \text{ g P}$$
$$1 \text{ mol Cl}_2 = 70.90 \text{ g Cl}_2$$
$$3 \text{ mol Cl}_2 \Leftrightarrow 2 \text{ mol P}$$

For the percentage yield our tool is Equation 4.2.

■**Solution:** In any limiting reactant problem, we can arbitrarily pick one reactant and do a calculation to see whether it can be entirely used up. We'll choose phosphorus and see whether there is enough to react with 35.0 g of chlorine. The following calculation gives us the answer.

$$12.0 \text{ g P} \times \frac{1 \text{ mol P}}{30.97 \text{ g P}} \times \frac{3 \text{ mol Cl}_2}{2 \text{ mol P}} \times \frac{70.90 \text{ g Cl}_2}{1 \text{ mol Cl}_2} = 41.2 \text{ g Cl}_2$$

Thus, with 35.0 g of Cl_2 provided but 41.2 g of Cl_2 needed, there is not enough Cl_2 to react with all 12.0 g of P. The Cl_2 will be all used up before the P is used up, so Cl_2 is the limiting reactant. We therefore base the calculation of the theoretical yield of PCl_3 on Cl_2.

(We must be careful to use the 35.0 g of Cl_2 given in the problem, *not* the 41.2 g calculated while we determined the limiting reactant.)

To find the *theoretical yield* of PCl_3, we calculate how many grams of PCl_3 could be made from 35.0 g of Cl_2 if everything went perfectly according to the equation given.

$$35.0 \text{ g } Cl_2 \times \frac{1 \text{ mol } Cl_2}{70.90 \text{ g } Cl_2} \times \frac{2 \text{ mol } PCl_3}{3 \text{ mol } Cl_2} \times \frac{137.32 \text{ g } PCl_3}{1 \text{ mol } PCl_3} = 45.2 \text{ g } PCl_3$$

$$\text{grams } Cl_2 \longrightarrow \text{moles } Cl_2 \longrightarrow \text{moles } PCl_3 \longrightarrow \text{grams } PCl_3$$

The actual yield was 42.4 g of PCl_3, not 45.2 g, so the percentage yield is calculated as follows.

$$\text{Percentage yield} = \frac{42.4 \text{ g } PCl_3}{45.2 \text{ g } PCl_3} \times 100\% = 93.8\%$$

Thus 93.8% of the theoretical yield of PCl_3 was obtained.

■ **Is the Answer Reasonable?** The obvious check is that the calculated or theoretical yield can never be *less* than the actual yield. Second, our theoretical yield is within the range of 1/5 to 5 times the starting amount. Finally, one way to estimate the theoretical yield, after checking that all units cancel properly, is

$$\frac{40 \times 2 \times 100}{70 \times 3} = \frac{80 \times 100}{210} \approx \frac{80}{2} \approx 40 \text{ g } PCl_3$$

which is close to the 45.2 g PCl_3 we calculated.

Practice Exercises

4.32 | In the synthesis of aspirin we react salicylic acid with acetic anhydride. The balanced chemical equation is:

$$\underset{\text{salicylic acid}}{2HOOCC_6H_4OH} + \underset{\text{acetic anhydride}}{C_4H_6O_3} \longrightarrow \underset{\text{acetyl salicylic acid}}{2HOOCC_6H_4O_2C_2H_3} + \underset{\text{water}}{H_2O}$$

If we mix together 28.2 grams of salicylic acid with 15.6 grams of acetic anhydride in this reaction, we obtain 30.7 grams of aspirin. What are the theoretical and percentage yields of our experiment? (*Hint:* What is the limiting reactant?)

4.33 | Ethanol, C_2H_5OH, can be converted to acetic acid (the acid in vinegar), $HC_2H_3O_2$, by the action of sodium dichromate in aqueous sulfuric acid according to the following equation.

$$3C_2H_5OH(aq) + 2Na_2Cr_2O_7(aq) + 8H_2SO_4(aq) \longrightarrow$$
$$3HC_2H_3O_2(aq) + 2Cr_2(SO_4)_3(aq) + 2Na_2SO_4(aq) + 11H_2O$$

In one experiment, 24.0 g of C_2H_5OH, 90.0 g of $Na_2Cr_2O_7$, and an excess of sulfuric acid were mixed, and 26.6 g of acetic acid ($HC_2H_3O_2$) was isolated. Calculate the theoretical and percentage yields of $HC_2H_3O_2$.

Multi-Step Reactions

Many chemical synthesis reactions involve more than one step to produce a product. Sometimes there can be more than ten separate reactions from the initial reactants to the final products. In such reactions, the product of one reaction is the reactant for the next. As a result, the overall percentage yield is the product of the percentage yields for all the steps along the way. The following equation is used to calculate percent yields for multi-step syntheses.

$$\text{Overall \% yield} = \left(\frac{\% \text{ yield}_1}{100} \times \frac{\% \text{ yield}_2}{100} \times \cdots \right) 100\%$$

TOOLS

Multi-step percentage yield

Practice Exercise   **4.34** | In producing a certain drug, one synthetic route involves three steps with percentage yields of 87.2%, 91.1%, and 86.3%. An alternate synthesis uses two steps with percentage yields of 85.5% and 84.3%. Based on the overall percent yield, which is the preferred synthesis?

Summary

Mole Concept, Avogadro's Number, and the Laboratory Scale. In the SI definition, one mole of any substance is an amount with the same number, 6.022×10^{23}, of atoms, molecules, or formula units as there are atoms in 12 g (exactly) of carbon-12. **Avogadro's number** is the title given to the number 6.022×10^{23}. Chemical equations show how atoms and molecules react (the molecular scale), whereas the **mole concept** uses the same equations in terms of moles of atoms and moles of molecules. Moles of substances have masses that are convenient for **laboratory scale** experiments.

Atomic, Molecular, and Formula Mass. Atomic masses listed on the periodic table are relative to an atomic mass of 12 (exactly) for C-12. The atomic mass of one mole of a monatomic element is often called the **gram atomic mass**. The mass of a mole of molecules is equal to the sum of the atomic masses of all the atoms in the formula and is called the **gram molecular mass**. Similarly, the mass of a mole of an ionic substance is equal to the masses of all the atoms in the ionic formula and is called the **gram formula mass**.

Molar Mass. This is a general term that may be used in place of the gram atomic mass, gram molecular mass, or gram formula mass. The **molar mass** is a tool for grams-to-moles or moles-to-grams conversions.

Empirical Formulas. An empirical formula gives the smallest whole-number ratio of the atoms in a substance. Empirical formulas may be calculated if we know the mass or percentage of each element in the compound.

Chemical Formulas. The actual composition of a molecule is given by its **molecular formula**. An **empirical formula** is generally the *only* formula we write for ionic compounds. In the case of a molecular compound, the molecular mass is a small whole-number multiple of the empirical formula mass.

Formula Stoichiometry. A chemical formula is a tool for stoichiometric calculations, because its subscripts tell us the mole ratios in which the various elements are combined.

Balanced Equations and Reaction Stoichiometry. A balanced equation is a tool for reaction stoichiometry because its coefficients disclose the stoichiometric equivalencies. When balancing an equation, only the coefficients can be adjusted, never the subscripts. All problems of reaction stoichiometry must be solved by first converting to moles.

Yields of Products. A reactant taken in a quantity less than required by another reactant, as determined by the reaction's stoichiometry, is called the **limiting reactant.** The **theoretical yield** of a product can be no more than permitted by the limiting reactant. Sometimes **competing reactions** (side reactions) producing by-products reduce the **actual yield**. The ratio of the actual to the theoretical yields, expressed as a percentage, is the **percentage yield**.

Stoichiometric Calculations. These are generally problems in which units are converted in a logical sequence of steps (see Figure 4.6). Conversion factors used in these calculations are found in the molar mass, Avogadro's number, the chemical formula, or the balanced chemical reaction.

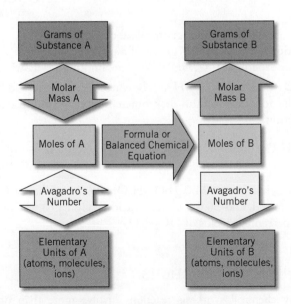

Figure 4.6 | Stoichiometry pathways. This diagram summarizes all of the possible stoichiometric calculations encountered in this chapter. The boxes represent the units that we start with and want to end at. Arrows between the boxes indicate the tools that provide the needed conversion factors.

TOOLS

Tools for Problem Solving
The following tools were introduced in this chapter. Study them carefully so you can select the appropriate tool when needed.

Atomic mass (page 108)
Used to form a conversion factor to calculate mass from moles of an element or moles from the mass of an element.

$$\text{Gram atomic mass of } X = \text{molar mass of } X = 1 \text{ mole } X$$

Formula mass; molecular mass (page 108)
Used to form a conversion factor to calculate mass from moles of a compound or moles from the mass of a compound.

$$\text{Gram molecular mass of } X = \text{molar mass of } X = 1 \text{ mole } X$$
$$\text{Gram formula mass of } X = \text{molar mass of } X = 1 \text{ mole } X$$

Molar Mass (page 108)
This is a general term encompassing atomic, molecular, and formula masses. All are the sum of the masses of the elements in a chemical formula.

$$\text{Molar mass of } X = 1 \text{ mole of } X$$

Avogadro's number (page 110)
It relates macroscopic lab-sized quantities (e.g., moles) to numbers of individual atomic-sized particles such as atoms, molecules, or ions.

$$1 \text{ mole } X = 6.02 \times 10^{23} \text{ particles of } X$$

Mole ratios (page 111)
Subscripts in a formula establish atom ratios and mole ratios between the elements in the substance.

Mass-to-mass conversions using formulas (page 114)
These steps are required for a mass-to-mass conversion problem using a chemical formula; also see Figure 4.6.

Percentage composition (page 116)
This describes the composition of a compound and can be the basis for computing the empirical formula. Comparing experimental and theoretical percentage compositions can help establish the identity of a compound.

$$\text{Percent of } X = \frac{\text{mass of } X \text{ in the sample}}{\text{mass of the entire sample}} \times 100\%$$

Empirical formula (page 119)
The empirical formula expresses the simplest ratio of the atoms of each element in a compound.

Determination of integer subscripts (page 121)
When determining an empirical formula, dividing all molar amounts by the smallest value often normalizes subscripts to integers. If decimals remain, multiplication by a small whole number can result in integer subscripts.

Empirical formulas from percentage composition (page 122)
Analysis of a substance often requires more than one procedure. Percentage composition (see above) helps correlate information from these different experiments, particularly when each method used may require a different mass of sample.

Balancing chemical equations (page 129)
Balancing equations involves writing the unbalanced equation and then adjusting the coefficients to get equal numbers of each kind of atom on both sides of the arrow.

Equivalencies obtained from balanced equations (page 130)

The coefficients in balanced chemical equations give us relationships between all reactants and products that can be used in factor-label calculations.

Mass-to-mass calculations using balanced equations (page 132)

A logical sequence of conversions allows calculation of all components of a chemical reaction. See Figure 4.6.

Limiting reactant calculations (page 137)

When the amount of at least two reactants is known, stoichiometry questions are answered by identifying the limiting reactant and then using the given amount of the limiting reactant to perform the required conversions.

Theoretical, actual, and percentage yields (page 140)

The theoretical yield is calculated from the limiting reactant whether stated, implied, or calculated. The actual yield must be determined by experiment, and the percentage yield relates the magnitude of the actual yield to the percentage yield.

$$\text{Percentage yield} = \frac{\text{actual mass by experiment}}{\text{theoretical mass by calculation}} \times 100\%$$

Multi-step percentage yield (page 141)

Modern chemical synthesis often involves more than one distinct reaction or step. The overall percentage yield of a multi-step synthesis is

$$\text{Overall percentage yield} = \left(\frac{\text{actual yield}_1}{\text{theoretical yield}_1} \times \frac{\text{actual yield}_2}{\text{theoretical yield}_2} \times \cdots \right) 100\%$$

PLUS = WileyPLUS, an online teaching and learning solution. *Note to instructors:* Many of the end-of-chapter problems are available for assignment via the *WileyPLUS* system. **www.wileyplus.com. ILW** = An Interactive Learningware solution is available for this problem. **OH** = An Office Hour video is available for this problem. Review Problems are presented in pairs separated by blue rules. Answers to problems whose numbers appear in blue are given in Appendix B. More challenging problems are marked with an asterisk ∗.

| Review Questions

Mole Concept

4.1 Using atomic mass units, how would you estimate the number of atoms in a gram of iron?

4.2 What is the definition of the mole?

4.3 Why are moles used, when all stoichiometry problems could be done using only atomic mass units?

4.4 Which contains more molecules: 2.5 mol of H_2O or 2.5 mol of H_2? Which contains more atoms? Which weighs more?

Chemical Formulas

4.5 How many moles of iron atoms are in one mole of Fe_2O_3? How many iron atoms are in one mole of Fe_2O_3?

4.6 Write all the mole-to-mole conversion factors that can be written based on the following chemical formulas: (a) SO_2, (b) As_2O_3, (c) K_2SO_4, (d) Na_2HPO_4.

4.7 Write all the mole-to-mole conversion factors that can be written based on the following chemical formulas: (a) Mn_3O_4, (b) Sb_2S_5, (c) $(NH_4)_2SO_4$, (d) Hg_2Cl_2,

4.8 What information is required to convert grams of a substance into moles of that same substance?

4.9 Why is the expression "1.0 mol of oxygen" ambiguous? Why doesn't a similar ambiguity exist in the expression "64 g of oxygen?"

4.10 The atomic mass of aluminum is 26.98. What specific conversion factors does this value make available for relating a mass of aluminum (in grams) and a quantity of aluminum given in moles?

Empirical Formulas

4.11 In general, what fundamental information, obtained from experimental measurements, is required to calculate the empirical formula of a compound?

4.12 Why are empirical formulas always used for ionic compounds?

4.13 Under what circumstances can we change, or assign, subscripts in a chemical formula?

4.14 How many distinct empirical formulas are shown by the following models for compounds formed between elements A and B? Explain. (Element A is represented by a black sphere and element B by a light gray sphere.)

Avogadro's Number

4.15 How would Avogadro's number change if the atomic mass unit were to be redefined as 2×10^{-27} kg, exactly?

4.16 What information is required to convert grams of a substance into molecules of that same substance?

Stoichiometry with Balanced Equations

4.17 The balanced chemical equation for the combustion of propane, a common heating fuel, is

$$C_3H_8 + 5O_2 \longrightarrow 3CO_2 + 4H_2O$$

Draw a molecular-level diagram of this chemical reaction. Use the color chart on page 11 to distinguish the atoms from each other.

4.18 Draw a molecular-level diagram for the reaction in which sulfur dioxide reacts with molecular oxygen to form sulfur trioxide. Be sure to write and balance the equation first. Use the color chart on page 11 to distinguish the atoms from each other.

4.19 When given the *unbalanced* equation

$$Na(s) + Cl_2(g) \longrightarrow NaCl(s)$$

and asked to balance it, student A wrote

$$Na(s) + Cl_2(g) \longrightarrow NaCl_2(s)$$

and student B wrote

$$2Na(s) + Cl_2(g) \longrightarrow 2NaCl(s)$$

Both equations are balanced, but which student is correct? Explain why the other student's answer is incorrect.

4.20 Give a step-by-step procedure for estimating the number grams of A required to completely react with 10 moles of B, given the following information:

A and B react to form A_5B_2.

A has a molecular mass of 100.0.

B has a molecular mass of 200.0.

There are 6.02×10^{23} molecules of A in a mole of A.

Which of these pieces of information weren't needed?

4.21 If two substances react completely in a 1-to-1 ratio *both* by mass and by moles, what must be true about these substances?

4.22 What information is required to determine how many grams of sulfur would react with a gram of arsenic?

4.23 A mixture of 0.020 mol of Mg and 0.020 mol of Cl_2 reacted completely to form $MgCl_2$ according to the equation

$$Mg + Cl_2 \longrightarrow MgCl_2$$

What information describes the *stoichiometry* of this reaction? What information gives the *scale* of the reaction?

4.24 In a report to a supervisor, a chemist described an experiment in the following way: "0.0800 mol of H_2O_2 decomposed into 0.0800 mol of H_2O and 0.0400 mol of O_2." Express the chemistry and stoichiometry of this reaction by a conventional chemical equation.

4.25 On April 16, 1947, in Texas City, Texas, two cargo ships, the *Grandcamp* and the *High Flier*, were each loaded with approximately 2000 tons of ammonium nitrate fertilizer. The *Grandcamp* caught fire and exploded, followed by the *High Flier*. More than 600 people were killed and one-third of the city was destroyed. Considering a much smaller mass, how would you count the number of N_2 molecules that could be produced after the explosion of 1.00 kg of NH_4NO_3?

4.26 Molecules containing *A* and *B* react to form *AB* as shown below. Based on the equations and the contents of the boxes labeled "Initial," sketch for each reaction the molecular models of what is present after the reaction is over. (In both cases, the species *B* exists as B_2. In reaction 1, *A* is monatomic; in reaction 2, *A* exists as diatomic molecules A_2.)

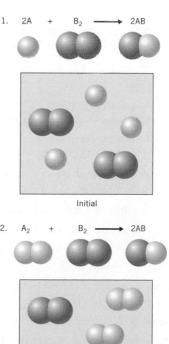

Review Problems

The Mole Concept and Stoichiometric Equivalencies

4.27 In what smallest whole-number ratio must N and O atoms combine to make dinitrogen tetroxide, N_2O_4? What is the mole ratio of the elements in this compound?

4.28 In what atom ratio are the elements present in methane, CH_4 (the chief component of natural gas)? In what mole ratio are the atoms of the elements present in this compound?

4.29 How many moles of tantalum atoms correspond to 1.56×10^{21} atoms of tantalum?

4.30 How many moles of iodine molecules correspond to 1.80×10^{24} molecules of I_2?

4.31 Sucrose (table sugar) has the formula $C_{12}H_{22}O_{11}$. In this compound, what is the

(a) atom ratio of C to H?   (c) atom ratio of H to O?

(b) mole ratio of C to O?   (d) mole ratio of H to O?

4.32 Nail polish remover is usually the volatile liquid ethyl acetate, $CH_3COOC_2H_5$. In this compound, what is the

(a) atom ratio of C to O?   (c) atom ratio of C to H?

(b) mole ratio of C to O?   (d) mole ratio of C to H?

4.33 How many moles of Bi atoms are needed to combine with 1.58 mol of O atoms to make bismuth oxide, Bi_2O_3?

4.34 How many moles of vanadium atoms, V, are needed to combine with 0.565 mol of O atoms to make vanadium pentoxide, V_2O_5?

4.35 How many moles of Cr are in 2.16 mol of Cr_2O_3?

4.36 How many moles of O atoms are in 4.25 mol of calcium carbonate, $CaCO_3$, the chief constituent of seashells?

4.37 Aluminum sulfate, $Al_2(SO_4)_3$, is a compound used in sewage treatment plants.

(a) Construct a pair of conversion factors that relate moles of aluminum to moles of sulfur for this compound.

(b) Construct a pair of conversion factors that relate moles of sulfur to moles of $Al_2(SO_4)_3$.

(c) How many moles of Al are in a sample of this compound if the sample also contains 0.900 mol S?

(d) How many moles of S are in 1.16 mol $Al_2(SO_4)_3$?

4.38 Magnetite is a magnetic iron ore. Its formula is Fe_3O_4.

(a) Construct a pair of conversion factors that relate moles of Fe to moles of Fe_3O_4.

(b) Construct a pair of conversion factors that relate moles of Fe to moles of O in Fe_3O_4.

(c) How many moles of Fe are in 2.75 mol of Fe_3O_4?

(d) If this compound could be prepared from Fe_2O_3 and O_2, how many moles of Fe_2O_3 would be needed to prepare 4.50 mol Fe_3O_4?

4.39 How many moles of H_2 and N_2 can be formed by the decomposition of 0.145 mol of ammonia, NH_3?

4.40 How many moles of S are needed to combine with 0.225 mol Al to give Al_2S_3?

ILW 4.41 How many moles of UF_6 would have to be decomposed to provide enough fluorine to prepare 1.25 mol of CF_4? (Assume sufficient carbon is available.)

4.42 How many moles of Fe_3O_4 are required to supply enough iron to prepare 0.260 mol Fe_2O_3? (Assume sufficient oxygen is available.)

4.43 How many atoms of carbon are combined with 4.13 moles of hydrogen atoms in a sample of the compound propane, C_3H_8? (Propane is used as the fuel in gas barbecues.)

4.44 How many atoms of hydrogen are found in 2.31 mol of propane, C_3H_8?

4.45 What is the total number of C, H, and O atoms in 0.260 moles of glucose, $C_6H_{12}O_6$?

4.46 What is the total number of N, H, and O atoms in 0.356 mol of ammonium nitrate, NH_4NO_3, an important fertilizer?

Measuring Moles of Elements and Compounds

4.47 How many atoms are in 6.00 g of carbon-12?

OH 4.48 How many atoms are in 1.50 mol of carbon-12? How many grams does this much carbon-12 weigh?

4.49 Determine the mass in grams of each of the following: (a) 1.35 mol Fe, (b) 24.5 mol O, (c) 0.876 mol Ca.

4.50 Determine the mass in grams of each of the following: (a) 0.546 mol S, (b) 3.29 mol N, (c) 8.11 mol Al.

4.51 A nanotechnology experiment requires 2×10^{12} atoms of potassium. What is the mass of this sample?

4.52 What is the mass, in grams, of 4×10^{17} atoms of gold present in one nanoparticle?

4.53 How many moles of nickel are in 17.7 g of Ni?

4.54 How many moles of chromium are in 85.7 g of Cr?

4.55 Calculate the formula mass of each of the following to the maximum number of significant figures possible using the table of atomic masses inside the front cover.

(a) $NaHCO_3$ (d) potassium dichromate

(b) $(NH_4)_2CO_3$ (e) aluminum sulfate

(c) $CuSO_4 \cdot 5H_2O$

4.56 Calculate the formula mass of each of the following to the maximum number of significant figures possible using the table of atomic masses inside the front cover.

(a) calcium nitrate   (d) $Fe_4[Fe(CN)_6]_3$

(b) $Pb(C_2H_5)_4$ (e) magnesium phosphate

(c) $Na_2SO_4 \cdot 10H_2O$

4.57 Calculate the mass in grams of the following.

(a) 1.25 mol $Ca_3(PO_4)_2$

(b) 0.625 mmol iron(III) nitrate

(c) 0.600 μmol C_4H_{10}

(d) 1.45 mol ammonium carbonate

4.58 What is the mass in grams of the following?

(a) 0.754 mol zinc chloride

(b) 0.194 μmol potassium chlorate

(c) 0.322 mmol $POCl_3$

(d) 4.31×10^{-3} mol $(NH_4)_2HPO_4$

4.59 Calculate the number of moles of each compound in the following samples.

(a) 21.5 g calcium carbonate

(b) 1.56 ng NH_3

(c) 16.8 g strontium nitrate

(d) 6.98 μg Na_2CrO_4

4.60 Calculate the number of moles of each compound in the following samples.

(a) 9.36 g calcium hydroxide

(b) 38.2 kg lead(II)sulfate

(c) 4.29 g H_2O_2

(d) 4.65 mg $NaAuCl_4$

ILW 4.61 One sample of CaC_2 contains 0.150 mol of carbon. How many moles and how many grams of calcium are also in the sample? [Calcium carbide, CaC_2, was once used to make signal flares for ships. Water dripped onto CaC_2 reacts to give acetylene (C_2H_2), which burns brightly.]

OH 4.62 How many moles of iodine are in 0.500 mol of $Ca(IO_3)_2$? How many grams of calcium iodate are needed to supply this much iodine? [Iodized salt contains a trace amount of calcium iodate, $Ca(IO_3)_2$, to help prevent a thyroid condition called goiter.]

4.63 How many moles of nitrogen, N, are in 0.650 mol of ammonium carbonate? How many grams of this compound supply this much nitrogen?

4.64 How many moles of nitrogen, N, are in 0.556 mol of ammonium nitrate? How many grams of this compound supply this much nitrogen?

4.65 How many kilograms of a fertilizer made of pure $(NH_4)_2CO_3$ would be required to supply 1 kilogram of nitrogen to the soil?

4.66 How many kilograms of a fertilizer made of pure P_2O_5 would be required to supply 1 kilogram of phosphorus to the soil?

Percentage Composition

4.67 Calculate the percentage composition by mass for each of the following:

(a) sodium dihydrogen phosphate

(b) $NH_4H_2PO_4$

(c) $(CH_3)_2CO$

(d) calcium sulfate dihydrate

(e) $CaSO_4 \cdot 2H_2O$

4.68 Calculate the percentage composition by mass of each of the following: (a) $(CH_3)_2N_2H_2$ (b) $CaCO_3$ (c) iron(III) nitrate (d) C_3H_8 (e) aluminum sulfate

4.69 Which has a higher percentage of oxygen: morphine ($C_{17}H_{19}NO_3$) or heroin ($C_{21}H_{23}NO_5$)?

4.70 Which has a higher percentage of nitrogen: carbamazepine ($C_{15}H_{12}N_2O$) or carbetapentane ($C_{20}H_{31}NO_3$)?

4.71 Freon is a trade name for a group of gaseous compounds once used as propellants in aerosol cans. Which has a higher percentage of chlorine: Freon-12 (CCl_2F_2) or Freon 141b ($C_2H_3Cl_2F$)?

4.72 Which has a higher percentage of fluorine: Freon-12 (CCl_2F_2) or Freon 113 ($C_2Cl_3F_3$)?

OH 4.73 It was found that 2.35 g of a compound of phosphorus and chlorine contained 0.539 g of phosphorus. What are the percentages by mass of phosphorus and chlorine in this compound?

4.74 An analysis revealed that 5.67 g of a compound of nitrogen and oxygen contained 1.47 g of nitrogen. What are the percentages by mass of nitrogen and oxygen in this compound?

4.75 Phencyclidine ("angel dust") is $C_{17}H_{25}N$. A sample suspected of being this illicit drug was found to have a percentage composition of 84.71% C, 10.42% H, and 5.61% N. Do these data acceptably match the theoretical data for phencyclidine?

4.76 The hallucinogenic drug LSD has the molecular formula $C_{20}H_{25}N_3O$. One suspected sample contained 74.07% C, 7.95% H, and 9.99% N.

(a) What is the percentage of O in the sample?

(b) Are these data consistent for LSD?

4.77 How many grams of O are combined with 7.14×10^{21} atoms of N in the compound dinitrogen pentoxide?

4.78 How many grams of C are combined with 4.25×10^{23} atoms of H in the compound C_5H_{12}?

Empirical Formulas

4.79 Write empirical formulas for the following compounds.

(a) S_2Cl_2 (c) NH_3 (e) H_2O_2

(b) $C_6H_{12}O_6$ (d) As_2O_6

4.80 What are the empirical formulas of the following compounds?

(a) $C_2H_4(OH)_2$ (c) C_4H_{10} (e) C_2H_5OH

(b) $H_2S_2O_8$ (d) B_2H_6

4.81 Quantitative analysis of a sample of sodium pertechnetate with a mass of 0.896 g found 0.111 g of sodium and 0.477 g of technetium. The remainder was oxygen. Calculate the empirical formula of sodium pertechnetate. (Radioactive sodium pertechnetate is used as a brain-scanning agent in medicine.)

4.82 A sample of Freon was found to contain 0.423 g of C, 2.50 g of Cl, and 1.34 g of F. What is the empirical formula of this compound?

4.83 A dry-cleaning fluid composed of only carbon and chlorine was found to be composed of 14.5% C and 85.5% Cl (by mass). What is the empirical formula of this compound?

4.84 One compound of mercury with a molar mass of 519 contains 77.26% Hg, 9.25% C, and 1.17% H (with the balance being O). Calculate the empirical and molecular formulas.

4.85 Cinnamic acid, a compound related to the flavor component of cinnamon, is 72.96% carbon, 5.40% hydrogen, and the rest is oxygen. What is the empirical formula of this acid?

4.86 Vanillin, a compound used as a flavoring agent in food products, has the following percentage composition: 64.2% C, 5.26% H, and 31.6% O. What is the empirical formula of vanillin?

ILW 4.87 When 0.684 g of an organic compound containing only carbon, hydrogen, and oxygen was burned in oxygen, 1.312 g of CO_2 and 0.805 g of H_2O were obtained. What is the empirical formula of the compound?

4.88 Methyl ethyl ketone (often abbreviated MEK) is a powerful solvent with many commercial uses. A sample of this compound (which contains only C, H, and O) weighing 0.822 g was burned in oxygen to give 2.01 g of CO_2 and 0.827 g of H_2O. What is the empirical formula for MEK?

4.89 When 6.853 mg of a sex hormone was burned in a combustion analysis, 19.73 mg of CO_2 and 6.391 mg of H_2O were obtained. What is the empirical formula of the compound?

4.90 When a sample of a compound in the vitamin D family was burned in a combustion analysis, 5.983 mg of the compound gave 18.490 mg of CO_2 and 6.232 mg of H_2O. What is the empirical formula of the compound?

Molecular Formulas

4.91 The following are empirical formulas and the masses per mole for three compounds. What are their molecular formulas?
(a) NaS_2O_3; 270.4 g/mol
(b) C_3H_2Cl; 147.0 g/mol
(c) C_2HCl; 181.4 g/mol

4.92 The following are empirical formulas and the masses per mole for three compounds. What are their molecular formulas?
(a) Na_2SiO_3; 732.6 g/mol
(b) $NaPO_3$; 305.9 g/mol
(c) CH_3O; 62.1 g/mol

4.93 The compound described in Problem 4.89 was found to have a molecular mass of 290. What is its molecular formula?

4.94 The compound described in Problem 4.90 was found to have a molecular mass of 399. What is the molecular formula of this compound?

ILW 4.95 A sample of a compound of mercury and bromine with a mass of 0.389 g was found to contain 0.111 g bromine. Its molecular mass was found to be 561. What are its empirical and molecular formulas?

4.96 A 0.6662 g sample of "antimonal saffron," which is a red pigment used in painting, was found to contain 0.4017 g of antimony. The remainder was sulfur. The formula mass of this compound is 404. What are the empirical and molecular formulas of this pigment?

4.97 A sample of a compound of C, H, N, and O, with a mass of 0.6216 g was found to contain 0.1735 g of C, 0.01455 g of H, and 0.2024 g of N. Its formula mass is 129. Calculate its empirical and molecular formulas.

4.98 Strychnine, a deadly poison, has a formula mass of 334 and a percentage composition of 75.42% C, 6.63% H, 8.38% N, and the balance oxygen. Calculate the empirical and molecular formulas of strychnine.

Balancing Chemical Equations

4.99 A balanced chemical equation contains the term "$2Ba(OH)_2 \cdot 8H_2O$." How many atoms of each element does this represent in the molecular view? How many moles of each element does this represent on the laboratory scale?

4.100 A balanced chemical equation contains the term "$3Ca_3(PO_4)_2$." How many atoms of each element does this represent in the molecular view? How many moles of each element does this represent on the laboratory scale?

OH 4.101 Write the equation that expresses in acceptable chemical shorthand the following statement: "Iron can be made to react with molecular oxygen to give iron(III) oxide."

4.102 The conversion of one air pollutant, nitrogen monoxide, produced in vehicle engines, into another pollutant, nitrogen dioxide, occurs when nitrogen monoxide reacts with molecular oxygen in the air. Write the balanced equation for this reaction.

4.103 Balance the following equations.
(a) Calcium hydroxide reacts with hydrogen chloride to form calcium chloride and water.
(b) Silver nitrate and calcium chloride react to form calcium nitrate and silver chloride.
(c) Lead nitrate reacts with sodium sulfate to form lead sulfate and sodium nitrate.
(d) Iron(III) oxide and carbon react to form iron and carbon dioxide.
(e) Butane reacts with oxygen to form carbon dioxide and water.

4.104 Balance the following equations.
(a) $SO_2 + O_2 \longrightarrow SO_3$
(b) $NaHCO_3 + H_2SO_4 \longrightarrow Na_2SO_4 + H_2O + CO_2$
(c) $P_4O_{10} + H_2O \longrightarrow H_3PO_4$
(d) $Fe_2O_3 + H_2 \longrightarrow Fe + H_2O$
(e) $Al + H_2SO_4 \longrightarrow Al_2(SO_4)_3 + H_2$

4.105 Balance the following equations.

    (a) $Mg(OH)_2 + HBr \longrightarrow MgBr_2 + H_2O$

    (b) $HCl + Ca(OH)_2 \longrightarrow CaCl_2 + H_2O$

    (c) $Al_2O_3 + H_2SO_4 \longrightarrow Al_2(SO_4)_3 + H_2O$

    (d) $KHCO_3 + H_3PO_4 \longrightarrow K_2HPO_4 + H_2O + CO_2$

    (e) $C_9H_{20} + O_2 \longrightarrow CO_2 + H_2O$

4.106 Balance the following equations.

    (a) $CaO + HNO_3 \longrightarrow Ca(NO_3)_2 + H_2O$

    (b) $Na_2CO_3 + Mg(NO_3)_2 \longrightarrow MgCO_3 + NaNO_3$

    (c) $(NH_4)_3PO_4 + NaOH \longrightarrow Na_3PO_4 + NH_3 + H_2O$

    (d) $LiHCO_3 + H_2SO_4 \longrightarrow Li_2SO_4 + H_2O + CO_2$

    (e) $C_4H_{10}O + O_2 \longrightarrow CO_2 + H_2O$

4.107 Using the diagram below, write the balanced chemical equation.

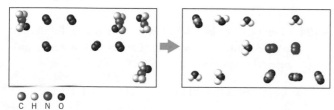

C H N O

4.108 Using the diagram below, write the balanced chemical equation.

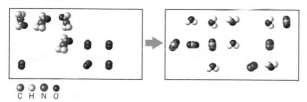

C H N O

Stoichiometry Based on Chemical Equations

4.109 Chlorine is used by textile manufacturers to bleach cloth. Excess chlorine is destroyed by its reaction with sodium thiosulfate, $Na_2S_2O_3$, as follows.

$$Na_2S_2O_3(aq) + 4Cl_2(g) + 5H_2O \longrightarrow$$
$$2NaHSO_4(aq) + 8HCl(aq)$$

    (a) How many moles of $Na_2S_2O_3$ are needed to react with 0.12 mol of Cl_2?

    (b) How many moles of HCl can form from 0.12 mol of Cl_2?

    (c) How many moles of H_2O are required for the reaction of 0.12 mol of Cl_2?

    (d) How many moles of H_2O react if 0.24 mol HCl is formed?

4.110 The octane in gasoline burns according to the following equation.

$$2C_8H_{18} + 25O_2 \longrightarrow 16CO_2 + 18H_2O$$

(a) How many moles of O_2 are needed to react fully with 6.84 mol of octane?

(b) How many moles of CO_2 can form from 0.511 mol of octane?

(c) How many moles of water are produced by the combustion of 8.20 mol of octane?

(d) If this reaction is used to synthesize 6.00 mol of CO_2, how many moles of oxygen are needed? How many moles of octane?

4.111 The following reaction is used to extract gold from pretreated gold ore:

$$2Au(CN)_2^-(aq) + Zn(s) \longrightarrow 2Au(s) + Zn(CN)_4^{2}\ (aq)$$

(a) How many grams of Zn are needed to react with 0.11 mol of $Au(CN)_2^-$?

(b) How many grams of Au can form from 0.11 mol of $Au(CN)_2^-$?

(c) How many grams of $Au(CN)_2^-$ are required for the reaction of 0.11 mol of Zn?

OH **4.112** Propane burns according to the following equation.

$$C_3H_8 + 5O_2 \longrightarrow 3CO_2 + 4H_2O$$

(a) How many grams of O_2 are needed to react fully with 3.45 mol of propane?

(b) How many grams of CO_2 can form from 0.177 mol of propane?

(c) How many grams of water are produced by the combustion of 4.86 mol of propane?

4.113 The incandescent white of a fireworks display is caused by the reaction of phosphorus with O_2 to give P_4O_{10}.

(a) Write the balanced chemical equation for the reaction.

(b) How many grams of O_2 are needed to combine with 6.85 g of P?

(c) How many grams of P_4O_{10} can be made from 8.00 g of O_2?

(d) How many grams of P are needed to make 7.46 g of P_4O_{10}?

4.114 The combustion of butane, C_4H_{10}, produces carbon dioxide and water. When one sample of C_4H_{10} was burned, 4.46 g of water was formed.

(a) Write the balanced chemical equation for the reaction.

(b) How many grams of butane were burned?

(c) How many grams of O_2 were consumed?

(d) How many grams of CO_2 were formed?

ILW **4.115** In *dilute* nitric acid, HNO_3, copper metal dissolves according to the following equation.

$$3Cu(s) + 8HNO_3(aq) \longrightarrow$$
$$3Cu(NO_3)_2(aq) + 2NO(g) + 4H_2O$$

How many grams of HNO_3 are needed to dissolve 11.45 g of Cu according to this equation?

4.116 The reaction of hydrazine, N_2H_4, with hydrogen peroxide, H_2O_2, has been used in rocket engines. One way these compounds react is described by the equation

$$N_2H_4 + 7H_2O_2 \longrightarrow 2HNO_3 + 8H_2O$$

According to this equation, how many grams of H_2O_2 are needed to react completely with 852 g of N_2H_4?

4.117 Oxygen gas can be produced in the laboratory by decomposition of hydrogen peroxide (H_2O_2):

$$2H_2O_2 \longrightarrow 2H_2O + O_2(g)$$

How many kg of O_2 can be produced from 1.0 kg of H_2O_2?

4.118 Oxygen gas can be produced in the laboratory by decomposition of potassium chlorate ($KClO_3$):

$$2KClO_3 \longrightarrow 2KCl + 3O_2(g)$$

How many kg of O_2 can be produced from 1.0 kg of $KClO_3$?

Limiting Reactant Calculations

4.119 Using the balanced equation

$$2C_2H_6S(g) + 9O_2(g) \longrightarrow 4CO_2(g) + 2SO_2(g) + 6H_2O(g)$$

determine the number of SO_2 units formed in the following molecular representation.

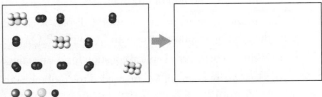

C H S O

4.120 Using the balanced chemical equation in Problem 4.119 and the diagram below, determine what the limiting reactant was.

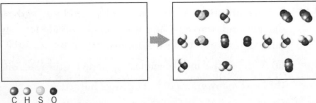

C H S O

4.121 The reaction of powdered aluminum and iron(III) oxide,

$$2Al + Fe_2O_3 \longrightarrow Al_2O_3 + 2Fe$$

produces so much heat the iron that forms is molten. Because of this, railroads have used this reaction to provide molten iron to weld steel rails together when laying track. Suppose that in one batch of reactants 4.20 mol of Al was mixed with 1.75 mol of Fe_2O_3.

(a) Which reactant, if either, was the limiting reactant?

(b) Calculate the number of grams of iron that can be formed from this mixture of reactants.

4.122 Ethanol (C_2H_5OH) is synthesized for industrial use by the following reaction, carried out at very high pressure:

$$C_2H_4(g) + H_2O(g) \longrightarrow C_2H_5OH(l)$$

What is the maximum amount, in kg, of ethanol that can be produced when 1.62 kg of ethylene (C_2H_4) and 0.0148 kg of steam are placed into the reaction vessel?

ILW 4.123 Silver nitrate, $AgNO_3$, reacts with iron(III) chloride, $FeCl_3$, to give silver chloride, $AgCl$, and iron(III) nitrate, $Fe(NO_3)_3$. A solution containing 18.0 g of $AgNO_3$ was mixed with a solution containing 32.4 g of $FeCl_3$. How many grams of which reactant remains after the reaction is over?

4.124 Chlorine dioxide, ClO_2, has been used as a disinfectant in air-conditioning systems. It reacts with water according to the equation

$$6ClO_2 + 3H_2O \longrightarrow 5HClO_3 + HCl$$

If 142.0 g of ClO_2 is mixed with 38.0 g of H_2O, how many grams of which reactant remain if the reaction is complete?

ILW 4.125 Some of the acid in acid rain is produced by the following reaction:

$$3NO_2(g) + H_2O(l) \longrightarrow 2HNO_3(aq) + NO(g)$$

If a falling raindrop weighing 0.050 g comes into contact with 1.0 mg of $NO_2(g)$, how many milligrams of HNO_3 can be produced?

4.126 Phosphorus pentachloride reacts with water to give phosphoric acid and hydrogen chloride according to the following equation.

$$PCl_5 + 4H_2O \longrightarrow H_3PO_4 + 5HCl$$

In one experiment, 0.360 mol of PCl_5 was slowly added to 2.88 mol of water.

(a) Which reactant, if either, was the limiting reactant?

(b) How many grams of HCl were formed in the reaction?

Theoretical Yield and Percentage Yield

4.127 Barium sulfate, $BaSO_4$, is made by the following reaction.

$$Ba(NO_3)_2(aq) + Na_2SO_4(aq) \longrightarrow$$
$$BaSO_4(s) + 2NaNO_3(aq)$$

An experiment was begun with 75.00 g of $Ba(NO_3)_2$ and an excess of Na_2SO_4. After collecting and drying the product, 64.45 g of $BaSO_4$ was obtained. Calculate the theoretical yield and percentage yield of $BaSO_4$.

4.128 The Solvay process for the manufacture of sodium carbonate begins by passing ammonia and carbon dioxide through a solution of sodium chloride to make sodium bicarbonate and ammonium chloride. The equation for the overall reaction is

$$H_2O + NaCl + NH_3 + CO_2 \longrightarrow$$
$$NH_4Cl + NaHCO_3$$

In the next step, sodium bicarbonate is heated to give sodium carbonate and two gases, carbon dioxide and steam.

$$2NaHCO_3 \longrightarrow Na_2CO_3 + CO_2 + H_2O$$

What is the theoretical yield of sodium carbonate, expressed in grams, if 120 g of NaCl was used in the first reaction? If 85.4 g of Na_2CO_3 was obtained, what was the percentage yield?

4.129 Aluminum sulfate can be made by the following reaction.

$$2AlCl_3(aq) + 3H_2SO_4(aq) \longrightarrow$$
$$Al_2(SO_4)_3(aq) + 6HCl(aq)$$

It is quite soluble in water, so to isolate it the solution has to be evaporated to dryness. This drives off the volatile HCl, but the residual solid has to be heated to a little over 200 °C to drive off all of the water. In one experiment, 25.0 g of $AlCl_3$ was mixed with 30.0 g of H_2SO_4. Eventually, 28.46 g of pure $Al_2(SO_4)_3$ was isolated. Calculate the percentage yield.

4.130 The combustion of methyl alcohol in an abundant excess of oxygen follows the equation

$$2CH_3OH + 3O_2 \longrightarrow 2CO_2 + 4H_2O$$

When 6.40 g of CH_3OH was mixed with 10.2 g of O_2 and ignited, 6.12 g of CO_2 was obtained. What was the percentage yield of CO_2?

*4.131 The potassium salt of benzoic acid, potassium benzoate ($KC_7H_5O_2$), can be made by the action of potassium permanganate on toluene (C_7H_8) as follows.

$$C_7H_8 + 2KMnO_4 \longrightarrow$$
$$KC_7H_5O_2 + 2MnO_2 + KOH + H_2O$$

If the yield of potassium benzoate cannot realistically be expected to be more than 71%, what is the minimum number of grams of toluene needed to produce 11.5 g of potassium benzoate?

OH ***4.132** Manganese(III) fluoride, MnF_3, can be prepared by the following reaction.

$$2MnI_2(s) + 13F_2(g) \longrightarrow 2MnF_3(s) + 4IF_5(l)$$

If the percentage yield of MnF_3 is always approximately 56%, how many grams of MnF_3 can be expected if 10.0 grams of each reactant is used in an experiment?

Additional Exercises

4.133 Mercury is an environmental pollutant because it can be converted by certain bacteria into the very poisonous substance dimethyl mercury, $(CH_3)_2Hg$. This compound ends up in the food chain and accumulates in the tissues of aquatic organisms, particularly fish, which renders them unsafe to eat. It is estimated that in the United States 263 tons of mercury are released into the atmosphere each year. If only 1.0 percent of this mercury is eventually changed to $(CH_3)_2Hg$, how many pounds of this compound are formed annually?

*4.134 Lead compounds are often highly colored and are toxic to mold, mildew, and bacteria, properties that in the past were useful for paints used before 1960. Today we know lead is very hazardous and it is not used in paint, however, old paint is still a problem. If a certain lead-based paint contains 14.5% $PbCr_2O_7$ and 73% of the paint evaporates as it dries, what mass of lead will be in a paint chip that weighs 0.15 g?

4.135 A superconductor is a substance that is able to conduct electricity without resistance, a property that is very desirable in the construction of large electromagnets. Metals have this property if cooled to temperatures a few degrees above absolute zero, but this requires the use of expensive liquid helium (boiling point 4 K). Scientists have discovered materials that become superconductors at higher temperatures, but they are ceramics. Their brittle nature has so far prevented them from being made into long wires. A recently discovered compound of magnesium and boron, which consists of 52.9 % Mg and 47.1 % B, shows special promise as a high-temperature superconductor because it is inexpensive to make and can be fabricated into wire relatively easily. What is the formula of this compound?

*4.136 A 0.1246 g sample of a compound of chromium and chlorine was dissolved in water. All of the chloride ion was then captured by silver ion in the form of AgCl. A mass of 0.3383 g of AgCl was obtained. Calculate the empirical formula of the compound of Cr and Cl.

*4.137 A compound of Ca, C, N, and S was subjected to quantitative analysis and formula mass determination, and the following data were obtained. A 0.250 g sample was mixed with Na_2CO_3 to convert all of the Ca to 0.160 g of $CaCO_3$. A 0.115 g sample of the compound was carried through a series of reactions until all of its S was changed to 0.344 g of $BaSO_4$. A 0.712 g sample was processed to liberate all of its N as NH_3, and 0.155 g of NH_3 was obtained. The formula mass was found to be 156. Determine the empirical and molecular formulas of this compound.

4.138 Ammonium nitrate will detonate if ignited in the presence of certain impurities. The equation for this reaction at a high temperature is

$$2NH_4NO_3(s) \xrightarrow{>300\ °C} 2N_2(g) + O_2(g) + 4H_2O(g)$$

Notice that all of the products are gases, so they occupy a vastly greater volume than the solid reactant.
(a) How many moles of *all* gases are produced from 1 mol of NH_4NO_3?
(b) If 1.00 ton of NH_4NO_3 exploded according to this equation, how many moles of *all* gases would be produced? (1 ton = 2000 lb.)

4.139 A lawn fertilizer is rated as 6.00% nitrogen, meaning 6.00 g of N in 100 g of fertilizer. The nitrogen is present in the form of urea, $(NH_2)_2CO$. How many grams of urea are present in 100 g of the fertilizer to supply the rated amount of nitrogen?

*4.140 Nitrogen is the "active ingredient" in many quick-acting fertilizers. You are operating a farm of 1500 acres to produce soybeans. Which of the following fertilizers will you choose as the most economical for your farm? **(a)** NH_4NO_3 at \$625 for 25 kg; **(b)** $(NH_4)_2HPO_4$ at \$55 for 1 kg; **(c)** urea, CH_4ON_2, at \$60 for 5 kg; or **(d)** ammonia, NH_3 at \$128 for 50 kg.

4.141 Based solely on the amount of available carbon, how many grams of sodium oxalate, $Na_2C_2O_4$, could be obtained from 125 g of C_6H_6? (Assume that no loss of carbon occurs in any of the reactions needed to produce the $Na_2C_2O_4$.)

4.142 According to NASA, the space shuttle's external fuel tank for the main propulsion system carries 1,361,936 lb of liquid oxygen and 227,641 lb of liquid hydrogen. During takeoff, these chemicals are consumed as they react to form water. If the reaction is continued until all of one reactant is gone, how many pounds of which reactant are left over?

*4.143 For a research project, a student decided to test the effect of the lead(II) ion (Pb^{2+}) on the ability of salmon eggs to hatch. This ion was obtainable from the water-soluble salt, lead(II) nitrate, $Pb(NO_3)_2$, which the student decided to make by the following reaction. (The desired product was to be isolated by the slow evaporation of the water.)

$$PbO(s) + 2HNO_3(aq) \longrightarrow Pb(NO_3)_2(aq) + H_2O$$

Losses of product for various reasons were expected, and a yield of 86.0% was expected. In order to have 5.00 g of product at this yield, how many grams of PbO should be taken? (Assume that sufficient nitric acid, HNO_3, would be used.)

4.144 Chlorine atoms cause chain reactions in the stratosphere that destroy ozone that protects the Earth's surface from ultraviolet radiation. The chlorine atoms come from chlorofluorocarbons, compounds that contain carbon, fluorine, and chlorine, which were used for many years as refrigerants. One of these compounds is Freon-12, CF_2Cl_2. If a sample contains 1.0×10^{-9} g of Cl, how many grams of F should be present if all of the F and Cl atoms in the sample came from CF_2Cl_2 molecules?

*4.145 Lime, CaO, can be produced in two steps as shown in the equations below. If the percentage yield of the first step is 83.5% and the percentage yield of the second step is 71.4%, what is the expected overall percentage yield for producing CaO from $CaCl_2$?

$$CaCl_2(aq) + CO_2(g) + H_2O \longrightarrow$$
$$CaCO_3(s) + 2HCl(aq)$$
$$CaCO_3(s) \xrightarrow{heat} CaO(s) + H_2O(g)$$

| Exercises in Critical Thinking

4.146 A newspaper story describing the local celebration of Mole Day on October 23 (selected for Avogadro's number, 6.02×10^{23}) attempted to give the readers a sense of the size of the number by stating that a mole of M&Ms would be equal to 18 tractor trailers full. Assuming that an M&M occupies a volume of about 0.5 cm^3, calculate the dimensions of a cube required to hold one mole of M&Ms. Would 18 tractor trailers be sufficient?

4.147 Suppose you had one mole of pennies and you were going to spend 500 million dollars each and every second until

you spent your entire fortune. How many years would it take you to spend all this cash? (Assume 1 year = 365 days.)

4.148 Using the above two questions as examples, devise a creative way to demonstrate the size of the mole, or Avogadro's number.

4.149 List the different ways in which a chemist could use the information used to determine empirical formulas.

Chapters 1–4

[**Bringing It Together**] Many of the fundamental concepts and problem-solving skills developed in the preceding chapters will carry forward into the rest of this book. Therefore, we recommend that you pause here to see how well you have grasped the concepts, how familiar you are with important terms, and how able you are at working chemistry problems.

Don't be discouraged if some of the problems here seem to be difficult at first. Many require using tools developed in more than one chapter. In some cases, necessary data are not included in the problem, so you will need to refer to tables in the book, including those inside the front and back covers. For problems that require mathematical solutions, we recommend that you follow the approach used in the worked examples. Begin with an analysis of the problem. If you get stuck, keep in mind that all the neccessary tools have been discussed in the preceding chapters. Next, assemble the necessary tools and set up the required conversion factors needed to obtain the answers, and then proceed to the solution. Don't forget to check your answers!

1. A rectangular block of zinc was found to be 24.6 cm wide, 0.35140 m high, and 7,424 mm deep.
   (a) How many significant figures are in each measurement?
   (b) Calculate the volume of the block in units of cm^3. Be sure to express your answer to the correct number of significant figures.
   (c) Calculate the volume of the zinc block in cubic feet.
   (d) Zinc has a density of 7.140 g/cm^3. What is the mass of the block in kilograms?
   (e) How many moles of zinc are contained in the block?
   (f) If all of the zinc were converted to zinc phosphate, how many grams of this compound would be obtained?

2. What is the difference between an atom and a molecule? What is the difference between a molecule and a mole? If you were forming a conversion factor, what relationship exists between molecules and moles?

3. If a 10.0 g sample of element X contains twice as many atoms as a 10.0 g sample of element Y, how does the atomic mass of X compare with the atomic mass of Y?

4. What is the percentage composition by mass of the substance shown below? How many molecules are in 12.0 g of this substance?

5. When the substance shown below burns in oxygen, the products are carbon dioxide and water. How many grams of water are obtained from burning 4.76 g of this substance?

6. What is the total number of protons and electrons in one molecule of the substance described in Question 4?

7. Derive a single conversion factor that would enable you to convert a volume of 3.14 ft^3 into cubic centimeters (cm^3).

8. A silver nitrate solution was added to an aqueous solution of 1.223 g of an iron–chlorine compound. When dried and weighed, the silver chloride that formed weighed 3.243 g. What is the name of the iron–chlorine compound?

9. A sample of the compound shown below contains 5.22 g of nitrogen. How many grams of oxygen does it contain? What is the percentage by mass of nitrogen in the compound?

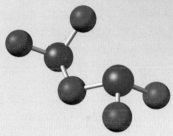

10. Ethanol, C_2H_5OH, is a renewable energy resource that is added to gasoline to help reduce the U.S. dependence on foreign oil imports. How many molecules of ethanol are in 1.00 fluid ounce of the liquid? The density of ethanol is 0.798 g/mL (1 fluid oz = 29.6 mL). How many grams of O_2 are needed for the complete combustion of 1.00 gallons of ethanol to give CO_2 and H_2O?

11. How did Dalton's atomic theory account for the law of conservation of mass? How did it explain the law of definite proportions?

12. What are the formula and name of the compound formed from chlorine and a substance in which the atoms contain 20 protons? What is the molar mass of this compound?

13. The atoms of one of the isotopes of plutonium, Pu, contain 94 protons, 150 neutrons, and 94 electrons. Write a symbol for this isotope that incorporates its mass number and atomic number. Write the symbol for a different isotope of plutonium.

14. Give chemical formulas for the following.
   (a) potassium nitrate   (h) copper(II) perchlorate
   (b) calcium carbonate   (i) bromine pentafluoride
   (c) cobalt(II) phosphate   (j) dinitrogen pentaoxide
   (d) magnesium sulfite   (k) strontium acetate
   (e) iron(III) bromide   (l) ammonium dichromate
   (f) magnesium nitride   (m) copper(I) sulfide
   (g) aluminum selenide

15. Give chemical names for the following.
   (a) $NaClO_3$ (e) ICl_3 (i) $MnCl_2$
   (b) $Ca_3(PO_4)_2$ (f) PCl_3 (j) $NaNO_2$
   (c) $NaMnO_4$ (g) K_2CrO_4 (k) $Fe(NO_3)_2$
   (d) AlP   (h) $Ca(CN)_2$

16. For each of the following, indicate whether it is possible to see the item specified with the naked eye. If not, explain
   (a) A molar mass of iron   (d) A mole of water
   (b) An atom of iron   (e) An ion of sodium
   (c) A molecule of water   (f) A formula unit of sodium chloride

17. Which of the following are binary substances: Al_2O_3, Cl_2, MgO, NO_2, $NaClO_4$? Which are molecular and which are ionic?

18. If 2.56 g of chlorine, Cl_2, will be used to prepare dichlorine heptaoxide, how many moles and how many grams of molecular oxygen are needed?

19. How many grams of O_2 are consumed in the complete combustion of 25.0 mL of ethylene glycol, $C_2H_4(OH)_2$, which has a density of 1.11 g mL^{-1}? The products of the combustion are CO_2 and H_2O. How many molecules of CO_2 are formed in the reaction?

20. A sample of 0.5866 g of nicotine was analyzed and found to consist of 0.4343 g C, 0.05103 g H, and 0.1013 g N. Calculate the percentage composition of nicotine.

21. A compound of potassium had the following percentage composition: K, 37.56%; H, 1.940%; P, 29.79%. The rest was oxygen. Calculate the empirical formula of this compound (arranging the atomic symbols in the order K H P O.)

22. How many milliliters of pure nitric acid, HNO_3, are needed to react with 2.56 mol of Cu in the following reaction? The density of nitric acid is 1.51 g cm^{-3}.

$$3Cu + 8HNO_3 \longrightarrow 3Cu(NO_3)_2 + 2NO + 4H_2O$$

23. Under the right conditions, ammonia can be converted to nitrogen monoxide, NO, according to the following unbalanced equation.

$$NH_3 + O_2 \longrightarrow NO + H_2O$$

How many moles and how many grams of O_2 are needed to react with 56.8 g of ammonia by this reaction?

24. Dolomite is a mineral consisting of calcium carbonate and magnesium carbonate. When dolomite is strongly heated, its carbonates decompose to their oxides (CaO and MgO) and carbon dioxide is expelled.
   (a) Write the separate equations for the decomposition of calcium carbonate and magnesium carbonate.
   (b) When a dolomite sample with a mass of 5.78 g was heated strongly, the residue had a mass of 3.02 g. Calculate the masses in grams and the percentages of calcium carbonate and magnesium carbonate in this sample of dolomite.

25. Adipic acid, $C_6H_{10}O_4$, is a raw material for making nylon, and it can be prepared in the laboratory by the following reaction between cyclohexene, C_6H_{10}, and sodium dichromate, $Na_2Cr_2O_7$, in sulfuric acid, H_2SO_4.

$$3C_6H_{10}(l) + 4Na_2Cr_2O_7(aq) + 16H_2SO_4(aq) \longrightarrow$$
$$3C_6H_{10}O_4(s) + 4Cr_2(SO_4)_3(aq) + 4Na_2SO_4(aq) + 16H_2O$$

There are side reactions. These plus losses of product during its purification reduce the overall yield. A typical yield of purified adipic acid is 68.6%.
   (a) To prepare 12.5 g of adipic acid in 68.6% yield requires how many grams of cyclohexene?

   (b) The only available supply of sodium dichromate is its dihydrate, $Na_2Cr_2O_7 \cdot 2H_2O$. (Since the reaction occurs in an aqueous medium, the water in the dihydrate causes no problems, but it does contribute to the mass of what is taken of this reactant.) How many grams of this dihydrate are also required in the preparation of 12.5 g of adipic acid in a yield of 68.6%?

26. One of the ores of iron is hematite, Fe_2O_3, mixed with other rock. One sample of this ore is 31.4% hematite. How many tons of this ore are needed to make 1.00 ton of iron if the percentage recovery of iron from the ore is 91.5% (1 ton = 2000 lb)?

27. Gold occurs in the ocean in a range of concentration of 0.1 to 2 mg of gold per ton of seawater. Near one coastal city the gold concentration of the ocean is 1.5 mg/ton.
   (a) How many tons of seawater have to be processed to obtain 1.0 troy ounce of gold if the recovery is 65% successful? (The troy ounce, 31.1 g, is the standard "ounce" in the gold trade.)
   (b) If gold can be sold for $1152.84 per troy ounce, what is the breakeven point in the dollar cost per ton of processed seawater for extracting gold from the ocean at this location?

28. *C.I. Pigment Yellow 45* ("sideran yellow") is a pigment used in ceramics, glass, and enamel. When analyzed, a 2.164 g sample of this substance was found to contain 0.5259 g of Fe and 0.7345 g of Cr. The remainder was oxygen. Calculate the empirical formula of this pigment. What additional data are needed to calculate the molecular mass of this compound?

29. When 6.584 mg of one of the hydrates of sodium sulfate was heated so as to drive off all of its water of hydration, the residue of anhydrous sodium sulfate had a mass of 2.889 mg. What is the formula of the hydrate?

30. In an earlier problem we described the reaction of ammonia with oxygen to form nitrogen monoxide, NO:
$$NH_3 + O_2 \longrightarrow NO + H_2O \qquad \text{(unbalanced)}$$
How many moles and how many grams of NO could be formed from a mixture of 45.0 g of NH_3 and 58.0 g of O_2? How many grams of which reactant would remain unreacted?

31. A sample of 14.0 cm^3 of aluminum, in powdered form, was mixed with an excess of iron(III) oxide. A reaction between them was initiated that formed aluminum oxide and metallic iron. How many cubic centimeters of metallic iron were formed?

32. Give the balanced equation for the reaction shown below. Is there a limiting reactant? How many molecules of the excess reactant are left?

33. What principle forms the basis for the arrangement of elements in the periodic table? If the periodic table was arranged in a spiral, what elements would be to the right of helium, neon, argon, krypton, and radon, respectively?

5 Molecular View of Reactions in Aqueous Solutions

Chapter Outline

The Coca-Cola shown in this photo is a complex mixture that contains, among other things, a small amount of phosphoric acid, which is added to provide just a bit of tartness to the beverage. Many of the foods we eat contain acids and many of the products we use around the house contain substances called bases. The nature of acids and bases and how they behave in aqueous solutions are among the topics discussed later in this chapter. (Photocuisine/Masterfile)

This Chapter in Context

Water is an amazing substance. Composed of just three atoms, it is one of the most common compounds on earth, and its ability to dissolve so many different kinds of materials is responsible, to a large degree, for the evolution of life as we know it. Our bodies are composed of approximately 60% water; it is the major component of the fluids in and around our cells, and it serves to transport nutrients throughout our systems.

A property of water that sets it apart from other liquids is its ability to dissolve many ionic compounds, enabling their particles to mix at the molecular level where they are able to easily react. In this chapter we will study in detail what happens when ionic substances dissolve in water, the nature of the chemical reactions they undergo, and the products that form. We will also introduce you to another important class of compounds called acids and bases, and we will examine the reactions of these substances in aqueous solutions. Finally, we will extend the principles of stoichiometry that you learned in Chapter 4 to deal quantitatively with chemical reactions in solution.

5.1 | Describing Solutions

Before we get to the meat of our subject, we first must define some terms. A **solution** is a homogeneous mixture in which the molecules or ions of the components freely intermingle (Figure 5.1). When a solution forms, at least two substances are involved. One is the *solvent* and all of the others are *solutes*. The **solvent** is the medium into which the solutes are mixed or dissolved. In this chapter we deal with *aqueous solutions*, so the solvent will be liquid water.[1] A **solute** is any substance dissolved in the solvent. It might be a gas, like the carbon dioxide dissolved in the Coca-Cola shown in the photo on the preceding page. Some solutes are liquids, like ethylene glycol dissolved in water to protect a car's radiator against freezing in the winter and boiling over in the summer. Solids, of course, can be solutes, like the sugar dissolved in lemonade or the salt dissolved in seawater.

■ When water is a component of a solution, it is usually considered to be the solvent even when it is present in small amounts.

To describe the composition of a solution, we often specify a **concentration**, which is the *ratio* of the amount of solute either to the amount of solvent or to the amount of solution. A **percentage concentration**, for example, is the number of grams of solute per 100 g of solution, a "solute-to-solution" ratio. Thus, the concentration of sodium chloride in seawater is often given as 3% NaCl, which means 3 g NaCl/100 g seawater.

The *relative* amounts of solute and solvent are often loosely given without specifying actual quantities. In a **dilute solution** the ratio of solute to solvent is small—such as when a few crystals of salt are dissolved in a glass of water. In a **concentrated solution**, the ratio of solute to solvent is large (Figure 5.2). Pancake syrup, for example, is a very concentrated solution of sugar in water.

Concentrated and dilute are relative terms. For example, a solution of 100 g of sugar in 100 mL of water is concentrated compared to one with just 10 g of sugar in 100 mL of water, but the latter solution is more concentrated than one that has 1 g of sugar in 100 mL of water.

Usually there is a limit to how much solute will dissolve in a solution. When a solution contains as much solute as it will hold at a given temperature, it is a **saturated solution** and any excess solute that's added simply sits at the bottom of the solution. The **solubility** of a solute is the amount required to give a saturated solution, usually expressed as grams dissolved in 100 g of solvent at a given temperature. The temperature must be specified because solubilities vary with temperature. A solution having less solute than required for saturation is called an **unsaturated solution**. It is able to dissolve more solute.

---

[1] Liquid water is a typical and very common solvent, but the solvent can actually be in any physical state: solid, liquid, or gas.

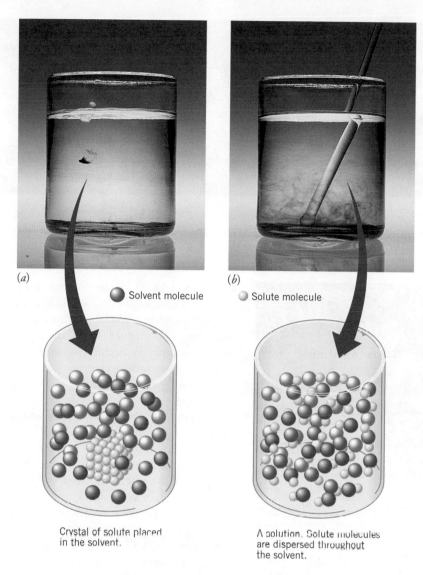

(a)

● Solvent molecule

(b)

○ Solute molecule

Crystal of solute placed in the solvent.

A solution. Solute molecules are dispersed throughout the solvent.

Figure 5.1 | Formation of a solution of iodine molecules in alcohol. *(a)* A crystal of iodine, I_2, on its way to the bottom of the beaker is already beginning to dissolve, the purplish iodine crystal forming a reddish brown solution. In the hugely enlarged view beneath the photo, we see the iodine molecules still bound in a crystal. For simplicity, the solute and solvent particles are shown as spheres. *(b)* Stirring the mixture helps the iodine molecules to disperse in the solvent, as illustrated in the molecular view below the photo. The solution is commonly called "tincture of iodine." *(Richard Megna/Fundamental Photographs)*

In most cases, the solubility of a solute increases with temperature, so more solute can be dissolved by heating a saturated solution in the presence of excess solute. If the temperature of such a warm saturated solution is subsequently lowered, the additional solute should separate from the solution, and indeed, this tends to happen spontaneously. However, sometimes the solute doesn't separate, leaving us with a **supersaturated solution**, a solution that actually contains more solute than required for saturation. Supersaturated solutions are unstable and can only be prepared if there are no traces of undissolved solute. If even a tiny crystal of the solute is present or is added, the extra solute crystallizes (Figure 5.3). A solid that forms in a solution is called a **precipitate,** and a chemical reaction that produces a precipitate is called a **precipitation reaction.**

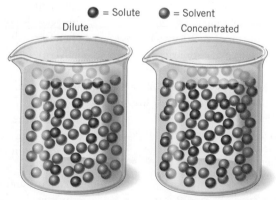

● = Solute   ● = Solvent
Dilute   Concentrated

Figure 5.2 | Dilute and concentrated solutions. The dilute solution on the left has fewer solute molecules per unit volume than the more concentrated solution on the right.

5.2 | Electrolytes, Strong Electrolytes, and Nonelectrolytes

Water itself is a very poor electrical conductor because it consists of electrically neutral molecules that are unable to transport electrical charges. However, as we noted in Chapter 3, when an ionic compound dissolves in water the resulting solution conducts

Figure 5.3 | **Crystallization.** When a small seed crystal of sodium acetate is added to a supersaturated solution of the compound, excess solute crystallizes rapidly until the solution is just saturated. The crystallization shown in this sequence took less than 10 seconds! *(Andy Washnik)*

(a)   *(b)*

Figure 5.4 | **Electrical conductivity of solutions.** (*a*) The copper sulfate solution is a strong conductor of electricity, so $CuSO_4$ is classified as a strong electrolyte. (*b*) Neither sugar nor water is an electrolyte, so this sugar solution is a nonconductor. *(Michael Watson)*

■ Solutions of electrolytes conduct electricity in a way that's different from metals. This is discussed more completely in Chapter 20.

■ Ethylene glycol, $C_2H_4(OH)_2$, is a type of alcohol. Other alcohols, such as ethanol and methanol, are also nonelectrolytes.

electricity well. This is illustrated in Figure 5.4*a* for a solution of copper sulfate, $CuSO_4$.

Solutes such as $CuSO_4$, which yield electrically conducting aqueous solutions, are called **electrolytes.** Their ability to conduct electricity suggests the presence of electrically charged particles that are able to move within the solution. The generally accepted reason is that when an ionic compound dissolves in water, the ions separate from each other and enter the solution as more or less independent particles that are surrounded by molecules of the solvent. This change is called the **dissociation** (*breaking apart*) of the ionic compound, and is illustrated in Figure 5.5. In general, *we will assume that in water the dissociation of any* **salt** (*a term that applies to any ionic compound*) *is complete* and that the solution contains no undissociated formula units of the salt. Thus, an aqueous solution of $CuSO_4$ is really a solution that contains Cu^{2+} and SO_4^{2-} ions, with virtually no undissociated formula units of $CuSO_4$. Because solutions of ionic compounds contain so many freely moving ions, they are strong conductors of electricity. Therefore, salts are said to be **strong electrolytes.**

Many ionic compounds have low solubilities in water. An example is AgBr, the light-sensitive compound in most photographic film. Although only a tiny amount of this compound dissolves in water, all of it that does dissolve is completely dissociated. However, because of the extremely low solubility, the number of ions in the solution is extremely small and the solution doesn't conduct electricity well. Nevertheless, it is still convenient to think of AgBr as a strong electrolyte because it serves to remind us that salts are completely dissociated in aqueous solution.

Aqueous solutions of most molecular, covalently bonded compounds do not conduct electricity, and such solutes are called **nonelectrolytes.** Examples are sugar (Figure 5.4*b*) and ethylene glycol (the solute in antifreeze solutions). Both consist of uncharged molecules that stay intact and simply intermingle with water molecules when they dissolve (Figure 5.6).

Dissociation Reactions

A convenient way to describe the dissociation of an ionic compound is with a chemical equation. Thus, for the dissociation of calcium chloride in water we write

$$CaCl_2(s) \longrightarrow Ca^{2+}(aq) + 2Cl^-(aq)$$

We use the symbol (*aq*) after a charged particle to mean that it is **hydrated** (*surrounded by water molecules in the solution*). By writing the formulas of the ions separately, we mean

Figure 5.5 | **Dissociation of an ionic compound as it dissolves in water.** Ions separate from the solid and become surrounded by water molecules. The ions are said to be hydrated. In the solution the ions are able to move freely, which enables the solution to conduct electricity.

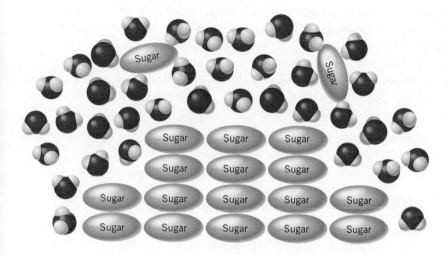

Figure 5.6 | **Formation of an aqueous solution of a nonelectrolyte.** When a nonelectrolyte dissolves in water, the molecules of solute separate from each other and mingle with the water molecules. The solute molecules stay intact and do not dissociate into smaller particles.

that they are essentially independent of each other in the solution. Notice that each formula unit of $CaCl_2(s)$ releases three ions, one $Ca^{2+}(aq)$ and two $Cl^-(aq)$.

Often, when the context is clear that the system is aqueous, the symbols (*s*) and (*aq*) are omitted. They are "understood." You should not be disturbed, therefore, when you see an equation such as

$$CaCl_2 \longrightarrow Ca^{2+} + 2Cl^-$$

Polyatomic ions generally remain intact as dissociation occurs. When copper sulfate dissolves, for example, both Cu^{2+} and SO_4^{2-} ions are released.

$$CuSO_4(s) \longrightarrow Cu^{2+}(aq) + SO_4^{2-}(aq)$$

■ Be sure you know the formulas and charges on the polyatomic ions listed in Table 3.5 on page 84.

Example 5.1
Writing the Equation for the Dissociation of an Ionic Compound

Ammonium sulfate is used as a fertilizer to supply nitrogen to crops. Write the equation for the dissociation of this compound when it dissolves in water.

■**Analysis:** This is actually a two-part problem. First, we have to write the correct formula for ammonium sulfate. Then we have to write the equation of the dissociation.

■**Assembling the Tools:** First we need the formula for ammonium sulfate, which means we need to know the formulas and charges of the ions that make up the salt. You should already know this information, but if you forgot it, the tool to use is Table 3.5 in Section 3.4. To write the equation, we need to follow the style presented above.

■ **Solution:** In this case, the cation is NH_4^+ (ammonium ion) and the anion is SO_4^{2-} (sulfate ion). The correct formula of the compound is therefore $(NH_4)_2SO_4$, which means there are *two* NH_4^+ ions for each SO_4^{2-} ion. We have to be sure to indicate this in the ionic equation.

We write the formula for the solid on the left of the equation and indicate its state by (*s*). The ions are written on the right side of the equation and are shown to be in aqueous solution by the symbol (*aq*) following their formulas.

$$(NH_4)_2SO_4(s) \longrightarrow 2NH_4^+(aq) + SO_4^{2-}(aq)$$

The subscript 2 becomes the coefficient for NH_4^+.

■ **Is the Answer Reasonable?** There are two things to check when writing equations such as this. First, be sure you have the correct formulas for the ions, including their charges. Second, be sure you've indicated the number of ions of each kind that comes from one formula unit when the compound dissociates. Performing these checks here confirms we've solved the problem correctly.

Practice Exercises

5.1 | Write equations that show the dissociation of the following compounds in water: (a) $FeCl_3$ and (b) potassium phosphate. (*Hint:* Identify the ions present in each compound.)

5.2 | Write equations that show what happens when the following solid ionic compounds dissolve in water: (a) $MgCl_2$, (b) $Al(NO_3)_3$, and (c) sodium carbonate.

Equations for Ionic Reactions

Often, ionic compounds react with each other when their aqueous solutions are combined. For example, when solutions of lead(II) nitrate, $Pb(NO_3)_2$, and potassium iodide, KI, are mixed, a bright yellow precipitate of lead(II) iodide, PbI_2, forms (Figure 5.7). The chemical equation for the reaction is

$$Pb(NO_3)_2(aq) + 2KI(aq) \longrightarrow PbI_2(s) + 2KNO_3(aq) \tag{5.1}$$

where we have noted the insolubility of PbI_2 by writing (*s*) following its formula. This is called a **molecular equation** because all the formulas are written with the ions together, as if

CHEMISTRY OUTSIDE THE CLASSROOM | 5.1

Painful Precipitates—Kidney Stones

Each year, more than a million people in the United States are hospitalized because of very painful kidney stone attacks. Kidney stone is a hard mass developed from crystals that separate from the urine and build up on the inner surfaces of the kidney. The formation of the stones is caused primarily by the buildup of Ca^{2+}, $C_2O_4^{2-}$, and PO_4^{3-} ions in the urine. When the concentrations of these ions become large enough, the urine becomes supersaturated with respect to calcium oxalate and/or calcium phosphate and precipitates begin to form (70% to 80% of all kidney stones are made up of calcium oxalate and phosphate). If the crystals remain tiny enough, they can travel through the urinary tract and pass out of the body in the urine without being noticed. Sometimes, however, they continue to grow without

being passed and can cause intense pain if they become stuck in the urinary tract.

Kidney stones don't all look alike. Their color depends on what substances are mixed with the inorganic precipitates (e.g., proteins or blood). Most are yellow or brown, as seen in the accompanying photo, but they can be tan, gold, or even black. Stones can be round, jagged, or even have branches. They vary in size from mere specks to pebbles to stones as big as golf balls!

A calcium oxalate kidney stone. Kidney stones such as this can be extremely painful. *(Custom Medical Stock Photo, Inc.)*

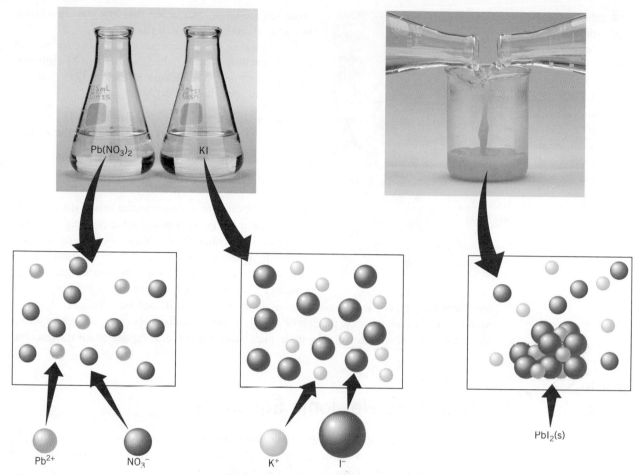

Figure 5.7 | **The reaction of Pb(NO₃)₂ with KI.** On the left are flasks containing solutions of lead(II) nitrate and potassium iodide. These solutes exist as separated ions in their respective solutions. On the right, we observe that when the solutions of the ions are combined, there is an immediate reaction as the Pb^{2+} ions join with the I^- ions to give a precipitate of small crystals of solid, yellow PbI_2. The reaction is so rapid that the yellow color develops where the two streams of liquid come together. If the $Pb(NO_3)_2$ and KI are combined in a 1-to-2 mole ratio, the solution surrounding the precipitate would now contain only K^+ and NO_3^- ions (the ions of KNO_3). *(Andy Washnik)*

the substances in solution consist of neutral "molecules." Equation 5.1 is fine for performing stoichiometric calculations, but let's look at other ways we might write the chemical equation.

Soluble ionic compounds are fully dissociated in solution, so $Pb(NO_3)_2$, KI, and KNO_3 are not present in the solution as intact units or "molecules." To show this, we can write the formulas of all soluble strong electrolytes in "dissociated" form to give the **ionic equation** for the reaction.

$$Pb(NO_3)_2(aq) \quad + \quad 2KI(aq) \longrightarrow PbI_2(s) \quad + \quad 2KNO_3(aq)$$

$$Pb^{2+}(aq) + 2NO_3^-(aq) + 2K^+(aq) + 2I^-(aq) \longrightarrow PbI_2(s) + 2K^+(aq) + 2NO_3^-(aq)$$

Notice that we have *not* separated PbI_2 into its ions in this equation. This is because PbI_2 has an extremely low solubility in water; it is essentially insoluble. When the Pb^{2+} and I^- ions meet in the solution, insoluble PbI_2 forms and separates as a precipitate. Therefore, after the reaction is over, the Pb^{2+} and I^- ions are no longer able to move independently. They are trapped in the insoluble product.

The ionic equation gives a clearer picture of what is actually going on in the solution during the reaction. The Pb^{2+} and I^- ions come together to form the product. The other ions, K^+ and NO_3^-, are unchanged by the reaction. Ions that do not actually take part in

Figure 5.8 | **Another reaction that forms lead iodide.** The net ionic equation tells us that any soluble lead(II) compound will react with any soluble iodide compound to give lead(II) iodide. This prediction is born out here as a precipitate of lead(II) iodide is formed when a solution of sodium iodide is added to a solution of lead(II) acetate. *(Andy Washnik)*

a reaction are sometimes called **spectator ions**; in a sense, they just "stand by and watch the action."

To emphasize the actual reaction that occurs, we can write the **net ionic equation**, which is obtained by eliminating spectator ions from the ionic equation. Let's cross out the spectator ions, K^+ and NO_3^-.

$$Pb^{2+}(aq) + 2\cancel{NO_3^-}(aq) + 2\cancel{K^+}(aq) + 2I^-(aq) \longrightarrow \\ PbI_2(s) + 2\cancel{K^+}(aq) + 2\cancel{NO_3^-}(aq)$$

What remains is the net ionic equation,

$$Pb^{2+}(aq) + 2I^-(aq) \longrightarrow PbI_2(s)$$

Notice how it calls our attention to the ions that are actually participating in the reaction as well as the change that occurs.

The net ionic equation is especially useful because it permits us to *generalize*. It tells us that if we combine *any* solution that contains Pb^{2+} with *any* other solution that contains I^-, we ought to expect a precipitate of PbI_2. This is exactly what happens if we mix aqueous solutions of lead(II) acetate, $Pb(C_2H_3O_2)_2$, and sodium iodide, NaI. A yellow precipitate of PbI_2 forms immediately (Figure 5.8). Example 5.2 demonstrates how we construct the molecular, ionic, and net ionic equations for the reaction.

Example 5.2
Writing Molecular, Ionic, and Net Ionic Equations

Write the molecular, ionic, and net ionic equations for the reaction of aqueous solutions of lead(II) acetate and sodium iodide, which yields a precipitate of lead(II) iodide and leaves the compound sodium acetate in solution.

■**Analysis:** Once again, this is a multi-part question. To write the equations, we first need to know the formulas of the reactants and products, so that's the first thing we have to work on. Then we can proceed to construct the three equations to answer the questions.

■**Assembling the Tools:** The first tool we need to apply is the set of rules of nomenclature you learned in Chapter 3. (If necessary, review them.) These rules tell us the ions involved are: Pb^{2+}, $C_2H_3O_2^-$, Na^+, and I^-. The requirement for electrical neutrality is the next tool we use to obtain the correct formulas of the reactants and products. Then we can use the methods for writing, balancing, and constructing the three kinds of equations asked for in the question.

■**Solution:** Following the rules we discussed in Chapter 3, we have:

Reactants		Products	
lead(II) acetate	$Pb(C_2H_3O_2)_2$	lead(II) iodide	PbI_2
sodium iodide	NaI	sodium acetate	$NaC_2H_3O_2$

The Molecular Equation We assemble the chemical formulas into the molecular equation and balance it.

$$Pb(C_2H_3O_2)_2(aq) + 2NaI(aq) \longrightarrow PbI_2(s) + 2NaC_2H_3O_2(aq)$$

Notice that we've indicated which substances are in solution and which substance is a precipitate. This is the *balanced molecular equation*.

The Ionic Equation To write the ionic equation, we write the formulas of all soluble salts in dissociated form and the formulas of precipitates in "molecular" form. We are careful to use the subscripts and coefficients in the molecular equation to properly obtain the coefficients of the ions in the ionic equation.

$$Pb(C_2H_3O_2)_2 \qquad\qquad 2NaI \qquad\qquad 2NaC_2H_3O_2$$

$$Pb^{2+}(aq) + 2C_2H_3O_2^-(aq) + 2Na^+(aq) + 2I^-(aq) \longrightarrow$$

$$PbI_2(s) + 2Na^+(aq) + 2C_2H_3O_2^-(aq)$$

This is the *balanced ionic equation*. Notice that to properly write the ionic equation it is necessary to know both the formulas and charges of the ions.

The Net Ionic Equation We obtain the net ionic equation from the ionic equation by eliminating spectator ions, which are Na^+ and $C_2H_3O_2^-$ (they're the same on both sides of the arrow). Let's cross them out.

$$Pb^{2+}(aq) + \cancel{2C_2H_3O_2^-(aq)} + \cancel{2Na^+(aq)} + 2I^-(aq) \longrightarrow PbI_2(s) + \cancel{2Na^+(aq)} + \cancel{2C_2H_3O_2^-(aq)}$$

What's left is the *net ionic equation*.

$$Pb^{2+}(aq) + 2I^-(aq) \longrightarrow PbI_2(s)$$

Notice that this is the same net ionic equation as in the reaction of lead(II) nitrate with potassium iodide.

■ **Are the Answers Reasonable?** When you look back over a problem such as this, things to ask yourself are (1) "Have I written the correct formulas for the reactants and products?" (2) "Is the molecular equation balanced correctly?" (3) "Have I divided the soluble ionic compounds into their ions correctly, being careful to properly apply the subscripts of the ions and the coefficients in the molecular equation?" and (4) "Have I identified and eliminated the correct ions from the ionic equation to obtain the net ionic equation?" If each of these questions can be answered in the affirmative, as they can here, you have solved the problem correctly.

Practice Exercises

5.3 | When solutions of $(NH_4)_2SO_4$ and $Ba(NO_3)_2$ are mixed, a precipitate of $BaSO_4$ forms, leaving soluble NH_4NO_3 in the solution. Write the molecular, ionic, and net ionic equations for the reaction. (*Hint:* Remember that polyatomic ions do not break apart when ionic compounds dissolve in water.)

5.4 | Write molecular, ionic, and net ionic equations for the reaction of aqueous solutions of cadmium chloride and sodium sulfide to give a precipitate of cadmium sulfide and a solution of sodium chloride.

Criteria for Balanced Ionic and Net Ionic Equations

In the ionic and net ionic equations we've written, not only are the atoms in balance, but so is the net electrical charge, which is the same on both sides of the equation. Thus, in the ionic equation for the reaction of lead(II) nitrate with potassium iodide, the sum of the charges of the ions on the left (Pb^{2+}, $2NO_3^-$, $2K^+$, and $2I^-$) is zero, which matches the sum of the charges on all of the formulas of the products (PbI_2, $2K^+$, and $2NO_3^-$).[2] In the net ionic equation the charges on both sides are also the same: on the left we have Pb^{2+} and $2I^-$, with a net charge of zero, and on the right we have PbI_2, also with a charge of zero. We now have an additional requirement for an ionic equation or net ionic equation to be balanced: *the net electrical charge on both sides of the equation must be the same.*

---

[2]There is no charge written for the formula of a compound such as PbI_2, so as we add up charges, we take the charge on PbI_2 to be zero.

TOOLS

Criteria for a balanced
ionic equation

Criteria for Balanced Ionic and Net Ionic Equations
1. **Material balance.** There must be the same number of atoms of each kind on both sides of the arrow.
2. **Electrical balance.** The *net* electrical charge on the left must equal the *net* electrical charge on the right (although the charge does not necessarily have to be zero).

5.3 | Acids and Bases

Acids and bases constitute a class of compounds that include some of our most familiar chemicals and important laboratory reagents. Many foods, for example, would not be as flavorful if it were not for the tartness imparted by the acids in vinegar or citrus juices. Cola beverages contain an acid that helps give them their unique taste. More powerful acids find uses in cleaning rust from metals and as the liquid in automobile batteries. The white crystals of lye in some drain cleaners, the white substance that makes milk of magnesia opaque, and household ammonia are all bases.

There are some general properties that are common to aqueous solutions of acids and bases. As noted above, foods that contain acids generally have a tart (sour) taste, whereas bases have a somewhat bitter taste and have a soapy "feel." (CAUTION: Taste is *never* used as a laboratory test for acids or bases; some are extremely corrosive to animal tissue and some are quite poisonous. *Never taste any chemicals in the laboratory!*)

Acids and bases also affect the colors of certain dyes we call **acid–base indicators**. An example is litmus (Figure 5.9), which has a pink or red color in an acidic solution and a blue color in a basic solution.[3]

One of the most important properties of acids and bases is their reaction with each other, a reaction referred to as **neutralization**. For example, when solutions of hydrochloric acid, $HCl(aq)$, and the base sodium hydroxide, $NaOH(aq)$, are mixed the following reaction occurs.

$$HCl(aq) + NaOH(aq) \longrightarrow NaCl(aq) + H_2O$$

When the reactants are combined in a 1-to-1 ratio by moles, the acidic and basic properties of the solutes disappear and the resulting solution is neither acidic nor basic. We say an *acid–base neutralization* has occurred. Svante Arrhenius,[4] a Swedish chemist, was the first to suggest that an acid–base neutralization is simply the combination of a hydrogen ion with a hydroxide ion to produce a water molecule, thus making H^+ ions and OH^- ions disappear.

Today we know that in aqueous solutions hydrogen ions, H^+, attach themselves to water molecules to form **hydronium ions**, H_3O^+. When H_3O^+ reacts with something, it gives up a hydrogen ion, so we can think of H^+ as the active ingredient in H_3O^+. Therefore, we often use the term *hydrogen ion* as a substitute for *hydronium ion*, and in many equations, we use $H^+(aq)$ to stand for $H_3O^+(aq)$. Whenever you see the symbol $H^+(aq)$, we are actually referring to $H_3O^+(aq)$.

For most purposes, we find that the following modified versions of Arrhenius' definitions work satisfactorily when we deal with aqueous solutions.

Arrhenius' Definition of Acids and Bases
An **acid** is a substance that reacts with water to produce hydronium ion, H_3O^+.
A **base** is a substance that produces hydroxide ion, OH^-, in water.

Figure 5.9 | **An acid-base indicator.** Litmus paper, a strip of paper impregnated with the dye litmus, becomes blue in aqueous ammonia (a base) and pink in lemon juice (which contains citric acid). *(Ken Karp)*

■ Acids and bases should be treated with respect because of their potential for causing bodily injury if spilled on the skin. If you spill an acid or base on yourself in the lab, be sure to notify your instructor at once.

■ Even the formula H_3O^+ is something of a simplification. In water the H^+ ion is associated with more than one molecule of water, but we use the formula H_3O^+ as a simple representation.

---

[3]Litmus paper, commonly found among the items in a locker in the general chemistry lab, consists of strips of absorbent paper that have been soaked in a solution of litmus and dried. Red litmus paper is used to test whether a solution is basic. A basic solution turns red litmus blue. To test whether the solution is acidic, blue litmus paper is used. Acidic solutions turn blue litmus red.
[4]Arrhenius proposed his theory of acids and bases in 1884 in his Ph.D. thesis. He won the Nobel Prize for his work in 1903.

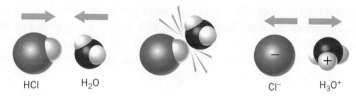

Figure 5.10 | **Ionization of HCl in water.** Collisions between HCl molecules and water molecules lead to a transfer of H^+ from HCl to H_2O, giving Cl^- and H_3O^+ as products.

In general, the reaction of an acid with a base produces an ionic compound as one of the products. In the reaction of HCl(*aq*) with NaOH(*aq*), the compound is sodium chloride, or salt. This reaction is so general, in fact, that *we use the word* **salt** *to mean any ionic compound that doesn't contain either hydroxide ion, OH^-, or oxide ion, O^{2-}*. (Ionic compounds that contain OH^- or O^{2-} are bases, as described below.) Note that we have now slightly modified our definition of the term *salt* given on page 158.

Formation of H_3O^+ by Acids

In general, **acids** are molecular substances that react with water to produce ions, one of which is H_3O^+. For example, when gaseous molecular HCl dissolves in water, a hydrogen ion (H^+) transfers from the HCl molecule to a water molecule. The reaction at the molecular level is depicted in Figure 5.10 using space-filling models,[5] and is represented by the chemical equation

$$HCl(g) + H_2O \longrightarrow H_3O^+(aq) + Cl^-(aq)$$

This is an **ionization reaction** because ions form where none existed before. Because the solution contains ions, it conducts electricity, so acids are electrolytes.

Sometimes acids also contain hydrogen atoms that are not able to form H_3O^+. An example is ethanoic acid, better known as acetic acid, $HC_2H_3O_2$, the acid that gives vinegar its sour taste. Acetic acid forms H_3O^+ by the following reaction.

$$HC_2H_3O_2(aq) + H_2O \longrightarrow H_3O^+(aq) + C_2H_3O_2^-(aq)$$

As a general rule, only the hydrogen written first in the formula transfers to H_2O to give H_3O^+. The structures of the acetic acid molecule and the acetate ion are shown in Figure 5.11, with the hydrogen that can be lost by the acetic acid molecule indicated in the drawing.[6]

As noted earlier, the "active ingredient" in the hydronium ion is H^+, which is why $H^+(aq)$ is often used in place of $H_3O^+(aq)$ in equations. Using this simplification, the ionization of HCl and $HC_2H_3O_2$ in water can be represented as

$$HCl(g) \xrightarrow{\text{H}_2\text{O}} H^+(aq) + Cl^-(aq)$$

and

$$HC_2H_3O_2(aq) \xrightarrow{\text{H}_2\text{O}} H^+(aq) + C_2H_3O_2^-(aq)$$

In both reactions, an anion is formed when the acid transfers an H^+ to the water molecule. If we represent the acid molecule by the general formula H*A*, we can represent the ionization of an acid in general terms by the equation

$$HA + H_2O \longrightarrow H_3O^+ + A^- \qquad (5.2)$$

Acetic acid molecule
$HC_2H_3O_2$

Only this H comes off as H^+.

Acetate ion
$C_2H_3O_2^-$

Figure 5.11 | **Acetic acid and acetate ion.** The structures of acetic acid and acetate ion are illustrated here. In acetic acid, only the hydrogen attached to an oxygen can come off as H^+.

Ionization of an acid in water

---

[5]To emphasize the transfer of the H^+, we have shown the positive charge to be on just one of the H atoms in H_3O^+. Actually the charge is distributed evenly over all three H atoms. In effect, the entire H_3O unit carries a single positive charge.
[6]The single negative charge is actually distributed evenly over the two O atoms in the acetate ion.

The molecules HCl and $HC_2H_3O_2$ are capable of furnishing only one H^+ per molecule and are said to be **monoprotic acids.** **Polyprotic acids** can furnish more than one H^+ per molecule. They undergo reactions similar to those of HCl and $HC_2H_3O_2$, except that the loss of H^+ by the acid occurs in two or more steps. Thus, the ionization of sulfuric acid, a **diprotic acid,** takes place by two successive steps.

$$H_2SO_4(aq) + H_2O \longrightarrow H_3O^+(aq) + HSO_4^-(aq)$$

$$HSO_4^-(aq) + H_2O \longrightarrow H_3O^+(aq) + SO_4^{2-}(aq)$$

Triprotic acids *ionize in three steps,* as illustrated in Example 5.3.

Example 5.3
Writing Equations for Ionization Reactions of Acids

Phosphoric acid, H_3PO_4, is a triprotic acid found in some soft drinks such as Coca-Cola (shown in the photo at the start of this chapter) where it adds a touch of tartness to the beverage. Write equations for its stepwise ionization in water.

■ **Analysis:** We are told that H_3PO_4 is a triprotic acid, which is also indicated by the three hydrogens at the beginning of the formula. Because there are three hydrogens to come off the molecule, we expect there to be three steps in the ionization. Each step removes one H^+, and we can use that knowledge to deduce the formulas of the products. Let's line them up so we can see the progression.

$$H_3PO_4 \xrightarrow{-H^+} H_2PO_4^- \xrightarrow{-H^+} HPO_4^{2-} \xrightarrow{-H^+} PO_4^{3-}$$

Notice that the loss of H^+ decreases the number of hydrogens by one and increases the negative charge by one unit. Also, the product of one step serves as the reactant in the next step.

■ **Assembling the Tools:** We'll use Equation 5.2 for the ionization of an acid as a tool in writing the chemical equation for each step.

■ **Solution:** The first step is the reaction of H_3PO_4 with water to give H_3O^+ and $H_2PO_4^-$.

$$H_3PO_4(aq) + H_2O \longrightarrow H_3O^+(aq) + H_2PO_4^-(aq)$$

The second and third steps are similar to the first.

$$H_2PO_4^-(aq) + H_2O \longrightarrow H_3O^+(aq) + HPO_4^{2-}(aq)$$

$$HPO_4^{2-}(aq) + H_2O \longrightarrow H_3O^+(aq) + PO_4^{3-}(aq)$$

■ **Is the Answer Reasonable?** Check to see whether the equations are balanced in terms of atoms and charge. If any mistakes were made, something would be out of balance and we would discover the error. In this case, all of the equations are balanced, so we can feel confident we've written them correctly.

Practice Exercises

5.5 | Write the equation for the ionization of $HCHO_2$ (methanoic acid, commonly called formic acid) in water. Formic acid is used industrially to remove hair from animal skins prior to tanning. (*Hint:* Formic acid and acetic acid are both examples of organic acids.)

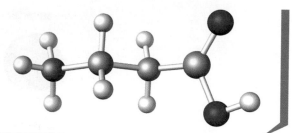

5.6 | Butanoic acid, an organic acid with an unpleasant odor found in rancid butter and some fermented cheeses, has the structure shown in the margin. Sketch the structure for the anion formed when butanoic acid is ionized. (*Hint:* Use acetic acid as a guide.) Write the chemical equation for the ionization of butanoic acid in water.

5.7 | Write equations for the stepwise ionization in water of citric acid, $H_3C_6H_5O_7$, the acid in citrus fruits.

Acidity of Nonmetal Oxides

The acids we've discussed so far have been molecules containing hydrogen atoms that can be transferred to water molecules. Nonmetal oxides form another class of compounds that yield acidic solutions in water. Examples are SO_3, CO_2, and N_2O_5 whose aqueous solutions contain H_3O^+ and turn litmus red. These oxides are called **acid anhydrides**, where *anhydride* means "without water." They react with water to form molecular acids containing hydrogen, which are then able to undergo reaction with water to yield H_3O^+.

$$SO_3(g) + H_2O \longrightarrow H_2SO_4(aq) \qquad \text{sulfuric acid}$$

$$N_2O_5(g) + H_2O \longrightarrow 2HNO_3(aq) \qquad \text{nitric acid}$$

$$CO_2(g) + H_2O \longrightarrow H_2CO_3(aq) \qquad \text{carbonic acid}$$

Although carbonic acid is too unstable to be isolated as a pure compound, its solutions in water are quite common. Carbon dioxide from the atmosphere dissolves in rainwater and the waters of lakes and streams where it exists partly as carbonic acid and its ions (i.e., H_3O^+, HCO_3^-, and CO_3^{2-}). This makes these waters naturally slightly acidic. Carbonic acid is also present in carbonated beverages.

Not all nonmetal oxides are acidic anhydrides, just those that are able to react with water. For example, carbon monoxide doesn't react with water, so its solutions in water are not acidic; carbon monoxide, therefore, is not classified as an acidic anhydride.

Formation of OH⁻ by Bases

Bases fall into two categories: ionic compounds that contain OH^- or O^{2-}, and molecular compounds that react with water to give hydroxide ions. Because solutions of bases contain ions, they conduct electricity. Therefore, bases are electrolytes.

Ionic Hydroxides and Oxides

Ionic bases include metal hydroxides, such as NaOH and $Ca(OH)_2$. When dissolved in water, they dissociate just like other soluble ionic compounds.

$$NaOH(s) \longrightarrow Na^+(aq) + OH^-(aq)$$

$$Ca(OH)_2(s) \longrightarrow Ca^{2+}(aq) + 2OH^-(aq)$$

Soluble metal oxides are **base anhydrides** because they react with water to form the hydroxide ion as one of the products. Calcium oxide is typical.

$$CaO(s) + H_2O \longrightarrow Ca(OH)_2(aq)$$

This reaction occurs when water is added to dry cement or concrete because calcium oxide or "quicklime" is an ingredient in these materials. In this case it is the oxide ion, O^{2-}, that actually forms the OH^-. See Figure 5.12.

$$O^{2-} + H_2O \longrightarrow 2OH^-$$

■ Continued contact of your hands with fresh Portland cement or grout for ceramic tile can lead to irritation because the mixture is quite basic.

Figure 5.12 | **Oxide ion reacts with water.** When a soluble metal oxide dissolves, the oxide ion takes an H^+ from a water molecule. The result is two hydroxide ions.[7]

Even insoluble metal hydroxides and oxides are bases because they are able to neutralize acids. We will study these reactions in Section 5.5.

Molecular Bases

The most common molecular base is the gas ammonia, NH_3, which dissolves in water and reacts to give a basic solution by the ionization reaction

$$NH_3(aq) + H_2O \longrightarrow NH_4^+(aq) + OH^-(aq)$$

Organic compounds called amines, in which fragments of hydrocarbons replace hydrogen atoms in ammonia, are similar to ammonia in their behavior toward water. An example is methylamine, CH_3NH_2, in which a *methyl group*, CH_3, replaces a hydrogen in ammonia.

$$CH_3NH_2(aq) + H_2O \longrightarrow CH_3NH_3^+(aq) + OH^-(aq)$$

The hydrogen taken from the H_2O molecule becomes attached to the nitrogen atom of the amine. This is how nitrogen-containing bases behave, which is why we've included the H^+ with the other two hydrogens on the nitrogen.

Notice that when a molecular base reacts with water, an H^+ is lost by the water molecule and gained by the base. (See Figure 5.13.) One product is a cation that has one more H and one more positive charge than the reactant base. Loss of H^+ by the water gives the other product, the OH^- ion, which is why the solution is basic. We might represent this by the general equation

$$base + H_2O \longrightarrow base\ H^+ + OH^-$$

If we signify the base by the symbol B, this becomes

Ionization of a molecular base in water

$$B + H_2O \longrightarrow BH^+ + OH^- \tag{5.3}$$

Figure 5.13 | **Ionization of ammonia in water.** Collisions between NH_3 molecules and water molecules lead to a transfer of H^+ from H_2O to NH_3, giving NH_4^+ and OH^- ions.

[7]You might notice that the sizes of the oxygen atoms in O^{2-}, OH^-, and H_2O are not the same. In Chapter 8 we will discuss how the sizes of atoms change as they gain or lose electrons.

Example 5.4
Writing the Equation for the Ionization of a Molecular Base

Dimethylamine, $(CH_3)_2NH$, is a base in water. It is used commercially as an attractant for boll weevils so they can be destroyed. This insect has caused a more than $14 billion loss to the yield of cotton in the United States since it arrived from Mexico in 1892. Write an equation for the ionization of $(CH_3)_2NH$ in water.

■ **Analysis:** We've been told that $(CH_3)_2NH$ is a base, so it's going to react with water to form hydroxide ion. To write the equation correctly we need to know precisely what the products are. Equation 5.3 is our guide.

■ **Assembling the Tools:** The tool is Equation 5.3, which we use as a template for writing the formulas of reactants and products.

■ **Solution:** The reactants in the equation are $(CH_3)_2NH$ and H_2O. According to Equation 5.3, when the base reacts with water it takes an H^+ from H_2O, leaving OH^- behind. Therefore, when an H^+ is picked up by $(CH_3)_2NH$, the product will be $(CH_3)_2NH_2^+$. The equation for the reaction is

$$(CH_3)_2NH(aq) + H_2O \longrightarrow (CH_3)_2NH_2^+(aq) + OH^-(aq)$$

■ **Is the Answer Reasonable?** Compare the equation we've written with the general equation for reaction of a base with water. Notice that the formula for the product has one more H and a positive charge, and that the H^+ has been added to the nitrogen. Also, notice that the water has become OH^- when it loses H^+. The equation is therefore correct.

5.8 | Triethylamine, $(C_2H_5)_3N$, is a base in water. Write an equation for its reaction with the solvent. (*Hint:* How do nitrogen-containing bases react toward water?)

5.9 | Hydroxylamine, $HONH_2$, is a molecular base in water. Write an equation for its reaction with the solvent.

5.10 | Ethylamine, a base in water, has the following structure:

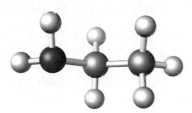

It is used in the manufacture of many herbicides. Sketch the structure of the nitrogen-containing product that is formed when it reacts with water. Write the equation for the ionization of ethylamine in water.

Strong and Weak Acids and Bases

Ionic compounds such as NaCl and $CaCl_2$ break up essentially 100% into ions in water. No "molecules" or formula units of either NaCl or $CaCl_2$ are detectable in their aqueous solutions. Because these solutions contain so many ions, they are strong conductors of electricity, so ionic compounds are said to be **strong electrolytes.**

Hydrochloric acid is also a strong electrolyte. Its ionization in water is essentially complete; its solutions are strongly acidic, and it is said to be a *strong acid*. In general, acids

■ All strong acids are strong electrolytes.

that are strong electrolytes are called **strong acids**. There are relatively few strong acids; the most common ones are as follows:

TOOLS

List of strong acids

Strong Acids	
$HClO_4(aq)$	perchloric acid
$HClO_3(aq)$	chloric acid
$HCl(aq)$	hydrochloric acid
$HBr(aq)$	hydrobromic acid
$HI(aq)$	hydroiodic acid[8]
$HNO_3(aq)$	nitric acid
$H_2SO_4(aq)$	sulfuric acid

Metal hydroxides are ionic compounds, so they are also strong electrolytes. Those that are soluble are the hydroxides of Group 1A and the hydroxides of calcium, strontium, and barium of Group 2A. Solutions of these compounds are strongly basic, so these substances are considered to be **strong bases.** The hydroxides of other metals have very low solubilities in water. They are strong electrolytes in the sense that the small amounts of them that dissolve in solution are completely dissociated. However, because of their low solubility in water, their solutions are very weakly basic.

Weak Acids and Bases: Weak Electrolytes

Most acids are not completely ionized in water. For instance, a solution of acetic acid, $HC_2H_3O_2$, is a relatively poor conductor of electricity compared to a solution of HCl with the same concentration (Figure 5.14). An acid, such as acetic acid, that is not fully ionized in water is classified as a **weak electrolyte** and is a **weak acid.**

An acetic acid solution is a poor conductor because in the solution only a small fraction of the acid exists as H_3O^+ and $C_2H_3O_2^-$ ions. The rest is present as molecules of $HC_2H_3O_2$. This is because $C_2H_3O_2^-$ ions have a strong tendency to react with H_3O^+ when the ions meet in the solution. As a result, there are two opposing reactions occurring simultaneously (Figure 5.15). One reaction forms the ions,

$$HC_2H_3O_2(aq) + H_2O \longrightarrow H_3O^+(aq) + C_2H_3O_2^-(aq)$$

and the other removes ions,

$$H_3O^+(aq) + C_2H_3O_2^-(aq) \longrightarrow HC_2H_3O_2(aq) + H_2O$$

A balance is reached when ions form and disappear at the same rate, and for acetic acid this happens when only a small percentage of the $HC_2H_3O_2$ is ionized.

The condition we've just described, with two opposing reactions occurring at the same rate, is called a **chemical equilibrium** or **dynamic equilibrium**. It is an *equilibrium* because the concentrations of the substances present in the solution do not change with time; it is *dynamic* because the opposing reactions continue endlessly.

The two opposing processes in a dynamic equilibrium are usually represented in a single equation by using double arrows, $\rightleftharpoons$. For acetic acid, we write

$$HC_2H_3O_2(aq) + H_2O \rightleftharpoons H_3O^+(aq) + C_2H_3O_2^-(aq)$$

The **forward reaction** (read from left to right) forms the ions; the **reverse reaction** (from right to left) removes them from the solution.

Molecular bases, such as ammonia and methylamine, are also weak electrolytes and have a low percentage ionization; they are classified as **weak bases**. See Figure 5.14c. In a solution of ammonia, only a small fraction of the solute is ionized to give NH_4^+ and OH^- because the ions have a strong tendency to react with each other. This leads to the dynamic equilibrium (Figure 5.16)

$$NH_3(aq) + H_2O \rightleftharpoons NH_4^+(aq) + OH^-(aq)$$

in which most of the base is present as NH_3 molecules.

---

[8]Sometimes the first "o" in the name of HI(aq) is dropped for ease of pronunciation to give *hydriodic acid*.

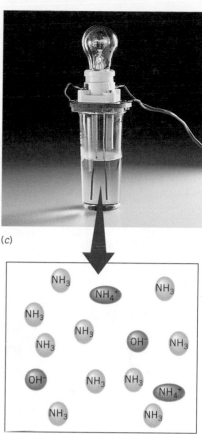
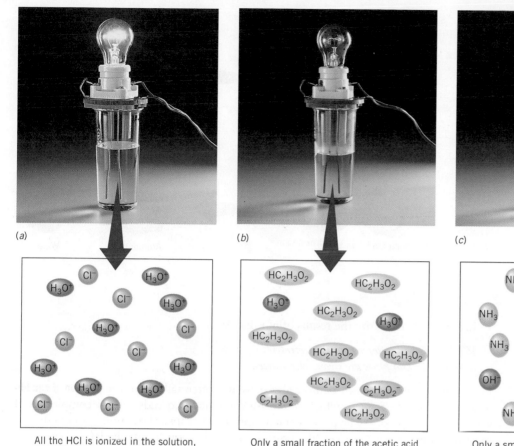

All the HCl is ionized in the solution, so there are many ions present.

Only a small fraction of the acetic acid is ionized, so there are few ions to conduct electricity. Most of the acetic acid is present as neutral molecules of $HC_2H_3O_2$.

Only a small fraction of the ammonia is ionized, so few ions are present to conduct electricity. Most of the ammonia is present as neutral molecules of NH_3.

Figure 5.14 | **Electrical conductivity of solutions of strong and weak acids and bases at equal concentrations.** (*a*) HCl is 100% ionized and is a strong conductor, enabling the light to glow brightly. (*b*) $HC_2H_3O_2$ is a weaker conductor than HCl because the extent of its ionization is far less, so the light is dimmer. (*c*) NH_3 also is a weaker conductor than HCl because the extent of its ionization is low, and the light remains dim. (*Michael Watson*)

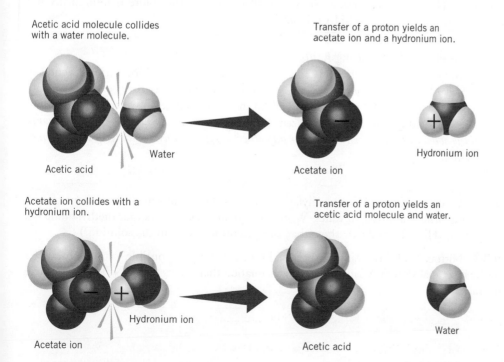

Acetic acid molecule collides with a water molecule.

Transfer of a proton yields an acetate ion and a hydronium ion.

Water

Acetic acid

Acetate ion

Hydronium ion

Acetate ion collides with a hydronium ion.

Transfer of a proton yields an acetic acid molecule and water.

Acetate ion

Hydronium ion

Acetic acid

Water

Figure 5.15 | **Equilibrium in a solution of acetic acid.** Two opposing reactions take place simultaneously in a solution of acetic acid. Molecules of acid collide with molecules of water and form acetate ions and H_3O^+ ions. Meanwhile, acetate ions collide with H_3O^+ ions to give acetic acid molecules and water molecules.

Figure 5.16 | **Equilibrium in a solution of the weak base ammonia.** Collisions between water and ammonia molecules produce ammonium and hydroxide ions. The reverse process, which involves collisions between ammonium ions and hydroxide ions, removes ions from the solution and forms ammonia and water molecules.

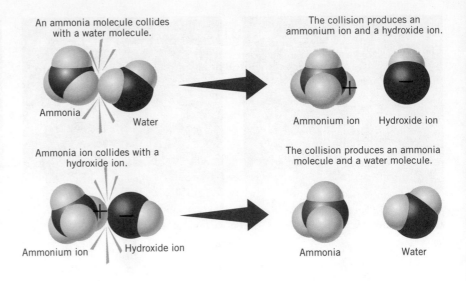

An ammonia molecule collides with a water molecule.

Ammonia   Water

The collision produces an ammonium ion and a hydroxide ion.

Ammonium ion   Hydroxide ion

Ammonia ion collides with a hydroxide ion.

Ammonium ion   Hydroxide ion

The collision produces an ammonia molecule and a water molecule.

Ammonia   Water

Let's briefly summarize the results of our discussion.

Weak acids and bases are weak electrolytes.
Strong acids and bases are strong electrolytes.

In describing equilibria such as those above, we will often talk about the **position of equilibrium**, which is the extent to which the forward reaction proceeds toward completion. If very little of the products are present at equilibrium, the forward reaction has not gone far toward completion and we say "the position of equilibrium lies to the left," toward the reactants. On the other hand, if large amounts of the products are present at equilibrium, we say "the position of equilibrium lies to the right."

For any weak electrolyte, when equilibrium is reached only a small percentage of the solute is actually ionized, so the position of equilibrium lies to the left. To call acetic acid a *weak* acid, for example, is just another way of saying that the forward reaction in the equilibrium is far from completion. It is also important to understand that calling acetic acid a weak acid does not imply a small concentration of $HC_2H_3O_2$. Rather, the concentration of H_3O^+ is small because only a small fraction of the solute is ionized. Even a concentrated solution of $HC_2H_3O_2$ is weakly acidic.

Complete Ionization of Strong Acids

With strong electrolytes such as HCl, the tendency of the forward ionization reaction to occur is very large, while the tendency of the reverse reaction to occur is extremely small. As a result, all of the HCl molecules dissolved in water become converted to H_3O^+ and Cl^- ions; the acid becomes 100% ionized. For this reason, *we do not use double arrows in describing what happens when HCl(g) or any other strong electrolyte undergoes ionization or dissociation.*

Practice Exercises

5.11 | Earlier you learned that methylamine, CH3NH2 (a fishy-smelling substance found in herring brine), is a base in water. Write the equation that shows that methylamine is a weak base. (Hint: How do we show that an equilibrium exists in the solution?)

5.12 | Nitrous acid, HNO_2, is a weak acid thought to be responsible for certain cancers of the intestinal system. Write the chemical equation that shows that HNO_2 is a weak acid in water.

5.4 | Acid-Base Nomenclature

Although at first there seems to be little order in the naming of acids, there are patterns that help organize names of acids and the anions that come from them when the acids are neutralized.

Hydrogen Compounds of Nonmetals

The binary compounds of hydrogen with many of the nonmetals are acidic, and in their aqueous solutions they are referred to as **binary acids**. Some examples are HCl, HBr, and H_2S. In naming these substances as acids, we add the prefix *hydro-* and the suffix *-ic* to the stem of the nonmetal name, followed by the word *acid*. For example, aqueous solutions of hydrogen chloride and hydrogen sulfide are named as follows:

Name of the molecular compound	Name of the binary acid in water
HCl(g) hydrogen chloride	HCl(aq) *hydrochloric acid*
H_2S(g) hydrogen sulfide	H_2S(aq) *hydrosulfuric acid*

Notice that the gaseous molecular substances are named in the usual way as binary compounds. *It is their aqueous solutions that are named as acids.*

When an acid is neutralized, the salt that is produced contains the anion formed by removing a hydrogen ion, H^+, from the acid molecule. Thus HCl yields salts containing the chloride ion, Cl^-. Similarly, HBr gives salts containing the bromide ion, Br^-. In general, then, neutralization of a binary acid yields the simple anion of the nonmetal.

> ■ In the name of an acid, the prefix *hydro-* tells us it is a binary acid. If the prefix *hydro-* is absent, it tells us the substance is not a binary acid.

Naming Oxoacids

Acids that contain hydrogen, oxygen, plus another element are called **oxoacids**. Examples are H_2SO_4 and HNO_3. These acids do not take the prefix *hydro-*. Many nonmetals form two or more oxoacids that differ in the number of oxygen atoms in their formulas. When there are two oxoacids, the one with the larger number of oxygens takes the suffix *-ic* and the one with the fewer number of oxygens takes the suffix *-ous*.

H_2SO_4 sulfur*ic acid* HNO_3 nitr*ic acid*
H_2SO_3 sulfur*ous acid* HNO_2 nitr*ous acid*

The halogens can form as many as four different oxoacids. The oxoacid with the most oxygens has the prefix *per-*, and the one with the least has the prefix *hypo-*.

HClO   *hypochlorous acid* (usually written HOCl) $HClO_3$ chlor*ic acid*
$HClO_2$ chlor*ous acid* $HClO_4$ per*chloric acid*

The neutralization of oxoacids produces negative polyatomic ions. The name of the polyatomic ion is related to that of its parent acid.

(1) *-ic* acids give *-ate* anions: HNO_3 (nitr*ic acid*) $\longrightarrow$ NO_3^- (nitr*ate* ion)
(2) *-ous* acids give *-ite* anions: H_2SO_3 (sulfur*ous acid*) $\longrightarrow$ SO_3^{2-} (sulf*ite* ion)

This relationship between the name of the acid and name of the anion carries over to other acids that end in the suffix *-ic*. For example, acetic acid gives the anion acetate, and citric acid gives the anion citrate.

In naming polyatomic anions, the prefixes *per-* and *hypo-* carry over from the name of the parent acid. Thus perchloric acid, $HClO_4$, gives perchlorate ion, ClO_4^-, and hypochlorous acid, HClO, gives hypochlorite ion, ClO^-.

Knowing the names and formulas of the polyatomic ions in Table 3.5 will help you in naming the acids as well. For example, the thiocyanate ion, SCN^-, has a name that ends in *-ate*. The anion is derived by removing an H^+ from an acid with a name that ends in *-ic*. Therefore, thiocyan*ate* ion, SCN^-, comes from thiocyan*ic* acid, HSCN.

TOOLS

Acid and anion names

Example 5.5
Naming Acids and Their Salts

Bromine forms four oxoacids, similar to those of chlorine. What is the name of the acid $HBrO_2$ and what is the name of the salt $NaBrO_3$?

■**Analysis:** In this problem we will reason by analogy and begin by analyzing the names of the acids of the halogens. Then we can apply the nomenclature rules above to deduce the answers.

■**Assembling the Tools:** There are two tools we can use here: (1) how names are related to the number of oxygens in the acid, and (2) how the ending on the name of the anion relates to the ending on the name of the acid.

■**Solution:**

Naming $HBrO_2$: The oxoacids of chlorine are

HClO	hypochlorous acid	$HClO_3$	chloric acid
$HClO_2$	chlorous acid	$HClO_4$	perchloric acid

The acid $HBrO_2$ is similar to chlorous acid, so to name it we will use the stem of the element name bromine (brom-) in place of chlor-. Therefore, the name of $HBrO_2$ is *bromous acid*.

Naming $NaBrO_3$: $NaBrO_3$ is a salt that would form by neutralization of an acid with the formula $HBrO_3$ (the H^+ of the acid is replaced by Na^+). This acid has one more oxygen than bromous acid, $HBrO_2$, so its name would have the ending *-ic*. This means $HBrO_3$ is bromic acid. Neutralizing an acid that has a name that ends in *-ic* gives an anion with a name that ends in *-ate*, so the anion BrO_3^- is the bromate ion. Therefore, the salt $NaBrO_3$ is *sodium bromate*.

■**Are the Answers Reasonable?** There's really not much we can do to check the answers here. For the salt, if $HClO_3$ is chloric acid, then it seems reasonable that $HBrO_3$ would be bromic acid, which would mean that BrO_3^- is the bromate ion and $NaBrO_3$ is sodium bromate. Alternatively, if you remember the polyatomic ions from Chapter 3, you know that ClO_3^- is the chlorate ion. By analogy, BrO_3^- would be bromate ion, so $NaBrO_3$ is sodium bromate.

Practice Exercises

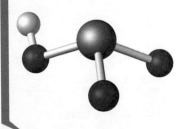

5.13 | The formula for arsenic acid is H_3AsO_4. What is the name of the salt Na_3AsO_4? (*Hint:* Recall how the name of the anion is related to the name of the acid.)

5.14 | Methanoic acid is also called formic acid and has the formula $HCHO_2$. What are two names for the salt $Ca(CHO_2)_2$?

5.15 | Name the water solutions of the following acids: HF, HBr. Name the sodium salts formed by neutralizing these acids with NaOH.

5.16 | What is the name of the acid having the structure shown in the margin? (Use the colors of the atoms to identify the elements in the acid.)

Acid Salts

If a polyprotic acid is neutralized stepwise, the neutralization can be halted before all the hydrogens have been removed. For example, partial neutralization of H_2SO_4 gives the HSO_4^- ion, which forms salts such as $NaHSO_4$. This compound is called an **acid salt** because its anion, HSO_4^-, is capable of furnishing additional H^+.

In naming ions such as HSO_4^-, we specify the number of hydrogens that can still be neutralized if the anion were to be treated with additional base. Thus, HSO_4^- is called the hydrogen sulfate ion; it's the active ingredient in Sani-Flush (Figure 5.17). Similarly, $H_2PO_4^-$ is the dihydrogen phosphate ion. These two anions give the following salts with Na^+:

$NaHSO_4$	sodium hydrogen sulfate
NaH_2PO_4	sodium dihydrogen phosphate

For acid salts of diprotic acids, the prefix **bi**- is still often used.

$NaHCO_3$ sodium bicarbonate

or

sodium hydrogen carbonate

Notice that the prefix bi- does *not* mean "two"; instead, it means that there is an acidic hydrogen in the compound.

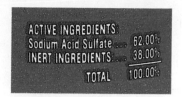

Figure 5.17 | **Applications of acid salts.** The label on a can of Sani-Flush shows the active ingredient to be sodium hydrogen sulfate, which the manufacturer calls "sodium acid sulfate." *(Robert Capece)*

5.17 | What is the formula for sodium bisulfite? What is the chemically correct name for this compound? (*Hint:* What information do we get from the prefix bi- and the suffix -ite?)

5.18 | Write molecular equations for the stepwise neutralization of phosphoric acid by sodium hydroxide. What are the names of the salts that are formed?

Practice Exercises

Naming Bases

Metal compounds that contain the ions OH^- or O^{2-}, such as NaOH and Na_2O, are ionic and are named just like any other ionic compound. Thus, NaOH is sodium hydroxide and Na_2O is sodium oxide.

Molecular bases such as NH_3 (ammonia) and CH_3NH_2 (methylamine) are specified by just giving the name of the molecule.[9] There is nothing in their names that specifically tells us they are bases.

■ Knowing that methylamine is a base requires that you know that amines in general are bases.

5.5 | Double Replacement (Metathesis) Reactions

In our discussion of the reaction of KI with $Pb(NO_3)_2$, you saw that the net ionic equation reveals a change in the number of ions in solution when the reaction takes place. Such changes characterize ionic reactions in general. In this section you will learn how we can use the existence or nonexistence of a net ionic equation as a criterion to determine whether or not an ionic reaction occurs in a solution of mixed solutes.

In general, a net ionic equation will exist (and a reaction will occur) under the following conditions:

A precipitate is formed from a mixture of soluble reactants.
An acid reacts with a base.
A weak electrolyte is formed from a mixture of strong electrolytes. ✓
A gas is formed from a mixture of reactants.

TOOLS

Predicting net ionic equations

It is also important to note that *no net reaction will occur if all of the substances in the ionic equation cancel.* There will be no net ionic equation, and therefore no net reaction!

■ If all the ions are spectator ions, there is no net reaction.

Predicting Precipitation Reactions

The reaction between $Pb(NO_3)_2$ and KI,

$$Pb(NO_3)_2(aq) + 2KI(aq) \longrightarrow PbI_2(s) + 2KNO_3(aq)$$

---

[9]Solutions of ammonia in water are sometimes called *ammonium hydroxide*, although there is no evidence that the species NH_4OH actually exists.

Solubility rules

Table 5.1	**Solubility Rules for Ionic Compounds in Water**

Soluble Compounds

1. All componds of the alkali metals (Group 1A) are soluble.
2. All salts containing NH_4^+, NO_3^-, ClO_4^-, ClO_3^-, and $C_2H_3O_2^-$ are soluble.
3. All chlorides, bromides, and iodides (salts containing Cl^-, Br^-, or I^-) are soluble *except* when combined with Ag^+, Pb^{2+}, and Hg_2^{2+} (note the subscript 2).
4. All sulfates (salts containing SO_4^{2-}) are soluble *except* those of Pb^{2+}, Ca^{2+}, Sr^{2+}, Hg_2^{2+}, and Ba^{2+}.

Insoluble Compounds

5. All metal hydroxides (ionic compounds containing OH^-) and all metal oxides (ionic compounds containing O^{2-}) are insoluble *except* those of Group 1A and those of Ca^{2+}, Sr^{2+}, and Ba^{2+}.

   When metal oxides do dissolve, they react with water to form hydroxides. The oxide ion, O^{2-}, does not exist in water. For example:

$$Na_2O(s) + H_2O \longrightarrow 2NaOH(aq)$$

6. All salts that contain PO_4^{3-}, CO_3^{2-}, SO_3^{2-}, and S^{2-} are insoluble, *except* those of Group 1A and NH_4^+.

is just one example of a large class of ionic reactions, called **metathesis reactions**, in which cations and anions change partners. Metathesis reactions are also sometimes called **double replacement reactions**. (In the formation of the products, PbI_2 and KNO_3, the I^- replaces NO_3^- in the lead compound and NO_3^- replaces I^- in the potassium compound.) Metathesis reactions in which a precipitate forms are also called **precipitation reactions.**

Lead(II) nitrate and potassium iodide react because one of the products is insoluble. Such reactions can be predicted if we know which substances are soluble and which are insoluble. To help us, we can apply a set of **solubility rules** (Table 5.1) that tell us, in many cases, whether an ionic compound is soluble or insoluble. To make the rules easier to remember, they are divided into two categories. The first includes compounds that are soluble, with some exceptions. The second describes compounds that are generally insoluble, with some exceptions. Some examples will help clarify their use.

Rule 1 states that all compounds of the alkali metals are soluble in water. This means that you can expect *any* compound containing Na^+ or K^+, or any of the Group 1A metal ions, *regardless of the anion*, to be soluble. If one of the reactants in a metathesis is Na_3PO_4, you now know from Rule 1 that it is soluble. Therefore, you would write it in *dissociated* form in the ionic equation. Similarly, Rule 6 states, in part, that all carbonate compounds are *insoluble* except those of the alkali metals and the ammonium ion. If one of the products in a metathesis reaction is $CaCO_3$, you'd expect it to be insoluble because the cation is not an alkali metal or NH_4^+. Therefore, you would write its formula in the *undissociated* form as $CaCO_3(s)$ in the ionic equation.

Example 5.6 illustrates how we can use the rules to predict the outcome of a reaction.

Example 5.6
Predicting Reactions and Writing Their Equations

Predict whether a reaction will occur when aqueous solutions of $Pb(NO_3)_2$ and $Fe_2(SO_4)_3$ are mixed. Write molecular, ionic, and net ionic equations for it.

■ **Analysis:** For the molecular equation, let's start by writing the reactants on the left.

$$Pb(NO_3)_2 + Fe_2(SO_4)_3 \longrightarrow$$

To complete the equation we have to determine the makeup of the products. We begin, therefore, by predicting what a double replacement (metathesis) might produce. Next, we proceed to construct the ionic equation, and then convert it to a net ionic equation by crossing out spectator ions. If a net ionic equation exists at this point, it tells us that a reaction does indeed take place.

■ The critical link in determining whether a reaction occurs is obtaining a net ionic equation.

■ **Assembling the Tools:** The tools you've learned that apply here are (1) rules for writing the formula of a salt from the formulas of its ions, (2) the rules for writing ionic and net ionic equations, and (3) the solubility rules.

■ **Solution:** The reactants, $Pb(NO_3)_2$ and $Fe_2(SO_4)_3$, contain the ions Pb^{2+} and NO_3^-, and Fe^{3+} and SO_4^{2-}, respectively. To write the formulas of the products, we interchange anions, being careful to require that the formula units be electrically neutral. This gives $PbSO_4$ as one possible product and $Fe(NO_3)_3$ as the other. The unbalanced molecular equation at this point is

$$Pb(NO_3)_2 + Fe_2(SO_4)_3 \longrightarrow PbSO_4 + Fe(NO_3)_3 \quad \text{(unbalanced)}$$

Next, let's determine solubilities. The reactants are ionic compounds and we are told that they are in solution, so we know they are water soluble. Solubility Rules 2 and 4 tell us this also. For the products, we find that Rule 2 says that all nitrates are soluble, so $Fe(NO_3)_3$ is soluble; Rule 4 tells us that the sulfate of Pb^{2+} is *insoluble*. This means that a precipitate of $PbSO_4$ will form. Writing (*aq*) and (*s*) following appropriate formulas, the unbalanced molecular equation is

$$Fe_2(SO_4)_3(aq) + Pb(NO_3)_2(aq) \longrightarrow Fe(NO_3)_3(aq) + PbSO_4(s) \quad \text{(unbalanced)}$$

■ Always write equations in two steps. First write correct formulas for the reactants and products, then adjust the coefficients to balance the equation.

When balanced, we obtain the *molecular equation*.

$$Fe_2(SO_4)_3(aq) + 3Pb(NO_3)_2(aq) \longrightarrow 2Fe(NO_3)_3(aq) + 3PbSO_4(s)$$

Next, we expand this to give the *ionic equation* in which soluble compounds are written in dissociated (separated) form as ions, and insoluble compounds are written in "molecular" form. Once again, we are careful to apply the subscripts of the ions and the coefficients.

$$2Fe^{3+}(aq) + 3SO_4^{2-}(aq) + 3Pb^{2+}(aq) + 6NO_3^-(aq) \longrightarrow 2Fe^{3+}(aq) + 6NO_3^-(aq) + 3PbSO_4(s)$$

By removing spectator ions (Fe^{3+} and NO_3^-), we obtain

$$3Pb^{2+}(aq) + 3SO_4^{2-}(aq) \longrightarrow 3PbSO_4(s)$$

Finally, we reduce the coefficients to give us the correct *net ionic equation*.

$$Pb^{2+}(aq) + SO_4^{2-}(aq) \longrightarrow PbSO_4(s)$$

The existence of the net ionic equation confirms that a reaction does take place between lead(II) nitrate and iron(III) sulfate.

■ **Is the Answer Reasonable?** One of the main things we have to check in solving a problem such as this is that we've written the correct formulas of the products. For example, in this problem some students might be tempted (without thinking) to write $Pb(SO_4)_2$ and $Fe_2(NO_3)_3$, or even $Pb(SO_4)_3$ and $Fe_2(NO_3)_2$. *This is a common error.* Always be careful to figure out the charges on the ions that must be combined in the formula. Then take the ions in a ratio that gives an electrically neutral formula unit.

Once we're sure the formulas of the products are right, we check that we've applied the solubility rules correctly, which we have. Then we check that we've properly balanced the equation (We have.), that we've correctly divided the soluble compounds into their ions (We have.), and that we've eliminated the spectator ions to obtain the net ionic equation (We have.).

Practice Exercises

5.19 | Show that in aqueous solutions there is no net reaction between $Zn(NO_3)_2$ and $Ca(C_2H_3O_2)_2$. (*Hint:* Write molecular, ionic, and net ionic equations.)

5.20 | Predict the reaction that occurs on mixing the following solutions. Write molecular, ionic, and net ionic equations for the reactions that take place. (a) $AgNO_3$ and NH_4Cl, (b) sodium sulfide and lead(II) acetate.

Figure 5.18 | **Net reaction of acetic acid with a strong base.** The neutralization of acetic acid by hydroxide ion occurs primarily by the removal of H^+ from acetic acid molecules by OH^- ions.

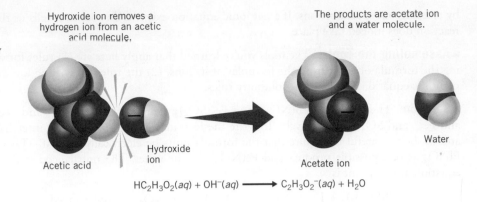

Hydroxide ion removes a hydrogen ion from an acetic acid molecule.

The products are acetate ion and a water molecule.

Acetic acid

Hydroxide ion

Acetate ion

Water

$$HC_2H_3O_2(aq) + OH^-(aq) \longrightarrow C_2H_3O_2^-(aq) + H_2O$$

Predicting Acid–Base Reactions

Recall from Section 5.3 that neutralization is one of the key properties of acids and bases. Many such reactions can be viewed as metathesis. An example is the reaction between HCl and NaOH.

$$HCl(aq) + NaOH(aq) \longrightarrow NaCl(aq) + H_2O$$

Writing this as an ionic equation gives

$$H^+(aq) + Cl^-(aq) + Na^+(aq) + OH^-(aq) \longrightarrow Na^+(aq) + Cl^-(aq) + H_2O$$

where we have used H^+ as shorthand for H_3O^+. The net ionic equation is obtained by removing spectator ions.

$$\checkmark \quad H^+(aq) + OH^-(aq) \longrightarrow H_2O$$

In this case, a net ionic equation exists because of the formation of a very weak electrolyte, H_2O, instead of a precipitate. In fact, we find this same net ionic equation for any reaction between a strong acid and a soluble strong base.

The formation of water in a neutralization reaction is such a strong driving force for reaction that it will form even if the acid is weak or if the base is insoluble, or both. Here are some examples.

not disassociate well

Reaction of a Weak Acid with a Strong Base

Molecular equation:

$$HC_2H_3O_2(aq) + NaOH(aq) \longrightarrow NaC_2H_3O_2(aq) + H_2O$$

weak acid   strong base

Net ionic equation: *stay the same*

$$HC_2H_3O_2(aq) + OH^-(aq) \longrightarrow C_2H_3O_2^-(aq) + H_2O$$

This reaction is illustrated in Figure 5.18.

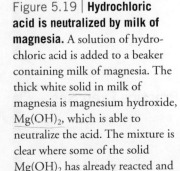

Figure 5.19 | **Hydrochloric acid is neutralized by milk of magnesia.** A solution of hydrochloric acid is added to a beaker containing milk of magnesia. The thick white solid in milk of magnesia is magnesium hydroxide, $Mg(OH)_2$, which is able to neutralize the acid. The mixture is clear where some of the solid $Mg(OH)_2$ has already reacted and dissolved. (*Andy Washnik*)

Reaction of a Strong Acid with an Insoluble Base

Figure 5.19 shows the reaction of hydrochloric acid with milk of magnesia, which contains $Mg(OH)_2$.

Molecular equation:

$$2HCl(aq) + Mg(OH)_2(s) \longrightarrow MgCl_2(aq) + 2H_2O$$

strong acid   insoluble base

combined together

$2H^+ + 2Cl^- + Mg(OH)_2 (s) \rightarrow Mg^{2+} + 2Cl^- + 2H_2O$

Net ionic equation:

$$2H^+(aq) + Mg(OH)_2(s) \longrightarrow Mg^{2+}(aq) + 2H_2O$$

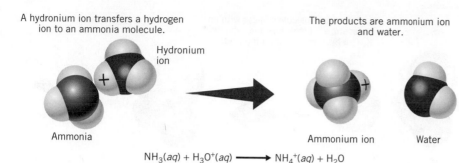

A hydronium ion transfers a hydrogen ion to an ammonia molecule.

Hydronium ion

Ammonia

The products are ammonium ion and water.

Ammonium ion   Water

Figure 5.20 | Reaction of ammonia with a strong acid. The reaction occurs primarily by the direct attack of H_3O^+ on NH_3 molecules. Transfer of a proton to the ammonia molecule produces an ammonium ion and a water molecule.

$$NH_3(aq) + H_3O^+(aq) \longrightarrow NH_4^+(aq) + H_2O$$

Reaction of a Weak Acid with an Insoluble Base

Molecular equation:

$$\underset{\text{weak acid}}{2HC_2H_3O_2(aq)} + \underset{\text{insoluble base}}{Mg(OH)_2(s)} \longrightarrow Mg(C_2H_3O_2)_2(aq) + 2H_2O$$

Net ionic equation:

$$2HC_2H_3O_2(aq) + Mg(OH)_2(s) \longrightarrow Mg^{2+}(aq) + 2C_2H_3O_2^-(aq) + 2H_2O$$

Notice that in the last two examples, the formation of water drives the reaction, even though one of the reactants is insoluble. To correctly write the ionic and net ionic equations, it is important to know both the solubility rules and which acids are strong and weak. If you've learned the list of strong acids, you can expect that any acid *not* on the list will be a weak acid. (Unless specifically told otherwise, you should assume weak acids to be water soluble.)

Reaction of an Acid with a Weak Base

Acid–base neutralization doesn't always involve the formation of water. We see this in the reaction of an acid with a weak base such as NH_3. For a strong acid such as HCl, we have

Molecular equation:

stay

$$HCl(aq) + NH_3(aq) \longrightarrow NH_4Cl(aq)$$

weak base

Net ionic equation (using H^+ as shorthand for H_3O^+):

$$H^+(aq) + NH_3(aq) \longrightarrow NH_4^+(aq)$$

Figure 5.20 depicts the transfer of H^+ from H_3O^+ to NH_3.

With a weak acid such as $HC_2H_3O_2$, we have

Molecular equation:

weak

$$HC_2H_3O_2(aq) + NH_3(aq) \longrightarrow NH_4C_2H_3O_2(aq)$$

Ionic and net ionic equation: stay

$$HC_2H_3O_2(aq) + NH_3(aq) \longrightarrow NH_4^+(aq) + C_2H_3O_2^-(aq)$$

Even though solutions of $HC_2H_3O_2$ contain some H^+, and solutions of NH_3 contain some OH^-, when these solutions are mixed the predominant reaction is between molecules of acid and base. This is illustrated in Figure 5.21.

5.21 | Write the molecular, ionic, and net ionic equations for the neutralization of $HNO_3(aq)$ by $Ca(OH)_2(aq)$. (*Hint:* First determine whether the acid and base are strong or weak.)

5.22 | Write molecular, ionic, and net ionic equations for the reaction of (a) HCl with KOH, (b) $HCHO_2$ with LiOH, and (c) N_2H_4 with HCl.

5.23 | Write molecular, ionic, and net ionic equations for the reaction of the weak base methylamine, CH_3NH_2, with formic acid, $HCHO_2$ (a weak acid).

Practice Exercises

Figure 5.21 | **Reaction of acetic acid with ammonia.** The collision of an ammonia molecule with an acetic acid molecule leads to a transfer of H$^+$ from the acetic acid to ammonia and the formation of ions.

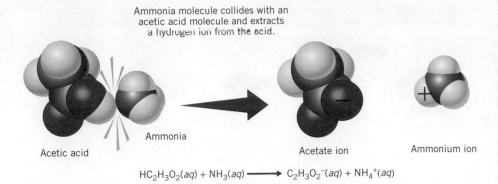

Ammonia molecule collides with an acetic acid molecule and extracts a hydrogen ion from the acid.

Acetic acid   Ammonia   Acetate ion   Ammonium ion

$$HC_2H_3O_2(aq) + NH_3(aq) \longrightarrow C_2H_3O_2^-(aq) + NH_4^+(aq)$$

Predicting Reactions in Which a Gas Is Formed

Sometimes a product of a metathesis reaction is a substance that normally is a gas at room temperature and is not very soluble in water. The most common example is carbon dioxide. This product forms when an acid reacts with either a bicarbonate or carbonate. For example, as a sodium bicarbonate solution is added to hydrochloric acid, bubbles of carbon dioxide are released (Figure 5.22). This is the same reaction that occurs if you take sodium bicarbonate to soothe an upset stomach. Stomach acid is HCl and its reaction with the NaHCO$_3$ both neutralizes the acid and produces CO$_2$ gas (burp!). The molecular equation for the metathesis reaction is

$$HCl(aq) + NaHCO_3(aq) \longrightarrow NaCl(aq) + H_2CO_3(aq)$$

Carbonic acid, H$_2$CO$_3$, is too unstable to be isolated in pure form. When it forms in appreciable amounts as a product in a metathesis reaction, it decomposes into its anhydride, CO$_2$, and water. Carbon dioxide is only slightly soluble in water, so most of the CO$_2$ bubbles out of the solution. The decomposition reaction is

$$\checkmark \quad H_2CO_3(aq) \longrightarrow H_2O + CO_2(g)$$

Figure 5.22 | **The reaction of sodium bicarbonate with hydrochloric acid.** The bubbles contain the gas carbon dioxide. *(Michael Watson)*

Therefore, the overall molecular equation for the reaction is

$$HCl(aq) + NaHCO_3(aq) \longrightarrow NaCl(aq) + H_2O + CO_2(g)$$

The ionic equation is

$$H^+(aq) + Cl^-(aq) + Na^+(aq) + HCO_3^-(aq) \longrightarrow Na^+(aq) + Cl^-(aq) + H_2O + CO_2(g)$$

and the net ionic equation is

$$H^+(aq) + HCO_3^-(aq) \longrightarrow H_2O + CO_2(g)$$

Similar results are obtained if we begin with a carbonate instead of a bicarbonate. In this case, hydrogen ions combine with carbonate ions to give H$_2$CO$_3$, which subsequently decomposes to water and CO$_2$.

$$2H^+(aq) + CO_3^{2-}(aq) \rightarrow H_2CO_3(aq) \longrightarrow H_2O + CO_2(g)$$

The net reaction is

$$2H^+(aq) + CO_3^{2-}(aq) \longrightarrow H_2O + CO_2(g)$$

Figure 5.23 | **Limestone reacts with acid.** Bubbles of CO$_2$ are formed in the reaction of limestone (CaCO$_3$) with hydrochloric acid. *(Andy Washnik)*

The release of CO$_2$ by the reaction of a carbonate with an acid is such a strong driving force for reaction that it enables insoluble carbonates to dissolve in acids (strong and weak). The reaction of limestone, CaCO$_3$, with hydrochloric acid is shown in Figure 5.23. The molecular and net ionic equations for the reaction are as follows:

$$CaCO_3(s) + 2HCl(aq) \longrightarrow CaCl_2(aq) + CO_2(g) + H_2O$$
$$CaCO_3(s) + 2H^+(aq) \longrightarrow Ca^{2+}(aq) + CO_2(g) + H_2O$$

Carbon dioxide is not the only gas formed in metathesis reactions. Table 5.2 lists others and the reactions that form them.

Table 5.2   Gases Formed in Metathesis Reactions

Gases Formed in Reactions with Acids		
Gas	Reactant Type	Equation for Formation[a]
H_2S	Sulfides	$2H^+ + S^{2-} \longrightarrow H_2S$
HCN	Cyanides	$H^+ + CN^- \longrightarrow HCN$
CO_2	Carbonates	$2H^+ + CO_3^{2-} \longrightarrow (H_2CO_3) \longrightarrow H_2O + CO_2$
	Bicarbonates (hydrogen carbonates)	$H^+ + HCO_3^- \longrightarrow (H_2CO_3) \longrightarrow H_2O + CO_2$
SO_2	Sulfites	$2H^+ + SO_3^{2-} \longrightarrow (H_2SO_3) \longrightarrow H_2O + SO_2$
	Bisulfites (hydrogen sulfites)	$H^+ + HSO_3^- \longrightarrow (H_2SO_3) \longrightarrow H_2O + SO_2$
Gases Formed in Reactions with Bases		
Gas	Reactant Type	Equation for Formation
NH_3	Ammonium salts[b]	$NH_4^+ + OH^- \longrightarrow NH_3 + H_2O$

[a]Formulas in parentheses are of unstable compounds that break down according to the continuation of the sequence.

[b]In writing a metathesis reaction, you may be tempted sometimes to write NH_4OH as a formula for "ammonium hydroxide." This compound does not exist. In water, it is nothing more than a solution of NH_3.

TOOLS

Gases formed in metathesis reactions

CHEMISTRY OUTSIDE THE CLASSROOM | 5.2

Hard Water and Its Problems

Precipitation reactions occur around us all the time, and we hardly ever take notice until they cause a problem. One common problem is caused by **hard water**—ground water that contains the "hardness ions," Ca^{2+}, Mg^{2+}, Fe^{2+}, or Fe^{3+}, in concentrations high enough to form precipitates with ordinary soap. Soap normally consists of the sodium salts of organic acids derived from animal fats or oils (so-called *fatty acids*). An example is sodium stearate, $NaC_{18}H_{35}O_2$. The negative ion of the soap forms an insoluble "scum" with hardness ions, which reduces the effectiveness of the soap for removing dirt and grease.

Hardness ions can be removed from water in a number of ways. One way is to add hydrated sodium carbonate, $Na_2CO_3 \cdot 10H_2O$, often called washing soda, to the water. The carbonate ion forms insoluble precipitates with the hardness ions; an example is $CaCO_3$.

$$Ca^{2+}(aq) + CO_3^{2-}(aq) \longrightarrow CaCO_3(s)$$

Once precipitated, the hardness ions are not available to interfere with the soap.

In localities where the earth contains limestone, which is composed mainly of $CaCO_3$, a particularly bothersome type of hard water is often found. Rain and other natural waters contain dissolved CO_2, which the water picks up from the atmosphere. Carbon dioxide is the anhydride of carbonic acid, H_2CO_3, a weak diprotic acid. This causes the water to be slightly acidic, primarily from the first step in the ionization of the acid,

$$CO_2(g) + H_2O \rightleftharpoons H_2CO_3(aq)$$
$$H_2CO_3(aq) + H_2O \rightleftharpoons H_3O^+(aq) + HCO_3^-(aq)$$

As the slightly acidic water seeps through the limestone, some of the insoluble $CaCO_3$ dissolves to give soluble calcium bicarbonate.

$$CaCO_3(s) + H_2CO_3(aq) \longrightarrow Ca^{2+}(aq) + 2HCO_3^-(aq)$$

When this ground water is pumped and distributed in a community water supply, the presence of Ca^{2+} gives the kinds of problems discussed above.

A more serious problem occurs when this hard water is heated in hot water heaters or spattered onto glassware and the walls of shower stalls. When solutions containing Ca^{2+} and HCO_3^- are heated or when the water evaporates, the reverse reactions occur and insoluble $CaCO_3$ precipitates as follows.

$$Ca^{2+}(aq) + 2HCO_3^-(aq) \longrightarrow H_2O + CO_2(g) + CaCO_3(s)$$

Evaporation of the hard water leaves spots of $CaCO_3$ on glass and other surfaces that are difficult to remove. In hot water heaters, the problem is more troublesome. The $CaCO_3$ precipitate sticks to the inner walls of pipes and the heating elements in hot water boilers and is called *boiler scale*. In locations that have high concentrations of Ca^{2+} and HCO_3^- in the water supply, boiler scale is a very serious problem, as illustrated in the photograph.

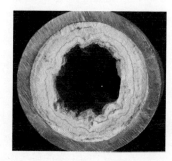

Boiler scale built up on the inside of a water pipe.
(Science VU/Betz/Visuals Unlimited.)

Example 5.7
Predicting Reactions and Writing Their Equations

What reaction (if any) occurs when solutions of ammonium carbonate, $(NH_4)_2CO_3$, and propanoic acid (also called propionic acid), $HC_3H_5O_2$, are mixed?

■ **Analysis:** To determine whether a reaction occurs, we need to know whether a net ionic equation exists after we drop spectator ions from the ionic equation. We begin by writing a potential metathesis equation in molecular form. Then we examine the reactants and products to see whether any are weak electrolytes or substances that give gases. We also look for soluble or insoluble ionic compounds. Then we form the ionic equation and search for spectator ions, which we eliminate to obtain the net ionic equation.

■ **Assembling the Tools:** Our tools for working a problem such as this are the list of strong acids, the solubility rules (Table 5.1), and the list of gases formed in metathesis reactions (Table 5.2).

■ **Solution:** First we construct a molecular equation, treating the reaction as a metathesis. For the acid, we take the cation to be H^+ and the anion to be $C_3H_5O_2^-$. Therefore, after exchanging cations between the two anions we can obtain the following balanced molecular equation:

$$(NH_4)_2CO_3 + 2HC_3H_5O_2 \longrightarrow 2NH_4C_3H_5O_2 + H_2CO_3$$

In the statement of the problem we are told that we are working with a *solution* of $HC_3H_5O_2$, so we know it's soluble. Also, it is not on the list of strong acids (the first tool mentioned above), so we expect it to be a weak acid; we will write it in molecular form in the ionic equation.

Next, we recognize that H_2CO_3 decomposes into $CO_2(g)$ and H_2O. (This information is also found in Table 5.2.) Let's rewrite the molecular equation taking this into account.

$$(NH_4)_2CO_3 + 2HC_3H_5O_2 \longrightarrow 2NH_4C_3H_5O_2 + CO_2(g) + H_2O$$

Now we need to determine which of the ionic substances are soluble. According to the solubility rules, all ammonium salts are soluble, and we know that all salts are strong electrolytes. Therefore, we will write $(NH_4)_2CO_3$ and $NH_4C_3H_5O_2$ in dissociated form. Now we are ready to expand the molecular equation into the ionic equation.

$$2NH_4^+(aq) + CO_3^{2-}(aq) + 2HC_3H_5O_2(aq) \longrightarrow 2NH_4^+(aq) + 2C_3H_5O_2^-(aq) + CO_2(g) + H_2O$$

The only spectator ion is NH_4^+. Dropping this gives the net ionic equation.

$$CO_3^{2-}(aq) + 2HC_3H_5O_2(aq) \longrightarrow 2C_3H_5O_2^-(aq) + CO_2(g) + H_2O$$

A net reaction *does* occur, as indicated by the existence of a net ionic equation.

■ **Is the Answer Reasonable?** There are some common errors that people make in working problems of this kind, so it is important to double check. Be sure you've written the formulas of the products correctly. (If you need review, you might look at Example 5.6 on page 176.) Look for weak acids. (You need to know the list of strong ones; if an acid isn't on the list, it's a weak acid.) Look for gases, or substances that decompose into gases. (Be sure you've studied Table 5.2.) Check for insoluble compounds. (You need to know the solubility rules in Table 5.1.) If you've checked each step, it is likely your result is correct.

Example 5.8
Predicting Reactions and Writing Their Equations

What reaction (if any) occurs in water between potassium nitrate and ammonium chloride?

■ **Analysis:** Once again, we need to know whether a net ionic equation exists. We follow the same path as in Example 5.7, but first we have to convert the names of the compounds into chemical formulas. Then we construct molecular, ionic, and net ionic equations.

■ **Assembling the Tools:** The tools we need are (1) nomenclature rules from Chapter 3 and (2) the solubility rules (Table 5.1). No acids are mentioned among the reactants, so we don't need the list of strong acids. We're also not going to need Table 5.2. The products shown in that table are formed from the reaction of either an acid or a strong base, neither of which is among our reactants here.

■ **Solution:** First we apply the nomenclature rules. The ions in potassium nitrate are K^+ and NO_3^-, so the salt has the formula KNO_3. In ammonium chloride, the ions are NH_4^+ and Cl^-, so the salt is NH_4Cl.

Next we write the molecular equation, being sure to construct correct formulas for the products.

$$KNO_3 + NH_4Cl \longrightarrow KCl + NH_4NO_3$$

Looking over the substances in the equation, we don't find any that are weak acids or that decompose to give gases. Next, we check solubilities.

According to solubility Rule 2, both KNO_3 and NH_4Cl are soluble. By solubility Rules 1 and 2, both products are also soluble in water. The anticipated molecular equation is therefore

$$KNO_3(aq) + NH_4Cl(aq) \longrightarrow KCl(aq) + NH_4NO_3(aq)$$

soluble   soluble   soluble   soluble

and the ionic equation is

$$K^+(aq) + NO_3^-(aq) + NH_4^+(aq) + Cl^-(aq) \longrightarrow K^+(aq) + Cl^-(aq) + NH_4^+(aq) + NO_3^-(aq)$$

Notice that the right side of the equation is the same as the left side except for the order in which the ions are written. When we eliminate spectator ions, everything goes. There is no net ionic equation, which means there is no net reaction.

■ **Is the Answer Reasonable?** Once again, we perform the same checks here as in Example 5.7, and they tell us our answer is right.

Practice Exercises

5.24 | Knowing that salts of the formate ion, CHO_2^-, are water soluble, predict the reaction between $Co(OH)_2$ and formic acid, $HCHO_2$. Write molecular, ionic, and net ionic equations. (*Hint:* Apply the tools we used in Example 5.7.)

5.25 | Predict whether a reaction will occur in aqueous solution between the following pairs of substances: (a) $KCHO_2$ and HCl, (b) $CuCO_3$ and $HC_2H_3O_2$, (c) calcium acetate and silver nitrate, and (d) sodium hydroxide and nickel(II) chloride. Write molecular, ionic, and net ionic equations.

Using Metathesis Reactions to Synthesize Salts

One practical use for metathesis reactions is the synthesis of chemical compounds. For example, in the manufacture of photographic film, the light-sensitive component is a mixture of silver bromide and silver iodide formed by the reaction of silver nitrate with potassium bromide and iodide. Both reactants are water soluble, but the silver bromide and iodide are insoluble.

In planning a synthesis, the most important criterion is that the desired compound should be easily separated from the reaction mixture, uncontaminated by either the reactant starting materials or by any other product of the reaction. This leads to two principal approaches.

Synthesis by metathesis

1. If the desired compound is insoluble in water, then we can start with two soluble reactants. After the reaction is over, the compound can be separated from the mixture by filtration.
2. If the desired compound is soluble, the best route is either by an acid—base neutralization in which the anion is supplied by the acid and the cation by the base, or by a reaction in which the cation is from a metal carbonate and the anion is provided by an acid. (Metal sulfides or sulfites would work as well, but a product would then be H_2S or SO_2, both of which are poisonous gases.) In both cases, if the conditions are controlled correctly, the resulting solution can be evaporated to recover the desired product. These methods work best if one of the reactants is insoluble and is present in excess, so that the only soluble product remaining in the reaction mixture is the desired compound.

Example 5.9
Synthesizing a Compound by Metathesis

What reaction might we use to synthesize nickel sulfate, $NiSO_4$?

■ **Analysis:** Questions of this kind are somewhat open ended because there is often more than one reaction we can use to make the same compound. First we need to know whether $NiSO_4$ is soluble or not. Then we can select our reactants.

■ **Assembling the Tools:** One tool we are definitely going to need is the solubility rules. The better you know them, the easier answering the question will be. After deciding solubility, we use the decision-making tool above to determine our path. We may also need to know how to write equations for acid—base neutralization or reactions of acids with carbonates.

■ **Solution:** According to the solubility rules, $NiSO_4$ is soluble in water. This means our path is best followed by reaction of an acid with a base or a carbonate. The acid supplies the anion, so we would use H_2SO_4. The base would be $Ni(OH)_2$, and if we use a carbonate it would be $NiCO_3$. The solubility rules tell us both of these nickel-containing reactants are insoluble. Here are the two possible reactions written in molecular form.

$$H_2SO_4(aq) + Ni(OH)_2(s) \longrightarrow NiSO_4(aq) + 2H_2O$$
$$H_2SO_4(aq) + NiCO_3(s) \longrightarrow NiSO_4(aq) + CO_2(g) + H_2O$$

■ **Is the Answer Reasonable?** All we can do here is check the reasoning, which seems sound. The two equations yield the desired product, and if the reaction is carried out with an excess of the insoluble reactant, filtration will give a solution containing only $NiSO_4$.

Practice Exercises

5.26 | Write an equation for the preparation of copper(II) nitrate using an acid—base neutralization reaction.

5.27 | Suppose you wished to prepare cobalt(II) sulfide using a metathesis reaction. What criteria would the reactants have to satisfy *in this particular case*? Write an equation for a reaction utilizing a set of reactants that meet these criteria.

5.6 | Molarity

Solutions are very convenient for carrying out many reactions, and to deal with their stoichiometry we need to develop some quantitative tools. One of these is a way to express their *concentrations*. Earlier we used percentage concentration (grams of solute per 100 g of solution) as an example of a concentration unit. To deal with the stoichiometry of reactions in solution, however, percentage concentration is inconvenient. Instead, we express the amount of solute in moles and the amount of solution in liters.

The **molar concentration**, or **molarity** (abbreviated M), of a solution is defined as *the number of moles of solute per liter of solution*. It is a ratio of moles of solute to the volume of the solution expressed in liters.

$$\text{Molarity } (M) = \frac{\text{moles of solute}}{\text{liters of solution}} \qquad (5.4)$$

TOOLS

Molarity

Thus, a solution that contains 0.100 mol of NaCl in 1.00 L has a molarity of 0.100 M, and we would refer to this solution as 0.100 *molar* NaCl or as 0.100 M NaCl. The same concentration would result if we dissolved 0.0100 mol of NaCl in 0.100 L (100 mL) of solution, because the *ratio* of moles of solute to volume of solution is the same.

$$\frac{0.100 \text{ mol NaCl}}{1.00 \text{ L NaCl soln}} = \frac{0.0100 \text{ mol NaCl}}{0.100 \text{ L NaCl soln}} = 0.100 \ M \text{ NaCl}$$

Using Molarity as a Conversion Factor

Whenever we have to deal with a stoichiometry problem that involves an amount of a chemical and a volume of a solution of that substance, you can expect that solving the problem will involve molarity.

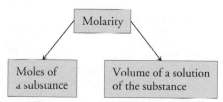

Molarity is a tool that provides the conversion factors we need to convert between moles and volume (either in liters or milliliters). Consider, for example, a solution labeled 0.100 M NaCl. The unit M always translates to mean "moles per liter," so we can write

$$0.100 \ M \text{ NaCl} = \frac{0.100 \text{ mol NaCl}}{1.00 \text{ L soln}}$$

This gives us an equivalence relationship between "mol NaCl" and "L soln" that we can use to form two conversion factors[10].

$$0.100 \text{ mol NaCl} \Leftrightarrow 1.00 \text{ L soln}$$

$$\frac{0.100 \text{ mol NaCl}}{1.00 \text{ L NaCl soln}} \qquad \frac{1.00 \text{ L NaCl soln}}{0.100 \text{ mol NaCl}}$$

---

[10]Some students find it easier to translate the "1.00 L" part of these factors into the equivalent 1000 mL here rather than convert between liters and milliliters at some other stage of the calculation. Factors such as the two above, therefore, can be rewritten as follows whenever it is convenient. (Remember that "1000" in the following is regarded as having an infinite number of significant figures because, standing as it does for 1 L, it is part of the definition of molarity and is an exact number.)

$$\frac{0.100 \text{ mol NaCl}}{1000 \text{ mL NaCl soln}} \quad \text{and} \quad \frac{1000 \text{ mL NaCl soln}}{0.100 \text{ mol NaCl}}$$

Example 5.10
Calculating the Molarity of a Solution

To study the effect of dissolved salt on the rusting of an iron sample, a student prepared a solution of NaCl by dissolving 1.461 g of NaCl in enough water to make 250.0 mL of solution. What is the molarity of this solution?

■ **Analysis:** When given the amount of solute and the volume of a solution, we go back to the definition of molarity to calculate the concentration.

■ **Assembling the Tools:** The tool we'll use to solve this problem is Equation 5.4, which defines molarity as the ratio of *moles of solute* to *liters of solution*. If we can find these two pieces of information, we can arrange them as a ratio,

$$\text{molarity} = \frac{?\,\text{mol NaCl}}{?\,\text{L soln}}$$

Therefore, we have to convert 1.461 g of NaCl to moles of NaCl, and the tool for this is the molar mass. We also have to change 250.0 mL to liters. The tool for this is 1000 mL = 1 L.

■ If necessary, practice converting between liters and milliliters. It's a task you will have to perform frequently.

■ **Solution:** The number of moles of NaCl is found using the formula mass of NaCl, 58.443 g mol^{-1}.

$$1.461\ \text{g NaCl} \times \frac{1\ \text{mol NaCl}}{58.443\ \text{g NaCl}} = 0.024999\ \text{mol NaCl}$$

■ Once again, we carry one extra significant figure in intermediate calculations.

To find the volume of the solution in liters, we move the decimal three places to the left, so 250.0 mL equals 0.2500 L.
The ratio of moles to liters, therefore, is

$$\frac{0.024999\ \text{mol NaCl}}{0.2500\ \text{L}} = 0.1000\ M\ \text{NaCl}$$

■ **Is the Answer Reasonable?** Let's use our answer to do a rough calculation of the amount of NaCl in the solution. If our answer is right, we should find a value not too far from the amount given in the problem (1.461 g). If we round the formula mass of NaCl to 60, and use 0.1 M as an approximate concentration, then one liter of the solution contains 0.1 mol of NaCl, or approximately 6 g of NaCl (one-tenth of 60 g). But 250 mL is only 1/4 of a liter, so the mass of NaCl will be approximately 1/4 of 6 g, or about 1.5 g. This is pretty close to the amount that was given in the problem, so our answer is probably correct.

Practice Exercises

5.28 | A certain solution contains 16.9 g of HNO$_3$ dissolved in 125 mL of solution. Water is added until the volume is 175 mL. What is the molarity of HNO$_3$ in the final solution? (*Hint:* Does the amount of HNO$_3$ change when the water is added?)

5.29 | Suppose 1.223 g of NaCl is added to the 250.0 mL of NaCl solution described in Example 5.10. If there is no change in the total volume of the solution, what is the new molarity of the NaCl?

Example 5.11
Using Molar Concentrations

How many milliliters of 0.250 M NaCl solution must be measured to obtain 0.100 mol of NaCl?

■ **Analysis:** We can restate the problem as follows:

$$0.100 \text{ mol NaCl} \Leftrightarrow ? \text{ mL soln}$$

To find the answer, we need a conversion factor to take us from moles to milliliters. In the discussion above we say that moles and volume are related by the molarity.

■ **Assembling the Tools:** Our tool will be the molarity, which translates to

$$0.250\,M \text{ NaCl} = \frac{0.250 \text{ mol NaCl}}{1 \text{ L NaCl soln}}$$

The fraction on the right relates moles of NaCl to liters of the solution and provides us with two conversion factors.

$$\frac{0.250 \text{ mol NaCl}}{1.00 \text{ L NaCl soln}} \quad \text{and} \quad \frac{1.00 \text{ L NaCl soln}}{0.250 \text{ mol NaCl}}$$

To obtain the answer, we select the one on the right, which will allow us to cancel the unit "mol NaCl."

■ **Solution:** We operate with the second factor on 0.100 mol NaCl.

$$0.100 \text{ mol NaCl} \times \frac{1.00 \text{ L NaCl soln}}{0.250 \text{ mol NaCl}} = 0.400 \text{ L of } 0.250\,M \text{ NaCl}$$

Because 0.400 L corresponds to 400 mL, our answer is that 400 mL (or 4.00×10^2 mL) of 0.250 M NaCl provides 0.100 mol of NaCl.

■ **Is the Answer Reasonable?** The molarity tells us that one liter contains 0.250 mol NaCl, so we need somewhat less than half of a liter (1000 mL) to obtain just 0.100 mol. The answer, 400 mL, is reasonable.

Practice Exercises

5.30 | A student measured 175 mL of 0.250 M HCl solution into a beaker. How many moles of HCl were in the beaker? (*Hint:* Molarity gives the equivalence between moles of solute and volume of solution in liters.)

5.31 | How many milliliters of 0.250 M HCl solution contain 1.30 g of HCl?

Obtaining Moles of Solute from Molarity and Volume

If you worked Practice Exercise 5.30 you learned that we can use the volume and molarity of a solution to calculate the number of moles of solute in it. This is such a useful relationship that it warrants special attention. Solving Equation 5.4 for *moles of solute* gives

TOOLS

$$\boxed{\text{molarity} \times \text{volume (L)} = \text{moles of solute}} \qquad (5.5)$$

Molarity times volume gives moles

$$\frac{\text{mol solute}}{\text{L soln}} \times \text{L soln} = \text{mol solute}$$

(a)   *(b)*   *(c)*   *(d)*   *(e)*

Figure 5.24 | **The preparation of a solution having a known molarity.** (*a*) The 250 mL volumetric flask shown is one of a number of sizes available for preparing solutions. When filled to the line etched around its neck, this flask contains exactly 250 mL of solution. The flask here already contains a weighed amount of solute. (*b*) Water is being added. (*c*) The solute is completely dissolved into solution before the level is brought up to the narrow neck of the flask. (*d*) More water is added to bring the level of the solution to the etched line. (*e*) The flask is stoppered and then inverted several times to mix its contents thoroughly. *(Michael Watson)*

Thus, *any time you know both the molarity and volume of a solution, you can easily calculate the number of moles of solute in it.* As you will see, this concept will be very useful in solving a variety of problems.

One situation in which Equation 5.5 is useful is when we must prepare some specific volume of a solution having a desired molarity (e.g., 250.0 mL of 0.0800 *M* Na$_2$CrO$_4$). To proceed, we have to calculate the amount of solute that will be in the solution after it's made. Thus, in 250.0 mL of 0.0800 *M* Na$_2$CrO$_4$ there are

■ In this calculation, we're using molarity as a conversion factor to change volume to moles.

$$\frac{0.0800 \text{ mol Na}_2\text{CrO}_4}{1 \text{ L soln}} \times 0.2500 \text{ L soln} = 0.0200 \text{ mol Na}_2\text{CrO}_4$$

Figure 5.24 shows how we would use a 250-mL volumetric flask to prepare such a solution.[11] (A **volumetric flask** is a narrow-necked flask having an etched mark high on its neck. When filled to the mark, the flask contains precisely the volume given by the flask's label.)

Example 5.12
Preparing a Solution with a Known Molarity

Strontium nitrate, Sr(NO$_3$)$_2$, is used in fireworks to produce brilliant red colors. Suppose we need to prepare 250.0 mL of 0.100 *M* Sr(NO$_3$)$_2$ solution. How many grams of strontium nitrate are required?

■**Analysis:** The *critical link* in solving this problem is realizing that we know both the volume and molarity of the final solution, which permits us to calculate the number of moles of Sr(NO$_3$)$_2$ that will be in it. Once we know the number of moles of Sr(NO$_3$)$_2$, we can calculate its mass using the molar mass of the salt.

■**Assembling the Tools:** The first tool we will use is Equation 5.5.

molarity of Sr(NO$_3$)$_2$ × volume of solution in liters = moles Sr(NO$_3$)$_2$

---

[11]Note that in preparing the solution described in Figure 5.24, we do not simply add 250 mL of water to the solute. If we did, the final volume would be slightly larger than 250 mL, which would make the molarity slightly less than desired. To obtain an accurate molarity, we add enough water to give a total volume of 250 mL. The actual volume of water added is not important, only that the *total final volume* is 250 mL.

Then we will use the molar mass of Sr, which gives us

$$1 \text{ mol Sr(NO}_3)_2 = 211.62 \text{ g Sr(NO}_3)_2$$

from which we will construct the necessary conversion factor.

■ **Solution:** First we apply Equation 5.5. The volume 250.0 mL converts to 0.2500 L. Multiplying the molarity by the volume in liters takes the following form.

$$\underbrace{\frac{0.100 \text{ mol Sr(NO}_3)_2}{1.00 \text{ L Sr(NO}_3)_2 \text{ soln}}}_{\text{molarity}} \times \underbrace{0.2500 \text{ L Sr(NO}_3)_2 \text{ soln}}_{\text{volume (L)}} = \underbrace{0.02500 \text{ mol Sr(NO}_3)_2}_{\text{moles of solute}}$$

Finally, we convert from moles to grams using the molar mass of $Sr(NO_3)_2$.

$$0.02500 \text{ mol Sr(NO}_3)_2 \times \frac{211.62 \text{ g Sr(NO}_3)_2}{1 \text{ mol Sr(NO}_3)_2} = 5.29 \text{ g Sr(NO}_3)_2$$

Thus, to prepare the solution we need to dissolve 5.29 g of $Sr(NO_3)_2$ in a total volume of 250.0 mL.

We could also have set this up as a chain calculation as follows, with the conversion factors strung together.

$$0.2500 \text{ L Sr(NO}_3)_2 \text{ soln} \times \frac{0.100 \text{ mol Sr(NO}_3)_2}{1.00 \text{ L Sr(NO}_3)_2 \text{ soln}} \times \frac{211.62 \text{ g Sr(NO}_3)_2}{1 \text{ mol Sr(NO}_3)_2} = 5.29 \text{ g Sr(NO}_3)_2$$

■ **Is the Answer Reasonable?** If we were working with a full liter of this solution, it would contain 0.1 mol of $Sr(NO_3)_2$. The molar mass of the salt is 211.62 g mol^{-1}, so 0.1 mol is slightly more than 20 g. However, we are working with just a quarter of a liter (250 mL), so the amount of $Sr(NO_3)_2$ needed is slightly more than a quarter of 20 g, or 5 g. The answer, 5.29 g, is close to this, so it makes sense.

Practice Exercises

5.32 | Suppose you wanted to prepare 50 mL of 0.2 M $Sr(NO_3)_2$ solution. Using the kind of approximate arithmetic we employed in the *Is the Answer Reasonable* step in Example 5.12, estimate the number of grams of $Sr(NO_3)_2$ required. (*Hint:* How many moles of $Sr(NO_3)_2$ would be in one liter of the solution?)

5.33 | How many grams of $AgNO_3$ are needed to prepare 250.0 mL of 0.0125 M $AgNO_3$ solution?

Diluting Solutions

Laboratory chemicals are usually purchased in concentrated form and must be *diluted* (made less concentrated) before being used. This is accomplished by adding more solvent to the solution, which spreads the solute through a larger volume and causes the concentration (the amount per unit volume) to decrease.

During dilution, the number of moles of solute remains constant. This means that the product of molarity and volume, which equals the moles of solute, must be the same for both the concentrated and diluted solution.

$$\underbrace{\left(\begin{array}{c} \text{Volume of} \\ \text{dilute solution} \\ \text{to be prepared} \end{array} \right) \times M_{\text{dilute}}}_{\substack{\text{Moles of solute in} \\ \text{the dilute solution}}} = \underbrace{\left(\begin{array}{c} \text{Volume of} \\ \text{concentrated solution} \\ \text{to be used} \end{array} \right) \times M_{\text{conc}}}_{\substack{\text{Moles of solute in the} \\ \text{concentrated solution}}}$$

Or,

$$V_{\text{dil}} \cdot M_{\text{dil}} = V_{\text{conc}} \cdot M_{\text{conc}} \qquad (5.6)$$

TOOLS

Dilution equation

Any units can be used for volume in Equation 5.6 provided that they are the same on both sides of the equation. This means we can solve dilution problems using *milliliters* directly in Equation 5.6.

Example 5.13
Preparing a Solution of Known Molarity by Dilution

How can we prepare 100.0 mL of 0.0400 M K$_2$Cr$_2$O$_7$ from 0.200 M K$_2$Cr$_2$O$_7$?

■ **Analysis:** This is the way such a question comes up in the lab, but what it is really asking is, "How many milliliters of 0.200 M K$_2$Cr$_2$O$_7$ (the more concentrated solution) must be diluted to give a solution with a final volume of 100.0 mL and a final molarity of 0.0400 M?" Once we see the question this way, it becomes clear what we have to do.

■ **Assembling the Tools:** Because it's a dilution problem, the tool we need to solve the problem is Equation 5.6.

$$V_{dil} \cdot M_{dil} = V_{conc} \cdot M_{conc}$$

■ **Solution:** It's a good idea to assemble the data first, noting what is missing (and therefore what has to be calculated).

$$V_{dil} = 100.0 \text{ mL} \qquad\qquad M_{dil} = 0.0400 \text{ } M$$

$$V_{conc} = ? \qquad\qquad M_{conc} = 0.200 \text{ } M$$

Next, we substitute into Equation 5.6.

$$100.0 \text{ mL} \times 0.0400 \text{ } M = V_{conc} \times 0.200 \text{ } M$$

Solving for V_{conc} gives

$$V_{conc} = \frac{100.0 \text{ mL} \times 0.0400 \, M}{0.200 \, M}$$

$$= 20.0 \text{ mL}$$

Therefore, the answer to the question as asked is: We would withdraw 20.0 mL of 0.200 M K$_2$Cr$_2$O$_7$, place it in a 100 mL volumetric flask, and then add water until the final volume is exactly 100 mL. (See Figure 5.25.)

■ **Is the Answer Reasonable?** Notice that the concentrated solution is 5 times more concentrated than the dilute solution (5 × 0.04 = 0.2). To reduce the concentration by a factor of 5 requires that we increase the volume by a factor of 5, and we see that 100 mL is 5 times 20 mL. The answer appears to be correct.

Practice Exercises

5.34 | To what final volume must 100.0 mL of 0.125 M H$_2$SO$_4$ solution be diluted to give a 0.0500 M H$_2$SO$_4$ solution? (*Hint:* Write the equation we used for dilution problems.)

5.35 | How many milliliters of water have to be *added* to 150 mL of 0.50 M HCl to reduce the concentration to 0.10 M HCl?

5.7 | Solution Stoichiometry

When we deal quantitatively with reactions in solution, we often work with volumes of solutions and molarity. The following is an example.

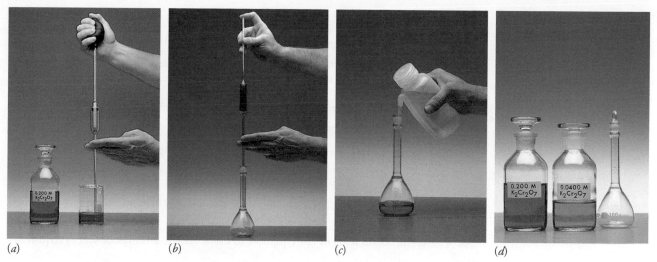

(a)   (b)   (c)   (d)

Figure 5.25 | **Preparing a solution by dilution.** (*a*) The calculated volume of the more concentrated solution is withdrawn from the stock solution by means of a volumetric pipet. (*b*) The solution is allowed to drain entirely from the pipet into the volumetric flask. (*c*) Water is added to the flask, the contents are mixed, and the final volume is brought up to the etch mark on the narrow neck of the flask. (*d*) The new solution is put into a labeled container. (*OPC, Inc.*)

Example 5.14
Stoichiometry Involving Reactions in Solution

One of the solids present in photographic film is silver bromide, AgBr. Suppose we wanted to prepare AgBr by the following precipitation reaction.

$$2AgNO_3(aq) + CaBr_2(aq) \longrightarrow 2AgBr(s) + Ca(NO_3)_2(aq)$$

How many milliliters of 0.125 *M* CaBr$_2$ solution must be used to react with the solute in 50.0 mL of 0.115 *M* AgNO$_3$?

■ **Analysis:** In general, when we deal with the stoichiometry of a reaction, we work with a balanced chemical equation, which we're given. The coefficients in the equation will relate moles of CaBr$_2$ to moles of AgNO$_3$, so this will be one of the tools we will use. However, we're not given moles directly. Instead we have molarities and the volume of the AgNO$_3$ solution. The *critical link* in solving the problem is recognizing that the molarity and volume of the AgNO$_3$ solution provides a path to finding the number of moles of AgNO$_3$.

At this point we can go in two steps from the data given for the AgNO$_3$ solution to the number of moles of CaBr$_2$ that react. The last step will be to go from moles of CaBr$_2$ to milliliters of the solution, and these two quantities are related by the molarity of the CaBr$_2$ solution. The calculation flow will look like the following.

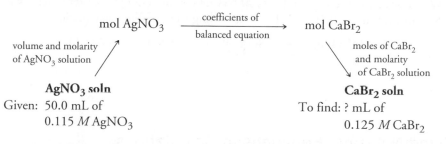

mol AgNO$_3$ $\xrightarrow{\substack{\text{coefficients of} \\ \text{balanced equation}}}$ mol CaBr$_2$

volume and molarity
of AgNO$_3$ solution ↗

moles of CaBr$_2$
and molarity
of CaBr$_2$ solution ↘

AgNO$_3$ soln   **CaBr$_2$ soln**
Given: 50.0 mL of   To find: ? mL of
      0.115 *M* AgNO$_3$ 0.125 *M* CaBr$_2$

■ **Assembling the Tools:** Here are the tools we will use. First, we need the relationship to calculate moles of AgNO$_3$

$$\text{molarity AgNO}_3 \text{ soln} \times \text{volume AgNO}_3 \text{ soln(L)} = \text{moles AgNO}_3$$

Silver bromide (AgBr) precipitates when solutions of calcium bromide and silver nitrate are mixed. (*Michael Watson*)

The next tool uses the coefficients of the equation.

$$2 \text{ mol AgNO}_3 \Leftrightarrow 1 \text{ mol CaBr}_2$$

Finally, we go from moles of $CaBr_2$ to volume of solution using the relationship derived from the molarity (0.125 M $CaBr_2$),

$$0.125 \text{ mol CaBr}_2 \Leftrightarrow 1.00 \text{ L CaBr}_2 \text{ soln}$$

to form the necessary conversion factor.

■ **Solution:** First, we find the moles of $AgNO_3$ taken. Changing 50.0 mL to 0.0500 L,

$$\underset{\text{volume}}{\underbrace{0.0500 \text{ L AgNO}_3 \text{ soln}}} \times \underset{\text{molarity}}{\underbrace{\frac{0.115 \text{ mol AgNO}_3}{1.00 \text{ L AgNO}_3 \text{ soln}}}} = 5.75 \times 10^{-3} \text{ mol AgNO}_3$$

Next, we use the coefficients of the equation to calculate the amount of $CaBr_2$ required.

$$5.75 \times 10^{-3} \text{ mol AgNO}_3 \times \frac{1 \text{ mol CaBr}_2}{2 \text{ mol AgNO}_3} = 2.875 \times 10^{-3} \text{ mol CaBr}_2$$

Finally we calculate the volume (mL) of 0.125 M $CaBr_2$ that contains this many moles of $CaBr_2$. Here we use the fact that the molarity of the $CaBr_2$ solution, 0.125 M, gives two possible conversion factors:

$$\frac{0.125 \text{ mol CaBr}_2}{1.00 \text{ L CaBr}_2 \text{ soln}} \quad \text{and} \quad \frac{1.00 \text{ L CaBr}_2 \text{ soln}}{0.125 \text{ mol CaBr}_2}$$

We use the one that cancels the unit "mol $CaBr_2$."

$$2.875 \times 10^{-3} \text{ mol CaBr}_2 \times \frac{1.00 \text{ L CaBr}_2 \text{ soln}}{0.125 \text{ mol CaBr}_2} = 0.0230 \text{ L CaBr}_2 \text{ soln}$$

Thus 0.0230 L, or 23.0 mL, of 0.125 M $CaBr_2$ has enough solute to combine with the $AgNO_3$ in 50.0 mL of 0.115 M $AgNO_3$.

■ **Is the Answer Reasonable?** The molarities of the two solutions are about the same, but only 1 mol $CaBr_2$ is needed for each 2 mol $AgNO_3$. Therefore, the volume of $CaBr_2$ solution needed (23.0 mL) should be about half the volume of $AgNO_3$ solution taken (50.0 mL), which it is.

Practice Exercises

5.36 | How many milliliters of 0.0475 M H_3PO_4 could be completely neutralized by 45.0 mL of 0.100 M KOH? The balanced equation for the reaction is

$$H_3PO_4(aq) + 3KOH(aq) \longrightarrow K_3PO_4(aq) + 3H_2O$$

(*Hint:* Outline the path of the calculations as in Example 5.14.)

5.37 | How many milliliters of 0.124 M NaOH contain enough NaOH to react with the H_2SO_4 in 15.4 mL of 0.108 M H_2SO_4 according to the following equation?

$$2NaOH(aq) + H_2SO_4(aq) \longrightarrow Na_2SO_4(aq) + 2H_2O$$

Using Net Ionic Equations in Calculations

In the preceding problem, we worked with a molecular equation in solving a stoichiometry problem. Ionic and net ionic equations can also be used, but this requires that we work with the concentrations of the ions in solution.

Calculating Concentrations of Ions in Solutions of Electrolytes

The concentrations of the ions in a solution of a strong electrolyte are obtained from the formula and molar concentration of the solute. For example, suppose we are working with a solution labeled "0.20 M $CaCl_2$." In 1.0 L of this solution there is 0.20 mol of $CaCl_2$, which is fully dissociated into Ca^{2+} and Cl^- ions.

$$CaCl_2 \longrightarrow Ca^{2+} + 2Cl^-$$

Based on the stoichiometry of the dissociation, 1 mol Ca^{2+} and 2 mol Cl^- are formed from each 1 mol of $CaCl_2$. We can find the ion concentrations in the solution using dimensional analysis.

$$\frac{0.20 \text{ mol } CaCl_2}{1.0 \text{ L soln}} \times \frac{1 \text{ mol } Ca^{2+}}{1 \text{ mol } CaCl_2} = \frac{0.20 \text{ mol } Ca^{2+}}{1.0 \text{ L soln}} = 0.20\, M\, Ca^{2+}$$

$$\frac{0.20 \text{ mol } CaCl_2}{1.0 \text{ L soln}} \times \frac{2 \text{ mol } Cl^-}{1 \text{ mol } CaCl_2} = \frac{0.40 \text{ mol } Cl^-}{1.0 \text{ L soln}} = 0.40\, M\, Cl^-$$

■ If you should ever become confused, you can always fall back on dimensional analysis to check the calculation.

In 0.20 M $CaCl_2$, then, the concentration of Ca^{2+} is 0.20 M and the concentration of Cl^- is 0.40 M.

In the example just given, notice that the ion concentrations are equal to the concentration of $CaCl_2$ multiplied by the number of ions of each kind that are released when a formula unit of $CaCl_2$ dissociates. This provides a very simple way to find the concentrations of the ions.

TOOLS

> The concentration of a particular ion equals the concentration of the salt multiplied by the number of ions of that kind in one formula unit of the salt.

Molarity of ions in a salt solution

Example 5.15
Calculating the Concentrations of Ions in a Solution

What are the molar concentrations of the ions in 0.20 M aluminum sulfate?

■ **Analysis:** To find the molar concentrations, we first need the formulas of the ions so we can write the correct formula of aluminum sulfate. Then we will have to examine how the salt dissociates and use that information to calculate ion concentrations.

■ **Assembling the Tools:** Several tools are required: (1) the formulas of the ions and the rules for writing chemical formulas, both from Chapter 3, (2) the equation for the dissociation of the salt in water, and (3) the method we just developed for finding molar concentrations of the ions using the coefficients in the dissociation equation.

■ **Solution:** The ions are Al^{3+} and SO_4^{2-}, so the salt must be $Al_2(SO_4)_3$. When $Al_2(SO_4)_3$ dissolves, it dissociates as follows:

$$Al_2(SO_4)_3(s) \longrightarrow 2Al^{3+}(aq) + 3SO_4^{2-}(aq)$$

Each formula unit of $Al_2(SO_4)_3$ yields two Al^{3+} ions and three SO_4^{2-} ions. Therefore, 0.20 mol $Al_2(SO_4)_3$ yields 0.40 mol Al^{3+} and 0.60 mol SO_4^{2-}, and we conclude that the solution contains 0.40 M Al^{3+} and 0.60 M SO_4^{2-}.

■ **Is the Answer Reasonable?** The answers here have been obtained by simple mole reasoning. We could have found the answers in a more formal manner using dimensional analysis. For example, for Al^{3+}, we have

$$\frac{0.20 \text{ mol } Al_2(SO_4)_3}{1.0 \text{ L soln}} \times \frac{2 \text{ mol } Al^{3+}}{1 \text{ mol } Al_2(SO_4)_3} = \frac{0.40 \text{ mol } Al^{3+}}{1.0 \text{ L soln}} = 0.40\, M\, Al^{3+}$$

A similar calculation would give the concentration of SO_4^{2-} as 0.60 M. Study both methods. With just a little practice, you will have little difficulty with the reasoning approach we used first.

Example 5.16
Calculating the Concentration of a Salt from the Concentration of One of Its Ions

A student found that the sulfate ion concentration in a solution of $Al_2(SO_4)_3$ was 0.90 M. What was the concentration of $Al_2(SO_4)_3$ in the solution?

■ **Analysis:** Once again, we use the formula of the salt to determine the number of ions released when it dissociates. This time we use the information to work backward to find the salt concentration.

■ **Assembling the Tools:** The tools are the same as in Example 5.15.

■ **Solution:** Let's set up the problem using dimensional analysis to be sure of our procedure. We will use the fact that 1 mol $Al_2(SO_4)_3$ yields 3 mol SO_4^{2-} in solution.

$$1 \text{ mol } Al_2(SO_4)_3 \Leftrightarrow 3 \text{ mol } SO_4^{2-}$$

therefore,

$$\frac{0.90 \text{ mol } SO_4^{2-}}{1.0 \text{ L soln}} \times \frac{1 \text{ mol } Al_2(SO_4)_3}{3 \text{ mol } SO_4^{2-}} = \frac{0.30 \text{ mol } Al_2(SO_4)_3}{1.0 \text{ L soln}} = 0.30 \, M \, Al_2(SO_4)_3$$

The concentration of $Al_2(SO_4)_3$ is 0.30 M.

■ **Is the Answer Reasonable?** We'll use the reasoning approach to check our answer. We know that 1 mol $Al_2(SO_4)_3$ yields 3 mol SO_4^{2-} in solution. Therefore, the number of moles of $Al_2(SO_4)_3$ is only one-third the number of moles of SO_4^{2-}. So the concentration of $Al_2(SO_4)_3$ must be one-third of 0.90 M, or 0.30 M.

Practice Exercises

5.38 | What are the molar concentrations of the ions in 0.40 M $FeCl_3$? (*Hint:* How many ions of each kind are formed when $FeCl_3$ dissociates?)

5.39 | In a solution of Na_3PO_4, the PO_4^{3-} concentration was determined to be 0.250 M. What was the sodium ion concentration in the solution?

Stoichiometry Calculations

You have seen that a net ionic equation is convenient for describing the net chemical change in an ionic reaction. Example 5.17 illustrates how such equations can be used in stoichiometric calculations.

Example 5.17
Stoichiometric Calculations Using a Net Ionic Equation

How many milliliters of 0.100 M $AgNO_3$ solution are needed to react completely with 25.0 mL of 0.400 M $CaCl_2$ solution? The net ionic equation for the reaction is

$$Ag^+(aq) + Cl^-(aq) \longrightarrow AgCl(s)$$

■ **Analysis:** In many ways, this problem is similar to Example 5.14. However, to use the net ionic equation, we will need to work with the concentrations of the ions. Therefore, to solve the problem, the first step will be to calculate the molarities of the ions in the solutions being mixed. Next, using the volume and molarity of the Cl^- solution, we will calculate the moles of Cl^- available. Then we'll use the coefficients of the equation to find the moles of Ag^+ that react. Finally, we'll use the molarity of the Ag^+ solution to determine the volume of the 0.100 M $AgNO_3$ solution needed.

■**Assembling the Tools:** To obtain the concentrations of the ions in the solutions of reactants, the tool will be chemical formulas themselves: one $AgNO_3$ yields one Ag^+ and one NO_3^-; one $CaCl_2$ yields one Ca^{2+} and two Cl^-.

The second tool will be Equation 5.5,

$$\text{volume } Cl^- \text{ soln} \times \text{molarity of } Cl^- \text{ soln} = \text{moles } Cl^-$$

The next tool is provided by the coefficients in the equation:

$$1 \text{ mol } Ag^+ \Leftrightarrow 1 \text{ mol } Cl^-$$

The molarity of the Ag^+ solution gives us the relationship required to convert from moles of Ag^+ to the volume of solution.

■**Solution:** We begin by applying the first tool and finding the concentrations of the ions in the reacting solutions.

$$0.100 \; M \; AgNO_3 \quad \text{contains } 0.100 \; M \; Ag^+ \quad \text{and} \quad 0.100 \; M \; NO_3^-$$
$$0.400 \; M \; CaCl_2 \quad \text{contains } 0.400 \; M \; Ca^{2+} \quad \text{and} \quad 0.800 \; M \; Cl^-$$

A solution of $AgNO_3$ is added to a solution of $CaCl_2$, producing a precipitate of AgCl. *(Andy Washnik)*

We're only interested in the Ag^+ and Cl^-; the Ca^{2+} and NO_3^- are spectator ions. For our purposes, then, the solution concentrations are $0.100 \; M \; Ag^+$ and $0.800 \; M \; Cl^-$. Having these values, we can now restate the problem: How many milliliters of $0.100 \; M \; Ag^+$ solution are needed to react completely with 25.0 mL of $0.800 \; M \; Cl^-$ solution?

$$25.0 \text{ mL } Cl^- \text{ soln} \Leftrightarrow ? \text{ mL } Ag^+ \text{ soln}$$

The moles of Cl^- available for reaction are obtained from the molarity and volume (0.0250 L) of the Cl^- solution by applying our second tool.

$$0.0250 \; L\; Cl^- \text{ soln} \times \frac{0.800 \text{ mol } Cl^-}{1.00 \; L\; Cl^- \text{ soln}} = 0.0200 \text{ mol } Cl^-$$

$$\text{volume} \quad \times \quad \text{molarity} \quad = \text{moles of solute}$$

The coefficients of the equation tell us the Ag^+ and Cl^- combine in a 1-to-1 mole ratio, so $0.0200 \text{ mol } Cl^- \longleftrightarrow 0.0200 \text{ mol } Ag^+$. Finally, we calculate the volume of the Ag^+ solution using its molarity as a conversion factor. As we've done previously, we use the factor that makes the units cancel correctly.

$$0.0200 \; \text{mol}\; Ag^+ \times \frac{1.00 \text{ L } Ag^+ \text{ soln}}{0.100 \; \text{mol}\; Ag^+} = 0.200 \text{ L } Ag^+ \text{ soln}$$

■ Simple reasoning works well here. Since the coefficients of Ag^+ and Cl^- are the same, the numbers of moles that react must be equal.

Our calculations tell us that we must use 0.200 L or 200 mL of the $AgNO_3$ solution. We could also have used the following chain calculation.

$$0.0250 \; L\; Cl^- \text{ soln} \times \frac{0.800 \; \text{mol}\; Cl^-}{1.00 \; L\; Cl^- \text{ soln}} \times \frac{1 \; \text{mol}\; Ag^+}{1 \; \text{mol}\; Cl^-} \times \frac{1.00 \text{ L } Ag^+ \text{ soln}}{0.100 \; \text{mol}\; Ag^+} = 0.200 \text{ L } Ag^+ \text{ soln}$$

■**Is the Answer Reasonable?** The silver ion concentration is one-eighth as large as the chloride ion concentration. Since the ions react one-for-one, we will need eight times as much silver ion solution as chloride solution. Eight times the amount of chloride solution, 25 mL, is 200 mL, which is the answer we obtained. Therefore, the answer appears to be correct.

Practice Exercises

5.40 | Suppose 18.4 mL of $0.100 \; M \; AgNO_3$ solution was needed to react completely with 20.5 mL of $CaCl_2$ solution. What is the molarity of the $CaCl_2$ solution? Use the net ionic equation in Example 5.17 to work the problem. (*Hint:* How can you calculate molarity from moles and volume, and how can you calculate the molarity of the $CaCl_2$ solution from the molarity of Cl^-?)

5.41 | How many milliliters of $0.500 \; M$ KOH are needed to react completely with 60.0 mL of $0.250 \; M \; FeCl_2$ solution to precipitate $Fe(OH)_2$? The net ionic equation is: $Fe^{2+}(aq) + 2OH^-(aq) \longrightarrow Fe(OH)_2(s)$.

5.8 | Titrations and Chemical Analysis

Chemical analyses fall into two categories. In a **qualitative analysis** we simply determine which substances are present in a sample without measuring their amounts. In a **quantitative analysis**, our goal is to measure the amounts of the various substances in a sample.

When chemical reactions are used in a quantitative analysis, a useful strategy is to capture *all* of a desired chemical species in a compound with a known formula. From the amount of this compound obtained, we can determine how much of the desired chemical species was present in the original sample. Such an analysis was described in Example 4.12 on page 125 in which we described the combustion analysis of a compound of carbon, hydrogen, and oxygen. The following example illustrates a similar analysis using solution chemistry.

Example 5.18
Calculation Involving a Quantitative Analysis

A chemist was asked to analyze a solution of chlordane, $C_{10}H_6Cl_8$, dissolved in a hydrocarbon solvent that was discovered by construction workers during demolition of an old work shed. This insecticide was banned for sale in the United States in 1988 by the EPA because of its potential for causing cancer. Reactions were carried out on a 1.446 g sample of the solution which converted all of the chlorine to chloride ion dissolved in water. This aqueous solution required 91.22 mL of 0.1400 M $AgNO_3$ to precipitate all of the chloride ion as AgCl. What was the percentage of chlordane in the original solution? The precipitation reaction was

$$Ag^+(aq) + Cl^-(aq) \longrightarrow AgCl(s)$$

■ **Analysis:** The percentage of chlordane in the sample will be calculated as follows:

$$\% \ C_{10}H_6Cl_8 \ \text{by mass} = \frac{\text{mass of } C_{10}H_6Cl_8 \ \text{in sample}}{\text{mass of sample}} \times 100\%$$

We already have the mass of the sample, so we need to use the data to calculate the mass of $C_{10}H_6Cl_8$. In doing this, we will assume that all the chlorine that was ultimately precipitated as AgCl originated in the chlordane and that none was lost in the reactions that had converted it to chloride ion.

From the molarity and volume of the $AgNO_3$ solution, we can calculate the moles of Ag^+ that reacts with Cl^-. The net ionic equation tells us Ag^+ and Cl^- react in a 1-to-1 mole ratio, so the moles of Ag^+ equals the moles of Cl^- that react. This equals the number of moles of Cl in the chlordane present in the sample of the solution. We will use the moles of Cl to calculate the moles of $C_{10}H_6Cl_8$ and then the grams of $C_{10}H_6Cl_8$. Once we have the mass of $C_{10}H_6Cl_8$ we can calculate the percentage of $C_{10}H_6Cl_8$.

■ **Assembling the Tools:** Equation 5.5 is the tool with which we calculate moles of Ag^+ that react.

$$\text{molarity of } Ag^+ \text{ soln} \times \text{volume of } Ag^+ \text{ soln} = \text{moles of } Ag^+$$

As noted, the net ionic equation tells us that moles of Ag^+ equals moles of Cl^-, which equals moles Cl.

The formula for chlordane gives us the equivalence

$$1 \text{ mol } C_{10}H_6Cl_8 \Leftrightarrow 8 \text{ mol Cl}$$

which allows us to calculate the moles of $C_{10}H_6Cl_8$ in the sample from the moles of Cl. To find grams of $C_{10}H_6Cl_8$, we need the molar mass of $C_{10}H_6Cl_8$, which is 409.778 g mol^{-1}.

$$1 \text{ mol } C_{10}H_6Cl_8 \Leftrightarrow 409.778 \text{ g}$$

■ **Solution:** In 0.1400 M AgNO$_3$, the molarity of Ag$^+$ is 0.1400 M. Applying Equation 5.5,

$$0.09122 \ \text{L Ag}^+ \ \text{soln} \times \frac{0.1400 \ \text{mol Ag}^+}{1.000 \ \text{L Ag}^+ \ \text{soln}} = 0.012771 \ \text{mol Ag}^+$$

■ 91.22 mL = 0.09122 L.

From the stoichiometry of the equation,

$$0.012771 \ \text{mol Ag}^+ \Leftrightarrow 0.012771 \ \text{mol Cl}^-$$

This is the amount of Cl$^-$ that came from the sample, so the chlordane in the sample must have contained 0.012771 mol Cl. Now we use the formula for chlordane to calculate moles of $C_{10}H_6Cl_8$ in the sample.

$$0.012771 \ \text{mol Cl} \times \frac{1 \ \text{mol } C_{10}H_6Cl_8}{8 \ \text{mol Cl}} = 1.5964 \times 10^{-3} \ \text{mol } C_{10}H_6Cl_8$$

Using the formula mass of chlordane, we calculate the mass of the insecticide in the sample.

$$1.5964 \times 10^{-3} \ \text{mol } C_{10}H_6Cl_8 \times \frac{409.778 \ \text{g } C_{10}H_6Cl_8}{1 \ \text{mol } C_{10}H_6Cl_8} = 0.65417 \ \text{g } C_{10}H_6Cl_8$$

The percentage of chlordane in the sample was

$$\% \ C_{10}H_6Cl_8 = \frac{0.65417 \ \text{g } C_{10}H_6Cl_8}{1.446 \ \text{g sample}} \times 100\% = 45.24\% \quad \text{(rounded correctly)}$$

The solution of insecticide contained 45.24% chlordane by mass.

■ **Is the Answer Reasonable?** We have used approximately 0.1 L of 0.14 M Ag$^+$ solution, which contains 0.014 mol of Ag$^+$. The amount of Cl$^-$ consumed is also 0.014 mol, which is the amount of Cl in the chlordane. The moles of chlordane are 1/8th of 0.014. For simplicity, suppose it was 1/10th. The moles of chlordane would then be 0.0014 mol. With a molar mass of about 400 g mol^{-1}, 0.001 mol of $C_{10}H_6Cl_8$ would weigh 0.4 g and 0.0014 mol would weigh around 0.6 g. Our answer, 0.654 g, is not far from this, so the calculations seem to be correct.

Practice Exercises

5.42 | A solution containing Na$_2$SO$_4$ was treated with 0.150 M BaCl$_2$ solution until all the sulfate ion had reacted to form BaSO$_4$. The net reaction

$$Ba^{2+}(aq) + SO_4{}^{2-}(aq) \longrightarrow BaSO_4(s)$$

required 28.40 mL of the BaCl$_2$ solution. How many grams of Na$_2$SO$_4$ were in the solution? (*Hint:* How do moles of SO$_4{}^{2-}$ relate to moles of Na$_2$SO$_4$?)

5.43 | A sample of a mixture containing CaCl$_2$ and MgCl$_2$ weighed 2.000 g. The sample was dissolved in water, and H$_2$SO$_4$ was added until the precipitation of CaSO$_4$ was complete.

$$CaCl_2(aq) + H_2SO_4(aq) \longrightarrow CaSO_4(s) + 2HCl(aq)$$

The CaSO$_4$ was filtered, dried completely, and weighed. A total of 0.736 g of CaSO$_4$ was obtained.

(a) How many moles of Ca^{2+} were in the CaSO$_4$?
(b) How many moles of Ca^{2+} were in the original 2.000 g sample?
(c) How many moles of CaCl$_2$ were in the 2.000 g sample?
(d) How many grams of CaCl$_2$ were in the 2.000 g sample?
(e) What was the percentage by mass of CaCl$_2$ in the original mixture?
(f) What was the percentage by mass of MgCl$_2$ in the original mixture?

Figure 5.26 | **Titration.** (*a*) A buret. (*b*) The titration of an acid by a base in which an acid-base indicator is used to signal the end point, which is the point at which all of the acid has been neutralized and addition of the base is halted.

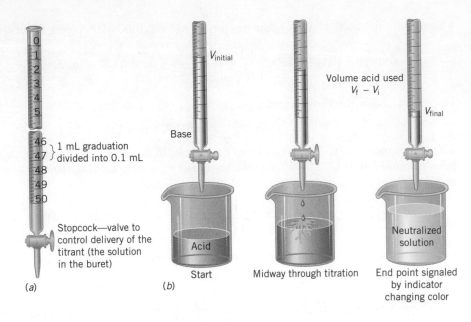

Stopcock—valve to control delivery of the titrant (the solution in the buret)

1 mL graduation divided into 0.1 mL

$V_{initial}$

Base

V_{final}

Volume acid used $V_f - V_i$

Acid

Neutralized solution

Start

Midway through titration

End point signaled by indicator changing color

(*a*)

(*b*)

Acid–Base Titrations

Titration is an important laboratory procedure used in performing chemical analyses. The apparatus is shown in Figure 5.26. The long tube is called a **buret**, which is marked for volumes, usually in increments of 0.10 mL. The valve at the bottom of the buret is called a **stopcock**, and it permits the analyst to control the amount of **titrant** (*the solution in the buret*) that is delivered to the receiving vessel (the beaker shown in the drawing).

In a typical titration, a solution containing one reactant is placed in the receiving vessel. A solution of the other reactant is then added gradually from the buret. (One of the two solutions has a precisely known concentration and is called a **standard solution**.) This addition is continued until something (usually a visual effect, like a color change) signals that the two reactants have been combined in just the right proportions to give a complete reaction.

In acid–base titrations, an **acid–base indicator** is used to detect the completion of the reaction by a change in color. Indicators are dyes that have one color in an acidic solution and a different color in a basic solution. Litmus was mentioned earlier. Phenolphthalein is a common indicator for titrations; it changes from colorless to pink when a solution changes from acidic to basic. This color change is very abrupt, and occurs with the addition of only one final drop of the titrant just as the end of the reaction is reached. When we observe the color change, the **end point** has been reached and the addition of titrant is stopped. We then record the total volume of the titrant that's been added to the receiving flask.

■ The theory of acid–base indicators is discussed in Chapter 17.

Example 5.19
Calculation Involving an Acid–Base Titration

A student prepares a solution of hydrochloric acid that is approximately 0.1 *M* and wants to determine its precise concentration. A 25.00 mL portion of the HCl solution is transferred to a flask, and after a few drops of indicator are added, the HCl solution is titrated with 0.0775 *M* NaOH solution. The titration requires exactly 37.46 mL of the standard NaOH solution to reach the end point. What is the molarity of the HCl solution?

■ **Analysis:** This is really a straightforward stoichiometry calculation involving a chemical reaction. The first step in solving it is to write the balanced equation, which will give us the stoichiometric equivalency between HCl and NaOH. The reaction is an acid–base neutralization, so the product is a salt plus water. Following the procedures developed earlier, the reaction is

$$HCl(aq) + NaOH(aq) \longrightarrow NaCl(aq) + H_2O$$

We have to go from molarity and volume of the NaOH solution to the molarity of the HCl solution. Solving the problem will follow essentially the same route as in Example 5.14 on page 191.

■**Assembling the Tools:** Our tools will be the molarity and volume of the NaOH solution (to calculate moles of NaOH that react), the coefficients of the equation (to obtain moles of HCl), and the definition of molarity (to calculate the molarity of the HCl solution from moles of HCl and the volume of the HCl sample taken).

■**Solution:** From the molarity and volume of the NaOH solution, we calculate the number of moles of NaOH consumed in the titration.

$$0.03746 \ \text{L NaOH soln} \times \frac{0.0775 \ \text{mol NaOH}}{1.000 \ \text{L NaOH soln}} = 2.903 \times 10^{-3} \ \text{mol NaOH}$$

The coefficients in the equation tell us that NaOH and HCl react in a one-to-one mole ratio,

$$2.903 \times 10^{-3} \ \text{mol NaOH} \times \frac{1 \ \text{mol HCl}}{1 \ \text{mol NaOH}} = 2.903 \times 10^{-3} \ \text{mol HCl}$$

A solution of HCl is titrated with a solution of NaOH using phenolphthalein as the acid-base indicator. The pink color that phenolphthalein has in a basic solution can be seen where a drop of the NaOH solution has entered the HCl solution, to which a few drops of the indicator had been added. *(Michael Watson)*

so in this titration, 2.903×10^{-3} mol HCl was in the flask. To calculate the molarity of the HCl, we simply apply the definition of molarity. We take the ratio of the number of moles of HCl that reacted (2.903×10^{-3} mol HCl) to the volume (in liters) of the HCl solution used (25.00 mL, or 0.02500 L).

$$\text{Molarity of HCl soln} = \frac{2.903 \times 10^{-3} \ \text{mol HCl}}{0.02500 \ \text{L HCl soln}}$$
$$= 0.116 \ M \ \text{HCl (rounded)}$$

The molarity of the hydrochloric acid is 0.116 M. (Note that we've rounded the answer to three significant figures to match the data given in the problem.)

■**Is the Answer Reasonable?** If the concentrations of the NaOH and HCl were the same, the volumes used would have been equal. However, the volume of the NaOH solution used is larger than the volume of HCl solution. This must mean that the HCl solution is more concentrated than the NaOH solution. The value we obtained, 0.116 M, is larger than 0.0775 M, so our answer makes sense.

Practice Exercises

5.44 | In a titration, a sample of H_2SO_4 solution having a volume of 15.00 mL required 36.42 mL of 0.147 M NaOH solution for *complete* neutralization. What is the molarity of the H_2SO_4 solution? (*Hint:* Check to be sure your chemical equation is correctly written and balanced.)

5.45 | "Stomach acid" is hydrochloric acid. A sample of gastric juice having a volume of 5.00 mL required 11.00 mL of 0.0100 M KOH solution for neutralization in a titration. What was the molar concentration of HCl in this fluid? If we assume a density of 1.00 g mL^{-1} for the fluid, what was the percentage by weight of HCl?

■ Multi-Concept Problems

The worked examples we've provided so far have been relatively simple, and each has focused on one topic or concept. However, in life and in chemistry, problems are not always that simple. Often they involve multiple concepts that are not immediately obvious, so it is difficult to see how to proceed. Although each problem is unique, there is a general strategy you can learn to apply. The key is realizing that almost all difficult problems can be broken down into some set of simpler tasks that you already know how to do. In fact, in real-life problems, the analysis will sometimes reveal tasks that you have not yet learned how to accomplish and point the way to learning new concepts or tools.

In the *Analyzing and Solving Multi-Concept Problems* section in this and subsequent chapters, our approach will be to look at the big picture first and deal with the details later. The goal will be to break the problem down into manageable parts. There is no simple "formula" for doing this, so don't be discouraged if solving these kinds of problems takes some considerable thought. You should also realize that with complex problems there is often more than one path to the solution. As you study the examples we provide, you may see an alternative way to arrive at the answer. As long as the reasoning is sound and leads to the same answer as ours, you are to be applauded!

Finally, by way of assurance, keep in mind that none of the multi-concept problems you encounter in this text will involve concepts that have not been previously discussed.

Analyzing and Solving Multi-Concept Problems

Milk of magnesia is a suspension of $Mg(OH)_2$ in water. It can be made by adding a base to a solution containing Mg^{2+}. Suppose that 40.0 mL of 0.200 M NaOH solution is added to 25.0 mL of 0.300 M $MgCl_2$ solution. What mass of $Mg(OH)_2$ will be formed, and what will be the concentrations of the ions in the solution after the reaction is complete?

■ **Analysis:** Our goal here is to break the problem down into parts that we already know how to solve. The approach is to read the problem carefully and extract from it the various pieces to the puzzle.

First, we're dealing with the stoichiometry of a chemical reaction, so we know we're going to need a balanced chemical equation. We will also need to determine the concentrations of ions, so we will have to be prepared to write an ionic equation, or at least to take into account the dissociation of each solute. These are things you know how to do, so we have that figured out.

Creamy milk of magnesia is an aqueous suspension of magnesium hydroxide. (*Robert Capece*)

Notice that we've been given the volume and molarity for *both* solutions. By now, you should realize that volume and molarity give us moles, so in effect *we have been given the number of moles of two reactants*. This means we have a limiting reactant problem. You learned how

to solve this kind of problem in Chapter 4, so working this part of the problem isn't anything new.

The problem also asks for the concentrations of the ions in the final mixture. The easiest way to find the answers here is to determine the number of moles of each of the ions present before and after the reaction, and then divide the latter by the total final volume of solution to calculate the molar concentrations. Because this is an ionic reaction, two of the ions will be reactants. One will be completely used up, but some of the other will be left over, and we will have to calculate how much. The other two ions are spectator ions and their amounts will not change.

At this point, we have a broad outline of what we have to do. To further clarify our thinking, let's refine and summarize each part so we can select appropriate tools to accomplish our tasks.

Part 1: Write a balanced molecular equation and then convert it to an ionic equation. (This comes first because all the rest of the reasoning is based on the equation.)

Part 2: Calculate the number of moles of each ion present before reaction, determine the limiting reactant, and then use it to calculate the moles and grams of $Mg(OH)_2$ formed.

Part 3: We already know the moles of the spectator ions from Part 2, but we have to calculate the moles of unreacted Mg^{2+} or OH^-. We also need to determine the total volume of the mixture and then calculate the molarities of the ions.

PART 1

■**Assembling the Tools**   We need to set up a metathesis equation and balance it. We follow the procedure developed earlier, making use of the solubility rules.

■**Solution**

The balanced molecular equation for the reaction is

$$MgCl_2(aq) + 2NaOH(aq) \longrightarrow Mg(OH)_2(s) + 2NaCl(aq)$$

from which we construct the ionic and net ionic equations.

$$Mg^{2+}(aq) + 2Cl^-(aq) + 2Na^+(aq) + 2OH^-(aq) \longrightarrow Mg(OH)_2(s) + 2Na^+(aq) + 2Cl^-(aq)$$
$$Mg^{2+}(aq) + 2OH^-(aq) \longrightarrow Mg(OH)_2(s)$$

These are the equations we will use in Part 2.

PART 2

■**Assembling the Tools**   For each reactant solution,

$$molarity \times volume(L) = moles\ of\ solute$$

The chemical formulas of the reactants will be used to find the number of moles of each ion prior to reaction. The method of finding the limiting reactant developed in Chapter 4 will be applied. A tool we will use is the set of coefficients in the equation, which relates moles of the reactants and product. The molar mass tool will be used to convert moles of $Mg(OH)_2$ to grams.

$$58.31\ g\ Mg(OH)_2 = 1\ mol\ Mg(OH)_2$$

■**Solution**   Let's begin by determining the number of moles of NaOH and $MgCl_2$ supplied by the volumes of their solutions. The conversion factors are taken from their molarities: 0.200 M NaOH and 0.300 M $MgCl_2$.

$$0.0400\ \cancel{L\ NaOH}\ soln \times \frac{0.200\ mol\ NaOH}{1.00\ \cancel{L\ NaOH}\ soln} = 8.00 \times 10^{-3}\ mol\ NaOH$$

$$0.0250\ \cancel{L\ MgCl_2}\ soln \times \frac{0.300\ mol\ MgCl_2}{1.00\ \cancel{L\ MgCl_2}\ soln} = 7.50 \times 10^{-3}\ mol\ MgCl_2$$

From this information, we obtain the number of moles of each ion present *before* any reaction occurs. In doing this, notice that we take into account that 1 mol of $MgCl_2$ gives 2 mol Cl^-. Here is a summary of the data.

Moles of Ions before Reaction

Mg^{2+}	7.50×10^{-3} mol	Cl^-	15.0×10^{-3} mol
Na^+	8.00×10^{-3} mol	OH^-	8.00×10^{-3} mol

Now we refer to the net ionic equation, where we see that only Mg^{2+} and OH^- react. From the coefficients of the equation,

$$1\ mol\ Mg^{2+} \Leftrightarrow 2\ mol\ OH^-$$

This means that 7.50×10^{-3} mol Mg^{2+} (the amount of Mg^{2+} *available*) would require 15.0×10^{-3} mol OH^-. But we have only 8.00×10^{-3} mol OH^-. Insufficient OH^- is available to react with all of the Mg^{2+}, so OH^- must be the limiting reactant. Therefore, all of the OH^- will be used up and some Mg^{2+} will be unreacted. The amount of Mg^{2+} that *does* react to form $Mg(OH)_2$ can be found as follows.

$$8.00 \times 10^{-3}\ \cancel{mol\ OH^-} \times \frac{1\ mol\ Mg^{2+}}{2\ \cancel{mol\ OH^-}} = 4.00 \times 10^{-3}\ mol\ Mg^{2+}$$
$$\text{(This amount reacts.)}$$

One mole of Mg^{2+} gives 1 mole of $Mg(OH)_2$. Therefore, the amount of $Mg(OH)_2$ that forms is

$$4.00 \times 10^{-3} \text{ mol Mg}^{2+} \times \frac{1 \text{ mol Mg(OH)}_2}{1 \text{ mol Mg}^{2+}} \times \frac{58.32 \text{ g Mg(OH)}_2}{1 \text{ mol Mg(OH)}_2} = 0.233 \text{ g Mg(OH)}_2$$

The reaction mixture will produce 0.223 g $Mg(OH)_2$.

PART 3

■ **Assembling the Tools** To calculate the concentrations of the ions, we can use the number of moles of each present in the final mixture divided by the *total volume* of the solution. This tool is the defining equation for molarity,

$$\text{molarity} = \frac{\text{number of moles of solute}}{\text{volume of solution in L}}$$

■ **Solution** Let's begin by tabulating the number of moles of each ion left in the mixture *after* the reaction is complete. For Mg^{2+}, the amount remaining equals the initial number of moles minus the moles that react (which we found in Part 2). Let's put all of the numbers into one table to make them easier to understand.

Ion	Moles Present before Reaction	Moles That React	Moles Present after Reaction
Mg^{2+}	7.50×10^{-3} mol	4.00×10^{-3} mol	3.50×10^{-3} mol
Cl^-	15.0×10^{-3} mol	0.00 mol	15.0×10^{-3} mol
Na^+	8.00×10^{-3} mol	0.00 mol	8.00×10^{-3} mol
OH^-	8.00×10^{-3} mol	8.00×10^{-3} mol	0.00 mol

The problem asks for the concentrations of the ions in the final reaction mixture, so we must now divide each quantity in the last column by the *total volume of the final solution* (40.0 mL + 25.0 mL = 65.0 mL). This volume must be expressed in liters (0.0650 L). For example, for Mg^{2+}, its concentration is

$$\frac{3.50 \times 10^{-3} \text{ mol Mg}^{2+}}{0.0650 \text{ L soln}} = 0.0538 \, M \text{ Mg}^{2+}$$

Performing similar calculations for the other ions gives the following;

Concentrations of Ions after Reaction

Mg^{2+}	0.0538 M	Cl^-	0.231 M
Na^+	0.123 M	OH^-	0.00 M

■ **Are the Answers Reasonable?** All the reasoning we've done seems to be correct, which is reassuring. For the amount of $Mg(OH)_2$ that forms, 0.001 mol would weigh approximately 0.06 g, so 0.004 mol would weigh 0.24 g. Our answer, 0.233 g $Mg(OH)_2$, is reasonable. The final concentrations of the spectator ions are lower than the initial concentrations, so that makes sense, too, because of the dilution effect.

| Summary

Solution Vocabulary. A **solution** is a homogeneous mixture in which one or more **solutes** are dissolved in a **solvent**. A solution may be **dilute** or **concentrated**, depending on the amount of solute dissolved in a given amount of solvent. **Concentration** (e.g., **percentage concentration**) is a ratio of the amount of solute to either the amount of solvent or the amount of solution. The amount of solute required to give a **saturated** solution at a given temperature is called the solute's **solubility**. **Unsaturated** solutions will dissolve more solute, but **supersaturated** solutions are unstable and tend to give a **precipitate**.

Electrolytes. Substances that **dissociate** or **ionize** in water to produce cations and anions are **electrolytes**; those that do not are called **nonelectrolytes**. Electrolytes include salts and metal hydroxides as well as molecular acids and bases that ionize by reaction with water. In water, ionic compounds are completely dissociated into ions and are **strong electrolytes**.

Ionic and Net Ionic Equations. Reactions that occur in solution between ions are called **ionic reactions**. Solutions of soluble strong electrolytes often yield an insoluble product that appears as a **precipitate**. Equations for these reactions can be written in three different ways. In **molecular equations**, complete formulas for all reactants and products are used. In an **ionic equation**, soluble strong electrolytes are written in dissociated (ionized) form; "molecular" formulas are used for solids and weak electrolytes. A **net ionic equation** is obtained by eliminating **spectator ions** from the ionic equation, and such an equation allows us to identify other combinations of reactants that give the same net reaction. An ionic or net ionic equation is balanced only if both atoms *and* net charge are balanced.

Acids and Bases. An **acid** is a substance that produces hydronium ions, H_3O^+, when dissolved in water, and a **base** produces hydroxide ions, OH^-, when dissolved in water. The oxides of nonmetals are generally **acidic anhydrides** and react with water to give acids. Metal oxides are usually **basic anhydrides** because they tend to react with water to give metal hydroxides or bases.

Strong acids and **strong bases** are also strong electrolytes. **Weak acids** and **weak bases** are **weak electrolytes**, which are incompletely ionized in water. In a solution of a weak electrolyte there is a **chemical equilibrium (dynamic equilibrium)** between the non-ionized molecules of the solute and the ions formed by the reaction of the solute with water.

Predicting Metathesis Reactions. Metathesis or **double replacement** reactions take place when anions and cations of two salts change partners. A metathesis reaction will occur if there is a net ionic equation. This happens if (1) a precipitate forms from soluble reactants, (2) an acid-base neutralization occurs, (3) a gas is formed, or (4) a weak electrolyte forms from soluble strong electrolytes. You should learn the **solubility rules** (Table 5.1), and remember that all salts are strong electrolytes. All strong acids and bases are strong electrolytes, too. Strong acids react with strong bases in neutralization reactions to produce a salt and water. Acids react with insoluble oxides and hydroxides to form water and the corresponding salt. Many acid—base neutralization reactions can be viewed as a type of metathesis reaction in which one product is water. Be sure to learn the reactions that produce gases in metathesis reactions, which are listed in Table 5.2.

Molar Concentration, Dilution, and Solution Stoichiometry. Molarity is the ratio of moles of solute to liters of solution. Molarity provides two conversion factors relating moles of solute and the volume of a solution.

$$\frac{\text{mol solute}}{1\text{ L soln}} \quad \text{and} \quad \frac{1\text{ L soln}}{\text{mol solute}}$$

Concentrated solutions of known molarity can be diluted quantitatively using volumetric glassware such as pipets and volumetric flasks. When a solution is diluted by adding solvent, the amount of solute doesn't change but the concentration decreases.

In ionic reactions, the concentrations of the ions in a solution of a salt can be derived from the molar concentration of the salt, taking into account the number of ions formed per formula unit of the salt.

Titration is a technique used to make quantitative measurements of the amounts of solutions needed to obtain a complete reaction. The apparatus is a long graduated tube called a **buret** that has a **stopcock** at the bottom, which is used to control the flow of **titrant**. In an acid—base titration, the **end point** is normally detected visually using an **acid—base indicator**. A color change indicates complete reaction, at which time the addition of titrant is stopped and the volume added is recorded.

Tools for Problem Solving
The following tools were introduced in this chapter. Study them carefully so you can select the appropriate tool when needed.

Criteria for a balanced ionic equation (page 164)
To be balanced, an equation that includes the formulas of ions must satisfy the following two criteria: (1) the number of atoms of each kind must be the same on both sides of the equation, and (2) the net electrical charge shown on each side of the equation must be the same.

Ionization of an acid in water (page 165)
Equation 5.2 describes how an acid reacts with water to form hydronium ion plus an anion.

$$HA + H_2O \longrightarrow H_3O^+ + A^-$$

Use this tool to write equations for the ionizations of acids and to determine the formulas of the anions formed when the acid molecules lose H^+. The equation also applies to acid anions such as HSO_4^-, which gives SO_4^{2-} when it loses an H^+. Often H_2O is omitted from the equation and the hydronium ion is abbreviated as H^+.

Ionization of a molecular base in water (page 165)
Equation 5.3 describes how molecules of a molecular base acquire H^+ from H_2O to form a cation plus a hydroxide ion.

$$B + H_2O \longrightarrow BH^+ + OH^-$$

Use this tool to write equations for the ionizations of bases and to determine the formula of the cation formed when a base molecule gains an H^+. *Molecular bases are weak and are not completely ionized.*

List of strong acids (page 170)
Formulas of the most common strong acids are given here. If you learn this list and encounter an acid that's *not* on the list, you can assume it is a weak acid. The most common strong acids are HCl, HNO_3, and H_2SO_4. *Remember that strong acids are completely ionized in water.*

Acid and anion names (page 173)
This relationship helps us remember the names of acids and anions.

Acid ends in *-ic*   Anion ends in *-ate*
Acid ends in *-ous*   Anion ends in *-ite*

Predicting net ionic equations (page 175)
A net ionic equation will exist and a reaction will occur when:
• A precipitate is formed from a mixture of soluble reactants.
• An acid reacts with a base. *This includes strong or weak acids reacting with strong or weak bases or insoluble metal hydroxides or oxides.*
• A weak electrolyte is formed from a mixture of strong electrolytes.
• A gas is formed from a mixture of reactants.

These criteria are tools to determine whether or not a net reaction will occur in a solution.

Solubility rules (page 176)
The rules in Table 5.1 serve as the tool we use to determine whether a particular salt is soluble in water. (If a salt is soluble, it's completely dissociated into ions.) They also serve as a tool to help predict the course of metathesis reactions.

Gases formed in metathesis reactions (page 181)
Use Table 5.2 as a tool to help predict the outcome of metathesis reactions. The most common gas formed in such reactions is CO_2, which comes from the reaction of an acid with a carbonate or bicarbonate.

Synthesis by metathesis (page 184)
Useful guidelines to use when selecting reactants in the synthesis of a salt are as follows:

1. Start with soluble reactants if the desired product is an insoluble salt.

2. Use an acid–base reaction or a reaction of an acid with a metal carbonate if the desired product is soluble in water. This works best if the metal hydroxide or oxide, or the metal carbonate, is insoluble in water.

Molarity (page 185)

Molarity provides the connection between moles of a solute and the volume of its solution. The definition serves as a tool for calculating molarity from values of moles of solute and volume of solution (in liters).

$$\text{Molarity } (M) = \frac{\text{moles of solute}}{\text{liters of solution}}$$

Molarity is the tool we use to write an equivalence between moles of solute and volume of solution, from which appropriate conversion factors can be formed.

Molarity times volume gives moles (page 187)

For any problem in which you're given both molarity and volume of a solution of a substance, you can always calculate the number of moles of the substance.

$$\text{molarity} \times \text{volume (L)} = \text{moles of solute}$$

Recognizing this relationship is very important when working stoichiometry problems involving solutions.

Dilution equation (page 189)

Equation 5.6 is the tool we use for working dilution problems.

$$V_{dil} \cdot M_{dil} = V_{conc} \cdot M_{conc}$$

The volume units must be the same on both sides of the equation.

Molarity of ions in a salt solution (page 193)

When using a net ionic equation to work stoichiometry problems, we need the concentrations of the ions in the solutions. *The concentration of a particular ion equals the concentration of the salt multiplied by the number of ions of that kind in one formula unit of the salt.*

Paths through stoichiometry problems

In this chapter you encountered another way that the data in stoichiometry problems are presented. Figure 5.27 gives an overview of the various paths through problems that involve chemical reactions. All funnel through the coefficients of the balanced chemical equation as the means to convert from moles of one substance to moles of another. The starting and finishing quantities can be moles, grams, or volumes of solutions of known molarity.

TOOLS

Paths through stoichiometry problems

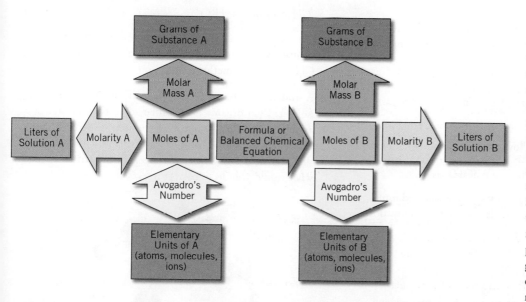

Figure 5.27 | **Paths for working stoichiometry problems involving chemical reactions.** The critical step is the conversion between moles of one substance and moles of another using the coefficients of the balanced chemical equation or the subscripts in a chemical formula. We can calculate moles in several ways: from numbers of atomic-sized formula units, and from laboratory units of grams or the volumes of solutions of known molarities. Similarly, we can present the answer either in moles, grams, number of formula units, or a volume of solution of known molarity.

PLUS — *WileyPLUS*, an online teaching and learning solution. *Note to instructors:* Many of the end-of-chapter problems are available for assignment via the *WileyPLUS* system. **www.wileyplus.com. ILW** = An Interactive Learningware solution is available for this problem. **OH** = An Office Hour video is available for this problem. Review Problems are presented in pairs separated by blue rules. Answers to problems whose numbers appear in blue are given in Appendix B. More challenging problems are marked with an asterisk *.

Review Questions

Solution Terminology

5.1 Define the following: (a) solvent, (b) solute, (c) concentration.

5.2 Define the following: (a) concentrated, (b) dilute, (c) saturated, (d) unsaturated, (e) supersaturated, (f) solubility.

5.3 Why are chemical reactions often carried out using solutions?

5.4 Describe what will happen if a crystal of sugar is added to (a) a saturated sugar solution, (b) a supersaturated solution of sugar, and (c) an unsaturated solution of sugar.

5.5 What is the meaning of the term *precipitate*? What condition must exist for a precipitate to form spontaneously in a solution?

Electrolytes

5.6 Which of the following compounds are likely to be electrolytes and which are likely to be nonelectrolytes? $CuBr_2$, $C_{12}H_{22}O_{11}$, CH_3OH, iron(II) chloride, $(NH_4)_2SO_4$.

5.7 Why is an electrolyte able to conduct electricity while a nonelectrolyte cannot? What does it mean when we say that an ion is "hydrated?"

5.8 Define "dissociation" as it applies to ionic compounds that dissolve in water.

5.9 Write equations for the dissociation of the following in water: (a) $CaCl_2$, (b) $(NH_4)_2SO_4$, (c) sodium acetate, (d) copper(II) perchlorate.

Ionic Reactions

5.10 The following equation shows the formation of cobalt(II) hydroxide, a compound used to improve the drying properties of lithographic inks.

$$Co^{2+}(aq) + 2Cl^-(aq) + 2Na^+(aq) + 2OH^-(aq) \longrightarrow$$
$$Co(OH)_2(s) + 2Na^+(aq) + 2Cl^-(aq)$$

Which are the spectator ions? Write the net ionic equation.

5.11 How can you tell that the following is a net ionic equation?

$$Al^{3+}(aq) + 3OH^-(aq) \longrightarrow Al(OH)_3(s)$$

5.12 What two conditions must be fulfilled by a balanced ionic equation? The following equation is not balanced. How do we know? Find the errors and fix them.

$$3Co^{3+}(aq) + 2HPO_4{}^{2-}(aq) \longrightarrow Co_3(PO_4)_2(s) + 2H^+(aq)$$

Acids, Bases, and Their Reactions

5.13 Give two general properties of an acid. Give two general properties of a base.

5.14 If you believed a solution was basic, which color litmus paper (blue or pink) would you use to test the solution to see whether you were correct? What would you observe if you've selected correctly? Why would the other color litmus paper not lead to a conclusive result?

5.15 How did Arrhenius define an acid and a base?

5.16 Which of the following undergo dissociation in water? Which undergo ionization? (a) NaOH, (b) HNO_3, (c) NH_3, (d) H_2SO_4

5.17 Which of the following would yield an acidic solution when they react with water? Which would give a basic solution? (a) P_4O_{10}, (b) K_2O, (c) SeO_3, (d) Cl_2O_7

5.18 What is a *dynamic equilibrium*? Using acetic acid as an example, describe why all the $HC_2H_3O_2$ molecules are not ionized in water.

5.19 Why don't we use double arrows in the equation for the reaction of a strong acid with water?

5.20 Which of the following are strong acids? (a) HCN, (b) HNO_3, (c) H_2SO_3, (d) HCl, (e) $HCHO_2$, (f) HNO_2

5.21 Which of the following produce a strongly basic solution when dissolved in water? (a) C_5H_5N, (b) $Ba(OH)_2$ (c) KOH, (d) $C_6H_5NH_2$, (e) Cs_2O, (f) N_2O_5

5.22 Methylamine, CH_3NH_2, reacts with hydronium ions in very much the same manner as ammonia.

$$CH_3NH_2(aq) + H_3O^+(aq) \longrightarrow CH_3NH_3{}^+(aq) + H_2O$$

On the basis of what you have learned so far in this course, sketch the molecular structures of CH_3NH_2 and $CH_3NH_3{}^+$ (the methylammonium ion).

5.23 A student was shown the structure of a molecule of propanoic acid (an organic acid similar to acetic acid) and was asked to draw the structure of the ion formed when the acid underwent ionization in water. Below is the structure the student drew. What is wrong with the structure, and what would you do to correct it?

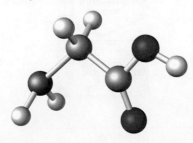

5.24 Would the molecule shown below be acidic or basic in water? What would you do to the structure to show what happens when the substance reacts with water? Write an equation for the ionization of this compound in water. (The compound is a weak electrolyte.)

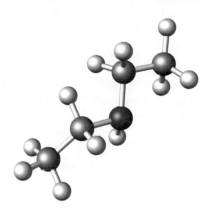

Nomenclature of Acids and Bases

5.25 Name the following: **(a)** $H_2Se(g)$, **(b)** $H_2Se(aq)$

5.26 Iodine, like chlorine, forms several acids. What are the names of the following? **(a)** HIO_4, **(b)** HIO_3, **(c)** HIO_2 **(d)** HIO, **(e)** HI

5.27 For the acids in the preceding question, **(a)** write the formulas and, **(b)** name the ions formed by removing a hydrogen ion (H^+) from each acid.

5.28 Write the formula for **(a)** chromic acid, **(b)** carbonic acid and **(c)** oxalic acid. (*Hint:* Check the table of polyatomic ions.)

5.29 Name the following acid salts: **(a)** $NaHCO_3$, **(b)** KH_2PO_4, **(c)** $(NH_4)_2HPO_4$.

5.30 Write the formulas for all the acid salts that could be formed from the reaction of $NaOH$ with the acid H_3PO_4.

5.31 Name the following oxoacids and give the names and formulas of the salts formed from them by neutralization with $NaOH$: **(a)** $HOCl$, **(b)** HIO_2, **(c)** $HBrO_3$, **(d)** $HClO_4$.

5.32 The formula for the arsenate ion is AsO_4^{3-}. What is the formula for arsenous acid?

5.33 Butanoic acid (also called butyric acid), $HC_4H_7O_2$, gives rancid butter its bad odor. What is the name of the salt $NaC_4H_7O_2$?

5.34 Calcium propanoate, $Ca(C_3H_5O_2)_2$, is used in baked foods as a preservative and to prevent the growth of mold. Based on the name of the salt, what is the name of the acid $HC_3H_5O_2$?

Predicting Ionic Reactions

5.35 What factors lead to the existence of a net ionic equation in a reaction between ions?

5.36 What is another name for a *metathesis reaction*?

5.37 Silver bromide is "insoluble." What does this mean about the concentrations of Ag^+ and Br^- in a saturated solution of AgBr? Explain why a precipitate of AgBr forms when solutions of the soluble salts $AgNO_3$ and $NaBr$ are mixed.

5.38 If a solution of sodium phosphate (also known as trisodium phosphate, or TSP), Na_3PO_4, is poured into seawater, precipitates of calcium phosphate and magnesium phosphate are formed. (Magnesium and calcium ions are among the principal ions found in seawater.) Write net ionic equations for these reactions.

5.39 Washing soda is $Na_2CO_3 \cdot 10H_2O$. Explain, using chemical equations, how this substance is able to remove Ca^{2+} ions from "hard water."

5.40 With which of the following will the weak acid $HCHO_2$ react? For those with which there is a reaction, write the formulas of the products. **(a)** KOH **(b)** MgO **(c)** NH_3

5.41 Suppose you suspected that a certain solution contained ammonium ions. What simple chemical test could you perform that would tell you whether your suspicion was correct?

5.42 What gas is formed if HCl is added to **(a)** $NaHCO_3$, **(b)** Na_2S, and **(c)** potassium sulfite?

Molarity and Dilution

5.43 What is the definition of molarity? Show that the ratio of millimoles (mmol) to milliliters (mL) is equivalent to the ratio of moles to liters.

5.44 A solution is labeled 0.25 *M* HCl. Construct two conversion factors that relate moles of HCl to the volume of solution expressed in liters.

5.45 When the units *molarity* and *liter* are multiplied, what are the resulting units?

5.46 When a solution labeled 0.50 *M* HNO_3 is diluted with water to give 0.25 *M* HNO_3, what happens to the number of moles of HNO_3 in the solution?

5.47 Two solutions, A and B, are labeled "0.100 *M* $CaCl_2$" and "0.200 *M* $CaCl_2$," respectively. Both solutions contain the same number of moles of $CaCl_2$. If solution A has a volume of 50.0 mL, what is the volume of solution B?

Chemical Analyses and Titrations

5.48 What is the difference between a qualitative analysis and a quantitative analysis?

5.49 Describe each of the following: **(a)** buret, **(b)** titration, **(c)** titrant, and **(d)** end point.

5.50 What is the function of an indicator in a titration? What color is phenolphthalein in **(a)** an acidic solution and **(b)** a basic solution?

Review Problems

Ionic Reactions

5.51 Write balanced ionic and net ionic equations for these reactions.

(a) $(NH_4)_2CO_3(aq) + MgCl_2(aq) \longrightarrow$
$$NH_4Cl(aq) + MgCO_3(s)$$

(b) $CuCl_2(aq) + NaOH(aq) \longrightarrow$
$$Cu(OH)_2(s) + NaCl(aq)$$

(c) $FeSO_4(aq) + Na_3PO_4(aq) \longrightarrow$
$$Fe_3(PO_4)_2(s) + Na_2SO_4(aq)$$

(d) $AgC_2H_3O_2(aq) + NiCl_2(aq) \longrightarrow$
$$AgCl(s) + Ni(C_2H_3O_2)_2(aq)$$

OH **5.52** Write balanced ionic and net ionic equations for these reactions.

(a) $CuSO_4(aq) + BaCl_2(aq) \longrightarrow CuCl_2(aq) + BaSO_4(s)$

(b) $Fe(NO_3)_3(aq) + LiOH(aq) \longrightarrow$
$$LiNO_3(aq) + Fe(OH)_3(s)$$

(c) $Na_3PO_4(aq) + CaCl_2(aq) \longrightarrow$
$$Ca_3(PO_4)_2(s) + NaCl(aq)$$

(d) $Na_2S(aq) + AgC_2H_3O_2(aq) \longrightarrow$
$$NaC_2H_3O_2(aq) + Ag_2S(s)$$

Acids and Bases as Electrolytes

5.53 Pure $HClO_4$ is molecular. In water it is a strong acid. Write an equation for its ionization in water.

5.54 Hydrogen bromide is a molecular substance that is a strong acid in water. Write an equation for its ionization in water.

OH **5.55** Hydrazine is a toxic substance that can form when household ammonia is mixed with a bleach such as Clorox. Its formula is N_2H_4, and it is a weak base. Write a chemical equation showing its reaction with water.

5.56 Pyridine, C_5H_5N, is a fishy-smelling compound used as an intermediate in making insecticides. It is a weak base. Write a chemical equation showing its reaction with water.

5.57 Nitrous acid, HNO_2, is a weak acid that can form when sodium nitrite, a meat preservative, reacts with stomach acid (HCl). Write an equation showing the ionization of HNO_2 in water.

5.58 Pentanoic acid, $HC_5H_9O_2$, is found in a plant called valerian, which cats seem to like almost as much as catnip. Also called valeric acid, it is a weak acid. Write an equation showing its reaction with water.

5.59 Carbonic acid is a weak diprotic acid formed in rainwater as it passes through the atmosphere and dissolves carbon dioxide. Write chemical equations for the equilibria involved in the stepwise ionization of carbonic acid in water.

5.60 Phosphoric acid is a weak acid found in some soft drinks. It undergoes ionization in three steps. Write chemical equations for the equilibria involved in each of these reactions.

Metathesis Reactions

5.61 Aqueous solutions of sodium sulfide and copper(II) nitrate are mixed. A precipitate of copper(II) sulfide forms at once. The solution that remains contains sodium nitrate. Write the molecular, ionic, and net ionic equations for this reaction.

5.62 If an aqueous solution of iron(III) sulfate (a compound used in dyeing textiles and also for etching aluminum) is mixed with a solution of barium chloride, a precipitate of barium sulfate forms and the solution that remains contains iron(III) chloride. Write the molecular, ionic, and net ionic equations for this reaction.

5.63 Use the solubility rules to decide which of the following compounds are *soluble* in water.

(a) $Ca(NO_3)_2$ (d) silver nitrate

(b) $FeCl_2$ (e) barium sulfate

(c) $Ni(OH)_2$ (f) copper(II) carbonate

5.64 Predict which of the following compounds are *soluble* in water.

(a) $HgBr_2$ (d) ammonium phosphate

(b) $Sr(NO_3)_2$ (e) lead(II) iodide

(c) Hg_2Br_2 (f) lead(II) acetate

5.65 Complete and balance the following molecular equations, being careful to apply the solubility rules. Write balanced ionic and net ionic equations for the reactions.

(a) $FeSO_4(aq) + K_3PO_4(aq) \longrightarrow$

(b) $AgC_2H_3O_2(aq) + AlCl_3(aq) \longrightarrow$

(c) chromium(III) chloride + barium hydroxide $\longrightarrow$

5.66 Complete and balance the following molecular equations, being careful to apply the solubility rules. Write balanced ionic and net ionic equations for the reactions.

(a) $Fe(NO_3)_3(aq) + KOH(aq) \longrightarrow$

(b) $Na_3PO_4(aq) + SrCl_2(aq) \longrightarrow$

(c) lead(II) acetate + ammonium sulfate $\longrightarrow$

Acid–Base Neutralization Reactions

5.67 Complete and balance the following equations. For each, write the molecular, ionic, and net ionic equations. (All the products are soluble in water.)

(a) $Ca(OH)_2(aq) + HNO_3(aq) \longrightarrow$

(b) $Al_2O_3(s) + HCl(aq) \longrightarrow$

(c) $Zn(OH)_2(s) + H_2SO_4(aq) \longrightarrow$

5.68 Complete and balance the following equations. For each, write the molecular, ionic, and net ionic equations. (All the products are soluble in water.)

(a) $HC_2H_3O_2(aq) + Mg(OH)_2(s) \longrightarrow$

(b) $HClO_4(aq) + NH_3(aq) \longrightarrow$

(c) $H_2CO_3(aq) + NH_3(aq) \longrightarrow$

5.69 How would the electrical conductivity of a solution of barium hydroxide change as a solution of sulfuric acid is added slowly to it? Use a net ionic equation to justify your answer.

5.70 How would the electrical conductivity of a solution of acetic acid change as a solution of ammonia is added slowly to it? Use a net ionic equation to justify your answer.

Ionic Reactions That Produce Gases

5.71 Write balanced net ionic equations for the reaction between:

(a) $HNO_3(aq) + K_2CO_3(aq)$

(b) $Ca(OH)_2(aq) + NH_4NO_3(aq)$

5.72 Write balanced net ionic equations for the reaction between:

(a) $H_2SO_4(aq) + NaHSO_3(aq)$

(b) $HNO_3(aq) + (NH_4)_2CO_3(aq)$

Predicting Ionic Reactions

5.73 Explain why the following reactions take place.

(a) $CrCl_3 + 3NaOH \longrightarrow Cr(OH)_3 + 3NaCl$

(b) $ZnO + 2HBr \longrightarrow ZnBr_2 + H_2O$

OH **5.74** Explain why the following reactions take place.

(a) $MnCO_3 + H_2SO_4 \longrightarrow MnSO_4 + H_2O + CO_2$

(b) $Na_2C_2O_4 + 2HNO_3 \longrightarrow 2NaNO_3 + H_2C_2O_4$

5.75 Complete and balance the molecular, ionic, and net ionic equations for the following reactions.

(a) $HNO_3 + Cr(OH)_3 \longrightarrow$

(b) $HClO_4 + NaOH \longrightarrow$

(c) $Cu(OH)_2 + HC_2H_3O_2 \longrightarrow$

(d) $ZnO + H_2SO_4 \longrightarrow$

5.76 Complete and balance the molecular, ionic, and net ionic equations for the following reactions.

(a) $NaHSO_3 + HBr \longrightarrow$

(b) $(NH_4)_2CO_3 + NaOH \longrightarrow$

(c) $(NH_4)_2CO_3 + Ba(OH)_2 \longrightarrow$

(d) $FeS + HCl \longrightarrow$

ILW **5.77** Write balanced molecular, ionic, and net ionic equations for the following pairs of reactants. If all ions cancel, indicate that no reaction (N.R.) takes place.

(a) sodium sulfite and barium nitrate

(b) formic acid ($HCHO_2$) and potassium carbonate

(c) ammonium bromide and lead(II) acetate

(d) ammonium perchlorate and copper(II) nitrate

5.78 Write balanced molecular, ionic, and net ionic equations for the following pairs of reactants. If all ions cancel, indicate that no reaction (N.R.) takes place.

(a) ammonium sulfide and sodium hydroxide

(b) chromium(III) sulfate and potassium carbonate

(c) silver nitrate and chromium(III) acetate

(d) strontium hydroxide and magnesium chloride

*5.79 Choose reactants that would yield the following net ionic equations. Write molecular equations for each.

(a) $HCO_3^-(aq) + H^+(aq) \longrightarrow H_2O + CO_2(g)$

(b) $Fe^{2+}(aq) + 2OH^-(aq) \longrightarrow Fe(OH)_2(s)$

(c) $Ba^{2+}(aq) + SO_3^{2-}(aq) \longrightarrow BaSO_3(s)$

(d) $2Ag^+(aq) + S^{2-}(aq) \longrightarrow Ag_2S(s)$

(e) $ZnO(s) + 2H^+(aq) \longrightarrow Zn^{2+}(aq) + H_2O$

*5.80 Suppose that you wanted to prepare copper(II) carbonate by a precipitation reaction involving Cu^{2+} and CO_3^{2-}. Which of the following pairs of reactants could you use as solutes?

(a) $Cu(OH)_2 + Na_2CO_3$ (d) $CuCl_2 + K_2CO_3$

(b) $CuSO_4 + (NH_4)_2CO_3$ (e) $CuS + NiCO_3$

(c) $Cu(NO_3)_2 + CaCO_3$

Molar Concentration

OH **5.81** Calculate the molarity of a solution prepared by dissolving

(a) 4.00 g of sodium hydroxide in a total volume of 100.0 mL of solution.

(b) 16.0 g of calcium chloride in a total volume of 250.0 mL of solution.

5.82 Calculate the molarity of a solution that contains

(a) 3.60 g of sulfuric acid in 450.0 mL of solution.

(b) 2.00×10^{-3} mol iron(II) nitrate in 12.0 mL of solution.

5.83 How many milliliters of $0.265\ M\ NaC_2H_3O_2$ are needed to supply 14.3 g $NaC_2H_3O_2$?

5.84 How many milliliters of $0.615\ M\ HNO_3$ contain 1.67 g HNO_3?

ILW **5.85** Calculate the number of grams of each solute that has to be taken to make each of the following solutions.

(a) 125 mL of 0.200 M NaCl

(b) 250.0 mL of 0.360 M $C_6H_{12}O_6$ (glucose)

(c) 250.0 mL of 0.250 M H_2SO_4

5.86 How many grams of solute are needed to make each of the following solutions?

(a) 250.0 mL of 0.100 M potassium sulfate

(b) 100.0 mL of 0.250 M iron(III) chloride

(c) 500.0 mL of 0.400 M barium acetate

Dilution of Solutions

5.87 If 25.0 mL of 0.56 M H_2SO_4 is diluted to a volume of 125 mL, what is the molarity of the resulting solution?

5.88 A 150 mL sample of 0.450 M HNO_3 is diluted to 450 mL. What is the molarity of the resulting solution?

ILW 5.89 To what volume must 25.0 mL of 18.0 M H_2SO_4 be diluted to produce 1.50 M H_2SO_4?

5.90 To what volume must 50.0 mL of 1.50 M HCl be diluted to produce 0.200 M HCl?

5.91 How many milliliters of water must be added to 150.0 mL of 2.50 M KOH to give a 1.00 M solution? (Assume the volumes are additive.)

5.92 How many milliliters of water must be added to 120.0 mL of 1.50 M HCl to give 1.00 M HCl? (Assume the volumes are additive.)

Concentrations of Ions in Solutions of Electrolytes

5.93 Calculate the number of moles of each of the ions in the following solutions.

(a) 32.3 mL of 0.455 M $CaCl_2$

(b) 50.0 mL of 0.408 M $AlCl_3$

5.94 Calculate the number of moles of each of the ions in the following solutions.

(a) 18.5 mL of 0.402 M $(NH_4)_2CO_3$

(b) 30.0 mL of 0.359 M $Al_2(SO_4)_3$

5.95 Calculate the concentrations of each of the ions in (a) 0.25 M $Cr(NO_3)_2$, (b) 0.10 M $CuSO_4$, (c) 0.16 M Na_3PO_4, (d) 0.075 M $Al_2(SO_4)_3$.

5.96 Calculate the concentrations of each of the ions in (a) 0.060 M $Ca(OH)_2$, (b) 0.15 M $FeCl_3$, (c) 0.22 M $Cr_2(SO_4)_3$, (d) 0.60 M $(NH_4)_2SO_4$.

5.97 In a solution of $Al_2(SO_4)_3$ the Al^{3+} concentration is 0.125 M. How many grams of $Al_2(SO_4)_3$ are in 50.0 mL of this solution?

5.98 In a solution of $NiCl_2$, the Cl^- concentration is 0.0556 M. How many grams of $NiCl_2$ are in 225 mL of this solution?

Solution Stoichiometry

OH 5.99 How many milliliters of 0.258 M $NiCl_2$ solution are needed to react completely with 20.0 mL of 0.153 M Na_2CO_3 solution? How many grams of $NiCO_3$ will be formed? The reaction is

$$Na_2CO_3(aq) + NiCl_2(aq) \longrightarrow NiCO_3(s) + 2NaCl(aq)$$

5.100 How many milliliters of 0.100 M NaOH are needed to completely neutralize 25.0 mL of 0.250 M $H_2C_4H_4O_6$? The reaction is

$$2NaOH(aq) + H_2C_4H_4O_6(aq) \longrightarrow Na_2C_4H_4O_6(aq) + 2H_2O$$

5.101 What is the molarity of an aqueous solution of potassium hydroxide if 21.34 mL is exactly neutralized by 20.78 mL of 0.116 M HCl? Write and balance the molecular equation for the reaction.

5.102 What is the molarity of an aqueous phosphoric acid solution if 12.88 mL is completely neutralized by 26.04 mL of 0.1024 M NaOH? Write and balance the molecular equation for the reaction.

5.103 Aluminum sulfate, $Al_2(SO_4)_3$, is used in water treatment to remove fine particles suspended in the water. When made basic, a gel-like precipitate forms that removes the fine particles as it settles. In an experiment, a student planned to react $Al_2(SO_4)_3$ with $Ba(OH)_2$. How many grams of $Al_2(SO_4)_3$ are needed to react with 85.0 mL of 0.0500 M $Ba(OH)_2$?

5.104 How many grams of baking soda, $NaHCO_3$, are needed to react with 162 mL of stomach acid having an HCl concentration of 0.052 M?

5.105 How many milliliters of 0.150 M $FeCl_3$ solution are needed to react completely with 20.0 mL of 0.0450 M $AgNO_3$ solution? How many grams of AgCl will be formed? The net ionic equation for the reaction is

$$Ag^+(aq) + Cl^-(aq) \longrightarrow AgCl(s)$$

5.106 How many grams of cobalt(II) chloride are needed to react completely with 60.0 mL of 0.200 M KOH solution? The net ionic equation for the reaction is

$$Co^{2+}(aq) + 2OH^-(aq) \longrightarrow Co(OH)_2(s)$$

ILW 5.107 Consider the reaction of aluminum chloride with silver acetate. How many milliliters of 0.250 M aluminum chloride would be needed to react completely with 20.0 mL of 0.500 M silver acetate solution? The net ionic equation for the reaction is

$$Ag^+(aq) + Cl^-(aq) \longrightarrow AgCl(s)$$

5.108 How many milliliters of ammonium sulfate solution having a concentration of 0.250 M are needed to react completely with 50.0 mL of 1.00 M sodium hydroxide solution? The net ionic equation for the reaction is

$$NH_4^+(aq) + OH^-(aq) \longrightarrow NH_3(g) + H_2O$$

*5.109 Suppose that 4.00 g of solid Fe_2O_3 is added to 25.0 mL of 0.500 M HCl solution. What will the concentration of the Fe^{3+} be when all of the HCl has reacted? What mass of Fe_2O_3 will not have reacted?

*5.110 Suppose 3.50 g of solid $Mg(OH)_2$ is added to 30.0 mL of 0.500 M H_2SO_4 solution. What will the concentration of Mg^{2+} be when all of the acid has been neutralized? How many grams of $Mg(OH)_2$ will not have dissolved?

Titrations and Chemical Analyses

5.111 In a titration, 23.25 mL of 0.105 M NaOH was needed to react with 21.45 mL of HCl solution. What is the molarity of the acid?

5.112 A 12.5 mL sample of vinegar, containing acetic acid, was titrated using 0.504 M NaOH solution. The titration required 20.65 mL of the base.

(a) What was the molar concentration of acetic acid in the vinegar?

(b) Assuming the density of the vinegar is 1.01 g mL^{-1}, what was the percent (by mass) of acetic acid in the vinegar?

ILW **5.113** Lactic acid, $HC_3H_5O_3$, is a monoprotic acid that forms
OH when milk sours. An 18.5 mL sample of a solution of lactic acid required 17.25 mL of 0.155 M NaOH to reach an end point in a titration. (a) How many moles of lactic acid were in the sample? (b) How many grams of lactic acid were in the sample?

5.114 Ascorbic acid (vitamin C) is a diprotic acid having the formula $H_2C_6H_6O_6$. A sample of a vitamin supplement was analyzed by titrating a 0.1000 g sample dissolved in water with 0.0200 M NaOH. A volume of 15.20 mL of the base was required to completely neutralize the ascorbic acid. What was the percentage by mass of ascorbic acid in the sample?

5.115 A certain lead ore contains the compound $PbCO_3$. A sample of the ore weighing 1.526 g was treated with nitric acid, which dissolved the $PbCO_3$. The resulting solution was filtered from undissolved rock and required 29.22 mL of 0.122 M Na_2SO_4 to completely precipitate all of the lead as $PbSO_4$. (a) How many moles of lead were in the ore sample? (b) How many grams of lead were in the ore sample? (c) What is the percentage by mass of lead in the ore?

5.116 An ore of barium contains $BaCO_3$. A 1.542 g sample of the ore was treated with HCl to dissolve the $BaCO_3$. The resulting solution was filtered to remove insoluble material and then treated with H_2SO_4 to precipitate $BaSO_4$. The precipitate was filtered, dried, and found to weigh 1.159 g. What is the percentage by mass of barium in the ore? (Assume all of the barium is precipitated as $BaSO_4$.)

| Additional Exercises

*5.117 Suppose that 25.0 mL of 0.440 M NaCl is added to 25.0 mL of 0.320 M $AgNO_3$.

(a) How many moles of AgCl would precipitate?

(b) What would be the concentrations of each of the ions in the reaction mixture after the reaction?

*5.118 A mixture is prepared by adding 25.0 mL of 0.185 M Na_3PO_4 to 34.0 mL of 0.140 M $Ca(NO_3)_2$.

(a) What mass of $Ca_3(PO_4)_2$ will be formed?

(b) What will be the concentrations of each of the ions in the mixture after reaction?

5.119 Classify each of the following as a strong electrolyte, weak electrolyte, or nonelectrolyte.

(a) KCl

(b) $C_3H_5(OH)_3$ (glycerin)

(c) NaOH

(d) $C_{12}H_{22}O_{11}$ (sucrose, or table sugar)

(e) $HC_2H_3O_2$ (acetic acid)

(f) CH_3OH (methyl alcohol)

(g) H_2SO_4

(h) NH_3

OH **5.120** Complete the following and write molecule, ionic, and net ionic equations. State whether a net reaction occurs in each case.

(a) $CaCO_3 + HNO_3 \longrightarrow$ (c) $FeS + HBr \longrightarrow$

(b) $CaCO_3 + H_2SO_4 \longrightarrow$ (d) $KOH + SnCl_2 \longrightarrow$

OH ***5.121** Aspirin is a monoprotic acid called acetylsalicylic acid. Its formula is $HC_9H_7O_4$. A certain pain reliever was analyzed for aspirin by dissolving 0.250 g of it in water and titrating it with 0.0300 M KOH solution. The titration required 29.40 mL of base. What is the percentage by weight of aspirin in the drug?

*5.122 In an experiment, 40.0 mL of 0.270 M barium hydroxide was mixed with 25.0 mL of 0.330 M aluminum sulfate.

(a) Write the net ionic equation for the reaction that takes place.

(b) What is the total mass of precipitate that forms?

(c) What are the molar concentrations of the ions that remain in the solution after the reaction is complete?

*5.123 How many milliliters of 0.10 M HCl must be added to 50.0 mL of 0.40 M HCl to give a final solution that has a molarity of 0.25 M?

5.124 Write an equation for the reaction of sodium hydroxide with the chloride salt of the cation with the following structure. How many grams of sodium hydroxide are needed to completely react with 12.4 g of the salt?

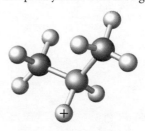

Multi-Concept Problems

* 5.125 Magnesium sulfate forms a hydrate known as *Epsom salts*. A student dissolved 1.24 g of this hydrate in water and added a barium chloride solution until the precipitation reaction was complete. The precipitate was filtered, dried, and found to weigh 1.174 g. Determine the formula for Epsom salts.

*5.126 Qualitative analysis of an unknown acid found only carbon, hydrogen, and oxygen. In a quantitative analysis, a 10.46 mg sample was burned in oxygen and gave 22.17 mg CO_2 and 3.40 mg H_2O. The molecular mass was determined to be 166 g mol^{-1}. When a 0.1680 g sample of the acid was titrated with 0.1250 M NaOH, the end point was reached after 16.18 mL of the base had been added. **(a)** What is the molecular formula for the acid? **(b)** Is the acid mono-, di-, or triprotic?

*5.127 A mixture was known to contain both KNO_3 and K_2SO_3. To 0.486 g of the mixture, dissolved in enough water to give 50.00 mL of solution, was added 50.00 mL of 0.150 M HCl (an excess of HCl). The reaction mixture was heated to drive off all of the SO_2, and then 25.00 mL of the reaction mixture was titrated with 0.100 M KOH.

The titration required 13.11 mL of the KOH solution to reach an end point. What was the percentage by mass of K_2SO_3 in the original mixture of KNO_3 and K_2SO_3?

*5.128 A white substance was known to be either magnesium hydroxide, calcium hydroxide, or zinc oxide. A 1.25 g sample of the substance was mixed with 50.0 mL of water and 100.0 mL of 0.500 M HCl was added. The mixture was stirred, causing all of the sample to dissolve. The excess HCl in the solution required 36.0 mL of 0.200 M NaOH for complete neutralization in a titration. What was the identity of the white substance?

*5.129 A steel cylinder with a diameter of 10.0 cm and a length of 30.0 cm was coated with a thin layer of zinc. The cylinder was dipped briefly in hydrochloric acid, which completely dissolved the coating of zinc, giving Zn^{2+} in the solution. When made basic, the mixture yielded 0.226 g of a $Zn(OH)_2$ precipitate. If a zinc atom occupies an average area of 6.31×10^4 pm^2 on the surface of the cylinder, how many layers of atoms thick was the zinc coating on the cylinder?

Exercises in Critical Thinking

5.130 Compare the advantages and disadvantages of performing a titration using the mass of the sample and titrant rather than the volume.

5.131 What kinds of experiments could you perform to measure the solubility of a substance in water? Describe the procedure you would use and the measurements you would make. What factors would limit the precision of your measurements?

5.132 Describe experiments, both qualitative and quantitative, that you could perform to show that lead chloride is more soluble in water than lead iodide.

5.133 How could you check the accuracy of a 100 mL volumetric flask?

5.134 Suppose a classmate doubted that an equilibrium really exists between acetic acid and its ions in an aqueous solution. What argument would you use to convince the person that such an equilibrium does exist?

5.135 When Arrhenius originally proposed that ions exist in solution, his idea was not well received. Propose another explanation for the conduction of electricity in molten salts and aqueous salt solutions.

5.136 Carbon dioxide is one obvious contributor to excessive global warming. What is your plan for controlling CO_2 emissions? What are the advantages and disadvantages of your plan?

6 Oxidation–Reduction Reactions

The beautiful, wispy, smoke-like fog that hangs over the Smoky Mountains in Tennessee and North Carolina comes from emissions from the deciduous trees and shrubs native to the mountains.[1] This natural haze is a result of photochemical smog: the compounds emitted by the trees react with sunlight and natural oxidants (compounds that remove electrons from other compounds) to form substances called *carboxylic acids*, which come together to form particles that scatter sunlight and produce a haze. In this chapter we will study reactions that occur by electron transfer—reactions of great importance in our everyday lives. Besides being involved in the formation of smog, these reactions have practical applications that range from the functioning of batteries to the burning of fossil fuels. (Carr Clifton/Minden Pictures, Inc.)

[1] F. Paulot et al., Unexpected Epoxide Formation in the Gas-Phase Photooxidation of Isoprene, *Science*, **325**, 730–733.

This Chapter in Context

In Chapter 5 you learned about some important reactions that take place in aqueous solutions. This chapter expands on that knowledge with a discussion of a class of reactions that can be viewed as involving the transfer of one or more electrons from one reactant to another. Our goal is to teach you how to recognize and analyze the changes that occur in these reactions and how to balance equations for reactions that involve electron transfer. You will also learn how to apply the principles of stoichiometry to these reactions and how to predict a type of reaction called single replacement. The reactions discussed here constitute a very broad class with many practical examples that range from combustion to batteries to the metabolism of foods by our bodies. Although we will introduce you to some of them in this chapter, we will wait until Chapter 20 to discuss some of the others.

6.1 | Oxidation–Reduction Reactions

Among the first reactions studied by early scientists were those that involved oxygen. The combustion of fuels and the reactions of metals with oxygen to give oxides were described by the word *oxidation*. The removal of oxygen from metal oxides to give the metals in their elemental forms was described as *reduction*.

In 1789, the French chemist Antoine Lavoisier discovered that *combustion* involves the reaction of chemicals in various fuels, like wood and coal, not just with air but specifically with the oxygen in air. Over time, scientists came to realize that such reactions were actually special cases of a much more general phenomenon, one in which electrons are transferred from one substance to another. Collectively, electron transfer reactions came to be called **oxidation–reduction reactions,** or simply **redox reactions.** The term **oxidation** was used to describe the loss of electrons by one reactant, and **reduction** to describe the gain of electrons by another. For example, the reaction between sodium and chlorine to yield sodium chloride involves a loss of electrons by sodium (*oxidation* of sodium) and a gain of electrons by chlorine (*reduction* of chlorine). We can write these changes in equation form including the electrons, which we represent by the symbol e^-.

$$Na \longrightarrow Na^+ + e^- \qquad \text{(oxidation)}$$
$$Cl_2 + 2e^- \longrightarrow 2Cl^- \qquad \text{(reduction)}$$

We say that sodium, Na, is oxidized and chlorine, Cl_2, is reduced.

Oxidation and reduction always occur together. No substance is ever oxidized unless something else is reduced, and the total number of electrons lost by one substance is always the same as the total number gained by the other. If this were not true, electrons would appear as a product of the overall reaction, and this is never observed.[2] In the reaction of sodium with chlorine, for example, the overall reaction is

$$2Na + Cl_2 \longrightarrow 2NaCl$$

When two sodium atoms are oxidized, two electrons are lost, which is exactly the number of electrons gained when one Cl_2 molecule is reduced.

For a redox reaction to occur, one substance must accept electrons from the other. The substance that accepts the electrons is called the **oxidizing agent**; it is the agent that allows the other substance to lose electrons and be oxidized. Similarly, the substance that supplies the electrons is called the **reducing agent** because it helps something else to be reduced.

■ Oxygen had just been discovered by Joseph Priestley in 1774.

■ The term redox was coined to emphasize that reduction and oxidation must always occur together in chemical reactions.

■ Notice that when we write equations of this type, the electron appears as a "product" if the process is oxidation and as a "reactant" if the process is reduction.

■ The *oxidizing agent* causes oxidation to occur by accepting electrons (it gets reduced). The *reducing agent* causes reduction by supplying electrons (it gets oxidized).

[2]If electron loss didn't equal electron gain, it would also violate the law of conservation of mass, and that doesn't happen in chemical reactions.

In our example above, sodium serves as a reducing agent when it supplies electrons to chlorine. In the process, sodium is oxidized. Chlorine is an oxidizing agent when it accepts electrons from the sodium, and when that happens, chlorine is reduced to chloride ion. One way to remember this is by the following summary:

The reducing agent is the substance that is oxidized.

The oxidizing agent is the substance that is reduced.

Redox reactions are very common. They occur in batteries, which are built so that the electrons transferred can pass through some external circuit where they are able to light a flashlight or power an iPod. The metabolism of foods, which supplies our bodies with energy, also occurs by a series of redox reactions. In the Smoky Mountains, the photochemical haze is produced by oxidation of isoprene (emitted by trees) by oxygen in the air. And ordinary household bleach works by oxidizing substances that stain fabrics, making them colorless or easier to remove from the fabric (see Figure 6.1).

Figure 6.1 | **"Chlorine" bleach.** This common household product is a dilute aqueous solution of sodium hypochlorite, NaOCl, which destroys fabric stains by oxidizing them to colorless products. *(OPC, Inc.)*

Oxidizing and reducing agents

Example 6.1
Identifying Oxidation–Reduction

The bright light produced by the reaction between magnesium and oxygen often is used in fireworks displays. The product of the reaction is magnesium oxide, an ionic compound. Which element is oxidized and which is reduced? What are the oxidizing and reducing agents?

■ **Analysis:** This question asks us to apply the definitions presented above, so we need to know how the electrons are transferred in the reaction.

■ **Assembling the Tools:** As stated, magnesium oxide is an ionic compound. Using the tools you learned in Chapter 3, the locations of the elements in the periodic table tell us that the ions are Mg^{2+} and O^{2-}, so the formula for magnesium oxide is MgO. The reactants are magnesium, Mg, and molecular oxygen, O_2. The equation for the reaction is therefore

$$2Mg + O_2 \longrightarrow 2MgO$$

Now that we have the balanced chemical equation and the formulas of the ions, we can determine how electrons are exchanged and use the definitions of oxidizing and reducing agent as tools to answer the question.

Fireworks display over Washington, D.C. *(Pete Saloutos/ Corbis Images)*

■ **Solution:** When a magnesium atom becomes a magnesium ion, it must lose two electrons, and they appear in the products when we express the reaction as an equation.

$$Mg \longrightarrow Mg^{2+} + 2e^-$$

By losing electrons, *magnesium is oxidized, so it is the reducing agent.*

When oxygen reacts to yield O^{2-} ions, each oxygen atom must gain two electrons, so an O_2 molecule must gain four electrons; these electrons appear on the reactant side of the equation.

$$O_2 + 4e^- \longrightarrow 2O^{2-}$$

By gaining electrons, *O_2 is reduced* and *must be the oxidizing agent.*

■ **Is the Answer Reasonable?** There are two things we can do to check our answers. First, we can check to be sure that we've placed electrons on the correct sides of the equations. As with ionic equations, *the number of atoms of each kind and the net charge must be the same on both sides.* We see that this is true for both equations. (If we had placed the electrons on the wrong side, the charges would not balance.) By observing the locations of the electrons in the equations (on the right for oxidation; on the left for reduction), we come to the same conclusions that Mg is oxidized and O_2 is reduced.

Another check is noting that we've identified one substance as being oxidized and the other as being reduced. If we had made a mistake, we might have concluded that both were oxidized, or both were reduced. But that's impossible, because in every reaction in which there is oxidation, there must also be reduction.

Practice Exercises

6.1 | When sodium reacts with molecular oxygen, O_2, the product is sodium peroxide, Na_2O_2, which contains the peroxide ion, O_2^{2-}. In this reaction, is O_2 oxidized or reduced? (*Hint:* Which reactant gains electrons, and which loses electrons?)

6.2 | Identify the substances oxidized and reduced, and the oxidizing and reducing agents in the reaction of aluminum and chlorine to form aluminum chloride.

6.3 | On page 134 we described the thermite reaction in which iron(III) oxide reacts with aluminum to form metallic iron and aluminum oxide. Identify the substances oxidized and reduced and the oxidizing and reducing agents in this reaction.

Using Oxidation Numbers to Follow Redox Changes

Unlike the reaction of magnesium with oxygen, not all reactions with oxygen produce ionic products. For example, sulfur reacts with oxygen to give sulfur dioxide, SO_2, which is molecular. Nevertheless, it is convenient to also view this as a redox reaction, but this requires that we change the way we define oxidation and reduction. To do this, chemists developed a bookkeeping system called **oxidation numbers,** which provides a way to keep tabs on electron transfers.

The oxidation number of an element in a particular compound is assigned according to a set of rules, which are described below. For simple, monatomic ions in a compound such as NaCl, the oxidation numbers are the same as the charges on the ions, so in NaCl the oxidation number of Na^+ is +1 and the oxidation number of Cl^- is −1. The real value of oxidation numbers is that they can also be assigned to atoms in molecular compounds. In such cases, it is important to realize that the oxidation number does not actually equal a charge on an atom. To be sure to differentiate oxidation numbers from actual electrical charges, we will specify the sign *before* the number when writing oxidation numbers, and *after* the number when writing electrical charges. Thus, a sodium ion has a charge of 1+ and an oxidation number of +1.

A term that is frequently used interchangeably with *oxidation number* is **oxidation state.** In NaCl, sodium has an oxidation number of +1 and is said to be "in the +1 oxidation state." Similarly, the chlorine in NaCl is said to be in the −1 oxidation state. When there are more than one possible oxidation states, the oxidation state of an element is given by writing the oxidation number as a Roman numeral in parentheses after the name of the element. For example, "iron(III)" means iron in the +3 oxidation state. A summary of the terms used in oxidation and reduction reactions is given in Table 6.1.

We can use these new terms now to redefine a redox reaction.

A **redox reaction** is a chemical reaction in which changes in oxidation numbers occur.

Table 6.1	Summary of Oxidation and Reduction Using $2Na + Cl_2 \longrightarrow 2NaCl$	
Sodium	**Chlorine**
Oxidized Na	Reduced Cl
Reducing agent	Oxidizing agent
Oxidation number increases	Oxidation number decreases
Loses electrons	Gains electrons

We can follow redox reactions by taking note of the changes in oxidation numbers. To do this, however, we must be able to assign oxidation numbers to atoms in a quick and simple way.

Rules for the Assignment of Oxidation Numbers

We can use some basic knowledge learned earlier plus the set of rules below to determine the oxidation numbers of the atoms in almost any compound. These rules are a hierarchy; use the lower numbered rule first, and then apply the higher numbered rule. This allows us to deal with conflicts between two rules.

A Hierarchy of Rules for Assigning Oxidation Numbers

1. Oxidation numbers must add up to the charge on the molecule, formula unit, or ion.
2. The atoms of free elements have oxidation numbers of zero.
3. Metals in Groups 1A, 2A, and Al have +1, +2, and +3 oxidation numbers, respectively.
4. H and F in compounds have +1 and −1 oxidation numbers, respectively.
5. Oxygen has a −2 oxidation number.
6. Group 7A elements have a −1 oxidation number.
7. Group 6A elements have a −2 oxidation number.
8. Group 5A elements have a −3 oxidation number.
9. When there is a conflict between two of these rules or an ambiguity in assigning an oxidation number, apply the rule with the lower number and ignore the conflicting rule.

TOOLS

Assigning oxidation numbers

■ Rule 2 means that O in O_2, P in P_4, and S in S_8 all have oxidation numbers of zero.

■ For example, hydrogen can have an oxidation number of −1 when combined with a metal in Group 1A. If we follow Rules 1 and 3 first, then we can ignore Rule 4 and give H the −1 oxidation number.

These rules can be applied to elements, molecules, and ionic compounds. For example, oxygen, O_2, is a free element and has a zero charge, the oxidation number for each oxygen atom in O_2 must be zero, following Rules 1 and 2. Or, take the simple ionic compound, NaCl: the sodium is in Group 1A and has an oxidation number of +1, from Rule 3; and from Rule 6, chlorine has an oxidation number of −1. These add up to zero, which is the overall charge of the formula unit.

The numbered rules and their order in the list given above come into play when an element is capable of having more than one oxidation state. For example, you learned that transition metals can form more than one ion. Iron, for example, forms Fe^{2+} and Fe^{3+} ions, so in an iron compound we have to use the rules to figure out which iron ion is present. Similarly, when nonmetals are combined with hydrogen and oxygen in compounds or polyatomic ions, their oxidation numbers can vary and must be calculated using the rules. For example, one of the products of the oxidation of isoprene is formaldehyde, CH_2O. The oxidation of the carbon atom can be calculated using the numbered rules. The two hydrogens together are $2 \times (+1)$ and the oxygen has an oxidation number of −2. Together they add up to zero, and since the molecule is neutral, the carbon must have an oxidation number of 0, according to Rule 1.

With this as background, let's look at some more examples that illustrate how we apply the rules.

Example 6.2
Assigning Oxidation Numbers

Titanium dioxide, TiO_2, is a white pigment used in making paint. A now outmoded process of making TiO_2 from its ore involved $Ti(SO_4)_2$ as an intermediate. What is the oxidation number of titanium in $Ti(SO_4)_2$?

■**Analysis:** The key here is recognizing SO_4 as the sulfate ion, SO_4^{2-}. Because we're only interested in the oxidation number of titanium, we use the charge on SO_4^{2-} to equal the net oxidation number of the polyatomic ion.

■**Assembling the Tools:** We will use the rules for assigning oxidation numbers and most important, Rule 1, to sum the oxidation numbers to equal the overall charge of the formula unit. The charge on a polyatomic ion is the *net* oxidation number of the ion.

■**Solution:** The sulfate ion has a charge of $2-$, which we can take to be its net oxidation number. Then, we apply the summation rule (Rule 1) to find the oxidation number of titanium, which we will represent by x.

$$\begin{array}{lll} \text{Ti} & (1 \text{ atom}) \times (x) = & x \\ SO_4^{2-} & (2 \text{ ions}) \times (-2) = & -4 \\ \hline & \text{Sum} = & 0 \qquad \text{(Rule 1)} \end{array}$$

Obviously, the oxidation number of titanium is $+4$ so that the sum can be zero.

■**Is the Answer Reasonable?** We have the sum of oxidation numbers adding up to zero, the charge on $Ti(SO_4)_2$, so our answer is reasonable.

As we have already discussed, transition metals can have more than one oxidation state. In addition, the oxidation states of the nonmetals can vary depending on the compound they are in. For example, sulfur can be found in H_2S, S (elemental sulfur), SO_2, SO_3, and H_2SO_4. The oxidation states for sulfur are -2, 0, $+4$, $+6$, and $+6$, respectively. Example 6.3 illustrates this same point with oxygen.

Example 6.3
Assigning Oxidation Numbers

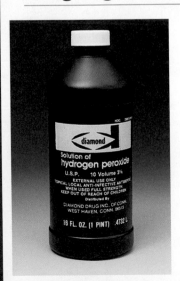

Hydrogen peroxide destroys bacteria by oxidizing them.
(Robert Capece)

Determine the oxidation numbers of the atoms in hydrogen peroxide, H_2O_2, a common antiseptic purchased in pharmacies, which can also be used to bleach hair.

■**Analysis:** The compound is molecular, so there are no ions to work with; we have to find the oxidation numbers for the hydrogen and the oxygen.

■**Assembling the Tools:** Just as in Example 6.2, we will use the tool for assigning oxidation numbers, and apply the appropriate rules. We can start by scanning the rules, and we see we have one for hydrogen and another for oxygen. We always have to keep in mind Rule 1, adding up the oxidation numbers, and Rule 9, how to handle conflicts between rules.

■**Solution:** Let us start with hydrogen and Rule 4, which tells us to assign an oxidation number of $+1$ to hydrogen. Rule 5 tells us to give oxygen an oxidation number of -2. Both of these can't be correct, because the sum must be zero (Rule 1).

$$\begin{array}{lll} \text{H} & (2 \text{ atoms}) \times (+1) = +2 & \text{(Rule 4)} \\ \text{O} & (2 \text{ atoms}) \times (-2) = -4 & \text{(Rule 5)} \\ \hline & \text{Sum} \neq 0 & \text{(violates Rule 1)} \end{array}$$

As mentioned above, when there is a conflict between the rules, we ignore the higher numbered rule that causes the conflict.

Rule 5 is the higher numbered rule causing the conflict, so we have to ignore it and just apply Rules 1 (the sum rule) and 4 (the rule that tells us the oxidation number of hydrogen is +1). Because we don't have a rule that applies to oxygen in this case, we'll represent the oxidation number of O by x.

$$H \quad (2 \text{ atoms}) \times (+1) = +2 \qquad (\text{Rule } 4)$$
$$\underline{O \quad (2 \text{ atoms}) \times (x) = 2x}$$
$$\text{Sum} = 0 \qquad (\text{Rule } 1)$$

For the sum to be zero, $2x = -2$, so $x = -1$. Therefore, in this compound, oxygen has an oxidation number of -1.

$$H = +1 \qquad O = -1$$

■ **Is the Answer Reasonable?** A conflict between the rules occurs only rarely, but when it happens the conflict becomes apparent because it causes a violation of the sum rule. However, *the sum rule (Rule 1) always applies.*

Sometimes, oxidation numbers calculated by the rules have fractional values, as illustrated in Example 6.4.

Example 6.4
Assigning Oxidation Numbers

The air bags used as safety devices in modern autos are inflated by the very rapid decomposition of the ionic compound sodium azide, NaN_3. The reaction gives elemental sodium and gaseous nitrogen. What is the average oxidation number of the nitrogen in sodium azide?

■ **Analysis:** We're told that NaN_3 is ionic, so we know that there is a cation and an anion. The cation is the sodium ion, Na^+, which means that the remainder of the formula unit, "N_3" must carry one unit of negative charge. However, there could not be three nitrogen anions each with a charge of $\frac{1}{3}-$, because it would mean that each nitrogen atom had acquired one-third of an electron. Whole numbers of electrons are always involved in electron transfers. Therefore, the anion must be a single particle with a negative one charge, namely, N_3^-. For this anion, the sum of the oxidation numbers of the three nitrogen atoms must be -1. We can use this information to solve the problem.

The explosive decomposition of sodium azide releases nitrogen gas, which rapidly inflates an air bag during a crash. *(Corbis-Bettmann)*

■ **Assembling the Tools:** We will use the same tools as in Example 6.3—namely, the assignment of oxidation numbers, and we will focus on Rules 1 and 3.

■ **Solution:** The sum of the oxidation numbers of the nitrogen must be equal to -1. If we let x stand for the oxidation number of just one of the nitrogen atoms, then

$$(3 \text{ atoms}) \times (x) = 3x = -1$$

$$x = -\tfrac{1}{3}$$

We could have also tackled the problem just using the rules for assigning oxidation numbers. We know that sodium exists as the ion Na^+ and that the compound is neutral overall. Therefore,

$$Na \quad (1 \text{ atom}) \times (+1) = +1 \qquad (\text{Rule } 3)$$
$$\underline{N \quad (3 \text{ atoms}) \times (x) = 3x}$$
$$\text{Sum} = 0 \qquad (\text{Rule } 1)$$

The sum of the oxidation numbers of the three nitrogen atoms in this ion must add up to -1, so each nitrogen must have an oxidation number of $-\frac{1}{3}$.

■**Is the Answer Reasonable?** As with Example 6.3, we've solved it two ways, so we can certainly feel confident the answer is correct.

Practice Exercises

6.4 | The chlorite ion, ClO_2^-, is a potent disinfectant, and solutions of it are sometimes used to disinfect air-conditioning systems in cars. What is the oxidation number of chlorine in this ion? (*Hint:* The sum of the oxidation numbers is not zero.)

6.5 | Assign oxidation numbers to each atom in (a) $NiCl_2$, (b) Mg_2TiO_4, (c) $K_2Cr_2O_7$, (d) HPO_4^{2-}, (e) $V(C_2H_3O_2)_3$, and (f) NH_4^+.

6.6 | Iron forms a magnetic oxide with the formula Fe_3O_4 that contains both Fe^{2+} and Fe^{3+} ions. What is the *average* oxidation number of iron in this oxide?

6.7 | Molybdenum can form compounds with many different oxidation numbers. Assign the oxidation numbers for molybdenum in (a) $MoCl_3$, (b) MoS_2, (c) $MoOCl_4$, and (d) MoP_2.

Identifying Oxidation and Reduction Processes

Oxidation and reduction reactions

Oxidation numbers can be used in several ways. One is to define oxidation and reduction in the most comprehensive manner, as follows:

Oxidation involves an increase in oxidation number.

Reduction involves a decrease in oxidation number.

Let's see how these definitions apply to the reaction of hydrogen with chlorine. To avoid confusing oxidation numbers with actual electrical charges, we will write oxidation numbers directly above the chemical symbols of the elements.

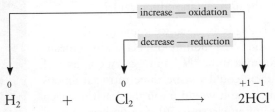

Notice that we have assigned the atoms in H_2 and Cl_2 oxidation numbers of zero, since they are free elements. The changes in oxidation number tell us that hydrogen is oxidized and chlorine is reduced.

Example 6.5
Using Oxidation Numbers to Follow Redox Reactions

Is the following a redox reaction?

$$2KCl + MnO_2 + 2H_2SO_4 \longrightarrow K_2SO_4 + MnSO_4 + Cl_2 + 2H_2O$$

If so, identify the substance oxidized and the substance reduced, as well as the oxidizing and reducing agents.

■**Analysis:** To determine whether the reaction is redox and to give the specific answers requested, we will need to determine whether oxidation numbers are changing and how they are changing in the reaction.

■**Assembling the Tools:** Our tools will be the rules for assigning oxidation numbers and the revised definitions of oxidation and reduction. Applying the tool to each element will tell us whether redox is occurring, and if so, what is oxidized and what is reduced. Then, applying the tool for the definition of oxidizing and reducing agents, we recall that the substance oxidized is the reducing agent, and the substance reduced is the oxidizing agent.

■ **Solution:** To determine whether redox is occurring here, we first assign oxidation numbers to each atom on both sides of the equation. Following the rules, we get

$$\overset{+1\ -1}{2KCl} + \overset{+4\ -2}{MnO_2} + \overset{+1+6-2}{H_2SO_4} \longrightarrow \overset{+1+6-2}{K_2SO_4} + \overset{+2\ +6-2}{MnSO_4} + \overset{0}{Cl_2} + \overset{+1\ -2}{2H_2O}$$

Next, we look for changes, keeping in mind that an increase in oxidation number is oxidation and a decrease is reduction.

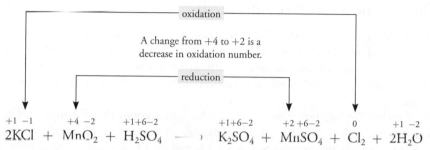

Thus, the Cl in KCl is oxidized and the Mn in MnO_2 is reduced. The reducing agent is KCl and the oxidizing agent is MnO_2. (Notice that when we identify the oxidizing and reducing agents, we give the entire formulas for the substances that contain the atoms with oxidation numbers that change.)

■ **Is the Answer Reasonable?** There are lots of things we could check here. We have found changes that lead us to conclude that redox is happening. We can also identify one change as oxidation and the other as reduction, which gives us confidence that we've done the rest of the work correctly.

Practice Exercises

6.8 | Consider the following reactions:

$$N_2O_5 + 2NaHCO_3 \longrightarrow 2NaNO_3 + 2CO_2 + H_2O$$

$$KClO_3 + 3HNO_2 \longrightarrow KCl + 3HNO_3$$

Which one is a redox reaction? For the redox reaction, which compound is oxidized and which is reduced? (*Hint:* How is redox defined using oxidation numbers?)

6.9 | Chlorine dioxide, ClO_2, is used to kill bacteria in the dairy industry, meat industry, and other food and beverage industry applications. It is unstable, but can be made by the following reaction:

$$Cl_2 + 2NaClO_2 \longrightarrow 2ClO_2 + 2NaCl$$

Identify the substances oxidized and reduced, as well as the oxidizing and reducing agents in the reaction.

6.10 | When hydrogen peroxide is used as an antiseptic, it kills bacteria by oxidizing them. When the H_2O_2 serves as an oxidizing agent, which product might be formed from it, O_2 or H_2O? Why?

6.11 | Burning methane in oxygen gives carbon dioxide and water according to the following reaction:

$$CH_4 + 2O_2 \longrightarrow CO_2 + 2H_2O$$

What species is being oxidized and what species is being reduced? Identify the reducing agent and the oxidizing agent.

6.2 | Balancing Redox Equations

Many redox reactions take place in aqueous solution and many of these involve ions. An example is the reaction of laundry bleach with substances in the wash water. The active ingredient in the bleach is hypochlorite ion, OCl^-, which is the oxidizing agent in these reactions. To study redox reactions, it is often helpful to write the ionic and net ionic equations, just as we did in our analysis of metathesis reactions earlier in Chapter 5. In addition, one of the easiest ways to balance equations for redox reactions is to follow a procedure called the ion–electron method.

The Ion–Electron Method: A Divide and Conquer Approach

■ Equations for redox reactions are often more complex than those for metathesis reactions and can be difficult to balance by inspection. The ion–electron method provides a systematic procedure for balancing redox equations.

■ For simplicity, we are using H^+ to stand for H_3O^+ throughout our discussions in this chapter.

In the **ion–electron method**, we divide the oxidation and reduction processes into individual equations called **half-reactions** that are balanced separately. Each half-reaction is made to obey *both* criteria for a balanced ionic equation: *both atoms and charge have to balance.* Then, we combine the balanced half-reactions to obtain the fully balanced net ionic equation.

In balancing the half-reactions, we must take into account that for many redox reactions in aqueous solutions, H^+ or OH^- ions play an important role, as do water molecules. For example, when solutions of $K_2Cr_2O_7$ and $FeSO_4$ are mixed, the acidity of the mixture decreases as dichromate ion, $Cr_2O_7^{2-}$, oxidizes Fe^{2+} (Figure 6.2). This is because the reaction uses up H^+ as a reactant and produces H_2O as a product. In other reactions, OH^- is consumed, while in still others, H_2O is a reactant. Another fact is that in many cases the products (or even the reactants) of a redox reaction will differ depending on the acidity of the solution. For example, in an acidic solution, MnO_4^- is reduced to the Mn^{2+} ion, but in a neutral or slightly basic solution, the reduction product is insoluble the MnO_2.

Figure 6.2 | **A redox reaction taking place in an acidic solution.** A solution of $K_2Cr_2O_7$ oxidizes Fe^{2+} to Fe^{3+} in an acidic solution, while the orange dichromate ion is reduced to Cr^{3+}. *(Peter Lerman)*

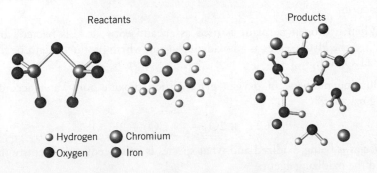

Reactants   Products

● Hydrogen   ● Chromium
● Oxygen   ● Iron

Because of these factors, redox reactions are generally carried out in solutions containing a substantial excess of either acid or base, so before we can apply the ion–electron method, we have to know whether the reaction occurs in an acidic or a basic solution. (This information will always be given to you in this book.)

Balancing Redox Equations in Acidic Solutions

As you just learned, $Cr_2O_7^{2-}$ reacts with Fe^{2+} in an acidic solution to give Cr^{3+} and Fe^{3+} as products. This information permits us to write the **skeleton equation**, which shows only the ions (or molecules) involved in the redox changes. We will leave out the spectator ions, K^+ and SO_4^{2-}, since they do not react in this redox reaction.

$$Cr_2O_7^{2-} + Fe^{2+} \longrightarrow Cr^{3+} + Fe^{3+}$$

1 skeleton equation

2 balance the atom number

3. balance the charge

We then proceed through the steps described below to find the balanced equation. As you will see, the ion–electron method will tell us how H^+ and H_2O are involved in the reaction; we don't need to know this in advance.

Step 1. ***Divide the skeleton equation into half-reactions.*** We choose one of the reactants, $Cr_2O_7^{2-}$, and write it at the left of an arrow. On the right, we write what $Cr_2O_7^{2-}$ changes to, which is Cr^{3+}. This gives us the beginnings of one half-reaction. For the second half-reaction, we write the other reactant, Fe^{2+}, on the left and the other product, Fe^{3+}, on the right. *Notice that we are careful to use the complete formulas for the ions that appear in the skeleton equation.* Except for hydrogen and oxygen, the same elements must appear on both sides of a given half-reaction.

$$Cr_2O_7^{2-} \longrightarrow Cr^{3+}$$
$$Fe^{2+} \longrightarrow Fe^{3+}$$

Step 2. ***Balance atoms other than H and O.*** There are two Cr atoms on the left and only one on the right, so we place a coefficient of 2 in front of Cr^{3+}. The second half-reaction is already balanced in terms of atoms, so we leave it as is.

$$Cr_2O_7^{2-} \longrightarrow 2Cr^{3+}$$
$$Fe^{2+} \longrightarrow Fe^{3+}$$

■ Many students tend to forget this step. If you do, you may end up in trouble later on.

Step 3. ***Balance oxygen by adding H_2O to the side that needs O.*** There are seven oxygen atoms on the left of the first half-reaction and none on the right. Therefore, we add $7H_2O$ to the right side of the first half-reaction to balance the oxygens. (There is no oxygen imbalance in the second half-reaction, so there's nothing to do there.)

$$Cr_2O_7^{2-} \longrightarrow 2Cr^{3+} + 7H_2O$$
$$Fe^{2+} \longrightarrow Fe^{3+}$$

■ We use H_2O, not O or O_2, to balance oxygen atoms, because H_2O is what is actually reacting or being produced in the solution.

The oxygen atoms now balance, but we've created an imbalance in hydrogen. We address that issue next.

Step 4. ***Balance hydrogen by adding H^+ to the side that needs H.*** After adding the water, we see that the first half-reaction has 14 hydrogens on the right and none on the left. To balance hydrogen, we add $14H^+$ to the left side of the half-reaction. When you do this step (or others) *be careful to write the charges on the ions.* If they are omitted, you will not obtain a balanced equation in the end.

$$14H^+ + Cr_2O_7^{2-} \longrightarrow 2Cr^{3+} + 7H_2O$$
$$Fe^{2+} \longrightarrow Fe^{3+}$$

Now each half-reaction is balanced in terms of atoms. Next, we will balance the charge.

Step 5. ***Balance the charge by adding electrons.*** First, we compute the net electrical charge on each side. For the first half-reaction we have

$$\underbrace{14H^+ + Cr_2O_7^{2-}}_{\text{Net charge} = (14+) + (2-) = 12+} \longrightarrow \underbrace{2Cr^{3+} + 7H_2O}_{\text{Net charge} = 2(3+) + 0 = 6+}$$

The algebraic difference between the net charges on the two sides equals the number of electrons that must be added to the more positive (or less negative) side. In this instance, we must add $6e^-$ to the left side of the half-reaction.

$$6e^- + 14H^+ + Cr_2O_7^{2-} \longrightarrow 2Cr^{3+} + 7H_2O$$

This half-reaction is now complete; it is balanced in terms of both atoms and charge. (We can check this by recalculating the charge on both sides.)

To balance the other half-reaction, we add one electron to the right.

$$Fe^{2+} \longrightarrow Fe^{3+} + e^-$$

Now this reaction is balanced for both mass and charge.

Step 6. ***Make the number of electrons gained equal to the number lost and then add the two half-reactions.*** At this point we have the two balanced half-reactions

$$6e^- + 14H^+ + Cr_2O_7^{2-} \longrightarrow 2Cr^{3+} + 7H_2O$$
$$Fe^{2+} \longrightarrow Fe^{3+} + e^-$$

Six electrons are gained in the first, but only one is lost in the second. Therefore, before combining the two equations we multiply all of the coefficients of the second half-reaction by 6.

$$6e^- + 14H^+ + Cr_2O_7^{2-} \longrightarrow 2Cr^{3+} + 7H_2O$$
$$6(Fe^{2+} \longrightarrow Fe^{3+} + e^-)$$

$$\text{(Sum)}\ 6e^- + 14H^+ + Cr_2O_7^{2-} + 6Fe^{2+} \longrightarrow 2Cr^{3+} + 7H_2O + 6Fe^{3+} + 6e^-$$

■ Because we know the electrons will cancel, we really don't have to carry them down into the combined equation. We've done so here just for emphasis.

Step 7. ***Cancel anything that is the same on both sides.*** This is the final step. Six electrons cancel from both sides to give the final balanced equation.

$$14H^+ + Cr_2O_7^{2-} + 6Fe^{2+} \longrightarrow 2Cr^{3+} + 7H_2O + 6Fe^{3+}$$

Notice that both the charge and the atoms balance.

In some reactions, after adding the two half-reactions you may have H_2O or H^+ on both sides—for example, $6H_2O$ on the left and $2H_2O$ on the right. Cancel as many as you can. Thus,

$$\ldots + 6H_2O \ldots \longrightarrow \ldots + 2H_2O \ldots$$

reduces to

$$\ldots + 4H_2O \ldots \longrightarrow \ldots$$

The following is a summary of the steps we've followed for balancing an equation for a redox reaction in an acidic solution. If you don't skip any steps and you perform them in the order given, you will always obtain a properly balanced equation.

TOOLS

Ion–electron method for acidic solutions

■ At both Steps 5 and 7, check that the equations are balanced for both mass and charge.

Ion–Electron Method—Acidic Solution
Step 1. Divide the equation into two half-reactions.
Step 2. Balance atoms other than H and O.
Step 3. Balance O by adding H_2O.
Step 4. Balance H by adding H^+.
Step 5. Balance net charge by adding e^-.
Step 6. Make e^- gain equal e^- loss; then add half-reactions.
Step 7. Cancel anything that's the same on both sides.

Example 6.6
Using the Ion–Electron Method

Balance the following equation:

$$MnO_4^- + H_2SO_3 \longrightarrow SO_4^{2-} + Mn^{2+}$$

The reaction occurs in an acidic solution.

■ **Analysis:** In using the ion–electron method, there's not much to analyze. It's necessary to know the steps and to follow them in sequence.

■ **Assembling the Tools:** Follow the seven steps of the ion–electron method for acidic solutions to balance the equation.

■ **Solution:** We follow the steps given above.

Step 1. Divide the skeleton equation into two half-reactions.

$$MnO_4^- \longrightarrow Mn^{2+}$$

$$H_2SO_3 \longrightarrow SO_4^{2-}$$

Step 2. Balance atoms other than H and O. There is nothing to do for this step. All the atoms except H and O are already in balance.

Step 3. Add H_2O to balance oxygens.

$$MnO_4^- \longrightarrow Mn^{2+} + 4H_2O$$

$$H_2O + H_2SO_3 \longrightarrow SO_4^{2-}$$

balance atom,
add H₂O & H⁺
↓
balance the charge of half-reactions
↓
balance the electron loss and gain
of the combined equation
↓
Cancel the same thing
↓
get the final equation

Step 4. Add H^+ to balance H.

$$8H^+ + MnO_4^- \longrightarrow Mn^{2+} + 4H_2O$$

$$H_2O + H_2SO_3 \longrightarrow SO_4^{2-} + 4H^+$$

Step 5. Balance the charge by adding electrons to the more positive side.

$$5e^- + 8H^+ + MnO_4^- \longrightarrow Mn^{2+} + 4H_2O$$

$$H_2O + H_2SO_3 \longrightarrow SO_4^{2-} + 4H^+ + 2e^-$$

Step 6. Make electron loss equal to electron gain, then add the half-reactions.

$$2(5e^- + 8H^+ + MnO_4^- \longrightarrow Mn^{2+} + 4H_2O)$$

$$5(H_2O + H_2SO_3 \longrightarrow SO_4^{2-} + 4H^+ + 2e^-)$$

$$10e^- + 16H^+ + 2MnO_4^- + 5H_2O + 5H_2SO_3 \longrightarrow$$
$$2Mn^{2+} + 8H_2O + 5SO_4^{2-} + 20H^+ + 10e^-$$

Step 7. Cancel $10e^-$, $16H^+$, and $5H_2O$ from both sides. The final equation is

$$2MnO_4^- + 5H_2SO_3 \longrightarrow 2Mn^{2+} + 3H_2O + 5SO_4^{2-} + 4H^+$$

■ **Is the Answer Reasonable?** The check involves *two* steps. First, we check that each side of the equation has the same number of atoms of each element, which it does. Second, we check to be sure that the net charge is the same on both sides. On the left we have $2MnO_4^-$ with a net charge of 2−. On the right we have $2Mn^{2+}$ and $4H^+$ (total charge = 8+) along with $5SO_4^{2-}$ (total charge = 10−), so the net charge is also 2−. Having both atoms *and* charge in balance makes it a balanced equation and confirms that we've worked the problem correctly.

Practice Exercises

6.12 | Explain why the following equation is not balanced. Balance it using the ion–electron method. (*Hint:* What are the criteria for a balanced ionic equation?)

$$Al + Cu^{2+} \longrightarrow Al^{3+} + Cu$$

6.13 | The element technetium (atomic number 43) is radioactive and one of its isotopes, ^{99}Tc, is used in medicine for diagnostic imaging. The isotope is usually obtained in the form of the pertechnetate anion, TcO_4^-, but its use sometimes requires the technetium to be in a lower oxidation state. Reduction can be carried out using Sn^{2+} in an acidic solution. The skeleton equation is

$$TcO_4^- + Sn^{2+} \longrightarrow Tc^{4+} + Sn^{4+} \qquad \text{(acidic solution)}$$

Balance the equation by the ion–electron method.

6.14 | What is the balanced net ionic equation for the following reaction in an acidic solution?

$$Cu + NO_3^- \longrightarrow Cu^{2+} + N_2O$$

6.15 | When pyridine (C_5H_5N), a compound used in the manufacturing of drugs and vitamins, is burned, carbon dioxide, nitrogen dioxide, and water are formed. Balance the following equation by the ion–electron method.

$$C_5H_5N + O_2 \longrightarrow CO_2 + NO_2 + H_2O$$

Balancing Redox Equations for Basic Solutions

In a basic solution, the concentration of H^+ is very small; the dominant species are H_2O and OH^-. Strictly speaking, these should be used to balance the half-reactions. However, the simplest way to obtain a balanced equation for a basic solution is to first *pretend* that the solution is acidic. We balance the equation using the seven steps just described, and then we use a simple three-step procedure described below to convert the equation to the correct form for a basic solution. The conversion uses the fact that H^+ and OH^- react in a 1-to-1 ratio to give H_2O.

Ion–electron method for basic solutions

■ Again, checking that the equation is balanced for both mass and charge is essential at the end of this process.

Additional Steps in the Ion–Electron Method for Basic Solutions
Step 8. Add to *both* sides of the equation the same number of OH^- as there are H^+.
Step 9. Combine H^+ and OH^- to form H_2O.
Step 10. Cancel any H_2O that you can.

As an example, suppose we wanted to balance the following equation for a basic solution.

$$SO_3^{2-} + MnO_4^- \longrightarrow SO_4^{2-} + MnO_2$$

Following Steps 1 through 7 for acidic solutions gives

$$2H^+ + 3SO_3^{2-} + 2MnO_4^- \longrightarrow 3SO_4^{2-} + 2MnO_2 + H_2O$$

Conversion of this equation to one appropriate for a basic solution proceeds as follows.

Step 8. *Add to **both** sides of the equation the same number of OH^- as there are H^+.*
The equation for acidic solution has $2H^+$ on the left, so we add $2OH^-$ to *each* side. This gives

$$2OH^- + 2H^+ + 3SO_3^{2-} + 2MnO_4^- \longrightarrow 3SO_4^{2-} + 2MnO_2 + H_2O + 2OH^-$$

Step 9. ***Combine*** H^+ ***and*** OH^- ***to form*** H_2O. The left side has $2OH^-$ and $2H^+$, which become $2H_2O$. So in place of $2OH^- + 2H^+$ we write $2H_2O$.

$$2OH^- + 2H^+ + 3SO_3^{2-} + 2MnO_4^- \longrightarrow 3SO_4^{2-} + 2MnO_2 + H_2O + 2OH^-$$

$$2H_2O + 3SO_3^{2-} + 2MnO_4^- \longrightarrow 3SO_4^{2-} + 2MnO_2 + H_2O + 2OH^-$$

Step 10. ***Cancel any*** H_2O ***that you can.*** In this equation, one H_2O can be eliminated from both sides. The final equation, balanced for basic solution, is

$$H_2O + 3SO_3^{2-} + 2MnO_4^- \longrightarrow 3SO_4^{2-} + 2MnO_2 + 2OH^-$$

Practice Exercises

6.16 | Consider the following half-reaction balanced for an acidic solution:

$$2H_2O + SO_2 \longrightarrow SO_4^{2-} + 4H^+ + 2e^-$$

What is the balanced half-reaction for a basic solution? (*Hint:* Remember that H^+ and OH^- react to form H_2O.)

6.17 | Balance the following equation for a basic solution.

$$MnO_4^- + C_2O_4^{2-} \longrightarrow MnO_2 + CO_3^{2-}$$

6.18 | The reaction of Br_2 with itself can be carried out in basic solutions.

$$Br_2 \longrightarrow BrO_3^- + Br^-$$

Balance the equation in a basic solution.

6.19 | Alkaline batteries last longer than if the reaction were carried out under acidic conditions. The reaction for alkaline batteries is

$$Zn + MnO_2 \longrightarrow ZnO + Mn_2O_3$$

Balance the equation in a basic solution.

6.3 | Acids as Oxidizing Agents

Earlier you learned that one of the properties of acids is that they react with bases. Another important property is their ability to react with certain metals. These are redox reactions in which the metal is oxidized and the acid is reduced. However, in these reactions, the part of the acid that's reduced depends on the composition of the acid itself as well as on the metal.

When a piece of zinc is placed into a solution of hydrochloric acid, bubbling is observed and the zinc gradually dissolves (Figure 6.3). The chemical reaction is

$$Zn(s) + 2HCl(aq) \longrightarrow ZnCl_2(aq) + H_2(g)$$

for which the net ionic equation is

$$Zn(s) + 2H^+(aq) \longrightarrow Zn^{2+}(aq) + H_2(g)$$

In this reaction, zinc is oxidized and hydrogen ions are reduced. Stated another way, *the* H^+ *of the acid is the oxidizing agent.*

Many metals react with acids just as zinc does—by being oxidized by hydrogen ions. In these reactions a metal salt and gaseous hydrogen are the products.

Figure 6.3 | **Zinc reacts with hydrochloric acid.** Bubbles of hydrogen are formed when a solution of hydrochloric acid comes in contact with metallic zinc. The same reaction takes place if hydrochloric acid is spilled on galvanized (zinc-coated) steel. In the molecular view (not balanced), the hydronium ions react with the zinc metal atoms (dark gray spheres). Two hydrogen ions gain two electrons from the metal atom and form a hydrogen molecule, and the zinc is oxidized to a cation with a 2+ charge. *(Richard Megna/Fundamental Photographs)*

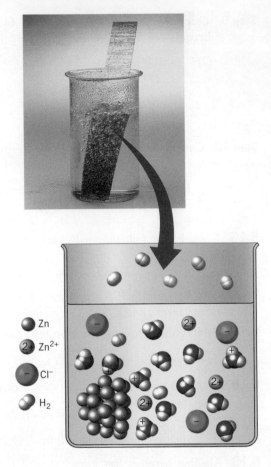

Zn
Zn^{2+}
Cl^-
H_2

Metals that are able to react with acids such as HCl and H_2SO_4 to give hydrogen gas are said to be *more active* than hydrogen (H_2). For other metals, however, hydrogen ions are not powerful enough to cause their oxidation. Copper, for example, is significantly less reactive than zinc or iron, and H^+ cannot oxidize it. Copper is an example of a metal that is *less active* than H_2.

The Anion Determines the Oxidizing Power of an Acid

Hydrochloric acid contains H_3O^+ ions (which is sometimes abbreviated as H^+) and Cl^- ions. The hydronium ion in hydrochloric acid can be an oxidizing agent because it can be reduced to H_2. However, the Cl^- ion in the solution has no tendency at all to be an oxidizing agent, so in a solution of HCl the only oxidizing agent is H_3O^+. The same applies to dilute solutions of sulfuric acid, H_2SO_4.

The hydrogen ion in water is actually a rather poor oxidizing agent, so hydrochloric acid and sulfuric acid have rather poor oxidizing abilities. They are often called **nonoxidizing acids,** even though their hydronium ions are able to oxidize certain metals. Therefore, in a nonoxidizing acid, the *anion* of the acid is a weaker oxidizing agent than H_3O^+ and the anion of the acid is more difficult to reduce than H_3O^+. Some acids contain anions that are stronger oxidizing agents than H_3O^+ and are called **oxidizing acids.** (See Table 6.2.)

■ The strongest oxidizing agent in a solution of a "nonoxidizing" acid is H^+.

Nitrate Ion as an Oxidizing Agent

Nitric acid, HNO_3, ionizes in water to give H^+ and NO_3^- ions. In this solution, the nitrate ion is a more powerful oxidizing agent than the hydrogen ion. This makes it able to oxidize metals that H^+ cannot, such as copper and silver. For example, the molecular equation for the reaction of concentrated HNO_3 with copper, shown in Figure 6.4, is

$$Cu(s) + 4HNO_3(aq) \longrightarrow Cu(NO_3)_2(aq) + 2NO_2(g) + 2H_2O$$

Table 6.2	Nonoxidizing and Oxidizing Acids	
Nonoxidizing Acids		
$HCl(aq)$		
$H_2SO_4(aq)^a$		
$H_3PO_4(aq)$		
Most organic acids (e.g., $HC_2H_3O_2$)		
Oxidizing Acids	**Conditions**	**Reduction Reaction**
HNO_3	Concentrated	$NO_3^- + 2H^+ + e^- \longrightarrow NO_2(g) + H_2O$
	Dilute	$NO_3^- + 4H^+ + 3e^- \longrightarrow NO(g) + 2H_2O$
	Very dilute, with strong reducing agent	$NO_3^- + 10H^+ + 8e^- \longrightarrow NH_4^+ + 3H_2O$
H_2SO_4	Hot, concentrated, with strong reducing agent	$SO_4^{2-} + 10H^+ + 8e^- \longrightarrow H_2S(g) + 4H_2O$
	Hot, concentrated	$SO_4^{2-} + 4H^+ + 2e^- \longrightarrow SO_2(g) + 2H_2O$

$^a H_2SO_4$ is a nonoxidizing acid when cold and dilute.

TOOLS

Oxidizing and nonoxidizing acids

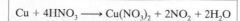

$$Cu + 4HNO_3 \longrightarrow Cu(NO_3)_2 + 2NO_2 + 2H_2O$$

Figure 6.4 | **The reaction of copper with concentrated nitric acid.** A copper penny reacts vigorously with concentrated nitric acid, as this sequence of photographs shows. The dark red-brown vapors are nitrogen dioxide, the same gas that gives smog its characteristic color. The atomic view shows the copper in the solid, the addition of nitric acid, and finally, the formation of the copper nitrate, nitrogen dioxide as a gas, and water molecules. *(Michael Watson)*

If we convert this to a net ionic equation and then assign oxidation numbers, we can see that NO_3^- is the oxidizing agent and Cu is the reducing agent.

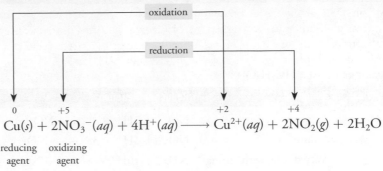

$$Cu(s) + 2NO_3^-(aq) + 4H^+(aq) \longrightarrow Cu^{2+}(aq) + 2NO_2(g) + 2H_2O$$

Notice that in this reaction, *no hydrogen gas is formed*. The H^+ ions of the HNO_3 are an essential part of the reaction, but they just become part of water molecules without a change in oxidation number.

The nitrogen-containing product formed in the reduction of nitric acid depends on the concentration of the acid and the reducing power of the metal. With *concentrated* nitric acid, nitrogen dioxide, NO_2, is often the reduction product. With *dilute* nitric acid, the product is often nitrogen monoxide (also called nitric oxide), NO, instead. Copper, for example, reacts as follows:

Concentrated HNO_3

$$Cu(s) + 4H^+(aq) + 2NO_3^-(aq) \longrightarrow Cu^{2+}(aq) + 2NO_2(g) + 2H_2O$$

Dilute HNO_3

$$3Cu(s) + 8H^+(aq) + 2NO_3^-(aq) \longrightarrow 3Cu^{2+}(aq) + 2NO(g) + 4H_2O$$

Nitric acid is a very effective oxidizing acid. All metals except the most unreactive ones, such as platinum and gold, are attacked by it. Nitric acid also does a good job of oxidizing organic compounds, so it is wise to be especially careful when working with this acid in the laboratory. Very serious accidents have occurred when inexperienced people have used concentrated nitric acid around organic substances.

■ Nitric acid causes severe skin burns, so be careful when you work with it in the laboratory. If you spill any on your skin, wash it off immediately and seek the help of your lab teacher.

Hot Concentrated Sulfuric Acid: Another Oxidizing Acid

In a dilute solution, the sulfate ion of sulfuric acid has little tendency to serve as an oxidizing agent. However, if the sulfuric acid is both concentrated and hot, it becomes a fairly potent oxidizer. For example, copper is not bothered by cool dilute H_2SO_4, but it is attacked by hot concentrated H_2SO_4 according to the following equation:

$$Cu + 2H_2SO_4(\text{hot, conc.}) \longrightarrow CuSO_4 + SO_2 + 2H_2O$$

Because of this oxidizing ability, hot concentrated sulfuric acid can be very dangerous. The liquid is viscous and can stick to the skin, causing severe burns.

Practice Exercises

6.20 | Write the balanced half-reactions for the reaction of zinc with hydrogen ions. (*Hint:* Be sure to place the electrons on the correct sides of the half-reactions.)

6.21 | Write balanced molecular, ionic, and net ionic equations for the reaction of hydrochloric acid with (a) magnesium and (b) aluminum. (Both are oxidized by hydrogen ions.)

6.22 | Hot concentrated sulfuric acid is reduced to hydrogen sulfide by hydroiodic acid, which forms iodine. Balance the equation that describes the reaction.

$$H_2SO_4 + HI \longrightarrow H_2S + I_2$$

6.4 | Redox Reactions of Metals

The formation of hydrogen gas in the reaction of a metal with an acid is a special case of a more general phenomenon—one element displacing (pushing out) another element from a compound by means of a redox reaction. In the case of a metal–acid reaction, it is the metal that displaces hydrogen from the acid, changing $2H^+$ to H_2.

Another reaction of this same general type occurs when one metal displaces another metal from its compounds, and is illustrated by the experiment shown in Figure 6.5. Here we see a brightly polished strip of metallic zinc that is dipped into a solution of copper sulfate. After the zinc is in the solution for a while, a reddish brown deposit of metallic copper forms on the zinc, and if the solution were analyzed, we would find that it now contains zinc ions, as well as some remaining unreacted copper ions.

Figure 6.5 | **The reaction of zinc with copper ion.** (*Left*) A piece of shiny zinc next to a beaker containing a copper sulfate solution. (*Center*) When the zinc is placed in the solution, copper ions are reduced to the free metal while the zinc dissolves. (*Right*) After a while the zinc becomes coated with a red-brown layer of copper. Notice that the solution is a lighter blue than before, showing that some of the copper ions have left the solution. (*Michael Watson*)

The results of this experiment can be summarized by the following net ionic equation:

$$Zn(s) + Cu^{2+}(aq) \longrightarrow Cu(s) + Zn^{2+}(aq)$$

■ Sulfate ion is a spectator ion in this reaction.

Metallic zinc is oxidized as copper ion is reduced. In the process, Zn^{2+} ions have taken the place of the Cu^{2+} ions, so a solution of copper sulfate is changed to a solution of zinc sulfate. An atomic-level view of what's happening at the surface of the zinc during the reaction is depicted in Figure 6.6. A reaction such as this, in which one element replaces another in a compound, is sometimes called a **single replacement reaction**.

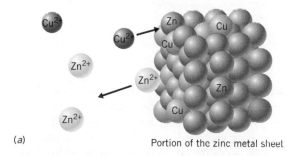

(a)   Portion of the zinc metal sheet

Two electrons are transferred from the zinc atom to the copper ion.

The result is a zinc ion and a copper atom.

(b)

Figure 6.6 | **An atomic-level view of the reaction of copper ions with zinc.** (*a*) Copper ions (blue) collide with the zinc surface, where they pick up electrons from zinc atoms (gray). The zinc atoms become zinc ions (yellow) and enter the solution. The copper ions become copper atoms (red-brown) and stick to the surface of the zinc. (For clarity, the water molecules of the solution and the sulfate ions are not shown.) (*b*) A close-up view of the exchange of electrons that leads to the reaction.

Activity Series of Metals

In the reaction of zinc with copper ion, the more "active" zinc displaces the less "active" copper in a compound, where we have used the word *active* to mean "easily oxidized." This is actually a general phenomenon: *an element that is more easily oxidized will displace one that is less easily oxidized from its compounds.* By comparing the relative ease of oxidation of various metals using experiments like the one pictured in Figure 6.5, we can arrange metals in order of their ease of oxidation. This yields the **activity series** shown in Table 6.3. In this table, metals at the bottom are more easily oxidized (are more active) than those at the top. *This means that a given element will be displaced from its compounds by any metal below it in the table.*

Activity series of metal

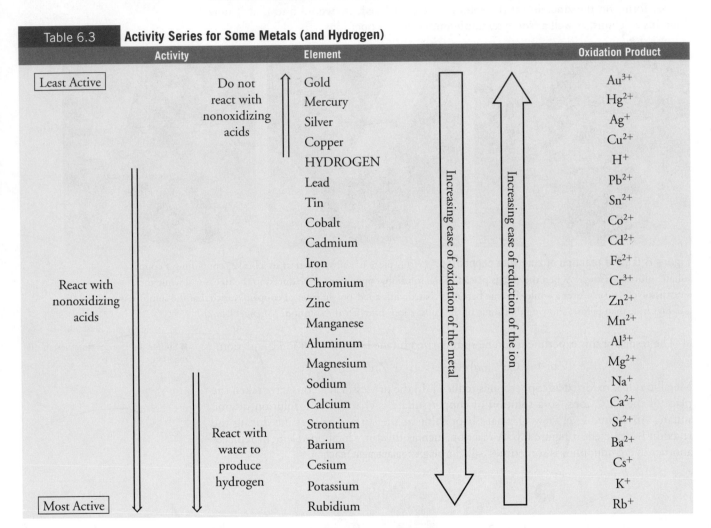

Table 6.3	Activity Series for Some Metals (and Hydrogen)		
Activity		**Element**	**Oxidation Product**
Least Active	Do not react with nonoxidizing acids	Gold	Au^{3+}
		Mercury	Hg^{2+}
		Silver	Ag^+
		Copper	Cu^{2+}
		HYDROGEN	H^+
React with nonoxidizing acids		Lead	Pb^{2+}
		Tin	Sn^{2+}
		Cobalt	Co^{2+}
		Cadmium	Cd^{2+}
		Iron	Fe^{2+}
		Chromium	Cr^{3+}
		Zinc	Zn^{2+}
		Manganese	Mn^{2+}
		Aluminum	Al^{3+}
		Magnesium	Mg^{2+}
		Sodium	Na^+
		Calcium	Ca^{2+}
		Strontium	Sr^{2+}
	React with water to produce hydrogen	Barium	Ba^{2+}
		Cesium	Cs^+
		Potassium	K^+
Most Active		Rubidium	Rb^+

Increasing ease of oxidation of the metal

Increasing ease of reduction of the ion

Notice that we have included hydrogen in the activity series. Metals below hydrogen in the series can displace hydrogen from solutions containing H^+. These are the metals that are capable of reacting with nonoxidizing acids. On the other hand, metals above hydrogen in the table do not react with acids having H^+ as the strongest oxidizing agent.

Metals at the very bottom of the table are very easily oxidized and are extremely strong reducing agents. They are so reactive, in fact, that they are able to reduce the hydrogen in water molecules. Sodium, for example, reacts vigorously (see Figure 6.7).

$$2Na(s) + 2H_2O \longrightarrow H_2(g) + 2NaOH(aq)$$

For metals below hydrogen in the activity series, there's a parallel between the ease of oxidation of the metal and the speed with which it reacts with H^+. For example, in

Figure 6.7 | **Metallic sodium reacts violently with water.** The heat of the reaction ignites the sodium metal, which can be seen burning and sending sparks from the surface of the water. In the reaction, sodium is oxidized to Na$^+$ and water molecules are reduced to give hydrogen gas and hydroxide ions. When the reaction is over, the solution contains sodium hydroxide. *(OPC, Inc.)*

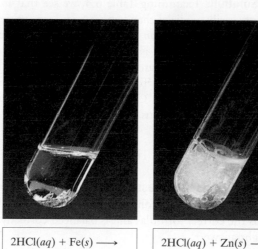

$$2HCl(aq) + Fe(s) \longrightarrow FeCl_2(aq) + H_2(g)$$

$$2HCl(aq) + Zn(s) \longrightarrow ZnCl_2(aq) + H_2(g)$$

$$2HCl(aq) + Mg(s) \longrightarrow MgCl_2(aq) + H_2(g)$$

Figure 6.8 | **The relative ease of oxidation of metals as demonstrated by their reaction with hydrogen ions of an acid.** The products are hydrogen gas and the metal ion in solution. All three test tubes contain HCl(*aq*) at the same concentration. The first also contains pieces of iron, the second, pieces of zinc, and the third, pieces of magnesium. Among these three metals, the ease of oxidation increases from iron to zinc to magnesium. *(OPC, Inc.)*

Figure 6.8, we see samples of iron, zinc, and magnesium reacting with solutions of hydrochloric acid. In each test tube the initial HCl concentration is the same, but we see that the magnesium reacts more rapidly than zinc, which reacts more rapidly than iron. You can see that this matches the order of reactivity in Table 6.3—namely, magnesium is more easily oxidized than zinc, which is more easily oxidized than iron.

Using the Activity Series to Predict Reactions

The activity series in Table 6.3 makes it possible to predict the outcome of single replacement redox reactions, as illustrated in Examples 6.7 and 6.8.

Example 6.7
Using the Activity Series

What will happen if an iron nail is dipped into a solution containing copper(II) sulfate? If a reaction occurs, write its molecular equation.

■**Analysis:** Before deciding what *will* happen, we have to consider, what *could* happen? If a chemical reaction were to occur, iron would have to react with the copper sulfate. A *metal* possibly reacting with the *salt of another metal?* This suggests the possibility of a single replacement reaction.

■**Assembling the Tools:** The tool we use to predict such reactions is the activity series of the metals in Table 6.3.

■ **Solution:** Examining Table 6.3, we see that iron is below copper. This means iron is more easily oxidized than copper, so we expect metallic iron to displace copper ions from the solution. *A reaction will occur.* (We've answered one part of the question.) The formula for copper(II) sulfate is $CuSO_4$. To write an equation for the reaction, we have to know the final oxidation state of the iron. In the table, this is indicated as +2, so the Fe atoms change to Fe^{2+} ions. To write the formula of the salt in the solution we pair Fe^{2+} with SO_4^{2-} to give $FeSO_4$. Copper(II) ions are reduced to copper atoms.

Our analysis told us that a reaction *will* occur and it also gave us the products, so the equation is

$$Fe(s) + CuSO_4(aq) \longrightarrow Cu(s) + FeSO_4(aq)$$

■ **Is the Answer Reasonable?** We can check the activity series again to be sure we've reached the correct conclusion, and we can check to be sure the equation we've written has the correct formulas and is balanced correctly. Doing this confirms that we've got the right answers.

CHEMISTRY OUTSIDE THE CLASSROOM | **6.1**

Polishing Silver—The Easy Way

Using an active metal to reduce a compound of a less active metal has a number of practical applications. One that is handy around the home is using aluminum to remove the tarnish from silver. Generally, silver tarnishes by a gradual reaction with hydrogen sulfide, present in very small amounts in the air. The product of the reaction is silver sulfide, Ag_2S, which is black and forms a dull film over the bright metal. Polishing a silver object using a mild abrasive restores the shine, but it also gradually removes silver from the object as the silver sulfide is rubbed away.

An alternative method, and one that requires little effort, involves lining the bottom of a sink with aluminum foil, adding warm water and detergent (which acts as an electrolyte), and then submerging the tarnished silver object in the detergent–water mixture and placing it in contact with the aluminum (Figure 1). In a short time, the silver sulfide is reduced, restoring the shine and depositing the freed silver metal on the object. As this happens, a small amount of the aluminum foil is oxidized and caused to dissolve. Besides requiring little physical effort, this silver polishing technique doesn't remove silver from the object being polished. Also, *the silver, considered a heavy metal, is being kept out of the water.*

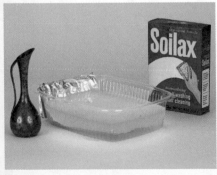 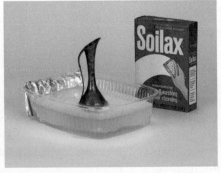 

(*a*)   (*b*)   (*c*)

Figure 1 Using aluminum to remove tarnish from silver. (*a*) A badly tarnished silver vase stands next to a container of detergent (Soilax) dissolved in water. The bottom of the container is lined with aluminum foil. (*b*) The vase, shown partly immersed in the detergent, rests on the aluminum foil. (*c*) After a short time, the vase is removed, rinsed with water, and wiped with a soft cloth. Where the vase was immersed in the liquid, much of the tarnish has been reduced to metallic silver. (*Andy Washnik*)

Example 6.8
Using the Activity Series

What happens if an iron nail is dipped into a solution of aluminum sulfate? If a reaction occurs, write the molecular equation.

■ **Analysis:** Once again, we have to realize that we're looking for a potential single replacement reaction.

■ **Assembling the Tools:** We will use the activity series of the metals in Table 6.3 as our tool to solve this problem.

■ **Solution:** Scanning the activity series, we see that aluminum metal is *more* easily oxidized than iron metal. This means that aluminum atoms would be able to displace iron ions from an iron compound. But it also means that iron atoms cannot displace aluminum ions from its compounds, and iron *atoms* plus aluminum *ions* are what we're given. Our analysis has told us that iron atoms will not reduce aluminum ions, so we must conclude that no reaction can occur.

$$Fe(s) + Al_2(SO_4)_3(aq) \longrightarrow \text{no reaction}$$

■ **Is the Answer Reasonable?** Checking the activity series again, we are confident we've come to the correct answer. In writing the equation, we've also been careful to correctly write the formula of aluminum sulfate.

6.23 | Suppose an aqueous mixture is prepared containing magnesium sulfate ($MgSO_4$), copper(II) sulfate ($CuSO_4$), metallic magnesium, and metallic copper. What reaction, if any, will occur? (*Hint:* What reactions could occur?)

6.24 | Write a chemical equation for the reaction that will occur, if any, when (a) aluminum metal is added to a solution of copper(II) chloride and (b) silver metal is added to a solution of magnesium sulfate. If no reaction will occur, write "no reaction" in place of the products.

Practice Exercises

6.5 | Molecular Oxygen as an Oxidizing Agent

Oxygen is a plentiful chemical; it's in the air and available to anyone who wants to use it, chemist or not. Furthermore, O_2 is a very reactive oxidizing agent, so its reactions have been well studied. When these reactions are rapid, with the evolution of light and heat, we call them **combustion**. The products of reactions with oxygen are generally oxides—*molecular oxides* when oxygen reacts with nonmetals and *ionic oxides* when oxygen reacts with metals.

Oxidation of Organic Compounds

Experience has taught you that certain materials burn. For example, if you had to build a fire to keep warm, you no doubt would look for combustible materials like twigs, logs, or other pieces of wood to use as fuel. The car you drive is probably powered by the combustion of gasoline. Wood and gasoline are examples of substances or mixtures of substances that chemists call *organic compounds*—compounds whose structures are determined primarily by the linking together of carbon atoms. When organic compounds burn, the products of the reactions are usually easy to predict.

Hydrocarbons as Fuels
Fuels such as natural gas, gasoline, kerosene, heating oil, and diesel fuel are examples of *hydrocarbons*—compounds containing only the elements carbon and hydrogen. Natural gas is composed principally of methane, CH_4. Gasoline is a mixture of hydrocarbons, the

most familiar of which is octane, C_8H_{18}. Kerosene, heating oil, and diesel fuel are mixtures of hydrocarbons in which the molecules contain even more atoms of carbon and hydrogen. When hydrocarbons are burned in air, besides water, a mixture of carbon containing products are formed, such as carbon dioxide, carbon monoxide, and carbon as soot. If the conditions are carefully managed, the products can be controlled.

*When hydrocarbons burn in a **plentiful** supply of oxygen, the products of combustion are mainly carbon dioxide and water.* Thus, methane and octane combine with oxygen according to the equations

$$CH_4 + 2O_2 \longrightarrow CO_2 + 2H_2O$$
$$2C_8H_{18} + 25O_2 \longrightarrow 16CO_2 + 18H_2O$$

Many people don't realize that water is one of the products of the combustion of hydrocarbons, even though they have seen evidence for it. Perhaps you've seen clouds of condensed water vapor coming from the exhaust pipes of automobiles on cold winter days, or you may have noticed that shortly after you first start a car, drops of water fall from the exhaust pipe. This is water that has been formed during the combustion of the gasoline. Similarly, the "smokestacks" of power stations release clouds of condensed water vapor (Figure 6.9), which is often mistaken for smoke from fires used to generate power to make electricity. Actually, many of today's power stations produce very little smoke because they burn natural gas instead of coal.

Figure 6.9 | **Water is a product of the combustion of hydrocarbons.** Here we see clouds of condensed water vapor coming from the stacks of an oil-fired electric generating plant during the winter. *(PictureNet/©Corbis)*

TOOLS

Hydrocarbon combustion with a limited supply of O_2

When the supply of oxygen is somewhat restricted during the combustion of a hydrocarbon, some of the carbon is converted to carbon monoxide. The formation of CO is a pollution problem associated with the use of gasoline engines, as you may know.

$$2CH_4 + 3O_2 \longrightarrow 2CO + 4H_2O \qquad \text{(in a limited oxygen supply)}$$

TOOLS

Hydrocarbon combustion with an extremely limited supply of O_2

When the oxygen supply is extremely limited, only the hydrogen of a hydrocarbon mixture is converted to the oxide (water) and the carbon atoms emerge as elemental carbon. For example, when a candle burns, the fuel is a high-molecular-weight hydrocarbon (e.g., $C_{20}H_{42}$) and incomplete combustion forms tiny particles of carbon that glow brightly, creating the candle's light. If a cold surface is held in the flame, the unburned carbon deposits, as seen in Figure 6.10.

An important commercial reaction is the incomplete combustion of methane in a very limited oxygen supply, which follows the equation

$$CH_4 + O_2 \longrightarrow C + 2H_2O$$
(in a very limited oxygen supply)

The carbon that forms is very finely divided and would be called *soot* by almost anyone observing the reaction. Nevertheless, such soot has considerable commercial value when collected and marketed under the name *lampblack*. This sooty form of carbon is used to manufacture inks and tons of it are used in the production of rubber tires, where it serves as a binder and a filler. When soot from incomplete combustion is released into air, its tiny particles constitute a component of air pollution referred to as *particulates,* which contribute to the haziness of smog.

■ Hydrocarbon combustion with a plentiful supply of O_2

■ You can tell whether smoke or water vapor is coming from a smokestack. If the cloud is steam, there will be a clear region just above the smokestack. If the emissions are smoke, no clear region will exist.

■ In all three of these reactions of hydrocarbons with oxygen, some of the other carbon products are formed. However, we will assume that just one product is formed: for a plentiful supply of oxygen, carbon dioxide; for a limited supply of oxygen, carbon monoxide; and for an extremely limited supply of oxygen, carbon.

■ This finely divided form of carbon is also called *carbon black*.

Figure 6.10 | **Incomplete combustion of a hydrocarbon.** The bright yellow color of a candle flame is caused by glowing particles of elemental carbon. Here we see that a black deposit of carbon is formed when the flame contacts a cold porcelain surface. *(Andy Washnik)*

Combustion of Organic Compounds That Contain Oxygen

Earlier we mentioned that you might choose wood to build a fire. The chief combustible ingredient in wood is cellulose, a fibrous material that gives plants their structural strength. Cellulose is composed of the elements carbon, hydrogen, and oxygen. Each cellulose molecule consists of many small, identical groups of atoms that are linked together to form a very long molecule, although the lengths of the molecules differ. For this reason we cannot specify a molecular formula for cellulose. Instead, we use the empirical formula, $C_6H_{10}O_5$, which represents the small, repeating "building block" units in large cellulose molecules. When cellulose burns, the products are mainly carbon dioxide and water. The only difference between its reaction and the reaction of a hydrocarbon with oxygen is that some of the oxygen in the products comes from the cellulose.

$C_{12}H_{22}O_{11}$ sugar

$$C_6H_{10}O_5 + 6O_2 \longrightarrow 6CO_2 + 5H_2O$$

The complete combustion of all other organic compounds containing only carbon, hydrogen, and oxygen produces the same products, CO_2 and H_2O, and follows similar equations.

Burning Organic Compounds That Contain Sulfur

A major pollution problem is caused by the release into the atmosphere of sulfur dioxide formed by the combustion of fuels that contain sulfur or its compounds. *The products of the combustion of organic compounds of sulfur are carbon dioxide, water, and sulfur dioxide.* A typical reaction is

$$2C_2H_5SH + 9O_2 \longrightarrow 4CO_2 + 6H_2O + 2SO_2$$

A solution of sulfur dioxide in water is acidic, and when rain falls through polluted air it picks up SO_2 and becomes "acid rain." Some SO_2 is also oxidized to SO_3, which reacts with moisture to give H_2SO_4, making the acid rain even more acidic.

■ The formula for cellulose can be expressed as $(C_6H_{10}O_5)_n$, which indicates that the molecule contains the $C_6H_{10}O_5$ unit repeated some large number n times.

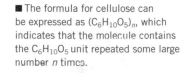 **TOOLS**

Combustion of an organic compound containing C, H, and O

■ These reactions can also be balanced using the ion–electron method, with oxygen going to water and the organic compound going to carbon dioxide, carbon monoxide, or carbon, depending on the amount of oxygen available.

 TOOLS

Combustion of an organic compound containing sulfur

6.25 | Write a balanced chemical equation for the combustion of candle wax, $C_{20}H_{42}$, in a very limited supply of oxygen. (*Hint:* What happens to methane under these conditions?)

6.26 | Write a balanced equation for the combustion of isoprene, C_5H_8, in an abundant supply of oxygen. Isoprene is emitted by trees and is used in the production of synthetic rubber.

6.27 | Ethanol, C_2H_5OH, is now mixed with gasoline, and the mixture is sold under the name *gasohol*. Write a chemical equation for the complete combustion of ethanol.

Practice Exercises

Figure 6.11 | **A flashbulb, before and after firing.** Fine magnesium wire in an atmosphere of oxygen fills the flashbulb at the left. After being used (*right*), the interior of the bulb is coated with a white film of magnesium oxide. *(Robert Capece)*

Reactions of Metals with Oxygen

We don't often think of metals as undergoing combustion, but have you ever lit a sparkler on the Fourth of July? The source of light is the reaction of the metal magnesium with oxygen. A close look at a fresh flashbulb reveals a fine web of thin magnesium wire within the glass envelope (see Figure 6.11). The wire is surrounded by an atmosphere of oxygen, a clear colorless gas. When the flashbulb is used, a small electric current surges through the thin wire, causing it to become hot enough to ignite, and it burns rapidly in the oxygen atmosphere. The equation for the reaction is

$$2Mg + O_2 \longrightarrow 2MgO$$

Most metals react directly with oxygen, although not so spectacularly, and usually we refer to the reaction as **corrosion** or **tarnishing** because the oxidation products dull the shiny metal surface. Iron, for example, is oxidized fairly easily, especially in the presence of moisture. As you know, under these conditions the iron corrodes—it rusts. Rust is a form of iron(III) oxide, Fe_2O_3, that also contains an appreciable amount of absorbed water. The formula for rust is therefore normally given as $Fe_2O_3 \cdot xH_2O$ to indicate its somewhat variable composition. Although the rusting of iron is a slow reaction, the combination of iron with oxygen can be speeded up if the metal is heated to a very high temperature under a stream of pure O_2 (see Figure 6.12).

An aluminum surface, unlike that of iron, is not noticeably dulled by the reaction of aluminum with oxygen. Aluminum is a common metal found around the home in uses ranging from aluminum foil to aluminum window frames, and it surely appears shiny. However, aluminum is a rather easily oxidized metal, as can be seen from its position in the activity series (Table 6.3). A *freshly* exposed surface of the metal does react very quickly with oxygen and becomes coated with a very thin film of aluminum oxide, Al_2O_3, so thin that it doesn't obscure the shininess of the metal beneath. Fortunately, the oxide coating adheres very tightly to the surface of the metal and makes it very difficult for additional oxygen to combine with the aluminum. Therefore, further oxidation of aluminum occurs very slowly. On the other hand, powdered aluminum, which has a large surface area, reacts violently when ignited and is part of the propellant in the booster rockets for the space shuttle.

Practice Exercises

6.28 | Write a balanced chemical equation for the reaction of molecular oxygen with strontium metal to form the oxide. (*Hint:* Strontium, Sr, is in the same group in the periodic table as calcium.)

6.29 | The oxide formed in the reaction shown in Figure 6.12 is iron(III) oxide. Write a balanced chemical equation for the reaction.

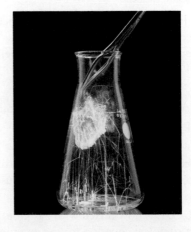

Figure 6.12 | **Hot steel wool burns in oxygen.** The reaction of hot steel wool with oxygen speeds up the oxidation process and the sparks and flames result. *(© 1993 Richard Megna/Fundamental Photographs)*

Reaction of Nonmetals with Oxygen

Most nonmetals combine as readily with oxygen as do the metals, and their reactions usually occur rapidly enough to be described as combustion. To most people, the most important nonmetal combustion reaction is that of carbon because the reaction is a source of heat. Coal and charcoal, for example, are common carbon fuels. Coal is used worldwide in large amounts to generate electricity, and charcoal is a popular fuel for grilling hamburgers. If plenty of oxygen is available, the combustion of carbon gives CO_2, but when the supply of O_2 is limited, some CO forms as well. Manufacturers that package charcoal briquettes, therefore, print a warning on the bag that the charcoal shouldn't be used indoors for cooking or heating because of the danger of carbon monoxide poisoning.

Sulfur is another nonmetal that burns readily in oxygen to produce sulfur dioxide. One important use for this reaction is in the manufacture of sulfuric acid. The first step in the manufacturing process is the combustion of sulfur to produce sulfur dioxide. In addition, sulfur dioxide also forms when sulfur compounds burn, and the presence of sulfur and sulfur compounds in coal and petroleum is a major source of air pollution. Power plants that burn coal are making strides to remove the SO_2 from their exhausts.

Nitrogen also reacts with oxygen to form nitrogen oxides: NO, NO_2, N_2O, N_2O_3, N_2O_4, and N_2O_5. Nitrogen oxide and nitrogen dioxide are formed when nitrogen and oxygen are heated to high enough temperatures and pressures such as the temperature of a car engine. Dinitrogen oxide, also known as nitrous oxide or laughing gas, is used as an anesthetic by dentists and as the propellant in canned whipped cream, Reddi-wip®.

The label on a bag of charcoal displays a warning about carbon monoxide. (*Andy Washnik*)

Titration

6.6 | Stoichiometry of Redox Reactions

In general, working stoichiometry problems involving redox reactions follows the same principles we've applied to other reactions. The principal difference is that the chemical equations are more complex. Nevertheless, once we have a balanced equation, the moles of substances involved in the reaction are related by the coefficients in the balanced equation.

Because so many reactions involve oxidation and reduction, it should not be surprising that they have useful applications in the lab. Some redox reactions are especially useful in chemical analyses, particularly in titrations. In acid–base titrations, we often need a specific indicator for each reaction to detect the end point. However, there are no simple indicators that can be used to conveniently detect the end points in redox titrations. Conveniently, there are a few oxidizing agents that are highly colored and can act as their own indicator, so we have to rely on color changes among the reactants themselves.

One of the most useful reactants for redox titrations is potassium permanganate, $KMnO_4$, especially when the reaction can be carried out in an acidic solution. Permanganate ion is a powerful oxidizing agent, so it oxidizes most substances that are capable of being oxidized. That's one reason why it is used. Especially important, though, is the fact that the MnO_4^- ion has an intense purple color and its reduction product in acidic solution is the almost colorless Mn^{2+} ion. Therefore, when a solution of $KMnO_4$ is added from a buret to a solution of a reducing agent, the chemical reaction that occurs forms a nearly colorless product. This is illustrated in Figure 6.13, where we see a solution of $KMnO_4$ being poured into an acidic solution containing Fe^{2+}. As the $KMnO_4$ solution is added, the purple color continues to be destroyed as long as there is any reducing agent left. In a titration, after the last trace of the reducing agent has been consumed, the MnO_4^- ion in the next drop of titrant has nothing to react with, so it colors the solution pink. This signals the end of the titration. In this way, permanganate ion serves as its own indicator in redox titrations. The next multi-concept problem illustrates a typical analysis using $KMnO_4$ in a redox titration.

■ In concentrated solutions, MnO_4^- is purple, but dilute solutions of the ion appear pink.

Figure 6.13 | **Reduction of MnO₄⁻ by Fe²⁺.**
A solution of KMnO₄ is added to a stirred
acidic solution containing Fe²⁺. The reaction
oxidizes the pale blue-green Fe²⁺ to Fe³⁺, while
the MnO₄⁻ is reduced to the almost colorless
Mn²⁺ ion. The purple color of the permanganate will continue to be destroyed until all of
the Fe²⁺ has reacted. Only then will the
iron-containing solution take on a pink or
purple color. This ability of MnO₄⁻ to signal
the completion of the reaction makes it
especially useful in redox titrations, where it
serves as its own indicator. *(Andy Washnik)*

Analyzing and Solving Multi-Concept Problems

All the iron in a 2.00 g sample of an iron ore was dissolved
in an acidic solution and converted to Fe²⁺, which was then
titrated with 0.100 *M* KMnO₄ solution. In the titration the
iron was oxidized to Fe³⁺. The titration required 27.45 mL of
the KMnO₄ solution to reach the end point.

(a) How many grams of iron were in the sample?
(b) What was the percentage of iron in the sample?
(c) If the iron was present in the sample as Fe₂O₃, what was
    the percentage by mass of Fe₂O₃ in the sample?

■ **Analysis** This problem has several parts to it, so to solve
it we will divide it into three parts. The first will be to construct a balanced equation to get the correct stoichiometry,
the second will be to find the mass of iron and the percentage of iron in the sample, and the third will be to find the
percentage by mass of the Fe₂O₃. In the final two parts, we
will use tools we learned in Chapters 4 and 5, as well as tools
from this chapter.

PART 1

■ **Assembling the Tools:** To start with, let's use the method for balancing redox reactions in
acidic solutions as a tool, even though the question does not explicitly state that it is needed.

■ **Solution:** The compound KMnO₄ provides MnO₄⁻, and the K⁺ is a spectator ion and is not
included in balancing the equation. The skeleton equation for the reaction is

$$Fe^{2+} + MnO_4^- \longrightarrow Fe^{3+} + Mn^{2+}$$

Balancing it by the ion–electron method for acidic solutions gives

$$5Fe^{2+} + MnO_4^- + 8H^+ \longrightarrow 5Fe^{3+} + Mn^{2+} + 4H_2O$$

PART 2

■ **Assembling the Tools:** With this information, let's look over the tools we'll use to answer the
first two questions. We'll tackle the calculation of percent Fe₂O₃ afterward.

• Molarity and volume of the KMnO₄: These will give us moles of KMnO₄ used in the titration
  [remember: volume (in liters) × molarity = moles].
• Coefficients of the equation: These permit us to find moles of iron from the moles of KMnO₄ used.
• Molar mass of iron: This lets us calculate the mass of iron in the sample from moles of iron.
• Equation to calculate the percentage of iron: %Fe = $\dfrac{g\,Fe}{g\,sample}$ × 100%.

■ **Solution:** The number of moles of MnO_4^- consumed in the reaction is calculated from the volume of the solution used in the titration and its concentration.

$$0.02745 \text{ L } MnO_4^- \text{ soln} \times \frac{0.100 \text{ mol } MnO_4^-}{1.00 \text{ L } MnO_4^- \text{ soln}} = 0.002745 \text{ mol } MnO_4^-$$

Next, we use the coefficients of the equation to calculate the number of moles of Fe^{2+} that reacted. The balanced chemical equation tells us five moles of Fe^{2+} react per mole of MnO_4^- consumed.

$$0.002745 \text{ mol } MnO_4^- \times \frac{5 \text{ mol } Fe^{2+}}{1 \text{ mol } MnO_4^-} = 0.01372 \text{ mol } Fe^{2+}$$

This is the number of moles of iron in the ore sample, so the mass of iron in the sample is

$$0.01372 \text{ mol Fe} \times \frac{55.845 \text{ g Fe}}{1 \text{ mol Fe}} = 0.766 \text{ g Fe}$$

Next, we calculate the percentage of iron in the sample, which is the mass of iron divided by the mass of the sample, all multiplied by 100%.

$$\% \text{ Fe} = \frac{\text{mass of Fe}}{\text{mass of sample}} \times 100\%.$$

Substituting gives

$$\% \text{ Fe} = \frac{0.766 \text{ g Fe}}{2.00 \text{ g sample}} \times 100\% = 38.3\% \text{ Fe}$$

The answer to part (b) is that the sample is 38.3% iron.

PART 3

■ **Assembling the Tools:** In Part 2 we determined that 0.0137 mol Fe had reacted. How many moles of Fe_2O_3 would have contained this number of moles of iron? Once we know this, we can calculate the mass of the Fe_2O_3 and the percentage of Fe_2O_3 in the original sample. The tools we'll use in solving this part of the problem are:

• The chemical formula, Fe_2O_3: The formula relates moles of iron to moles Fe_2O_3.
• The molar mass of Fe_2O_3: This lets us calculate the mass of Fe_2O_3.

• The formula for calculating the percentage of Fe_2O_3: $\% \text{ Fe}_2\text{O}_3 = \frac{\text{g Fe}_2\text{O}_3}{\text{g sample}} \times 100\%.$

■ **Solution:** (c) The chemical formula for the iron oxide gives us

$$1 \text{ mol } Fe_2O_3 \Leftrightarrow 2 \text{ mol Fe}$$

This provides the conversion factor we need to determine how many moles of Fe_2O_3 were present in the sample. Working with the number of moles of Fe,

$$0.0137 \text{ mol Fe} \times \frac{1 \text{ mole } Fe_2O_3}{2 \text{ mol Fe}} = 0.00685 \text{ mol } Fe_2O_3$$

This is the number of moles of Fe_2O_3 in the sample. The formula mass of Fe_2O_3 is 159.69 g mol^{-1}, so the mass of Fe_2O_3 in the sample was

$$0.00685 \text{ mol } Fe_2O_3 \times \frac{159.69 \text{ g } Fe_2O_3}{1 \text{ mol } Fe_2O_3} = 1.094 \text{ g } Fe_2O_3$$

Finally, the percentage of Fe_2O_3 in the sample was

$$\% \ Fe_2O_3 = \frac{1.094 \ g \ Fe_2O_3}{2.00 \ g \ sample} \times 100\% \ = 54.7\% \ Fe_2O_3$$

The ore sample contained 54.8% Fe_2O_3.

■ **Are the Answers Reasonable?** For the first part, which involved balancing redox reactions, there are two steps to making sure the reaction is properly balanced: checking mass and charge. For the mass, we have to make sure each side of the equation has the same number of atoms of each element, and for the charge we need to check that the net charge is the same on both sides.

For the second part, we can use some approximate arithmetic to estimate the answer. In the titration we used approximately 30 mL, or 0.030 L, of the $KMnO_4$ solution, which is 0.10 M. Multiplying these tells us we've used approximately 0.003 mol of $KMnO_4$. From the coefficients of the equation, five times as many moles of Fe^{2+} react, so the amount of Fe in the sample is approximately $5 \times 0.003 = 0.015$ mol. The atomic mass of Fe is about 55 g/mol, so the mass of Fe in the sample is approximately $0.015 \times 55 = 0.8$ g. Our answer (0.766 g) is reasonable.

For the last part, we've noted that the amount of Fe in the sample is approximately 0.015 mol. The amount of Fe_2O_3 that contains this much Fe is 0.0075 mol. The formula mass of Fe_2O_3 is about 160, so the mass of Fe_2O_3 in the sample was approximately $0.0075 \times 160 = 1.2$ g, which isn't too far from the mass we obtained (1.095 g). Since 1.09 g is about half of the total sample mass of 2.00 g, the sample was approximately 50% Fe_2O_3, in agreement with the answer we obtained.

| Summary

Oxidation–Reduction. **Oxidation** is the loss of electrons or an algebraic increase in oxidation number; **reduction** is the gain of electrons or an algebraic decrease in oxidation number. Both always occur together in **redox** reactions. The substance oxidized is the **reducing agent;** the substance reduced is the **oxidizing agent. Oxidation numbers** are a bookkeeping device that we use to follow changes in redox reactions. They are assigned according to the rules on page 217. The term **oxidation state** is equivalent to oxidation number. These terms are summarized in Table 6.1.

Ion–Electron Method. In a balanced redox equation, the number of electrons gained by one substance is always equal to the number lost by another substance. This fact forms the basis for the **ion–electron method,** which provides a systematic method for deriving a net ionic equation for a redox reaction in aqueous solution. According to this method, the *skeleton* net ionic equation is divided into two **half-reactions,** which are balanced separately before being recombined to give the final balanced net ionic equation. For reactions in basic solutions the equation is balanced as if it occurred in an acidic solution, and then the balanced equation is converted to its proper form for basic solutions by adding an appropriate number of OH^- to both sides and canceling H_2O if possible.

Metal–Acid Reactions. In **nonoxidizing acids,** the strongest oxidizing agent is H^+ (Table 6.2). The reaction of a metal with a nonoxidizing acid gives hydrogen gas and a salt of the acid. Only metals more active than hydrogen react this way. These are metals that are located below hydrogen in the **activity series** (Table 6.3). **Oxidizing acids,** like HNO_3, contain an anion that is a stronger oxidizing agent than H^+, and they are able to oxidize many metals that nonoxidizing acids cannot.

Metal–Displacement Reactions. If one metal is more easily oxidized than another, it can displace the other metal from its compounds by a redox reaction. Such reactions are sometimes called **single replacement reactions.** Atoms of the more active metal become ions; ions of the less active metal generally become atoms. In this manner, any metal in the **activity series** can displace any of the others above it in the series from their compounds.

Oxidations by Molecular Oxygen. **Combustion** is the rapid reaction of a substance with oxygen accompanied by the evolution of heat and light. Combustion of a hydrocarbon in the presence of excess oxygen gives mostly CO_2 and H_2O. When the supply of oxygen is limited, mainly CO also forms, and in a very limited supply of oxygen the products are H_2O and very finely divided, mostly elemental carbon (as soot or lampblack). When hydrocarbons are burned in air, a mixture of CO_2, CO, and C are formed. The combustion of organic compounds containing only carbon, hydrogen, and oxygen also gives the same products, CO_2 and H_2O. Most nonmetals also burn in oxygen to give molecular oxides. Sulfur burns to give SO_2, which also forms when sulfur-containing fuels burn. Nitrogen reacts with oxygen to give a variety of nitrogen oxides, including NO and NO_2.

Many metals combine with oxygen in a process often called **corrosion,** but only sometimes is the reaction rapid enough to be considered combustion. The products are metal oxides.

Redox Titrations. Potassium permanganate is often used in redox titrations because it is a powerful oxidizing agent and serves as its own indicator. In acidic solutions, the purple MnO_4^- ion is reduced to the nearly colorless Mn^{2+} ion.

TOOLS
Tools for Problem Solving The following tools were introduced in this chapter. Study them carefully so that you can select the appropriate tool when needed.

Oxidizing and reducing agents (page 215)
The substance reduced is the oxidizing agent; the substance oxidized is the reducing agent.

Assigning oxidation numbers (page 217)
The rules permit us to assign oxidation numbers to elements in compounds and ions. You use changes in oxidation numbers to identify oxidation and reduction processes. Remember that when there is a conflict between two rules, the rule with the lower number is followed and the rule with the higher number is ignored.

Oxidation and reduction reactions (page 220)
In an oxidation reaction, the substance loses electrons; in a reduction reaction, the reactant gains electrons. Oxidation and reduction reactions always occur together.

Ion–electron method for acidic solutions (page 224)
Use this method when you need to obtain a balanced net ionic equation for a redox reaction in an acidic solution. Be sure to follow the steps in the order given and do not skip steps. Also, be sure to include charges on all ions.

Ion–electron method for basic solutions (page 226)
Use this method when you need to obtain a balanced net ionic equation for a redox reaction in a basic solution.

Oxidizing and nonoxidizing acids (Table 6.2, page 229)
Refer to this table to identify oxidizing and nonoxidizing acids, which enables you to anticipate the products of reactions of metals with acids. Nonoxidizing acids will react with metals below hydrogen in Table 6.3 to give H_2 and the metal ion.

Activity series of metals (Table 6.3, page 232)
When a question deals with the possible reaction of one metal with the salt of another, refer to the activity series to determine the outcome. A metal in the table will reduce the ion of any metal above it in the table, leading to a single replacement reaction.

Hydrocarbon combustion with plentiful supply of oxygen (page 236)

$$\text{hydrocarbon} + O_2 \longrightarrow CO_2 + H_2O \qquad \text{(plentiful supply of } O_2\text{)}$$

Hydrocarbon combustion with limited supply of oxygen (page 236)

$$\text{hydrocarbon} + O_2 \longrightarrow CO + H_2O \qquad \text{(limited supply of } O_2\text{)}$$

Hydrocarbon combustion with extremely limited supply of oxygen (page 236)

$$\text{hydrocarbon} + O_2 \longrightarrow C + H_2O \qquad \text{(very limited supply of } O_2\text{)}$$

Combustion of compounds containing C, H, and O (page 237)
Complete combustion gives CO_2 and H_2O,

$$(\text{C, H, O compound}) + O_2 \longrightarrow CO_2 + H_2O \qquad \text{(complete combustion)}$$

Combustion of organic compounds containing sulfur (page 237)
If an organic compound contains sulfur, SO_2 is formed in addition to CO_2 and H_2O when the compound is burned.

PLUS = WileyPLUS, an online teaching and learning solution. *Note to instructors:* Many of the end-of-chapter problems are available for assignment via the *WileyPLUS* system. **www.wileyplus.com. ILW** = An Interactive Learningware solution is available for this problem. **UH** = An Office Hour video is available for this problem. Review Problems are presented in pairs separated by blue rules. Answers to problems whose numbers appear in blue are given in Appendix B. More challenging problems are marked with an asterisk ∗.

Review Questions

Oxidation–Reduction

6.1 Define oxidation and reduction in terms of **(a)** electron transfer and **(b)** oxidation numbers.

6.2 Why must both oxidation and reduction occur simultaneously during a redox reaction? What is an oxidizing agent? What happens to it in a redox reaction? What is a reducing agent? What happens to it in a redox reaction?

6.3 In the compound As_4O_6, arsenic has an *oxidation number* of $+3$. What is the *oxidation state* of arsenic in this compound?

6.4 Are the following redox reactions? Explain.

$$2NO_2 \longrightarrow N_2O_4$$
$$2CrO_4{}^{2-} + 2H^+ \longrightarrow Cr_2O_7{}^{2-} + H_2O$$

6.5 If the oxidation number of nitrogen in a certain molecule changes from $+3$ to -2 during a reaction, is the nitrogen oxidized or reduced? How many electrons are gained (or lost) by each nitrogen atom?

Ion–Electron Method

6.6 The following equation is not balanced.

$$Ag + Fe^{2+} \longrightarrow Ag^+ + Fe$$

Why? Use the ion–electron method to balance it.

6.7 What are the net charges on the left and right sides of the following equations? Add electrons as necessary to make each of them a balanced half-reaction.

(a) $NO_3{}^- + 10H^+ \longrightarrow NH_4{}^+ + 3H_2O$

(b) $Cl_2 + 4H_2O \longrightarrow 2ClO_2{}^- + 8H^+$

6.8 In Question 6.7, which half-reaction represents oxidation? Which represents reduction?

Acids as Oxidizing Agents and the Activity Series

6.9 What is a *single replacement reaction*?

6.10 What is a nonoxidizing acid? Give two examples. What is the oxidizing agent in a nonoxidizing acid?

6.11 What is the strongest oxidizing agent in an aqueous solution of nitric acid?

6.12 If a metal is able to react with a solution of HCl, where must the metal stand relative to hydrogen in the activity series?

6.13 Where in the activity series do we find the best reducing agents? Where do we find the best oxidizing agents?

6.14 Which metals in Table 6.3 will not react with nonoxidizing acids?

6.15 Which metals in Table 6.3 will react with water? Write chemical equations for each of these reactions.

6.16 When manganese reacts with silver ion, is manganese oxidized or reduced? Is it an oxidizing agent or a reducing agent?

Oxygen as an Oxidizing Agent

6.17 Define combustion.

6.18 Why is "loss of electrons" described as oxidation?

6.19 What are the major products produced in the combustion of $C_{10}H_{22}$ under the following conditions **(a)** an excess of oxygen **(b)** a slightly limited oxygen supply **(c)** a very limited supply of oxygen **(d)** the compound is burned in air?

6.20 If one of the impurities in diesel fuel has the formula C_2H_6S, what products will be formed when it burns? Write a balanced chemical equation for the reaction.

6.21 Burning ammonia in an atmosphere of oxygen produces stable N_2 molecules as one of the products. What is the other product? Write the balanced chemical equation for the reaction.

6.22 What does burning sulfur in air produce? What is the limiting reactant in this reaction?

Review Problems

Oxidation–Reduction; Oxidation Numbers

6.23 Assign oxidation numbers to the atoms in the following: **(a)** S^{2-}, **(b)** SO_2, **(c)** P_4, and **(d)** PH_3.

OH 6.24 Assign oxidation numbers to the atoms in the following: **(a)** $ClO_4{}^-$, **(b)** Cl^-, **(c)** SF_6, and **(d)** $Au(NO_3)_3$.

6.25 Assign oxidation numbers to each atom in the following: **(a)** $NaOCl$, **(b)** $NaClO_2$, **(c)** $NaClO_3$, and **(d)** $NaClO_4$.

6.26 Assign oxidation numbers to the elements in the following: **(a)** $MnCl_2$, **(b)** $MnO_4{}^-$, **(c)** $MnO_4{}^{2-}$, and **(d)** MnO_2.

6.27 Assign oxidation numbers to the elements in the following: **(a)** PbS, **(b)** $TiCl_4$, **(c)** CsO_2, and **(d)** O_2F_2.

6.28 Assign oxidation numbers to the elements in the following: **(a)** $Sr(IO_3)_2$, **(b)** Cr_2S_3, **(c)** OF_2, and **(d)** HOF.

6.29 Titanium burns in pure nitrogen to form TiN. What are the oxidation states of titanium and nitrogen in TiN?

6.30 Zirconia, which is zirconium oxide, is used to make ceramic knives. What are the oxidation states of zirconium and oxygen in zircon?

6.31 Ozone, O_3, is one of the oxidants responsible for the haze over the Smoky Mountains. What is the oxidation number of the oxygens in ozone?

6.32 The other major oxidizing agent in the Smoky Mountains is OH. What is the oxidation number of the oxygen in OH?

6.33 When chlorine is added to drinking water to kill bacteria, some of the chlorine is changed into ions by the following equilibrium:

$$Cl_2(aq) + H_2O \rightleftharpoons H^+(aq) + Cl^-(aq) + HOCl(aq)$$

In the forward reaction (the reaction going from left to right), which substance is oxidized and which is reduced? In the reverse reaction, which is the oxidizing agent and which is the reducing agent?

6.34 A pollutant in smog is nitrogen dioxide, NO_2. The gas has a reddish brown color and is responsible for the red-brown color associated with this type of air pollution. Nitrogen dioxide is also a contributor to acid rain because when rain passes through air contaminated with NO_2, it dissolves and undergoes the following reaction:

$$3NO_2(g) + H_2O \longrightarrow NO(g) + 2H^+(aq) + 2NO_3^-(aq)$$

In this reaction, which element is reduced and which is oxidized? Which are the oxidizing agent and the reducing agent?

6.35 For the following reactions, identify the substance oxidized, the substance reduced, the oxidizing agent, and the reducing agent.

(a) $2HNO_3 + 3H_3AsO_3 \longrightarrow 2NO + 3H_3AsO_4 + H_2O$

(b) $NaI + 3HOCl \longrightarrow NaIO_3 + 3HCl$

(c) $2KMnO_4 + 5H_2C_2O_4 + 3H_2SO_4 \longrightarrow$
$$10CO_2 + K_2SO_4 + 2MnSO_4 + 8H_2O$$

(d) $6H_2SO_4 + 2Al \longrightarrow Al_2(SO_4)_3 + 3SO_2 + 6H_2O$

6.36 For the following reactions, identify the substance oxidized, the substance reduced, the oxidizing agent, and the reducing agent.

(a) $Cu + 2H_2SO_4 \longrightarrow CuSO_4 + SO_2 + 2H_2O$

(b) $3SO_2 + 2HNO_3 + 2H_2O \longrightarrow 3H_2SO_4 + 2NO$

(c) $5H_2SO_4 + 4Zn \longrightarrow 4ZnSO_4 + H_2S + 4H_2O$

(d) $I_2 + 10HNO_3 \longrightarrow 2HIO_3 + 10NO_2 + 4H_2O$

Ion-Electron Method

ILW **6.37** Balance the following equations for reactions occurring in an acidic solution.

(a) $S_2O_3^{2-} + OCl^- \longrightarrow Cl^- + S_4O_6^{2-}$

(b) $NO_3^- + Cu \longrightarrow NO_2 + Cu^{2+}$

(c) $IO_3^- + H_3AsO_3 \longrightarrow I^- + H_3AsO_4$

(d) $SO_4^{2-} + Zn \longrightarrow Zn^{2+} + SO_2$

(e) $NO_3^- + Zn \longrightarrow NH_4^+ + Zn^{2+}$

(f) $Cr^{3+} + BiO_3^- \longrightarrow Cr_2O_7^{2-} + Bi^{3+}$

(g) $I_2 + OCl^- \longrightarrow IO_3^- + Cl^-$

(h) $Mn^{2+} + BiO_3^- \longrightarrow MnO_4^- + Bi^{3+}$

(i) $H_3AsO_3 + Cr_2O_7^{2-} \longrightarrow H_3AsO_4 + Cr^{3+}$

6.38 Balance the following equations for reactions occurring in an acidic solution.

(a) $Sn + NO_3^- \longrightarrow SnO_2 + NO$

(b) $PbO_2 + Cl^- \longrightarrow PbCl_2 + Cl_2$

(c) $Ag + NO_3^- \longrightarrow NO_2 + Ag^+$

(d) $Fe^{3+} + NH_3OH^+ \longrightarrow Fe^{2+} + N_2O$

(e) $HNO_2 + I^- \longrightarrow I_2 + NO$

(f) $H_2C_2O_4 + HNO_2 \longrightarrow CO_2 + NO$

(g) $HNO_2 + MnO_4^- \longrightarrow Mn^{2+} + NO_3^-$

(h) $H_3PO_2 + Cr_2O_7^{2-} \longrightarrow H_3PO_4 + Cr^{3+}$

(i) $XeF_2 + Cl^- \longrightarrow Xe + F^- + Cl_2$

6.39 Balance the equations for the following reactions occurring in a basic solution.

(a) $CrO_4^{2-} + S^{2-} \longrightarrow S + CrO_2^-$

(b) $MnO_4^- + C_2O_4^{2-} \longrightarrow CO_2 + MnO_2$

(c) $ClO_3^- + N_2H_4 \longrightarrow NO + Cl^-$

(d) $NiO_2 + Mn(OH)_2 \longrightarrow Mn_2O_3 + Ni(OH)_2$

(e) $SO_3^{2-} + MnO_4^- \longrightarrow SO_4^{2-} + MnO_2$

6.40 Balance the equations for the following reactions occurring in a basic solution.

(a) $CrO_2^- + S_2O_8^{2-} \longrightarrow CrO_4^{2-} + SO_4^{2-}$

(b) $SO_3^{2-} + CrO_4^{2-} \longrightarrow SO_4^{2-} + CrO_2^-$

(c) $O_2 + N_2H_4 \longrightarrow H_2O_2 + N_2$

(d) $Fe(OH)_2 + O_2 \longrightarrow Fe(OH)_3 + OH^-$

(e) $Au + CN^- + O_2 \longrightarrow Au(CN)_4^- + OH^-$

6.41 When very dilute nitric acid reacts with a strong reducing agent such as magnesium, the nitrate ion is reduced to ammonium ion. Write a balanced net ionic equation for the reaction.

6.42 Hydroiodic acid reduces chlorine to hydrochloric acid and iodine. Write a balanced net ionic equation for the reaction.

6.43 Laundry bleach such as Clorox is a dilute solution of sodium hypochlorite, NaOCl. Write a balanced net ionic equation for the reaction of NaOCl with $Na_2S_2O_3$. The OCl^- is reduced to chloride ion and the $S_2O_3^{2-}$ is oxidized to sulfate ion.

OH **6.44** Calcium oxalate is one of the minerals found in kidney stones. If a strong acid is added to calcium oxalate, the compound will dissolve and the oxalate ion will be changed to oxalic acid (a weak acid). Oxalate ion is a moderately strong reducing agent. Write a balanced net ionic equation for the oxidation of $H_2C_2O_4$ by $K_2Cr_2O_7$ in an acidic solution. The reaction yields Cr^{3+} and CO_2 among the products.

6.45 Ozone, O_3, is a very powerful oxidizing agent, and in some places ozone is used to treat water to kill bacteria and make it safe to drink. One of the problems with this method of purifying water is that if there is any bromide ion in the water, it becomes oxidized to bromate ion, which has shown evidence of causing cancer in test animals. Assuming that ozone is reduced to water, write a balanced chemical equation for the reaction. (Assume an acidic solution.)

6.46 Chlorine is a good bleaching agent because it is able to oxidize substances that are colored to give colorless reaction products. It is used in the pulp and paper industry as a bleach, but after it has done its work, residual chlorine must be removed. This is accomplished using sodium thiosulfate, $Na_2S_2O_3$, which reacts with the chlorine, reducing it to chloride ion. The thiosulfate ion is changed to sulfate ion, which is easily removed by washing with water. Write a balanced chemical equation for the reaction of chlorine with thiosulfate ion, assuming an acidic solution.

Acids as Oxidizing Agents

6.47 Write balanced molecular, ionic, and net ionic equations for the reactions of the following metals with hydrochloric acid to give hydrogen plus the metal ion in solution.

(a) Manganese (gives Mn^{2+})

(b) Cadmium (gives Cd^{2+})

(c) Tin (gives Sn^{2+})

6.48 Write balanced molecular, ionic, and net ionic equations for the reaction of each of the following metals with dilute sulfuric acid.

(a) Nickel (gives Ni^{2+})

(b) Chromium (gives Cr^{3+})

(c) Aluminum (gives Al^{3+})

6.49 On the basis of the discussions in this chapter, suggest balanced chemical equations for the oxidation of metallic silver to Ag^+ ion with (a) dilute HNO_3 and (b) concentrated HNO_3.

OH **6.50** Hot, concentrated sulfuric acid is a fairly strong oxidizing agent. Write a balanced net ionic equation for the oxidation of metallic copper to copper(II) ion by hot, concentrated H_2SO_4, in which the sulfur is reduced to SO_2. Write a balanced molecular equation for the reaction.

Single Replacement Reactions and the Activity Series

6.51 Use Table 6.3 to predict the outcome of the following reactions. If no reaction occurs, write N.R. If a reaction occurs, write a balanced chemical equation for it.

(a) $Fe + Mg^{2+} \longrightarrow$

(b) $Cr + Pb^{2+} \longrightarrow$

(c) $Ag^+ + Fe \longrightarrow$

(d) $Ag + Au^{3+} \longrightarrow$

OH **6.52** Use Table 6.3 to predict the outcome of the following reactions. If no reaction occurs, write N.R. If a reaction occurs, write a balanced chemical equation for it.

(a) $Mn + Fe^{2+} \longrightarrow$

(b) $Cd + Zn^{2+} \longrightarrow$

(c) $Mg + Co^{2+} \longrightarrow$

(d) $Cr + Sn^{2+} \longrightarrow$

6.53 The following reactions occur spontaneously.

$$Pu + 3Tl^+ \longrightarrow Pu^{3+} + 3Tl$$
$$Ru + Pt^{2+} \longrightarrow Ru^{2+} + Pt$$
$$2Tl + Ru^{2+} \longrightarrow 2Tl^+ + Ru$$

List the metals Pu, Pt, and Tl in order of increasing ease of oxidation.

6.54 The following reactions occur spontaneously.

$$2Y + 3Ni^{2+} \longrightarrow 2Y^{3+} + 3Ni$$
$$2Mo + 3Ni^{2+} \longrightarrow 2Mo^{3+} + 3Ni$$
$$Y^{3+} + Mo \longrightarrow Y + Mo^{3+}$$

List the metals Y, Ni, and Mo in order of increasing ease of oxidation.

6.55 The following reaction occurs spontaneously.

$$Ru^{2+}(aq) + Cd(s) \longrightarrow Ru(s) + Cd^{2+}(aq)$$

What reaction will occur if a mixture is prepared containing the following: $Cd(s)$, $Cd(NO_3)_2(aq)$, $Pt(s)$, and $PtCl_2(aq)$? (Refer to the information in Problem 6.53.)

6.56 When magnesium metal is dipped into a solution of nickel(II) chloride, some of the magnesium dissolves and nickel metal is deposited on the surface of the magnesium. Referring to Problem 6.54 which one of the following reactions will occur spontaneously? Explain the reason for your choice.

(a) $2Mo^{3+} + 3Mg \longrightarrow 3Mg^{2+} + 2Mo$

(b) $2Mo + 3Mg^{2+} \longrightarrow 2Mo^{3+} + 3Mg$

6.57 Write a balanced equation for the reaction depicted in the following visualization:

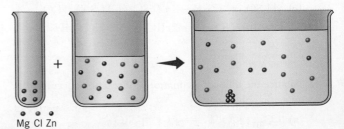

Mg Cl Zn

6.58 Write a balanced equation for the reaction depicted in the following visualization:

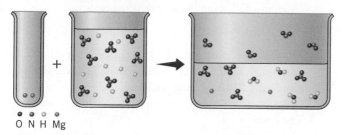

O N H Mg

6.59 Write the balanced chemical equation for the following reaction.

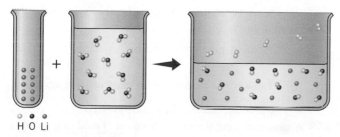

H O Li

6.60 Write the balanced chemical equation for the following reaction.

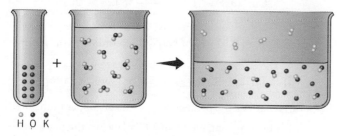

H O K

Reactions of Oxygen

6.61 Write balanced chemical equations for the complete combustion (in the presence of excess oxygen) of the following:

(a) C_6H_6 (benzene, an important industrial chemical and solvent)

(b) C_4H_{10} (butane, a fuel used in cigarette lighters)

(c) $C_{21}H_{44}$ (a component of paraffin wax used in candles)

6.62 Write balanced chemical equations for the complete combustion (in the presence of excess oxygen) of the following:

(a) $C_{12}H_{26}$ (a component of kerosene)

(b) $C_{18}H_{36}$ (a component of diesel fuel)

(c) C_7H_8 (toluene, a raw material in the production of the explosive TNT)

6.63 Write balanced equations for the combustion of the hydrocarbons in Problem 6.61 in (a) a slightly limited supply of oxygen and (b) a very limited supply of oxygen.

6.64 Write balanced equations for the combustion of the hydrocarbons in Problem 6.62 in (a) a slightly limited supply of oxygen and (b) a very limited supply of oxygen.

6.65 Methanol, CH_3OH, has been suggested as an alternative to gasoline as an automotive fuel. Write a balanced chemical equation for its complete combustion.

OH **6.66** The metabolism of carbohydrates such as glucose, $C_6H_{12}O_6$, produces the same products as combustion in excess oxygen. Write a chemical equation representing the metabolism (combustion) of glucose.

6.67 Write the balanced equation for the combustion of dimethylsulfide, $(CH_3)_2S$, in an abundant supply of oxygen.

6.68 Thiophene, C_4H_4S, is an impurity in crude oil and is a source of pollution if not removed. Write an equation for the combustion of thiophene.

6.69 Write chemical equations for the reaction of oxygen with (a) zinc, (b) aluminum, (c) magnesium, and (d) iron to form iron(III) oxide.

6.70 Write chemical equations for the reaction of oxygen with (a) beryllium, (b) lithium, (c) barium, and (d) bismuth to form bismuth(III) oxide.

Redox Reactions and Stoichiometry

6.71 Iodate ion reacts with sulfite ion to give sulfate ion and iodide ion.

(a) Write a balanced net ionic equation for the reaction.

(b) How many grams of sodium sulfite are needed to react with 5.00 g of sodium iodate?

6.72 Potable water (drinking water) should not have manganese concentrations in excess of 0.05 mg/mL. If the manganese concentration is greater than 0.1 mg/mL, it imparts a foul taste to the water and discolors laundry and porcelain surfaces. Manganese(II) ion is oxidized to permanganate ion by bismuthate ion, BiO_3^-, in an acidic solution. In the reaction, BiO_3^- is reduced to Bi^{3+}.

(a) Write a balanced net ionic equation for the reaction.

(b) How many milligrams of $NaBiO_3$ are needed to oxidize the manganese in 18.5 mg of manganese(II) sulfate?

OH **6.73** How many grams of copper must react to displace 12.0 g of silver from a solution of silver nitrate?

6.74 How many grams of aluminum must react to displace all of the silver from 25.0 g of silver nitrate? The reaction occurs in aqueous solution.

6.75 In an acidic solution, permanganate ion reacts with tin(II) ion to give manganese(II) ion and tin(IV) ion.

(a) Write a balanced net ionic equation for the reaction.

(b) How many milliliters of 0.230 M potassium permanganate solution are needed to react completely with 40.0 mL of 0.250 M tin(II) chloride solution?

6.76 In an acidic solution, bisulfite ion reacts with chlorate ion to give sulfate ion and chloride ion.

(a) Write a balanced net ionic equation for the reaction.

(b) How many milliliters of 0.150 M sodium chlorate solution are needed to react completely with 30.0 mL of 0.450 M sodium bisulfite solution?

6.77 Sulfites are used worldwide in the wine industry as antioxidant and antimicrobial agents. However, sulfites have also been identified as causing certain allergic reactions suffered by asthmatics, and the FDA mandates that sulfites be identified on the label if they are present at levels of 10 ppm (parts per million) or higher. The analysis of sulfites in wine uses the "Ripper method" in which a standard iodine solution, prepared by the reaction of iodate and iodide ions, is used to titrate a sample of the wine. The iodine is formed in the reaction

$$IO_3^- + 5I^- + 6H^+ \longrightarrow 3I_2 + 3H_2O$$

The iodine is held in solution by adding an excess of I^-, which combines with I_2 to give I_3^-. In the titration, the SO_3^{2-} is converted to SO_2 by acidification, and the reaction during the titration is

$$SO_2(aq) + I_3^-(aq) + 2H_2O \longrightarrow SO_4^{2-} + 3I^- + 4H^+$$

Starch is added to the wine sample to detect the end point, which is signaled by the formation of a dark blue color when excess iodine binds to the starch molecules. In a certain analysis, 0.0421 g of $NaIO_3$ was dissolved in dilute acid and excess NaI was added to the solution, which was then diluted to a total volume of 100.0 mL. A 50.0 mL sample of wine was then acidified and titrated with the iodine-containing solution. The volume of iodine solution required was 2.47 mL.

(a) What was the molarity of the iodine (actually, I_3^-) in the standard solution?

(b) How many grams of SO_2 were in the wine sample?

(c) If the density of the wine was 0.96 g/mL, what was the percentage of SO_2 in the wine?

(d) Parts per million (ppm) is calculated in a manner similar to percent (which is equivalent to *parts per hundred*).

$$ppm = \frac{\text{grams of component}}{\text{grams of sample}} \times 10^6 \ ppm$$

What was the concentration of sulfite in the wine, expressed as parts per million SO_2?

6.78 Methylbromide, CH_3Br, is used in agriculture to fumigate soil to rid it of pests such as nematodes. It is injected directly into the soil, but over time it has a tendency to escape before it can undergo natural degradation to innocuous products. Soil chemists have found that ammonium thiosulfate, $(NH_4)_2S_2O_3$, a nitrogen and sulfur fertilizer, drastically reduces methylbromide emissions by causing it to degrade.

In a chemical analysis to determine the purity of a batch of commercial ammonium thiosulfate, a chemist first prepared a standard solution of iodine following the procedure in Problem 6.77. First, 0.462 g KIO_3 was dissolved in

water to make 125 mL of solution. The solution was made acidic and treated with excess potassium iodide, which caused the following reaction to take place:

$$IO_3^- + 8I^- + 6H^+ \longrightarrow 3I_3^- + 3H_2O$$

The solution containing the I_3^- ion was then diluted to exactly 250.0 mL in a volumetric flask. Next, the chemist dissolved 0.2180 g of the fertilizer in water, added starch indicator, and titrated it with the standard I_3^- solution. The reaction was

$$2S_2O_3^{2-} + I_3^- \longrightarrow S_4O_6^{2-} + 3I^-$$

The titration required 27.99 mL of the I_3^- solution.

(a) What was the molarity of the I_3^- solution used in the titration?

(b) How many grams of $(NH_4)_2S_2O_3$ were in the fertilizer sample?

(c) What was the percentage by mass of $(NH_4)_2S_2O_3$ in the fertilizer?

ILW 6.79 A sample of a copper ore with a mass of 0.4225 g was dissolved in acid. A solution of potassium iodide was added, which caused the reaction

$$2Cu^{2+}(aq) + 5I^-(aq) \longrightarrow I_3^-(aq) + 2CuI(s)$$

The I_3^- that formed reacted quantitatively with exactly 29.96 mL of 0.02100 M $Na_2S_2O_3$ according to the following equation.

$$I_3^-(aq) + 2S_2O_3^{2-}(aq) \longrightarrow 3I^-(aq) + S_4O_6^{2-}(aq)$$

(a) What was the percentage by mass of copper in the ore?

(b) If the ore contained $CuCO_3$, what was the percentage by mass of $CuCO_3$ in the ore?

6.80 A 1.362 g sample of an iron ore that contained Fe_3O_4 was dissolved in acid and all of the iron was reduced to Fe^{2+}. The solution was then acidified with H_2SO_4 and titrated with 39.42 mL of 0.0281 M $KMnO_4$, which oxidized the iron to Fe^{3+}. The net ionic equation for the reaction is

$$5Fe^{2+} + MnO_4^- + 8H^+ \longrightarrow 5Fe^{3+} + Mn^{2+} + 4H_2O$$

(a) What was the percentage by mass of iron in the ore?

(b) What was the percentage by mass of Fe_3O_4 in the ore?

6.81 Hydrogen peroxide, H_2O_2, solution can be purchased in drug stores for use as an antiseptic. A sample of such a solution weighing 1.000 g was acidified with H_2SO_4 and titrated with a 0.02000 M solution of $KMnO_4$. The net ionic equation for the reaction is

$$6H^+ + 5H_2O_2 + 2MnO_4^- \longrightarrow 5O_2 + 2Mn^{2+} + 8H_2O$$

The titration required 17.60 mL of $KMnO_4$ solution.

(a) How many grams of H_2O_2 reacted?

(b) What is the percentage by mass of the H_2O_2 in the original antiseptic solution?

6.82 Sodium nitrite, $NaNO_2$, is used as a preservative in meat products such as frankfurters and bologna. In an acidic solution, nitrite ion is converted to nitrous acid, HNO_2, which reacts with permanganate ion according to the equation

$$H^+ + 5HNO_2 + 2MnO_4^- \longrightarrow 5NO_3^- + 2Mn^{2+} + 3H_2O$$

A 1.000 g sample of a water-soluble solid containing $NaNO_2$ was dissolved in dilute H_2SO_4 and titrated with 0.01000 M $KMnO_4$ solution. The titration required 12.15 mL of the $KMnO_4$ solution. What was the percentage by mass of $NaNO_2$ in the original 1.000 g sample?

6.83 A sample of a chromium-containing alloy weighing 3.450 g was dissolved in acid, and all the chromium in the sample was oxidized to CrO_4^{2-}. It was then found that 3.18 g of Na_2SO_3 was required to reduce the CrO_4^{2-} to CrO_2^- in a basic solution, with the SO_3^{2-} being oxidized to SO_4^{2-}.

(a) Write a balanced equation for the reaction of CrO_4^{2-} with SO_3^{2-} in a basic solution.

(b) How many grams of chromium were in the alloy sample?

(c) What was the percentage by mass of chromium in the alloy?

6.84 Solder is an alloy containing the metals tin and lead. A particular sample of this alloy weighing 1.50 g was dissolved in acid. All of the tin was then converted to the +2 oxidation state. Next, it was found that 0.368 g of $Na_2Cr_2O_7$ was required to oxidize the Sn^{2+} to Sn^{4+} in an acidic solution. In the reaction the chromium was reduced to Cr^{3+} ion.

(a) Write a balanced net ionic equation for the reaction between Sn^{2+} and $Cr_2O_7^{2-}$ in an acidic solution.

(b) Calculate the number of grams of tin that were in the sample of solder.

(c) What was the percentage by mass of tin in the solder?

6.85 Both calcium chloride and sodium chloride are used to melt ice and snow on roads in the winter. A certain company

was marketing a mixture of these two compounds for this purpose. A chemist, wanting to analyze the mixture, dissolved 2.463 g of it in water and precipitated calcium oxalate by adding sodium oxalate, $Na_2C_2O_4$. The calcium oxalate was carefully filtered from the solution, dissolved in sulfuric acid, and titrated with 0.1000 M $KMnO_4$ solution. The reaction that occurred was

$$6H^+ + 5H_2C_2O_4 + 2MnO_4^- \longrightarrow 10CO_2 + 2Mn^{2+} + 8H_2O$$

The titration required 21.62 mL of the $KMnO_4$ solution.

(a) How many moles of $C_2O_4^{2-}$ were present in the calcium oxalate precipitate?

(b) How many grams of calcium chloride were in the original 2.463 g sample?

(c) What was the percentage by mass of calcium chloride in the sample?

6.86 A way to analyze a sample for nitrite ion is to acidify a solution containing NO_2^- and then allow the HNO_2 that is formed to react with iodide ion in the presence of excess I^-. The reaction is

$$2HNO_2 + 2H^+ + 3I^- \longrightarrow 2NO + 2H_2O + I_3^-$$

Then the I_3^- is titrated with $Na_2S_2O_3$ solution using starch as an indicator.

$$I_3^- + 2S_2O_3^{2-} \longrightarrow 3I^- + S_4O_6^{2-}$$

In a typical analysis, a 1.104 g sample that was known to contain $NaNO_2$ was treated as described above. The titration required 29.25 mL of 0.3000 M $Na_2S_2O_3$ solution to reach the end point.

(a) How many moles of I_3^- had been produced in the first reaction?

(b) How many moles of NO_2^- had been in the original 1.104 g sample?

(c) What was the percentage by mass of $NaNO_2$ in the original sample?

| Additional Exercises

6.87 Waste water treatment often has at least one oxidation–reduction step. In the collection of waste water, chlorine can be added to control corrosion by hydrogen sulfide to give sulfur and chloride ions. What is the balanced equation for the reaction that occurs in this step?

6.88 Bromine gas is used to make fire-retardant chemicals used on children's pajamas. However, to dispose of excess bromine, it is passed through a solution of sodium hydroxide. The products are NaBr and NaOBr. What is being reduced and what is being oxidized? Write a balanced equation for the reaction.

6.89 Biodiesel is formed from the reaction of oils with methanol or ethanol. One of the products is methyl octanoate, $C_9H_{18}O_2$, which burns completely in a diesel engine. Give a balanced equation for this reaction. If the density of methyl octanoate is 0.877 g/mL, how many grams of CO_2 will be formed from the burning of 1 gallon of methyl octanoate?

6.90 What is the oxidation number of sulfur in the tetrathionate ion, $S_4O_6^{2-}$?

*6.91 In Practice Exercise 6.9 (page 221), some of the uses of chlorine dioxide were described along with a reaction that could be used to make ClO_2. Another reaction that is used to make this substance is

$$HCl + NaOCl + 2NaClO_2 \longrightarrow 2ClO_2 + 2NaCl + NaOH$$

Which element is oxidized? Which element is reduced? Which substance is the oxidizing agent and which is the reducing agent?

6.92 What is the average oxidation number of carbon in (a) C_2H_5OH (grain alcohol), (b) $C_{12}H_{22}O_{11}$ (sucrose, table sugar), (c) $CaCO_3$ (limestone), and (d) $NaHCO_3$ (baking soda)?

6.93 The following chemical reactions are *observed to occur* in aqueous solution.

$$2Al + 3Cu^{2+} \longrightarrow 2Al^{3+} + 3Cu$$
$$2Al + 3Fe^{2+} \longrightarrow 3Fe + 2Al^{3+}$$
$$Pb^{2+} + Fe \longrightarrow Pb + Fe^{2+}$$
$$Fe + Cu^{2+} \longrightarrow Fe^{2+} + Cu$$
$$2Al + 3Pb^{2+} \longrightarrow 3Pb + 2Al^{3+}$$
$$Pb + Cu^{2+} \longrightarrow Pb^{2+} + Cu$$

Arrange the metals Al, Pb, Fe, and Cu in order of increasing ease of oxidation without referring to Table 6.3.

6.94 In Problem 6.93, were all of the experiments described actually necessary to establish the order?

6.95 According to the activity series in Table 6.3, which of the following metals react with nonoxidizing acids: (a) silver, (b) gold, (c) zinc, (d) magnesium?

6.96 In each of the following pairs, choose the metal that would most likely react more rapidly with a nonoxidizing acid such as HCl: (a) aluminum or iron, (b) zinc or nickel, and (c) cadmium or magnesium.

6.97 Use Table 6.3 to predict whether the following displacement reactions should occur. If no reaction occurs, write N.R. If a reaction does occur, write a balanced chemical equation for it.

(a) $Zn + Sn^{2+} \longrightarrow$ (d) $Zn + Co^{2+} \longrightarrow$

(b) $Cr + H^+ \longrightarrow$ (e) $Mn + Pb^{2+} \longrightarrow$

(c) $Pb + Cd^{2+} \longrightarrow$

6.98 Sucrose, $C_{12}H_{22}O_{11}$, is ordinary table sugar. Write a balanced chemical equation representing the metabolism of sucrose. (See Review Problem 6.66.)

*6.99 Balance the following equations by the ion–electron method.

(a) $NBr_3 \longrightarrow N_2 + Br^- + HOBr$ (basic solution)

(b) $Cl_2 \longrightarrow Cl^- + ClO_3^-$ (basic solution)

(c) $H_2SeO_3 + H_2S \longrightarrow S + Se$ (acidic solution)

(d) $MnO_2 + SO_3^{2-} \longrightarrow Mn^{2+} + S_2O_6^{2-}$ (acidic solution)

(e) $XeO_3 + I^- \longrightarrow Xe + I_2$ (acidic solution)

(f) $(CN)_2 \longrightarrow CN^- + OCN^-$ (basic solution)

6.100 Lead(IV) oxide reacts with hydrochloric acid to give chlorine. The unbalanced equation for the reaction is

$$PbO_2 + Cl^- \longrightarrow PbCl_2 + Cl_2$$

How many grams of PbO_2 must react to give 15.0 g of Cl_2?

*6.101 A solution contains $Ce(SO_4)_3^{2-}$ at a concentration of 0.0150 M. It was found that in a titration, 25.00 mL of this solution reacted completely with 23.44 mL of 0.032 M $FeSO_4$ solution. The reaction gave Fe^{3+} as a product in the solution. In this reaction, what is the final oxidation state of the Ce?

*6.102 A copper bar with a mass of 12.340 g is dipped into 255 mL of 0.125 M $AgNO_3$ solution. When the reaction that occurs has finally ceased, what will be the mass of unreacted copper in the bar? If all the silver that forms adheres to the copper bar, what will be the total mass of the bar after the reaction?

*6.103 A bar of copper weighing 32.00 g was dipped into 50.0 mL of 0.250 M $AgNO_3$ solution. If all of the silver that deposits adheres to the copper bar, how much will the bar weigh after the reaction is complete? Write and balance any necessary chemical equations.

6.104 As described in the *Chemistry Outside the Classroom 6.1*, silver tarnishes in the presence of hydrogen sulfide to form Ag_2S, which is how silver spoons tarnish. The silver can be polished and made lustrous again by placing the piece of tarnished silver in a pan with aluminum foil and detergent solution. The silver must touch the aluminum foil. Write balanced equations for both the tarnishing and the polishing of silver.

6.105 Titanium(IV) can be reduced to titanium(III) by the addition of zinc metal. Sulfur dioxide can be reduced to elemental sulfur by hydrogen. For both of these reactions, write the balanced equations. Why could we not include these compounds in the activity series table?

6.106 A researcher planned to use chlorine gas in an experiment and wished to trap excess chlorine to prevent it from escaping into the atmosphere. To accomplish this, the reaction of sodium thiosulfate ($Na_2S_2O_3$) with chlorine gas in an acidic aqueous solution to give sulfate ion and chloride ion would be used. How many grams of $Na_2S_2O_3$ are needed to trap 4.25 g of chlorine?

6.107 A sample of a tin ore weighing 0.3000 g was dissolved in an acid solution and all the tin in the sample was changed to tin(II). In a titration, 8.08 mL of 0.0500 M $KMnO_4$ solution was required to oxidize the tin(II) to tin(IV).

(a) What is the balanced equation for the reaction in the titration?

(b) How many grams of tin were in the sample?

(c) What was the percentage by mass of tin in the sample?

(d) If the tin in the sample had been present in the compound SnO_2, what would have been the percentage by mass of SnO_2 in the sample?

| Multi-Concept Problems

6.108 In June 2002, the Department of Health and Children in Ireland began a program to distribute tablets of potassium iodate to households as part of Ireland's National Emergency Plan for Nuclear Accidents. Potassium iodate provides iodine, which when taken during a nuclear emergency, works by "topping off" the thyroid gland to prevent the uptake of radioactive iodine that might be released into the environment by a nuclear accident.

To test the potency of the tablets, a chemist dissolved one in 100.0 mL of water, made the solution acidic, and then added excess potassium iodide, which caused the following reaction to occur.

$$IO_3^- + 8I^- + 6H^+ \longrightarrow 3I_3^- + 3H_2O$$

The resulting solution containing I_3^- was titrated with 0.0500 M $Na_2S_2O_3$ solution, using starch indicator to detect the end point. (In the presence of iodine, starch turns dark blue. When the $S_2O_3^{2-}$ has consumed all of the iodine, the solution becomes colorless.) The titration required 22.61 mL of the thiosulfate solution to reach the end point. The reaction during the titration was

$$I_3^- + 2S_2O_3^{2-} \longrightarrow 3I^- + S_4O_6^{2-}$$

How many milligrams of KIO_3 were in the tablet?

*6.109 An organic compound contains carbon, hydrogen, and sulfur. A sample of it with a mass of 1.045 g was burned in oxygen to give gaseous CO_2, H_2O, and SO_2. These gases were passed through 500.0 mL of an acidified 0.0200 M $KMnO_4$ solution, which caused the SO_2 to be oxidized to SO_4^{2-}. Only part of the available $KMnO_4$ was reduced to Mn^{2+}. Next, 50.00 mL of 0.0300 M $SnCl_2$ was added to a 50.00 mL portion of this solution, which still contained unreduced $KMnO_4$. There was more than enough added $SnCl_2$ to cause all of the remaining MnO_4^- in the 50 mL portion to be reduced to Mn^{2+}. The excess Sn^{2+} that still remained after the reaction was then titrated with 0.0100 M $KMnO_4$, requiring 27.28 mL of the $KMnO_4$ solution to reach the end point. What was the percentage of sulfur in the original sample of the organic compound that had been burned?

*6.110 A mixture is made by combining 325 mL of 0.0200 M $Na_2Cr_2O_7$ with 425 mL of 0.060 M $Fe(NO_3)_2$. Initially, the H^+ concentration in the mixture is 0.400 M. Dichromate ion oxidizes Fe^{2+} to Fe^{3+} and is reduced to Cr^{3+}. After the reaction in the mixture has ceased, how many milliliters of 0.0100 M NaOH will be required to neutralize the remaining H^+?

6.111 A solution containing 0.1244 g of $K_2C_2O_4$ was acidified, changing the $C_2O_4^{2-}$ ions to $H_2C_2O_4$. The solution was then titrated with 13.93 mL of a $KMnO_4$ solution to reach a faint pink end point. In the reaction, $H_2C_2O_4$ was oxidized to CO_2 and MnO_4^- was reduced to Mn^{2+}. What was the molarity of the $KMnO_4$ solution used in the titration?

*6.112 It was found that a 20.0 mL portion of a solution of oxalic acid, $H_2C_2O_4$, requires 6.25 mL of 0.200 M $K_2Cr_2O_7$ for complete reaction in an acidic solution. In the reaction, the oxidation product is CO_2 and the reduction product is Cr^{3+}. How many milliliters of 0.450 M NaOH are required to completely neutralize the $H_2C_2O_4$ in a separate 20.00 mL sample of the same oxalic acid solution?

*6.113 A 15.00 mL sample of a solution containing oxalic acid, $H_2C_2O_4$, was titrated with 0.02000 M $KMnO_4$. The titration required 18.30 mL of the $KMnO_4$ solution. If 19.69 mL of a solution of NaOH is needed to react completely with 25.00 mL of this same oxalic acid solution, what is the concentration of the NaOH solution? In the reaction, oxalate ion ($C_2O_4^{2-}$) is oxidized to CO_2 and MnO_4^- is reduced to Mn^{2+}.

*6.114 A solution with a volume of 500.0 mL contained a mixture of SO_3^{2-} and $S_2O_3^{2-}$. A 100.0 mL portion of the solution was found to react with 80.00 mL of 0.0500 M CrO_4^{2-} in a basic solution to give CrO_2^-. The only sulfur-containing product was SO_4^{2-}. After the reaction, the solution was treated with excess 0.200 M $BaCl_2$ solution, which precipitated $BaSO_4$. This solid was filtered from the solution, dried, and found to weigh 0.9336 g. Explain in detail how you can determine the molar concentrations of SO_3^{2-} and $S_2O_3^{2-}$ in the original solution.

Exercises in Critical Thinking

6.115 The ion $OSCN^-$ is found in human saliva. Discuss the problems in assigning oxidation numbers to the atoms in this ion. Suggest a reasonable set of oxidation numbers for the atoms in $OSCN^-$.

6.116 We described the ion–electron method for balancing redox equations in Section 6.2. Can you devise an alternate method using oxidation numbers?

6.117 Assuming that a chemical reaction with DNA could lead to damage causing cancer, would a very strong or a weak oxidizing agent have a better chance of being a carcinogen? Justify your answer.

6.118 Would you expect atomic oxygen and chlorine to be better or worse oxidizing agents than molecular oxygen and molecular chlorine? Justify your answer.

6.119 Do we live in an oxidizing or reducing environment? What effect might our environment have on chemistry we do in the laboratory? What effect might the environment have on the nature of the chemicals (minerals, etc.) we find on earth?

6.120 Antioxidants are touted as helping people live longer. What are antioxidants? What role do they play in longevity? In terms of this chapter, how else could antioxidants be defined? What from this chapter would make a good antioxidant?

8 The Quantum Mechanical Atom

Chapter Outline

The "strip" of Las Vegas is world famous for its dazzling array of lighted signs and creative displays of all shapes and colors. Behind these displays are the promise and excitement of many forms of entertainment. To chemists, these same lights and colors revolutionized physics and chemistry in the last century, while, importantly, providing a window into the structure of the atom itself. Tim Gartside USA/Alamy

This Chapter in Context

In previous chapters we have described how the existence and basic structure of atoms were deduced from a variety of experiments. However, there were many unanswered questions about the elements. Why do metals tend to form cations and why do nonmetals tend to form anions? Why do nonmetals combine to form molecules, while molecules made of metals are very rare? Why are the noble gases virtually inert? Why does the periodic table have the arrangement and shape it has? Many more questions could also be posed, but they are minor compared to major problems that were becoming apparent in the classical physics of the late 1800s and early 1900s.

First, classical physics, the physics of the late 1800s, predicted that atoms simply could not exist. It predicted that electrons must quickly lose energy and collapse into the nucleus—the *collapsing atom paradox*. Classical physics also predicted that heated objects should emit vast quantities of ultraviolet light. That they emit very little UV radiation led physicists to call this the *ultraviolet catastrophe*. Finally, particles, such as electrons, passing through very small openings gave results that could be explained only if we regarded particles as waves leading to the concept of the **wave/particle duality** of matter. These problems in describing the fundamental nature of matter made it clear that an entirely new set of theoretical concepts was needed. These concepts are commonly embodied in **quantum mechanics** (also called **wave mechanics** or **quantum theory**), which is now the cornerstone of modern chemistry.

■ When experiment and theory do not agree, the theory must be modified or discarded. Classical physics could not resolve the collapsing atom paradox. It also could not correctly predict the crucial characteristics of the radiation emitted by hot objects or hot samples of the elements.

8.1 | Electromagnetic Radiation

The Nature of Light

You've learned that objects can have energy in only two ways, as kinetic energy and as potential energy. You also learned that energy can be transferred between things, and in Chapter 7 our principal focus was on the transfer of heat. Energy can also be transferred between atoms and molecules in the form of light or electromagnetic radiation. As we will see in this chapter, light is a very important form of energy in chemistry since it allows us to delve into the structure of atoms and molecules and, in some cases, their reactions. For example, many chemical systems emit visible light as they react often by a process called chemiluminescence (see Figure 8.1).

■ Like shaking a birthday present to try to guess its contents, scientists can "shake up" an atom by adding energy. Instead of hearing the rattle of a present, light is emitted. The energy and intensity of the light emitted helps to describe the inner workings of the atom.

Figure 8.1 | **Light is given off in a variety of chemical reactions.** (*a*) Combustion. (*b*) Cyalume light sticks. (*c*) A lightning bug. (*Jim Richardson/Corbis, © Marc Steinmetz/Visum/The Image Works, © Phil Degginger/Alamy*)

Many experiments show that radiation carries energy through space by means of **waves**. Waves are an oscillation that moves outward from a disturbance (think of ripples moving away from a pebble dropped into a pond). In the case of **electromagnetic radiation**, the disturbance can be a pulsing, or oscillating, electric charge that creates an oscillating electric field. The oscillating electric field creates an oscillating magnetic field, and the two together are known as **electromagnetic waves**.

Wavelength and Frequency

An electromagnetic wave is often depicted as a sine wave that has an amplitude, wavelength, and frequency (for simplicity we do not show the magnetic component of the wave). Figure 8.2 shows how the amplitude or intensity of the wave varies with time and with distance as the wave travels through space. The **amplitude** of the wave is related to the intensity or brightness of the radiation. In Figure 8.2a, we see two complete oscillations or *cycles* of the wave during a one-second interval. The number of cycles per second is called the **frequency** of the electromagnetic radiation, and its symbol is ν, the Greek letter nu. In the SI, the unit of time is the second (s), so frequency is given the unit "per second," which is $\dfrac{1}{\text{second}}$, or second^{-1}. This unit is given the special name **hertz (Hz)**.

$$1 \text{ Hz} = 1 \text{ s}^{-1}$$

As electromagnetic radiation moves away from its source, the positions of maximum and minimum amplitude (peaks and troughs) are regularly spaced. The peak-to-peak distance is called the radiation's **wavelength**, symbolized by λ (the Greek letter *lambda*). See Figure 8.2b. Because wavelength is a distance, it has distance units (for example, meters).

If we multiply the wavelength by frequency, the result is the velocity of the wave. We can see this if we analyze the units.

$$\text{meters} \times \frac{1}{\text{second}} = \frac{\text{meters}}{\text{second}} = \text{velocity}$$

$$\text{m} \times \frac{1}{\text{s}} = \frac{\text{m}}{\text{s}} = \text{m s}^{-1}$$

The velocity of electromagnetic radiation in a vacuum is a constant and is commonly called the *speed of light*. Its value to three significant figures is 3.00×10^8 m s^{-1}. This important physical constant is given the symbol c.

$$c = 3.00 \times 10^8 \text{ m s}^{-1}$$

From the preceding discussion we obtain a very important relationship that allows us to convert between λ and ν.

$$\lambda \times \nu = c = 3.00 \times 10^8 \text{ m s}^{-1} \qquad \textbf{(8.1)}$$

- Electricity and magnetism are closely related to each other. A moving charge creates an electric current, which in turn creates a magnetic field around it. This is the fundamental idea behind electric motors. A moving magnetic field creates an electric field or current. This is also the idea behind electric generators and turbines.

- Electromagnetic waves don't need a medium to travel through, as water and sound waves do. They can cross empty space. The speed of the electromagnetic wave in a vacuum is the same, about 3.00×10^8 m/s, no matter how the radiation is created.

- ν, the symbol for frequency, is the Greek letter nu, pronounced "new."

- The SI symbol for the second is s.

$$s^{-1} = \frac{1}{s}$$

- The speed of light is one of our most carefully measured constants because it is used to define the meter. The precise value of the speed of light in a vacuum is 2.99792458×10^8 m/s, and a meter is defined as exactly the distance traveled by light in 1/299792458 of a second.

TOOLS

Wavelength–frequency relationship

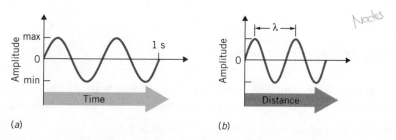

(a)　　　　　　　　　(b)

Figure 8.2 | Two views of electromagnetic radiation. (a) The frequency, ν, of a light wave is the number of complete oscillations each second. Here two cycles span a one-second time interval, so the frequency is 2 cycles per second, or 2 Hz. (b) Electromagnetic radiation frozen in time. This curve shows how the amplitude varies along the direction of travel. The distance between two peaks is the wavelength, λ, of the electromagnetic radiation.

Example 8.1
Calculating Frequency from Wavelength

Mycobacterium tuberculosis, the organism that causes tuberculosis, can be completely destroyed by irradiation with ultraviolet light with a wavelength of 254 nm. What is the frequency of this radiation?

■ **Analysis:** Our analysis includes the realization that this question is not a conversion as our stoichiometry problems were. This will require an equation to solve.

■ **Assembling the Tools:** The tool needed is expressed by Equation 8.1. When rearranged it becomes

$$\nu = \frac{c}{\lambda}$$

However, we must be very careful about the units, and may need to consult the table of SI prefixes in Chapter 2.

■ **Solution:** We substitute 3.00×10^8 m s^{-1} for c and 254 nm for λ, the wavelength. However, to cancel units correctly, we must convert the wavelength to meters. Recall that nm means nanometer and the prefix nano implies the factor "$\times 10^{-9}$."

$$1 \text{ nm} = 1 \times 10^{-9} \text{ m}$$

Therefore, 254 nm equals 254×10^{-9} m. Substituting gives

$$\nu = \frac{3.00 \times 10^8 \text{ m s}^{-1}}{254 \text{ nm}} \times \frac{1 \text{ nm}}{1 \times 10^{-9} \text{ m}}$$

$$= 1.18 \times 10^{15} \text{ s}^{-1}$$

$$= 1.18 \times 10^{15} \text{ Hz}$$

■ **Is the Answer Reasonable?** One way to test whether our answer is correct is to see if the given wavelength, multiplied by our calculated frequency, gives us the speed of light. To estimate the answer we round the numbers to one or two significant figures so we can do the calculation without a calculator. Rounding 254 nm to 250×10^{-9} m and our answer to 1×10^{15} s^{-1} we calculate

$$(250 \times 10^{-9} \text{ m}) \times (1 \times 10^{15} \text{ s}^{-1}) = 250 \times 10^6 \text{ m s}^{-1} = 2.5 \times 10^8 \text{ m s}^{-1}$$

which is close to the actual speed of light, within one significant figure. Using the actual data and a calculator gives us the exact value for the speed of light.

Example 8.2
Calculating Wavelength from Frequency

Radio station WKXR is an AM radio station broadcasting from Asheboro, North Carolina, at a frequency of 1260 kHz. What is the wavelength of these radio waves expressed in meters?

■ **Analysis:** We use the same analysis as in Example 8.1.

■ **Assembling the Tools:** This question will use the same equation as Example 8.1. This time we solve for wavelength in meters, as asked for in the problem.

$$\lambda = \frac{c}{\nu}$$

■**Solution:** Solving Equation 8.1 for the wavelength we first have to consider units. The frequency in kilohertz has two parts. The prefix kilo stands for 10^3 and hertz stands for s^{-1}. Making those substitutions, we write

$$\lambda = \frac{c}{\nu} = \frac{3.00 \times 10^8 \text{ m s}^{-1}}{1260 \text{ kHz}} = \frac{3.00 \times 10^8 \text{ m s}^{-1}}{1260 \times 10^3 \text{ s}^{-1}}$$

When we cancel the units in the last term and work out the mathematics, we find that the wavelength is 238 meters.

■**Is the Answer Reasonable?** If this wavelength is correct, we should be able to multiply it by the original frequency (in Hz) and get the speed of light, as we did in the previous example. Another approach is to test our answer by dividing the speed of light by the wavelength to get back the frequency. Rounding to one significant figure, we get

$$\frac{3 \times 10^8 \text{ m/s}}{2 \times 10^2 \text{ m}} = 1.5 \times 10^6 \text{ Hz} = 1500 \text{ kHz}$$

which is reasonably close to the original frequency of 1260 kHz.

Practice Exercises

8.1 | Helium derives it name from the Latin name for the sun. Helium was discovered when spectroscopists found that the 588 nm wavelength (among others) was missing from the sun's spectrum. What is the frequency of this radiation? (*Hint:* Recall the metric prefixes so units will cancel correctly.)

8.2 | The most intense radiation emitted by the Earth has a wavelength of about 10.9 μm. What is the frequency of this radiation in hertz?

8.3 | Radio station KRED in Eureka, California, broadcasts electromagnetic radiation at a frequency of 92.3 MHz (megahertz). What is the wavelength of these radio waves, expressed in meters?

Electromagnetic Spectrum

Electromagnetic radiation comes in a broad range of frequencies called the **electromagnetic spectrum**, illustrated in Figure 8.3. Some portions of the spectrum have popular names. For example, radio waves are electromagnetic radiations having very low frequencies (and therefore very long wavelengths as we just calculated). Microwaves, which also have low frequencies, are emitted by radar instruments such as those the police use to monitor the speeds of cars. In microwave ovens, similar radiation is used to heat water in foods, causing the food to cook quickly. Infrared radiation is emitted by hot objects and consists of the range of frequencies that can make molecules of most substances vibrate internally. You can't see infrared radiation, but you can feel how your body absorbs it by holding your hand near a hot radiator; the absorbed radiation makes your hand warm. Gamma rays are at the high-frequency end of the electromagnetic spectrum. They are produced by certain elements that are radioactive. X rays are very much like gamma rays, but they are usually made by special equipment. Both X rays and gamma rays penetrate living things easily.

Most of the time, you are bombarded with electromagnetic radiation from all portions of the electromagnetic spectrum, Figure 8.3*a*. Radio and TV signals pass through you; you feel infrared radiation when you sense the warmth of a radiator; X rays and gamma rays fall on you from space; and light from a lamp reflects into your eyes from the page you're reading. Of all these radiations, your eyes are able to sense only a very narrow band of wavelengths ranging from about 400 to 700 nm, Figure 8.3*b*. This band is called the **visible spectrum** and consists of all the colors you can see, from red through orange, yellow, green, blue, and violet. White light is composed of all these colors and can be separated into them by focusing a beam of

■ There is an inverse relationship between wavelength and frequency. The lower the frequency, the longer the wavelength.

■ The speed of electromagnetic radiation was computed to be about 3×10^8 m/s. The fact that the same speed was determined experimentally for light supported the hypothesis that light was a form of electromagnetic radiation.

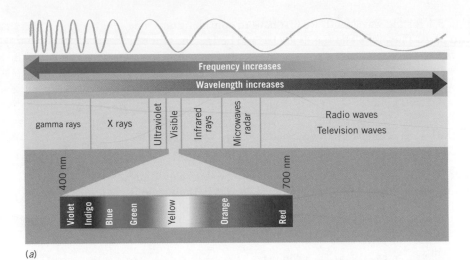

(a)

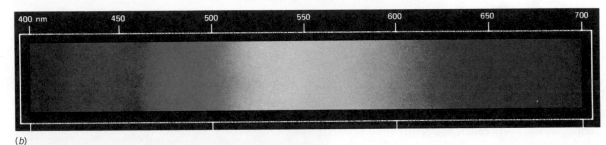

(b)

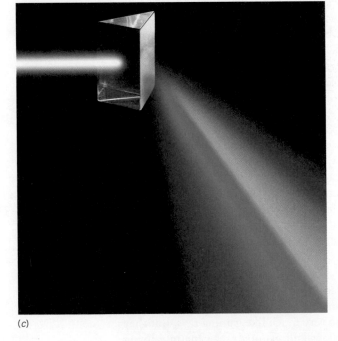

prism

(c)

Figure 8.3 | **The electromagnetic spectrum.**
(a) The electromagnetic spectrum is divided into
regions according to the wavelengths of the radiation.
(b) The visible spectrum is composed of wavelengths
that range from about 400 to 700 nm. (c) The
production of a visible spectrum by splitting white
light into its rainbow of colors.

white light through a prism, which spreads the various wavelengths apart. The visible spectrum is shown in Figure 8.3b. An illustration showing the production of a visible spectrum is given in Figure 8.3c.

The way substances absorb electromagnetic radiation often can help us characterize them. For example, each substance absorbs a uniquely different set of infrared frequencies. A plot of the intensities of absorption versus the wavelength is called an infrared absorption spectrum. It can be used to identify a compound, because each infrared spectrum is as unique as a set of fingerprints. (See Figure 8.4.) Many substances absorb visible and ultraviolet radiations in unique ways, too, and they have characteristic visible and ultraviolet absorption spectra (Figure 8.5).

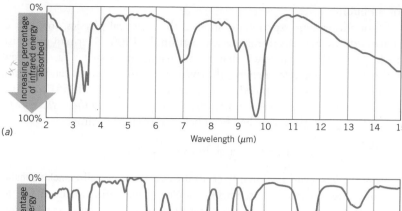

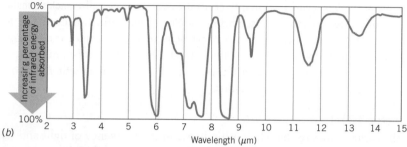

Figure 8.4 | **Absorption of infrared radiation by an organic compound.** (*a*) Infrared absorption spectrum of methanol. In an infrared spectrum, the usual practice is to show the amount of light absorbed increasing from top to bottom in the graph. Thus, for example, there is a peak in the percentage of light absorbed at about 3 μm. (*Spectrum courtesy Sadtler Research Laboratories, Inc., Philadelphia, Pa.*). (*b*) Infrared spectrum of acetone, which is found in nail polish remover mixed with water, fragrance, dyes, and sometimes moisturizers such as lanolin.

Light as a Stream of Photons

When an electromagnetic wave passes an object, the oscillating electric and magnetic fields may interact with it, as ocean waves interact with a buoy in a harbor. A tiny charged particle placed in the path of the wave will be yanked back and forth by the changing electric and magnetic fields. For example, when a radio wave strikes an antenna, electrons within the antenna begin to bounce up and down, creating an alternating current that can be detected and decoded electronically. Because the wave exerts a force on the antenna's electrons and moves them through a distance, work is done. Thus, as energy is lost by the source of the wave (the radio transmitter), energy is gained by the electrons in the antenna.

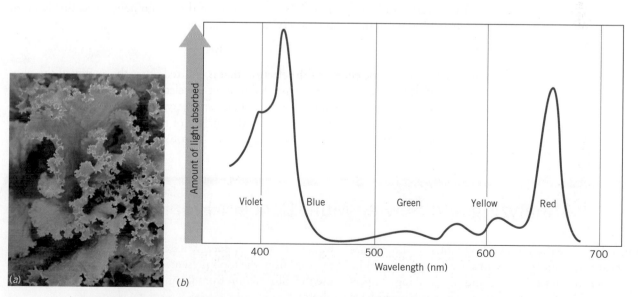

Figure 8.5 | **Absorption of light by chlorophyll.** (*a*) Chlorophyll is the green pigment plants use to harvest solar energy for photosynthesis. (*Gary Braasch/Riser/Getty*) (*b*) In this visible absorption spectrum of chlorophyll, the percentage of light absorbed increases from bottom to top. Thus, there is a peak in the light absorbed at about 420 nm and another at about 660 nm. This means the pigment strongly absorbs blue-violet and red light. The green color we *see* is the light that is *not* absorbed. It's composed of the wavelengths of visible light that are reflected. (Our eyes are most sensitive to green, so we don't notice the yellow components of the reflected light.)

Energy of a Photon

A series of groundbreaking experiments showed that classical physics does not correctly describe energy transfer by electromagnetic radiation. In 1900 a German physicist named Max Planck (1858–1947) proposed that electromagnetic radiation can be viewed as a stream of tiny packets or **quanta** of energy that were later called **photons**. Each photon travels at the speed of light. Planck proposed, and Albert Einstein (1879–1955) confirmed, that *the energy of a photon of electromagnetic radiation is proportional to the radiation's frequency,* not to its intensity or brightness as had been believed up to that time.

■ The energy of one photon is called one **quantum** of energy.

Energy of a photon

■ The value of Planck's constant is 6.626 × 10⁻³⁴ J s. It has units of energy (joules) multiplied by time (seconds).

$$\text{Energy of a photon:} \qquad E = h\nu \qquad (8.2)$$

In this expression, h is a proportionality constant that we now call **Planck's constant**. Note that Equation 8.2 relates two representations of electromagnetic radiation. The left-hand side of the equation deals with a property of particles (energy per photon); the right-hand side deals with a property of waves (the frequency). Quantum theory unites the two representations, so we can use whichever representation of electromagnetic radiation is convenient for describing experimental results.

Photoelectric Effect

One of the earliest clues to the relationship between the frequency of light and its energy was the discovery of the **photoelectric effect**. In the latter part of the nineteenth century, it was found that certain metals acquired a positive charge when they were illuminated by light. Apparently, light is capable of kicking electrons out of the surface of the metal.

When this phenomenon was studied in detail, it was discovered that electrons could only be made to leave a metal's surface if the frequency of the incident radiation was above some minimum value, which was named the threshold frequency. This threshold frequency differs for different metals, depending on how tightly the metal atom holds onto electrons. Above the threshold frequency, the kinetic energy of the emitted electron increases with increasing frequency of the light. Interestingly, however, its kinetic energy does not depend on the intensity of the light. In fact, if the frequency of the light is below the minimum frequency, no electrons are observed at all, no matter how bright the light is. To physicists of that time, this was very perplexing because they believed the energy of light was related to its brightness. The explanation of the phenomenon was finally given by Albert Einstein in the form of a very simple equation.

$$\text{KE} = h\nu - \text{BE}$$

■ Brighter light delivers more photons; higher frequency light delivers more energetic photons.

where KE is the kinetic energy of the electron that is emitted, $h\nu$ is the energy of the photon, and BE is the minimum energy needed to eject the electron from the metal's surface (this can be considered the *binding energy*). Stated another way, part of the energy of the photon is needed just to get the electron off the surface of the metal, and this amount is BE. Any energy left over ($h\nu - \text{BE}$) appears as the electron's kinetic energy.

Analyzing and Solving Multi-Concept Problems

Using your microwave oven, how many moles of photons are needed to heat your cup of tea? Consider a cup of tea to be 237 mL of water starting at 25.0 °C and the drinking temperature to be a warm 85.5 °C. Also, most microwave ovens have Klystron tubes tuned to emit microwaves that are absorbed by water molecules at a wavelength of 12.24 cm.

■ **Analysis** This problem requires that we calculate the energy needed to heat a cup of tea. We can calculate the total energy needed using the tools presented in Chapter 7. Once

we know the total energy, we can determine the number of photons from the tools presented in this section. Then we can use the information from Chapter 4 to calculate the moles of photons.

■ **Strategy** We have delineated three parts for this calculation: (1) calculate the total energy needed, (2) calculate the number of photons needed, and (3) convert the number of photons to moles of photons.

PART 1

■ **Assembling the Tools** To determine the energy needed to heat a cup of water, we need the calorimetry equation, Equation 7.7 on page 261, from Chapter 7.

$$\text{Heat energy (J)} = (\text{specific heat})(\text{mass})(\text{temperature change})$$

■ **Solution** We know that the specific heat of water is $4.184\ \text{J g}^{-1}\ ^\circ\text{C}^{-1}$, and the mass is determined by converting 237 mL of water to 237 g of water using the density of water from Chapter 2. The change in temperature is $85.5\ ^\circ\text{C} - 25.0\ ^\circ\text{C}$ or $60.5\ ^\circ\text{C}$. Putting this together we get

$$\text{Heat energy (J)} = (4.184\ \text{J g}^{-1}\ ^\circ\text{C}^{-1})\,(237\ \text{g})\,(60.5\ ^\circ\text{C}) = 5.999 \times 10^4\ \text{J}$$

Notice that we will keep one extra significant figure until the final result is calculated.

PART 2

■ **Assembling the Tools** We can calculate the energy of one photon using Equation 8.2 combined with Equation 8.1 to get

$$E = \frac{hc}{\lambda}$$

Then we divide that into the total energy from Part 1 to determine the number of photons.

■ **Solution** The energy of one photon is

$$E = \frac{(6.626 \times 10^{-34}\ \text{J s})\,(2.998 \times 10^8\ \text{m s}^{-1})}{(12.24 \times 10^{-2}\ \text{m})} = 1.623 \times 10^{-24}\ \text{J photon}^{-1}$$

The number of photons is

$$\text{Number of photons} = \frac{(5.999 \times 10^4\ \text{J})}{(1.623 \times 10^{-24}\ \text{J photon}^{-1})} = 3.696 \times 10^{28}\ \text{photons}$$

PART 3

■ **Assembling the Tools** We use the tool for converting between elementary particles to moles, more commonly known as Avogadro's number.

$$1\ \text{mole photons} = 6.022 \times 10^{23}\ \text{photons}$$

■ **Solution** We use our conversion factor to calculate moles from elementary units:

$$3.696 \times 10^{28}\ \text{photons}\left(\frac{1\ \text{mol photons}}{6.022 \times 10^{23}\ \text{photons}}\right) = 6.138 \times 10^4\ \text{mol photons}$$

Correctly rounded the answer is 6.14×10^4 mol photons.

■ **Is the Answer Reasonable?** First of all, we expect that it will take a large number of photons to heat a cup of tea, and our answer supports that expectation. We then check our calculations, first by being sure that all units cancel and second by estimating the answers. For Part 1 we estimate the answer as $4 \times 250 \times 60 = 1000 \times 60 = 60,000$ which is very close to the 5.999×10^4 we got. For Part 2 the numerical part of the numbers is $(6 \times 3)/12 = 3/2$. The exponential part of Part 2 is $-34 + 8 - (-2) = -24$. Our estimate is 1.5×10^{-24}, close to the answer we got. Similar estimates for the last two calculations also indicate that the math was done correctly.

The idea that electromagnetic radiation can be represented as either a stream of photons or a wave is a cornerstone of the quantum theory. Physicists were able to use this concept to understand many experimental results that classical physics simply could not explain. The success of the quantum theory in describing radiation paved the way for a second startling realization: that electrons, like radiation, could be represented as both waves and particles. We now turn our attention to the first experimental evidence that led to our modern quantum mechanical model of atomic structure: the existence of discrete lines in atomic spectra.

8.2 | Line Spectra and the Rydberg Equation

The spectrum described in Figure 8.3 is called a **continuous spectrum** because it contains a continuous unbroken distribution of light of *all* colors. It is formed when the light from an object that's been heated to a very high temperature (such as the filament in an electric light bulb), is split by a prism and displayed on a screen. A rainbow after a summer shower appears as a continuous spectrum that most people have seen. In this case, tiny water droplets in the air spread out the colors contained in sunlight.

A rather different kind of spectrum is observed if we examine the light that is given off when an *electric discharge*, or spark, passes through a gas such as hydrogen. The electric discharge is an electric current that *excites*, or energizes, the electrons in the atoms of the gas. When this occurs we say that an atom is in an **excited state**. The atoms then emit the absorbed energy in the form of light as the electrons return to a lower energy state. When a narrow beam of this light is passed through a prism, as shown in Figure 8.6, we do *not* see a continuous spectrum. Instead, only a few colors are observed, displayed as a series of individual lines. This series of lines is called the element's **atomic spectrum** or **emission spectrum**. Figure 8.7 shows the visible portions of the atomic spectra of two common elements, sodium and hydrogen, and how they compare with a continuous spectrum. Notice that the spectra of these elements are quite different. In fact, each element has its own unique atomic spectrum that is as characteristic as a fingerprint.

■ Atoms of an element can often be excited thermally by adding them to the flame of a Bunsen burner.

■ An emission spectrum is also called a *line spectrum* because the light corresponding to the individual emissions appear as lines on the screen.

Figure 8.6 | **Production and observation of an atomic spectrum.** Light emitted by excited atoms is formed into a narrow beam by the slits. It then passes through a prism, which divides the light into relatively few narrow beams with frequencies that are characteristic of the particular element that's emitting the light. When these beams fall on a screen, a series of lines is observed, which is why the spectrum is also called a line spectrum.

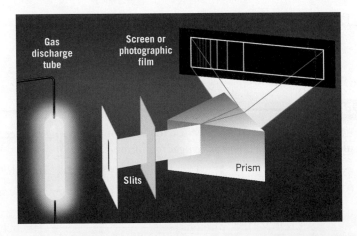

Figure 8.7 | **Continuous and atomic emission spectra.**
(*a*) The continuous visible spectrum produced by the sun or an incandescent lamp. (*b*) The atomic emission spectrum produced by sodium. The emission spectrum of sodium actually contains more than 90 lines in the visible region. The two brightest lines are shown here. All the others are less than 1% as bright as these. (*c*) The atomic spectrum (line spectrum) produced by hydrogen. There are only four lines in this visible spectrum. They vary in brightness by only a factor of five, so they are all shown.

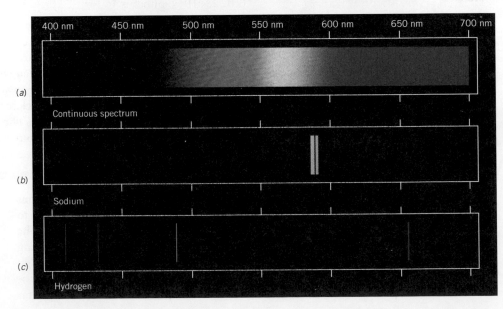

The Spectrum of Hydrogen

The first success in explaining atomic spectra quantitatively came with the study of the spectrum of hydrogen. This is the simplest element, because its atoms have only one electron, and it produces the simplest spectrum with the fewest lines.

The Rydberg Equation

The atomic spectrum of hydrogen actually consists of several series of lines. One series is in the visible region of the electromagnetic spectrum and is shown in Figure 8.7. A second series is in the ultraviolet region, and another is in the infrared. In 1885, J. J. Balmer found an equation that was able to give the wavelengths of the lines in the visible portion of the spectrum. This was soon extended to a more general equation, called the **Rydberg equation**, that could be used to calculate the wavelengths of *all* the spectral lines of hydrogen.

$$\frac{1}{\lambda} = R_H\left(\frac{1}{n_1^2} - \frac{1}{n_2^2}\right)$$

TOOLS

Rydberg equation

The symbol λ stands for the wavelength, R_H is a constant ($109{,}678$ cm^{-1}), and n_1 and n_2 are variables whose values are positive integers: 1, 2, 3 . . . . The only restriction is that the value of n_2 must be larger than n_1. (This ensures that the calculated wavelength has a positive value.) Thus, if $n_1 = 1$, acceptable values of n_2 are 2, 3, 4 . . . . The Rydberg constant, R_H, is an *empirical constant*, which means its value was chosen so that the equation gives values for λ that match the ones determined experimentally. The use of the Rydberg equation is straightforward, as illustrated in the following example.

Example 8.3
Calculating the Wavelength of a Line in the Hydrogen Spectrum

The lines in the visible portion of the hydrogen spectrum are called the Balmer series, for which $n_1 = 2$ in the Rydberg equation. Calculate, to four significant figures, the wavelength in nanometers of the spectral line in this series for which $n_2 = 4$.

■ **Analysis:** The wording of the question clearly indicates that the Rydberg equation will be used for this calculation.

■ **Assembling the Tools:** The Rydberg equation is given above. The values for n_1 and n_2 are clearly given and the only unknown left is the wavelength. We will also need the SI prefixes from Chapter 2.

■ **Solution:** To solve this problem, we substitute values into the Rydberg equation, which will give us $1/\lambda$. Substituting $n_1 = 2$ and $n_2 = 4$ into the Rydberg equation gives

$$\frac{1}{\lambda} = 109{,}678 \text{ cm}^{-1}\left(\frac{1}{2^2} - \frac{1}{4^2}\right)$$

$$= 109{,}678 \text{ cm}^{-1}\left(\frac{1}{4} - \frac{1}{16}\right)$$

$$= 109{,}678 \text{ cm}^{-1}(0.25000 - 0.06250)$$

$$= 109{,}678 \text{ cm}^{-1}(0.18750)$$

$$= 2.05646 \times 10^4 \text{ cm}^{-1}$$

Now that we have $\frac{1}{\lambda}$, taking the reciprocal gives the wavelength in centimeters.

$$\lambda = \frac{1}{2.05646 \times 10^4 \text{ cm}^{-1}}$$

$$= 4.86272 \times 10^{-5} \text{ cm}$$

Finally, we convert centimeters to nanometers.

$$\lambda = 4.86272 \times 10^{-5} \text{ cm} \times \frac{10^{-2} \text{ m}}{1 \text{ cm}} \times \frac{1 \text{ nm}}{10^{-9} \text{ m}}$$

$$= 486.272 \text{ nm}$$

The answer rounded to four significant figures is 486.3 nm. Notice that the values for n are exact numbers, and we could have kept all six significant figures.

■ **Is the Answer Reasonable?** Besides double-checking the arithmetic, we can note that the wavelength falls within the visible region of the spectrum, 400 to 700 nm. We can also check the answer against the experimental spectrum of hydrogen in Figure 8.7. This wavelength corresponds to the turquoise line in the hydrogen spectrum.

Practice Exercises

8.4 | Calculate the wavelength in micrometers, μm, of radiation expected when $n_1 = 4$ and $n_2 = 6$. Report your result to three significant figures. (*Hint:* The values of n_1 and n_2 are used to calculate the term in parentheses first.)

8.5 | Calculate the wavelength in nanometers of the spectral line in the visible spectrum of hydrogen for which $n_1 = 2$ and $n_2 = 3$. What color is this line?

The discovery of the Rydberg equation was both exciting and perplexing. The fact that the wavelength of any line in the hydrogen spectrum can be calculated by a simple equation involving just one constant and the reciprocals of the squares of two whole numbers is remarkable. What is there about the behavior of the electron in the atom that could account for such simplicity?

8.3 | The Bohr Theory

Quantized Energies of Electrons in Atoms

Earlier you saw that there is a simple relationship between the frequency of light and its energy, $E = h\nu$. Because excited atoms emit light of only certain frequencies, it must be true that only specific energy changes are able to take place within the atoms. For instance, in the spectrum of hydrogen there is a red line (see Figure 8.7) that has a wavelength of 656.4 nm and a frequency of 4.567×10^{14} Hz. As shown in the margin, the energy of a photon of this light is 3.026×10^{-19} J. Whenever a hydrogen atom emits red light, the frequency of the light is always precisely 4.567×10^{14} Hz and the energy of the atom decreases by *exactly* 3.026×10^{-19} J, never more and never less. Atomic spectra, then, tell us that *when an excited atom loses energy, not just any arbitrary amount can be lost*. The same is true if the atom gains energy.

How is it that atoms of a given element always undergo exactly the same specific energy changes? The answer seems to be that in an atom an electron can have only certain definite amounts of energy and no others. We say that the electron is restricted to certain **energy levels**, and that the energy of the electron is **quantized**.

The energy of an electron in an atom might be compared to the energy of the rabbit in the exhibit shown in Figure 8.8*b*. The rabbit trapped inside this zoo exhibit can be "stable" on only one of the ledges, so it has certain specific amounts of potential energy

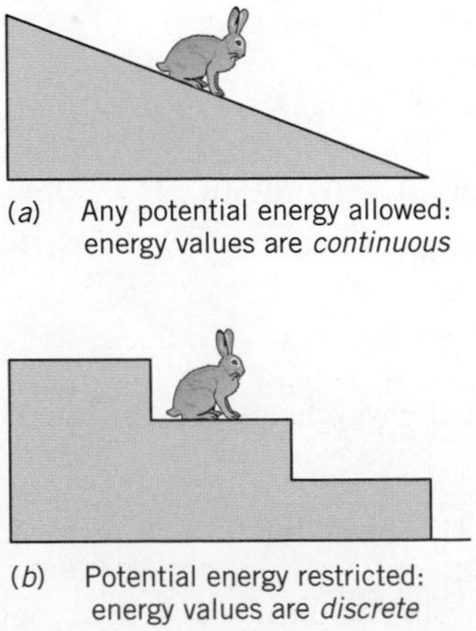

■ $E = h\nu$
  $h = 6.626 \times 10^{-34}$ J s
  $E = (6.626 \times 10^{-34}$ J s$)$
     $\times (4.567 \times 10^{14} \text{ s}^{-1})$
     $= 3.026 \times 10^{-19}$ J

Figure 8.8 | **An analogy of quantized states.**
(*a*) The rabbit is free to move to any height less than the height of the hill. Its potential energy can take on any value between the maximum (at the hill top) and the minimum (at the bottom). Similarly, the energy of a free electron can take on any value. (*b*) The rabbit trapped inside a zoo exhibit is found only at one of the three heights: at the bottom (the lowest, or *ground state*), middle, or top step. Similarly, the energy of the electron trapped inside an atom is restricted to certain values, which correspond to the various energy levels in an atom. Some of the energy levels may be unoccupied.

(*a*)   Any potential energy allowed: energy values are *continuous*

(*b*)   Potential energy restricted: energy values are *discrete* as determined by the "energy levels" of the various ledges. If the rabbit jumps to a higher ledge, its potential energy is increased. When it hops to a lower ledge, its potential energy decreases. If the rabbit tries to occupy heights between the ledges, it immediately falls to the lower ledge. Therefore, the energy changes for the rabbit are restricted to the differences in potential energy between the ledges.

■ In a certain sense we can consider that the potential energy of the rabbit at rest is quantized.

So it is with an electron in an atom. The electron can only have energies corresponding to the set of electron energy levels in the atom. When the atom is supplied with energy (by an electric discharge, for example), an electron is raised from a low-energy level to a higher one. When the electron drops back, energy equal to the difference between the two levels is released and emitted as a photon. Because only certain energy jumps can occur, only certain frequencies of light can appear in the spectrum.

The existence of specific energy levels in atoms, as implied by atomic spectra, forms the foundation of all theories about electronic structure. Any model of the atom that attempts to describe the positions or motions of electrons must also account for atomic spectra.

The Bohr Model of Hydrogen

The first theoretical model of the hydrogen atom that successfully accounted for the Rydberg equation was proposed in 1913 by Niels Bohr (1885–1962), a Danish physicist. In his model, Bohr likened the electron moving around the nucleus to a planet circling the sun. He suggested that the electron moves around the nucleus along fixed paths, or orbits. This model broke with the classical laws of physics by placing restrictions on the sizes of the orbits and the energies that electrons could have in given orbits. This ultimately led Bohr to propose an equation that described the energy of the electron in the atom. The equation includes a number of physical constants such as the mass of the electron, its charge, and Planck's constant. It also contains an integer, n, that Bohr called a **quantum number**. Each of the orbits is identified by its value of n. When all the constants are combined, Bohr's equation becomes

■ Niels Bohr won the 1922 Nobel Prize in physics for his work on his model of the hydrogen atom.

■ Classical physical laws, such as those discovered by Isaac Newton, place no restrictions on the sizes or energies of orbits.

$$E = \frac{-b}{n^2} \qquad (8.3)$$

where E is the energy of the electron and b is the combined constant (its value is 2.18×10^{-18} J). The allowed values of n are whole numbers that range from 1 to ∞ (i.e., n could equal 1, 2, 3, 4, . . . , ∞). From this equation the energy of the electron in any particular orbit could be calculated.

■ Bohr's equation for the energy actually is $E - \frac{2\pi^2 me^4}{n^2 h^2}$, where m is the mass of the electron, e is the charge on the electron, n is the quantum number, and h is Planck's constant. Therefore, in Equation 8.3, $b = \frac{2\pi^2 me^4}{h^2} = 2.18 \times 10^{-18}$ J .

Because of the negative sign in Equation 8.3, the lowest (most negative) energy value occurs when $n = 1$, which corresponds to the *first Bohr orbit*. The lowest energy state of an atom is the most stable one and is called the **ground state**. For hydrogen, the ground state occurs when its electron has $n = 1$. According to Bohr's theory, this orbit brings the electron closest to the nucleus. Conversely, an atom with $n = \infty$ would correspond to an "unbound" electron that had escaped from the nucleus. Such an electron has an energy of zero in Bohr's theory. The negative sign in Equation 8.3 ensures that any electron with a finite value of n has a lower energy than an unbound electron. Thus, energy is released when a free electron is bound to a proton to form a hydrogen atom.

When a hydrogen atom absorbs energy, as it does when an electric discharge passes through it, the electron is raised from the orbit having $n = 1$ to a higher orbit: $n = 2$ or $n = 3$ or even higher. The hydrogen atom is now in an excited state. These higher orbits are less stable than the lower ones, so the electron quickly drops to a lower orbit. When this happens, energy is emitted in the form of light (see Figure 8.9). Since the energy of the electron in a given orbit is fixed, a drop from one particular orbit to another, say, from $n = 2$ to $n = 1$, always releases the same amount of energy, and the frequency of the light emitted because of this change is always precisely the same.

The success of Bohr's theory was in its ability to account for the Rydberg equation. When the atom emits a photon, an electron drops from a higher initial energy E_{high} to a lower final energy E_{low}. If the initial quantum number of the electron is n_{high} and the final

The solar system model of the atom was the way that Niels Bohr's model was presented to the public. Today this simple picture of the atom makes a nice corporate logo, but the idea of an atom with electrons orbiting a nucleus as planets orbit a sun has been replaced by the wave mechanical model.

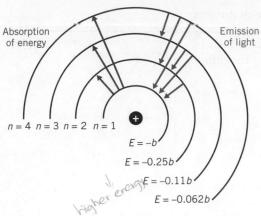

Figure 8.9 | **Absorption of energy and emission of light by the hydrogen atom.** When the atom absorbs energy, the electron is raised to a higher energy level. When the electron falls to a lower energy level, light of a particular energy and frequency is emitted.

quantum number is n_{low}, then the energy change, calculated as a positive quantity, is

$$\Delta E = E_{high} - E_{low}$$

$$= \left(\frac{-b}{n_{high}{}^2}\right) - \left(\frac{-b}{n_{low}{}^2}\right)$$

This can be rearranged to give

$$\Delta E = b\left(\frac{1}{n_{low}{}^2} - \frac{1}{n_{high}{}^2}\right) \quad \text{with } n_{high} > n_{low}$$

By combining Equations 8.1 and 8.2, the relationship between the energy "ΔE" of a photon and its wavelength λ is

$$\Delta E = \frac{hc}{\lambda} = hc\left(\frac{1}{\lambda}\right)$$

Substituting and solving for $1/\lambda$ give

$$\frac{1}{\lambda} = \frac{b}{hc}\left(\frac{1}{n_{low}{}^2} - \frac{1}{n_{high}{}^2}\right) \quad \text{with } n_{high} > n_{low}$$

Notice how closely this equation derived from Bohr's theory matches the Rydberg equation, which was obtained solely from the experimentally measured atomic spectrum of hydrogen. Equally satisfying is that the combination of constants, b/hc, has a value of 109,730 cm^{-1}, which differs by only 0.05% from the experimentally derived value of R_H in the Rydberg equation.

Because Bohr envisioned the electron as being in orbit around the nucleus, the quantized energy changes also implied that there were fixed, or quantized, orbits. Angular momentum, a quantity from classical physics, describes circular motion, and Bohr derived equations in which the angular momentum would be multiples of the quantum number n. Using these equations Bohr was able to calculate the radius of the electron orbits in his model. The smallest orbit had a size of 53 pm (picometers). This distance is now known as the Bohr radius.

Failure of the Bohr Model

Bohr's model of the atom was both a success and a failure. By calculating the energy changes that occur between energy levels, Bohr was able to account for the Rydberg equation and, therefore, for the atomic spectrum of hydrogen. However, the theory was not able to explain quantitatively the spectra of atoms with more than one electron, and all attempts to modify the theory to make it work met with failure. Gradually, it became clear that Bohr's picture of the atom was flawed and that another theory would have to be found. Nevertheless, the concepts of quantum numbers and fixed energy levels were important steps forward.

8.4 | The Wave Mechanical Model

■ All the objects that had been studied by scientists up until the time of Bohr's model of the hydrogen atom were large and massive in comparison with the electron, so no one had detected the limits of classical physics.

■ De Broglie was awarded the Nobel Prize in physics in 1929.

Bohr's efforts to develop a theory of electronic structure were doomed from the very beginning because the classical laws of physics—those known in his day—simply do not apply to objects as small as the electron. Classical physics fails for atomic particles because matter is not really as our physical senses perceive it. When physicists were proposing that photons (particles) and the waves of electromagnetic radiation were the same thing, it became apparent that particles such as electrons may behave as waves. This idea was proposed in 1924 by a young French graduate student, Louis de Broglie.

In Section 8.1 you learned that light waves are characterized by their wavelengths and their frequencies. The same is true of matter waves. De Broglie suggested that the wavelength of a matter wave, λ, is given by the equation

$$\lambda = \frac{h}{mv}$$ (8.4)

[handwritten annotations: F = mg (9.8 N/kg); N = kg m/s²; F = ma (m/s²); momenta, SI unit kg m/s or N/s; Js = h]

where h is Planck's constant, m is the particle's mass, and v is its velocity. Notice that this equation allows us to connect a wave property, wavelength, with mass, which is characteristic of a particle. We may describe the electron either as a particle or a wave, and the de Broglie relationship provides a link between the two descriptions.

When first encountered, the concept of a particle of matter behaving as a wave rather than as a solid object is difficult to comprehend. This book certainly seems solid enough, especially if you drop it on your toe! The reason for the book's apparent solidity is that in de Broglie's equation (Equation 8.4) the mass appears in the denominator. This means that heavy objects have extremely short wavelengths. The peaks of the matter waves for heavy objects are so close together that the wave properties go unnoticed and can't even be measured experimentally. But tiny particles with very small masses have much longer wavelengths, so their wave properties become an important part of their overall behavior.

Models of the Atom

Model	Approx. Date
Indivisible particle	ca 400 BC
Billiard ball elements	1803
Plum pudding model	1897
Nuclear model	1910
Solar system model	1913
Wave mechanical model	1926

Electron Diffraction and Wave Properties of Electrons

Perhaps by now you've begun to wonder whether there is any way to *prove* that matter has wave properties. Actually, these properties can be demonstrated by a phenomenon that you have probably witnessed. When raindrops fall on a quiet pond, ripples spread out from where the drops strike the water, as shown in Figure 8.10. When two sets of ripples cross, there are places where the waves are *in phase*, which means that the peak of one wave coincides with the peak of the other. At these points the amplitudes of the waves add and the height of the water is equal to the sum of the heights of the two crossing waves. At other places the crossing waves are *out of phase*, which means the peak of one wave occurs at the trough of the other. In these places the amplitudes of the waves cancel. This reinforcement and cancellation of wave amplitudes, referred to, respectively, as *constructive* and *destructive interference*, is a phenomenon called **diffraction**. It is examined more closely in Figure 8.11. Note how diffraction creates characteristic **interference fringes** when waves pass through adjacent pinholes or reflect off closely spaced grooves. You have seen interference fringes yourself if you've ever noticed the rainbow of colors that shine from the surface of a compact disk (Figure 8.12). When white light, which contains all the visible wavelengths, is reflected from the closely spaced "bumps" on the CD, it is divided into

■ Gigantic waves, called rogue waves, with heights up to 100 ft have been observed in the ocean and are believed to be formed when a number of wave sets moving across the sea become in phase simultaneously.

Figure 8.10 | **Diffraction of water waves on the surface of a pond.** As the waves cross, the amplitudes increase where the waves are in phase and cancel where they are out of phase. *(Mandy Collins/Alamy Images.)*

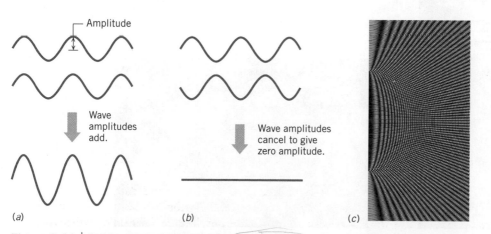

(a)   Amplitude — Wave amplitudes add.

(b)   Wave amplitudes cancel to give zero amplitude.

(c)

Figure 8.11 | **Constructive and destructive interference.** (*a*) Waves in phase produce constructive interference and an increase in intensity. (*b*) Waves out of phase produce destructive interference that results in the cancellation of intensity. (*c*) Waves passing through two pinholes fan out and interfere with each other, producing an interference pattern characteristic of waves. *(Zhen Lin/Wikipedia)*

Figure 8.12 | **Diffraction of light from a compact disc.** Colored interference fringes are produced by the diffraction of reflected light from the closely spaced spiral of "bumps" on the inner aluminum surface of a compact disc. *(Carol & Mike Werner/Visuals Unlimited)*

many individual light beams. For a given angle between the incoming and reflected light, the light waves experience interference with each other for all wavelengths (colors) except for one wavelength, which is reinforced. Our eye sees the wavelength of light that is reinforced, and as the angle changes the wavelengths that are reinforced change. The result is a rainbow of colors reflected from the CD.

Diffraction is a phenomenon that can be explained only as a property of waves, and we have seen how it can be demonstrated with water waves and light waves. Experiments can also be done to show that electrons, protons, and neutrons experience diffraction, which demonstrates their wave nature (see Figure 8.13). In fact, electron diffraction is the principle on which the electron microscope is based (See *Chemistry and Current Affairs 8.1*).

CHEMISTRY AND CURRENT AFFAIRS | 8.1

The Electron Microscope

The usefulness of a microscope in studying small specimens is limited by its ability to distinguish between closely spaced objects. We call this ability the *resolving power* of the microscope. Through optics, it is possible to increase the magnification and thereby increase the resolving power, but only within limits. These limits depend on the wavelength of the light that is used. Objects with diameters less than the wavelength of the light cannot be seen in detail. Since the smallest wavelength of visible light is about 400 nm, objects smaller than this can't be seen clearly with a microscope that uses visible light.

The electron microscope uses electron waves to "see" very small objects. De Broglie's equation, $\lambda = h/mv$, suggests that if an electron, proton, or neutron has a very high velocity, its wavelength will be very small. In the electron microscope, high-voltage electrodes accelerate electrons. This gives electron waves with typical wavelengths of about 2 pm to 12 pm that strike the sample and are then focused magnetically (using "magnetic lenses") onto a fluorescent screen where they form a visible image. Because of certain difficulties, the actual resolving power of the instrument is quite a bit less than the wavelength of the electron waves—generally on the order of 1 to 6 nm. Some high-resolution electron microscopes, however, are able to reveal the shadows of individual atoms in very thin specimens through which the electron beam passes.

(a)

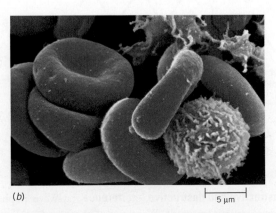

(b)

5 μm

Figure 1 A modern electron microscope (a) operated by a trained technician is used to obtain (b) electron micrographs such as the one shown here depicting red and white blood cells. *(Brand X/Superstock; Yorgos Nikas/Stone/Getty Images)*

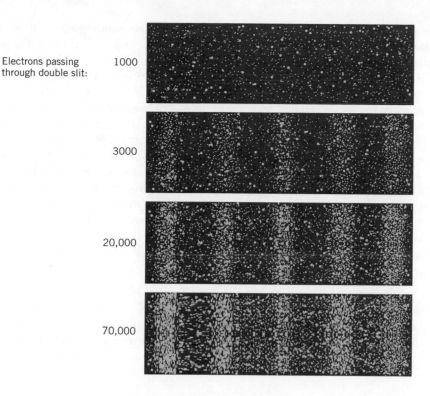

Electrons passing through double slit:

1000

3000

20,000

70,000

Figure 8.13 | **Experimental evidence of wave behavior in electrons.** (*a*) Electrons passing one at a time through a double slit. Each spot shows an electron impact on a detector. As more and more electrons are passed through the slits, interference fringes are observed. (*Semiconductor Surface Physics Group, Queen's University.*)

Quantized Energy of Bound Electrons

Standing Waves and Quantum Numbers

Before we can discuss how electron waves behave in atoms, we need to know a little more about waves in general. There are basically two kinds of waves, *traveling waves* and *standing waves*. On a lake or ocean the wind produces waves whose crests and troughs move across the water's surface, as shown in Figure 8.14. The water moves up and down while the crests and troughs travel horizontally in the direction of the wind. These are examples of **traveling waves.**

A more important kind of wave for us is the standing wave. An example is the vibrating string of a guitar. When the string is plucked, its center vibrates up and down while the ends, of course, remain fixed. The crest, or point of maximum amplitude of the wave, occurs at one position. At the ends of the string are points of zero amplitude, called **nodes**, and their positions are also fixed. A **standing wave**, then, is one in which the crests and nodes

■ The wavelength of this wave is actually twice the length of the string.

Figure 8.14 | **Traveling waves.** Waves breaking on this beach are the result of traveling waves from out in the ocean. (*Gallo Images/ Alamy*)

do not change position. One of the interesting things about standing waves is that they lead naturally to "quantum numbers." Let's see how this works using the guitar as an example.

As you know, many notes can be played on a guitar string by shortening its effective length with a finger placed at frets along the neck of the instrument. But even without shortening the string, we can play a variety of notes. For instance, if the string is touched momentarily at its midpoint at the same time it is plucked, the string vibrates as shown in Figure 8.15 and produces a tone an octave higher. The wave that produces this higher tone has a wavelength exactly half of that formed when the untouched string is plucked. In Figure 8.15 we see that other wavelengths are possible, too, and each gives a different note.

If you examine Figure 8.15, you will see that there are some restrictions on the wavelengths that can exist. Not just any wavelength is possible, because the nodes at either end of the string are in fixed positions. The only waves that can occur are those for which a half-wavelength is repeated *exactly* a whole number of times. Expressed another way, the length of the string is a whole-number multiple of half-wavelengths. In a mathematical form we could write this as

$$L = n\left(\frac{\lambda}{2}\right)$$

where L is the length of the string, λ is a wavelength (therefore, $\lambda/2$ is half the wavelength), and n is an integer. Rearranging this to solve for the wavelength gives

$$\lambda = \frac{2L}{n} \qquad (8.5)$$

We see that the waves that are possible are determined quite naturally by a set of whole numbers (similar to quantum numbers).

We are now in a position to demonstrate how quantum theory unites wave and particle descriptions to build a simple but accurate model of a bound electron. Let's look at an electron that is confined to a wire of length L. To keep things simple, let's assume that the wire is infinitely thin, so that the electron can only move in straight lines along the wire. The wire is clamped in place at either end, and its ends cannot move up or down.

First, let's consider a classical particle model: the "bead on a wire" model shown in Figure 8.16a. The bead can slide in either direction along the wire, like a bead on an abacus. If the bead's mass is m and its velocity is v, its kinetic energy is given by

$$E = \frac{1}{2}mv^2$$

The bead can have any velocity, even zero, so the energy E can have any value, even zero. No position on the wire is any more favorable than any other, and the bead is equally likely to be found anywhere on the wire. There is no reason why the bead's position and velocity cannot be known simultaneously.

Now consider a classical wave along the wire, Figure 8.16b. It is exactly like the guitar string we looked at in Figure 8.15. The ends of the wire are clamped in place, so there *must* be a whole number of peaks and troughs along the wire. The wavelength is restricted to values calculated by Equation 8.5. We can see that the quantum number, n, is just the

■ Notes played this way are called harmonics.

Notes played on a guitar rely on standing waves. The ends of the strings correspond to nodes of the standing waves. Different notes can be played by shortening the effective lengths of the strings with fingers placed along the neck of the instrument. *(SuperStock/Age Fotostock America, Inc.)*

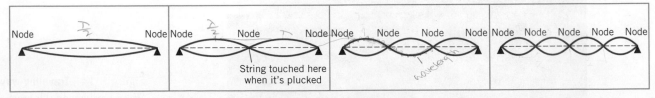

Figure 8.15 | **Standing waves on a guitar string.** Panes show 1, 2, 3, and 4 half-waves, respectively. The number of nodes is one more than the number of half-waves.

number of peaks and troughs along the wave. It has integer values (1, 2, 3, . . .) because you can't have half a peak or half a trough.

Now let's use the de Broglie relation, Equation 8.4, to unite these two classical models. Our goal is to derive an expression for the energy of an electron trapped on the wire (Figure 8.16c). The de Broglie relation lets us relate particle velocities with wavelengths. Rearranging Equation 8.4, we have

$$v = \left(\frac{h}{m\lambda}\right)$$

v = velocity of particles
m = mass of particles

and inserting this equation for kinetic energy gives

$$E = \frac{1}{2}mv^2 = \frac{1}{2}m\left(\frac{h}{m\lambda}\right)^2 = \frac{m}{2}\left(\frac{h^2}{m^2\lambda^2}\right)$$

$$= \frac{h^2}{2m\lambda^2}$$

$$\lambda = \frac{2L}{n}$$

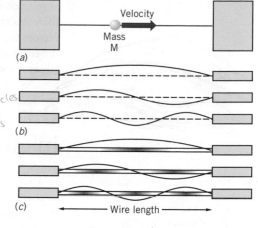

(a) Velocity Mass M

(b)

(c) Wire length

Figure 8.16 | **Three models of an electron on an infinitely thin wire of length L.** (*a*) Classical model. Bead can have any velocity or position. (*b*) Classical waves like a guitar string. (*c*) Quantum mechanical model where wave amplitude is related to the probability of the bead's position.

This equation will give us the energy of the electron from its wavelength. We can replace λ with its equivalent values shown Equation 8.5, which gives the wavelength of the standing wave in terms of the wire length L and the quantum number n. The result is

$$E = \frac{n^2h^2}{8mL^2}$$ $$\left(\frac{1}{\lambda}\right)^2 = \frac{n^2}{4L^2}$$ **(8.6)**

This equation has a number of profound implications. The fact that the electron's energy depends on an integer, n, means that *only certain energy states are allowed.* The allowed states are plotted on the energy level diagram shown in Figure 8.17. The lowest value of n is 1, so the lowest energy level (the ground state) is $E = h^2/8mL^2$. Energies lower than this are not allowed, so the energy cannot be zero! This indicates that the electron will always have some residual kinetic energy. The electron is never at rest. This is true for the electron trapped in a wire and it is also true for an electron trapped in an atom. Thus, *quantum theory resolves the collapsing atom paradox.*

Note that the spacing between energy levels is proportional to $1/L^2$. This means that when the wire is made longer, the energy levels become more closely spaced. In general, *the more room an electron has to move in, the smaller the spacings between its energy levels.* Chemical reactions sometimes change the way that electrons are confined in molecules. This causes changes in the wavelengths of light the reacting mixture absorbs. These wavelength changes are why color changes sometimes occur during chemical reactions.

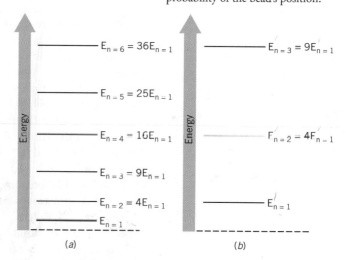

(a)   (b)

Figure 8.17 | **Energy level diagram for the electron-on-a-wire model.** (*a*) A long wire, with $L = 2$ nm, and (*b*) a short wire, with $L = 1$ nm. The value of n at each energy level indicates the number of peaks and troughs of the wave. Notice how the energy levels become more closely spaced when the electron has more room to move. Notice also that the energy in the ground state ($E_{n=1}$) is not zero.

Wave Functions

A **wave function** (symbolized by the symbol ψ, the Greek letter psi) is the quantum mechanical description of an electron. This mathematical construct, based on the quantum numbers, can be used to describe the shape of the electron wave and its energy. The wave function is not an oscillation of the wire, like a guitar wave, nor is it an electromagnetic wave. The wave's amplitude at any given point can be related to the probability of finding the electron there.

The electron waves shown in Figure 8.16c show that unlike the bead-on-a-wire model, the electron is more likely to be found at some places on the wire than others. For the ground state, with $n = 1$, the electron is most likely to be found in the center of the wire. Where the

■ The probability of finding an electron at a given point is proportional to the amplitude of the electron wave squared. Thus, peaks and troughs in the electron wave indicate places where there is the greatest buildup of negative charge.

amplitude is zero, such as at the ends of the wire or the center of the wire in the $n = 2$ state, there is a zero probability of finding the electron! Points where the amplitude of the electron wave is zero are called **nodes**. Notice that the higher the quantum number n, the more nodes the electron wave has, and from Equation 8.6, the more energy the electron has. It is generally true that *the more nodes an electron wave has, the higher its energy*.

8.5 | Quantum Numbers of Electrons in Atoms

In 1926 Erwin Schrödinger (1887–1961), an Austrian physicist, became the first scientist to successfully apply the concept of the wave nature of matter to an explanation of electronic structure. His work and the theory that developed from it are highly mathematical. Fortunately, we need only a qualitative understanding of electronic structure, and the main points of the theory can be understood without all the math.

Electron Waves in Atoms Are Called Orbitals

Schrödinger developed an equation that can be solved to give wave functions and energy levels for electrons trapped inside atoms. Wave functions for electrons in atoms are called **orbitals.** Not all of the energies of the waves are different, but most are. *Energy changes within an atom are simply the result of an electron changing from a wave pattern with one energy to a wave pattern with a different energy.*

We will be interested in two properties of orbitals, their energies and their shapes. Their energies are important because when an atom is in its most stable state (its *ground state*), the atom's electrons have waveforms with the lowest possible energies. The shapes of the wave patterns (i.e., where their amplitudes are large and where they are small) are important because the theory tells us that the amplitude of a wave at any particular place is related to the likelihood of finding the electron there. This will be important when we study how and why atoms form chemical bonds to each other.

In much the same way that the characteristics of a wave on a one-dimensional guitar string can be related to a single integer, wave mechanics tells us that the three-dimensional electron waves (orbitals) can be characterized by a set of *three* integer quantum numbers, n, ℓ, and m_ℓ. In discussing the energies of the orbitals, it is usually most convenient to sort the orbitals into groups according to these quantum numbers.

The Principal Quantum Number, n

The quantum number n is called the **principal quantum number**, and all orbitals that have the same value of n are said to be in the same **shell**. The values of n can range from $n = 1$ to $n = \infty$. The shell with $n = 1$ is called the *first shell,* the shell with $n = 2$ is the *second shell,* and so forth. The various shells are also sometimes identified by letters, beginning (for no significant reason) with K for the first shell ($n = 1$).

The principal quantum number is related to the size of the electron wave (i.e., how far the wave effectively extends from the nucleus). The higher the value of n, the larger is the electron's average distance from the nucleus. This quantum number is also related to the energy of the orbital. As n increases, the energies of the orbitals also increase.

Bohr's theory took into account only the principal quantum number n. His theory worked fine for hydrogen because hydrogen just happens to be the one element in which all orbitals having the same value of n also have the same energy. Bohr's theory failed for atoms other than hydrogen, however, because when the atom has more than one electron, orbitals with the same value of n can have different energies.

The Secondary Quantum Number, ℓ

The **secondary quantum number,** ℓ, divides the shells into smaller groups of orbitals called **subshells.** The value of n determines which values of ℓ are allowed. For a given n, ℓ can

---

■ Schrödinger won the Nobel Prize in physics in 1933 for his work. The equation he developed that gives electronic wave functions and energies is known as *Schrödinger's equation*. The equation is extremely difficult to solve. Even an approximate solution of the equation for large molecules can require hours or days of supercomputer time.

■ Electron waves are described by the term *orbital* to differentiate them from the notion of *orbits*, which was part of the Bohr model of the atom.

■ "Most stable" almost always means "lowest energy."

Regions that electron can not be found — Nodes

■ The term shell comes from an early notion that electrons are arranged in atoms in a manner similar to the layers, or shells, found within an onion.

■ Bohr was fortunate to have used the element hydrogen to develop his model of the atoms. If he had chosen a different element, his model would never have worked.

■ ℓ is also called the **azimuthal quantum number** and the **orbital angular momentum number**.

range from $\ell = 0$ to $\ell = (n - 1)$. Thus, when $n = 1$, $(n - 1) = 0$, so the only value of ℓ that's allowed is zero. This means that when $n = 1$, there is only one subshell (the shell and subshell are really identical). When $n = 2$, ℓ can have a value of 0 or 1. (The maximum value of $\ell = n - 1 = 2 - 1 = 1$.) This means that when $n = 2$, there are two subshells. One has $n = 2$ and $\ell = 0$, and the other has $n = 2$ and $\ell = 1$. The relationship between n and the allowed values of ℓ are summarized in the table in the margin.

Subshells could be identified by the numerical value of ℓ. However, to avoid confusing numerical values of n with those of ℓ, a letter code is normally used to specify the value of ℓ.

Value of ℓ	0	1	2	3	4	5	...
Letter designation	s	p	d	f	g	h	...

To designate a particular subshell, we write the value of its principal quantum number followed by the letter code for the subshell. For example, the subshell with $n = 2$ and $\ell = 1$ is the $2p$ subshell; the subshell with $n = 4$ and $\ell = 0$ is the $4s$ subshell. Notice that because of the relationship between n and ℓ, every shell has an s subshell ($1s$, $2s$, $3s$, etc.). All the shells except the first have a p subshell ($2p$, $3p$, $4p$, etc.). All but the first and second shells have a d subshell ($3d$, $4d$, etc.); and so forth.

8.6 | What are the values of n and ℓ for the following subshells? (a) $4d$, (b) $5f$, and (c) $7s$ (*Hint:* How are the subshell designations related to the value of ℓ?)

8.7 | What subshells would be found in the shells with $n = 2$ and $n = 5$? How is the number of subshells related to n?

> **Practice Exercises**

Relationship between n and ℓ

Value of n	Value of ℓ
1	0
2	0, 1
3	0, 1, 2
4	0, 1, 2, 3
5	0, 1, 2, 3, 4
n	0, 1, 2, ... $(n - 1)$

■ The number of subshells in a given shell equals the value of n for that shell. For example, when $n = 3$, there are three subshells.

The secondary quantum number determines the shape of the orbital, which we will examine more closely later. Except for the special case of hydrogen, which has only one electron, the value of ℓ also indicates the relative energies of the orbitals. This means that in atoms with two or more electrons, the subshells within a given shell differ slightly in energy, with the energy of the subshell increasing with increasing ℓ. Therefore, within a given shell, the s subshell is lowest in energy, p is the next lowest, followed by d, then f, and so on. For example,

$$4s < 4p < 4d < 4f$$
— increasing energy →

The Magnetic Quantum Number, m_ℓ

The third quantum number, m_ℓ, is known as the **magnetic quantum number**. It divides the subshells into individual orbitals, and its values are related to the way the individual orbitals are oriented relative to each other in space. As with ℓ, there are restrictions as to the possible values of m_ℓ, which can range from $+\ell$ to $-\ell$. When $\ell = 0$, m_ℓ can have only the value 0 because $+0$ and -0 are the same. An s subshell, then, has just a single orbital. When $\ell = 1$, the possible values of m_ℓ are $+1$, 0, and -1. A p subshell therefore has three orbitals: one with $\ell = 1$ and $m_\ell = 1$, another with $\ell = 1$ and $m_\ell = 0$, and a third with $\ell = 1$ and $m_\ell = -1$. Similarly, we find that a d subshell has five orbitals and an f subshell has seven orbitals. The numbers of orbitals in the subshells are easy to remember because they follow a simple arithmetic progression.

s	p	d	f	...
1	3	5	7	...

The Whole Picture

The relationships among all three quantum numbers are summarized in Table 8.1. In addition, the relative energies of the subshells in an atom containing two or more electrons are depicted in Figure 8.18. Several important features should be noted. First, observe that each orbital on this energy diagram is indicated by a separate circle—one for an s subshell,

The schrödinger Equation
$H\Psi = E\Psi$

$Df(x) = f(x)$
$D = \frac{d}{dx}$

■ Spectroscopists used m_ℓ to explain additional lines that appear in atomic spectra when atoms emit light while in a magnetic field. This explains how this quantum number got its name.

Table 8.1	Summary of Relationships among the Quantum Numbers n, ℓ, and m_ℓ			
Value of n	**Value of ℓ**	**Value of m_ℓ**	**Subshell**	**Number of Orbitals**
1	0	0	$1s$	1
2	0	0	$2s$	1
	1	$-1, 0, 1$	$2p$	3
3	0	0	$3s$	1
	1	$-1, 0, 1$	$3p$	3
	2	$-2, -1, 0, 1, 2$	$3d$	5
4	0	0	$4s$	1
	1	$-1, 0, 1$	$4p$	3
	2	$-2, -1, 0, 1, 2$	$4d$	5
	3	$-3, -2, -1, 0, 1, 2, 3$	$4f$	7

three for a p subshell, and so forth. Second, notice that all the orbitals of a given subshell have the *same* energy. Third, note that, in going upward on the energy scale, the spacing between successive shells decreases as the number of subshells increases. This leads to the overlapping of shells having different values of n. For instance, the $4s$ subshell is lower in energy than the $3d$ subshell, $5s$ is lower than $4d$, and $6s$ is lower than $5d$. In addition, the $4f$ subshell is below the $5d$ subshell and $5f$ is below $6d$.

We will see shortly that Figure 8.18 is very useful for predicting the electronic structures of atoms. Before discussing this, however, we must study another very important property of the electron, a property called spin. Electron spin gives rise to a fourth quantum number.

Figure 8.18 | **Approximate energy level diagram for atoms with two or more electrons.** The quantum numbers associated with the orbitals in the first two shells are also shown.

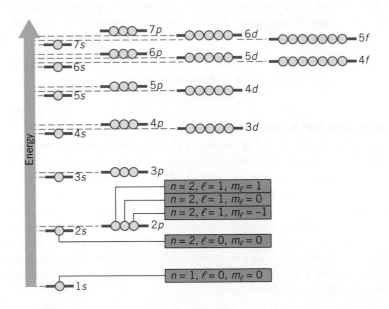

■ In an atom, an electron can take on many different energies and wave shapes, each of which is called an orbital that is identified by a set of values for n, ℓ, and m_ℓ. When the electron wave possesses a given set of n, ℓ, and m_ℓ, we say the electron "occupies the orbital" with that set of quantum numbers.

8.6 | Electron Spin

Recall from Section 8.3 that an atom is in its most stable state (its ground state) when its electrons have the lowest possible energies. This occurs when the electrons "occupy" the lowest energy orbitals that are available. But what determines how the electrons "fill" these orbitals? Fortunately, there are some simple rules that can help. These govern both the maximum number of electrons that can be in a particular orbital and how orbitals with the same energy become filled. One important factor that influences the distribution of electrons is the phenomenon known as *electron spin*.

Spin Quantum Number

When a beam of atoms with an odd number of electrons is passed through an uneven magnetic field, the beam is split in two, as shown in Figure 8.19. The splitting occurs because the electrons within the atoms interact with the magnetic field in two different ways. The electrons behave like tiny magnets, and they are attracted to one or the other of the poles depending on their orientation. This can be explained by imagining that an electron spins around its axis, like a toy top. A moving charge creates a moving electric field, which in turn creates a magnetic field. The spinning electrical charge of the electron creates its own magnetic field. This **electron spin** could occur in two possible directions, which accounts for the two beams.

Electron spin gives us a fourth quantum number for the electron, called the **spin quantum number, m_s**, which can take on two possible values: $m_s = +\frac{1}{2}$ or $m_s = -\frac{1}{2}$, corresponding to the two beams in Figure 8.19. The actual values of m_s and the reason they are not integers aren't very important to us, but the fact that there are *only* two values is very significant.

Pauli Exclusion Principle

In 1925 an Austrian physicist, Wolfgang Pauli (1900–1958), expressed the importance of electron spin in determining electronic structure. The **Pauli exclusion principle** states that *no two electrons in the same atom can have identical values for all four of their quantum numbers.* To understand the significance of this, suppose two electrons were to occupy the 1s orbital of an atom. Each electron would have $n = 1$, $\ell = 0$, and $m_\ell = 0$. Since these three quantum numbers are the same for both electrons, the exclusion principle requires that their fourth quantum numbers (their spin quantum numbers) be different; one electron must have $m_s = +\frac{1}{2}$ and the other, $m_s = -\frac{1}{2}$. No more than two electrons can occupy the 1s orbital of the atom simultaneously because there are only two possible values of m_s. Thus, the Pauli exclusion principle is really telling us that *the maximum number of electrons in any orbital is two*, and that *when two electrons are in the same orbital, they must have opposite spins*.

The limit of two electrons per orbital also limits the maximum electron populations of the shells and subshells. For the subshells we have

Subshell	Number of Orbitals	Maximum Number of Electrons
s	1	2
p	3	6
d	5	10
f	7	14

The electron can spin in either of two directions in the presence of an external magnetic field. Without a magnetic field the electrons and their spins are usually oriented in random directions.

■ Electrons don't actually spin, but it is useful to picture the electron as spinning.

■ Pauli received the 1945 Nobel Prize in physics for his discovery of the exclusion principle.

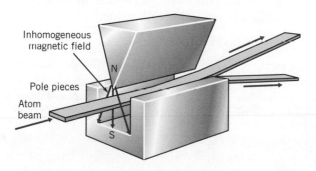

Inhomogeneous magnetic field

Pole pieces

Atom beam

Figure 8.19 | **The discovery of electron spin.** In this classic experiment by Stern and Gerlach, a beam of atoms with an odd number of electrons is passed through an uneven magnetic field, created by magnet pole faces of different shapes. The beam splits in two, indicating that the electrons in the atoms behave as tiny magnets, which are attracted to one or the other of the poles depending on their orientation. Electron spin was proposed to account for the two possible orientations for the electron's magnetic field.

The maximum electron population per shell is shown below.

Shell	Subshells	Maximum Shell Population	
1	1s	2	
2	2s 2p	8	$\overset{2s\quad 2p}{(2+6)}$
3	3s 3p 3d	18	$\overset{3s\quad 3p\quad 3d}{(2+6+10)}$
4	4s 4p 4d 4f	32	$\overset{4s\quad 4p\quad 4d\quad 4f}{(2+6+10+14)}$

The maximum electron population of a shell is $2n^2$.

Paramagnetism and Diamagnetism

We have seen that when two electrons occupy the same orbital they must have different values of m_s. When this occurs, we say that the spins of the electrons are *paired*, or simply that the electrons are *paired*. Such pairing leads to the cancellation of the magnetic effects of the electrons because the north pole of one electron magnet is opposite the south pole of the other. Atoms with more electrons that spin in one direction than in the other are said to contain *unpaired* electrons. For these atoms, the magnetic effects do not cancel and the atoms themselves become tiny magnets that can be attracted to an external magnetic field. This weak attraction of a substance containing unpaired electrons to a magnet is called **paramagnetism**. Substances in which all the electrons are paired are not attracted to a magnet and are said to be diamagnetic.

Paramagnetism and **diamagnetism** are measurable properties that provide experimental verification of the presence or absence of unpaired electrons in substances. In addition, the quantitative measurement of the strength of the attraction of a paramagnetic substance toward a magnetic field makes it possible to calculate the number of unpaired electrons in its atoms, molecules, or ions.

■ Remember that a shell is a group of orbitals with the same value of n. A subshell is a group of orbitals with the same values of n and ℓ.

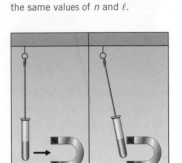

A paramagnetic substance is attracted to a magnetic field.

■ Diamagnetic substances are actually weakly repelled by a magnetic field.

8.7 | Energy Levels and Ground State Electron Configurations

The distribution of electrons among the orbitals of an atom is called the atom's **electronic structure** or **electron configuration**. This is very useful information about an element because the arrangement of electrons in the outer parts of an atom, which is determined by its electron configuration, controls the chemical properties of the element.

We are interested in the ground state electron configurations of the elements. This is the configuration that yields the lowest energy for an atom and can be predicted for many of the elements by the use of the energy level diagram in Figure 8.18 and application of the Pauli exclusion principle. To see how we go about this, let's begin with the simplest atom of all, hydrogen.

Hydrogen has an atomic number, Z, equal to 1, so a neutral hydrogen atom has one electron. In its ground state this electron occupies the lowest energy orbital that's available, which is the $1s$ orbital. To indicate symbolically the electron configuration we list the subshells that contain electrons and indicate their electron populations by appropriate superscripts. Thus, the electron configuration of hydrogen is written as

$$\text{H} \qquad 1s^1$$

Another way of expressing electron configurations that we will sometimes find useful is the **orbital diagram**. In it, a circle will represent each orbital and arrows will be used to indicate the individual electrons, head up for spin in one direction and head down for spin in the other. The orbital diagram for hydrogen is simply

$$\text{H} \qquad \underset{1s}{\text{⬆}}$$

Ground State Electron Configurations

To arrive at the electron configuration of an atom of another element, we imagine that we begin with a hydrogen atom and then add one proton after another (plus whatever neutrons are also needed) until we obtain the nucleus of the atom of interest. As we proceed, we also add electrons, one at a time to the lowest available orbital, until we have added enough electrons to give the neutral atom of the element. This imaginary process for obtaining the electronic structure of an atom is known as the **aufbau principle**. The word *aufbau* is German for *building up*.

How *s* Orbitals Fill

Let's look at the way this works for helium, which has $Z = 2$. This atom has two electrons, both of which occupy the 1*s* orbital. The electron configuration of helium can therefore be written as

$$\text{He} \qquad 1s^2 \qquad \text{or} \qquad \text{He} \quad \textcircled{$\uparrow\downarrow$}$$
$$1s$$

Notice that the orbital diagram shows that both electrons in the 1*s* orbital are paired.

We can proceed in the same fashion to predict successfully the electron configurations of most of the elements in the periodic table. For example, the next two elements in the table are lithium, Li ($Z = 3$), and beryllium, Be ($Z = 4$), which have three and four electrons, respectively. For each of these, the first two electrons enter the 1*s* orbital with their spins paired. The Pauli exclusion principle tells us that the 1*s* subshell is filled with two electrons, and Figure 8.18 shows that the orbital of next lowest energy is the 2*s*, which can also hold up to two electrons. Therefore, the third electron of lithium and the third and fourth electrons of beryllium enter the 2*s*. We can represent the electronic structures of lithium and beryllium as

$$\text{Li} \qquad 1s^2 2s^1 \qquad \text{or} \qquad \text{Li} \quad \textcircled{$\uparrow\downarrow$} \quad \textcircled{$\uparrow$}$$
$$1s \qquad 2s$$

$$\text{Be} \qquad 1s^2 2s^2 \qquad \text{or} \qquad \text{Be} \quad \textcircled{$\uparrow\downarrow$} \quad \textcircled{$\uparrow\downarrow$}$$
$$1s \qquad 2s$$

Filling *p* and *d* Orbitals

After beryllium comes boron, B ($Z = 5$). Referring to Figure 8.18, we see that the first four electrons of this atom complete the 1*s* and 2*s* subshells, so the fifth electron must be placed into the 2*p* subshell.

$$\text{B} \qquad 1s^2 2s^2 2p^1$$

In the orbital diagram for boron, the fifth electron can be put into any one of the 2*p* orbitals—which one doesn't matter because they are all of equal energy.

$$\text{B} \quad \textcircled{$\uparrow\downarrow$} \quad \textcircled{$\uparrow\downarrow$} \quad \textcircled{$\uparrow$}\bigcirc\bigcirc$$
$$1s \qquad 2s \qquad 2p$$

Notice, however, that when we give this orbital diagram we show *all* of the orbitals of the 2*p* subshell even though two of them are empty.

Next we come to carbon, which has six electrons. As before, the first four electrons complete the 1*s* and 2*s* orbitals. The remaining two electrons go in the 2*p* subshell to give

$$\text{C} \qquad 1s^2 2s^2 2p^2$$

Now, however, to write the orbital diagram we have to make a decision as to where to put the two *p* electrons. (At this point you may have an unprintable suggestion! But try to bear up. It's really not all that bad.) To make this decision, we apply **Hund's rule**, which states that *when electrons are placed in a set of orbitals of equal energy, they are spread out as much as*

■ It doesn't matter which two orbitals are shown as occupied. Any of these are okay for the ground state of carbon.

2p

possible to give as few paired electrons as possible. Both theory and experiment have shown that if we follow this rule, we obtain the electron configuration with the lowest energy. For carbon, it means that the two *p* electrons are in separate orbitals and their spins are in the same direction.[1]

Applying the Pauli exclusion principle and Hund's rule, we can now complete the electron configurations and orbital diagrams for the rest of the elements of the second period.

		1s	2s	2p

N $1s^2 2s^2 2p^3$ ⟨↑↓⟩ ⟨↑↓⟩ ⟨↑⟩⟨↑⟩⟨↑⟩

O $1s^2 2s^2 2p^4$ ⟨↑↓⟩ ⟨↑↓⟩ ⟨↑↓⟩⟨↑⟩⟨↑⟩

F $1s^2 2s^2 2p^5$ ⟨↑↓⟩ ⟨↑↓⟩ ⟨↑↓⟩⟨↑↓⟩⟨↑⟩

Ne $1s^2 2s^2 2p^6$ ⟨↑↓⟩ ⟨↑↓⟩ ⟨↑↓⟩⟨↑↓⟩⟨↑↓⟩

We can continue to predict electron configurations in this way, using Figure 8.18 as a guide to tell us which subshells become occupied and in what order. For instance, after completing the 2p subshell at neon, Figure 8.18 predicts that the next two electrons enter the 3s, followed by the filling of the 3p. Then we find the 4s lower in energy than the 3d, so it is filled first. Next, the 3d is completed before we go on to fill the 4p, and so forth.

You might be thinking that you'll have to consult Figure 8.18 whenever you need to write down the ground state electron configuration of an element. However, as you will see in the next section, all the information contained in this figure is also contained in the periodic table.

8.8 | Periodic Table and Ground State Electron Configurations

In Chapter 3 you learned that when Mendeleev constructed his periodic table, elements with similar chemical properties were arranged in vertical columns called groups. Later work led to the expanded version of the periodic table we use today. The basic structure of this table is one of the strongest empirical supports for the quantum theory, and it also permits us to use the periodic table as a device for predicting electron configurations.

Predicting Ground State Electron Configurations

Consider, for example, the way the table is laid out (Figure 8.20). On the left there is a block of *two* columns shown in blue; on the right there is a block of *six* columns shown in pink; in the center there is a block of *ten* columns shown in yellow, and below the table

---

[1]Hund's rule gives us the *lowest* energy (ground state) distribution of electrons among the orbitals. However, configurations such as

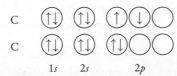

are not impossible—it is just that neither of them corresponds to the lowest energy distribution of electrons in the carbon atom.

there are two rows consisting of *fourteen* elements each shown in gray. These numbers—2, 6, 10, and 14—are *precisely* the numbers of electrons that the quantum theory tells us can occupy *s*, *p*, *d*, and *f* subshells, respectively. In fact, *we can use the structure of the periodic table to predict the filling order of the subshells when we write the electron configuration of an element.*

To use the periodic table to predict electron configurations, we follow the aufbau principle as before. We start with hydrogen and then move through the table row after row until we reach the element of interest, noting as we go along which regions of the table we pass through. For example, consider the element calcium. Using Figure 8.21, we obtain the electron configuration

$$\text{Ca} \qquad 1s^2 2s^2 2p^6 3s^2 3p^6 4s^2$$

Refer to a periodic table and Figure 8.21 as we go through the process of writing an electron configuration.

■ This would be an amazing coincidence if the theory were wrong!

TOOLS

Periodic table and electron configurations

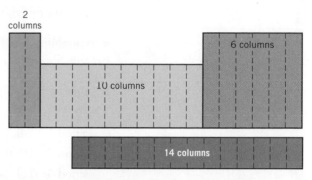

Figure 8.20 | The overall column structure of the periodic table. The table is naturally divided into regions of 2, 6, 10, and 14 columns, which are the numbers of electrons that can occupy *s*, *p*, *d*, and *f* subshells.

Filling Periods 1, 2, and 3

Notice that the first period has only two elements, H and He. Starting with hydrogen and passing through this period, two electrons are added to the atom. These enter the 1*s* subshell and are written as $1s^2$. Next we move across the second period, where the first two elements, Li and Be, are in the block of two columns. The two electrons added here enter the 2*s* subshell and are written as $2s^2$. Then we move to the block of six columns, and as we move across this region in the second row we fill the 2*p* subshell with six electrons, writing $2p^6$. Now we go to the third period, where we first pass through the block of two columns, filling the 3*s* subshell with two electrons, $3s^2$, and then through the block of six columns, filling the 3*p* subshell with six electrons, $3p^6$.

Filling Periods 4 and 5

Next, we move to the fourth period. To get to calcium in the example above we step through two elements in the two-column block, filling the 4*s* subshell with two electrons. Up to calcium we have only filled *s* and *p* subshells. Figure 8.21 shows that after calcium the 3*d* subshell is the next to be filled. Ten electrons are added for the ten elements in the first row of the transition elements. After the 3*d* subshell we complete the fourth period by filling the 4*p* subshell with six electrons. The fifth period fills the 5*s*, 4*d*, and 5*p* subshells in sequence with 2, 10, and 6 electrons, respectively.

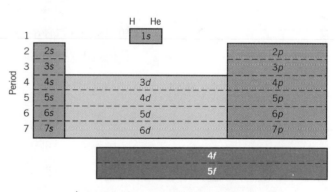

Figure 8.21 | Arrangement of subshells in the periodic table. This format illustrates the sequence for filling subshells.

Filling Periods 6 and 7

The inner transition elements (*f* subshells) begin to fill in the 6th and 7th periods. Period six fills the 6*s*, 4*f*, 5*d*, and 6*p* subshells with 2, 14, 10, and 6 electrons, respectively. There are many irregularities in this sequence, and Appendix C.1 should be consulted for the correct electron configurations. The seventh period fills the 7*s*, 5*f*, 6*d*, and 7*p* subshells. Once again, the sequence is based on the energies of the subshells, and there are many irregularities that make it advisable to consult Appendix C.1 for the correct electron configurations.

Notice that in the above patterns the *s* and *p* subshells always have the same number as the period they are in. The *d* subshells always have a number that is one less than the period they are in. Finally, the *f* subshells are always two less than the period in which they reside.

Example 8.4
Predicting Electron Configurations

What is the electron configuration of (a) Mn and (b) Bi?

■ **Analysis:** We need to write the correct sequence of subshells along with the correct number of electrons, written as superscripts, in each subshell until we have the correct number of electrons for (a) Mn and (b) Bi.

■ **Assembling the Tools:** We use the periodic table as a tool to tell us which subshells become filled. It is best to do this without referring to Figure 8.18, 8.20, or 8.21.

■ **Solution:** (a) To get to manganese, we cross the following regions of the table, with the results indicated.

Period 1   Fill the $1s$ subshell
Period 2   Fill the $2s$ and $2p$ subshells
Period 3   Fill the $3s$ and $3p$ subshells
Period 4   Fill the $4s$ and then move 5 places in the $3d$ region

The electron configuration of Mn is therefore

$$\text{Mn} \qquad 1s^2 2s^2 2p^6 3s^2 3p^6 4s^2 3d^5$$

This configuration is correct as is. However, in elements with electrons in d and f orbitals, we can also group all subshells of the same shell together. For manganese, this gives

$$\text{Mn} \qquad 1s^2 2s^2 2p^6 3s^2 3p^6 3d^5 4s^2 \qquad \text{Shell order}$$

We'll see later that writing the configuration in shell number order is convenient when working out ground state electronic configurations for ions.

(b) To get to bismuth, we fill the following subshells:

Period 1   Fill the $1s$
Period 2   Fill the $2s$ and $2p$
Period 3   Fill the $3s$ and $3p$
Period 4   Fill the $4s$, $3d$, and $4p$
Period 5   Fill the $5s$, $4d$, and $5p$
Period 6   Fill the $6s$, $4f$, $5d$, and then add 3 electrons to the $6p$

This gives

$$\text{Bi} \qquad 1s^2 2s^2 2p^6 3s^2 3p^6 4s^2 3d^{10} 4p^6 5s^2 4d^{10} 5p^6 6s^2 4f^{14} 5d^{10} 6p^3$$

Grouping subshells with the same value of n gives

$$\text{Bi} \qquad 1s^2 2s^2 2p^6 3s^2 3p^6 3d^{10} 4s^2 4p^6 4d^{10} 4f^{14} 5s^2 5p^6 5d^{10} 6s^2 6p^3$$

Again, either of these configurations is correct.

■ **Is the Answer Reasonable?** We can count the number of electrons to be sure we have 25 for Mn and 83 for Bi and none have been left out or added. Also, we can look at Appendix C.1 to check our configurations.

8.8 | Use the periodic table to predict the electron configurations of (a) Mg, (b) Ge, (c) Cd, and (d) Gd. Group subshells of the same shell together. (*Hint*: Recall which areas of the periodic table represent *s*, *p*, *d*, and *f* electrons.)

8.9 | Describe in your own words how to use the periodic table to write the electron configuration of an element.

8.10 | Use the periodic table to predict the electron configurations of (a) O, S, Se and (b) P, N, Sb. What is the same about all the elements in (a), all the elements in (b)?

8.11 | Draw orbital diagrams for (a) Na, (b) S, and (c) Fe. (*Hint:* Recall how we indicate paired electron spins.)

8.12 | Use orbital diagrams to determine how many unpaired electrons are in each of the elements (a) Mg, (b) Ge, (c) Cd, and (d) Gd.

Abbreviated Electron Configurations

It makes sense that when two atoms come together to form new chemical bonds, it must be due to the interactions of the electrons furthest from the nucleus. It also makes sense that electrons buried deep within the atomic structure most likely do not contribute significantly to the chemical properties of an atom. To emphasize and examine the nature of the electrons that are important for chemical reactions and properties, chemists often write **abbreviated electron configurations** (also called shorthand configurations).

When writing an abbreviated electron configuration for any element, Pb for example, the complete electron configuration is divided into two groups as shown below. The first group is represented by the symbol for the noble gas immediately preceding Pb in the periodic table—that is, [Xe]. The second group consists of the remaining electron configuration.

$$\text{Pb} \qquad 1s^2 2s^2 2p^6 3s^2 3p^6 4s^2 3d^{10} 4p^6 5s^2 4d^{10} 5p^6 \, 6s^2 4f^{14} 5d^{10} 6p^2$$

$$\text{Pb} \qquad\qquad\qquad [\text{Xe}] \qquad\qquad 6s^2 4f^{14} 5d^{10} 6p^2$$

The abbreviated electron configuration is often rearranged in the order of shell numbers.

$$\text{Pb} \qquad [\text{Xe}] \; 4f^{14} 5d^{10} 6s^2 6p^2$$

Some simple abbreviated electron configurations can be written for the representative elements sodium and magnesium. The complete electron configuration and the abbreviated configuration are shown below.

Na	$1s^2 2s^2 2p^6 3s^1$		Na	[Ne] $3s^1$
Mg	$1s^2 2s^2 2p^6 3s^2$		Mg	[Ne] $3s^2$

The complete and abbreviated electron configurations for a transition element such as iron are

$$\text{Fe} \qquad 1s^2 2s^2 2p^6 3s^2 3p^6 4s^2 3d^6 \qquad\qquad \text{Fe} \qquad [\text{Ar}] \, 4s^2 3d^6$$

In addition, the abbreviated electron configurations for Mn and Bi that we worked with in Example 8.4 are

$$\text{Mn} \qquad [\text{Ar}] \, 4s^2 3d^5 \qquad \text{and} \qquad \text{Bi} \qquad [\text{Xe}] \, 6s^2 4f^{14} 5d^{10} 6p^3$$

We can also write the configurations in order of shell numbers, n, as

$$\text{Mn} \quad [\text{Ar}]\, 3d^5 4s^2 \quad \text{and} \quad \text{Bi} \quad [\text{Xe}]\, 4f^{14} 5d^{10} 6s^2 6p^3$$

The discussion of valence shell electron configurations that follows illustrates how the abbreviated electron configuration, arranged in shell number order, helps emphasize the electrons that are of most interest with respect to chemical properties.

Example 8.5
Writing Shorthand Electron Configurations

What is the shorthand electron configuration of manganese? Draw the orbital diagram for manganese based on this shorthand configuration. Is manganese paramagnetic or diamagnetic?

■ **Analysis:** This is the same as the previous example except that we list only the electrons in Period 4, while the remaining electrons are represented by the symbol for the appropriate noble gas in square brackets.

■ **Assembling the Tools:** We will need the periodic table, the methods for drawing orbital diagrams, and the conditions that make an element paramagnetic (page 328).

■ **Solution:** Manganese is in Period 4. The preceding noble gas is argon, Ar, in Period 3. To write the abbreviated configuration we write the symbol for argon in brackets followed by the electron configuration that exists beyond argon. We can obtain this by noting that to get to Mn in Period 4, we first cross the "s region" by adding two electrons to the $4s$ subshell, and then go five steps into the "d region" where we add five electrons to the $3d$ subshell. Therefore, the shorthand electron configuration for Mn is

$$\text{Mn} \quad [\text{Ar}]\, 4s^2 3d^5$$

Placing the electrons that are in the highest shell farthest to the right gives

$$\text{Mn} \quad [\text{Ar}]\, 3d^5 4s^2$$

To draw the orbital diagram, we simply distribute the electrons in the $3d$ and $4s$ orbitals following Hund's rule. This gives

Mn [Ar] ↑ ↑ ↑ ↑ ↑ ↑↓
                $3d$ $4s$

Each of the $3d$ orbitals is half-filled. The atom contains five unpaired electrons and is paramagnetic.

■ **Is the Answer Reasonable?** From the left end of Period 4, count the groups needed to reach Mn. These should equal 7, the number of electrons in the orbitals beyond Ar as written above. The orbital diagram must have 7 electrons and must obey Hund's rule.

Practice Exercises

8.13 | Can an element with an even atomic number be paramagnetic? (*Hint:* Try writing the orbital diagrams of a few of the transition elements in Period 4.)

8.14 | Write shorthand configurations and abbreviated orbital diagrams for (a) P and (b) Sn. Where appropriate, place the electrons that are in the highest shell farthest to the right. How many unpaired electrons does each of these atoms have?

Valence Shell Electron Configurations

Each group within the periodic table has elements with similar chemical and physical properties that vary regularly within the group. We are now ready to understand the reason for these similarities in terms of the electronic structures of atoms.

Chemical Properties and Valence Shell Configurations

When we consider the chemical reactions of an atom (particularly one of the representative elements), our attention is usually focused on the distribution of electrons in the **outer shell** of the atom (those electrons where n is the largest). This is because the **outer electrons**, those in the outer shell, are the ones that are exposed to other atoms when the atoms react. (Later we will see that d electrons are also very important in reactions involving the transition elements.) It seems reasonable, therefore, that elements with similar properties should have similar outer shell electron configurations. This is, in fact, exactly what we observe. For example, let's look at the alkali metals of Group 1A. Going by our rules, we obtain the following abbreviated electron configurations and complete electron configurations.

Li	[He] $2s^1$	or	$1s^2 2s^1$
Na	[Ne] $3s^1$	or	$1s^2 2s^2 2p^6 3s^1$
K	[Ar] $4s^1$	or	$1s^2 2s^2 2p^6 3s^2 3p^6 4s^1$
Rb	[Kr] $5s^1$	or	$1s^2 2s^2 2p^6 3s^2 3p^6 3d^{10} 4s^2 4p^6 5s^1$
Cs	[Xe] $6s^1$	or	$1s^2 2s^2 2p^6 3s^2 3p^6 3d^{10} 4s^2 4p^6 4d^{10} 5s^2 5p^6 6s^1$

valence number = group number

The abbreviated electron configuration clearly illustrates the similarities of the outermost electron configurations in these elements. Each of these elements has only one outer shell electron that is in an s subshell (shown in bold, red, type). We know that when they react, the alkali metals each lose one electron to form ions with a charge of 1+. For each, the electron that is lost is this outer s electron, and the electron configuration of the ion that is formed is the same as that of the preceding noble gas.

Li$^+$	$1s^2$		He	$1s^2$
Na$^+$	$1s^2 2s^2 2p^6$		Ne	$1s^2 2s^2 2p^6$
K$^+$	$1s^2 2s^2 2p^6 3s^2 3p^6$		Ar	$1s^2 2s^2 2p^6 3s^2 3p^6$

etc.

If you write the abbreviated electron configurations of the members of any of the groups in the periodic table, you will find the same kind of similarity among the configurations of the outer shell electrons. The differences are in the value of the principal quantum number of these outer electrons.

For the representative elements (those in the longer columns), the only electrons that are normally important in controlling chemical properties are the ones in the outer shell. This outer shell is known as the **valence shell**, and it is always the occupied shell with the largest value of n. The electrons in the valence shell are called **valence electrons**. (The term *valence* comes from the study of chemical bonding and relates to the combining capacity of an element, but that's not important here.)

For the representative elements it is very easy to determine the electron configuration of the valence shell by using the periodic table. *The valence shell always consists of just the s and p subshells that we encounter crossing the period that contains the element in question.* Thus, to determine the valence shell configuration of sulfur, a Period 3 element, we note that to reach sulfur in Period 3 we need to place two electrons into the $3s$ and four electrons into the $3p$ subshells. The valence shell configuration of sulfur is therefore

S $3s^2 3p^4$

and we can say that sulfur has six valence electrons.

TOOLS

Periodic table and chemical properties

Example 8.6
Writing Valence Shell Configurations

Predict the electron configuration of the valence shell of arsenic ($Z = 33$).

■ **Analysis:** To determine the number of s and p electrons in the highest shell, we write the electron configuration grouping the subshells in each shell together.

■ **Assembling the Tools:** Our tools are the periodic table and the definition of valence shell electrons.

■ **Solution:** To reach arsenic in Period 4, we add electrons to the $4s$, $3d$, and $4p$ subshells. However, the $3d$ is not part of the fourth shell and therefore not part of the valence shell, so all we need be concerned with are the electrons in the $4s$ and $4p$ subshells. This gives us the valence shell configuration of arsenic,

$$\text{As} \qquad 4s^2 4p^3$$

■ **Is the Answer Reasonable?** We can check that only s and p electrons are counted and that there are five valence electrons. The answer does seem reasonable.

Practice Exercises

8.15 | Give an example of a valence shell with more than eight electrons. If that is not possible, explain why. (*Hint:* Are there any elements in which the highest numbered d subshell electrons are equal to the highest numbered s or p shell electrons?)

8.16 | What is the valence shell electron configuration of (a) Se, (b) Sn, and (c) I? How many valence electrons do each of these elements have?

Some Unexpected Electron Configurations

The rules you've learned for predicting electron configurations work most of the time, but not always. Appendix C.1 gives the electron configurations of all of the elements as determined experimentally. Close examination reveals that there are quite a few exceptions to the rules. Some of these exceptions are important to us because they occur with common elements.

Two important exceptions are for chromium and copper. Following the rules, we would expect the configurations of chromium and copper to be

$$\text{Cr} \qquad [\text{Ar}]\ 3d^4 4s^2$$
$$\text{Cu} \qquad [\text{Ar}]\ 3d^9 4s^2$$

However, the actual electron configurations, determined experimentally, are

$$\text{Cr} \qquad [\text{Ar}]\ 3d^5 4s^1$$
$$\text{Cu} \qquad [\text{Ar}]\ 3d^{10} 4s^1$$

The corresponding orbital diagrams are

Notice that for chromium, an electron is "borrowed" from the $4s$ subshell to give a $3d$ subshell that is exactly half-filled. For copper the $4s$ electron is borrowed to give a completely filled 3*d* subshell. A similar thing happens with silver and gold, which have filled 4*d* and 5*d* subshells, respectively.

$$\text{Ag} \qquad [\text{Kr}]\, 4d^{10}5s^1$$
$$\text{Au} \qquad [\text{Xe}]\, 4f^{14}5d^{10}6s^1$$

Apparently, half-filled and filled *d* subshells (particularly the latter) have some special stability that makes such borrowing energetically favorable. This subtle but nevertheless important phenomenon affects not only the ground state configurations of atoms but also the relative stabilities of some of the ions formed by the transition elements. Similar irregularities occur among the lanthanide and actinide elements.

8.9 | Atomic Orbitals: Shapes and Orientations

To picture what electrons are doing within the atom, we are faced with imagining an object that behaves like a particle in some experiments and like a wave in others. There is nothing in our worldly experience that is comparable. Fortunately we can still think of the electron as a particle in the usual sense by speaking in terms of the statistical probability of the electron being found at a particular place. We can then use quantum mechanics to mathematically connect the particle and wave representations of the electron. Even though we may have trouble imagining an object that can be represented both ways, mathematics describes its behavior very accurately.

Describing the electron's position in terms of statistical probability is based on more than simple convenience. The German physicist Werner Heisenberg showed mathematically that it is impossible to measure with complete precision both a particle's velocity and position at the same instant. To measure an electron's position or velocity, we have to bounce another particle, such as a photon, off it. Thus, the very act of making the measurement alters the electron's position and velocity. We cannot determine both exact position and exact velocity simultaneously, no matter how cleverly we make the measurements. This is the Heisenberg **uncertainty principle**. The theoretical limitations on measuring speed and position are not significant for large objects. However, for small particles such as the electron, these limitations prevent us from ever knowing or predicting where in an atom an electron will be at a particular instant, so we speak of probabilities instead.

Wave mechanics views the probability of finding an electron at a given point in space as equal to the square of the amplitude of the electron wave (given by the square of the wave function, ψ^2) at that point. It seems quite reasonable to relate probability to amplitude, or intensity, because where a wave is intense its presence is strongly felt. The amplitude is squared because, mathematically, the amplitude can be either positive or negative, but probability only makes sense if it is positive. Squaring the amplitude assures us that the probabilities will be positive. We need not be very concerned about this point, however.

The notion of electron probability leads to three very important and frequently used concepts. One is that an electron behaves as if it were spread out around the nucleus in a sort of **electron cloud**. Figure 8.22*a* is a *dot-density diagram* that illustrates the way the probability of finding the electron varies in space for a 1*s* orbital. In those places where the dot density is large (i.e., where there are large numbers of dots per unit volume), the amplitude of the wave is large and the probability of finding the electron is also large.

The second important concept that stems from the notion that the electron probability varies from place to place is **electron density**, which relates to how much of the electron's charge is packed into a given region of space. In regions of high probability there is a high concentration of electrical charge (and mass) and the electron density is large; in regions of low probability, the electron density is small. Figure 8.22*b* shows how the electron probability for a 1*s* orbital varies as we move away from the nucleus. As you might expect, the

■ The uncertainty principle is often stated mathematically as

$$\Delta x = \frac{h}{4\pi m}\left(\frac{1}{\Delta v}\right)$$

where Δx is the minimum uncertainty in the particle's location, h is Planck's constant, m is the mass of the particle, and Δv is the minimum uncertainty in the particle's velocity. Notice that we can generally measure the particle's location more precisely if the particle is heavier. Notice also that the greater the uncertainty in the velocity, the smaller the uncertainty in the particle's location.

■ The amplitude of an electron wave is described by a **wave function**, which is usually given the symbol ψ (the Greek letter psi). The probability of finding the electron in a given location is given by ψ^2. The sign of the wave function is important when they are combined, as we discuss in Chapter 10.

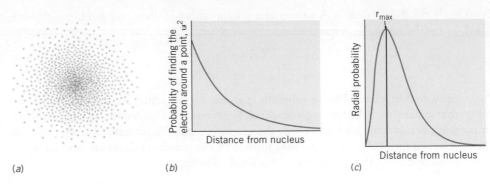

(a)   (b)   (c)

Figure 8.22 | **Electron distribution in the 1s orbital of a hydrogen atom.** (a) A dot-density diagram that illustrates the electron probability distribution for a 1s electron. (b) A graph that shows how the probability of finding the 1s electron around a given point, ψ^2, decreases as the distance from the nucleus increases. (c) A graph of the radial probability distribution of a 1s electron that shows the probability of finding the 1s electron in a volume between r and $r + x$ from the nucleus. The maximum is the same as the Bohr radius.

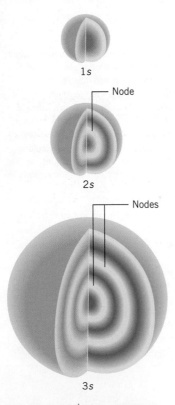

Figure 8.23 | **Size variations among s orbitals.** The orbitals become larger as the principal quantum number, n, becomes larger.

probability of finding the electron close to the nucleus is large and decreases with increasing distance from the nucleus.

In a third view we ask ourselves, "What is the probability that an electron will occupy a thin spherical shell from r to $r + x$, where x is very small, away from the nucleus?" If we plot the probabilities for these shells, the graph that we get looks like Figure 8.22c. This is called a radial distribution plot. Interestingly, the maximum for such a plot for the hydrogen atom falls precisely at 53 pm, the Bohr radius.

Remember that an electron confined to a tiny space no longer behaves much like a particle. It's more like a cloud of negative charge. Like clouds made of water vapor, the density of the cloud varies from place to place. In some places the cloud is dense; in others the cloud is thinner and may be entirely absent. This is a useful picture to keep in mind as you try to visualize the shapes of atomic orbitals.

Shapes and Sizes of s and p Orbitals

In looking at the way the electron density distributes itself in atomic orbitals, we are interested in three things—the *shape* of the orbital, its *size*, and its *orientation* in space relative to other orbitals.

The electron density in an orbital doesn't end abruptly at some particular distance from the nucleus. It gradually fades away. Therefore, to define the size and shape of an orbital, it is useful to picture some imaginary surface enclosing, say, 90% of the electron density of the orbital, and on which the probability of finding the electron is everywhere the same. For the 1s orbital in Figure 8.22, we find that if we go out a given distance from the nucleus in *any* direction, the probability of finding the electron is the same. This means that all the points of equal probability lie on the surface of a sphere, so we can say that the shape of the orbital is spherical. In fact, all s orbitals are spherical. As suggested earlier, their sizes increase with increasing n. This is illustrated in Figure 8.23. Notice that beginning with the 2s orbital, there are certain places where the electron density drops to zero. These are spherically shaped nodes of the s orbital electron waves. It is interesting that electron waves have nodes just like the waves on a guitar string. For s orbital electron waves, however, the nodes consist of imaginary spherical *surfaces* on which the electron density is zero.

The p orbitals are quite different from s orbitals, as shown in Figure 8.24. Notice that the electron density is equally distributed in two regions on opposite sides of the nucleus. Figure 8.24a illustrates the two "lobes" of *a single 2p orbital*. Between the lobes is a **nodal plane**—an imaginary flat surface on which every point has an electron density of zero. The

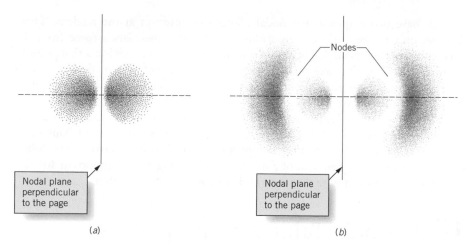

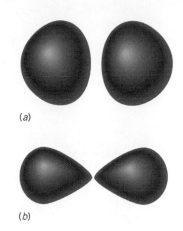

Figure 8.24 | **Distribution of electron density in *p* orbitals.** (*a*) Dot-density diagram that represents a cross section of the probability distribution in a 2*p* orbital. There is a nodal plane between the two lobes of the orbital. (*b*) Cross section of a 3*p* orbital. Note the nodes in the electron density that are in addition to the nodal plane passing through the nucleus.

Figure 8.25 | **Representations of the shapes of *p* orbitals.** (*a*) Shape of a surface of constant probability for a 2*p* orbital. (*b*) A simplified representation of a *p* orbital that emphasizes the directional nature of the orbital.

size of the *p* orbitals also increases with increasing *n* as illustrated by the cross section of a 3*p* orbital in Figure 8.24*b*. The 3*p* and higher *p* orbitals have additional nodes besides the nodal plane that passes through the nucleus.

Figure 8.25*a* illustrates the shape of a surface of constant probability for a 2*p* orbital. Often chemists will simplify this shape by drawing two "balloons" connected at the nucleus and pointing in opposite directions as shown in Figure 8.25*b*. Both representations emphasize the point that a *p* orbital has two equal-sized lobes that extend in opposite directions along a line that passes through the nucleus.

Orientations of *p* Orbitals

As you've learned, a *p* subshell consists of three orbitals of equal energy. Wave mechanics tells us that the lines along which the orbitals have their maximum electron densities are oriented at 90° angles to each other, corresponding to the axes of an imaginary *xyz* coordinate system (Figure 8.26). For convenience in referring to the individual *p* orbitals they are often labeled according to the axis along which they lie. The *p* orbital concentrated along the *x* axis is labeled p_x, and so forth.

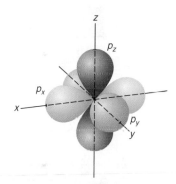

Figure 8.26 | **The orientations of the three *p* orbitals in a *p* subshell.** Because the directions of maximum electron density lie along lines that are mutually perpendicular, like the axes of an *xyz* coordinate system, it is convenient to label the orbitals p_x, p_y, and p_z.

Shapes and Orientations of *d* Orbitals in a *d* Subshell

The shapes of the *d* orbitals, illustrated in Figure 8.27, are a bit more complex than are those of the *p* orbitals. For clarity we do not attempt to draw all five *d* orbitals at the same time on the same set of coordinate axes as we did for the *p* orbitals. Notice that four of the five *d* orbitals have the same shape and consist of four lobes of electron density. These four *d*

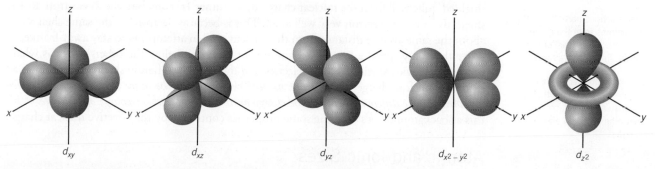

Figure 8.27 | **The shapes and directional properties of the five orbitals of a *d* subshell.**

orbitals each have two perpendicular nodal planes that intersect at the nucleus. These orbitals differ only in their orientations around the nucleus (their labels come from the mathematics of wave mechanics). The fifth d orbital, labeled d_{z^2}, has two lobes that point in opposite directions along the z axis plus a doughnut-shaped ring of electron density around the center that lies in the x–y plane. The two nodes for the d_{z^2} orbital are conic surfaces whose peaks meet at the nucleus. We will see that the d orbitals are important in the formation of chemical bonds in certain molecules, and that their shapes and orientations are important in understanding the properties of the transition metals, which we will discuss in Chapter 22.

The shapes of the f orbitals are more complex than the d orbitals, having more lobes, nodes, and a variety of shapes. Use of f orbitals for bonding is not important for this course. However, we should note that each f orbital has three nodal planes.

■ The f orbitals are even more complex than the d orbitals, but we will have no need to discuss their shapes.

8.10 | Periodic Table and Properties of the Elements

There are many chemical and physical properties that vary in a more or less systematic way according to an element's position in the periodic table. For example, in Chapter 3 we noted that the metallic character of the elements increases from top to bottom in a group and decreases from left to right across a period. In this section we discuss several physical properties of the elements that have an important influence on chemical properties. We will see how these properties correlate with an atom's electron configuration, and because electron configuration is also related to the location of an element in the periodic table, we will study their periodic variations as well.

Effective Nuclear Charge

Many of an atom's properties are determined by the amount of positive charge felt by the atom's outer electrons. Except for hydrogen, this positive charge is always *less* than the full nuclear charge, because the negative charge of the electrons in inner shells partially offsets, or "neutralizes," the positive charge of the nucleus.

To gain a better understanding of this, consider the element lithium, which has the electron configuration $1s^2 2s^1$. The **core electrons** ($1s^2$), which lie beneath the valence shell ($2s^1$), are tightly packed around the nucleus and for the most part lie between the nucleus and the electron in the outer shell. This core has a charge of 2– and it surrounds a nucleus that has a charge of 3+. When the outer $2s$ electron "looks toward" the center of the atom, it "sees" the 3+ charge of the nucleus reduced to only about 1+ because of the intervening 2– charge of the core. In other words, the 2– charge of the core effectively neutralizes two of the positive charges of the nucleus, so the net charge that the outer electron feels, which we call the **effective nuclear charge**, is only about 1+. This is illustrated in an overly simplified way in Figure 8.28.

Although electrons in inner shells shield the electrons in outer shells quite effectively from the nuclear charge, electrons in the *same* shell are much less effective at shielding each other. For example, in the element beryllium ($1s^2 2s^2$) each of the electrons in the outer $2s$ orbital is shielded quite well from the nuclear charge by the inner $1s^2$ core, but one $2s$ electron doesn't shield the other $2s$ electron very well at all. This is because electrons in the same shell are at about the same average distance from the nucleus, and in attempting to stay away from each other they only spend a very small amount of time one below the other, which is what's needed to provide shielding. Since electrons in the same shell hardly shield each other at all from the nuclear charge, *the effective nuclear charge felt by the outer electrons is determined primarily by the difference between the charge on the nucleus and the charge on the core.* With this as background, let's examine some properties controlled by the effective nuclear charge.

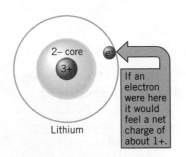

Figure 8.28 | Effective nuclear charge. If the 2– charge of the $1s^2$ core of lithium were 100% effective at shielding the $2s$ electron from the nucleus, the valence electron would feel an effective nuclear charge of only about 1+.

■ The inner electrons partially shield the outer electrons from the nucleus, so the outer electrons "feel" only a fraction of the full nuclear charge.

■ An electron spends very little time between the nucleus and another electron in the same shell, so it shields that other electron poorly.

Atomic and Ionic Sizes

The wave nature of the electron makes it difficult to define exactly what we mean by the "size" of an atom or ion. As we've seen, the electron cloud doesn't simply stop at some particular distance from the nucleus; instead it gradually fades away. Nevertheless, atoms and ions do behave in many ways as though they have characteristic sizes. For example, in a whole host of hydrocarbons, ranging from methane (CH_4, natural gas) to octane (C_8H_{18}, in gasoline) to many others, the distance between the nuclei of carbon and hydrogen atoms is virtually the same. This would suggest that carbon and hydrogen have the same relative sizes in each of these compounds.

■ The C—H distance in most hydrocarbons is about 110 pm (110×10^{-12} m).

Experimental measurements reveal that the diameters of atoms range from about 1.4×10^{-10} to 5.7×10^{-10} m. Their radii, which is the usual way that size is specified, range from about 7.0×10^{-11} to 2.9×10^{-10} m. Such small numbers are difficult to comprehend. A million carbon atoms placed side by side in a line would extend a little less than 0.2 mm, or about the diameter of the period at the end of this sentence.

The sizes of atoms and ions are rarely expressed in meters because the numbers are so cumbersome. Instead, a unit is chosen that makes the values easier to comprehend. A unit that scientists have traditionally used is called the **angstrom** (symbolized **Å**), which is defined as

$$1 \text{ Å} = 1 \times 10^{-10} \text{ m}$$

■ The angstrom is named after Anders Jonas Ångström (1814–1874), a Swedish physicist who was the first to measure the wavelengths of the four most prominent lines of the hydrogen spectrum.

However, the angstrom is not an SI unit, and in many current scientific journals, atomic dimensions are given in picometers, or sometimes in nanometers (l pm = 10^{-12} m and 1 nm = 10^{-9} m). In this book, we will normally express atomic dimensions in picometers, but because much of the scientific literature has these quantities in angstroms, you may someday find it useful to remember the conversions:

$$1 \text{ Å} = 100 \text{ pm}$$
$$1 \text{ Å} = 0.1 \text{ nm}$$

Periodic Variations

The variations in atomic radii within the periodic table are illustrated in Figure 8.29. There we see that atoms generally become larger going from top to bottom in a group, and they become smaller going from left to right across a period. To understand these variations we must consider two factors. One is the value of the principal quantum number of the valence electrons, and the other is the effective nuclear charge felt by the valence electrons.

■ Large atoms are found in the lower left of the periodic table, and small atoms are found in the upper right.

Going from top to bottom within a group, the effective nuclear charge felt by the outer electrons remains nearly constant, while the principal quantum number of the valence shell increases. For example, consider the elements of Group 1A. For lithium, the valence shell configuration is $2s^1$; for sodium, it is $3s^1$; for potassium, it is $4s^1$; and so forth. For each of these elements, the core has a negative charge that is one less than the nuclear charge, so the valence electron of each experiences a nearly constant effective nuclear charge of about 1+. However, as we descend the group, the value of n for the valence shell increases, and as you learned in Section 8.5, the larger the value of n, the larger the orbital. Therefore, the atoms become larger as we go down a group simply because the orbitals containing the valence electrons become larger. This same argument applies whether the valence shell orbitals are s or p.

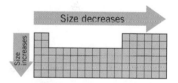

General variation of atomic size within the periodic table.

Periodic trends in atomic size

Moving from left to right across a period, electrons are added to the same shell. The orbitals holding the valence electrons all have the *same* value of n. In this case we have to examine the variation in the effective nuclear charge felt by the valence electrons.

As we move from left to right across a period, the nuclear charge increases, and the outer shells of the atoms become more populated but the inner core remains the same. For example, from lithium to fluorine the nuclear charge increases from 3+ to 9+. The core ($1s^2$) stays the same, however. As a result, the outer electrons feel an increase in positive charge (i.e., effective nuclear charge), which causes them to be drawn inward and thereby causes the sizes of the atoms to decrease.

Across a row of transition elements or inner transition elements, the size variations are less pronounced than among the representative elements. This is because the outer shell configuration remains essentially the same while an inner shell is filled. From atomic numbers 21 to 30, for example, the outer electrons occupy the $4s$ subshell while the underlying $3d$ subshell is gradually completed. The amount of shielding provided by the addition of electrons to this inner $3d$ level is greater than the amount of shielding that would occur if the electrons were added to the outer shell, so the effective nuclear charge felt by the outer

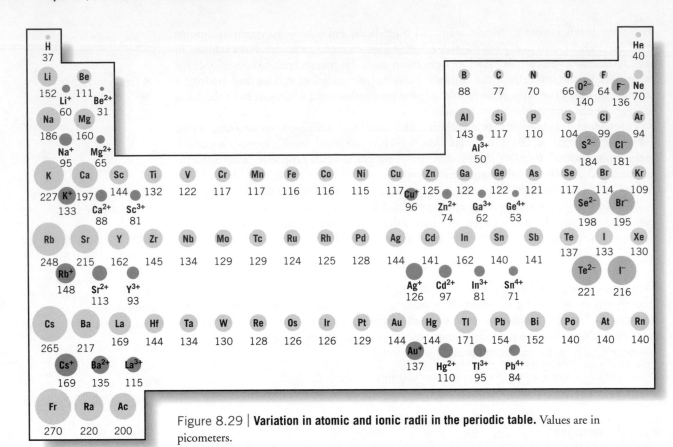

Figure 8.29 | **Variation in atomic and ionic radii in the periodic table.** Values are in picometers.

electrons increases more gradually. As a result, the decrease in size with increasing atomic number is also more gradual.

Ion Size Compared to Atomic Size

Figure 8.29 also illustrates how sizes of the ions compare with those of the neutral atoms. As you can see, when atoms gain or lose electrons to form ions, rather significant size changes take place. The reasons are easy to understand and remember.

Periodic trends in ionic size

■ Adding electrons creates an ion that is larger than the neutral atom; removing electrons produces an ion that is smaller than the neutral atom.

When electrons are added to an atom, the mutual repulsions between them increase. This causes the electrons to push apart and occupy a larger volume. Therefore, *negative ions are often about 1.5 to 2 times larger than the atoms from which they are formed* (Figure 8.30).

When electrons are removed from an atom, the electron–electron repulsions decrease, which allows the remaining electrons to be pulled closer together around the nucleus. Therefore, *positive ions are always smaller than*

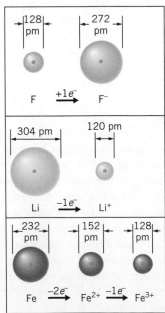

Figure 8.30 | **Changes in size when atoms gain or lose electrons to form ions.** Adding electrons leads to an increase in the size of the particle, as illustrated for fluorine. Removing electrons leads to a decrease in the size of the particle, as shown for lithium and iron.

the atoms from which they are formed. As Figure 8.29 shows, cations often are only 1/2 to 2/3 the size of their parent atom. This is also illustrated in Figure 8.30 for the elements lithium and iron. For lithium, removal of the outer $2s$ electron completely empties the valence shell and exposes the smaller $1s^2$ core. When a metal is able to form more than one positive ion, the sizes of the ions decrease as the amount of positive charge on the ion increases. To form the Fe^{2+} ion, an iron atom loses its outer $4s$ electrons. To form the Fe^{3+} ion, an additional electron is lost from the $3d$ subshell that lies beneath the $4s$. Comparing sizes, we see that the radius of an iron atom is 116 pm whereas the radius of the Fe^{2+} ion is 76 pm. Removing yet another electron to give Fe^{3+} decreases electron–electron repulsions in the d subshell and gives the Fe^{3+} ion a radius of 64 pm.

■ Li $1s^2 2s^1$
  Li$^+$ $1s^2$

■ Fe   [Ar] $3d^6 4s^2$
  Fe^{2+} [Ar] $3d^6$
  Fe^{3+} [Ar] $3d^5$

8.17 | Use the periodic table to choose the largest atom or ion in each set.

(a) Ge, Te, Se, Sn   (b) C, F, Br, Ga   (c) Cr, Cr^{2+}, Cr^{3+} (d) O, O^{2-}, S, S^{2-}
(*Hint:* Recall that electrons repel each other.)

8.18 | Use the periodic table to determine the smallest atom or ion in each group.

(a) Si, Ge, As, P   (b) Fe^{2+}, Fe^{3+}, Fe   (c) Db, W, Tc, Fe   (d) Br$^-$, I$^-$, Cl$^-$

Practice Exercises

Ionization Energy

The **ionization energy** (abbreviated **IE**) *is the energy required to remove an electron from an isolated, gaseous atom or ion in its ground state.* For an atom of an element X, it is the increase in potential energy associated with the change

$$X(g) \longrightarrow X^+(g) + e^-$$

In effect, the ionization energy is a measure of how much work is required to pull an electron from an atom, so it reflects how tightly the electron is held by the atom. Usually, the ionization energy is expressed in units of kilojoules per mole (kJ/mol), so we can also view it as the energy needed to remove one mole of electrons from one mole of gaseous atoms.

Table 8.2 lists the ionization energies of the first 12 elements. As you can see, atoms with more than one electron have more than one ionization energy. These correspond to

Table 8.2	**Successive Ionization Energies in kJ/mol for Hydrogen through Magnesium**							
	1st	**2nd**	**3rd**	**4th**	**5th**	**6th**	**7th**	**8th**
H	1312							
He	2372	5250						
Li	520	7297	11,810					
Be	899	1757	14,845	21,000				
B	800	2426	3659	25,020	32,820			
C	1086	2352	4619	6221	37,820	47,260		
N	1402	2855	4576	7473	9442	53,250	64,340	
O	1314	3388	5296	7467	10,987	13,320	71,320	84,070
F	1680	3375	6045	8408	11,020	15,160	17,860	92,010
Ne	2080	3963	6130	9361	12,180	15,240	—	—
Na	496	4563	6913	9541	13,350	16,600	20,113	25,666
Mg	737	1450	7731	10,545	13,627	17,995	21,700	25,662

Note the sharp increase in ionization energy when crossing the "staircase," indicating that the last of the valence electrons has been removed.

the stepwise removal of electrons, one after the other. Lithium, for example, has three ionization energies because it has three electrons. Removing the outer $2s$ electrons from one mole of isolated lithium atoms to give one mole of gaseous lithium ions, Li^+, requires 520 kJ; so the *first ionization energy* of lithium is 520 kJ/mol. The second IE of lithium is 7297 kJ/mol, and corresponds to the process

$$Li^+(g) \longrightarrow Li^{2+}(g) + e^-$$

This involves the removal of an electron from the now-exposed $1s$ core of lithium and requires more than thirteen times the energy used to remove the first electron. Removal of the third (and last) electron requires the third IE, which is 11,810 kJ/mol. In general, successive ionization energies always increase because each subsequent electron is being pulled away from an increasingly more positive ion, and that requires more work.

Earlier we saw that the explanation of the photoelectric effect by Einstein led to the concept of light quanta, or photons. This phenomena is used in a powerful research technique called photoelectron spectroscopy that described in *On the Cutting Edge 8.1*.

■ Ionization energies are additive. For example,

$Li(g) \longrightarrow Li^+(g) + e^-$
$\qquad\qquad IE_1 = 520 \ kJ$
$Li^+(g) \longrightarrow Li^{2+}(g) + e^-$
$\qquad\qquad IE_2 = 7297 \ kJ$
———————————————
$Li(g) \longrightarrow Li^{2+}(g) + 2e^-$
$\qquad IE_{total} = IE_1 + IE_2 = 7817 \ kJ$

ON THE CUTTING EDGE | 8.2

Photoelectron Spectroscopy

The photoelectric effect, where electrons can be ejected from a surface by a beam of light, was described earlier in this chapter. In 1921 Albert Einstein was awarded the Nobel Prize in physics for explaining this phenomenon. To do so he viewed electromagnetic radiation as particles, or photons, with each photon having a quantum of energy equal to its frequency multiplied by Planck's constant, $h\nu$. Einstein then postulated that electrons are attracted to the nucleus with a certain amount of energy that he called the binding energy, BE. He then reasoned that if a photon has more energy than an electron's binding energy, the photon would be able to eject an electron out of the atom. In simpler terms, he showed that it is the energy of the photon that ejects an electron rather than the number of photons.

In addition to the atomic view of the photoelectric process, we know that energy must be conserved. The total energy entering

the system is the energy of the photon, $h\nu$. That must exceed the binding energy, BE, and the excess energy appears as the kinetic energy, KE, of the ejected electron.

$$h\nu = BE + KE$$

Researchers can measure the energy of the incoming photon from its frequency and can measure the kinetic energies of the ejected electrons, to determine the binding energies of the ejected electrons. The binding energy is closely related to the ionization energy for a given electron.

In practice, photoelectron spectroscopy, PES, can be divided into two closely related methods. Ultraviolet photoelectron spectroscopy (UPS) uses UV radiation to eject electrons from a sample; X-ray photoelectron spectroscopy, XPS, that uses X rays. In 1981, Kai Siegbahn was awarded the Nobel

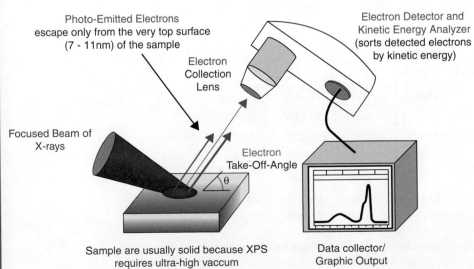

Photo-Emitted Electrons
escape only from the very top surface
(7 - 11nm) of the sample

Electron
Collection
Lens

Electron Detector and
Kinetic Energy Analyzer
(sorts detected electrons
by kinetic energy)

Focused Beam of
X-rays

Electron
Take-Off-Angle

θ

Sample are usually solid because XPS
requires ultra-high vaccum

Data collector/
Graphic Output

Figure 1 A conceptualized drawing of a photoelectron spectrometer.

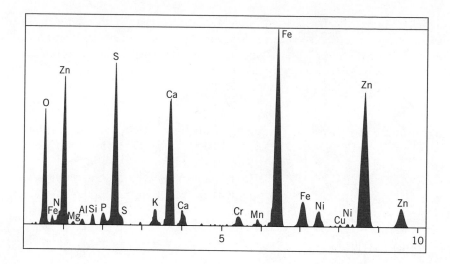

Figure 2 A conceptual graph of intensity versus kinetic energy generated by a PES experiment.

Prize in physics for the use of XPS in chemical analysis. Current research using PES involves chemical analysis, the study of surfaces and molecules that bind to them, and fine details about molecular structure. Under the appropriate conditions, the oxidation state of an atom can be determined based on the observed binding energy.

Instruments used for PES must provide a monochromatic beam (close to a single wavelength) of UV light or X rays. To ensure that the ejected electrons get to the detector before col-liding with another molecule, the sample chamber must have an ultra-high vacuum. The ejected electrons then enter a detector that monitors the number and the kinetic energy of the electrons. This information is collected by a computer and may be shown graphically on the computer monitor. See Figure 1.

The typical result of a PES experiment is a plot of the number of electrons versus the kinetic energy of the ejected electrons. Figure 2 illustrates an x-ray PES spectrum used for chemical analysis.

Periodic Trends in IE

Within the periodic table there are trends in the way IE varies that are useful to know and to which we will refer in later discussions. We can see these by examining Figure 8.31 that shows a graph of how the first ionization energy varies with an element's position in the periodic table. Notice that the elements with the largest ionization energies are the nonmetals in the upper right of the periodic table, and that those with the smallest ionization energies are the metals in the lower left of the table. In general, then, the following trends are observed.

Ionization energy generally increases from bottom to top within a group and increases from left to right within a period. Overall the ionization energy increases from the lower left corner of the periodic table to the upper right corner. This is usually referred to as a **diagonal trend**.

TOOLS

Periodic trends in ionization energy

■ It is often helpful to remember that the trends in IE are just the opposite of the trends in atomic size within the periodic table; when size increases, IE decreases.

The same factors that affect atomic size also affect ionization energy. As the value of n increases going down a group, the orbitals become larger and the outer electrons are farther from the nucleus. Electrons farther from the nucleus are bound less tightly, so IE decreases from top to bottom.

As you can see, there is a gradual overall increase in IE as we move from left to right across a period, although the horizontal variation of IE is somewhat irregular. The reason for the overall trend is the increase in effective nuclear charge felt by the valence electrons as we move across a period. As we've seen, this draws the valence electrons closer to the nucleus and leads to a decrease in atomic size as we move from left to right. However, the

Figure 8.31 | **Variation in first ionization energy with location in the periodic table.** Elements with the largest ionization energies are in the upper right of the periodic table. Those with the smallest ionization energies are at the lower left.

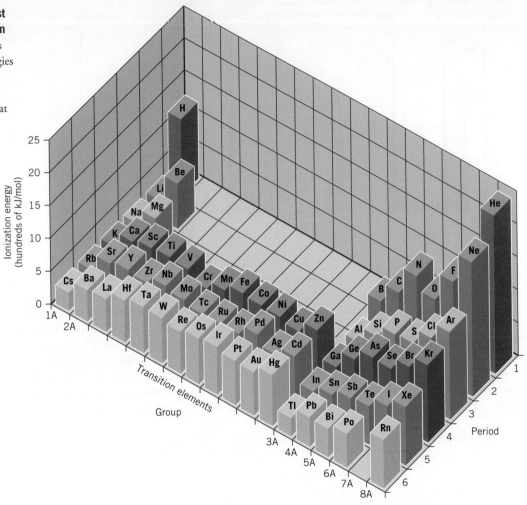

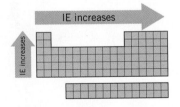

General variation of ionization energy (as an exothermic quantity) **within the periodic table.**

increasing effective nuclear charge also causes the valence electrons to be held more tightly, which makes it more difficult to remove them.

The results of these trends place elements with the largest IE in the upper right-hand corner of the periodic table. It is very difficult to cause these atoms to lose electrons. In the lower left-hand corner of the table are elements that have loosely held valence electrons. These elements form positive ions relatively easily, as you learned in Chapter 3.

Stability of Noble Gas Configurations

Table 8.2 shows that, for a given representative element, successive ionization energies increase gradually until the valence shell is emptied. Then a very much larger increase in IE occurs as the core is broken into. This is illustrated graphically in Figure 8.32 for the Period 2 elements lithium through fluorine. For lithium, we see that the first electron (the $2s$ electron) is removed rather easily, but the second and third electrons, which come from the $1s$ core, are much more difficult to dislodge. For beryllium, the large jump in IE occurs after two electrons (the two $2s$ electrons) are removed. In fact, for all of these elements, the large increase in IE happens when the core is broken into.

The data displayed in Figure 8.32 suggest that although it may be moderately difficult to empty the valence shell of an atom, it is *extremely* difficult to break into the noble gas configuration of the core electrons. As you will learn, this is one of the factors that influences the number of positive charges on ions formed by the representative metals.

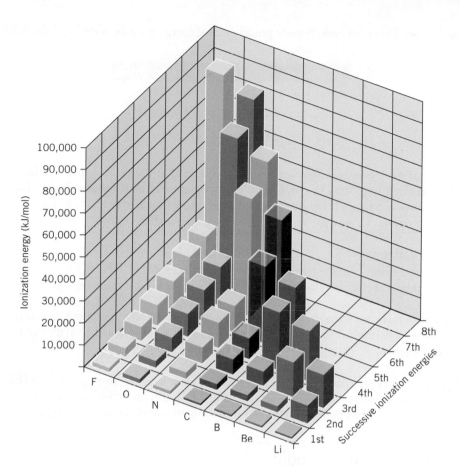

Figure 8.32 | **Variations in successive ionization energies for the elements lithium through fluorine.**

8.19 | Use the periodic table to select the atom with the most positive value for its first ionization energy, IE: (a) Na, Sr, Be, Rb; (b) B, Al, C, Si. (*Hint:* Use the diagonal relationships of the IE values within the periodic table.)

8.20 | Use Table 8.2 to determine which of the following elements is expected to have the most positive ionization energy, IE: (a) Na^+, Mg^+, H, C^{2+}; (b) Ne, F, Mg^{2+}, Li^+.

Practice Exercises

Electron Affinity

The **electron affinity** (abbreviated **EA**) *is the potential energy change associated with the addition of an electron to a gaseous atom or ion in its ground state.* For an element X, it is the change in potential energy associated with the process

$$X(g) + e^- \longrightarrow X^-(g)$$

As with ionization energy, electron affinities are usually expressed in units of kilojoules per mole, so we can also view the EA as the energy change associated with adding one mole of electrons to one mole of gaseous atoms or ions.

For nearly all the elements, the addition of one electron to the neutral atom is exothermic, and the EA is given as a negative value. This is because the incoming electron experiences an attraction to the nucleus that causes the potential energy to be lowered as the electron approaches the atom. However, when a second electron must be added, as in the formation of the oxide ion, O^{2-}, work must be done to force the electron into an already negative ion. This is an endothermic process where energy must be added and the EA has a positive value.

Change	EA (kJ/mol)
$O(g) + e^- \longrightarrow O^-(g)$	−141
$O^-(g) + e^- \longrightarrow O^{2-}(g)$	+844
$O(g) + 2e^- \longrightarrow O^{2-}(g)$	+703 (net)

Notice that more energy is absorbed adding an electron to the O^- ion than is released by adding an electron to the O atom. Overall, the formation of an isolated oxide ion leads to a net increase in potential energy (so we say its formation is *endothermic*). The same applies to the formation of *any* negative ion with a charge larger than 1−.

Periodic Variations

The electron affinities of the representative elements are listed in Table 8.3, and we see that periodic trends in electron affinity roughly parallel those for ionization energy.

> Although there are some irregularities, overall the electron affinities of the elements become more *exothermic* going from left to right across a period and from bottom to top in a group.

This shouldn't be surprising, because a valence shell that loses electrons easily (low IE) will have little attraction for additional electrons (small EA). On the other hand, a valence shell that holds its electrons tightly will also tend to bind an additional electron tightly.

Irregularities in Periodic Trends

As mentioned previously, the variation in first ionization energy across a period is not a smooth one, as seen in the graph in Figure 8.33 for the elements in Period 2. The first irregularity occurs between Be and B, where the IE increases from Li to Be but then decreases from Be to B. This happens because there is a change in the nature of the subshell from which the electron is being removed. For Li and Be, the electron is removed from the 2*s* subshell, but at boron the first electron comes from the higher energy 2*p* subshell where it is not bound so tightly.

Periodic trends in electron affinity

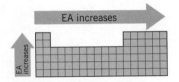

General variation of electron affinity (as an exothermic quantity) **within the periodic table.**

Table 8.3	Electron Affinities of the Representative Elements (kJ/mol)					
1A	**2A**	**3A**	**4A**	**5A**	**6A**	**7A**
H						
−73						
Li	Be	B	C	N	O	F
−60	+238	−27	−122	~ +9	−141	−328
Na	Mg	Al	Si	P	S	Cl
−53	+230	−44	−134	−72	−200	−348
K	Ca	Ga	Ge	As	Se	Br
−48	+155	−30	−120	−77	−195	−325
Rb	Sr	In	Sn	Sb	Te	I
−47	+167	−30	−121	−101	−190	−295
Cs	Ba	Tl	Pb	Bi	Po	At
−45	+50	−30	−110	−110	−183	−270

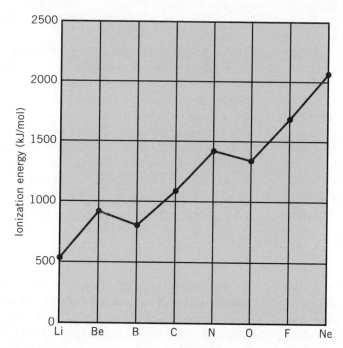

Figure 8.33 | **A closer look at the variation in ionization energy for the Period 2 elements Li through Ne.**

Another irregularity occurs between nitrogen and oxygen. For nitrogen, the electron that's removed comes from a singly occupied orbital. For oxygen, the electron is taken from an orbital that already contains an electron. We can diagram this as follows:

$$
\begin{array}{ccccc}
& 2s & 2p & & 2s & 2p \\
\text{N} & (\uparrow\downarrow) & (\uparrow)(\uparrow)(\uparrow) & \rightarrow \quad \text{N}^+ & (\uparrow\downarrow) & (\;)(\uparrow)(\uparrow) \quad + e \\
\text{O} & (\uparrow\downarrow) & (\uparrow\downarrow)(\uparrow)(\uparrow) & \longrightarrow \quad \text{O}^+ & (\uparrow\downarrow) & (\uparrow)(\uparrow)(\uparrow) \quad + e^-
\end{array}
$$

For oxygen, repulsions between the two electrons in the p orbital that's about to lose an electron help the electron leave. This "help" is absent for the electron that's about to leave the p orbital of nitrogen. As a result, it is not as difficult to remove one electron from an oxygen atom as it is to remove one electron from a nitrogen atom.

As with ionization energy, there are irregularities in the periodic trends for electron affinity. For example, the Group 2A elements have little tendency to acquire electrons because their outer shell s orbitals are filled. The incoming electron must enter a higher energy p orbital. We also see that the EA for elements in Group 5A are either endothermic or only slightly exothermic. This is because the incoming electron must enter an orbital already occupied by an electron.

One of the most interesting irregularities occurs between Periods 2 and 3 among the nonmetals. In any group, the element in Period 2 has a less exothermic electron affinity than the element below it. The reason seems to be the small size of the nonmetal atoms of Period 2, which are among the smallest elements in the periodic table. Repulsions between the many electrons in the small valence shells of these atoms leads to a lower than expected attraction for an incoming electron and a less exothermic electron affinity than the element below in Period 3.

Summary

Electromagnetic Energy. Electromagnetic energy, or light energy, travels through space at a constant speed of 3.00×10^8 m s^{-1} in the form of waves. The **wavelength**, λ, and **frequency**, ν, of the wave are related by the equation $\lambda \nu = c$, where c is the **speed of light**. The SI unit for frequency is the **hertz (Hz,** 1 Hz $= 1$ s^{-1}). Light also behaves as if it consists of small packets of energy called **photons** or **quanta**, based on the **photoelectric effect**. The energy delivered by a photon is proportional to the frequency of the light, and is given by the equation $E = h\nu$, where h is **Planck's constant**. White light is composed of all the frequencies visible to the eye and can be split into a **continuous spectrum**. Visible light represents only a small portion of the entire **electromagnetic spectrum**, which also includes **X rays, ultraviolet, infrared, microwaves,** and **radio** and **TV** waves.

Atomic Spectra. The occurrence of **line spectra** tells us that atoms can emit energy only in discrete amounts and suggests that the energy of the electron is **quantized**; that is, the electron is restricted to certain specific **energy levels** in an atom. Niels Bohr recognized this and, although his theory was later shown to be incorrect, he was the first to propose a model that was able to account for the **Rydberg equation**. Bohr was the first to introduce the idea of **quantum numbers**.

Matter Waves. The wave behavior of electrons and other tiny particles, which can be demonstrated by **diffraction** experiments, was suggested by de Broglie. Schrödinger applied wave theory to the atom and launched the theory we call **wave mechanics** or **quantum mechanics**. This theory tells us that electron waves in atoms are **standing waves** whose crests and **nodes** are stationary. Each standing wave, or **orbital**, is characterized by three quantum numbers, n, ℓ, and m_ℓ (**principal, secondary,** and **magnetic quantum numbers**, respectively). **Shells** are designated by n (which can range from 1 to ∞), **subshells** by ℓ (which can range from 0 to $n - 1$), and orbitals within subshells by m_ℓ (which can range from $-\ell$ to $+\ell$).

Electron Configurations. The electron has magnetic properties that are explained in terms of spin. The **spin quantum number**, m_s, can have values of $+\frac{1}{2}$ or $-\frac{1}{2}$. The **Pauli exclusion principle** limits orbitals to a maximum population of two electrons with **paired spins**. Substances with unpaired electrons are **paramagnetic** and are weakly attracted to a magnetic field. Substances with only paired electrons are **diamagnetic** and are slightly repelled by a magnetic field. The **electron configuration** of an element in its **ground state** is obtained by filling orbitals beginning with the 1s subshell and following the Pauli exclusion principle and **Hund's rule** (which states that electrons spread out as much as possible in orbitals of equal energy). The periodic table serves as a guide in predicting electron configurations. **Abbreviated configurations** show subshell populations outside a noble gas **core**. **Valence shell configurations** show the populations of subshells in the **outer shell** of an atom of the representative elements. Sometimes we represent electron configurations using **orbital diagrams**. Unexpected configurations occur for chromium and copper because of the extra stability of half-filled and filled subshells.

Orbital Shapes. The **Heisenberg uncertainty principle** says we cannot know exactly the position and velocity of an electron both at the same instant. Consequently, wave mechanics describes the probable locations of electrons in atoms. In each orbital the electron is conveniently viewed as an **electron cloud** with a varying **electron density**. All s orbitals are spherical; each p orbital consists of two lobes with a **nodal plane** between them. A p subshell has three p orbitals whose axes are mutually perpendicular and point along the x, y, and z axes of an imaginary coordinate system centered at the nucleus. Four of the five d orbitals in a d subshell have the same shape, with four lobes of electron density each. The fifth has two lobes of electron density pointing in opposite directions along the z axis and a ring of electron density in the x–y plane.

Atomic Properties. The amount of positive charge felt by the valence electrons of an atom is the **effective nuclear charge**. This is less than the actual nuclear charge because core electrons partially shield the valence electrons from the full positive charge of the nucleus. **Atomic radii** depend on the value of n of the valence shell orbitals and the effective nuclear charge experienced by the valence electrons. These radii are expressed in units of picometers or nanometers, or an older unit called the **angstrom (Å)**. 1 Å $= 100$ pm $= 0.1$ nm. Atomic radii decrease from left to right in a period and from bottom to top in a group in the periodic table. Negative ions are larger than the atoms from which they are formed; positive ions are smaller than the atoms from which they are formed.

Ionization energy (IE) is the energy needed to remove an electron from an isolated gaseous atom, molecule, or ion in its ground state; it is endothermic. The first ionization energies of the elements increase from left to right in a period and from bottom to top in a group. (Irregularities occur in a period when the nature of the orbital from which the electron is removed changes and when the electron removed is first taken from a doubly occupied p orbital.) Successive ionization energies become larger, but there is a very large jump when the next electron must come from the noble gas core beneath the valence shell.

Electron affinity (EA) is the potential energy change associated with the addition of an electron to a gaseous atom or ion in its ground state. For atoms, the first EA is usually exothermic. When more than one electron is added to an atom, the overall potential energy change is endothermic. In general, electron affinity becomes more exothermic from left to right in a period and from bottom to top in a group. (However, the EA of second period nonmetals is less exothermic than for the nonmetals of the third period. Irregularities across a period occur when the electron being added must enter the next higher-energy subshell and when it must enter a half-filled p subshell.)

Periodic trends are regular changes of properties within the periods and groups of the periodic table. These include the variation of atomic size, ionic size, ionization energy, electron affinity, and effective nuclear charge. Periodic and group trends in properties can often be combined into a **diagonal trend** from the lower left corner (Fr) to the upper right corner (F). Atomic size, ionization energy, and electron affinity can be viewed as diagonal trends.

Tools for Problem Solving
The following tools were introduced in this chapter. Study them carefully so you can select the appropriate tool when needed.

Wavelength–frequency relationship (page 307)
Use this equation to convert between frequency and wavelength: $\lambda \times \nu = c$

Energy of a photon (page 312)
With this tool you can calculate the energy carried by a photon of frequency ν. Also, ν can be calculated if E is known.

$$E = h\nu = h\frac{c}{\lambda}$$

Rydberg Equation (page 315)
The wavelengths of the emission spectrum of hydrogen are calculated using this equation.

Electron configurations using the periodic table (page 331)
In this chapter you learned to use the periodic table as an aid in writing electron configurations of the elements.

Periodic table and chemical properties (page 335)
Valence electrons define chemical properties of the elements. Elements within a group (family) have similarites in their valence electrons and thus similar chemical properties.

Periodic trends in atomic and ionic size (pages 341 and 342)
We use the periodic table to predict relative sizes of atoms and ions.

Periodic trends in ionization energy (page 345)
This is used to compare the case with which atoms of the elements lose electrons.

Periodic trends in electron affinity (page 348)
Trends help in comparing the tendency of atoms or ions to gain electrons.

PLUS = *WileyPLUS*, an online teaching and learning solution. *Note to instructors:* Many of the end-of-chapter problems are available for assignment via the *WileyPLUS* system. **www.wileyplus.com.** ILW = An Interactive Learningware solution is available for this problem. OH = An Office Hour video is available for this problem. Review Problems are presented in pairs separated by blue rules. Answers to problems whose numbers appear in blue are given in Appendix B. More challenging problems are marked with an asterisk *.

Review Questions

Electromagnetic Radiation

8.1 In general terms, why do we call light *electromagnetic radiation*?

8.2 In general, what does the term *frequency* imply? What is meant by the term *frequency of light*? What symbol is used for it, and what is the SI unit (and symbol) for frequency?

8.3 What is meant by the term *wavelength* of light? What symbol is used for it?

8.4 Sketch a picture of a wave and label its wavelength and its amplitude.

8.5 Which property of light waves is a measure of the brightness of the light? Which specifies the color of the light? Which is related to the energy of the light?

8.6 Arrange the following regions of the electromagnetic spectrum in order of increasing wavelength (i.e., shortest wavelength ⟶ longest wavelength): microwave, TV, X rays, ultraviolet, visible, infrared, gamma rays.

8.7 What wavelength range is covered by the *visible spectrum*?

8.8 Arrange the following colors of visible light in order of increasing wavelength: orange, green, blue, yellow, violet, red.

8.9 Write the equation that relates the wavelength and frequency of a light wave. (Define all symbols used.)

8.10 How is the frequency of a particular type of radiation related to the energy associated with it? (Give an equation, defining all symbols.)

8.11 What is a photon?

8.12 Show that the energy of a photon is given by the equation $E = hc/\lambda$.

8.13 Examine each of the following pairs and state which of the two has the higher energy:

(a) microwaves and infrared

(b) visible light and infrared

(c) ultraviolet light and X rays

(d) visible light and ultraviolet light

8.14 What is a quantum of energy?

Atomic Spectra

8.15 What is an atomic spectrum? How does it differ from a continuous spectrum?

8.16 What fundamental fact is implied by the existence of atomic spectra?

Bohr Atom and the Hydrogen Spectrum

8.17 Describe Niels Bohr's model of the structure of the hydrogen atom.

8.18 In qualitative terms, how did Bohr's model account for the atomic spectrum of hydrogen?

8.19 What is the "ground state"?

8.20 In what way was Bohr's theory a success? How was it a failure?

Wave Nature of Matter

8.21 How does the behavior of very small particles differ from that of the larger, more massive objects that we encounter in everyday life? Why don't we notice this same behavior for the larger, more massive objects?

8.22 Describe the phenomenon called diffraction. How can this be used to demonstrate that de Broglie's theory was correct?

8.23 What experiment could you perform to determine whether a beam was behaving as a wave or as a stream of particles?

8.24 What is wave/particle duality?

8.25 What is the difference between a traveling wave and a standing wave?

8.26 What is the collapsing atom paradox?

8.27 How does quantum mechanics resolve the collapsing atom paradox?

Electron Waves in Atoms

8.28 What are the names used to refer to the theories that apply the matter–wave concept to electrons in atoms?

8.29 What is the term used to describe a particular waveform of a standing wave for an electron?

8.30 What are the three properties of orbitals in which we are most interested? Why?

Quantum Numbers

8.31 What are the allowed values of the principal quantum number?

8.32 Why is (a) the d subshell in the Period 4 designated as $3d$ and (b) the f subshell in Period 7 designated as $5f$?

8.33 Why does every shell contain an s subshell?

8.34 How many orbitals are found in (a) an s subshell, (b) a p subshell, (c) a d subshell, and (d) an f subshell?

8.35 If the value of m_ℓ for an electron in an atom is 2, could another electron in the same subshell have $m_\ell = -3$?

8.36 Suppose an electron in an atom has the following set of quantum numbers: $n = 2$, $\ell = 1$, $m_\ell = 1$, $m_s = +\frac{1}{2}$. What set of quantum numbers is impossible for another electron in this same atom?

Electron Spin

8.37 What physical property of electrons leads us to propose that they spin like a toy top?

8.38 What is the name of the magnetic property exhibited by atoms that contain unpaired electrons?

8.39 What is the Pauli exclusion principle? What effect does it have on the populating of orbitals by electrons?

8.40 What are the possible values of the spin quantum number?

Electron Configuration of Atoms

8.41 What do we mean by the term *electronic structure*?

8.42 Within any given shell, how do the energies of the s, p, d, and f subshells compare?

8.43 What fact about the energies of subshells was responsible for the apparent success of Bohr's theory about electronic structure?

8.44 How do the energies of the orbitals belonging to a given subshell compare?

8.45 Give the electron configurations of the elements in Period 2 of the periodic table.

8.46 Give the correct electron configurations of (a) Cr and (b) Cu.

8.47 What is the correct electron configuration of silver?

8.48 How are the electron configurations of the elements in a given group similar? Illustrate your answer by writing shorthand configurations for the elements in Group 6A.

8.49 Define the terms *valence shell* and *valence electrons*.

Shapes of Atomic Orbitals

8.50 Why do we use probabilities when we discuss the position of an electron in the space surrounding the nucleus of an atom?

8.51 Sketch the approximate shape of (a) a $1s$ orbital and (b) a $2p$ orbital.

8.52 How does the size of a given type of orbital vary with n?

8.53 How are the *p* orbitals of a given *p* subshell oriented relative to each other?

8.54 What is a *nodal plane*?

8.55 What is a radial node?

8.56 How many nodal planes does a *p* orbital have? How many does a *d* orbital have?

8.57 On appropriate coordinate axes, sketch the shape of the following *d* orbitals: (a) d_{xy}, (b) $d_{x^2-y^2}$, (c) d_{z^2}.

Atomic and Ionic Size

8.58 What is the meaning of *effective nuclear charge?* How does the effective nuclear charge felt by the outer electrons vary going down a group? How does it change as we go from left to right across a period?

8.59 In what region of the periodic table are the largest atoms found? Where are the smallest atoms found?

8.60 Going from left to right in the periodic table, why are the size changes among the transition elements more gradual than those among the representative elements?

Ionization Energy

8.61 Define ionization energy. Why are ionization energies of atoms and positive ions endothermic quantities?

8.62 For oxygen, write an equation for the change associated with (a) its first ionization energy and (b) its third ionization energy.

8.63 Explain why ionization energy increases from left to right in a period and decreases from top to bottom in a group.

8.64 Why is an atom's second ionization energy always larger than its first ionization energy?

8.65 Why is the fifth ionization energy of carbon so much larger than its fourth?

8.66 Why is the first ionization energy of aluminum less than the first ionization energy of magnesium?

8.67 Why does phosphorus have a larger first ionization energy than sulfur?

Electron Affinity

8.68 Define *electron affinity*.

8.69 For sulfur, write an equation for the change associated with (a) its first electron affinity and (b) its second electron affinity. How should they compare?

8.70 Why does Cl have a more exothermic electron affinity than F? Why does Br have a less exothermic electron affinity than Cl?

8.71 Why is the second electron affinity of an atom always endothermic?

8.72 How is electron affinity related to effective nuclear charge? On this basis, explain the relative magnitudes of the electron affinities of oxygen and fluorine.

Review Problems

Electromagnetic Radiation

8.73 What is the frequency in hertz of blue light having a wavelength of 436 nm.

$$v = \frac{c}{\lambda} = \frac{3.0\times10^8 \text{ m/s}}{436\times10^{-6}\text{ m}}$$

OH 8.74 Ultraviolet light with a wavelength of more than 295 nm has little germicidal value. What is the frequency that corresponds to this wavelength?

8.75 A certain substance strongly absorbs infrared light having a wavelength of 6.85 μm. What is the frequency of this light in hertz?

8.76 The sun emits many wavelengths of light. The brightest light is emitted at about 0.48 μm. What frequency does this correspond to?

8.77 Ozone protects the earth's inhabitants from the harmful effects of ultraviolet light arriving from the sun. This shielding is a maximum for UV light having a wavelength of 295 nm. What is the frequency in hertz of this light?

8.78 The meter is defined as the length of the path light travels in a vacuum during the time interval of 1/299,792,458 of a second. The standards body recommends use of light from a helium–neon laser for defining the meter. The light from the laser has a wavelength of 632.99139822 nm. What is the frequency of this light, in hertz?

8.79 In New York City, radio station WCBS broadcasts its FM signal at a frequency of 101.1 megahertz (MHz). What is the wavelength of this signal in meters?

8.80 Sodium vapor lamps are often used in residential street lighting. They give off a yellow light having a frequency of 5.09×10^{14} Hz. What is the wavelength of this light in nanometers?

8.81 There has been some concern in recent times about possible hazards to people who live very close to high-voltage electric power lines. The electricity in these wires oscillates at a frequency of 60.0 Hz, which is the frequency of any electromagnetic radiation that they emit. What is the wavelength of this radiation in meters? What is it in kilometers?

8.82 An X-ray beam has a frequency of 1.50×10^{18} Hz. What is the wavelength of this light in nanometers and in picometers?

8.83 Calculate the energy in joules of a photon of red light having a frequency of 4.0×10^{14} Hz. What is the energy of one mole of these photons?

8.84 Calculate the energy in joules of a photon of green light having a wavelength of 563 nm.

Atomic Spectra

8.85 In the spectrum of hydrogen, there is a line with a wavelength of 410.3 nm. **(a)** What color is this line? **(b)** What is its frequency? **(c)** What is the energy of each of its photons?

8.86 In the spectrum of sodium, there is a line with a wavelength of 589 nm. **(a)** What color is this line? **(b)** What is its frequency? **(c)** What is the energy of each of its photons?

OH **8.87** Use the Rydberg equation to calculate the wavelength in nanometers of the spectral line of hydrogen for which $n_2 = 6$ and $n_1 = 3$. (Report your answer using three significant figures.) Would we be expected to see the light corresponding to this spectral line? Explain your answer.

8.88 Use the Rydberg equation to calculate the wavelength in nanometers of the spectral line of hydrogen for which $n_2 = 5$ and $n_1 = 2$. (Report your answer using three significant figures.) Would we be expected to see the light corresponding to this spectral line? Explain your answer.

8.89 Calculate the wavelength of the spectral line produced in the hydrogen spectrum when an electron falls from the tenth Bohr orbit to the fourth. (Report your answer using three significant figures.) In which region of the electromagnetic spectrum (UV, visible, or infrared) is the line?

8.90 Calculate the energy in joules and the wavelength in nanometers of the spectral line produced in the hydrogen spectrum when an electron falls from the fourth Bohr orbit to the first. (Report your answer using three significant figures.) In which region of the electromagnetic spectrum (UV, visible, or infrared) is the line?

Quantum Numbers

8.91 What is the letter code for a subshell with **(a)** $\ell = 1$ and **(b)** $\ell = 3$?

8.92 What is the value of ℓ for **(a)** an f orbital and **(b)** a d orbital?

8.93 What are the values of n and ℓ for the following subshells: **(a)** $3s$, **(b)** $5d$?

8.94 Give the values of n and ℓ for the following subshells: **(a)** $4p$, **(b)** $6f$.

8.95 For the shell with $n = 6$, what are the possible values of ℓ

8.96 In a particular shell, the largest value of ℓ is 7. What is the value of n for this shell?

8.97 What are the possible values of m_ℓ for a subshell with **(a)** $\ell = 1$ and **(b)** $\ell = 3$?

8.98 If the value of ℓ for an electron in an atom is 5, what are the possible values of m_ℓ that this electron could have?

8.99 If the value of m_ℓ for an electron in an atom is -4, what is the smallest value of ℓ that the electron could have? What is the smallest value of n that the electron could have?

8.100 How many orbitals are there in an h subshell ($\ell = 5$)? What are their values of m_ℓ?

OH **8.101** Give the complete set of quantum numbers for all of the electrons that could populate the $2p$ subshell of an atom.

8.102 Give the complete set of quantum numbers for all of the electrons that could populate the $3d$ subshell of an atom.

8.103 In an antimony atom, how many electrons have $\ell = 1$? How many electrons have $\ell = 2$ in an antimony atom?

8.104 In an atom of barium, how many electrons have **(a)** $\ell = 0$ and **(b)** $m_\ell = 1$?

Electron Configuration of Atoms

8.105 Give the electron configurations of **(a)** S, **(b)** K, **(c)** Ti, and **(d)** Sn.

8.106 Write the electron configurations of **(a)** As, **(b)** Cl, **(c)** Ni, and **(d)** Si.

8.107 Which of the following atoms in their ground states are expected to be paramagnetic: **(a)** Mn, **(b)** As, **(c)** S, **(d)** Sr, **(e)** Ar?

8.108 Which of the following atoms in their ground states are expected to be diamagnetic: **(a)** Ba, **(b)** Se, **(c)** Zn, **(d)** Si?

OH **8.109** How many unpaired electrons would be found in the
ILW ground state of **(a)** Mg, **(b)** P, and **(c)** V?

8.110 How many unpaired electrons would be found in the ground state of **(a)** Cs, **(b)** S, and **(c)** Ni?

8.111 Write the shorthand electron configurations for **(a)** Ni, **(b)** Cs, **(c)** Ge, **(d)** Br, and **(e)** Bi.

8.112 Write the shorthand electron configurations for **(a)** Al, **(b)** Se, **(c)** Ba, **(d)** Sb, and **(e)** Gd.

8.113 Draw complete orbital diagrams for **(a)** Mg and **(b)** Ti.

8.114 Draw complete orbital diagrams for **(a)** As and **(b)** Ni.

8.115 Draw orbital diagrams for the shorthand configurations of **(a)** Ni, **(b)** Cs, **(c)** Ge, and **(d)** Br.

8.116 Draw orbital diagrams for the shorthand configurations of **(a)** Al, **(b)** Se, **(c)** Ba, and **(d)** Sb.

8.117 What is the value of n for the valence shells of **(a)** Sn, **(b)** K, **(c)** Br, and **(d)** Bi?

8.118 What is the value of n for the valence shells of **(a)** Al, **(b)** Se, **(c)** Ba, and **(d)** Sb?

8.119 Give the configuration of the valence shell for **(a)** Na, **(b)** Al, **(c)** Ge, and **(d)** P.

8.120 Give the configuration of the valence shell for **(a)** Mg, **(b)** Br, **(c)** Ga, and **(d)** Pb.

8.121 Draw the orbital diagram for the valence shell of **(a)** Na, **(b)** Al, **(c)** Ge, and **(d)** P.

8.122 Draw the orbital diagram for the valence shell of **(a)** Mg, **(b)** Br, **(c)** Ga, and **(d)** Pb.

Atomic Properties

8.123 If the core electrons were 100% effective at shielding the valence electrons from the nuclear charge and the valence electrons provided no shielding for each other, what would be the effective nuclear charge felt by a valence electron in **(a)** Na, **(b)** S, **(c)** Cl?

8.124 If the core electrons were 100% effective at shielding the valence electrons from the nuclear charge and the valence electrons provided no shielding for each other, what would be the effective nuclear charge felt by a valence electron in (a) Mg, (b) Si, (c) Br?

8.125 Choose the larger atom in each pair: (a) Mg or S; (b) As or Bi.

8.126 Choose the larger atom in each pair: (a) Al or Ar; (b) Tl or In.

8.127 Choose the largest atom among the following: Ge, As, Sn, Sb.

8.128 Place the following in order of increasing size: N^{3-}, Mg^{2+}, Na^+, Ne, F^-, O^{2-}.

8.129 Choose the larger particle in each pair: (a) Na or Na^+; (b) Co^{3+} or Co^{2+}; (c) Cl or Cl^-.

OH 8.130 Choose the larger particle in each pair: (a) S or S^{2-}; (b) Al^{3+} or Al; (c) Au^+ or Au^{3+}.

8.131 Choose the atom with the larger ionization energy in each pair: (a) B or N; (b) Se or S; (c) Cl or Ge.

8.132 Choose the atom with the larger ionization energy in each pair: (a) Li or Rb; (b) Al or F; (c) F or C.

8.133 Choose the atom with the more exothermic electron affinity in each pair: (a) I or Br; (b) Ga or As.

8.134 Choose the atom with the more exothermic electron affinity in each pair: (a) S or As; (b) Si or N.

8.135 Use the periodic table to select the element in the following list for which there is the largest difference between the second and third ionization energies: Na, Mg, Al, Si, P, Se, Cl.

8.136 Use the periodic table to select the element in the following list for which there is the largest difference between the fourth and fifth ionization energies: Na, Mg, Al, Si, P, Se, Cl.

Additional Exercises

8.137 The human ear is sensitive to sound ranging from 20.0 to 2.00×10^4 Hz. The speed of sound is 330 m/s in air, and 1500 m/s under water. What is the longest and the shortest wavelength that can be heard (a) in air and (b) under water?

*8.138 Microwaves are used to heat food in microwave ovens. The microwave radiation is absorbed by moisture in the food. This heats the water, and as the water becomes hot, so does the food. How many photons having a wavelength of 3.00 mm would have to be absorbed by 1.00 g of water to raise its temperature by 1.00 °C?

8.139 In the spectrum of hydrogen, there is a line with a wavelength of 410.3 nm. Use the Rydberg equation to calculate the value of n for the higher energy Bohr orbit involved in the emission of this light. Assume the value of n for the lower energy orbit equals 2.

8.140 Calculate the wavelength in nanometers of the shortest wavelength of light emitted by a hydrogen atom.

8.141 Which of the following electronic transitions could lead to the emission of light from an atom?

$$1s \longrightarrow 4p \longrightarrow 3d \longrightarrow 5f \longrightarrow 4d \longrightarrow 2p$$

8.142 Calculate the wavelengths of the lines in the spectrum of hydrogen that result when an electron falls from a Bohr orbit with (a) $n = 5$ to $n = 1$, (b) $n = 4$ to $n = 2$, and (c) $n = 6$ to $n = 4$. (Report your answer using four significant figures.) In which regions of the electromagnetic spectrum are these lines?

OH 8.143 What, if anything, is wrong with the following electron configurations for atoms in their ground states?

(a) $1s^2 2s^1 2p^3$ (c) $1s^2 2s^2 2p^4$
(b) $[Kr]3d^7 4s^2$ (d) $[Xe]\, 4f^{14}5d^8 6s^1$

*8.144 Suppose students gave the following orbital diagrams for the 2s and 2p subshell in the ground state of an atom. What, if anything, is wrong with them? Are any of these electron distributions impossible?

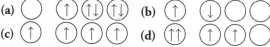

8.145 How many electrons are in p orbitals in an atom of germanium?

8.146 What are the quantum numbers of the electrons that are lost by an atom of iron when it forms the ion Fe^{2+}?

*8.147 The removal of an electron from the hydrogen atom corresponds to raising the electron to the Bohr orbit that has $n = \infty$. On the basis of this statement, calculate the ionization energy of hydrogen in units of (a) joules per atom and (b) kilojoules per mole.

8.148 Use orbital diagrams to illustrate what happens when an oxygen atom gains two electrons. On the basis of what you have learned about electron affinities and electron configurations, why is it extremely difficult to place a third electron on the oxygen atom?

*8.149 From the data available in this chapter, determine the ionization energy of (a) F^-, (b) O^-, and (c) O^{2-}. Are any of these energies exothermic?

8.150 For an oxygen atom, which requires more energy, the addition of two electrons or the removal of one electron?

| Multi-Concept Problems

*8.151 A neon sign is a gas discharge tube in which electrons traveling from the cathode to the anode collide with neon atoms in the tube and knock electrons off of them. As electrons return to the neon ions and drop to lower energy levels, light is given off. How fast would an electron have to be moving to eject an electron from an atom of neon, which has a first ionization energy equal to 2080 kJ mol^{-1}?

*8.152 How many grams of water could have its temperature raised by 5.0 °C by a mole of photons that have a wavelength of **(a)** 600 nm and **(b)** 300 nm?

OH

*8.153 It has been found that when the chemical bond between chlorine atoms in Cl_2 is formed, 328 kJ is released per

OH

mole of Cl_2 formed. What is the wavelength of light that would be required to break chemical bonds between chlorine atoms?

*8.154 Using the ionization energy for sodium, would a photon with a wavelength of 23.7 nm be able to transfer enough energy to an electron in a sodium atom to cause it to ionize if all of the energy of the photon is transferred to the $3s^1$ electron of sodium? What is the maximum kinetic energy of the ejected electron?

*8.155 Using photons with a wavelength of 23.7 nm, determine the kinetic energies of all of the electrons that can be observed from a sample of boron.

| Exercises in Critical Thinking

8.156 Our understanding of the quantum mechanical atom has been developing since the early 1900s. Has quantum mechanics had any effect on the daily lives of people?

8.157 When a copper atom loses an electron to become a Cu^+ ion, what are the possible quantum numbers of the electron that was lost?

8.158 Paired electrons cancel each other's magnetic fields. Why can't unpaired electrons have opposite spins and cancel each other's magnetic fields also?

8.159 Placing a small piece of an element from Group 1A in water results in increasingly rapid and violently spectacular reactions as we progress from lithium down to cesium. What information in this chapter makes this behavior understandable?

9 The Basics of Chemical Bonding

Chapter Outline

This mountain climber's fate hangs on the strength of the chemical bonds between the atoms forming the fibers in the rope keeping her from falling to her death. Chemical bonds affect the chemical and physical properties of substances, both of which are important criteria when selecting materials for practical uses. In this chapter we begin our study of the way atoms bond to each other. I Love Images/© Corbis

This Chapter in Context

In Chapter 3 you learned that we can classify substances into two broad categories, ionic or molecular. Ionic compounds, such as ordinary table salt, consist of electrically charged particles (ions) that bind to each other by electrostatic forces of attraction. We also said that in molecular substances, such as water, the atoms are held to each other by the sharing of electrons. Now that you've learned about the electronic structures of atoms, we can explore the attractions between atoms or ions, called **chemical bonds,** in greater depth. Our goal is to gain some insight into the reasons certain combinations of atoms prefer electron transfer and the formation of ions (leading to *ionic bonding*), while other combinations bind by electron sharing (leading to *covalent bonding*).

As with electronic structure, models of chemical bonding have also evolved, and in this chapter we introduce you to relatively simple theories. Although more complex theories exist (some of which we describe in Chapter 10), the basic concepts you will study in this chapter still find many useful applications in modern chemical thought.

9.1 | Energy Requirements for Bond Formation

■ The heat of reaction is just one factor that determines whether or not a chemical reaction can occur spontaneously. We will discuss this in detail in Chapter 19.

For a *stable* compound to be formed from its elements, the reaction must be exothermic. In other words, ΔH_f° must be negative. Two examples of such reactions are the formation of H_2O by the reaction of H_2 with O_2 (Figure 1.22, page 20) and the formation of NaCl by the reaction of Na with Cl_2, shown in Figure 9.1. Both of these reactions release a large amount of energy when they occur and produce very stable compounds. Typically, compounds with positive heats of formation tend to be unstable with respect to decomposition. Sometimes that decomposition can occur violently, as with nitroglycerine, a powerful explosive.

When a reaction is exothermic, the potential energy of the particles in the system decreases. Therefore, to understand the formation of chemical bonds, we need to understand how bond formation can lead to a lowering of the potential energy of the atoms involved. In the pages ahead we will examine this for both ionic and molecular substances.

9.2 | Ionic Bonding

Figure 9.1 | **Exothermic reaction of sodium with chlorine.** A small piece of melted sodium immediately ignites when dipped into a flask containing chlorine gas, producing light and releasing a lot of heat. The smoke coming from the flask is composed of fine crystals of sodium chloride. *(Richard Megna/Fundamental Photographs)*

You learned in Chapter 3 that when sodium chloride is formed from its elements, each sodium atom loses one electron to form a sodium ion, Na^+, and each chlorine atom gains one electron to become a chloride ion, Cl^-.

$$Na \longrightarrow Na^+ + e^-$$
$$Cl + e^- \longrightarrow Cl^-$$

Once formed, these ions become tightly packed together, as illustrated in Figure 9.2, because their opposite charges attract. *This attraction between positive and negative ions in an ionic compound is what we call an* **ionic bond.**

The attraction between Na^+ and Cl^- ions may seem reasonable, but *why* are electrons transferred between these and other atoms? *Why* does sodium form Na^+ and not Na^- or Na^{2+}? And *why* does chlorine form Cl^- instead of Cl^+ or Cl^{2-}? To answer such questions we have to consider factors that are related to the potential energy of the system of reactants and products. As noted above, for any stable compound to form from its elements, there must be a net lowering of the potential energy and the reaction must be exothermic.

Importance of the Lattice Energy

In the formation of an ionic compound such as NaCl, it is not the electron transfer itself that leads to a stable substance. We can see this if we examine the ionization energy of Na and the electron affinity of Cl. Dealing with a mole-sized collection of gaseous atoms, we have

$$Na(g) \longrightarrow Na^+(g) + e^- \quad +495.4 \text{ kJ mol}^{-1} \quad \text{(IE of sodium)}$$
$$Cl(g) + e^- \longrightarrow Cl^-(g) \quad \quad -348.8 \text{ kJ mol}^{-1} \quad \text{(EA of chlorine)}$$
$$\text{Net} \quad +146.6 \text{ kJ mol}^{-1}$$

■ Keep in mind the relationship between potential energy changes and endothermic and exothermic processes:

endothermic ⇔ increase in PE
exothermic ⇔ decrease in PE

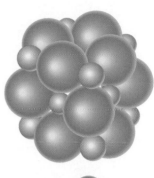

Notice that forming gaseous sodium and chloride ions from gaseous sodium and chlorine atoms requires a substantial *increase* in the potential energy. This tells us that if the IE and EA were the only energy changes involved, ionic sodium chloride would not form from atoms of sodium and chlorine. So where does the stability of the compound come from?

In the calculation above, we looked at the formation of gaseous ions, but salt is not a gas; it's a solid. Therefore, we need to see how the energy would change if the gaseous ions are condensed to give the solid, and to do this we must examine a quantity called the lattice energy.

The **lattice energy** *is the energy change that would occur if the ions at infinite separation (i.e., a cloud of gaseous ions) are brought together to form one mole of the solid compound.*[1] For sodium chloride, the change associated with the lattice energy is pictured in Figure 9.3, and in equation form can be represented as

$$Na^+(g) + Cl^-(g) \longrightarrow NaCl(s)$$

Because Na^+ and Cl^- ions attract each other, their potential energy decreases as they come together, so the process releases energy and is exothermic. In fact, the lattice energy for sodium chloride is very exothermic and is equal to -787 kJ mol^{-1}. If we include the lattice energy along with the ionization energy of Na and electron affinity of Cl, we have

$$Na(g) \longrightarrow Na^+(g) + e^- \quad +495.4 \text{ kJ} \quad \text{(IE of sodium)}$$
$$Cl(g) + e^- \longrightarrow Cl^-(g) \quad \quad -348.8 \text{ kJ} \quad \text{(EA of chlorine)}$$
$$Na^+(g) + Cl^-(g) \longrightarrow NaCl(s) \quad -787.0 \text{ kJ} \quad \text{(lattice energy)}$$
$$\text{Net} \quad -640.4 \text{ kJ}$$

Figure 9.2 | **The packing of ions in NaCl.** Electrostatic forces hold the ions in place in the solid. These forces constitute ionic bonds.

■ The name lattice energy comes from the word *lattice*, which is used to describe the regular pattern of ions or atoms in a crystal. Lattice energies are exothermic and so are given negative signs.

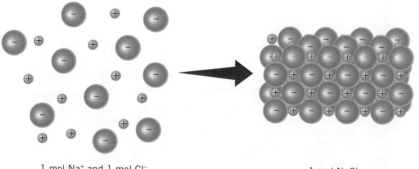

1 mol Na$^+$ and 1 mol Cl$^-$
(gaseous ions from NaCl)

1 mol NaCl
(solid, crystalline NaCl)

Figure 9.3 | **The lattice energy of NaCl.** The energy released when one mole of gaseous Na$^+$ and one mole of gaseous Cl$^-$ condenses to one mole of solid NaCl is the lattice energy. For NaCl, this amounts to 787 kJ.

---

[1] In some books, the lattice energy is defined as *the energy needed to separate the ions in one mole of a solid to give a cloud of gaseous ions.* This would correspond to the change

$$NaCl(s) \longrightarrow Na^+(g) + Cl^-(g)$$

The *magnitude* of the energy change is the same as for the process described above in the body of the text, but the algebraic sign of the energy change would be positive instead of negative (endothermic instead of exothermic).

Thus, the release of energy equal to the lattice energy provides a large net lowering of the potential energy as solid NaCl is formed. We can also say that *it is the lattice energy that provides the stabilization necessary for the formation of NaCl*. Without it, the compound could not exist.

Determining Lattice Energies

At this point, you may be wondering about our starting point in these energy calculations—namely, gaseous sodium atoms and chlorine atoms. In nature, sodium is a solid metal and chlorine consists of gaseous Cl_2 molecules. Let's look at a complete analysis of the energy changes taking this into account. To perform the analysis we will use an enthalpy diagram similar to the type discussed in Chapter 7. It is called a **Born–Haber cycle** after the scientists who were the first to use it to calculate lattice energies.

In Chapter 7 you learned that the enthalpy change for a process is the same regardless of the path we follow from start to finish. With this in mind, we will construct two different paths from the free elements (solid sodium and gaseous chlorine molecules) to the solid ionic compound, sodium chloride, as shown in Figure 9.4.

The starting point for both paths is the same: the free elements sodium and chlorine. The path that starts at the lower left takes us directly to the product, NaCl(s), and has as its enthalpy change the heat of formation of NaCl, ΔH_f°.

$$Na(s) + \tfrac{1}{2}Cl_2(g) \longrightarrow NaCl(s) \qquad \Delta H_f^\circ = -411.3 \text{ kJ}$$

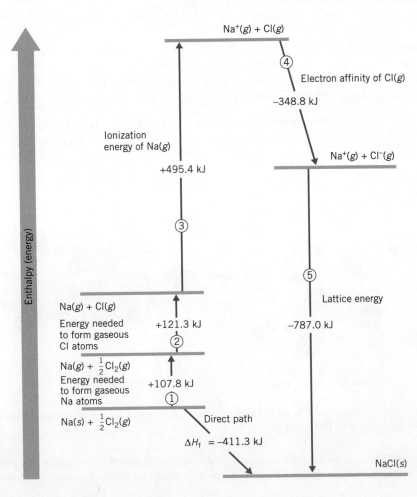

Figure 9.4 | **Analysis of the enthalpy changes in the formation of sodium chloride.** One path leads directly from the elements Na(s) and $Cl_2(g)$ to NaCl(s). The second (upper) path follows a series of changes that include the lattice energy and take us to the same final product, NaCl(s).

The alternative path is divided into a number of steps. The first two, labeled 1 and 2, have $\Delta H°$ values that can be measured experimentally and both are endothermic. They change $Na(s)$ and $Cl_2(g)$ into gaseous atoms, $Na(g)$ and $Cl(g)$. The next two steps (Steps 3 and 4) change the atoms to ions, first by the endothermic ionization energy (IE) of Na followed by the exothermic electron affinity (EA) of Cl. This brings us to the gaseous ions, $Na^+(g) + Cl^-(g)$, depicted on the right in Figure 9.4. Notice that at this point, if we add all the energy changes, the ions are at a considerably higher energy than the reactants. If these were the only energy terms involved in the formation of NaCl, the heat of formation would be endothermic and the compound would be unstable; it could not be formed by the direct combination of the elements.

The last step on the right in Figure 9.4 (Step 5) finally brings us to solid NaCl and corresponds to the lattice energy. To make the net energy changes the same along both paths, the energy released when the ions condense to form the solid must equal -787.0 kJ. Therefore, the calculated lattice energy of NaCl must be -787.0 kJ mol^{-1}.

What we see in this analysis is that it is the lattice energy that permits NaCl to be formed from its elements. In fact, *for any ionic compound, the chief stabilizing influence is the lattice energy, which when released is large enough to overcome the net energy input required to form the ions from the elements.*

Besides affecting the ability of ionic compounds to form, lattice energies are also important in determining the solubilities of ionic compounds in water and other solvents. We will explore this topic in Chapter 14.

Effect of Ionic Size and Charge on the Lattice Energy

The lattice energies of some ionic compounds are given in Table 9.1. As you can see, they are all very large exothermic quantities. Their magnitudes depend on a number of factors, including the charges on the ions and their sizes.

For two ions with charges q_1 and q_2 separated by a distance r, the potential energy can be calculated from **Coulomb's law:**

$$E = \frac{q_1\, q_2}{k\, r} \tag{9.1}$$

where k is a proportionality constant.[2] In an ionic solid, q_1 and q_2 have opposite signs, so E is calculated to be a negative quantity. That's why the lattice energy has a negative sign.

When the charges on the ions become larger (i.e., when q_1 and q_2 become larger), E becomes more negative, which means the potential energy becomes lower (more negative).

Table 9.1	Lattice Energies of Some Ionic Compounds	
Compound	**Ions**	**Lattice Energy (kJ mol^{-1})**
LiCl	Li^+ and Cl^-	−845
NaCl	Na^+ and Cl^-	−787
KCl	K^+ and Cl^-	−709
LiF	Li^+ and F^-	−1033
$CaCl_2$	Ca^{2+} and Cl^-	−2258
$AlCl_3$	Al^{3+} and Cl^-	−5492
CaO	Ca^{2+} and O^{2-}	−3401
Al_2O_3	Al^{3+} and O^{2-}	−15,916

[2]In this case, we're using the symbol q to mean electric charge, not heat as in Chapter 7. Because the number of letters in the alphabet is limited, it's not uncommon in science for the same letter to be used to stand for different quantities. This usually doesn't present a problem as long as the symbol is defined in the context in which it is used.

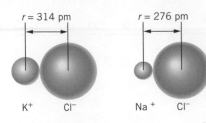

Figure 9.5 | **The effect of ionic size on the lattice energy.** Because Na⁺ is smaller than K⁺, the distance between ions is smaller in NaCl than in KCl. This causes the lattice energy of NaCl to be larger than that of KCl.

This explains why salts of Ca^{2+} have larger lattice energies than comparable salts of Na^+, and those containing Al^{3+} have even larger lattice energies.

Because the distance between the ions, r, appears in the denominator in Equation 9.1, E becomes a larger negative quantity as r becomes smaller. As a result, compounds formed from small ions (which can get close together) have larger lattice energies than those formed from large ions. For example, a Na^+ ion is smaller than a K^+ ion, and in Figure 9.5 we compare the cation–anion distances observed in solid NaCl and KCl. The smaller Na–Cl distance causes NaCl to have a larger lattice energy than KCl.

Factors That Determine the Formation of Cations and Anions

We've shown that for an ionic compound to form, the energy lowering produced by release of the lattice energy must exceed the energy rise associated with forming the ions from the neutral atoms. This requires that the cation be formed from an atom of relatively low ionization energy; such atoms are found among the metals. Nonmetals, at the upper right of the periodic table, have large ionization energies but generally exothermic electron affinities. A nonmetal atom has little tendency to lose electrons, but forming an anion from a nonmetal atom can actually help to lower the energy. As a result, cations are formed from metals and anions are formed from nonmetals because this leads to the greatest lowering of the energy. In fact, metals combine with nonmetals to form ionic compounds simply because ionic bonding is favored energetically over other types whenever atoms with small ionization energies combine with atoms that have large exothermic electron affinities.

9.3 | Electron Configurations of Ions

Stability of the Noble Gas Configuration

Earlier we raised the question about why sodium forms Na^+ and chlorine forms Cl^-. To find the answer, let's begin by examining what happens when a sodium atom loses an electron. The electron configuration of Na is

$$\text{Na} \qquad 1s^2 2s^2 2p^6 3s^1$$

The electron that is lost is the one least tightly held, which is the single outer $3s$ electron. The electronic structure of the Na^+ ion, then, is

$$\text{Na}^+ \qquad 1s^2 2s^2 2p^6$$

Notice that this is identical to the electron configuration of the noble gas neon. We say the Na^+ ion has achieved a *noble gas configuration*.

The energy needed to remove the first electron from Na is relatively small and can easily be recovered by the release of the lattice energy when an ionic compound containing Na^+ is formed. However, removal of a second electron from sodium is *very* difficult because it involves breaking into the $2s^2 2p^6$ core. Forming the Na^{2+} ion is therefore very endothermic, as we can see by adding the first and second ionization energies (Table 8.2, page 343).

$$\text{Na}(g) \longrightarrow \text{Na}^+(g) + e^- \qquad \text{1st IE} = 496 \text{ kJ mol}^{-1}$$
$$\text{Na}^+(g) \longrightarrow \text{Na}^{2+}(g) + e^- \qquad \text{2nd IE} = 4563 \text{ kJ mol}^{-1}$$
$$\overline{\qquad\qquad\qquad \text{Total} \qquad 5059 \text{ kJ mol}^{-1}}$$

This value is so large because the second electron is removed from the noble gas core beneath the outer shell of sodium.

Even though the Na^{2+} ion would give a compound such as $NaCl_2$ a larger lattice energy than NaCl (e.g., see the lattice energy for $CaCl_2$), it would not be large enough to make the formation of the compound exothermic. As a result, $NaCl_2$ cannot form. The same applies to other compounds of sodium, so when sodium forms a cation, electron loss stops once the Na^+ ion is formed and a noble gas electron configuration is reached.

Similar situations exist for other metals, too. For example, the first two electrons to be removed from a calcium atom come from the $4s$ valence shell (outer shell).

$$Ca \qquad 1s^2 2s^2 2p^6 3s^2 3p^6 4s^2$$
$$Ca^{2+} \qquad 1s^2 2s^2 2p^6 3s^2 3p^6$$

The energy needed to accomplish this can be recovered by the release of the lattice energy when a compound containing Ca^{2+} forms. Electron loss ceases at this point, however, because of the huge amount of energy needed to break into the noble gas core. As a result, a calcium atom loses just two electrons when it reacts.

For sodium and calcium, as well as other metals of Groups 1A and 2A and aluminum, the large ionization energy of the noble gas core just below their outer shells limits the number of electrons they lose, so the ions that are formed have noble gas electron configurations.

Nonmetals also tend to achieve noble gas configurations when they form anions. For example, when a chlorine atom reacts, it gains one electron.

$$Cl \qquad 1s^2 2s^2 2p^6 3s^2 3p^5$$
$$Cl^- \qquad 1s^2 2s^2 2p^6 3s^2 3p^6$$

At this point, we have a noble gas configuration (that of argon). Electron gain ceases, because if another electron were to be added, it would have to enter an orbital in the next higher shell, which is very energetically unfavorable. Similar arguments apply to the other nonmetals as well.

■ For calcium:

1st IE = 590 kJ/mol
2nd IE = 1146 kJ/mol
3rd IE = 4940 kJ/mol

The Octet Rule

In the preceding discussion you learned that a balance of energy factors causes many atoms to form ions that have a noble gas electron configuration. Historically, this is expressed in the form of a generalization: *When they form ions, atoms of most of the representative elements tend to gain or lose electrons until they have obtained an electron configuration identical to that of the nearest noble gas.* Because all the noble gases except helium have outer shells with eight electrons, this rule has become known as the **octet rule,** which can be stated as follows: *Atoms tend to gain or lose electrons until they have achieved an outer shell that contains an* **octet of electrons** *(eight electrons).*

Electron configurations of ions of the representative elements.

Cations That Do Not Obey the Octet Rule

The octet rule, as applied to ionic compounds, really works well only for the cations of the Group 1A and 2A metals and aluminum, and for the anions of the nonmetals. It does not work well for the transition metals and post-transition metals (the metals that follow a row of transition metals). Be ? P 399

To obtain the correct electron configurations of the cations of these metals, we apply the following rules:

Obtaining the Electron Configuration of a Cation
1. The first electrons to be lost by an atom or ion are *always* those from the shell with the largest value of n (i.e., the outer shell).
2. As electrons are removed from a given shell, they come from the highest-energy occupied subshell first, before any are removed from a lower-energy subshell. Within a given shell, the energies of the subshells vary as follows: $s < p < d < f$. This means that f is emptied before d, which is emptied before p, which is emptied before s.

Let's look at two examples.

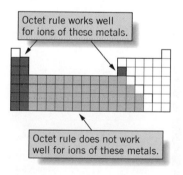

Octet rule works well for ions of these metals.

Octet rule does not work well for ions of these metals.

Order in which electrons are lost from an atom.

■ Applying these rules to the metals of Groups 1A and 2A also gives the correct electron configurations.

Tin (a post-transition metal) forms two ions, Sn^{2+} and Sn^{4+}. The electron configurations are

$$Sn \quad [Kr]\, 4d^{10}5s^25p^2$$
$$Sn^{2+} \quad [Kr]\, 4d^{10}5s^2$$
$$Sn^{4+} \quad [Kr]\, 4d^{10}$$

Notice that the Sn^{2+} ion is formed by the loss of the higher energy $5p$ electrons first. Then, further loss of the two $5s$ electrons gives the Sn^{4+} ion. However, neither of these ions has a noble gas configuration.

For the transition elements, the first electrons lost are the s electrons of the outer shell. Then, if additional electrons are lost, they come from the underlying d subshell. An example is iron, which forms the ions Fe^{2+} and Fe^{3+}. The element iron has the electron configuration

$$Fe \quad [Ar]\, 3d^64s^2$$

Iron loses its $4s$ electrons fairly easily to give Fe^{2+}, which has the electron configuration

$$Fe \quad [Ar]\, 3d^6$$

The Fe^{3+} ion results when another electron is removed, this time from the $3d$ subshell.

$$Fe^{3+} \quad [Ar]\, 3d^5$$

Iron is able to form Fe^{3+} because the $3d$ subshell is close in energy to the $4s$, so it is not very difficult to remove the third electron. Notice once again that the first electrons to be removed come from the shell with the largest value of n (the $4s$ subshell). Then, after this shell is emptied, the next electrons are removed from the shell below.

Because so many of the transition elements are able to form ions in a way similar to that of iron, the ability to form more than one positive ion is usually cited as one of the characteristic properties of the transition elements. Frequently, one of the ions formed has a $2+$ charge, which arises from the loss of the two outer s electrons. Ions with larger positive charges result when additional d electrons are lost. Unfortunately, it is not easy to predict exactly which ions can form for a given transition metal, nor is it simple to predict their relative stabilities with respect to being oxidized or reduced.

Example 9.1
Writing Electron Configurations of Ions

How do the electron configurations change (a) when a nitrogen atom forms the N^{3-} ion and (b) when an antimony atom forms the Sb^{3+} ion?

■ **Analysis:** For the nonmetals, you've learned that the octet rule does work, so the ion that is formed by nitrogen will have a noble gas configuration.

Antimony is a post-transition element, so we don't expect its cation to obey the octet rule. We will have to examine the electron configuration of the neutral atoms and determine which electrons are lost.

■ **Assembling the Tools:** The octet rule serves as the tool to determine the electron configuration of N^{3-}. To determine the electron configuration of Sb^{3+}, our tools will be the procedure for writing abbreviated electron configurations for atoms as well as the rules describing the order in which electrons are lost from an atom.

■ **Solution:** (a) Following the method for writing abbreviated configurations, the electron configuration for nitrogen is

$$N \quad [He]\, 2s^22p^3$$

To form N^{3-}, three electrons are gained. These enter the $2p$ subshell because it is the lowest available energy level. Filling the $2p$ subshell completes the octet; the configuration for the ion is therefore

$$N^{3-} \quad [He]\, 2s^22p^6$$

(b) The rules tell us that when a cation is formed, electrons are removed first from the outer shell of the atom (the shell with the largest value of the principal quantum number, n). Within a given shell, electrons are always removed first from the subshell highest in energy. Let's begin with the ground state electron configuration for antimony, obtained in the usual way.

$$\text{Sb} \qquad [\text{Kr}]\, 4d^{10}5s^25p^3$$

To form the Sb^{3+} ion, three electrons must be removed. These will come from the outer shell, which has $n = 5$. Within this shell, the energies of the subshells increase in the order $s < p < d < f$. Therefore, the $5p$ subshell is higher in energy than the $5s$, so all three electrons are removed from the $5p$. This gives

$$\text{Sb}^{3+} \qquad [\text{Kr}]\, 4d^{10}5s^2$$

■ **Are the Answers Reasonable?** In Chapter 3 you learned to use the periodic table to figure out the charges on the anions of the nonmetals. For nitrogen, we would take three steps to the right to get to the nearest noble gas, neon. The electron configuration we obtained for N^{3-} is that of neon, so our answer should be correct.

For antimony, we had to remove three electrons, which completely emptied the $5p$ subshell. That's also good news, because ions do not tend to have partially filled s or p subshells (although partially filled d subshells are not uncommon for the transition metals). If we had taken the electrons from any other subshells, the Sb^{3+} ion would have had a partially filled $5p$ subshell.

Example 9.2
Writing Electron Configurations of Ions

What is the electron configuration of the V^{3+} ion? Give the orbital diagram for the ion.

■ **Analysis:** To obtain the electron configuration of a cation, always begin with the electron configuration of the neutral atom. In this case we will remove three electrons to obtain the electron configuration of the ion.

■ **Assembling the Tools:** Once again, our tools will be the method for deriving electron configurations of atoms and the rules that tell us the order in which electrons are lost by an atom. We will also use Hund's rule, which tells us how electrons populate orbitals of a given subshell.

■ **Solution:** Following the usual method, the electron configuration of vanadium is

$$\text{V} \qquad 1s^22s^22p^63s^23p^63d^34s^2$$

Argon core

Notice that we've written the configuration showing the outer shell $4s$ electrons farthest to the right. To form the V^{3+} cation, three electrons must be removed from the neutral atom. We have to keep in mind that the electrons are lost first from the occupied shell with highest n. Therefore, the first two come from the $4s$ subshell and the third comes from the $3d$. This means we won't have to take any from the $3s$ or $3p$ subshells, so the argon core will remain intact. Therefore, let's rewrite the electron configuration in abbreviated form.

$$\text{V} \qquad [\text{Ar}]\, 3d^34s^2$$

Removing the three electrons gives

$$\text{V}^{3+} \qquad [\text{Ar}]\, 3d^2$$

To form the orbital diagram, we show all five orbitals of the $3d$ subshell and then spread out the two electrons with spins unpaired (Hund's rule). This gives

$$V^{3+} \quad [Ar] \; \uparrow \; \uparrow \; \bigcirc \; \bigcirc \; \bigcirc$$
$$3d$$

■ **Is the Answer Reasonable?** First, we check that we've written the correct electron configuration of vanadium, which we have. (A quick count of the electrons gives 23, which is the atomic number of vanadium.) We've also taken electrons away from the atom following the rules, so the electron configuration of the ion seems okay. Finally, we remembered to show all five orbitals of the $3d$ subshell, even though only two of them are occupied.

Practice Exercises

9.1 | What is wrong with the following electron configuration of the In^+ ion? What should the electron configuration be?

$$In^+ \qquad 1s^2 2s^2 2p^6 3s^2 3p^6 3d^{10} 4s^2 4p^6 4d^{10} 5s^1 5p^1$$

(*Hint:* Check the rules that tell us the order in which electrons are lost by an atom or ion.)

9.2 | How do the electron configurations change when a chromium atom forms the following ions: (a) Cr^{2+}, (b) Cr^{3+}, (c) Cr^{6+}?

9.3 | How are the electron configurations of S^{2-} and Cl^- related?

9.4 | Lewis Symbols: Keeping Track of Valence Electrons

In the previous section you saw how the valence shells of atoms change when electrons are transferred during the formation of ions. We will soon see the way many atoms share their valence electrons with each other when they form covalent bonds. In these discussions it is useful to be able to keep track of valence electrons. To help us do this, we use a simple bookkeeping device called Lewis symbols, named after their inventor, the American chemist, G. N. Lewis (1875–1946).

To draw the **Lewis symbol** for an element, we write its chemical symbol surrounded by dots (or some other similar mark), each of which represents a valence electron of the atom. For example, the element lithium has the Lewis symbol

$$Li\cdot$$

in which the single dot stands for lithium's single valence electron. In fact, each element in Group 1A has a similar Lewis symbol, because each has only one valence electron. The Lewis symbols for all of the Group 1A metals are

$$Li\cdot \quad Na\cdot \quad K\cdot \quad Rb\cdot \quad Cs\cdot$$

The Lewis symbols for the eight A-group elements of Period 2 are[3]

Group	1A	2A	3A	4A	5A	6A	7A	8A
Symbol	Li·	·Be·	·B̈·	·C̈·	·N̈:	·Ö:	·F̈:	:N̈e:

Gilbert N. Lewis, chemistry professor at the University of California, helped develop theories of chemical bonding. In 1916, he proposed that atoms form bonds by sharing pairs of electrons. (*Bettmann/© Corbis*)

Lewis symbols

---

[3]For beryllium, boron, and carbon, the number of unpaired electrons in the Lewis symbol doesn't agree with the number predicted from the atom's electron configuration. Boron, for example, has two electrons paired in its $2s$ orbital and a third electron in one of its $2p$ orbitals; therefore, there is actually only one unpaired electron in a boron atom. The Lewis symbols are drawn as shown, however, because when beryllium, boron, and carbon form bonds, they *behave* as if they have two, three, and four unpaired electrons, respectively.

The elements below each of these in their respective groups have identical Lewis symbols except, of course, for the chemical symbol of the element. Notice that when an atom has more than four valence electrons, the additional electrons are shown to be paired with others. Also notice that *for the representative elements, the group number is equal to the number of valence electrons* when the North American convention for numbering groups in the periodic table is followed.

■ This is one of the advantages of the North American convention for numbering groups in the periodic table.

Example 9.3
Writing Lewis Symbols

What is the Lewis symbol for arsenic?

■ **Analysis:** We need to know the number of valence electrons, which we can obtain from the group number. Then we distribute the electrons (dots) around the chemical symbol.

■ **Assembling the Tools:** Our tool is the method described above for constructing the Lewis symbol.

■ **Solution:** The symbol for arsenic is As and we find it in Group 5A. The element therefore has five valence electrons. The first four are placed around the symbol for arsenic as follows:

$$\cdot \overset{\cdot}{As} \cdot$$

The fifth electron is paired with one of the first four. This gives

$$\cdot \overset{\cdot}{As} :$$

The location of the fifth electron doesn't really matter, so equally valid Lewis symbols are

$$\cdot \overset{\cdot\cdot}{As} \cdot \quad \text{or} \quad : \overset{\cdot}{As} \cdot \quad \text{or} \quad \cdot \underset{\cdot\cdot}{\overset{\cdot}{As}} \cdot$$

■ **Is the Answer Reasonable?** There's not much to check here. Have we got the correct chemical symbol? Yes. Do we have the right number of dots? Yes.

Using Lewis Symbols to Represent Ionic Compounds

Although we will use Lewis symbols mostly to follow the fate of valence electrons in covalent bonds, they can also be used to describe what happens during the formation of ions. For example, when a sodium atom reacts with a chlorine atom, the sodium loses an electron to the chlorine, which we might depict as

$$Na \cdot + \cdot \overset{\cdot\cdot}{\underset{\cdot\cdot}{Cl}} : \longrightarrow Na^+ + \left[: \overset{\cdot\cdot}{\underset{\cdot\cdot}{Cl}} : \right]^-$$

The valence shell of the sodium atom is emptied, so no dots remain. The outer shell of chlorine, which formerly had seven electrons, gains one to give a total of eight. The brackets are drawn around the chloride ion to show that all eight electrons are the exclusive property of the Cl$^-$ ion.

We can diagram a similar reaction between calcium and chlorine atoms.

$$: \overset{\cdot\cdot}{\underset{\cdot\cdot}{Cl}} \cdot \quad \cdot Ca \cdot \quad \cdot \overset{\cdot\cdot}{\underset{\cdot\cdot}{Cl}} : \longrightarrow Ca^{2+} + 2 \left[: \overset{\cdot\cdot}{\underset{\cdot\cdot}{Cl}} : \right]^-$$

Example 9.4
Using Lewis Symbols

Use Lewis symbols to diagram the reaction that occurs between sodium and oxygen atoms to give Na^+ and O^{2-} ions.

■ **Analysis:** For electrical neutrality, the formula will be Na_2O, so we will use two sodium atoms and one oxygen atom. Each sodium will lose one electron to give Na^+ and the oxygen will gain two electrons to give O^{2-}.

■ **Assembling the Tools:** The principal tool is the method for constructing the Lewis symbol for an element and its ions.

■ **Solution:** Our first task is to draw the Lewis symbols for Na and O.

$$Na \cdot \qquad \cdot \ddot{O} \colon$$

It takes two electrons to complete the octet around oxygen. Each Na supplies one. Therefore,

$$Na \curvearrowright \cdot \ddot{O} \colon \curvearrowleft Na \longrightarrow 2Na^+ + \left[\colon \ddot{O} \colon \right]^{2-}$$

Notice that we have put brackets around the oxide ion.

■ **Is the Answer Reasonable?** We have accounted for all the valence electrons (an important check), the net charge is the same on both sides of the arrow (the equation is balanced), and we've placed the brackets around the oxide ion to emphasize that the octet belongs exclusively to that ion.

Practice Exercises

9.4 | Use Lewis symbols to diagram the formation of CaI_2 from Ca and I atoms. (*Hint:* Begin by determining how many electrons are gained or lost by each atom.)

9.5 | Diagram the reaction between magnesium and oxygen atoms to give Mg^{2+} and O^{2-} ions.

9.5 | Covalent Bonds

Most of the substances we encounter in our daily lives are not ionic. Instead, they are composed of electrically neutral molecules. The chemical bonds that bind the atoms to each other in such molecules are electrical in nature, but arise from the sharing of electrons rather than by electron transfer.

Energy Changes on Bond Formation

In Section 9.2 we saw that for ionic bonding to occur, the energy-lowering effect of the lattice energy must be greater than the combined net energy-raising effects of the ionization energy (IE) and electron affinity (EA). Many times this is not possible, particularly when the ionization energies of all the atoms involved are large. This happens, for example, when nonmetals combine with each other to form molecules. In such cases, nature uses a different way to lower the energy—electron sharing.

Let's look at what happens when two hydrogen atoms join to form an H_2 molecule (Figure 9.6). As the two atoms approach each other, the electron of each atom begins to feel the attraction of both nuclei. This causes the electron density around each nucleus to shift toward the region between the two atoms. Therefore, as the distance between the nuclei decreases, there is an increase in the probability of finding either electron near either nucleus. In effect, as the molecule is formed, each of the hydrogen atoms in the H_2 molecule acquires a share of two electrons.

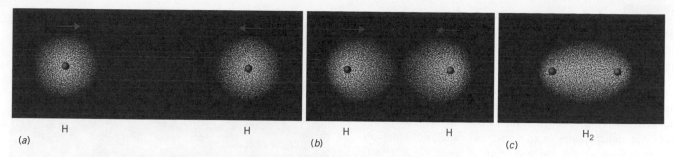

H   H   H   H H_2
(a)   (b)   (c)

Figure 9.6 | Formation of a covalent bond between two hydrogen atoms. (*a*) Two H atoms separated by a large distance. (*b*) As the atoms approach each other, their electron densities are pulled into the region between the two nuclei. (*c*) In the H_2 molecule, the electron density is concentrated between the nuclei. Both electrons in the bond are distributed over both nuclei.

In the H_2 molecule, the buildup of electron density between the two atoms attracts both nuclei and pulls them together. Being of the same charge, however, the two nuclei also repel each other, as do the two electrons. In the molecule that forms, therefore, the atoms are held at a distance at which all these attractions and repulsions are balanced. Overall, the nuclei are kept from separating, and the net force of attraction produced by sharing the pair of electrons is called a **covalent bond.**

Bond Energy and Bond Length

Every covalent bond is characterized by two quantities—namely, the average distance between the nuclei held together by the bond and the amount of energy needed to separate the two atoms to produce neutral atoms again. In the hydrogen molecule, the attractive forces pull the nuclei to a distance of 75 pm, and this distance is called the **bond length** (or sometimes the **bond distance**). Because a covalent bond holds atoms together, work must be done (energy must be supplied) to separate them. The amount of energy needed to "break" the bond (or the energy released when the bond is formed) is called the **bond energy.**

Figure 9.7 shows how the potential energy changes when two hydrogen atoms come together to form H_2. We see that the minimum potential energy occurs at a bond length of 75 pm, and that 1 mol of hydrogen molecules is more stable than 2 mol of hydrogen atoms by 435 kJ. In other words, the bond energy of H_2 is 435 kJ/mol.

In general, forming any covalent bond leads to a lowering of the energy and breaking covalent bonds leads to an increase in energy. As noted in Chapter 7, the net energy change we observe in a chemical reaction is the result of energies associated with the breaking and making of bonds.

◼ As the distance between the nuclei and the electron cloud that lies between them decreases, the potential energy decreases.

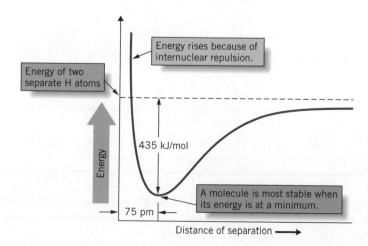

Energy rises because of internuclear repulsion.

Energy of two separate H atoms

435 kJ/mol

Energy

A molecule is most stable when its energy is at a minimum.

75 pm

Distance of separation ⟶

Figure 9.7 | Changes in the total potential energy of two hydrogen atoms as they form H_2. The energy of the molecule reaches a minimum when there is a balance between the attractions and repulsions.

Sunlight and Skin Cancer

The ability of light to provide the energy for chemical reactions enables life to exist on our planet. Green plants absorb sunlight and, with the help of chlorophyll, convert carbon dioxide and water into carbohydrates (e.g., sugars and cellulose), which are essential constituents of the food chain. However, not all effects of sunlight are so beneficial.

As you know, light packs energy that's proportional to its frequency, and if the photons that are absorbed by a substance have enough energy, they can rupture chemical bonds and initiate chemical reactions. Light that is able to do this has frequencies in the ultraviolet (UV) region of the electromagnetic spectrum, and the sunlight bombarding the earth contains substantial amounts of UV radiation. Fortunately, a layer of ozone (O_3) in the stratosphere, a region of the atmosphere extending from about 45 to 55 km altitude, absorbs most of the incoming UV, protecting life on the surface. However, some UV radiation does get through, and the part of the spectrum of most concern is called "UV-B" with wavelengths between 280 and 320 nm.

What makes UV-B so dangerous is its ability to affect the DNA in our cells. (The structure of DNA and its replication is discussed in Chapter 23.) Absorption of UV radiation causes constituents of the DNA, called *pyrimidine bases*, to undergo reactions that form bonds between them. This causes transcription errors when the DNA replicates during cell division, giving rise to genetic

Dawn of a new day brings the risk of skin cancer to those particularly susceptible. Fortunately, understanding the risk allows us to protect ourselves with clothing and sunblock creams. *© Mick Roessler/© Corbis*

mutations that can lead to skin cancers. These skin cancers fall into three classes—basal cell carcinomas, squamous cell carcinomas, and melanomas (the last being the most dangerous). Each year there are more than 1 million cases of skin cancer diagnosed. It is estimated that more than 90% of skin cancers are due to absorption of UV-B radiation.

In recent years, concern has grown over the depletion of the ozone layer in the stratosphere apparently caused by the release of gases called chlorofluorocarbons (CFCs), which have been widely used in refrigerators and air conditioners. Some scientists have estimated a substantial increase in the rate of skin cancer caused by increased amounts of UV-B reaching the earth's surface due to this ozone depletion.

Pairing of Electrons in Covalent Bonds

■ In Chapter 8 you learned that when two electrons occupy the same orbital and therefore share the same space, their spins must be paired. The pairing of electrons is an important part of the formation of a covalent bond.

Before joining to form H_2, each of the separate hydrogen atoms has one electron in a 1s orbital. When these electrons are shared, the 1s orbital of each atom is, in a sense, filled. Because the electrons now share the same space, they become paired as required by the Pauli exclusion principle; that is, m_s is $+\frac{1}{2}$ for one of the electrons and $-\frac{1}{2}$ for the other. In general, the electrons involved almost always become paired when atoms form covalent bonds. In fact, a covalent bond is sometimes referred to as an **electron pair bond**.

Lewis symbols are often used to keep track of electrons in covalent bonds. The electrons that are shared between two atoms are shown as a pair of dots placed between the symbols for the bonded atoms. The formation of H_2 from hydrogen atoms, for example, can be depicted as

$$H \cdot + H \cdot \longrightarrow H : H$$

Because the electrons are shared, each H atom is considered to have two electrons.

(Colored circles emphasize that two electrons can be counted around each of the H atoms.)

For simplicity, the electron pair in a covalent bond is usually depicted as a single dash. Thus, the hydrogen molecule is represented as

$$H—H$$

A formula such as this, which is drawn with Lewis symbols, is called a **Lewis formula** or **Lewis structure**. It is also called a **structural formula** because it shows which atoms are present in the molecule *and* how they are attached to each other.

The Octet Rule and Covalent Bonding

You have seen that when a nonmetal atom forms an anion, electrons are gained until the s and p subshells of its valence shell are completed. The tendency of a nonmetal atom to finish with a completed valence shell, usually consisting of eight electrons, also influences the number of electrons the atom tends to acquire by sharing, and it thereby affects the number of covalent bonds the atom forms.

Hydrogen, with just one electron in its $1s$ orbital, completes its valence shell by obtaining a share of just one electron from another atom, so a hydrogen atom forms just one covalent bond. When this other atom is hydrogen, the H_2 molecule is formed.

Many atoms form covalent bonds by sharing enough electrons to give them complete s and p subshells in their outer shells. This is the noble gas configuration mentioned earlier and is the basis of the octet rule described in Section 9.3. As applied to covalent bonding, the **octet rule** can be stated as follows: *When atoms form covalent bonds, they tend to share sufficient electrons so as to achieve an outer shell having eight electrons.*

Often, the octet rule can be used to explain the number of covalent bonds an atom forms. This number normally equals the number of electrons the atom must acquire to have a total of eight (an octet) in its outer shell. For instance, the halogens (Group 7A) all have seven valence electrons. The Lewis symbol for a typical member of this group, chlorine, is

$$\cdot \overset{\cdot\cdot}{\underset{\cdot\cdot}{Cl}}\colon$$

We can see that only one electron is needed to complete its octet. Of course, chlorine can actually gain this electron and become a chloride ion. This is what it does when it forms an ionic compound such as sodium chloride (NaCl). When chlorine combines with another nonmetal, however, the complete transfer of an electron is not energetically favorable. Therefore, in forming such molecules as HCl or Cl_2, chlorine gets the one electron it needs by forming a covalent bond.

$$H \cdot + \cdot \overset{\cdot\cdot}{\underset{\cdot\cdot}{Cl}}\colon \longrightarrow H \colon \overset{\cdot\cdot}{\underset{\cdot\cdot}{Cl}}\colon \quad \text{or} \quad H \!-\! \overset{\cdot\cdot}{\underset{\cdot\cdot}{Cl}}\colon$$

$$\colon\overset{\cdot\cdot}{\underset{\cdot\cdot}{Cl}}\cdot + \cdot \overset{\cdot\cdot}{\underset{\cdot\cdot}{Cl}}\colon \longrightarrow \colon\overset{\cdot\cdot}{\underset{\cdot\cdot}{Cl}}\colon\overset{\cdot\cdot}{\underset{\cdot\cdot}{Cl}}\colon \quad \text{or} \quad \colon\overset{\cdot\cdot}{\underset{\cdot\cdot}{Cl}}\!-\!\overset{\cdot\cdot}{\underset{\cdot\cdot}{Cl}}\colon$$

There are many nonmetals that form more than one covalent bond. For example, the three most important elements in biochemical systems are carbon, nitrogen, and oxygen.

$$\cdot \overset{\cdot}{\underset{\cdot}{C}}\cdot \qquad \cdot \overset{\cdot}{\underset{\cdot}{N}}\cdot \qquad \cdot \overset{\cdot}{\underset{\cdot\cdot}{O}}\colon$$

You've already encountered the simplest hydrogen compounds of these elements: methane, CH_4, ammonia, NH_3, and water, H_2O. Their Lewis structures are

$$
\begin{array}{ccc}
\text{H} & \text{H} & \text{H} \\
\text{H}\colon\!\overset{\cdot\cdot}{C}\!\colon\text{H} & \text{H}\colon\!\overset{\cdot\cdot}{N}\!\colon\text{H} & \text{H}\colon\!\overset{\cdot\cdot}{\underset{\cdot\cdot}{O}}\!\colon \\
\text{H} & & \\
\end{array}
$$

$$
\begin{array}{ccc}
\text{or} & \text{or} & \text{or} \\
\end{array}
$$

$$
\begin{array}{ccc}
\text{H} & \text{H} & \text{H} \\
| & | & | \\
\text{H}\!-\!\text{C}\!-\!\text{H} & \text{H}\!-\!\text{N}\!-\!\text{H} & \text{H}\!-\!\overset{}{\underset{\cdot\cdot}{O}}\colon \\
| & & \\
\text{H} & & \\
\end{array}
$$

■ As you will see, it is useful to remember that hydrogen atoms form only one covalent bond.

TOOLS

Octet rule and covalent bonding

Methane   Ammonia   Water

In the ball-and-stick drawings of the molecules, the "sticks" represent the covalent bonds between the atoms.

Multiple Bonds

The bond produced by the sharing of *one* pair of electrons between two atoms is called a **single bond**. So far, these have been the only kind we've discussed. There are, however, many molecules in which more than a single pair of electrons are shared between two atoms. For example, we can diagram the formation of the bonds in CO_2 as follows.

■ The arrows here simply indicate how the electrons can combine to form the electron pair bonds in the molecule.

The carbon atom shares two of its valence electrons with one oxygen and two with the other. At the same time, each oxygen shares two electrons with carbon. The result is the formation of two **double bonds**. Notice that in the Lewis formula, both of the shared electron pairs are placed between the symbols for the two atoms joined by the double bond. Once again, if we circle the valence shell electrons that "belong" to each atom, we see that each has an octet.

$$:\!\ddot{O}\!:\!:\!C\!:\!:\!\ddot{O}\!:$$
8 electrons

■ How we place the unshared pairs of electrons around the oxygen is unimportant. Two equally valid Lewis structure for CO_2 are

$$:\!\ddot{O}\!=\!C\!=\!\ddot{O}\!:\quad \text{and}\quad \ddot{O}\!=\!C\!-\!\ddot{\underset{..}{O}}$$

The Lewis structure for CO_2, using dashes, is

$$:\!\underset{..}{O}\!=\!C\!=\!\ddot{O}\!:$$

Sometimes three pairs of electrons are shared between two atoms. The most abundant gas in the atmosphere, nitrogen, occurs in the form of diatomic molecules, N_2. As we've seen, the Lewis symbol for nitrogen is

$$\cdot\!\dot{N}\!:$$

and each nitrogen atom needs three electrons to complete its octet. When the N_2 molecule is formed, each of the nitrogen atoms shares three electrons with the other.

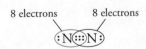

The result is called a **triple bond**. Again, notice that we place all three electron pairs of the bond between the two atoms. We count all of these electrons as though they belong to both of the atoms. Each nitrogen therefore has an octet.

8 electrons   8 electrons

The triple bond is usually represented by three dashes, so the bonding in the N_2 molecule is normally shown as

$$:\!N\!\equiv\!N\!:$$

9.6 | Covalent Compounds of Carbon

Covalent bonds are found in many of the substances we encounter on a daily basis. Most of them are classified as **organic compounds** in which carbon atoms are covalently bonded to other carbon atoms and to a variety of other nonmetals. They include the foods we eat, the fabrics we wear, the medicines that cure us, the fuels that power vehicles, and the fibers in the rope supporting the mountain climber in the opening photo of this chapter. Because they are so common, organic compounds will be used frequently as examples in our discussions later in the book. For this reason, you will find it helpful to learn something now about their makeup.

Organic compounds fall into different classes according to the elements that are bonded to carbon and how atoms of those elements are arranged in the molecules. The kinds of compounds we will study in this section will include those in which carbon is bonded to hydrogen, oxygen, and nitrogen. As you learned in Chapter 3, such substances can be considered to be derived from hydrocarbons—compounds of carbon and hydrogen in which the basic molecular "backbones" are composed of carbon atoms linked to one another in a chainlike fashion. (Hydrocarbons themselves are the principal constituents of petroleum.)

One of the chief features of organic compounds is the tendency of carbon to complete its octet by forming four covalent bonds. For example, in the alkane series of hydrocarbons (which we described briefly on page 92) all of the bonds are single bonds. The structures of the first three alkanes (methane, ethane, and propane) are

methane   ethane   propane

The shapes of their molecules are illustrated as space-filling models in Figure 3.19 on page 93.

When more than four carbon atoms are present, matters become more complex because there is more than one way to arrange the atoms. For example, butane has the formula C_4H_{10}, but there are two ways to arrange the carbon atoms. These two arrangements occur in compounds commonly called butane and isobutane.

Butane

C_4H_{10}
bp = −0.5 °C

Methylpropane
(isobutane)

C_4H_{10}
bp = −11.7 °C

■ If you are also enrolled in a course in biology, you will find some knowledge of organic chemistry useful in understanding that subject as well.

■ A more comprehensive discussion of organic compounds is found in Chapter 23. In this section we look at some simple ways carbon atoms combine with other atoms to form certain important classes of organic substances that we encounter frequently.

■ These structures can be written in a condensed form as
CH_4
CH_3CH_3
$CH_3CH_2CH_3$

■ Butane and isobutane are said to be isomers of each other. In condensed form, we can write their structures as
$CH_3CH_2CH_2CH_3$
$\qquad CH_3$
$\qquad |$
CH_3CHCH_3

Even though they have the same molecular formula, these are actually different compounds with different properties, as you can see from the boiling points listed below their structures. The ability of atoms to arrange themselves in more than one way to give different compounds that have the same molecular formula is called **isomerism** and is discussed more fully in Chapters 22 and 23. The existence of *isomers* is one of the reasons there are so many organic compounds. For example, there are 366,319 different compounds, or isomers, that have the formula $C_{20}H_{42}$; they differ only in the way the carbon atoms are attached to each other.

Carbon can also complete its octet by forming double or triple bonds. The Lewis structures of ethene, C_2H_4, and ethyne, C_2H_2 (commonly called ethylene and acetylene, respectively) are as follows:[4]

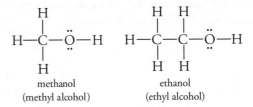

ethene
(ethylene)

ethyne
(acetylene)

Compounds That Also Contain Oxygen and Nitrogen

Most organic compounds contain elements in addition to carbon and hydrogen. As we mentioned in Chapter 3, it is convenient to consider such compounds to be derived from hydrocarbons by replacing one or more hydrogens by other groups of atoms. Such compounds can be divided into various families according to the nature of the groups, called **functional groups,** attached to the parent hydrocarbon fragment. Some such families are summarized in Table 9.2, in which the hydrocarbon fragment to which the functional group is attached is symbolized by the letter R.

Alcohols

In Chapter 3 we noted that alcohols are organic compounds in which one of the hydrogen atoms of a hydrocarbon is replaced by OH. The family name for these compounds is **alcohol**. Examples are methanol (methyl alcohol) and ethanol (ethyl alcohol), which have the following structures:

methanol
(methyl alcohol)

ethanol
(ethyl alcohol)

This container of "Canned Heat" contains methanol as the fuel. It is commonly used to heat food at buffets. *(Andy Washnik)*

Some **condensed formulas** that we might write for these are CH_3OH and CH_3CH_2OH, or CH_3—OH and CH_3CH_2—OH. Methanol is used as a solvent and a fuel; ethanol is found in alcoholic beverages and is blended with gasoline to yield a fuel called E85, containing 85% ethanol.

Ketones

In alcohols, the oxygen forms two single bonds to complete its octet, just as in water. But oxygen can also form double bonds, as you saw for CO_2. One family of compounds in which a doubly bonded oxygen replaces a pair of hydrogen atoms is called **ketones.** The

---

[4]In the IUPAC system for naming organic compounds, *meth-*, *eth-*, *prop-*, and *but-* indicate carbon chains of 1, 2, 3, and 4 carbon atoms, respectively. Organic nomenclature is discussed more fully in Chapter 23.

Family Name	General Formula[a]	Example
Alcohols	R—Ö—H	CH₃—Ö—H (methanol)

Table 9.2 — Some Families of Oxygen- and Nitrogen-Containing Organic Compounds

Alcohols: $R-\ddot{O}-H$; $CH_3-\ddot{O}-H$ methanol

Aldehydes: $R-\overset{:O:}{\overset{\|}{C}}-H$; $CH_3-\overset{:O:}{\overset{\|}{C}}-H$ ethanal (acetaldehyde)

Ketones: $R-\overset{:O:}{\overset{\|}{C}}-R$; $CH_3-\overset{:O:}{\overset{\|}{C}}-CH_3$ propanone (acetone)

Acids: $R-\overset{:O:}{\overset{\|}{C}}-\ddot{O}-H$; $CH_3-\overset{:O:}{\overset{\|}{C}}-\ddot{O}-H$ ethanoic acid (acetic acid)

Amines: $R-\ddot{N}H_2$; $R-\ddot{N}H-R$; $R-\overset{|}{\underset{R}{\ddot{N}}}-R$; $CH_3-\ddot{N}H_2$ methylamine

[a]R stands for a hydrocarbon fragment such as CH_3- or CH_3CH_2-.

simplest example is propanone, better known as acetone, a solvent often used in nail polish remover.

$$H-\overset{H}{\underset{H}{\overset{|}{C}}}-\overset{:O:}{\overset{\|}{C}}-\overset{H}{\underset{H}{\overset{|}{C}}}-H \quad \text{or} \quad CH_3-\overset{:O:}{\overset{\|}{C}}-CH_3$$
propanone (acetone)

Acetone

Ketones are found in many useful solvents that dissolve various plastics. An example is methyl ethyl ketone.

$$CH_3-\overset{:O:}{\overset{\|}{C}}-CH_2-CH_3$$
butanone (methyl ethyl ketone)

Aldehydes

Notice that in ketones the carbon bonded to the oxygen is also attached to *two* other carbon atoms. If at least one of the atoms attached to the C=O group (called a **carbonyl group,** pronounced *car-bon-EEL*) is a hydrogen, a different family of compounds is formed

Formaldehyde

called **aldehydes.** Examples are formaldehyde (used to preserve biological specimens, for embalming, and to make plastics) and acetaldehyde (used in the manufacture of perfumes, dyes, plastics, and other products).

$$
\begin{array}{cc}
\overset{\displaystyle :\!\ddot{O}\!:}{\underset{|}{\|}} & \overset{\displaystyle :\!\ddot{O}\!:}{\underset{|}{\|}} \\
H\!-\!C\!-\!H & CH_3\!-\!C\!-\!H \\
\text{methanal} & \text{ethanal} \\
\text{(formaldehyde)} & \text{(acetaldehyde)}
\end{array}
$$

Organic Acids

Organic acids, also called **carboxylic acids,** constitute another very important family of oxygen-containing organic compounds. An example is acetic acid, which we described in Chapter 5. The shape of the molecule was illustrated in Figure 5.11 (page 165), showing the single hydrogen atom that is capable of ionizing in the formation of H_3O^+. The Lewis structures of acetic acid and the acetate ion are

$$
\begin{array}{cc}
H \quad :\!\ddot{O}\!: & \left[H \quad :\!\ddot{O}\!: \right]^- \\
H\!-\!C\!-\!C\!-\!\ddot{O}\!-\!H & H\!-\!C\!-\!C\!-\!\ddot{O}\!: \\
H & H \\
\text{acetic acid} & \text{acetate ion}
\end{array}
$$

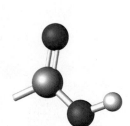

The carboxyl group

In general, the structures of organic acids are characterized by the presence of the **carboxyl group,** $-CO_2H$.

$$
\begin{array}{c}
:\!\ddot{O}\!: \\
\|\\
-C\!-\!\ddot{O}\!-\!H \\
\text{carboxyl group}
\end{array}
$$

Notice that organic acids have both a doubly bonded oxygen and an OH group attached to the end carbon atom.

Amines

Nitrogen atoms need three electrons to complete an octet, and in most of its compounds, nitrogen forms three bonds. The common nitrogen-containing organic compounds can be imagined as being derived from ammonia by replacing one or more of the hydrogens of NH_3 with hydrocarbon groups. They're called amines, and an example is methylamine, CH_3NH_2.

Methylamine

$$
\begin{array}{cc}
H & H \\
| & | \\
H\!-\!\ddot{N}\!-\!H & H\!-\!\ddot{N}\!-\!CH_3 \\
\text{ammonia} & \text{methylamine}
\end{array}
$$

Amines are strong-smelling compounds and often have a "fishy" odor. Like ammonia, they're weakly basic.[5]

$$CH_3NH_2(aq) + H_2O \rightleftharpoons CH_3NH_3^+(aq) + OH^-(aq)$$

As we noted in Chapter 5, the H^+ that is added to an amine becomes attached to the nitrogen atom.

---

[5]Amino acids, which are essential building blocks of proteins in our bodies, contain both an amine group ($-NH_2$) and a carboxyl group ($-CO_2H$). The simplest of these is the amino acid glycine,

$$
\begin{array}{c}
:\!\ddot{O}\!: \\
\|\\
:NH_2\!-\!CH_2\!-\!C\!-\!\ddot{O}H \\
\text{glycine}
\end{array}
$$

9.6 | Match the structural formulas on the left with the correct names of the families of organic compounds to which they belong.

$$CH_3—CH_2—\overset{\displaystyle :\overset{\displaystyle ..}{O}:}{\overset{\displaystyle \|}{C}}—H \qquad \text{amine}$$

$$CH_3—\overset{\displaystyle H}{\underset{\displaystyle ..}{\overset{\displaystyle |}{N}}}—CH_3 \qquad \text{alcohol}$$

$$H—\overset{\displaystyle :\overset{\displaystyle ..}{O}:}{\overset{\displaystyle \|}{C}}—\overset{\displaystyle ..}{\underset{\displaystyle ..}{O}}—H \qquad \text{ketone}$$

$$CH_3—CH_2—\overset{\displaystyle :\overset{\displaystyle ..}{O}:}{\overset{\displaystyle \|}{C}}—CH_2—CH_3 \qquad \text{aldehyde}$$

$$CH_3—CH_2—CH_2—\overset{\displaystyle ..}{\underset{\displaystyle ..}{O}}—H \qquad \text{acid}$$

9.7 | The following questions apply to the compounds in Practice Exercise 9.6. (a) Which produces a basic solution in water? (b) Which produces an acidic aqueous solution? (c) For the acid, what is the Lewis structure of the anion formed when it is neutralized?

9.7 | Bond Polarity and Electronegativity

When two identical atoms form a covalent bond, as in H_2 or Cl_2, each atom has an equal share of the bond's electron pair. The electron density at both ends of the bond is the same, because the electrons are equally attracted to both nuclei. However, when different kinds of atoms combine, as in HCl, one nucleus usually attracts the electrons in the bond more strongly than the other.

Polar and Nonpolar Bonds

The result of unequal attractions for the bonding electrons is an unbalanced distribution of electron density within the bond. For example, chlorine atoms have a greater attraction for electrons in a bond than do hydrogen atoms. In the HCl molecule, therefore, the electron cloud is pulled more tightly around the Cl, and that end of the molecule experiences a slight buildup of negative charge. The electron density that shifts toward the chlorine is removed from the hydrogen, which causes the hydrogen end to acquire a slight positive charge. These charges are less than full 1+ and 1− charges and are called **partial charges,** which are usually indicated by the lowercase Greek letter delta, δ (see Figure 9.8). Partial charges can also be indicated on Lewis structures. For example,

$$H—\overset{\displaystyle ..}{\underset{\displaystyle ..}{Cl}}:$$
$$\quad \delta+ \quad \delta-$$

A bond that carries partial positive and negative charges on opposite ends is called a **polar covalent bond,** or often simply a **polar bond** (the word *covalent* is understood). The term *polar* comes from the notion of *poles* of equal but opposite charge at either end of the bond. Because *two poles* of electric charge are involved, the bond is said to be an **electric dipole.**

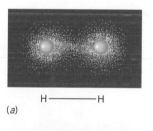

(a) H———H

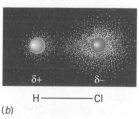

(b) H————Cl

Figure 9.8 | **Equal and unequal sharing of electrons in a covalent bond.** Each of the diagrams illustrate the distribution of electron density of the shared electron pair in a bond. (*a*) In H_2, the electron density in the bond is spread equally over both atoms. (*b*) In HCl, more than half of the electron density of the bond is concentrated around chlorine, causing opposite ends of the bond to carry partial electrical charges.

The polar bond in HCl causes the molecule as a whole to have opposite charges on either end, so the HCl molecule as a whole is an electric dipole. We say that HCl is a **polar molecule.** The magnitude of its polarity is expressed quantitatively by its **dipole moment** (symbol μ), which is equal to the amount of charge on either end of the molecule, q, multiplied by the distance between the charges, r.

Dipole moment

$$\mu = q \times r \qquad (9.2)^{6}$$

Table 9.3 lists the dipole moments and bond lengths for some diatomic molecules. The dipole moments are reported in **debye** units (symbol D), where $1\ D = 3.34 \times 10^{-30}$ C m (coulomb $\times$ meter).

By separate experiments, it is possible to measure both μ and r (which corresponds to the bond length in a diatomic molecule such as HCl). Knowledge of μ and r makes it possible to calculate the amount of charge on opposite ends of the dipole. For HCl, such calculations show that q equals 0.17 electronic charge units, which means the hydrogen carries a charge of $+0.17e^{-}$ and the chlorine a charge of $-0.17e^{-}$.

One of the main reasons we are concerned about whether a molecule is polar or not is because many physical properties, such as melting point and boiling point, are affected by it. This is because polar molecules attract each other more strongly than do nonpolar molecules. The positive end of one polar molecule attracts the negative end of another. The strength of the attraction depends on both the amount of charge on either end of the molecule and the distance between the charges; in other words, it depends on the molecule's dipole moment.

Table 9.3	Dipole Moments and Bond Lengths for Some Diatomic Molecules[a]	
Compound	**Dipole Moment (D)**	**Bond Length (pm)**
HF	1.83	91.7
HCl	1.09	127
HBr	0.82	141
HI	0.45	161
CO	0.11	113
NO	0.16	115

[a]Source: National Institute of Standards and Technology.

Example 9.5
Calculating the Charge on the End of a Polar Molecule

The HF molecule has a dipole moment of 1.83 D and a bond length of 91.7 pm. What is the amount of charge, in electronic charge units, on either end of the bond?

■ **Analysis:** This is going to involve substituting values into Equation 9.2. However, to answer the problem correctly, we will have to be especially careful of the units. The debye has charge expressed in coulombs, but we have to express the answer in electronic charge units.

■ **Assembling the Tools:** The primary tool for solving the problem is Equation 9.2. In the calculation we are also going to have to convert between coulombs (C) and electronic charge units. From the table on the inside rear cover of the book we find that the charge on an electron (i.e., an electronic charge unit) equals 1.602×10^{-19} C, which we can express as

$$1\ e^{-} \Leftrightarrow 1.602 \times 10^{-19}\ C$$

■ **Solution:** We will solve Equation 9.2 for q.

$$q = \frac{\mu}{r}$$

The debye unit, D, $= 3.34 \times 10^{-30}$ C m, so the dipole moment of HF is

$$\mu = (1.83\ \cancel{D}) (3.34 \times 10^{-30}\ C\ m/\cancel{D}) = 6.11 \times 10^{-30}\ C\ m$$

---

[6]Once again, we're using the symbol q to mean electric charge, not heat as in Chapter 7.

The SI prefix p (pico) means $\times\ 10^{-12}$, so the bond length $r = 91.7 \times 10^{-12}$ m. Substituting in the equation above gives

$$q = \frac{6.11 \times 10^{-30}\ C\ \cancel{m}}{91.7 \times 10^{-12}\ \cancel{m}} = 6.66 \times 10^{-20}\ C$$

The value of q in electronic charge units is therefore

$$q = 6.66 \times 10^{-20}\ \cancel{C} \times \left(\frac{1\ e^-}{1.602 \times 10^{-19}\ \cancel{C}}\right) = 0.416\ e^-$$

As in HCl, the hydrogen carries the positive charge, so the charge on the hydrogen end of the molecule is $+0.416\ e^-$ and the charge on the fluorine end is $-0.416\ e^-$.

■ **Is the Answer Reasonable?** If we look at the units, we see that they cancel correctly, so that gives us confidence that we've done the calculation correctly. The fact that our answer is between zero and one electronic charge unit, and therefore a partial electrical charge, further suggests we've solved the problem correctly.

9.8 | The chlorine end of the chlorine monoxide molecule carries a charge of $+0.167\ e^-$. The bond length is 154.6 pm. Calculate the dipole moment of the molecule in debye units. (*Hint:* Be sure to convert the charge to coulombs.)

9.9 | Although isolated Na^+ and Cl^- ions are unstable, these ions can exist in the gaseous state as *ion pairs*. An ion pair consists of an NaCl unit in which the bond length is 236 pm. The dipole moment of the ion pair is 9.00 D. What are the actual amounts of charge on the sodium and chlorine atoms in this NaCl pair? What percentage of full 1+ and 1− charges are these? (This is the *percentage ionic character* in the NaCl pair.)

Practice Exercises

Electronegativity

The degree to which a covalent bond is polar depends on the difference in the abilities of the bonded atoms to attract electrons. The greater the difference, the more polar the bond, and the more the electron density is shifted toward the atom that attracts electrons more.

The term that we use to describe the attraction an atom has for the electrons in a bond is called **electronegativity.** In HCl, for example, chlorine is *more electronegative* than hydrogen. This causes the electron pair of the covalent bond to spend more of its time around the more electronegative atom, which is why the Cl end of the bond acquires a partial negative charge.

The first scientist to develop numerical values for electronegativity was Linus Pauling (1901–1994). He observed that polar bonds have a bond energy larger than would be expected if the opposite ends of the bonds were electrically neutral. Pauling reasoned that the extra bond energy is caused by the attraction between the partial charges on opposite ends of the bond. By estimating the extra bond energy, he was able to develop a scale of electronegativities for the elements. Other scientists have used different approaches to measuring electronegativities, with similar results.

A set of numerical values for the electronegativities of the elements is shown in Figure 9.9. These data are useful because the *difference* in electronegativity provides an estimate of the degree of polarity of a bond. For instance, the data tell us fluorine is more electronegative than chlorine, so we expect HF to be more polar than HCl. (This is confirmed by the larger dipole moment of the HF molecule.) In addition, the relative magnitudes of the electronegativities indicate which ends of a bond carry the partial positive and negative charges. Thus, hydrogen is less electronegative than

Linus Pauling (1901–1994) contributed greatly to our understanding of chemical bonding. He was the winner of two Nobel Prizes, in 1954 for chemistry and in 1962 for peace. *(Ted Streshinsky/© Corbis)*

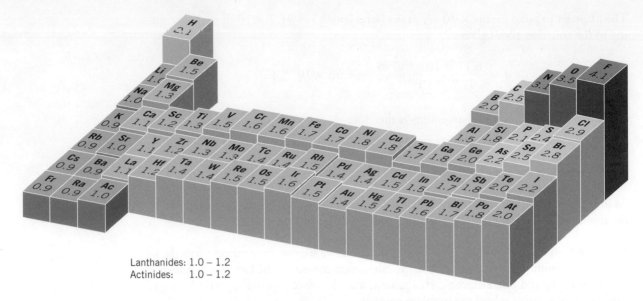

Lanthanides: 1.0 – 1.2
Actinides: 1.0 – 1.2

Figure 9.9 | **The electronegativities of the elements.** The noble gases are assigned electronegativities of zero and are omitted from the table.

either fluorine or chlorine, so in both of these molecules the hydrogen bears the partial positive charge.

$$H—\ddot{\underset{..}{F}}: \qquad H—\ddot{\underset{..}{C}l}:$$
$$\delta+ \quad \delta- \qquad \delta+ \quad \delta-$$

By studying electronegativity values and their differences we find that there is no sharp dividing line between ionic and covalent bonding. Ionic bonding and *nonpolar covalent bonding* simply represent the two extremes. A bond is mostly ionic when the difference in electronegativity between two atoms is very large; the more electronegative atom acquires essentially complete control of the bonding electrons. In a **nonpolar covalent bond,** there is no difference in electronegativity, so the pair of bonding electrons is shared equally.

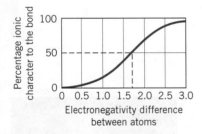

Figure 9.10 | **Variation in the percentage ionic character of a bond with electronegativity difference.** The bond becomes about 50% ionic when the electronegativity difference equals 1.7, which means that the atoms in the bond carry a partial charge of approximately $\pm 0.5 \, e^-$.

$$Cs^+ \left[:\ddot{\underset{..}{F}}: \right]^- \qquad\qquad :\ddot{\underset{..}{F}}:\ddot{\underset{..}{F}}:$$
"bonding pair" held   bonding pair
exclusively by fluorine   shared equally

The degree to which the bond is polar, which we might think of as the amount of **ionic character** of the bond, varies in a continuous way with changes in the electronegativity difference (Figure 9.10). The bond becomes more than 50% ionic when the electronegativity difference exceeds approximately 1.7.

Practice Exercises

9.10 | Bromine and chlorine form a molecular substance with the formula BrCl. Is the bond polar? If so, which atom carries the partial negative charge? (*Hint:* Compare electronegativities.)

9.11 | For each of the following bonds, choose the atom that carries the partial negative charge. Arrange them in order of increasing bond polarity: (a) P—Br, (b) Si—Cl, (c) S—Cl.

Periodic Trends in Electronegativity

An examination of Figure 9.9 reveals that within the periodic table, *electronegativity increases from bottom to top in a group, and from left to right in a period.* These trends follow those for ionization energy (IE); an atom that has a small IE will lose an electron more easily than an atom with a large IE, just as an atom with a small electronegativity will lose its share of an electron pair more readily than an atom with a large electronegativity.

Elements located in the same region of the table (for example, the nonmetals) have similar electronegativities, which means that if they form bonds with each other, the electronegativity differences will be small and the bonds will be more covalent than ionic. On the other hand, if elements from widely separated regions of the table combine, large electronegativity differences occur and the bonds will be predominantly ionic. This is what happens, for example, when an element from Group 1A or Group 2A reacts with a nonmetal from the upper right-hand corner of the periodic table.

Reactivities of the Elements and Electronegativity

There are parallels between an element's electronegativity and its **reactivity**—its tendency to undergo redox reactions.

Reactivities of Metals Relate to Their Ease of Oxidation

In nearly every compound containing a metal, the metal exists in a positive oxidation state. Therefore, for a metal, *reactivity* relates to how easily the metal is oxidized. For example, a metal like sodium, which is very easily oxidized, is said to be very reactive, whereas a metal like platinum, which is very difficult to oxidize, is said to be unreactive.

There are several ways to compare how easily metals are oxidized. In Chapter 6 we saw that by comparing the abilities of metals to displace each other from compounds we are able to establish their relative ease of oxidation. This was the basis for the activity series (Table 6.3).

Figure 9.11 illustrates how the ease of oxidation (reactivity) of metals varies in the periodic table. In general, these trends roughly follow the variations in electronegativity, with the metal being less easily oxidized as its electronegativity increases. You might expect this, because electronegativity is a measure of how strongly the atom of an element attracts electrons when combining with an atom of a different element. The more strongly the atom attracts electrons, the more difficult it is to oxidize. This relationship between reactivity and electronegativity is only approximate, however, because many other factors affect the stability of the compounds that are formed.

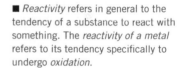

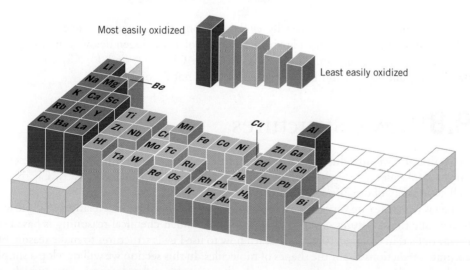

Most easily oxidized

Least easily oxidized

Figure 9.11 | Variations in the ease of oxidation of metals.

Elements of Groups 1A and 2A

In Figure 9.11, we see that the metals that are most easily oxidized are found at the far left in the periodic table. These are elements with very low electronegativities. The metals in Group 1A, for example, are so easily oxidized that all of them react with water to liberate hydrogen. Because of their reactivity toward moisture and oxygen, they have no useful applications that require exposure to the atmosphere, so we rarely encounter them as free metals. The same is true of the heavier metals in Group 2A, calcium through barium. These elements also react with water to liberate hydrogen. In Figure 9.9 we see that electronegativity decreases going down a group, which explains why the heavier elements in Group 2A are more reactive than those at the top of the group.

Noble Metals

In Figure 9.11 we can also locate the metals that are the most difficult to oxidize. They occur for the most part among the heavier transition elements in the center of the periodic table. Here we find the elements platinum and gold, which are sometimes called **noble metals** because of their extremely low degree of reactivity. Their bright luster and lack of any tendency to corrode in air or water combine to make them particularly attractive for use in fine jewelry. Their lack of reactivity also is responsible for their industrial uses. Gold, for example, is used to coat the electrical contacts in low-voltage circuits found in microcomputers, because even a small amount of corrosion on a more reactive metal would be sufficient to impede the flow of electricity so much as to make the devices unreliable.

The Oxidizing Power of Nonmetals

The reactivity of a nonmetal is determined by its ease of reduction, and therefore its ability to serve as an oxidizing agent. This ability also varies according to the element's electronegativity. Nonmetals with high electronegativities have strong tendencies to acquire electrons and are therefore strong oxidizing agents. In parallel with changes in electronegativities in the periodic table, *the oxidizing abilities of nonmetals increase from left to right across a period and from bottom to top in a group.* Thus, the most powerful oxidizing agent is fluorine, followed closely by oxygen, both of which appear in the upper right-hand corner of the periodic table.

Single replacement reactions (also called **displacement reactions**) occur among the nonmetals, just as with the metals (which you studied in Chapter 6). For example, heating a metal sulfide in oxygen causes the sulfur to be replaced by oxygen. The displaced sulfur then combines with additional oxygen to give sulfur dioxide. The equation for a typical reaction is

$$CuS(s) + \tfrac{3}{2}O_2(g) \longrightarrow CuO(s) + SO_2(g)$$

Displacement reactions are especially evident among the halogens, where a particular halogen in its elemental form will oxidize the *anion* of any halogen below it in Group 7A, as illustrated in the margin. Thus, F_2 will oxidize Cl^-, Br^-, and I^-; Cl_2 will oxidize Br^- and I^-, but not F^-; and Br_2 will oxidize I^-, but not F^- or Cl^-.

This statue of Prometheus overlooking the skating rink in Rockefeller Center in New York City is covered in a thin layer of gold, providing both beauty and weather resistance. *(Philipus/Alamy)*

TOOLS

Trends in the reactivity of nonmetals in the periodic table

■ Fluorine:

$$F_2 + 2Cl^- \longrightarrow 2F^- + Cl_2$$
$$F_2 + 2Br^- \longrightarrow 2F^- + Br_2$$
$$F_2 + 2I^- \longrightarrow 2F^- + I_2$$

Chlorine:

$$Cl_2 + 2Br^- \longrightarrow 2Cl^- + Br_2$$
$$Cl_2 + 2I^- \longrightarrow 2Cl^- + I_2$$

Bromine:

$$Br_2 + 2I^- \longrightarrow 2Br^- + I_2$$

9.8 | Lewis Structures

In Section 9.5 we introduced you to Lewis structures and we have used them to describe various molecules, all of which obey the octet rule. Examples included CO_2, Cl_2, N_2, as well as a variety of organic compounds.

Lewis structures are very useful in chemistry because they give us a relatively simple way to describe the structures of molecules. As a result, much chemical reasoning is based on them. In fact, in Chapter 10 you will learn how to use Lewis structures to make reasonably accurate predictions about the shapes of molecules. In this section we will develop a simple method for drawing Lewis structures for both molecules and polyatomic ions (which are also held together by covalent bonds).

Although the octet rule is important in covalent bonding, it is not always obeyed. For instance, there are some molecules in which one or more atoms must have more than an octet in the valence shell. Examples are PCl_5 and SF_6, whose Lewis structures are

```
      :Cl:                :F:
       |                 .. | ..
 :Cl — P — Cl:        :F   S   F:
     / |   ..            ..  /|\  ..
  :Cl: :Cl:           :F.  /  | \  .F:
    ..   ..              ..  :F:  ..
                            ..
```

In these molecules the formation of more than four bonds to the central atom requires that the central atom have a share of more than eight electrons.

There are also some molecules (but not many) in which the central atom behaves as though it has less than an octet. The most common examples involve compounds of beryllium and boron.

$\cdot \text{Be} \cdot \; + \; 2 \cdot \ddot{\text{Cl}}\!: \; \longrightarrow \; :\ddot{\text{Cl}} - \text{Be} - \ddot{\text{Cl}}:$

four electrons around Be

$:\ddot{\text{Cl}}:$
$\cdot \dot{\text{B}} \cdot \; + \; 3 \cdot \ddot{\text{Cl}}\!: \; \longrightarrow \; :\ddot{\text{Cl}} - \overset{\textstyle |}{\text{B}} - \ddot{\text{Cl}}:$

six electrons around B

Although Be and B sometimes have less than an octet, *the elements in Period 2 never exceed an octet.* The reason is because their valence shells, having $n = 2$, can hold a maximum of only 8 electrons. (This explains why the octet rule works so well for atoms of carbon, nitrogen, and oxygen.) However, elements in periods below Period 2, such as phosphorus and sulfur, sometimes do exceed an octet, because their valence shells can hold more than 8 electrons. For example, the valence shell for elements in Period 3, for which $n = 3$, could hold a maximum of 18 electrons, and the valence shell for Period 4 elements, which have s, p, d, and f subshells, could theoretically hold as many as 32 electrons.

A Procedure for Drawing Lewis Structures

Figure 9.12 outlines a series of steps that provides a systematic method for drawing Lewis structures. The first step is to decide which atoms are bonded to each other, so that we know where to put the dots or dashes. This is not always a simple matter. Many times the formula suggests the way the atoms are arranged because the central atom, which is usually the least electronegative one, is usually written first. Examples are CO_2 and ClO_4^-, which have the following **skeletal structures** (i.e., arrangements of atoms):

```
                    O
                    |
  O  C  O      O  Cl  O
                    |
                    O
```

Sometimes, obtaining the skeletal structure is not quite so simple, especially when more than two elements are present. Some generalizations are possible, however. For example, the skeletal structure of nitric acid, HNO_3, is

(correct)

■ Lewis structures just describe which atoms are bonded to each other and the kinds of bonds involved. Thus, the Lewis structure for water can be drawn as H—Ö—H, but it does not mean the water molecule is linear, with all the atoms in a straight line. Actually, water isn't linear; the two O—H bonds form an angle of about 104°.

■ Although beryllium is a metal, many of its compounds are not ionic. Pure $BeCl_2$ is molecular with covalent Be—Cl bonds.

Method for drawing Lewis structures

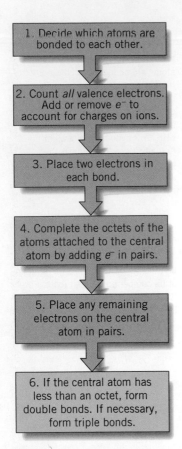

Figure 9.12 | Summary of the steps in drawing a Lewis structure. If you follow these steps, you will obtain a Lewis structure in which the octet rule is obeyed by the maximum number of atoms.

rather than one of the following:

$$\begin{array}{c} O \\ O\ N\ O \quad \text{or} \quad H\ O\ O\ N\ O \quad \text{(incorrect)} \\ H \end{array}$$

Nitric acid is an oxoacid (Section 5.4), and it happens that the hydrogen atoms that can be released from molecules of oxoacids are always bonded to oxygen atoms, which are in turn bonded to the third nonmetal atom. Therefore, recognizing HNO_3 as the formula of an oxoacid allows us to predict that the three oxygen atoms are bonded to the nitrogen, and the hydrogen is bonded to one of the oxygens. (It is also useful to remember that hydrogen forms only one bond, so we should not choose it to be a central atom.)

There are times when no reasonable basis can be found for choosing a particular skeletal structure. If you must make a guess, choose the most symmetrical arrangement of atoms, because it has the greatest chance of being correct.

After you've decided on the skeletal structure, the next step is to count all of the *valence electrons* to find out how many dots must appear in the final formula. Using the periodic table, locate the groups in which the elements in the formula occur to determine the number of valence electrons contributed by each atom. If the structure you wish to draw is that of an ion, *add one additional valence electron for each negative charge or remove a valence electron for each positive charge.* Some examples are as follows:

SO_3	Sulfur (Group 6A) contributes $6e^-$.	$1 \times 6 = 6e^-$
	Each oxygen (Group 6A) contributes $6e^-$.	$3 \times 6 = 18e^-$
		Total $24e^-$
ClO_4^-	Chlorine (Group 7A) contributes $7e^-$.	$1 \times 7 = 7e^-$
	Each oxygen (Group 6A) contributes $6e^-$.	$4 \times 6 = 24e^-$
	Add $1e^-$ for the 1− charge.	$+1e^-$
		Total $32e^-$
NH_4^+	Nitrogen (Group 5A) contributes $5e^-$.	$1 \times 5 = 5e^-$
	Each hydrogen (Group 1A) contributes $1e^-$.	$4 \times 1 = 4e^-$
	Subtract $1e^-$ for the 1+ charge.	$-1e^-$
		Total $8e^-$

After we have determined the number of valence electrons, we place them into the skeletal structure in pairs following the steps outlined in Figure 9.12. Let's look at some examples of how we go about this.

Example 9.6
Drawing Lewis Structures

What is the Lewis structure of the chloric acid molecule, $HClO_3$?

■ **Analysis:** The first step is to select a reasonable skeletal structure. Because the substance is an oxoacid, we can expect the hydrogen to be bonded to an oxygen, which in turn is bonded to the chlorine. The other two oxygens would also be bonded to the chlorine. This gives

$$\begin{array}{c} O \\ H\ O\ Cl\ O \end{array}$$

■ **Assembling the Tools:** Our tool is the procedure outlined in Figure 9.12.

■ **Solution:** The total number of valence electrons is 26 (1e^- from H, 6e^- from each O, and 7e^- from Cl). To distribute the electrons, we start by placing a pair of electrons in each bond, because we know that there must be at least one pair of electrons between each pair of atoms.

$$\text{O}$$
$$\text{H:O:}\overset{..}{\text{Cl}}\text{:O}$$

This has used 8e^-, so we still have 18e^- to go. Next, we work on the atoms surrounding the chlorine (which is the central atom in this structure). No additional electrons are needed around the H, because 2e^- are all that can occupy its valence shell. Therefore, we next complete the octets of the oxygens, which uses 16 more electrons.

$$:\overset{..}{\text{O}}:$$
$$\text{H:}\overset{..}{\underset{..}{\text{O}}}\text{:}\overset{..}{\text{Cl}}\text{:}\overset{..}{\underset{..}{\text{O}}}\text{:}$$

We have now used a total of 24e^-, so there are two electrons left. "Left-over" electrons are always placed on the central atom in pairs (the Cl atom, in this case). This gives

$$:\overset{..}{\text{O}}:$$
$$\text{H:}\overset{..}{\underset{..}{\text{O}}}\text{:}\overset{..}{\underset{..}{\text{Cl}}}\text{:}\overset{..}{\underset{..}{\text{O}}}\text{:}$$

which we can also write as follows, using dashes for the electron pairs in the bonds:

$$:\overset{..}{\text{O}}:$$
$$\text{H—}\overset{..}{\underset{..}{\text{O}}}\text{—}\overset{..}{\underset{..}{\text{Cl}}}\text{—}\overset{..}{\underset{..}{\text{O}}}:$$

The chlorine and the three oxygens have octets, and the valence shell of hydrogen is complete with 2e^-, so we are finished.

■ **Is the Answer Reasonable?** The most common error is to have either too many or too few valence electrons in the structure, so that's always the best place to begin your check. Doing this will confirm that the number of e^- is correct.

■ The valence shell of hydrogen contains only the 1s subshell, which can hold a maximum of two electrons. This means hydrogen can have a share of only two electrons and can form just one covalent bond.

Example 9.7
Drawing Lewis Structures

Draw the Lewis structure for the SO_3 molecule.

■ **Analysis:** Sulfur is less electronegative than oxygen and it is written first in the formula, so we expect it to be the central atom, surrounded by the three O atoms. This gives the skeletal structure

$$\text{O}$$
$$\text{O \quad S \quad O}$$

■ **Assembling the Tools:** We follow the procedure in Figure 9.12.

■ **Solution:** The total number of electrons in the formula is 24 (6e^- from the sulfur, plus 6e^- from each oxygen). We begin to distribute the electrons by placing a pair in each bond. This gives

$$\text{O}$$
$$\text{O:}\overset{..}{\text{S}}\text{:O}$$

We have used $6e^-$, so there are $18e^-$ left. We next complete the octets around the oxygens, which uses the remaining electrons.

$$:\overset{..}{\underset{}{O}}:$$
$$:\overset{..}{\underset{..}{O}}:\overset{}{\underset{..}{S}}:\overset{..}{\underset{..}{O}}:$$

At this point all of the electrons have been placed into the structure, but we see that the sulfur has only six electrons around it. We cannot simply add more dots because the total must be 24. Therefore, according to the last step of the procedure in Figure 9.12, we have to create a multiple bond. *To do this we move a pair of electrons that we have shown to belong solely to an oxygen into a sulfur–oxygen bond so that it can be counted as belonging to both the oxygen and the sulfur.* In other words, we place a double bond between sulfur and one of the oxygens. It doesn't matter which oxygen we choose for this honor.

gives   or

Notice that each atom has an octet.

■ **Is the Answer Reasonable?** The key step in completing the structure is recognizing what we have to do to obtain an octet around the sulfur. We have to add more electrons to the valence shell of sulfur, but without removing them from any of the oxygen atoms. By forming the double bond, we accomplish this. A quick check also confirms that we've placed exactly the correct number of valence electrons into the structure.

Example 9.8
Drawing Lewis Structures

What is the Lewis structure for the ion IF_4^-?

■ **Analysis:** Iodine is less electronegative than fluorine and is first in the formula, so we can anticipate that iodine will be the central atom. Our skeletal structure is

$$\begin{array}{ccc} & F & \\ F & I & F \\ & F & \end{array}$$

■ **Assembling the Tools:** As before, we follow the procedure in Figure 9.12. We begin by counting valence electrons, remembering to add an extra electron to account for the negative charge. Then we distribute the electrons in pairs.

■ **Solution:** The iodine and fluorine atoms are in Group 7A and each contribute 7 electrons, for a total of $35e^-$. The negative charge requires one additional electron to give a total of $36e^-$.

First we place $2e^-$ into each bond, and then we complete the octets of the fluorine atoms. This uses 32 electrons.

There are four electrons left, and according to Step 5 in Figure 9.12 they are placed on the central atom as *pairs* of electrons. This gives

$$
\begin{array}{c}
:\ddot{F}: \\
| \\
:\ddot{F}\!-\!I\!-\!\ddot{F}: \\
| \\
:\ddot{F}:
\end{array}
$$

The last step is to add brackets around the formula and write the charge outside as a superscript.

$$
\left[\begin{array}{c}
:\ddot{F}: \\
| \\
:\ddot{F}\!-\!I\!-\!\ddot{F}: \\
| \\
:\ddot{F}:
\end{array}\right]^{-}
$$

■ **Is the Answer Reasonable?** We can recount the valence electrons, which tells us we have the right number of them, and all are in the Lewis structure. Each fluorine atom has an octet, which is proper. Notice that we have placed the "left-over" electrons onto the central atom. This gives iodine more than an octet, but that's okay because iodine is not a Period 2 element.

Practice Exercises

9.12 | Predict a reasonable skeletal structure for $H_2PO_4^-$ and determine the number of valence electrons that should be in its Lewis structure. (*Hint:* It's an ion derived from an oxoacid.)

9.13 | Predict reasonable skeletal structures for SO_2, NO_3^-, $HClO_3$, and H_3AsO_4.

9.14 | How many valence electrons should appear in the Lewis structures of SO_2, SeO_4^{2-}, and NO^+?

9.15 | Draw Lewis structures for OF_2, NH_4^+, SO_2, NO_3^-, ClF_3, and $HClO_4$.

Formal Charges and Lewis Structures

Lewis structures are meant to describe how atoms share electrons in chemical bonds. Such descriptions are theoretical explanations or predictions that relate to the forces that hold molecules and polyatomic ions together. But, as you learned in Chapter 1, a theory is only as good as the observations on which it is based, so to have confidence in a theory about chemical bonding, we need to have a way to check it. We need experimental observations that relate to the description of bonding.

Bond Properties That Depend on Bond Order

To compare bonds between the same two elements, it's useful to define a quantity called the **bond order**, *which is the number of electron pairs shared between two atoms.* Thus, a single bond has a bond order of one, a double bond a bond order of two, and a triple bond a bond order of three.

Two properties that are related to the bond order are *bond length*, the distance between the nuclei of the bonded atoms, and *bond energy*, the energy required to separate the bonded atoms to give neutral particles. For example, we mentioned in Section 9.5 that measurements have shown the H_2 molecule has a bond length of 75 pm and a bond

Table 9.4	Average Bond Lengths and Bond Energies Measured for Carbon–Carbon Bonds	
Bond	**Bond Length (pm)**	**Bond Energy (kJ/mol)**
C—C	154	348
C=C	134	615
C≡C	120	812

energy of 435 kJ/mol, which means that it takes 435 kJ to break the bonds of 1 mol of H_2 molecules to give 2 mol of hydrogen atoms.

Bond order is a measure of the amount of electron density in the bond, and the greater the electron density, the more tightly the nuclei are held and the more closely they are drawn together. This is illustrated by the data in Table 9.4, which gives typical bond lengths and bond energies for single, double, and triple bonds between carbon atoms. In summary:

Correlation between bond properties and bond order

As the bond order increases, the bond length decreases and the bond energy increases, provided we are comparing bonds between the same elements.

With this as background, let's examine the Lewis structure of sulfuric acid, drawn according to the procedure given in Figure 9.12.

$$
\begin{array}{c}
:\!\ddot{O}\!: \\
| \\
H\!-\!\ddot{O}\!-\!S\!-\!\ddot{O}\!-\!H \\
| \\
:\!\ddot{O}\!:
\end{array}
\qquad \text{(Structure I)}
$$

It obeys the octet rule, and there doesn't seem to be any need to attempt to write any other structures for it. But a problem arises if we compare the predicted bond lengths with those found experimentally. In our Lewis structure, all four sulfur–oxygen bonds are shown as single bonds, which means they should have about the same bond lengths. However, experimentally it has been found that the bonds are not of equal length, as illustrated in Figure 9.13. The S—O bonds are shorter than the S—OH bonds, which means they must have a larger bond order. Therefore, we need to modify our Lewis structure to make it conform to reality.

Because sulfur is in Period 3, its valence shell has $3s$, $3p$, and $3d$ subshells, which together can accommodate more than eight electrons. Therefore, sulfur is able to form more than four bonds, so we are allowed to increase the bond order in the S—O bonds by moving electron pairs to create sulfur–oxygen double bonds as follows:

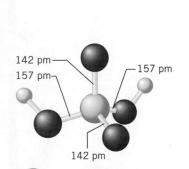

Figure 9.13 | The structure of sulfuric acid in the vapor state. Notice the difference in the sulfur–oxygen bond lengths.

142 pm
157 pm
157 pm
142 pm
Sulfur   Oxygen   Hydrogen

$$
\begin{array}{c}
:\!\ddot{O}\!: \\
\uparrow \\
H\!-\!\ddot{O}\!-\!S\!-\!\ddot{O}\!-\!H \\
\uparrow \\
:\!\ddot{O}\!:
\end{array}
\quad \text{gives} \quad
\begin{array}{c}
:\!\ddot{O} \\
\| \\
H\!-\!\ddot{O}\!-\!S\!-\!\ddot{O}\!-\!H \\
\| \\
:\!O\!:
\end{array}
\qquad \text{(Structure II)}
$$

Now we have a Lewis structure that better fits experimental observations because the sulfur–oxygen double bonds are expected to be shorter than the sulfur–oxygen single bonds. Because this second Lewis structure agrees better with the actual structure of the molecule, it is the *preferred* Lewis structure, even though it violates the octet rule.

Assigning Formal Charges to Atoms

Are there any criteria that we could have applied that would have allowed us to predict that the second Lewis structure for H_2SO_4 is better than the one with only single bonds, even though it seems to violate the octet rule unnecessarily? To answer this question, let's take a closer look at the two Lewis structures we've drawn.

In Structure I, there are only single bonds between the sulfur and oxygen atoms. If the electrons in the bonds are shared equally by S and O, then each atom "owns" half of the electron pair, or the equivalent of one electron. In other words, the four single bonds place the equivalent of four electrons in the valence shell of the sulfur. An isolated single atom of sulfur, however, has six valence electrons, so in Structure I the sulfur appears to have two electrons *less* than it does as just an isolated atom. Thus, at least in a *bookkeeping* sense, it would appear that if sulfur obeyed the octet rule in H_2SO_4, it would have a charge of 2+. This *apparent* charge on the sulfur atom is called its **formal charge.**

Notice that in defining formal charge, we've stressed the word "apparent." *The formal charge arises because of the bookkeeping we've done and should not be confused with whatever the actual charge is on an atom in the molecule.* (The situation is somewhat similar to the oxidation numbers you learned to assign in Chapter 6, which are artificial charges assigned according to a set of rules.) Here's how formal charges are assigned.

■ The actual charges on the atoms in a molecule are determined by the relative electronegativities of the atoms.

Calculating the Formal Charge on Atoms in a Lewis Structure

1. For each atom, write down the number of valence electrons in an isolated atom of the element.
2. Using the Lewis structure, add up the valence electrons that "belong to" the atom in the molecule or ion, and then subtract this total from the value in Step 1. The result is the formal charge on the atom.
3. The sum of the formal charges in a structure must equal the charge on the particle.

Calculating formal charges

In performing the calculation in Step 2, electrons in bonds are divided equally between the two atoms, while unshared electrons are assigned exclusively to the atom on which they reside. For example, for Structure I above, we have

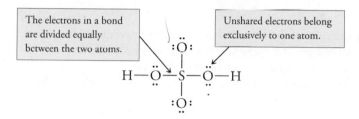

Therefore, the calculation of formal charge is summarized by the following equation:

Calculated number of electrons in the valence shell of the atom in the Lewis structure

$$\text{formal charge} = \left(\begin{array}{c}\text{number of } e^- \text{ in valence} \\ \text{shell of the isolated atom}\end{array}\right) - \left(\begin{array}{c}\text{number of bonds} \\ \text{to the atom}\end{array} + \begin{array}{c}\text{number of} \\ \text{unshared } e^-\end{array}\right) \quad (9.3)$$

For example, for the sulfur in Structure I, we get

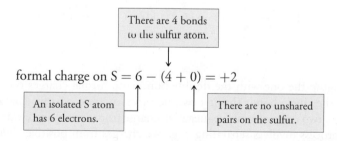

$$\text{formal charge on S} = 6 - (4 + 0) = +2$$

Let's also calculate the formal charges on the hydrogen and oxygen atoms in Structure I. An isolated H atom has one electron. In Structure I each H has one bond and no unshared electrons. Therefore,

$$\text{formal charge on H} = 1 - (1 + 0) = 0$$

In Structure I, we also see that there are two kinds of oxygen to consider. An isolated oxygen atom has six electrons, so we have, for the oxygens also bonded to hydrogen,

$$\text{formal charge} = 6 - (2 + 4) = 0$$

and for the oxygens not bonded to hydrogen,

$$\text{formal charge} = 6 - (1 + 6) = -1$$

$$\begin{array}{c} :\overset{\cdot\cdot}{O}: \\ | \\ \text{H} - \overset{\cdot\cdot}{O} - \text{S} - \overset{\cdot\cdot}{O} - \text{H} \\ | \\ :\overset{\cdot\cdot}{O}: \end{array} \qquad \text{(Structure I)}$$

| $6 - (2 \text{ bonds} + 4 \text{ unshared}) = 0$ | $6 - (1 \text{ bond} + 6 \text{ unshared}) = -1$ |

Nonzero formal charges are indicated in a Lewis structure by placing them in circles alongside the atoms, as follows:

$$\begin{array}{c} :\overset{\cdot\cdot}{O}:\ominus \\ | \\ \text{H} - \overset{\cdot\cdot}{O} - \text{S}\overset{(2+)}{-}\overset{\cdot\cdot}{O} - \text{H} \\ | \\ :\overset{\cdot\cdot}{O}:_{\ominus} \end{array}$$

Notice that the sum of the formal charges in the molecule adds up to zero. *After you've assigned formal charges, it is important to always check that the sum of the formal charges in the Lewis structure adds up to the charge on the particle.*

Now let's look at the formal charges in Structure II. For sulfur we have

$$\text{formal charge on S} = 6 - (6 + 0) = 0$$

so the sulfur has no formal charge. The hydrogens and the oxygens that are also bonded to H are the same in this structure as before, so they have no formal charges. And finally, the oxygens that are not bonded to hydrogen have

$$\text{formal charge} = 6 - (2 + 4) = 0$$

These oxygens also have no formal charges.

Now let's compare the two structures side by side.

$$\begin{array}{cc} \begin{array}{c} :\overset{\cdot\cdot}{O} \\ \| \\ \text{H} - \overset{\cdot\cdot}{O} - \text{S} - \overset{\cdot\cdot}{O} - \text{H} \\ \| \\ :\overset{\cdot\cdot}{O} \end{array} & \begin{array}{c} :\overset{\cdot\cdot}{O}:\ominus \\ | \\ \text{H} - \overset{\cdot\cdot}{O} - \text{S}\overset{(2+)}{-}\overset{\cdot\cdot}{O} - \text{H} \\ | \\ :\overset{\cdot\cdot}{O}:_{\ominus} \end{array} \end{array}$$

Imagine changing the one with the double bonds (no formal charges on any atoms) to the one with the single bonds (having two negative and two positive charges). In doing so, we've create two pairs of positive–negative charge from something electrically neutral. Because the process involves separating negative charges from positive charges, it would produce an increase in the potential energy. Our conclusion, therefore, is that the singly bonded structure on the right has a higher potential energy than the one with the double bonds. In general, the lower the potential energy of a molecule, the more stable it is. Therefore, the lower energy structure with the double bonds is, in principle, the more stable structure, so it is preferred over the one with only single bonds. This now gives us a rule that we can use in selecting the best Lewis structures for a molecule or ion:

Selecting the best Lewis structure

When several Lewis structures are possible, the one with formal charges closest to zero is the most stable and is preferred.

Example 9.9
Selecting Lewis Structures Based on Formal Charges

A student drew the following three Lewis structures for the nitric acid molecule:

(I)   (II)   (III)

Which one is preferred?

■ Analysis: When we have to select among several Lewis structures to find the best one, we first have to assign formal charges to each of the atoms. As a rule, the structure with the formal charges closest to zero will be the best structure. We have to be careful, however, that we don't select a structure in which an atom is assigned more electrons than its valence shell can actually hold. Such a structure must be eliminated from consideration.

■ Assembling the Tools: To assign the formal charges, the tool we use is Equation 9.3 on page 389.

■ Solution: Except for hydrogen, all of the atoms in the molecule are from Period 2, and therefore can have a maximum of eight electrons in their valence shells. (Period 2 elements *never* exceed an octet because their valence shells have only s and p subshells and can accommodate a maximum of eight electrons.) Scanning the structures, we see that I and II show octets around both N and O. However, the nitrogen in Structure III has 5 bonds to it, which require 10 electrons. Therefore, this structure is not acceptable and can be eliminated immediately. Our choice is then between Structures I and II. Let's calculate formal charges on the atoms in each of them.

■ In Structure III, the formal charges are zero on each of the atoms, but this cannot be the "preferred structure" because the nitrogen atom has too many electrons in its valence shell.

Structure I:

Structure II:

Next, we place the formal charges on the atoms in the structures.

(I)   (II)

Because Structure II has fewer formal charges than Structure I, it is the lower-energy, preferred Lewis structure for HNO_3.

■ **Is the Answer Reasonable?** One simple check we can do is to add up the formal charges in each structure. The sum must equal the net charge on the particle, which is zero for HNO_3. Adding formal charges gives zero for each structure, so we can be confident we've assigned them correctly. This gives us confidence in our answer, too.

Example 9.10
Selecting Lewis Structures Based on Formal Charges

The following two structures can be drawn for BCl_3:

$$
\begin{array}{cc}
\ddot{\text{Cl}}: & \ddot{\text{Cl}}: \\
| & | \\
:\ddot{\text{Cl}}-\text{B}-\ddot{\text{Cl}}: & :\text{Cl}=\text{B}-\ddot{\text{Cl}}: \\
\text{(I)} & \text{(II)}
\end{array}
$$

Why is the one that violates the octet rule preferred?

■ **Analysis:** We're asked to select between Lewis structures, which tells us that we have to consider formal charges. We'll assign them and then see whether we can answer the question.

■ **Assembling the Tools:** To assign formal charges we use Equation 9.3.

■ **Solution:** Assigning formal charges gives

$$
\begin{array}{cc}
\text{(I)} \quad :\ddot{\text{Cl}}: & \text{(II)} \quad :\ddot{\text{Cl}}: \\
| & | \\
:\ddot{\text{Cl}}-\text{B}-\ddot{\text{Cl}}: & :\overset{\oplus}{\text{Cl}}=\underset{\ominus}{\text{B}}-\ddot{\text{Cl}}:
\end{array}
$$

In Structure I all the formal charges are zero. In Structure II, two of the atoms have formal charges, so this alone would argue in favor of Structure I. There is another argument in favor as well. Notice that the formal charges in Structure II place the positive charge on the more electronegative chlorine atom and the negative charge on the less electronegative boron. If charges could form in this molecule, they certainly would not be expected to form in this way. Therefore, there are two factors that make the structure with the double bond unfavorable, so we usually write the Lewis structure for BCl_3 as shown in (I).

■ **Is the Answer Reasonable?** We've assigned the formal charges correctly, and our reasoning seems sound, so we appear to have answered the question adequately.

Practice Exercises

9.16 | A student drew the following Lewis structure for the sulfite ion, SO_3^{2-}:

$$
\left[\begin{array}{c}
:\text{O}: \\
\| \\
\ddot{\text{O}}=\text{S}=\ddot{\text{O}}
\end{array} \right]^{2-}
$$

Is this the best Lewis structure for the ion? (*Hint:* Negative formal charges should be on the more electronegative atoms.)

9.17 | Assign formal charges to the atoms in the following Lewis structures:

(a) $:\ddot{\text{N}}-\text{N}\equiv\text{O}:$ (b) $\left[\ddot{\text{S}}=\text{C}=\ddot{\text{N}} \right]^{-}$

9.18 | Select the preferred Lewis structure for (a) SO_2, (b) $HClO_3$, and (c) H_3PO_4.

Coordinate Covalent Bonds

Often we use Lewis structures to follow the course of chemical reactions. For example, we can diagram how a hydrogen ion combines with a water molecule to form the hydronium ion, a process that occurs in aqueous solutions of acids.

$$H^+ + \ddot{\,}\overset{\displaystyle H}{\underset{\displaystyle }{\ddot{O}}}-H \longrightarrow \left[\ H-\overset{\displaystyle H}{\underset{\displaystyle }{\ddot{O}}}-H\ \right]^+$$

The formation of the bond between H^+ and H_2O follows a different path than the covalent bonds we discussed earlier in this chapter. For instance, when two H atoms combine to form H_2, each atom brings one electron to the bond.

$$H\cdot + \cdot H \longrightarrow H-H$$

But in the formation of H_3O^+, both of the electrons that become shared between the H^+ and the O originate on the oxygen atom of the water molecule. *This type of bond, in which both electrons of the shared pair come from just one of the two atoms, is called a* **coordinate covalent bond.**

Although we can make a distinction about the origin of the electrons shared in the bond, once the bond is formed a coordinate covalent bond is really the same as any other covalent bond. In other words, we can't tell where the electrons in the bond came from *after* the bond has been formed. In the H_3O^+ ion, for example, all three O—H bonds are identical once they've been formed.

The concept of a coordinate covalent bond is helpful in explaining what happens to atoms in a chemical reaction. For example, when ammonia is mixed with boron trichloride, an exothermic reaction takes place and the compound NH_3BCl_3 is formed in which there is a boron–nitrogen bond. Using Lewis structures, we can diagram this reaction as follows.

■ All electrons are alike. We are using different colors for them so we can see where the electrons in the bond came from.

$$\overset{\displaystyle H}{\underset{\displaystyle H}{H-N}}\!\!:\ +\ \overset{\displaystyle :\ddot{Cl}:}{\underset{\displaystyle :\ddot{Cl}:}{B-\ddot{Cl}:}} \longrightarrow \overset{\displaystyle H}{\underset{\displaystyle H}{H-N}}:\overset{\displaystyle :\ddot{Cl}:}{\underset{\displaystyle :\ddot{Cl}:}{B-\ddot{Cl}:}}$$

In the reaction, we might say that "the boron forms a coordinate covalent bond with the nitrogen of the ammonia molecule."

An arrow sometimes is used to represent the donated pair of electrons in a coordinate covalent bond. The direction of the arrow indicates the direction in which the electron pair is donated, in this case from the nitrogen to the boron.

$$\overset{\displaystyle H}{\underset{\displaystyle H}{H-N}}\!\overset{\ominus}{}\ \overset{\displaystyle :\ddot{Cl}:}{\underset{\displaystyle :\ddot{Cl}:}{B-\ddot{Cl}:}} \longrightarrow \overset{\displaystyle H}{\underset{\displaystyle H}{H-N}}\!\longrightarrow\overset{\displaystyle :\ddot{Cl}:}{\underset{\displaystyle :\ddot{Cl}:}{B-\ddot{Cl}:}}$$

Compounds like BCl_3NH_3, which are formed by simply joining two smaller molecules, are sometimes called **addition compounds.**

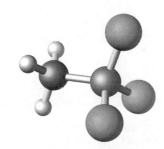

The addition compound formed from ammonia and boron trichloride. The light blue colored atom is boron.

9.19 | Use Lewis structures to show how the formation of NH_4^+ from NH_3 and H^+ involves formation of a coordinate covalent bond. How does this bond differ from the other N—H bonds in NH_4^+? (*Hint:* Keep in mind the definition of a coordinate covalent bond.)

9.20 | Use Lewis structures to explain how the reaction between hydroxide ion and hydrogen ion involves the formation of a coordinate covalent bond.

Practice Exercises

9.9 | Resonance Structures

■ The IUPAC name for formic acid is methanoic acid and the formate ion is the methanoate ion.

Formic acid is the substance that causes the stinging sensation in bites from fire ants. (*WildPicture/Alamy*)

There are some molecules and ions for which we cannot write Lewis structures that agree with experimental measurements of bond length and bond energy. An example is the formate ion, CHO_2^-, formed by neutralizing formic acid, $HCHO_2$. Following the usual steps, we would write the Lewis structure of the formate ion as shown on the right below.

formic acid   formate ion

This structure suggests that in the CHO_2^- ion, one carbon–oxygen bond should be longer than the other, but experiments show that the C—O bond lengths are identical, with lengths that are about halfway between the expected values for a single bond and a double bond. The Lewis structure doesn't match the experimental evidence, and there's no way to write one that does. It would require showing all of the electrons in pairs and, at the same time, showing 1.5 pairs of electrons in each carbon–oxygen bond.

The way we get around problems like this is through the use of a concept called **resonance.** We view the actual structure of the molecule or ion, which we cannot draw satisfactorily, as a composite, or average, of a number of Lewis structures that we can draw. For example, for formate ion we write

■ It is important to understand that when we draw resonance structures *no atoms are moved*; the electrons are just redistributed.

A zonkey is the hybrid offspring of a zebra and a donkey. It has characteristics of both of its parents, but is never exactly like either one of them. It certainly isn't a zebra one minute and a donkey the next! (*JIJIPRESS/AFP/Getty Images, Inc.*)

where we have simply shifted electrons around in going from one structure to the other. The bond between the carbon and a particular oxygen is depicted as a single bond in one structure and as a double bond in the other. The average of these is 1.5 bonds (halfway between a single and a double bond), which is in agreement with the experimental bond lengths. These two Lewis structures are called **resonance structures** or **contributing structures.** The actual structure of the ion, which we can't draw, is called a **resonance hybrid** of these two resonance structures. The double-ended arrow is used to show that we are drawing resonance structures and implies that the true hybrid structure is a composite of the two resonance structures.

Some students find the term *resonance* somewhat misleading. The word itself suggests that the actual structure flip-flops back and forth between the two structures shown. This is *not* the case! We are simply using structures that we are able to draw to describe an actual structure that we cannot draw. It's a bit like trying to imagine what a *zonkey* looks like by viewing photos of a zebra and a donkey. Although a zonkey may have characteristics of both, a zonkey is a zonkey; it doesn't flip back and forth between being a zebra one minute and a donkey the next. Similarly, a *resonance hybrid* also has characteristics of its "parents," but it doesn't flip back and forth between the contributing structures.

When We Draw Resonance Structures

Determining resonance structures

There is a simple way to determine when resonance should be applied to Lewis structures. If you find that you must move electrons to create one or more double bonds while following the procedures developed earlier, the number of resonance structures is equal to the number of equivalent choices for the locations of the double bonds. For example, in drawing the Lewis structure for the NO_3^- ion, we reach the stage

A double bond must be created to give the nitrogen an octet. Since it can be placed in any one of three locations, there are three resonance structures for this ion.

■ The three oxygens in NO_3^- are said to be equivalent; that is, they are all alike in their chemical environment. Each oxygen is bonded to a nitrogen atom that's attached to two other oxygen atoms.

Notice that each structure is the same, except for the location of the double bond.

In the nitrate ion, the extra bond that appears to "move around" from one structure to another is actually divided among all three bond locations. Therefore, the **average bond order** in the N—O bonds is expected to be $1\frac{1}{3}$, or 1.33. In general, we can calculate the average bond order by adding up the total number of bonds and dividing by the number of equivalent positions. In the NO_3^- ion, we have a total of *four* bonds (two single bonds and a double bond) distributed over *three* equivalent positions, so the bond order is $4/3 = 1\frac{1}{3}$.

TOOLS

Calculating average bond orders

Example 9.11
Drawing Resonance Structures

Use formal charges to show that resonance applies to the preferred Lewis structure for the sulfite ion, SO_3^{2-}. Draw the resonance structures and determine the average bond order of the S—O bonds.

■ **Analysis:** Following our usual procedure we obtain the following Lewis structure:

All of the valence electrons have been placed into the structure and we have octets around all of the atoms, so it doesn't seem that we need the concept of resonance. However, the question refers to the "preferred" structure, which suggests that we are going to have to assign formal charges and determine what the preferred structure is. Then we can decide whether the concept of resonance will apply.

■ **Assembling the Tools:** To assign formal charges, our tool is Equation 9.3. If a double bond occurs in the preferred structure, the number of equivalent positions equals the number of resonance structures. The average bond order will be calculated from the number of bonds distributed over the three equivalent bond locations.

■**Solution:** When we assign formal charges, we get

$$\left[\begin{array}{c} {}^{\ominus}\ddot{\text{O}}\!\!: \\ | \\ {}^{\ominus}\!\!:\!\ddot{\text{O}}\!-\!\underset{\oplus}{\text{S}}\!-\!\ddot{\text{O}}\!:^{\ominus} \end{array}\right]^{2-}$$

We can obtain a better Lewis structure if we can reduce the number of formal charges. This can be accomplished by moving an unshared electron pair from one of the oxygens into an S—O bond, thereby forming a double bond. Let's do this using the oxygen at the left.

$$\left[\begin{array}{c} {}^{\ominus}\ddot{\text{O}}\!\!: \\ | \\ :\!\ddot{\text{O}}\!\!\curvearrowright\!\text{S}\!-\!\ddot{\text{O}}\!:^{\ominus} \end{array}\right]^{2-} \quad \xrightarrow{\text{gives}} \quad \left[\begin{array}{c} {}^{\ominus}\ddot{\text{O}}\!\!: \\ | \\ :\!\text{O}\!=\!\text{S}\!-\!\ddot{\text{O}}\!:^{\ominus} \end{array}\right]^{2-}$$

However, we could have done this with any of the three S—O bonds, so there are three equivalent choices for the location of the double bond. Therefore, there are three resonance structures.

$$\left[\begin{array}{c} :\ddot{\text{O}}\!: \\ | \\ :\!\text{O}\!=\!\text{S}\!-\!\ddot{\text{O}}\!: \end{array}\right]^{2-} \longleftrightarrow \left[\begin{array}{c} :\ddot{\text{O}} \\ \| \\ :\!\ddot{\text{O}}\!-\!\text{S}\!-\!\ddot{\text{O}}\!: \end{array}\right]^{2-} \longleftrightarrow \left[\begin{array}{c} :\ddot{\text{O}}\!: \\ | \\ :\!\ddot{\text{O}}\!-\!\text{S}\!=\!\text{O}\!: \end{array}\right]^{2-}$$

As with the nitrate ion, we expect an average bond order of 1.33.

■**Is the Answer Reasonable?** If we can answer "yes" to the following questions, the problem is solved correctly: Have we counted valence electrons correctly? Have we properly placed the electrons into the skeletal structure? Do the formal charges we've calculated add up to the charge on the SO_3^{2-} ion? Have we correctly determined the number of equivalent positions for the double bond? Have we computed the average bond order correctly? All the answers are "yes", so we have solved the problem correctly.

Practice Exercises

9.21 | The phosphate ion has the following Lewis structure, where we've used formal charges to obtain the best structure.

$$\left[\begin{array}{c} :\text{O}\!: \\ \| \\ :\!\ddot{\text{O}}\!-\!\text{P}\!-\!\ddot{\text{O}}\!: \\ | \\ :\ddot{\text{O}}\!: \end{array}\right]^{3-}$$

How many resonance structures are there for this ion? (*Hint:* How many equivalent positions are there for the double bond?)

9.22 | Draw the resonance structures for HCO_3^-.

9.23 | Determine the preferred Lewis structure for the bromate ion, BrO_3^-, and, if appropriate, draw resonance structures.

Stability of Molecules with Resonance Structures

One of the benefits that a molecule or ion derives from existing as a resonance hybrid is that its total energy is lower than that of any one of its contributing structures. A particularly important example of this occurs with the compound benzene, C_6H_6. This is a flat hexagonal ring-shaped molecule (Figure 9.14) with a basic structure that appears in many important organic molecules, ranging from plastics to amino acids.

Two resonance structures are usually drawn for benzene.

These are generally represented as hexagons with dashes showing the locations of the double bonds. It is assumed that at each apex of the hexagon there is a carbon bonded to a hydrogen as well as to the adjacent carbon atoms.

Usually, the actual structure of benzene (that of its resonance hybrid) is represented as a hexagon with a circle in the center. This is intended to show that the electron density of the three extra bonds is evenly distributed around the ring.

This is the way the structure of benzene is usually represented

Although the individual resonance structures for benzene show double bonds, the molecule does not react like other organic molecules that have true carbon–carbon double bonds. The reason appears to be that the resonance hybrid is considerably more stable than either of the resonance forms. In fact, it has been calculated that the actual structure of the benzene molecule is more stable than either of its resonance structures by approximately 146 kJ/mol. This extra stability achieved through resonance is called the **resonance energy**.

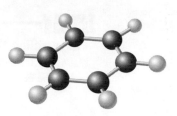

Figure 9.14 | **Benzene.** The molecule has a planar hexagonal structure.

Analyzing and Solving Multi-Concept Problems

Phosphorous acid has the formula H_3PO_3. It was found that a sample of the acid weighing 0.3066 g was neutralized completely by 0.4196 g of KOH. Use these data to write the preferred Lewis structure for H_3PO_3.

■**Analysis** At first, it seems like we should be able to follow the guidelines developed earlier in this chapter to arrive at the Lewis structure. For example, on page 384 you learned that for oxoacids, the hydrogens that can be released as H^+ are bonded to oxygen, which in turn is bonded to the central atom of the oxoacid. The formula H_3PO_3 suggests a triprotic acid, which would have the following skeletal structure.

H

O

H O P O H

We can use the data presented for the neutralization of the acid by KOH to confirm whether or not this is the correct arrangement of atoms.

From the neutralization data we can calculate the number of moles of KOH required to neutralize one mole of the acid. This will tell us the number of "acidic" hydrogens in a molecule of the acid. If the acid is indeed a triprotic acid as indicated by the skeletal structure above, three moles of KOH should be needed to neutralize one mole of acid.

If the stoichiometry of the neutralization reaction tells us the acid is triprotic, we can then proceed to add the necessary number of electrons to the skeletal structure above. However, if the neutralization reaction tells us H_3PO_3 is not triprotic, then we have to refine the skeletal structure before proceeding further. Here, then, is our strategy.

Part 1: Use the neutralization data to determine the number of moles of KOH that reacts with 1.00 mol of H_3PO_3.

Part 2: Refine the skeletal structure, if necessary, to make it conform to the results of the computation in Part 1.

Part 3: Add the necessary number of electrons to obtain the compete Lewis structure. Then reduce formal charges, if possible, to obtain the preferred structure.

PART 1

■ **Assembling the Tools** The data we need to perform the calculation are the molar masses of H_3PO_3 (81.994 g mol^{-1}) and KOH (56.108 g mol^{-1}). From the data in the problem, we can also set up the equivalence

$$0.3066 \text{ g } H_3PO_3 \Leftrightarrow 0.4196 \text{ g of KOH}$$

■ **Solution** This part of the problem can be expressed as

$$1 \text{ mol } H_3PO_3 \Leftrightarrow ? \text{ mol KOH}$$

Using dimensional analysis gives us.

$$1 \text{ mol } H_3PO_3 \times \frac{81.994 \text{ g } H_3PO_3}{1 \text{ mol } H_3PO_3} \times \frac{0.4196 \text{ g KOH}}{0.3066 \text{ g } H_3PO_3} \times \frac{1 \text{ mol KOH}}{56.108 \text{ g KOH}} = 2.00 \text{ mol KOH}$$

Because only 2 moles of KOH are needed to neutralize 1 mole of the acid, the acid must be diprotic. We are going to have to make changes in the skeletal structure to reflect this.

PART 2

■ **Assembling the Tools** We need to use the general guidelines for constructing skeletal structures, modified as necessary to make the structure conform to the results of Part 1.

■ **Solution** On page 384 you learned that acidic hydrogens in an oxoacid are bonded to oxygen atoms, which are bonded in turn to the central atom. Because H_3PO_3 is diprotic, only two such hydrogens are present. So what about the third hydrogen? If it's not bonded to oxygen, then it must be bonded to the phosphorus atom. This suggests the skeletal structure:

$$
\begin{array}{c}
\text{O} \\
\text{H O P O H} \\
\text{H}
\end{array}
$$

PART 3

■ **Assembling the Tools** Our tool is the procedure for drawing Lewis structures given on page 383. We will also use formal charges (page 389) to determine whether we have the preferred structure.

■ **Solution** Phosphorus (Group 5A) contributes 5 electrons; each oxygen (Group 6A) contributes 6 electrons, and each hydrogen contributes one electron. The total is $26e^-$. Following the usual procedure, the Lewis structure is

Assigning formal charges gives us

We can reduce the formal charges by moving a lone electron pair from the oxygen at the top into the phosphorus–oxygen bond, giving a double bond.

$$\begin{array}{c} \ddot{O}: \\ \parallel \\ H-\ddot{O}-P-\ddot{O}-H \\ | \\ H \end{array}$$

This structure has no formal charges and is the preferred structure of the molecule.

■ **Is the Answer Reasonable?** The fact that the stoichiometry calculation gives a whole number of moles of KOH per mole of H_3PO_3 suggests this part of the problem has been solved correctly. Dimensional analysis also gives the correct units, so we can conclude the calculation is correct. The alternative skeletal structure agrees with the stoichiometry, so it is reasonable. Finally, we can check to be sure we've supplied the correct number of electrons, which we have, so our Lewis structure appears to be reasonable.

Summary

polar

Ionic Bonding. In ionic compounds, the forces of attraction between positive and negative ions are called **ionic bonds.** The formation of ionic compounds by electron transfer is favored when atoms of low ionization energy react with atoms of high electron affinity. The chief stabilizing influence in the formation of ionic compounds is the release of the **lattice energy.** When atoms of the elements in Groups 1A and 2A as well as the nonmetals form ions, they usually gain or lose enough electrons to achieve a noble gas electron configuration. Transition elements lose their outer s electrons first, followed by loss of d electrons from the shell below the outer shell. Post-transition metals lose electrons from their outer p subshell first, followed by electrons from the outer s subshell.

Covalent Bonding. Electron sharing between atoms occurs when electron transfer is energetically too "expensive." Shared electrons attract the positive nuclei, and this leads to a lowering of the potential energy of the atoms as a covalent bond forms. Electrons generally become paired when they are shared. An atom tends to share enough electrons to complete its valence shell. Except for hydrogen, the valence shell usually holds eight electrons, which forms the basis of the octet rule. The **octet rule** states that atoms of the representative elements tend to acquire eight electrons in their outer shells when they form bonds. **Single, double,** and **triple bonds** involve the sharing of one, two, and three pairs of electrons, respectively, between two atoms. Boron and beryllium often have less than an octet in their compounds. Atoms of the elements of Period 2 cannot have more than an octet because their outer shells can hold only eight electrons. Elements in Periods 3, 4, 5, and 6 can exceed an octet if they form more than four bonds.

Bond energy (the energy needed to separate the bonded atoms) and **bond length** (the distance between the nuclei of the atoms connected by the bond) are two experimentally measurable quantities that can be related to the number of pairs of electrons in the bond. For bonds between atoms of the same elements, bond energy increases and bond length decreases as the bond order increases.

Electronegativity and Polar Bonds. The attraction an atom has for the electrons in a bond is called the atom's **electronegativity.** When atoms of different electronegativities form a bond, the electrons are shared unequally and the bond is **polar,** with **partial positive** and **partial negative** charges at opposite ends. This causes the bond to be an electric **dipole.** In a **polar molecule,** such as HCl, the product of the charge at either end multiplied by the distance between the charges gives the **dipole moment,** μ. When the two atoms have the same electronegativity, the bond is **nonpolar.** The extent of polarity of the bond depends on the electronegativity difference between the two bonded atoms. When the electronegativity difference is very large, ionic bonding results. A bond is approximately 50% ionic when the electronegativity difference is 1.7. In the periodic table, electronegativity increases from left to right across a period and from bottom to top in a group.

Reactivity and Electronegativity. The **reactivity** of metals is related to the ease with which they are oxidized (lose electrons); for nonmetals it is related to the ease with which they are reduced (gain electrons). Metals with low electronegativities lose electrons easily, are good reducing agents, and tend to be very reactive. The most reactive metals are located in Groups 1A and 2A, and their ease of oxidation increases going down the group. For nonmetals, the higher the electronegativity, the stronger is their ability to serve as oxidizing agents. In **displacement reactions,** a more electronegative nonmetal is often able to displace one of lower electronegativity from its compounds. The strongest oxidizing agent is fluorine. Among the halogens, oxidizing strength decreases from fluorine to iodine.

Lewis Symbols and Lewis Structures. Lewis symbols are a bookkeeping device used to keep track of valence electrons in ionic and covalent bonds. The **Lewis symbol** of an element consists of the element's chemical symbol surrounded by a number of dots equal to the number of valence electrons. In the **Lewis structure** for an ionic compound, the Lewis symbol for the anion is enclosed in brackets (with the charge written outside) to show that all the electrons belong entirely to the ion. The Lewis structure for a molecule or polyatomic ion uses pairs of dots between chemical symbols to represent shared pairs of electrons. The electron pairs in covalent bonds usually are represented by dashes; one dash equals two electrons. The following procedure is used to draw the Lewis structure: (1) decide on the **skeletal structure** (remember that the least electronegative atom is usually the central atom and is usually first in the formula); (2) count all the valence electrons, taking into account the charge, if any; (3) place a pair of electrons in each bond; (4) complete the octets of atoms other than the central atom (but remember that hydrogen can only have two electrons); (5) place any left-over electrons on the central atom in pairs; (6) if the central atom still has less than an octet, move electron pairs to make double or triple bonds.

Formal Charges. The **formal charge** assigned to an atom in a Lewis structure (which usually differs from the actual charge on the atom) is calculated as the difference between the number of valence electrons of an isolated atom of the element and the number of electrons that "belong" to the atom because of its bonds to other atoms and its unshared valence electrons. The sum of the formal charges always equals the net charge on the molecule or ion. The most stable (lowest energy) Lewis structure for a molecule or ion is the one with formal charges closest to zero. This is usually the preferred Lewis structure for the particle.

Coordinate Covalent Bonding. For bookkeeping purposes, we sometimes single out a covalent bond whose electron pair originated from one of the two bonded atoms. An arrow is sometimes used to indicate the donated pair of electrons. Once formed, a coordinate covalent bond is no different from any other covalent bond.

Resonance. Two or more atoms in a molecule or polyatomic ion are *chemically equivalent* if they are attached to the same kinds of atoms or groups of atoms. Bonds to chemically equivalent atoms must be the same; they must have the same bond length and the same bond energy, which means they must involve the sharing of the same number of electron pairs. Sometimes the Lewis structures we draw suggest that the bonds to chemically equivalent atoms are not the same. Typically, this occurs when it is necessary to form multiple bonds during the drawing of a Lewis structure. When alternatives exist for the location of a multiple bond among two or more equivalent atoms, then each possible Lewis structure is actually a **resonance structure** or **contributing structure,** and we draw them all. In drawing resonance structures, the relative locations of the nuclei must be identical in all. The **average bond order** is calculated from the total number of bonds distributed over the equivalent bond locations. Remember that none of the resonance structures corresponds to a real molecule, but their composite—the **resonance hybrid**—does approximate the actual structure of the molecule or ion.

Tools for Problem Solving

In this chapter you learned to apply the following concepts as tools in solving problems. Study each one carefully so that you know what each is used for. When faced with solving a problem, recall what each tool does and consider whether it will be helpful in finding a solution. This will aid you in selecting the tools you need.

Electron configurations of ions of the representative elements (page 363)
Metals in Groups 1A and 2A, aluminum, and the nonmetals obey the octet rule when they form ions. This knowledge is helpful when you have to write the electron configurations of ions of these elements.

Order in which electrons are lost from an atom (page 363)
Electrons are lost first from the shell with largest n. For a given shell, electrons are lost from subshells in the following order: f before d before p before s. Use this knowledge to obtain electron configurations of ions of the transition and post-transition metals.

Lewis symbols (page 366)
Lewis symbols are a bookkeeping device that we use to keep track of valence electrons in atoms and ions. For a neutral atom of the representative elements, the Lewis symbol consists of the atomic symbol surrounded by dots equal in number to the group number.

Octet rule and covalent bonding (page 371)
The octet rule helps us construct Lewis structures for covalently bonded molecules. Elements in Period 2 never exceed an octet in their valence shells.

Dipole moment (page 378)

Dipole moments are a measure of the polarity of molecules, so they can be used to compare molecular polarity. The dipole moment (μ) of a diatomic molecule is calculated as the charge on an end of the molecule, q, multiplied by the bond length, r. Dipole moments are expressed in debye units.

$$\mu = q \times r$$

Periodic trends in electronegativity (page 381)

The trends revealed in Figure 9.9 allow us to use the locations of elements in the periodic table to estimate the degree of polarity of bonds and to estimate which of two atoms in a bond is the most electronegative.

Trends in the reactivity of metals in the periodic table (page 381)

A knowledge of where the most reactive and least reactive metals are located in the periodic table gives a qualitative feel for how reactive a metal is.

Trends in the reactivity of nonmetals in the periodic table (page 382)

The periodic table correlates the position of a nonmetal with its strength as an oxidizing agent. Oxidizing ability increases from left to right across a period and from bottom to top in a group.

Method for drawing Lewis structures (page 383)

The method described in Figure 9.12 yields Lewis structures in which the maximum number of atoms obey the octet rule.

Correlation between bond properties and bond order (page 388)

The correlations allow us to compare experimental covalent bond properties (bond energy and bond length) with those predicted by theory.

Method for calculating formal charges (page 389)

Use formal charges to select the best Lewis structure for a molecule or polyatomic ion. The best structure is usually the one with the fewest formal charges. Assign formal charges to atoms as follows:

$$\text{Formal charge} = \begin{bmatrix} \text{number of } e^- \text{ in valence} \\ \text{shell of the isolated atom} \end{bmatrix} - \begin{bmatrix} \text{number of bonds} \\ \text{to the atom} \end{bmatrix} + \begin{bmatrix} \text{number of} \\ \text{unshared } e^- \end{bmatrix}$$

Selecting the best Lewis structure (page 390)

The structure having the smallest formal charges is preferred. Be sure none of the atoms in the structure appears to have more electrons than permitted by its location in the periodic table.

Determining resonance structures (page 394)

Expect resonance structures when there is more than one option for assigning the location of a double bond. Determine the number of equivalent positions for the double bond. That number is the number of resonance structures you should draw.

Calculating average bond order (page 395)

To calculate the average bond order for resonance structures, add up the total number of bonds and divide by the number of equivalent positions in which they are drawn.

WILEY **PLUS** = *WileyPLUS*, an online teaching and learning solution. *Note to instructors:* Many of the end-of-chapter problems are available for assignment via the *WileyPLUS* system. **www.wileyplus.com**. **ILW** = An Interactive Learningware solution is available for this problem. **OH** = An Office Hour video is available for this problem. Review Problems are presented in pairs separated by blue rules. Answers to problems whose numbers appear in blue are given in Appendix B. More challenging problems are marked with an asterisk ★.

| Review Questions

Ionic Bonding

9.1 What must be true about the change in the total potential energy of a collection of atoms for a stable compound to be formed from the elements?

9.2 What is an *ionic bond*?

9.3 How is the tendency to form ionic bonds related to the IE and EA of the atoms involved?

9.4 Define the term *lattice energy*. In what ways does the lattice energy contribute to the stability of ionic compounds?

9.5 Magnesium forms compounds containing the ion Mg^{2+} but not the ion Mg^{3+}. Why?

9.6 Why doesn't chlorine form the ion Cl^{2-} in compounds?

9.7 Why do many of the transition elements in Period 4 form ions with a 2+ charge?

9.8 If we were to compare the first, second, third, and fourth ionization energies of aluminum, between which pair of successive ionization energies would there be the largest difference? (Refer to the periodic table when answering this question.)

9.9 In each of the following pairs of compounds, which would have the larger lattice energy: **(a)** CaO or Al_2O_3, **(b)** BeO or SrO, **(c)** NaCl or NaBr?

Lewis Symbols

9.10 The Lewis symbol for an atom only accounts for electrons in the valence shell of the atom. Why are we not concerned with the other electrons?

9.11 Which of these Lewis symbols is incorrect?

(a) $:\!\overset{\cdot}{\underset{\cdot}{O}}\!:$ **(b)** $\cdot\overset{\cdot\cdot}{\underset{\cdot\cdot}{Cl}}\cdot$ **(c)** $:\!\overset{\cdot}{\underset{\cdot}{N}}e:$ **(d)** $:\!\overset{\cdot\cdot}{\underset{\cdot}{Sb}}\!:$

Electron Sharing

9.12 In terms of the potential energy change, why doesn't ionic bonding occur when two nonmetals react with each other?

9.13 Describe what happens to the electron density around two hydrogen atoms as they come together to form an H_2 molecule.

9.14 What happens to the energy of two hydrogen atoms as they approach each other? What happens to the spins of the electrons?

9.15 Is the formation of a covalent bond endothermic or exothermic?

9.16 What factors control the bond length in a covalent bond?

Covalent Bonding and the Octet Rule

9.17 What is the *octet rule*? What is responsible for it?

9.18 How many covalent bonds are normally formed by **(a)** hydrogen, **(b)** carbon, **(c)** oxygen, **(d)** nitrogen, and **(e)** chlorine?

9.19 Why do Period 2 elements never form more than four covalent bonds? Why are Period 3 elements able to exceed an octet?

9.20 Define **(a)** *single bond*, **(b)** *double bond*, and **(c)** *triple bond*.

9.21 The Lewis structure for hydrogen cyanide is $H—C\equiv N:$. Draw circles enclosing electrons to show that carbon and nitrogen obey the octet rule.

9.22 Why doesn't hydrogen obey the octet rule?

Compounds of Carbon

9.23 Sketch the Lewis structures for **(a)** methane, **(b)** ethane, and **(c)** propane.

9.24 Draw the structure for a hydrocarbon that has a chain of six carbon atoms linked by single bonds. How many hydrogen atoms does the molecule have? What is the molecular formula for the compound?

9.25 How many *different* molecules have the formula C_5H_{12}? Sketch their structures.

9.26 What is a carbonyl group? In which classes of organic molecules that we've studied do we find a carbonyl group?

9.27 Match the compounds on the left with the family types on the right.

$CH_3—CH_2—\overset{\overset{O}{\|\|}}{C}—OH$	hydrocarbon
$CH_3—\overset{\overset{O}{\|\|}}{C}—CH_2—CH_3$	aldehyde
$CH_3—CH_2—\overset{\overset{OH}{\|}}{CH}—CH_3$	amine
$CH_3—CH_2—\overset{\overset{O}{\|\|}}{C}—H$	acid
$CH_3—\overset{\overset{H}{\|}}{N}—CH_2—CH_3$	alcohol
$CH_3—CH_2—\overset{\underset{\underset{CH_3}{\|}}{}}{CH}—CH_3$	ketone

9.28 Write a chemical equation for the ionization in water of the acid in Question 9.27. Is the acid strong or weak? Draw the Lewis structure for the ion formed by the acid when it ionizes.

9.29 Write a chemical equation for the reaction of the amine in Question 9.27 with water. Draw the Lewis structure for the ion formed by the amine.

9.30 Write the net ionic equation for the aqueous reaction of the acid and amine in Question 9.27 with each other. (Use molecular formulas.)

9.31 Draw the structures of **(a)** ethylene and **(b)** acetylene.

Polar Bonds and Electronegativity

9.32 What is a polar covalent bond?

9.33 Define *dipole moment* in the form of an equation. What is the value of the *debye* (with appropriate units)?

9.34 Define electronegativity. On what basis did Pauling develop his scale of electronegativities?

9.35 Which element has the highest electronegativity? Which is the second most electronegative element?

9.36 Among the following bonds, which are more ionic than covalent? **(a)** Si—O, **(b)** Ba—O, **(c)** Se—Cl, **(d)** K—Br

9.37 If an element has a low electronegativity, is it likely to be classified as a metal or a nonmetal? Explain your answer.

Electronegativity and the Reactivities of the Elements

9.38 When we say that aluminum is more *reactive* than iron, which kind of reaction of these elements are we describing?

9.39 In what groups in the periodic table are the most reactive metals found? Where do we find the least reactive metals?

9.40 How is the electronegativity of a metal related to its reactivity?

9.41 Arrange the following metals in their approximate order of reactivity (most reactive first, least reactive last) based on their locations in the periodic table: **(a)** iridium, **(b)** silver, **(c)** calcium, **(d)** iron.

9.42 Complete and balance the following equations. If no reaction occurs, write "N.R."

    (a) $KCl + Br_2 \longrightarrow$ **(d)** $CaBr_2 + Cl_2 \longrightarrow$

    (b) $NaI + Cl_2 \longrightarrow$ **(e)** $AlBr_3 + F_2 \longrightarrow$

    (c) $KCl + F_2 \longrightarrow$ **(f)** $ZnBr_2 + I_2 \longrightarrow$

9.43 In each pair, choose the better oxidizing agent.

    (a) O_2 or F_2 **(d)** P_4 or S_8

    (b) As_4 or P_4 **(e)** Se_8 or Cl_2

    (c) Br_2 or I_2 **(f)** As_4 or S_8

Failure of the Octet Rule

9.44 How many electrons are in the valence shells of **(a)** Be in $BeCl_2$, **(b)** B in BCl_3, and **(c)** H in H_2O?

9.45 What is the minimum number of electrons that would be expected to be in the valence shell of As, in $AsCl_5$?

9.46 Nitrogen and arsenic are in the same group in the periodic table. Arsenic forms both $AsCl_3$ and $AsCl_5$, but with chlorine, nitrogen only forms NCl_3. On the basis of the electronic structures of N and As, explain why this is so.

Bond Length and Bond Energy

9.47 Define *bond length* and *bond energy*.

9.48 Define *bond order*. How are bond energy and bond length related to bond order? Why are there these relationships?

9.49 The energy required to break the H—Cl bond to give H^+ and Cl^- ions would not be called the H—Cl bond energy. Why?

Formal Charge

9.50 What is the definition of *formal charge*?

9.51 How are formal charges used to select the best Lewis structure for a molecule? What is the basis for this method of selection?

9.52 What are the formal charges on the atoms in the HCl molecule? What are the actual charges on the atoms in this molecule? (*Hint:* See Section 9.7.) Are formal charges the same as actual charges?

Coordinate Covalent Bonds

9.53 What is a *coordinate covalent bond*?

9.54 Once formed, how (if at all) does a coordinate covalent bond differ from an ordinary covalent bond?

9.55 BCl_3 has an incomplete valence shell. Use Lewis structures to show how it could form a coordinate covalent bond with a water molecule.

Resonance

9.56 Why is the concept of resonance needed?

9.57 What is a resonance hybrid? How does it differ from the resonance structures drawn for a molecule?

9.58 Draw the resonance structures of the benzene molecule. Why is benzene more stable than one would expect if the ring contained three carbon–carbon double bonds?

9.59 Polystyrene plastic is a hydrocarbon that consists of a long chain of carbon atoms joined by single bonds in which every other carbon is attached to a benzene ring. The ring is attached by replacing a hydrogen of benzene with a single bond to the carbon chain. Sketch a portion of a polystyrene molecule that contains five benzene rings.

| Review Problems

Lattice Energy

9.60 Use data from the tables of ionization energies and electron affinities on pages 343 and 348 to calculate the energy changes for the following reactions.

$$Na(g) + Cl(g) \longrightarrow Na^+(g) + Cl^-(g)$$
$$Na(g) + 2Cl(g) \longrightarrow Na^{2+}(g) + 2Cl^-(g)$$

Approximately how many times larger would the lattice energy of $NaCl_2$ have to be compared to the lattice energy of NaCl for $NaCl_2$ to be more stable than NaCl?

9.61 Changing 1 mol of Mg(s) and 1/2 mol of $O_2(g)$ to gaseous atoms requires a total of approximately 150 kJ of energy. The first and second ionization energies of magnesium are 737 and 1450 kJ/mol, respectively; the first and second electron affinities of oxygen are −141 and +844 kJ/mol, respectively; and the standard heat of formation of MgO(s) is −602 kJ/mol. Construct an enthalpy diagram similar to the one in Figure 9.4 (page 360) and use it to calculate the lattice energy of magnesium oxide. How does the lattice energy of MgO compare with that of NaCl? What might account for the difference?

Electron Configurations of Ions

9.62 Explain what happens to the electron configurations of Mg and Br when they react to form magnesium bromide.

9.63 Describe what happens to the electron configurations of lithium and nitrogen when they react to form the lithium nitride.

ILW OH **9.64** What are the electron configurations of the Pb^{2+} and Pb^{4+} ions?

9.65 What are the electron configurations of the Bi^{3+} and Bi^{5+} ions?

9.66 Write the abbreviated electron configuration of the Mn^{3+} ion. How many unpaired electrons does the ion contain?

9.67 Write the abbreviated electron configuration of the Co^{3+} ion. How many unpaired electrons does the ion contain?

Lewis Symbols

9.68 Write Lewis symbols for the following atoms: **(a)** Si, **(b)** Sb, **(c)** Ba, **(d)** Al, **(e)** S.

9.69 Write Lewis symbols for the following atoms: **(a)** K, **(b)** Ge, **(c)** As, **(d)** Br, **(e)** Se.

9.70 Use Lewis symbols to diagram the reactions between **(a)** Ca and Br, **(b)** Al and O, and **(c)** K and S.

OH **9.71** Use Lewis symbols to diagram the reactions between **(a)** Mg and S, **(b)** Mg and Cl, and **(c)** Mg and N.

Dipole Moments

9.72 Use the data in Table 9.3 (page 378) to calculate the amount of charge on the oxygen and nitrogen in the nitrogen monoxide molecule, expressed in electronic charge units ($e = 1.60 \times 10^{-19}$ C). Which atom carries the positive charge?

9.73 The molecule bromine monofluoride has a dipole moment of 1.42 D and a bond length of 176 pm. Calculate the charge on the ends of the molecule, expressed in electronic charge units ($e = 1.60 \times 10^{-19}$ C). Which atom carries the positive charge?

9.74 The dipole moment of HF is 1.83 D and the bond length is 917 pm. Calculate the amount of charge (in electronic charge units) on the hydrogen and the fluorine atoms in the HF molecule.

OH **9.75** In the vapor state, cesium and fluoride ions pair to give CsF formula units that have a bond length of 0.255 nm and a dipole moment of 7.88 D. What is the actual charge on the cesium and fluorine atoms in CsF? What percentage of full 1+ and 1− charges is this?

Bond Energy

9.76 How much energy, in joules, is required to break the bond in *one* chlorine molecule? The bond energy of Cl_2 is 242.6 kJ/mol.

9.77 How much energy is released in the formation of one molecule of HCl by the following reaction?

$$H^+(g) + Cl^-(g) \longrightarrow HCl(g)$$

The bond energy of HCl is 431 kJ mol^{-1}. Additional data can be found in tables in Chapter 8.

9.78 The reason there is danger in exposure to high-energy radiation (e.g., ultraviolet and X rays) is that the radiation can rupture chemical bonds. In some cases, cancer can be caused by it. A carbon–carbon single bond has a bond energy of approximately 348 kJ per mole. What wavelength of light is required to provide sufficient energy to break the C—C bond? In which region of the electromagnetic spectrum is this wavelength located?

9.79 A mixture of H_2 and Cl_2 is stable, but a bright flash of light passing through it can cause the mixture to explode. The light causes Cl_2 molecules to split into Cl atoms, which are highly reactive. What wavelength of light is necessary to cause the Cl_2 molecules to split? The bond energy of Cl_2 is 242.6 kJ per mole.

Covalent Bonds and the Octet Rule

9.80 Use Lewis structures to diagram the formation of **(a)** Br_2, **(b)** H_2O, and **(c)** NH_3 from neutral atoms.

OH **9.81** Chlorine tends to form only one covalent bond because it needs just one electron to complete its octet. What are the Lewis structures for the simplest compound formed by chlorine with **(a)** nitrogen, **(b)** carbon, **(c)** sulfur, and **(d)** bromine?

9.82 Use the octet rule to predict the formula of the simplest compound formed from hydrogen and **(a)** selenium, **(b)** arsenic, and **(c)** silicon. (Remember that the valence shell of hydrogen can hold only two electrons.)

9.83 What would be the formula for the simplest compound formed from **(a)** phosphorus and chlorine, **(b)** carbon and fluorine, and **(c)** iodine and chlorine?

Electronegativity

9.84 Use Figure 9.9 to choose the atom in each of the following bonds that carries the partial positive charge: **(a)** N—S, **(b)** Si—I, **(c)** N—Br, **(d)** C—Cl.

9.85 Use Figure 9.9 to choose the atom that carries the partial negative charge in each of the following bonds: **(a)** Hg—I, **(b)** P—I, **(c)** Si—F, **(d)** Mg—N.

9.86 Which of the bonds in Problem 9.84 is the most polar?

9.87 Which of the bonds in the Problem 9.85 is the least polar?

Drawing Lewis Structures

ILW **9.88** Draw Lewis structures for **(a)** $AsCl_4^+$, **(b)** ClO_2^-, **(c)** HNO_2, and **(d)** XeF_2.

9.89 Draw Lewis structures for **(a)** TeF_4, **(b)** ClF_5, **(c)** PF_6^-, and **(d)** XeF_4.

9.90 Draw Lewis structures for (**a**) $SiCl_4$, (**b**) PF_3, (**c**) PH_3, and (**d**) SCl_2.

9.91 Draw Lewis structures for (**a**) HIO_3, (**b**) H_2CO_3, (**c**) HCO_3^-, and (**d**) PCl_4^+.

9.92 Draw Lewis structures for (**a**) carbon disulfide and (**b**) cyanide ion.

9.93 Draw Lewis structures for (**a**) selenium trioxide and (**b**) selenium dioxide.

9.94 Draw Lewis structures for (**a**) AsH_3, (**b**) $HClO_2$, (**c**) H_2SeO_3, and (**d**) H_3AsO_4.

OH **9.95** Draw Lewis structures for (**a**) NO^+, (**b**) NO_2^-, (**c**) $SbCl_6^-$, and (**d**) IO_3^-.

9.96 Draw the Lewis structure for (**a**) CH_2O (the central atom is carbon, which is attached to two hydrogens and an oxygen), and (**b**) $SOCl_2$ (the central atom is sulfur, which is attached to an oxygen and two chlorines).

9.97 Draw Lewis structures for (**a**) $GeCl_4$, (**b**) CO_3^{2-}, (**c**) PO_4^{3-}, and (**d**) O_2^{2-}.

Formal Charge

9.98 Assign formal charges to each atom in the following structures:

(**a**) $H—\ddot{\underset{..}{O}}—\ddot{\underset{..}{Cl}}—\ddot{\underset{..}{O}}:$

(**b**) $\ddot{O}=\underset{\underset{:\ddot{O}:}{|}}{S}—\ddot{\underset{..}{O}}:$

(**c**) $\ddot{O}=\ddot{\underset{..}{S}}—\ddot{\underset{..}{O}}:$

9.99 Assign formal charges to each atom in the following structures:

(**a**) $:\ddot{\underset{..}{Cl}}—\underset{\underset{:\ddot{O}:}{||}}{N}—\ddot{\underset{..}{O}}:$

(**b**) $:\ddot{\underset{..}{F}}—\underset{\underset{:\ddot{F}:}{|}}{\overset{\overset{:\ddot{F}:}{|}}{N}}—\ddot{\underset{..}{O}}:$

(**c**) $:\ddot{\underset{..}{F}}—\underset{\underset{:\ddot{O}:}{|}}{\overset{\overset{:\ddot{O}:}{|}}{S}}—\ddot{\underset{..}{F}}:$

ILW **9.100** Draw the Lewis structure for $HClO_4$ according to the procedure described in Figure 9.12. Assign formal charges to each atom in the formula. Determine the preferred Lewis structure for this compound.

9.101 Draw the Lewis structure for SO_2Cl (sulfur bonded to two O and one Cl). Assign formal charges to each atom. Determine the preferred Lewis structure for this molecule.

9.102 Below are two structures for $BeCl_2$. Give two reasons why the one on the left is the preferred structure.

$:\ddot{\underset{..}{Cl}}—Be—\ddot{\underset{..}{Cl}}: \qquad :\ddot{\underset{..}{Cl}}—Be=\ddot{\underset{..}{Cl}}:$

9.103 The following are two Lewis structures that can be drawn for phosgene, a substance that has been used as a war gas.

$:\ddot{O}: \qquad\qquad \ddot{O}:$

$:\ddot{\underset{..}{Cl}}—\overset{\overset{|}{}}{C}=\ddot{\underset{..}{Cl}}: \qquad :\ddot{\underset{..}{Cl}}—\overset{\overset{||}{}}{C}—\ddot{\underset{..}{Cl}}:$

Which is the better Lewis structure? Why?

Coordinate Covalent Bonds

9.104 Use Lewis structures to show that the hydronium ion, H_3O^+, can be considered to be formed by the creation of a coordinate covalent bond between H_2O and H^+.

9.105 Use Lewis structures to show that the reaction

$$BF_3 + F^- \longrightarrow BF_4^-$$

involves the formation of a coordinate covalent bond.

Resonance

9.106 Draw the resonance structures for CO_3^{2-}. Calculate the average C—O bond order.

ILW **9.107** Draw all of the resonance structures for the N_2O_4 molecule and determine the average N—O bond order. The skeletal structure of the molecule is

$$\begin{matrix} O & & O \\ & N & N \\ O & & O \end{matrix}$$

OH **9.108** How should the N—O bond lengths compare in the NO_3^- and NO_2^- ions?

9.109 Arrange the following in order of increasing C—O bond length: CO, CO_3^{2-}, CO_2, HCO_2^- (formate ion, page 394).

9.110 The Lewis structure of CO_2 was given as

$$\ddot{O}=C=\ddot{O}$$

but two other resonance structures can also be drawn for it. What are they? On the basis of formal charges, why are they not preferred structures?

9.111 Use formal charges to establish the preferred Lewis structures for the ClO_3^- and ClO_4^- ions. Draw resonance structures for both ions and determine the average Cl—O bond order in each. Which of these ions would be expected to have the shorter Cl—O bond length?

Additional Exercises

9.112 Use an enthalpy diagram to calculate the lattice energy of $CaCl_2$ from the following information. Energy needed to vaporize one mole of Ca(s) is 192 kJ. For calcium, the first IE = 589.5 kJ mol^{-1}, the second IE = 1146 kJ mol^{-1}. The electron affinity of Cl is 348 kJ mol^{-1}. The bond energy of Cl_2 is 242.6 kJ per mole of Cl—Cl bonds. The standard heat of formation of $CaCl_2$ is −795 kJ mol^{-1}.

9.113 Use an enthalpy diagram and the following data to calculate the electron affinity of bromine. The standard heat of formation of NaBr is −360 kJ mol^{-1}. The energy needed to vaporize Na(s) to give of Na(g) is 107.8 kJ mol^{-1}. The energy needed to vaporize one mole of $Br_2(l)$ to give $Br_2(g)$ is 31 kJ mol^{-1}. The first ionization energy of Na is 495.4 kJ mol^{-1}. The bond energy of Br_2 is 192 kJ per mole of Br–Br bonds. The lattice energy of NaBr is −743.3 kJ mol^{-1}. The heat of vaporization of Na(s) to Na(g) is 107.8 kJ mol^{-1}.

9.114 In many ways, tin(IV) chloride behaves more like a covalent molecular species than like a typical ionic chloride. Draw the Lewis structure for the tin(IV) chloride molecule.

9.115 In each pair, choose the one with the more polar bonds. (Use the periodic table to answer the question.)

    (a) PCl_3 or $AsCl_3$ **(c)** $SiCl_4$ or SCl_2

    (b) SF_2 or GeF_4 **(d)** SrO or SnO

9.116 How many electrons are in the outer shell of the Zn^{2+} ion?

9.117 The Lewis structure for carbonic acid (formed when CO_2 dissolves in water) is usually given as

$$H—\overset{..}{\underset{..}{O}}—\overset{\overset{\displaystyle \overset{..}{O}:}{\|}}{C}—\overset{..}{\underset{..}{O}}—H$$

What is wrong with the following structures?

(a) $H—\overset{..}{\underset{..}{O}}—\overset{\overset{\displaystyle :\overset{..}{O}:}{|}}{C}—\overset{..}{\underset{..}{O}}—H$

(b) $H—\overset{..}{O}=\overset{\overset{\displaystyle :\overset{..}{O}:}{|}}{C}—\overset{..}{O}—H$

(c) $H—\overset{..}{O}=\overset{\overset{\displaystyle :\overset{..}{O}:}{|}}{C}=\overset{..}{O}—H$

9.118 Are the following Lewis structures considered to be resonance structures? Explain. Which is the more likely structure for $POCl_3$?

$$:\overset{..}{\underset{..}{Cl}}—\overset{\overset{\displaystyle :\overset{..}{Cl}:}{|}}{P}=\overset{..}{\underset{..}{O}} \qquad :\overset{..}{\underset{..}{Cl}}—\overset{\overset{\displaystyle :\overset{..}{Cl}:}{|}}{O}=\overset{..}{P}:$$

9.119 Assign formal charges to all the atoms in the following Lewis structure of hydrazoic acid, HN_3.

$$H—N\equiv N—\overset{..}{\underset{..}{N}}:$$

Suggest a lower-energy resonance structure for this molecule.

9.120 Assign formal charges to all the atoms in the Lewis structure

$$\begin{array}{c} :\overset{..}{O}—H \\ | \\ :\overset{..}{\underset{..}{O}}—As—\overset{..}{\underset{..}{O}}—H \\ | \\ H—\overset{..}{\underset{..}{O}}: \end{array}$$

Suggest a lower-energy Lewis structure for this molecule.

9.121 The inflation of an "air bag" when a car experiences a collision occurs by the explosive decomposition of sodium azide, NaN_3, which yields nitrogen gas that inflates the bag. The following resonance structures can be drawn for the azide ion, N_3^-. Identify the best and worst of them.

$$\left[:\overset{..}{N}=N=\overset{..}{N}:\right]^- \longleftrightarrow \left[\overset{..}{N}\equiv N—\overset{..}{\underset{..}{N}}:\right]^-$$

$$\updownarrow \qquad\qquad\qquad \updownarrow$$

$$\left[:N\equiv N=\overset{..}{\underset{..}{N}}:\right]^- \longleftrightarrow \left[:\overset{..}{\underset{..}{N}}—N—\overset{..}{\underset{..}{N}}:\right]^-$$

9.122 How should the sulfur–oxygen bond lengths compare for the species SO_3, SO_2, SO_3^{2-}, and SO_4^{2-}?

9.123 What is the most reasonable Lewis structure for S_2Cl_2?

*9.124 There are two acids that have the formula HCNO. Which of the following skeletal structures are most likely for them? Justify your answer.

   H C O N   H N O C   H O C N

   H C N O   H N C O   H O N C

9.125 In the vapor state, ion pairs of KF can be identified. The dipole moment of such a pair is measured to be 8.59 D and the K—F bond length is found to be 217 pm. Is the K—F bond 100% ionic? If not, what percent of full 1+ and 1− charges do the K and F atoms carry, respectively?

9.126 Below is a ball-and-stick model of a type of alcohol derived from a hydrocarbon. What is the formula for the hydrocarbon and what is its name?

| Multi-Concept Problems

9.127 Use Lewis structures to show the ionization of the following organic acid (a weak acid) in water.

9.128 The compound below is called an amine. It is a weak base and undergoes ionization in water following a path similar to that of ammonia. Use Lewis structures to diagram the reaction of this amine with water.

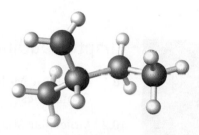

9.129 Use Lewis structures to diagram the reaction between the acid in Problem 9.127 with the base in Problem 9.128. If

12.5 g of the acid is mixed with 17.4 g of the base, how many grams of which reactant will remain unreacted after the reaction is complete?

9.130 How many grams of water could have its temperature raised from 25 °C (room temperature) to 100 °C (the boiling point of water) by the amount of energy released in the formation of 1 mol of H_2 from hydrogen atoms? The bond energy of H_2 is 435 kJ/mol.

*9.131 What wavelength of light, if absorbed by a hydrogen molecule, could cause the molecule to split into the ions H^+ and H^-? (The data required are available in this and previous chapters.)

*9.132 A 38.40 mg sample of an organic acid composed of just carbon, hydrogen, and oxygen was burned in pure oxygen to give 37.54 mg CO_2 and 7.684 mg H_2O in a combustion analysis. In a separate experiment, the molecular mass was determined to be 90. In a titration, 40.2 mg of the acid dissolved in 50 mL of water required 14.28 mL of 0.0625 M NaOH for complete neutralization. Use these data to draw a reasonable Lewis structure for the compound.

| Exercises in Critical Thinking

9.133 What is the average bond energy of a C—C covalent bond? What wavelength of light provides enough energy to break such a bond? Using this information, explain why unfiltered sunlight is damaging to the skin.

9.134 One way of estimating the electronegativity of an atom is to use an average of its ionization energy and electron affinity. Why would these two quantities, taken together, be related to electronegativity?

9.135 The attractions between molecules of a substance can be associated with the size of the molecule's dipole moment. Explain why this is so.

9.136 The positive end of the dipole in a water molecule is not located on an atom. Explain why this happens and suggest other simple molecules that show the same effect.

9.137 In describing the structures of molecules, we use Lewis structures, formal charges, and experimental evidence. Rank these in terms of importance in deciding on the true structure of a molecule, and defend your choice.

10 Theories of Bonding and Structure

In preceding chapters you've seen a variety of molecular shapes illustrated by molecular drawings. Molecular shape has many important consequences, among them our ability to detect odors, both pleasant and unpleasant. Olfactory receptors in our nasal passages bind selectively to molecules according to their shapes. The receptors then send signals to the brain that permit us to distinguish among an enormous number of odor molecules, including those that skunks use to defend themselves. In this chapter we will examine the nature of the shapes of molecules as well as theories of bonding that permit us to explain and sometimes predict molecular geometry. © Corbis RF/Alamy

This Chapter in Context

The structure of a solid ionic compound, such as NaCl, is controlled primarily by the sizes of the ions and their charges. The attractions between the ions have no preferred directions, so if an ionic compound is melted, this structure is lost and the ordered array of ions collapses into a jumbled liquid state. Molecular substances are quite different, however. Molecules have three-dimensional shapes that are determined by the relative orientations of their covalent bonds, and this structure is maintained regardless of whether the substance is a solid, a liquid, or a gas. You've seen some of these shapes in previous chapters.

Many of the properties of a molecule depend on the three-dimensional arrangement of its atoms. As described in the caption accompanying the chapter-opening photo, we detect various aromas because of a precise fit between "odor molecules" and odor receptors in our olfactory system. Similarly, the structures of polymer molecules in plastics have a strong influence on the properties of materials made from them.

In this chapter we will explore the topic of molecular geometry and study theoretical models that allow us to explain, and in some cases predict, the shapes of molecules. We will also examine theories that explain, in terms of wave mechanics and the electronic structures of atoms, *how* covalent bonds form and *why* they are so highly directional in nature. You will find the knowledge gained here helpful in later discussions of the physical properties of substances such as melting points and boiling points.

10.1 | Five Basic Molecular Geometries

Although we live in a three-dimensional world made up of three-dimensional molecules, the Lewis structures we've been using to describe the bonding in molecules do not convey any information about shape. They simply describe which atoms are bonded to each other. Our goal now is to examine theories that predict molecular shapes and explain covalent structures in terms of quantum theory. We begin by describing some of the kinds of shapes molecules have.

Molecular shape only becomes a question when there are at least three atoms present. If there are only two, there is no doubt as to how they are arranged; one is just alongside the other. But when there are three or more atoms in a molecule we find that its shape is often built from just one or another of five basic geometrical structures.

Linear Molecules

In a **linear molecule** the atoms lie in a straight line. When the molecule has three atoms, the angle formed by the covalent bonds, which we call the **bond angle**, equals 180° as illustrated below.

■ As you study these structures, you should try hard to visualize them in three dimensions. You should also learn how to sketch them in a way that conveys the three-dimensional information.

TOOLS

Basic molecular shapes

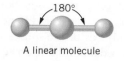

A linear molecule

Planar Triangular Molecules

A **planar triangular molecule** is one in which three atoms are located at the corners of a triangle and are bonded to a fourth atom that lies in the center of the triangle.

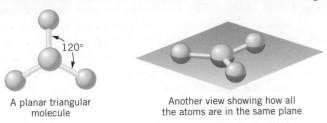

| A planar triangular molecule | Another view showing how all the atoms are in the same plane |

In this molecule, all four atoms lie in the same plane and the bond angles are all equal to 120°.

Tetrahedral Molecules

A **tetrahedron** is a four-sided geometric figure shaped like a pyramid with triangular faces. A **tetrahedral molecule** is one in which four atoms, located at the vertices of a tetrahedron, are bonded to a fifth atom in the center of the structure.

A tetrahedron   A tetrahedral molecule

All of the bond angles in a tetrahedral molecule are the same and are equal to 109.5°.

Trigonal Bipyramidal Molecules

A **trigonal bipyramid** consists of two *trigonal pyramids* (pyramids with triangular faces) that share a common base. In a **trigonal bipyramidal molecule**, the central atom is located in the middle of the triangular plane shared by the upper and lower trigonal pyramids and is bonded to five atoms that are at the vertices of the figure.

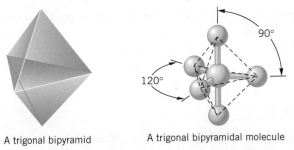

A trigonal bipyramid   A trigonal bipyramidal molecule

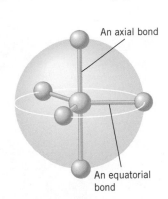

An axial bond

An equatorial bond

Figure 10.1 | **Axial and equatorial bonds in a trigonal bipyramidal molecule.**

Figure 10.2 | **A simplified way of drawing a trigonal bipyramid.** To form a trigonal bipyramidal molecule, atoms would be attached at the corners of the triangle in the center and at the ends of the bonds that extend vertically up and down.

In this molecule, not all the bonds are equivalent. If we imagine the trigonal bipyramid centered inside a sphere similar to earth, as illustrated in Figure 10.1, the atoms in the triangular plane are located around the equator. The bonds to these atoms are called **equatorial bonds**. The angle between any two equatorial bonds is 120°. The two vertical bonds pointing along the north and south axis of the sphere are 180° apart and are called **axial bonds**. The bond angle between an axial bond and an equatorial bond is 90°.

A simplified representation of a trigonal bipyramid is illustrated in Figure 10.2. The equatorial triangular plane is sketched as it would look tilted backward, so we're looking at it from its edge. The axial bonds are represented as lines pointing up and down. To add more three-dimensional character, notice that the bond pointing down appears to be partially hidden by the triangular plane in the center.

Octahedral Molecules

An **octahedron** is an eight-sided figure, which you might think of as two *square pyramids* sharing a common square base. The octahedron has only six vertices, and in an **octahedral molecule** we find an atom in the center of the octahedron bonded to six other atoms at the vertices.

An octahedron

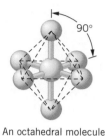

An octahedral molecule

All of the bonds in an octahedral molecule are equivalent, with angles between adjacent bonds equal to 90°.

A simplified representation of an octahedron is shown in Figure 10.3. The square plane in the center of the octahedron, when drawn in perspective and viewed from its edge, looks like a parallelogram. The bonds to the top and bottom of the octahedron are shown as vertical lines. Once again, the bond pointing down is drawn so it appears to be partially hidden by the square plane in the center.

Figure 10.3 | A simplified way of drawing an octahedron. To form an octahedral molecule, atoms would be attached at the corners of the square in the center and at the ends of the bonds that extend vertically up and down.

10.2 | Molecular Shapes and the VSEPR Model

In general, a useful theoretical model should explain known facts, and it should be capable of making accurate predictions. The **valence shell electron pair repulsion model** (called the **VSEPR model,** for short) is remarkably successful at both and is also conceptually simple. The model is based on the following idea:

> Electron pairs (or groups of electron pairs) in the valence shell of an atom repel each other and will position themselves so that they are as far apart as possible, thereby minimizing the repulsions.

The term we will use to describe the space occupied by a group of electrons in the valence shell of an atom is **electron domain,** so the preceding statement can be rephrased as: *electron domains stay as far apart as possible so as to minimize their mutual repulsions.*

As you will see, in describing the shapes of molecules it is useful to divide electron domains into two categories—domains that contain electrons in bonds and domains that contain unshared electrons. They are called *bonding domains* and *nonbonding domains,* respectively.

- A **bonding domain** contains the electrons that are shared between two atoms. *Therefore, all of the electrons within a given single, double, or triple bond are considered to be in the same bonding domain.* A double bond (containing 4 electrons) will occupy more space than a single bond (with only 2 electrons) but all electrons shared by the atoms occupy the same general region in space, so they all belong to the same bonding domain.
- A **nonbonding domain** contains valence electrons that are associated with *a single atom.* A nonbonding domain is either an unshared pair of valence electrons (called a **lone pair**) or, in some cases, a single unpaired electron (found in molecules with an odd number of valence electrons).

Figure 10.4 shows the orientations assumed by different numbers of electron domains, which permit them to minimize repulsions by remaining as far apart as possible. These

TOOLS

VSEPR model

■ An *electron domain* can be a bond, a lone pair, or an unpaired electron. Some prefer to call the VSEPR model (or VSEPR theory) the *electron domain model.*

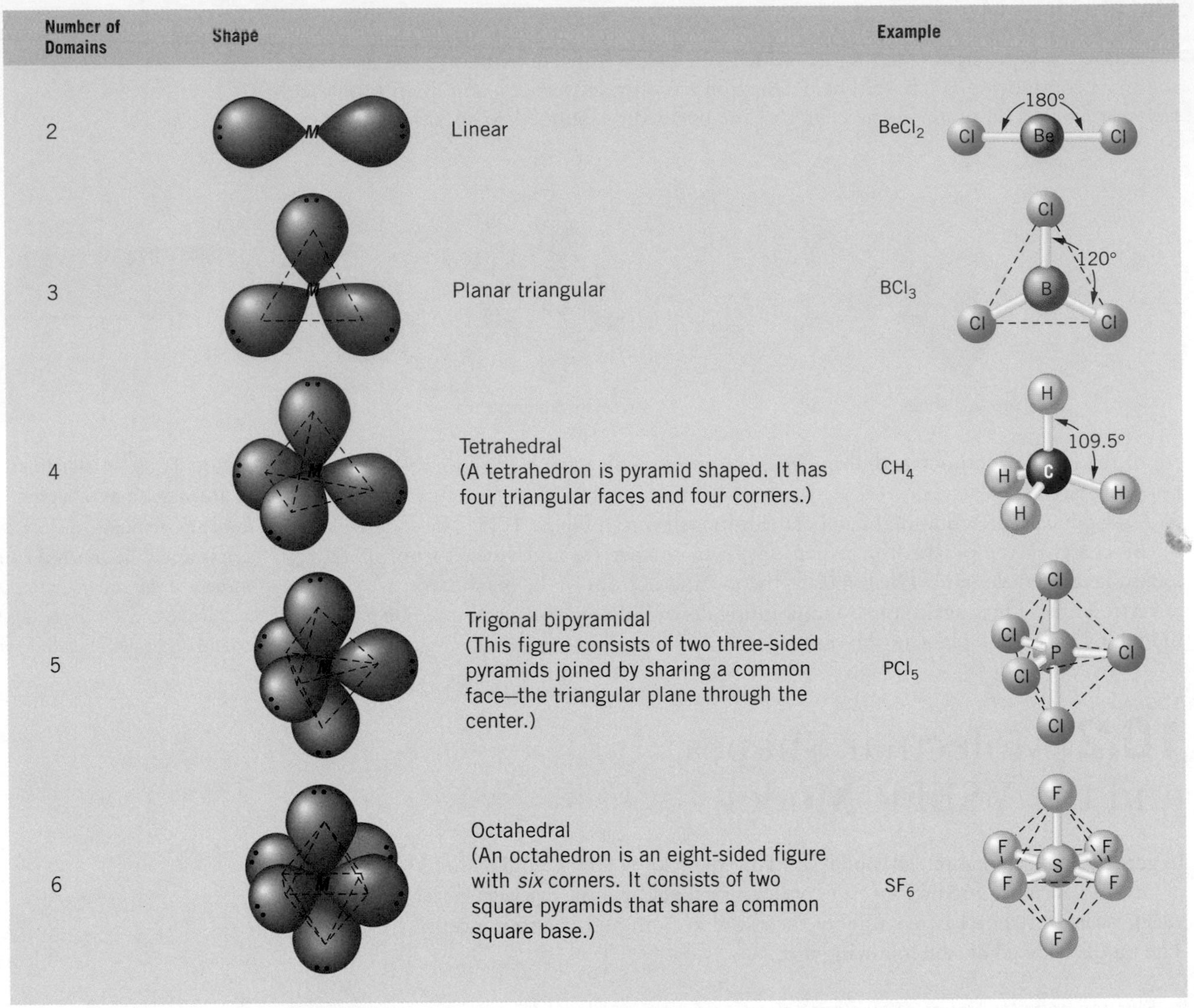

Number of Domains	Shape		Example
2		Linear	$BeCl_2$
3		Planar triangular	BCl_3
4		Tetrahedral (A tetrahedron is pyramid shaped. It has four triangular faces and four corners.)	CH_4
5		Trigonal bipyramidal (This figure consists of two three-sided pyramids joined by sharing a common face—the triangular plane through the center.)	PCl_5
6		Octahedral (An octahedron is an eight-sided figure with *six* corners. It consists of two square pyramids that share a common square base.)	SF_6

Figure 10.4 | **Shapes expected for different numbers of electron domains around a central atom, M.** Each lobe represents an electron domain.

same orientations are achieved whether the domains are bonding or nonbonding. If all of them are bonding domains, molecules are formed having the shapes described in the preceding section, as shown at the right in Figure 10.4.

Lewis Structures and the VSEPR Model

To apply the VSEPR model in predicting shape, we have to know how many electron domains are in the valence shell of the central atom. This is where Lewis structures are especially helpful.

Consider the $BeCl_2$ molecule. On page 383 we gave its Lewis structure as

$$:\ddot{Cl}—Be—\ddot{Cl}:$$

■ In Chapter 9 we noted that the bonds in $BeCl_2$ are covalent, rather than ionic.

Because there are just three atoms, only two shapes are possible. The molecule must be either linear or nonlinear; that is, the atoms lie in a straight line, or they form some angle less than 180°.

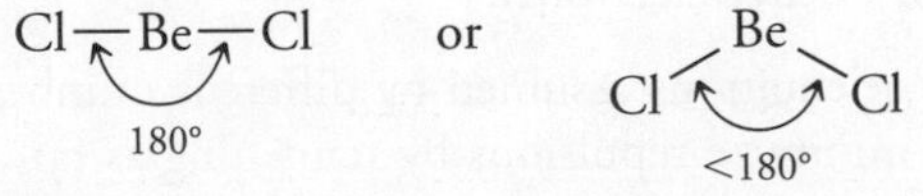

Cl—Be—Cl   or

180°

Cl — Be — Cl

<180°

To predict the structure, we begin by counting the number of electron domains in the valence shell of the Be atom. In this molecule Be forms two single bonds to Cl atoms, so Be has two bonding domains in its valence shell. In Figure 10.4, we see that when there are two electron domains in the valence shell of an atom, minimum repulsion occurs if they are on opposite sides of the nucleus, pointing in opposite directions. We can represent this as

Electron domains

to suggest the approximate locations of the electron clouds of the valence shell electron pairs. In order for the electrons to be in the Be—Cl bonds, the Cl atoms must be placed where the electrons are; the result is that we predict that a $BeCl_2$ molecule should be linear.

$$Cl—Be—Cl$$

Experimentally it has been shown that this is the shape of $BeCl_2$ molecules in the vapor state.

Example 10.1
Predicting Molecular Shapes

Carbon tetrachloride was once used as a cleaning fluid until it was discovered that it causes liver damage if absorbed by the body. What is the shape of the molecule?

■ **Analysis:** To find the shape of the molecule, we need its Lewis structure so that we can count electron domains and apply the VSEPR model. To write the Lewis structure, we need the formula for the compound, and that requires the application of the rules of chemical nomenclature.

■ **Assembling the Tools:** The primary tool for solving this kind of problem is the Lewis structure, which we will draw following the procedure in Chapter 9. First, however, we need the chemical formula. Applying the rules of nomenclature in Chapter 3 gives CCl_4. Finally, we'll use the VSEPR model as a tool to deduce the structure of the molecule.

■ **Solution:** Following the procedure in Figure 9.12, the Lewis structure of CCl_4 is

$$:\ddot{C}l:$$
$$|$$
$$:\ddot{C}l—C—\ddot{C}l:$$
$$|$$
$$:\ddot{C}l:$$

There are four bonds, each corresponding to a bonding domain around the carbon. According to Figure 10.4, the domains can be farthest apart when arranged tetrahedrally, so the molecule is expected to be tetrahedral. (This is, in fact, its structure.)

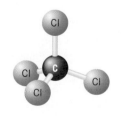

■ **Is the Answer Reasonable?** The answer depends critically on the Lewis structure, so be sure to check that you've constructed it correctly. Once we're confident in the Lewis structure the rest is straightforward. The arrangement of domains gives us the arrangement of Cl atoms around the C atom.

10.1 | What is the shape of the SeF_6 molecule? (*Hint:* If necessary, refer to Figure 9.12 on page 384.)

10.2 | What shape is expected for the $SbCl_5$ molecule?

Practice Exercises

Nonbonding Domains and Molecular Shapes

■ The electronegativity difference between tin and chlorine is only 1.1, which means that tin–chlorine bonds have a significant degree of covalent character. Many compounds of tin are molecular, especially those of Sn^{IV}. $SnCl_2$ is another example of a molecule that behaves as though it has less than an octet around the central atom.

Some molecules have a central atom with one or more nonbonding domains, each of which consists of an unshared electron pair (lone pair) or a single unpaired valence electron. These nonbonding domains affect the geometry of the molecule. An example is $SnCl_2$.

$$:\ddot{Cl}—\ddot{Sn}—\ddot{Cl}:$$

There are *three* domains around the tin atom: two bonding domains plus a nonbonding domain (the lone pair). According to Figure 10.4, the domains are farthest apart when at the corners of a triangle. For the moment, let's ignore the chlorine atoms and concentrate on how the electron domains are arranged.

We can find the shape of the molecule, now, by placing the two Cl atoms where two of the domains are (below, left).

We can't describe this molecule as triangular, even though that is how the domains are arranged. ***Molecular shape describes the arrangement of atoms, not the arrangement of electron domains***. Therefore, to describe the shape we ignore the lone pair, as shown above at the right, and say that the $SnCl_2$ molecule has a structure that is **nonlinear** or **bent** or **V-shaped**.

Notice that when there are three domains around the central atom, *two* different molecular shapes are possible. If all three are bonding domains, a molecule with a planar triangular shape is formed, as shown for BCl_3 in Figure 10.4. If one of the domains is nonbonding, as in $SnCl_2$, the arrangement of the atoms in the molecule is said to be non-linear. The predicted shapes of both, however, are *derived* by first noting the triangular arrangement of domains around the central atom and *then* adding the necessary number of atoms.

Molecules with Four Electron Domains around the Central Atom

There are many molecules with four electron pairs (an octet) in the valence shell of the central atom. When these electron pairs are used to form four single bonds, as in methane (CH_4), the resulting molecule is tetrahedral (Figure 10.4). There are many examples, however, where nonbonding domains are also present. For instance, two molecules you've encountered before are

$$H—\overset{\displaystyle ..}{N}—H$$
$$|$$
$$H$$
one lone pair

$$H—\underset{\displaystyle ..}{\overset{\displaystyle ..}{O}}—H$$
two lone pairs

Figure 10.5 shows how the nonbonding domains affect the shapes of molecules of this type.

■ Note once again that in describing the shape of the molecule, we look at how the atoms are arranged and ignore the nonbonding domains.

With one nonbonding domain, as in NH_3, the central atom is at the top of a pyramid with three atoms at the corners of the triangular base. The resulting structure is said to be **trigonal pyramidal**. When there are two nonbonding domains in the tetrahedron, as in H_2O,

Number of Bonding Domains	Number of Nonbonding Domains	Structure	
4	0	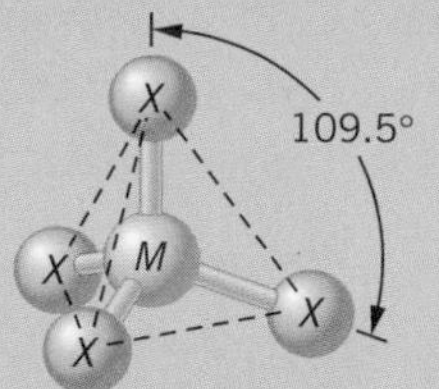	**Tetrahedral** (example, CH_4) All bond angles are 109.5°.
3	1	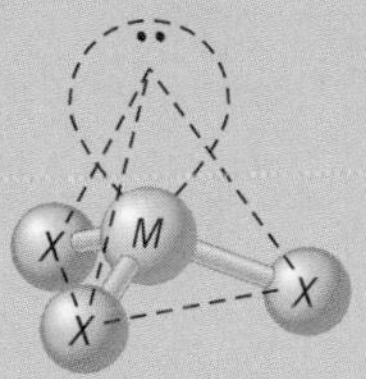	**Trigonal pyramidal** (pyramid shaped) (example, NH_3)
2	2	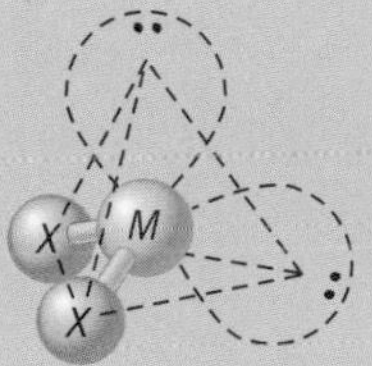	**Nonlinear, bent** (example, H_2O)

Figure 10.5 | **Molecular shapes with four domains around the central atom.** The molecules MX_4, MX_3, and MX_2 shown here all have four domains arranged tetrahedrally around the central atom. The names used to describe the shapes are derived from the way the X atoms are arranged around M, ignoring the nonbonding domains.

the three atoms of the molecule (the central atom plus the two atoms bonded to it) do not lie in a straight line, so the structure is described as nonlinear or bent.

Molecules with Five Electron Domains around the Central Atom

When five domains are present around the central atom, they are directed toward the vertices of a trigonal bipyramid. Molecules such as PCl_5 have this geometry, as shown in Figure 10.4, and are said to have a **trigonal bipyramidal** shape.

In the trigonal bipyramid, nonbonding domains always occupy positions in the *equatorial plane* (the triangular plane through the center of the molecule). This is because nonbonding domains, which have a positive nucleus only at one end, are larger than bonding domains, as illustrated in Figure 10.6. The larger nonbonding domains are less crowded in the equatorial plane, where they have just two closest neighbors at 90°, than they would be in an axial position, where they would have three closest neighbors at 90°.

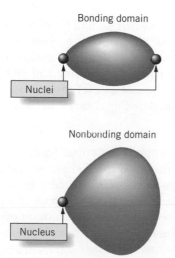

Bonding domain

Nuclei

Nonbonding domain

Nucleus

Figure 10.6 | **Relative sizes of bonding and nonbonding domains.**

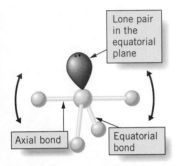

Figure 10.8 | **This distorted tetrahedron is sometimes described as a *seesaw structure.*** The origin of this description can be seen if we tip the structure over so it stands on the two atoms in the equatorial plane, with the nonbonding domain pointing up.

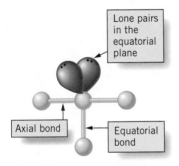

Figure 10.9 | **A molecule with two nonbonding domains in the equatorial plane of the trigonal bipyramid.** When tipped over, the molecule looks like a T, so it is called **T-shaped.**

■ No common molecule or ion with six electron domains around the central atom has more than two nonbonding domains.

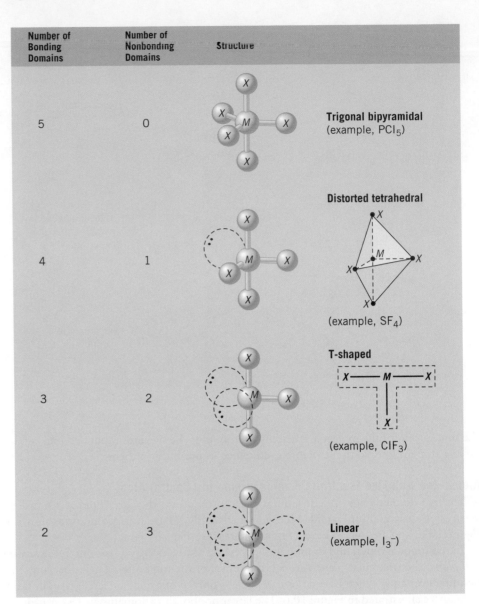

Number of Bonding Domains	Number of Nonbonding Domains	Structure
5	0	**Trigonal bipyramidal** (example, PCl_5)
4	1	**Distorted tetrahedral** (example, SF_4)
3	2	**T-shaped** (example, ClF_3)
2	3	**Linear** (example, I_3^-)

Figure 10.7 | **Molecular shapes with five domains around the central atom.** Four different molecular structures are possible, depending on the number of nonbonding domains around the central atom M.

Figure 10.7 shows the kinds of geometries that we find for different numbers of non-bonding domains in the trigonal bipyramid. When there is only one nonbonding domain, as in SF_4, the structure is described as a **distorted tetrahedron** or **seesaw** in which the central atom lies along one edge of a four-sided figure (Figures 10.7 and 10.8). With two non-bonding domains in the equatorial plane, the molecule is **T-shaped** (shaped like the letter T, Figure 10.9), and when there are three nonbonding domains in the equatorial plane, the molecule is **linear.**

Molecules with Six Electron Domains around the Central Atom

Finally, we come to molecules or ions that have six domains around the central atom. When all are in bonds, as in SF_6, the molecule is octahedral (Figure 10.4). When one nonbonding domain is present, the molecule or ion has the shape of a **square pyramid,** and when two nonbonding domains are present, they take positions on opposite sides of the nucleus and the molecule or ion has a **square planar** structure. These shapes are shown in Figure 10.10.

Steps in Using the VSEPR Model to Determine Molecular Shape

Now that we've seen how nonbonding and bonding domains influence molecular shape we can develop a strategy for applying the VSEPR model. In following this strategy it will be to your advantage to learn to sketch the five basic geometries (linear, planar triangular, tetrahedral, trigonal bipyramidal, and octahedral).

Determining Molecular Shape Using the VSEPR Model

Step 1. Use the procedure in Figure 9.12 to construct the Lewis formula for the molecule or ion.

Step 2. Count the total number of electron domains (bonding plus nonbonding).

Step 3. Using the result from Step 2, select the basic geometry upon which the shape of the molecule is based. [Make a drawing that shows the location of the central atom and the directions in which the domains (both bonding and nonbonding) are oriented.]

Step 4. Add the appropriate number of atoms to the bonding domains.

Step 5. If there are any nonbonding domains, ignore them and use the arrangement of atoms around the central atom to obtain the description of the molecular shape, as shown in Figures 10.5, 10.7, and 10.10.

Applying VSEPR theory

Number of Bonding Domains	Number of Nonbonding Domains	Structure	
6	0	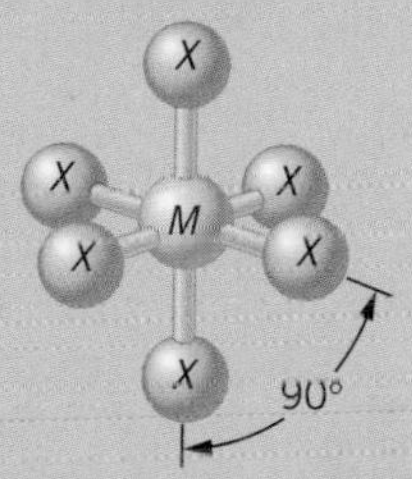	Octahedral (example, SF$_6$) All bond angles are 90°.
5	1	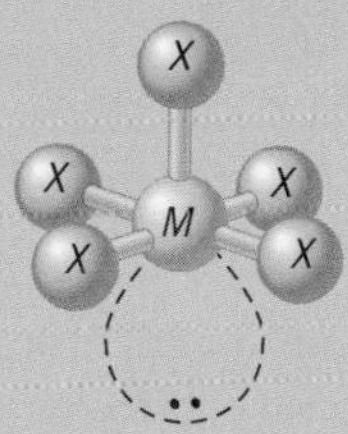	Square pyramidal 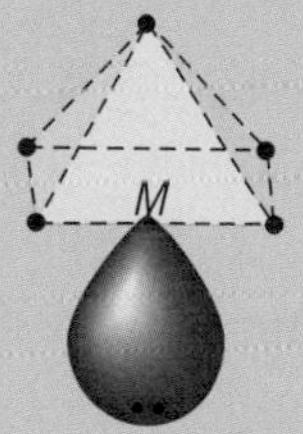 (example, BrF$_5$)
4	2	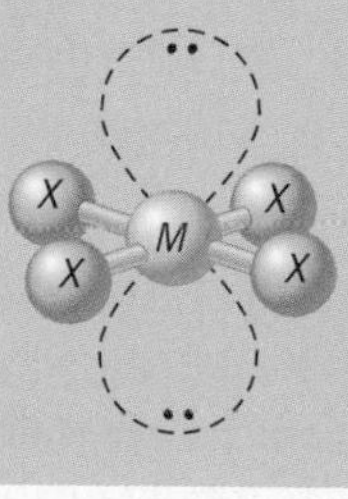	Square planar (example, XeF$_4$)

Figure 10.10 | **Molecular shapes with six domains around the central atom.** Although more are theoretically possible, only three different molecular shapes are observed, depending on the number of nonbonding domains around the central atom.

Example 10.2
Predicting the Shapes of Molecules and Ions

Do we expect the ClO_2^- ion to be linear?

■ **Analysis:** This is a pretty straightforward application of the VSEPR model.

■ **Assembling the Tools:** The strategy described above for applying the VSEPR model as a tool first requires construction of the Lewis formula. The tool for this is Figure 9.12 on page 384.

■ **Solution:** Following the usual procedure described in Figure 9.12, the Lewis structure for ClO_2^- is

$$\left[\ddot{\underset{..}{O}}-\underset{..}{\ddot{Cl}}-\ddot{\underset{..}{O}}\right]^-$$

Next, we count bonding and nonbonding domains around the central atom. There are four domains around the chlorine: two bonding and two nonbonding. Four domains (according to the theory) are always arranged tetrahedrally. This gives

Now we add the two oxygens, as shown below on the left. It doesn't matter which locations in the tetrahedron we choose because all the bond angles are equal. Below, on the right, we see how the structure of the ion looks when we ignore the lone pairs.

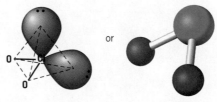

■ For a molecule with three atoms, there are only two ways they can be arranged: either in a straight line (linear) or in a nonlinear arrangement.

Notice that the O—Cl—O angle is less than 180°, so we predict the ion to be nonlinear (or bent or V-shaped).

■ **Is the Answer Reasonable?** Here are questions we have to answer to check our work. First, have we drawn the Lewis structure correctly? Have we counted the domains correctly? Have we selected the correct orientation of the domains? And finally, have we correctly described the structure obtained by adding the two oxygen atoms? Our answer to each of these questions is "Yes," so we can be confident our answer is right.

Example 10.3
Predicting the Shapes of Molecules and Ions

Xenon is one of the noble gases, and is generally quite unreactive. In fact, it was long believed that all the noble gases were totally unable to form compounds. It came as quite a surprise, therefore, when it was discovered that some compounds could be made. One of these is xenon difluoride. What would you expect the geometry of xenon difluoride to be—linear or nonlinear?

■**Analysis:** This problem is similar to previous examples we've worked out. The first step will be to correctly write the formula of the compound. Then we can construct the Lewis formula, from which we can derive the shape of the molecule by applying the VSEPR model.

■**Assembling the Tools:** First, we need the rules of nomenclature from Chapter 3 to obtain the formula of xenon tetrafluoride, which is XeF_2. We then follow the procedure in Figure 9.12 to construct the Lewis formula. From here, we follow the strategy for applying the VSEPR model.

■**Solution:** The outer shell of xenon, of course, has a noble gas configuration, which contains 8 electrons. Each fluorine has 7 valence electrons. Using this information we obtain the following Lewis structure for XeF_2.

Next we count domains around xenon; there are five of them, three nonbonding and two bonding. When there are five domains, they are arranged in a trigonal bipyramid.

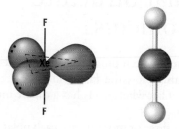

Now we must add the fluorine atoms. In a trigonal bipyramid, the nonbonding domains always occur in the equatorial plane through the center, so the fluorines go on the top and bottom. This gives

The three atoms, F—Xe—F, are arranged in a straight line, so the molecule is linear.

■**Is the Answer Reasonable?** Is the Lewis structure correct? Yes. Have we selected the correct basic geometry? Yes. Have we attached the F atoms to the Xe correctly? Yes. All is in order, so the answer is correct.

Example 10.4
Predicting the Shapes of Molecules and Ions

The Lewis structure for the very poisonous gas hydrogen cyanide, HCN, is

$$H—C≡N:$$

Is the HCN molecule linear or nonlinear?

■**Analysis:** We already have the Lewis structure, so we count electron domains and proceed as before. The critical link in this problem is remembering that a bonding domain connects one atom to the central atom and that *all the electron pairs in a given bond belong to the same bonding domain.*

■**Assembling the Tools:** As before, the tool required is the strategy for applying the VSEPR model.

■**Solution:** There are two bonding domains around the carbon: one for the triple bond with nitrogen and one for the single bond with hydrogen.

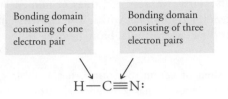

Therefore, we expect the two bonds to locate themselves 180° apart, yielding a linear HCN molecule.

■**Is the Answer Reasonable?** Have we correctly counted bonding domains? Yes. We can expect our answer to be correct.

Practice Exercises

10.3 | The first known compound of the noble gas argon is HArF. What shape is expected for the HArF molecule? (*Hint:* Remember that argon is a noble gas with 8 electrons in its valence shell.)

10.4 | What shape is expected for the IBr_2^- ion?

10.5 | What shape is expected for the RnF_4 molecule?

10.6 | Predict the shapes of SO_3^{2-}, $PbCl_4$, XeO_4, and OF_2.

10.3 | Molecular Structure and Dipole Moments

■ Any molecule composed of just two atoms that differ in electronegativity must be polar because the bond is polar.

For a diatomic molecule, the dipole moment is determined solely by the polarity of the bond between the two atoms. Thus, the HCl molecule has a nonzero dipole moment because the H—Cl bond is polar, whereas H_2 has a dipole moment equal to zero because the H—H bond is nonpolar.

For a molecule containing three or more atoms, each polar bond has its own **bond dipole**, which contributes to the overall dipole moment of the molecule. This happens because the bond dipoles have *vector properties*, with both direction and magnitude. In a molecule, the bond dipoles add as vectors do.

Figure 10.11 shows three molecules in which vector addition of the bond dipoles leads to complete cancellation and dipole moments equal to zero. In the figure, the bond dipoles

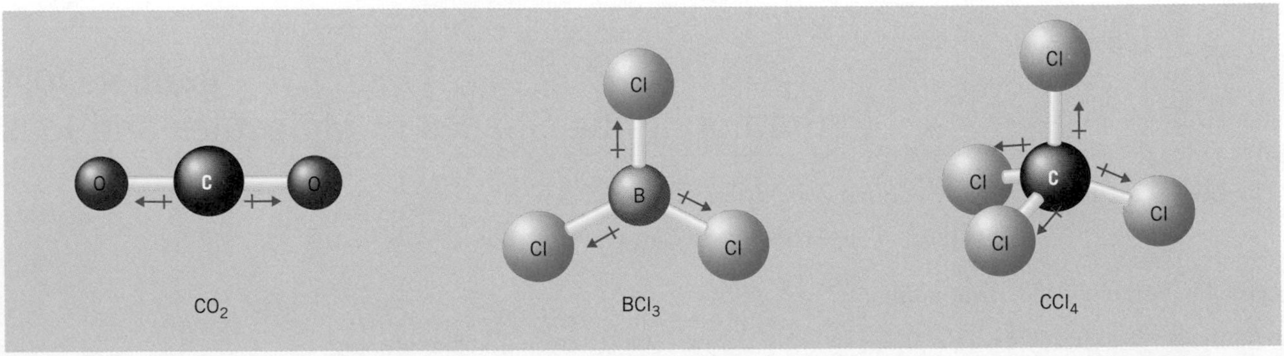

Figure 10.11 | **Molecular shape and its effect on the dipole moment.** Even though these molecules have polar bonds, vector addition of their bond dipoles leads to dipole moments of zero, which means the molecules are nonpolar.

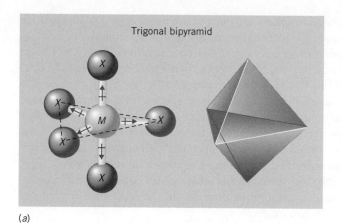

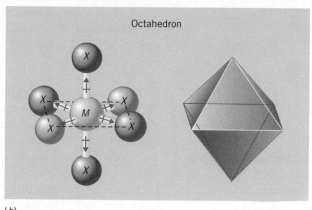

(a)

(b)

Figure 10.12 | **Cancellation of bond dipoles in symmetric trigonal bipyramidal and octahedral molecules.** In this figure, the colors of atoms are used to identify different sets of atoms within the molecule. (a) A trigonal bipyramidal molecule, MX_5, in which the central atom M is bonded to five identical atoms X. The set of three bond dipoles in the triangular plane in the center (in blue) cancel, as do the linear set of dipoles (red). Overall, the molecule is nonpolar. (b) An octahedral molecule MX_6 in which the central atom is bonded to six identical atoms. This molecule contains three linear sets of bond dipoles (red, blue, and green). Cancellation occurs for each set, so the molecule is nonpolar overall.

are indicated by arrows with plus signs at one end, $+\!\!\longrightarrow$, to show which end of the dipole is positive. On the left is the linear CO_2 molecule in which both C—O bonds are identical. The individual bond dipoles have the same magnitude, but they point in opposite directions. Vector addition leads to cancellation and a net dipole moment of zero, just as adding numbers such as $+5$ and -5 gives a sum of zero. Because the dipole moment is zero, the CO_2 molecule is nonpolar. Although it isn't so easy to visualize, the same thing also happens in BCl_3 and CCl_4. In each of these molecules, the influence of one bond dipole is canceled by the effects of the others, which causes the molecules to have net dipole moments of zero. As a result, BCl_3 and CCl_4 are **nonpolar molecules**.

Although the molecules in Figure 10.11 are nonpolar, the fact that they contain non-zero bond dipoles means that the atoms carry some partial positive or negative charge. In CO_2, for example, the carbon carries a partial positive charge and an equal negative charge is divided between the two oxygen atoms. Similarly, in BCl_3 and CCl_4, the central atoms have partial positive charges and the chlorine atoms have partial negative charges.

Perhaps you've noticed that the structures of the molecules in Figure 10.11 correspond to three of the basic shapes that we used to derive the shapes of molecules. Molecules with the remaining two structures, trigonal bipyramidal and octahedral, also are nonpolar if all the atoms attached to the central atom are the same. All of the basic shapes are "balanced," or **symmetric**,[1] if all of the domains and groups attached to them are identical. Examples are shown in Figure 10.12. The trigonal bipyramidal structure can be viewed as a planar triangular set of atoms (shown in blue) plus a pair of atoms arranged linearly (shown in red). All the bond dipoles in the planar triangle cancel, as do the two dipoles of the bonds arranged linearly, so the molecule is nonpolar overall. Similarly, we can look at the octahedral molecule as consisting of three linear sets of bond dipoles. Cancellation of bond dipoles occurs in each set, so overall the octahedral molecule is also nonpolar.

---

[1]Symmetry is a more complex subject than we present it here. When we describe the symmetry properties of a molecule, we are specifying the various ways the molecule can be turned and otherwise manipulated while leaving the molecule looking exactly as it appeared before the manipulation. For example, imagine the BCl_3 molecule in Figure 10.11 being rotated 120° around an axis perpendicular to the page, that passes through the B atom. Performing this rotation leaves the molecule looking just as it did before the rotation. This rotation axis is a symmetry property of BCl_3.

Intuitively, we can recognize when an object possesses symmetry elements such as rotation axes (as well as other symmetry properties we haven't mentioned). Comparing objects, we can usually tell when one is more symmetric than another, and in our discussions in this chapter we rely on this qualitative sense of symmetry.

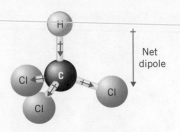

Figure 10.13 | Bond dipoles in the chloroform molecule, CHCl₃.
Because C is slightly more electronegative than H, the C—H bond dipole points toward the carbon. The small C—H bond dipole actually adds to the effects of the C—Cl bond dipoles. All the bond dipoles are additive, and this causes CHCl₃ to be a polar molecule.

■ The lone pairs also influence the polarity of a molecule, but we will not explore this any further here.

If all the atoms attached to the central atom are **not** *the same, or if there are lone pairs in the valence shell of the central atom, the molecule is* **usually** *polar.* For example, in CHCl₃, one of the atoms in the tetrahedral structure is different from the others. The C—H bond is less polar than the C—Cl bonds, and the bond dipoles do not cancel (Figure 10.13). An "unbalanced" structure such as this is said to be **dissymmetric.**

Two familiar molecules that have lone pairs in the valence shells of their central atoms are shown in Figure 10.14. In these molecules the bond dipoles are oriented in such a way that their effects do not cancel. In water, for example, each bond dipole points partially in the same direction, toward the oxygen atom. As a result, the bond dipoles partially add to give a net dipole moment for the molecule. The same thing happens in ammonia, where three bond dipoles point partially in the same direction and add to give a polar NH₃ molecule.

Not every structure that contains nonbonding domains on the central atom produces polar molecules. The following are two exceptions.

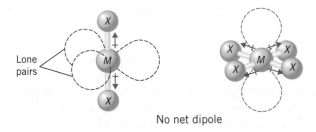

Lone pairs

No net dipole

In the first case, we have a pair of bond dipoles arranged linearly, just as they are in CO₂. In the second, the bonded atoms lie at the corners of a square, which can be viewed as two linear sets of bond dipoles. *If the atoms attached to the central atom are the same and are arranged linearly,* cancellation of bond dipoles occurs and produces nonpolar molecules. This means that molecules such as linear XeF₂ and square planar XeF₄ are nonpolar.

Molecular shape and molecular polarity

In Summary

- A molecule will be nonpolar if (a) the bonds are nonpolar or (b) there are no lone pairs in the valence shell of the central atom and all the atoms attached to the central atom are the same.

- A molecule in which the central atom has lone pairs of electrons will usually be polar, with the two exceptions described above in which the attached atoms are arranged so that their bond dipoles cancel.

On the basis of the preceding discussions, let's see how we apply these ideas to predict whether molecules are expected to be polar or nonpolar.

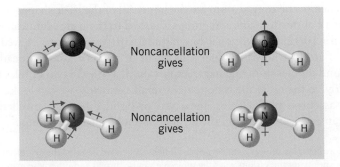

Noncancellation gives

Noncancellation gives

Figure 10.14 | Dipole moments in water and ammonia.
Each of these molecules contains nonbonding domains in the valence shell of the central atoms and has a net dipole moment. When nonbonding domains occur on the central atom, the bond dipoles usually do not cancel, and polar molecules result.

Example 10.5
Predicting Molecular Polarity

Do we expect the phosphorus trichloride molecule to be polar or nonpolar?

■ **Analysis:** Answering this seemingly simple question actually requires answering a number of questions. Are the bonds in the molecule polar or nonpolar? If they are polar, do the bond dipoles cancel? To answer that question, we need to know the shape of the molecule and whether there are lone pairs around the central atom. To find the shape of the molecule we have to construct the Lewis structure and apply the VSEPR model.

■ **Assembling the Tools:** First, we need to apply the nomenclature rules from Chapter 3 to convert the name of the compound into a chemical formula, which gives PCl_3. Next, we'll use electronegativities as a tool to determine whether the bonds in the molecule are polar. If they're not, the molecule will be nonpolar regardless of its structure. If the bonds are polar, we then need to determine the molecular structure. Our tools will be the procedure for drawing the Lewis structure and the VSEPR model. On the basis of the molecular structure, we can then decide whether the bond dipoles cancel.

■ **Solution:** The electronegativities of the atoms (P = 2.1, Cl = 2.9) tell us that the individual P—Cl bonds will be polar. Therefore, to predict whether or not the molecule is polar, we need to know its shape. First, we draw the Lewis structure following our usual procedure.

$$
\begin{array}{c}
: \ddot{C}l : \\
| \\
: \ddot{C}l - P - \ddot{C}l : \\
\end{array}
$$

There are four domains around the phosphorus, so they should be arranged tetrahedrally. This means that the PCl_3 molecule should have a trigonal pyramidal shape, as shown in the margin. Because of the structure, the bond dipoles do not cancel, and we expect the molecule to be polar.

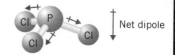
Net dipole

■ **Is the Answer Reasonable?** There's not much to do here except to carefully check the Lewis structure to be sure it's correct and to check that we've applied the VSEPR theory correctly.

Example 10.6
Predicting Molecular Polarity

Would you expect the molecule HCN to be polar or nonpolar?

■ **Analysis and Tools:** Our analysis proceeds as in Example 10.5, so we will apply the same tools.

■ **Solution:** To begin, we have polar bonds, because carbon is slightly more electronegative than hydrogen and nitrogen is slightly more electronegative than carbon. The Lewis structure of HCN is

$$
H - C \equiv N :
$$

There are two domains around the central carbon atom, so we expect a linear shape. However, the two bond dipoles do not cancel. One reason is that they are not of equal magnitude, which we know because the difference in electronegativity between C and H is 0.4, whereas the difference in electronegativity between C and N is 0.6. The other

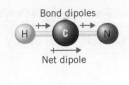

Bond dipoles

Net dipole

reason is because both bond dipoles point in the same direction, from the atom of low electronegativity to the one of high electronegativity. This is illustrated in the margin. Notice that the bond dipoles combine by vector addition to give a net dipole moment for the molecule that is larger than either of the individual bond dipoles. As a result, HCN is a polar molecule.

■**Is the Answer Reasonable?** As in the preceding example, we can check that we've obtained the correct Lewis structure and applied the VSEPR theory correctly, which we have. We can also check to see whether we've used the electronegativities to reach the right conclusions, which we have. We can be confident in our conclusions.

Practice Exercises

10.7 | Is the sulfur tetrafluoride molecule polar or nonpolar? (*Hint:* Use the VSEPR model to sketch the shape of the molecule.)

10.8 | Which of the following molecules would you expect to be polar? (a) TeF_6, (b) SeO_2, (c) $BrCl$, (d) AsH_3, (e) CF_2Cl_2

10.4 | Valence Bond Theory

So far we have described the bonding in molecules using Lewis structures. Lewis structures, however, tell us nothing about *why* covalent bonds are formed or *how* electrons manage to be shared between atoms. Nor does the VSEPR model explain *why* electrons group themselves into domains as they do. Thus, we must look beyond these simple models to understand more fully the covalent bond and the factors that determine molecular geometry.

There are fundamentally two theories of covalent bonding that have evolved based on quantum theory: the **valence bond theory** (or **VB theory**, for short) and the **molecular orbital theory (MO theory)**. They differ principally in the way they construct a theoretical model of the bonding in a molecule. The valence bond theory imagines individual atoms, each with its own orbitals and electrons, coming together to form the covalent bonds of the molecule. The molecular orbital theory doesn't concern itself with *how* the molecule is formed. It just views a molecule as a collection of positively charged nuclei surrounded in some way by electrons that occupy a set of *molecular orbitals*, in much the same way that the electrons in an atom occupy *atomic orbitals*. (In a sense, MO theory would look at an atom as if it were a special case—a molecule having only one positive center, instead of many.)

Bond Formation by Orbital Overlap

VB criteria for bond formation

According to VB theory, *a bond between two atoms is formed when **two electrons** with their **spins paired** are shared by two **overlapping** atomic orbitals, one orbital from each of the atoms joined by the bond.* By **overlap of orbitals** we mean that portions of two atomic orbitals from different atoms share the same space.[2]

An important part of the theory, as suggested by the bold italic type above, is that only *one* pair of electrons, with paired spins, can be shared by two overlapping orbitals. This electron pair becomes concentrated in the region of overlap and helps "cement" the nuclei together, so the amount that the potential energy is lowered when the bond is formed is determined in part by the extent to which the orbitals overlap. Therefore, *atoms tend to position themselves so that the maximum amount of orbital overlap occurs because this yields the minimum potential energy and therefore the strongest bonds.*

[2]The concept of orbital overlap is actually more complicated than this and requires the application of quantum theory. For our purposes, the current definition will suffice.

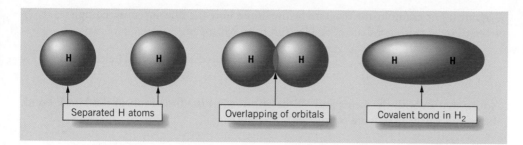

The way VB theory views the formation of a hydrogen molecule is shown in Figure 10.15. As the two atoms approach each other, their $1s$ orbitals begin to overlap and merge as the electron pair spreads out over both orbitals, thereby giving the H—H bond. The description of the bond in H_2 provided by VB theory is essentially the same as that discussed in Chapter 9.

Now let's look at the HF molecule, which is a bit more complex than H_2. Following the usual rules we can write its Lewis structure as

$$H-\ddot{\underset{\cdot\cdot}{F}}:$$

and we can diagram the formation of the bond as

$$H\cdot + \cdot\ddot{\underset{\cdot\cdot}{F}}: \longrightarrow H-\ddot{\underset{\cdot\cdot}{F}}:$$

Our Lewis symbols suggest that the H—F bond is formed by the pairing of electrons, one from hydrogen and one from fluorine. To explain this according to VB theory, we must have two half-filled orbitals, one from each atom, that can be joined by overlap. (They must be half-filled, because we cannot place more than two electrons into the bond.) To see clearly what must happen, it is best to look at the orbital diagrams of the valence shells of hydrogen and fluorine.

The requirements for bond formation are met by overlapping the half-filled $1s$ orbital of hydrogen with the half-filled $2p$ orbital of fluorine; there are then two orbitals plus two electrons whose spins can adjust so they are paired. The formation of the bond is illustrated in Figure 10.16.

The overlap of orbitals provides a means for sharing electrons, thereby allowing each atom to complete its valence shell. It is sometimes convenient to indicate this using orbital

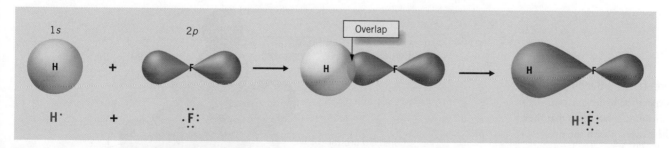

Figure 10.16 | **The formation of the hydrogen fluoride molecule according to valence bond theory.** For clarity, only the half-filled $2p$ orbital of fluorine is shown. The other $2p$ orbitals of fluorine are filled and cannot participate in bonding.

diagrams. For example, the diagram below shows how the fluorine atom completes its $2p$ subshell by acquiring a share of an electron from hydrogen.

F (in HF)   ⓘ↑↓ ⓘ↑↓ⓘ↑↓ⓘ↑↓   (Colored arrow is the H electron.)
             $2s$ $2p$

Notice that in both the Lewis and VB descriptions of the formation of the H—F bond, the atoms' valence shells are completed.

Overlap of Atomic Orbitals and Molecular Shapes

Let's look now at a more complex molecule, hydrogen sulfide, H_2S. Experiments have shown that it is a nonlinear molecule in which the H—S—H bond angle is about 92°.

■ H_2S is the compound that gives rotten eggs their foul odor.

$$\begin{matrix} & S & \\ & \diagup \ \diagdown & \\ H & \curvearrowright \ \curvearrowleft & H \\ & 92° & \end{matrix}$$

Using Lewis symbols, we would diagram the formation of H_2S as

$$2H\cdot + \cdot\ddot{\underset{\cdot\cdot}{S}}\cdot \longrightarrow H-\ddot{\underset{\cdot\cdot}{S}}-H$$

Our Lewis symbols suggest that each H—S bond is formed by the pairing of two electrons, one from H and one from S. Applying this to VB theory, each bond requires the overlap of two half-filled orbitals, one on H and one on S. Therefore, forming *two* H—S bonds in H_2S will require *two* half-filled orbitals on sulfur to form bonds to two separate H atoms. To clearly see what happens, let's look at the orbital diagrams of the valence shells of hydrogen and sulfur.

■ If necessary, review the procedure for drawing orbital diagrams on page 329 in Chapter 8.

H   ⓘ↑
     $1s$

S   ⓘ↑↓ ⓘ↑↓ⓘ↑ⓘ↑
     $3s$ $3p$

Sulfur has two $3p$ orbitals that each contain only one electron. Each of these can overlap with the $1s$ orbital of a hydrogen atom, as shown in Figure 10.17. This overlap completes the $3p$ subshell of sulfur because each hydrogen provides one electron.

S (in H_2S)   ⓘ↑↓ ⓘ↑↓ⓘ↑↓ⓘ↑↓   (Colored arrows are H electrons.)
                $3s$ $3p$

■ In VB theory, two orbitals from different atoms never overlap simultaneously with opposite ends of the same p orbital.

In Figure 10.17, notice that when the $1s$ orbital of a hydrogen atom overlaps with a p orbital of sulfur, the best overlap occurs when the hydrogen atom lies along the axis of the

Figure 10.17 | **Bonding in H_2S.** We expect the hydrogen $1s$ orbitals to position themselves so that they can best overlap with the two partially filled $3p$ orbitals of sulfur, which gives a predicted bond angle of 90°. The experimentally measured bond angle of 92° is very close to the predicted angle.

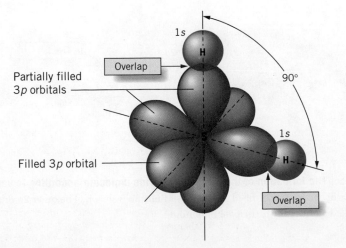

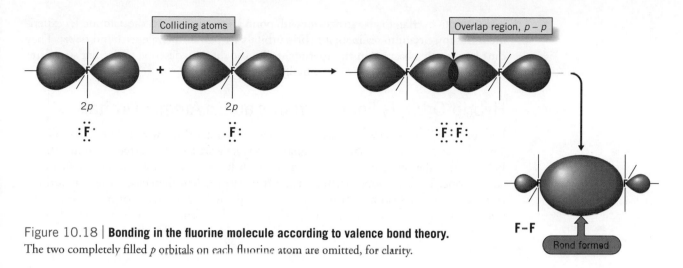

Figure 10.18 | **Bonding in the fluorine molecule according to valence bond theory.**
The two completely filled p orbitals on each fluorine atom are omitted, for clarity.

p orbital. Because p orbitals are oriented at 90° to each other, the H—S bonds are expected to be at this angle, too. Therefore, the predicted bond angle is 90°. This is very close to the actual bond angle of 92° found by experiment. Thus, the VB theory requirement for maximum overlap quite nicely explains the geometry of the hydrogen sulfide molecule. Also, notice that both the Lewis and VB descriptions of the formation of the H—S bonds account for the completion of the atoms' valence shells. Therefore, *a Lewis structure can be viewed, in a very qualitative sense, as a shorthand notation for the valence bond description of a molecule.*

Other kinds of orbital overlaps are also possible. For example, according to VB theory the bonding in the fluorine molecule, F_2, occurs by the overlap of two $2p$ orbitals, as shown in Figure 10.18. The formation of the other diatomic molecules of the halogens, all of which are held together by single bonds, could be similarly described.

Practice Exercises

10.9 | Use the principles of VB theory to explain the bonding in HCl. Give the orbital diagram for chlorine in the HCl molecule and indicate the orbital that shares the electron with one from hydrogen. Sketch the orbital overlap that gives rise to the H—Cl bond. (*Hint:* Remember that a half-filled orbital on each atom is required to form the covalent bond.)

10.10 | The phosphine molecule, PH_3, has a trigonal pyramidal shape with H—P—H bond angles equal to 93.7°, as shown in the margin. Give the orbital diagram for phosphorus in the PH_3 molecule and indicate the orbitals that share electrons with those from hydrogen. On a set of *xyz* coordinate axes, sketch the orbital overlaps that give rise to the P—H bonds.

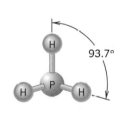

10.5 | Hybrid Orbitals and Molecular Geometry

There are many molecules for which the simple VB theory described in Section 10.4 fails to account for the correct shape. For example, there are no simple atomic orbitals that are oriented so they point toward the corners of a tetrahedron, yet there are many tetrahedral molecules. Therefore, to explain the bonds in molecules such as CH_4 we must study the way atomic orbitals *of the same atom* mix with each other to produce new orbitals, called **hybrid atomic orbitals.**[3] The new orbitals have new shapes and new directional properties,

---

[3]Mathematically, hybrid orbitals are formed by the addition and subtraction of the wave functions for the basic atomic orbitals. This process produces a new set of wave functions corresponding to the hybrid orbitals. The hybrid orbital wave functions describe the shape and directional properties of the hybrid orbitals.

and they can overlap to give structures with bond angles that match those found by experiment. It's important to realize that hybrid orbitals are part of the valence bond *theory*. They can't be directly observed in an experiment. We use them to describe molecular structures that have been determined experimentally.

Hybrid Orbitals Formed from *s* and *p* Atomic Orbitals

Let's begin by studying what happens when we mix a 2*s* orbital with a 2*p* orbital to form a new set of two orbitals that we designate as **sp hybrid orbitals,** illustrated in Figure 10.19. First, notice that each has the same shape; each has one large lobe and another much smaller one. The large lobe extends farther from the nucleus than either the *s* or *p* orbital from which the hybrid was formed. This allows the hybrid orbital to overlap more effectively with an orbital on another atom when a bond is formed. As a result, hybrid orbitals form stronger, more stable, bonds than would be possible if just simple atomic orbitals were used.

■ In general, the greater the overlap of two orbitals, the stronger is the bond. At a given distance between nuclei, the greater "reach" of a hybrid orbital gives better overlap than either an *s* or a *p* orbital.

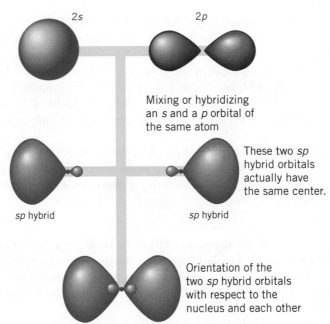

Figure 10.19 | Formation of *sp* hybrid orbitals.
Mixing of 2*s* and 2*p* atomic orbitals produces a pair of *sp* hybrid orbitals. The large lobes of these orbitals have their axes pointing in opposite directions.

Another point to notice in Figure 10.19 is that the large lobes of the two *sp* hybrid orbitals point in opposite directions; that is, they are 180° apart. If bonds are formed by the overlap of these hybrids with orbitals of other atoms, the other atoms will occupy positions on opposite sides of this central atom. Let's look at a specific example—the linear beryllium hydride molecule, BeH_2, as it would be formed in the gas phase.[4]

The orbital diagram for the valence shell of beryllium is

$$Be \quad \boxed{\uparrow\downarrow} \;\; \bigcirc\bigcirc\bigcirc$$
$$\qquad\quad 2s \qquad\; 2p$$

Notice that the 2*s* orbital is filled and the three 2*p* orbitals are empty. For bonds to form at a 180° angle between beryllium and the two hydrogen atoms, two conditions must be met: (1) the two orbitals that beryllium uses to form the Be—H bonds must point in opposite directions, and (2) each of the beryllium orbitals must contain only one electron. In satisfying these requirements, the electrons of the beryllium atom become unpaired and the resulting half-filled *s* and *p* atomic orbitals become hybridized.

---

[4]In the solid state, BeH_2 has a complex structure not consisting of simple BeH_2 molecules.

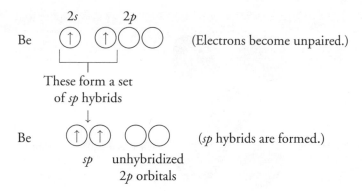

Be   2s   2p
       (↑) (↑)◯◯   (Electrons become unpaired.)

       These form a set
       of *sp* hybrids
           ↓

Be   (↑)(↑) ◯◯   (*sp* hybrids are formed.)
       sp   unhybridized
              2*p* orbitals

Now the 1*s* orbitals of the hydrogen atoms can overlap with the *sp* hybrids of beryllium to form the bonds, as shown in Figure 10.20. Because the two *sp* hybrid orbitals of beryllium are identical in shape and energy, the two Be—H bonds are alike except for the directions in which they point, and we say that the bonds are *equivalent*. Since the bonds point in opposite directions, the linear geometry of the molecule is also explained. The orbital diagram for beryllium in this molecule is

Be (in BeH₂)   (↑↓)(↑↓) ◯◯   (Colored arrows
               sp   unhybridized   are H electrons.)
                      2*p* orbitals

Even if we had not known the shape of the BeH₂ molecule, we could have obtained the same bonding picture by applying the VSEPR model first. The Lewis structure for BeH₂ is H:Be:H, with two bonding domains around the central atom, so the molecule is linear. Once the shape is known, we can apply the VB theory to explain the bonding in terms of orbital overlaps. Thus, the VB theory and VSEPR model complement each other well. The VSEPR model allows us to predict geometry in a simple way, and once the geometry is known, it is relatively easy to analyze the bonding in terms of VB theory.

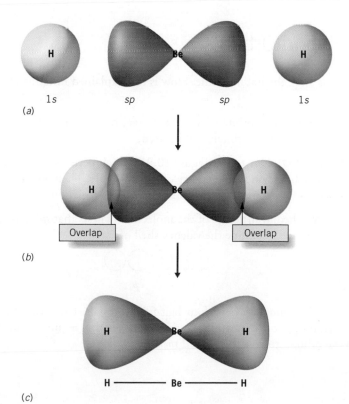

(a)   1*s*   *sp*   *sp*   1*s*

(b)   Overlap   Overlap

(c)   H —— Be —— H

Figure 10.20 | **Bonding in BeH₂ according to valence bond theory.** Only the larger lobe of each *sp* hybrid orbital is shown. (*a*) The two hydrogen 1*s* orbitals approach the pair of *sp* hybrid orbitals of beryllium. (*b*) Overlap of the hydrogen 1*s* orbitals with the *sp* hybrid orbitals. (*c*) A representation of the distribution of electron density in the two Be—H bonds after they have been formed.

Figure 10.21 | **Directional properties of hybrid orbitals formed from *s* and *p* atomic orbitals.** (*a*) *sp* hybrid orbitals oriented at 180° to each other. (*b*) *sp*² hybrid orbitals formed from an *s* orbital and two *p* orbitals. The angle between them is 120°. (*c*) *sp*³ hybrid orbitals formed from an *s* orbital and three *p* orbitals. The angle between any two of them is 109.5°.

Hybrid orbitals involving *s* and *p* atomic orbitals

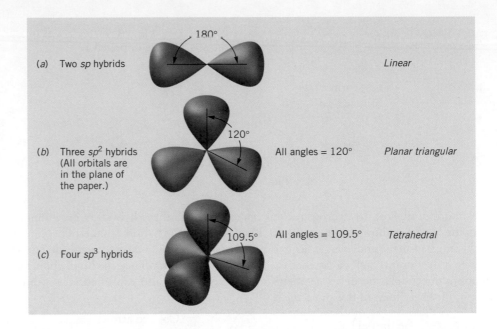

(*a*) Two *sp* hybrids — 180° — Linear

(*b*) Three *sp*² hybrids (All orbitals are in the plane of the paper.) — 120° — All angles = 120° — Planar triangular

(*c*) Four *sp*³ hybrids — 109.5° — All angles = 109.5° — Tetrahedral

In addition to *sp* hybrids, atomic *s* and *p* orbitals form two other kinds of hybrid orbitals. These are shown in Figure 10.21. In identifying hybrid orbitals, we specify which kinds of pure atomic orbitals, as well as the number of each, that are mixed to form the hybrids. Thus, hybrid orbitals labeled **sp³** are formed by blending one *s* orbital and three *p* orbitals. *The total number of hybrid orbitals in a set is equal to the number of basic atomic orbitals used to form them.* Therefore, a set of *sp*³ hybrids consists of four orbitals, whereas a set of **sp²** orbitals consists of three orbitals.

Example 10.7
Explaining Bonding with Hybrid Orbitals

Methane, CH_4, is a tetrahedral molecule. How is this explained in terms of valence bond theory?

■**Analysis:** No pure atomic orbitals have the correct orientations to form a tetrahedral molecule, so we expect hybrid orbitals will be used.

■**Assembling the Tools:** Our tool is Figure 10.21, which permits us to select which hybrids are appropriate based on the geometry of the molecule. Then we can use the orbital diagram of carbon to follow the changes leading to bond formation.

■**Solution:** The tetrahedral structure of the molecule suggests that *sp*³ hybrid orbitals are involved in bonding. Let's examine the valence shell of carbon.

C   (↑↓) (↑)(↑)( )
    2*s*   2*p*

To form four C—H bonds, we need four half-filled orbitals. Unpairing the electrons in the 2*s* and moving one to the vacant 2*p* orbital satisfies this requirement. Then we can hybridize all the orbitals to give the desired *sp*³ set.

C   2s   2p
(↑) (↑)(↑)(↑)   (Electrons become unpaired.)

These become hybridized.

↓

C   (↑)(↑)(↑)(↑)

sp^3 hybrids

Then we form the four bonds to hydrogen 1s orbitals.

C (in CH_4)   (↑↓)(↑↓)(↑↓)(↑↓)   (Colored arrows are H electrons.)

sp^3

This is illustrated in Figure 10.22.

■ **Is the Answer Reasonable?** The positions of the hydrogen atoms around the carbon give the correct tetrahedral shape for the molecule. The Lewis structure for CH_4 shows four bonding domains around the carbon atom, which is consistent with the idea of four sp^3 orbitals overlapping with hydrogen 1s orbitals to form four bonds.

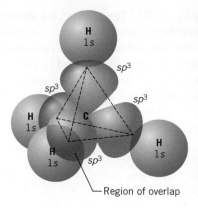

Figure 10.22 | **Formation of the bonds in methane.** Each bond results from the overlap of a hydrogen 1s orbital with an sp^3 hybrid orbital on the carbon atom.

10.11 | The BF_3 molecule has a planar triangular shape. What kind of hybrid orbitals does boron use in this molecule? Use orbital diagrams to explain how the bonds are formed. (*Hint:* Which kind of hybrid orbitals are oriented correctly to give this molecular shape?)

10.12 | In the gas phase, beryllium fluoride exists as linear molecules. Which kind of hybrid orbitals does Be use in this compound? Use orbital diagrams to explain how the bonds are formed.

Practice Exercises

In methane, carbon forms four single bonds with hydrogen atoms by using sp^3 hybrid orbitals. In fact, carbon uses these same kinds of orbitals in all of its compounds in which it is bonded to four other atoms by single bonds. This makes the tetrahedral orientation of atoms around carbon one of the primary structural features of organic compounds, and organic chemists routinely think in terms of "tetrahedral carbon."

In the alkane series of hydrocarbons (compounds with the general formula $C_nH_{(2n + 2)}$, page 92), carbon atoms are bonded to other carbon atoms. An example is ethane, C_2H_6.

$$
\begin{array}{ccc}
& H \quad H & \\
& | \quad\; | & \\
H- & C - C & -H \\
& | \quad\; | & \\
& H \quad H &
\end{array}
$$

In this molecule, the carbons are bonded together by the overlap of sp^3 hybrid orbitals (Figure 10.23). One of the most important characteristics of this bond is that the overlap of the orbitals in the C—C bond is hardly affected at all if one portion of the molecule rotates relative to the other around the bond axis. Such rotation, therefore, is said to occur freely and permits different possible relative orientations of the atoms in the molecule. These different relative orientations are called **conformations**. With complex molecules, the number of possible conformations is enormous. For example, Figure 10.24 illustrates three of the large number of possible conformations of the pentane molecule, C_5H_{12}, one of the low-molecular-weight organic compounds in gasoline.

Figure 10.23 | **The bonds in the ethane molecule**. (*a*) Overlap of orbitals. (*b*) The degree of overlap of the sp^3 orbitals in the carbon–carbon bond is not appreciably affected by the rotation of the two CH_3— groups relative to each other around the bond.

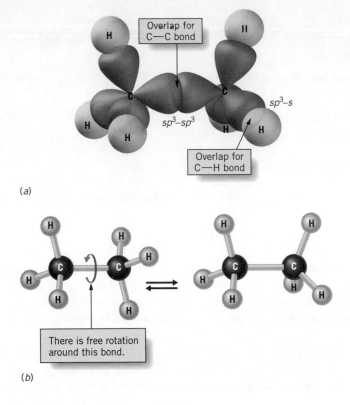

(*a*)

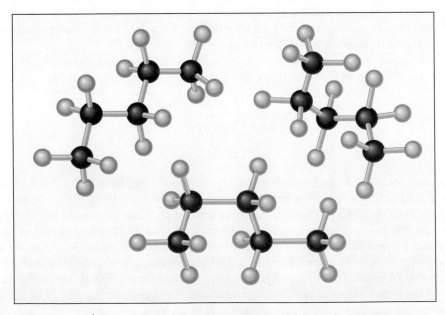

(*b*)

Using the VSEPR Model to Predict Hybridization

TOOLS

VSEPR model and hybridization

We've seen that if we know the structure of a molecule, we can make a reasonable guess as to the kind of hybrid orbitals that the central atom uses to form its bonds. Because the VSEPR model works so well in predicting geometry, we can use it to help us obtain VB descriptions of bonding. This is illustrated in the following example.

Figure 10.24 | **Three of the many conformations of the atoms in the pentane molecule, C_5H_{12}.** Free rotation around single bonds makes these different conformations possible.

Example 10.8
Using the VSEPR Model to Predict Hybridization

Predict the shape of the boron trichloride molecule and describe the bonding in the molecule in terms of valence bond theory.

■**Analysis:** This problem is similar to Example 10.7, except we're not given the shape of the molecule, which we need to select the kind of hybrid orbitals used by the central atom. The rules of nomenclature tell us the chemical formula is BCl_3. Based on the formula, we will write a Lewis structure for the molecule. This will permit us to determine its geometry by applying VSEPR theory. From the shape of the molecule, we can select the kind of hybrid orbitals used by the central atom and then use orbital diagrams to describe the bonding.

■**Assembling the Tools:** Our tools will include the method for constructing Lewis structures and the VSEPR model. On the basis of the geometry predicted by the VSEPR model, we can select the appropriate hybrid orbitals from Figure 10.21.

■**Solution:** Keeping in mind that boron is an element that is permitted to have less than an octet in its valence shell and following the procedure described in Chapter 9, the Lewis structure for BCl_3 is

$$\ddot{:}\overset{\displaystyle :\ddot{Cl}:}{\underset{\displaystyle}{}}$$

$$:\ddot{Cl}-B-\ddot{Cl}:$$

The VSEPR model tells us the molecule should be planar triangular, and referring to Figure 10.21, we find that the hybrid set that fits this structure is sp^2.

B (↑↓) (↑)( )( )
    $2s$ $2p$

To form the three bonds to chlorine, boron needs three half-filled orbitals. These can be obtained by unpairing the electrons in the $2s$ orbital and placing one of them in the $2p$. Then the $2s$ orbital and two of the $2p$ orbitals can be combined to give the set of three sp^2 hybrids.

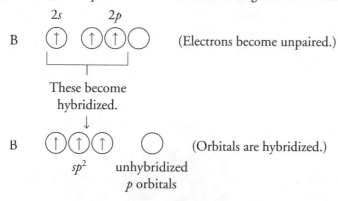

B $2s$ $2p$
    (↑) (↑)(↑)( )   (Electrons become unpaired.)

These become
hybridized.
↓

B   (↑)(↑)(↑) ( )   (Orbitals are hybridized.)
    sp^2 unhybridized
             p orbitals

Now let's look at the valence shell of chlorine.

Cl   (↑↓) (↑↓)(↑↓)(↓)
     $3s$ $3p$

The half-filled $3p$ orbital of each chlorine atom can overlap with a hybrid sp^2 orbital of boron to give three B—Cl bonds.

B (in BCl_3)   (↑↓)(↑↓)(↑↓) ( )   (Colored arrows are Cl electrons.)
                 sp^2 unhybridized
                          p orbital

Figure 10.25 illustrates the overlap of the orbitals to give the bonding in the molecule.

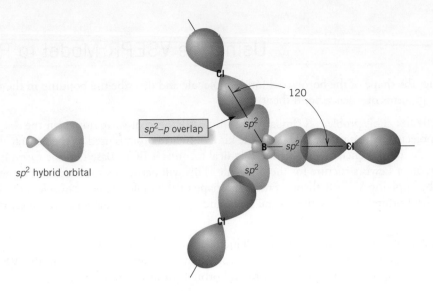

Figure 10.25 | **Description of the bonding in BCl₃.** Each B—Cl bond is formed by the overlap of a half-filled 3*p* orbital of a Cl atom with one of the *sp²* hybrid orbitals of boron. (For simplicity, only the half-filled 3*p* orbital of each Cl atom is shown.)

■ **Is the Answer Reasonable?** Notice that the arrangement of atoms yields a planar triangular molecule, in agreement with the structure predicted by the VSEPR model. This internal consistency is convincing evidence that we've answered the question correctly.

Practice Exercise

10.13 | What kind of hybrid orbitals are expected to be used by the central atom in SiH₄? Use orbital diagrams to describe the bonding in the molecule.

Hybrid Orbitals Formed from *s*, *p*, and *d* Orbitals

TOOLS

VSEPR theory and hybrid orbitals involving *s*, *p*, and *d* atomic orbitals

Earlier we saw that certain molecules have atoms that must violate the octet rule because they form more than four bonds. In these cases, the atom must reach beyond its *s* and *p* valence shell orbitals to form sufficient half-filled orbitals for bonding. This is because the *s* and *p* orbitals can be mixed to form a maximum of only four hybrid orbitals. When five or more hybrid orbitals are needed, *d* orbitals are brought into the mix. The two most common kinds of hybrid orbitals involving *d* orbitals are **sp³d** and **sp³d² hybrid orbitals.** Their directional properties are illustrated in Figure 10.26. Notice that the *sp³d* hybrids point toward the corners of a trigonal bipyramid and the *sp³d²* hybrids point toward the corners of an octahedron.

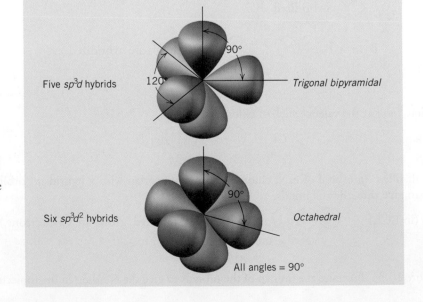

Figure 10.26 | **Orientations of hybrid orbitals that involve *d* orbitals.** (*a*) *sp³d* hybrid orbitals formed from an *s* orbital, three *p* orbitals, and a *d* orbital. The orbitals point toward the vertices of a trigonal bipyramid. (*b*) *sp³d²* hybrid orbitals formed from an *s* orbital, three *p* orbitals, and two *d* orbitals. The orbitals point toward the vertices of an octahedron.

Example 10.9
Explaining Bonding with Hybrid Orbitals

Predict the shape of the sulfur hexafluoride molecule and describe the bonding in the molecule in terms of valence bond theory.

■ **Analysis:** The rules of nomenclature tell us the chemical formula is SF_6. Based on the formula, we will write a Lewis structure for the molecule. This will permit us to determine its geometry. From the shape of the molecule, we can select the kind of hybrid orbitals used by the central atom and then use orbital diagrams to describe the bonding.

■ **Assembling the Tools:** Our tools will include the method for constructing Lewis structures and the VSEPR model. On the basis of the geometry predicted by the VSEPR model, we would then select the appropriate hybrid orbitals from Figures 10.21 or 10.26. However, the formula SF_6 tells us that we have more than four bonds in the molecules, so we can anticipate using Figure 10.26.

■ **Solution:** Following the procedure discussed earlier, the Lewis structure for SF_6 is

$$
\begin{array}{ccc}
 & :\!\ddot{F}\!: & \\
:\!\ddot{F} & | & \ddot{F}\!: \\
 & \diagdown\!S\!\diagup & \\
:\!\ddot{F} & | & \ddot{F}\!: \\
 & :\!\ddot{F}\!: &
\end{array}
$$

The VSEPR model tells us the molecule should be octahedral, and referring to Figure 10.26, we find that the hybrid set that fits this structure is sp^3d^2.

Now let's examine the valence shell of sulfur.

$$S \quad \boxed{\uparrow\downarrow} \; \boxed{\uparrow\downarrow}\boxed{\uparrow}\boxed{\uparrow}$$
$$\quad\quad 3s \quad\quad\quad 3p$$

To form six bonds to fluorine atoms we need six half-filled orbitals, but we show only four orbitals altogether. However, sp^3d^2 orbitals tell us we need to look for *d* orbitals to include in the set of hybrids.

An isolated sulfur atom has electrons only in its 3*s* and 3*p* subshells, so these are the only subshells we usually show in the orbital diagram. But the third shell also has a *d* subshell, which is empty in a sulfur atom. Therefore, let's rewrite the orbital diagram to show the vacant 3*d* subshell.

$$S \quad \boxed{\uparrow\downarrow} \; \boxed{\uparrow\downarrow}\boxed{\uparrow}\boxed{\uparrow} \; \bigcirc\bigcirc\bigcirc\bigcirc\bigcirc$$
$$\quad\quad 3s \quad\quad\quad 3p \quad\quad\quad\quad 3d$$

Unpairing all of the electrons to give six half-filled orbitals, followed by hybridization, gives the required set of half-filled sp^3d^2 orbitals (Figure 10.27).

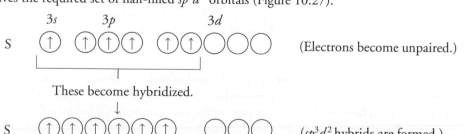
(Electrons become unpaired.)

These become hybridized.

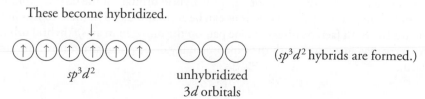
(sp^3d^2 hybrids are formed.)

■ Sulfur is able to exceed an octet because of the availability of *d* orbitals in its valence shell.

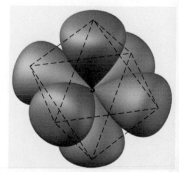

Figure 10.27 | **The sp^3d^2 hybrid orbitals of sulfur in SF₆.**

Finally, the six S—F bonds are formed by overlap of the half-filled $2p$ orbitals of the fluorine atoms with these half-filled sp^3d^2 hybrids.

S (in SF$_6$)   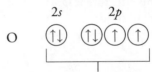   (Colored arrows are F electrons.)

sp^3d^2 unhybridized 3d orbitals

■ **Is the Answer Reasonable?** Once again, the fact that all the parts fit together so well to account for the structure of SF$_6$ makes us feel that our explanation of the bonding is reasonable.

Practice Exercises

10.14 | What kind of hybrid orbitals are expected to be used by the central atom in PCl$_5$? (*Hint:* Which hybrid orbitals have the same geometry as the molecule?)

10.15 | Use the VSEPR model to predict the shape of the AsCl$_5$ molecule and then describe the bonding in the molecules using valence bond theory.

Molecules with Nonbonding Domains

Methane is a tetrahedral molecule with sp^3 hybridization of the orbitals of carbon and H—C—H bond angles that are each equal to 109.5°. In ammonia, NH$_3$, the H—N—H bond angles are 107°, and in water the H—O—H bond angle is 104.5°. Both NH$_3$ and H$_2$O have H—X—H bond angles that are close to the bond angles expected for a molecule whose central atom has sp^3 hybrids. The use of sp^3 hybrids by oxygen and nitrogen, therefore, is often used to explain the geometry of H$_2$O and NH$_3$.

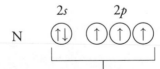

O

Hybridization and bond formation occur.

O (in H$_2$O)   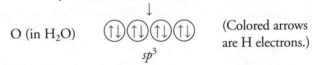   (Colored arrows are H electrons.)

sp^3

N

Hybridization and bond formation occur.

N (in NH$_3$)   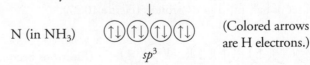   (Colored arrows are H electrons.)

sp^3

According to these descriptions, not all of the hybrid orbitals of the central atom must be used for bonding. Lone pairs of electrons can be accommodated in them too, as illustrated in Figure 10.28. In fact, putting the lone pair on the nitrogen in an sp^3 hybrid orbital gives a geometry that agrees well with the experimentally determined structure of the ammonia molecule.

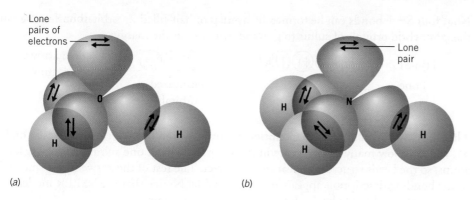

Lone pairs of electrons

Lone pair

(a)   (b)

Figure 10.28 | **Hybrid orbitals can hold lone pairs of electrons.** (*a*) In water, two lone pairs on oxygen are held in sp^3 hybrid orbitals. (*b*) Ammonia has one lone pair in an sp^3 hybrid orbital.

Example 10.10
Explaining Bonding with Hybrid Orbitals

Use valence bond theory to explain the bonding in the SF_4 molecule.

■**Analysis:** In solving this problem we will follow the same steps as in Example 10.9: (1) Draw the Lewis structure, (2) predict the geometry of the molecule, (3) select the hybrid orbital set that fits the structure, and (4) construct orbital diagrams to explain the bonding.

■**Assembling the Tools:** Our tools are the same as before. We apply our method for drawing Lewis structures from Chapter 9. We apply the VSEPR theory. We use Figures 10.21 or 10.26 to select the hybrid orbital set.

■**Solution:** We begin by constructing the Lewis structure for the molecule.

$$
\begin{array}{c}
\ddot{\mathrm{F}}\mathbin{:}\\
|\\
\mathbin{:}\ddot{\mathrm{F}}\!\!-\!\!\underset{\displaystyle\cdot\cdot}{\mathrm{S}}\!\!-\!\!\ddot{\mathrm{F}}\mathbin{:}\\
|\\
\mathbin{:}\ddot{\mathrm{F}}\mathbin{:}
\end{array}
$$

The VSEPR model predicts that the electron pairs around the sulfur should be in a trigonal bipyramidal arrangement, and the only hybrid set that fits this geometry is sp^3d (according to Figure 10.26). To see how the hybrid orbitals are formed, we look at the valence shell of sulfur, including the vacant $3d$ subshell.

S   (↑↓) (↑↓)(↑)(↑) ○○○○○
    $3s$ $3p$ $3d$

To form the four bonds to fluorine atoms, we need four half-filled orbitals, so we unpair the electrons in one of the filled orbitals. This gives

        $3s$ $3p$ $3d$
S   (↑↓) (↑)(↑)(↑) (↑)○○○○

Next, we form the hybrid orbitals. In doing this, we use all the valence shell orbitals that have electrons in them.

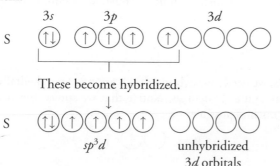

        $3s$ $3p$ $3d$
S   (↑↓) (↑)(↑)(↑) (↑)○○○○

These become hybridized.
↓

S   (↑↓)(↑)(↑)(↑)(↑) ○○○○
        sp^3d unhybridized
                       $3d$ orbitals

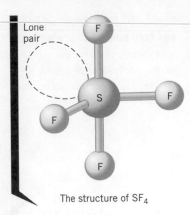

Lone pair

The structure of SF$_4$

Now, four S—F bonds can be formed by overlap of half-filled $2p$ orbitals of fluorine with the sp^3d hybrid orbitals of sulfur to give the structure in the margin.

S (in SF$_4$)   (Colored arrows are F electrons.)

Lone pair ⎯⎯⎯↑ sp^3d unhybridized $3d$ orbitals

■ **Is the Answer Reasonable?** Counting electrons in the Lewis structure gives a total of 34, which is how many electrons are in the valence shells of one sulfur and four chlorine atoms, so the Lewis structure appears to be correct. The rest of the answer flows smoothly, so the bonding description appears to be reasonable. Notice that the VSEPR model even shows us which of the hybrid orbitals contains the lone pair.

Practice Exercises

10.16 | What kind of orbitals are used by Xe in the XeF$_4$ molecule? (*Hint:* An Xe atom has 8 valence electrons.)

10.17 | What kind of hybrid orbitals would we expect the central atom to use for bonding in (a) PCl$_3$ and (b) BrCl$_3$?

Formation of Coordinate Covalent Bonds

In Section 9.8 we defined a coordinate covalent bond as one in which both of the shared electrons are provided by just one of the joined atoms. Such a bond is formed when boron trifluoride, BF$_3$, combines with an additional fluoride ion to form the tetrafluoroborate ion, BF$_4^-$.

$$BF_3 + F^- \longrightarrow BF_4^-$$

tetrafluoroborate ion

We can diagram this reaction as follows:

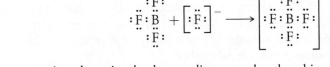

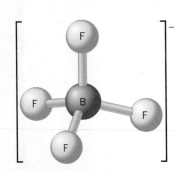

Figure 10.29 | **The tetrahedral structure of the BF$_4^-$ ion.**

As we mentioned previously, the coordinate covalent bond is really no different from any other covalent bond once it has formed. The distinction is made *only* for bookkeeping purposes. One place where such bookkeeping is useful is in keeping track of the orbitals and electrons used when atoms bond together.

The VB theory requirements for bond formation—two overlapping orbitals sharing two paired electrons—can be satisfied in two ways. One, as we have already seen, is by the overlapping of two half-filled orbitals. This gives an "ordinary" covalent bond. The other is by overlapping one filled orbital with one empty orbital. The atom with the filled orbital donates the shared pair of electrons, and a coordinate covalent bond is formed.

The structure of the BF$_4^-$ ion, which the VSEPR model predicts to be tetrahedral (Figure 10.29), can be explained as follows. First, we examine the orbital diagram for boron.

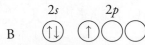

$2s$ $2p$

B

To form four bonds, we need four hybrid orbitals arranged tetrahedrally around the boron, so we expect boron to use sp^3 hybrids. Notice that we spread the electrons out over the hybrid orbitals as much as possible.

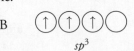

B

sp^3

Boron forms three ordinary covalent bonds with fluorine atoms plus one coordinate covalent bond with a fluoride ion.

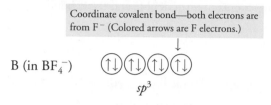

Coordinate covalent bond—both electrons are from F$^-$ (Colored arrows are F electrons.)

B (in BF$_4^-$)

sp^3

Practice Exercises

10.18 | If we assume that nitrogen uses sp^3 hybrid orbitals in NH$_3$, use valence bond theory to account for the formation of NH$_4^+$ from NH$_3$ and H$^+$. (*Hint:* Which atom donates the pair of electrons in the formation of the bond between H$^+$ and NH$_3$?)

10.19 | What is the shape of the PCl$_6^-$ ion? What hybrid orbitals are used by phosphorus in PCl$_6^-$? Draw the orbital diagram for phosphorus in PCl$_6^-$.

10.6 | Hybrid Orbitals and Multiple Bonds

The types of orbital overlap that we have described so far produce bonds in which the electron density is concentrated most heavily between the nuclei of the two atoms along an imaginary line that joins their centers. Any bond of this kind, whether formed from the overlap of *s* orbitals, *p* orbitals, or hybrid orbitals (Figure 10.30), is called a **sigma bond** (or *σ* **bond**).

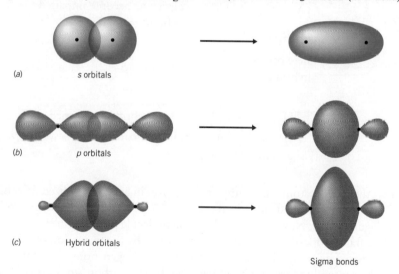

(a) *s* orbitals

(b) *p* orbitals

(c) Hybrid orbitals

Sigma bonds

Figure 10.30 | Formation of *σ* bonds. Sigma bonds concentrate electron density along the line between the two atoms joined by the bond. (*a*) From the overlap of *s* orbitals. (*b*) From the end-to-end overlap of *p* orbitals. (*c*) From the overlap of hybrid orbitals.

Another way that *p* orbitals can overlap is shown in Figure 10.31. This produces a bond in which the electron density is divided between two separate regions that lie on opposite sides of an imaginary line joining the two nuclei. This kind of bond is called a **pi bond**

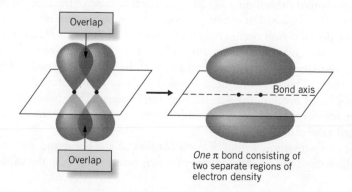

Overlap

Overlap

Bond axis

One π bond consisting of two separate regions of electron density

Figure 10.31 | Formation of a *π* bond. Two *p* orbitals overlap sideways instead of end-to-end. The electron density is concentrated in two regions on opposite sides of the bond axis, and taken together they constitute one *π* bond.

(or π **bond**). Notice that a π bond, like a p orbital, consists of two parts, and each part makes up just half of the π bond; it takes both of them to equal one π bond. The formation of π bonds allows atoms to form double and triple bonds.

Double Bonds

A hydrocarbon that contains a double bond is ethene (also called ethylene), C_2H_4. It has the Lewis structure

H   H

C=C

H   H

ethene
(ethylene)

The molecule is planar, and each carbon atom lies in the center of a triangle surrounded by three other atoms (two H and one C atom). A planar triangular arrangement of bonds suggests that carbon uses sp^2 hybrid orbitals. Therefore, let's look at the distribution of electrons among the orbitals that carbon has available in its valence shell, assuming sp^2 hybridization.

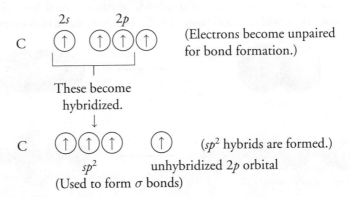

Notice that the carbon atom has an unpaired electron in an unhybridized $2p$ orbital. This p orbital is oriented perpendicular to the triangular plane of the sp^2 hybrid orbitals, as shown in Figure 10.32. Now we can see how the molecule goes together.

The basic framework of the molecule is determined by the formation of σ bonds. Each carbon uses two of its sp^2 hybrids to form σ bonds to hydrogen atoms. The third sp^2 hybrid on each carbon is used to form a σ bond between the two carbon atoms, thereby accounting for one of the two bonds of the double bond. Finally, the remaining unhybridized $2p$ orbitals, one from each carbon atom, overlap to produce a π bond, which accounts for the second bond of the double bond.

This description of the bonding in C_2H_4 accounts for one of the most important properties of double bonds: rotation of one portion of the molecule relative to the rest around the axis of the double bond occurs only with great difficulty. The reason for this is illustrated in Figure 10.33. We see that as one CH_2 group rotates relative to the other around the carbon–carbon bond, the unhybridized p orbitals become misaligned and can no longer overlap effectively. This destroys the π bond. In effect, then, rotation around a double bond involves bond breaking, which requires more energy than is normally available to molecules at room temperature. As a result, rotation around the axis of a double bond usually doesn't take place.

In almost every instance, a double bond consists of a σ bond and a π bond. Another example is the compound methanal (better known as formaldehyde, the substance used as

■ The double bond is a little like a hot dog on a bun. The sigma bond is like the hot dog, and the π bond is like the two parts of the bun.

■ Restricted rotation around double bonds affects the properties of organic and biochemical molecules.

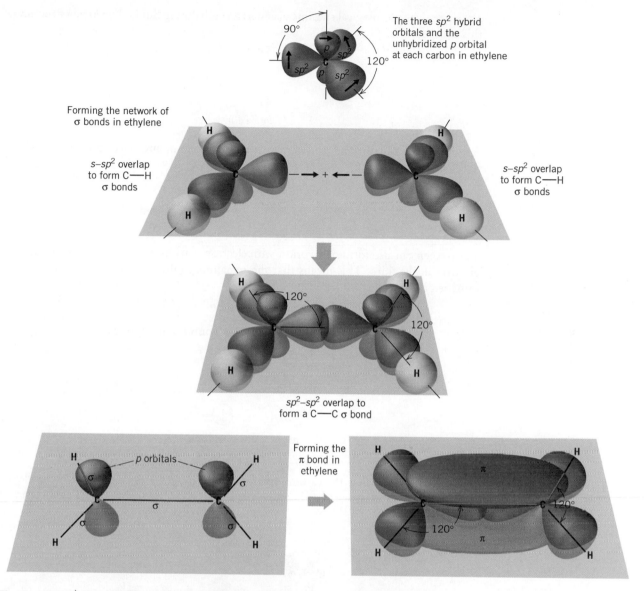

Figure 10.32 | **The carbon–carbon double bond.**

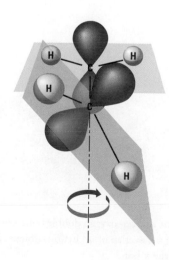

Figure 10.33 | **Restricted rotation around a double bond.** As the CH_2 group closest to us rotates relative to the one at the rear, the unhybridized p orbitals become misaligned, as shown here. This destroys the overlap and breaks the π bond. Bond breaking requires a lot of energy, more than is available to the molecule through the normal bending and stretching of its bonds at room temperature. Because of this, rotation around the double bond axis is hindered or "restricted."

a preservative for biological specimens and as an embalming fluid). The Lewis structure of this compound is

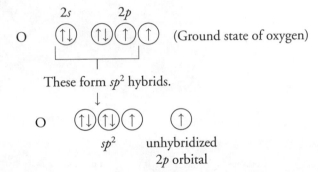

formaldehyde

As with ethene, the carbon forms sp^2 hybrids, leaving an unpaired electron in an unhybridized p orbital.

C ⟳⟳⟳   ⟳
  sp^2 unhybridized
         $2p$ orbital

The oxygen can also form sp^2 hybrids, with electron pairs in two of them and an unpaired electron in the third. This means that the remaining unhybridized p orbital also has an unpaired electron.

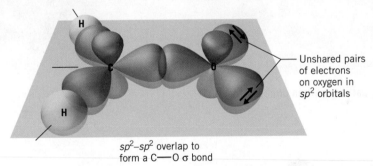

O ⟳⟳ ⟳⟳⟳⟳   (Ground state of oxygen)

These form sp^2 hybrids.
↓

O ⟳⟳⟳⟳⟳   ⟳
  sp^2 unhybridized
         $2p$ orbital

■ The two filled sp^2 hybrids on the oxygen become lone pairs on the oxygen atom in the molecule.

Figure 10.34 shows how the carbon, hydrogen, and oxygen atoms form the molecule. As before, the basic framework of the molecule is formed by the σ bonds. These determine

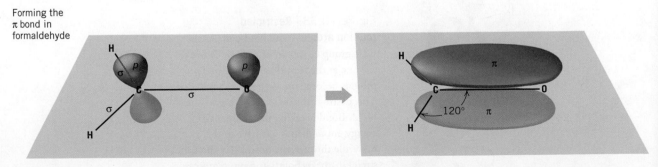

Formaldehyde

Unshared pairs
of electrons
on oxygen in
sp^2 orbitals

sp^2–sp^2 overlap to
form a C—O σ bond

Forming the
π bond in
formaldehyde

Figure 10.34 | **Bonding in formaldehyde.** The carbon–oxygen double bond consists of a σ bond and a π bond. The σ bond is formed by the overlap of sp^2 hybrid orbitals. The overlap of unhybridized p orbitals on the two atoms gives the π bond.

the molecular shape. The carbon–oxygen double bond also contains a π bond formed by the overlap of the unhybridized p orbitals.

Triple Bonds

An example of a molecule containing a triple bond is ethyne, also known as acetylene, C_2H_2 (a gas used as a fuel for welding torches).

$$H-C\equiv C-H$$
ethyne
(acetylene)

In the linear ethyne molecule, each carbon needs two hybrid orbitals to form two σ bonds—one to a hydrogen atom and one to the other carbon atom. These can be provided by mixing the $2s$ and one of the $2p$ orbitals to form sp hybrids. To help us visualize the bonding, we will imagine that there is an xyz coordinate system centered at each carbon atom and that it is the $2p_z$ orbital that becomes mixed in the hybrid orbitals.

■ We label the orbitals p_x, p_y, and p_z just for convenience; they are really all equivalent.

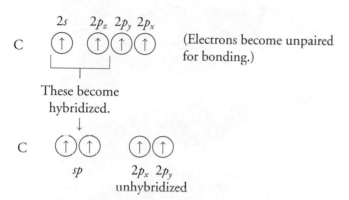

Figure 10.35 shows how the bonds in the molecule are formed. The sp orbitals point in opposite directions and are used to form the σ bonds. The unhybridized $2p_x$ and $2p_y$ orbitals are perpendicular to the C—C bond axis and overlap sideways to form two separate π bonds that surround the C—C σ bond. Notice that we now have three pairs of electrons in three bonds—one σ bond and two π bonds—whose electron densities are concentrated in different places. Also notice that the use of sp hybrid orbitals for the σ bonds allows us to explain the linear arrangement of atoms in the molecule.

Similar descriptions can be used to explain the bonding in other molecules that have triple bonds. Figure 10.36, for example, shows how the nitrogen molecule, N_2, is formed. In it, too, the triple bond is composed of one σ bond and two π bonds.

Sigma Bonds and Molecular Structure

In the preceding discussions we examined several polyatomic molecules that contain both single and multiple bonds. The following observations will be helpful in applying the valence bond theory to a variety of similar molecules.

A Brief Summary
1. The basic molecular framework of a molecule is determined by the arrangement of its σ bonds.
2. Hybrid orbitals are used by an atom to form its σ bonds and to hold lone pairs of electrons.
3. The number of hybrid orbitals needed by an atom in a structure equals the number of atoms to which it is bonded *plus* the number of lone pairs of electrons in its valence shell.
4. When there is a double bond in a molecule, it consists of one σ bond and one π bond.
5. When there is a triple bond in a molecule, it consists of one σ bond and two π bonds.

σ and π bonds and hybridization

Figure 10.35 | The carbon–carbon triple bond in ethyne. (*a*) The *sp* hybrid orbitals on the carbon atoms are used to form sigma bonds to the hydrogen atoms and to each other. This accounts for one of the three bonds between the carbon atoms.
(*b*) Sideways overlap of unhybridized $2p_x$ and $2p_y$ orbitals of the carbon atoms produces two π bonds.
(*c*) The two π bonds in acetylene after they've formed surround the σ bond.

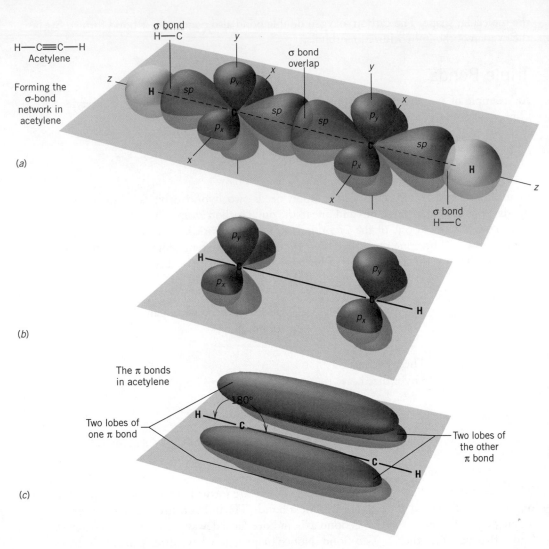

Practice Exercises

10.20 | Consider the molecule below. What kind of hybrid orbitals are used by atoms 1, 2, and 3? How many sigma bonds and pi bonds are in the molecule? (*Hint:* Study the brief summary above.)

10.21 | Consider the molecule below. What kind of hybrid orbitals are used by atoms 1, 2, and 3? How many σ bonds and π bonds are in the molecule?

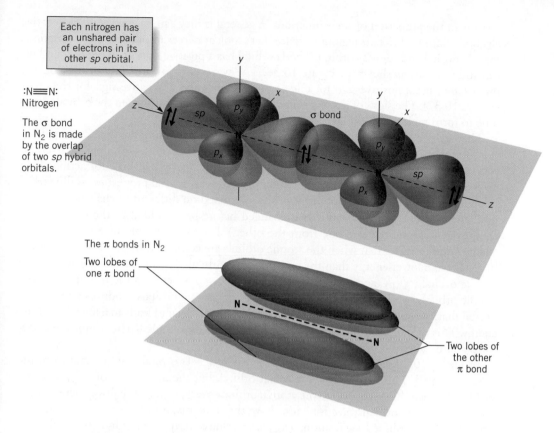

Each nitrogen has an unshared pair of electrons in its other *sp* orbital.

:N≡N:
Nitrogen

The σ bond in N_2 is made by the overlap of two *sp* hybrid orbitals.

The π bonds in N_2

Two lobes of one π bond

Two lobes of the other π bond

Figure 10.36 | Bonding in molecular nitrogen. The triple bond in nitrogen, N_2, is formed like the triple bond in ethyne. A sigma bond is formed by the overlap of *sp* hybrid orbitals. The two unhybridized *2p* orbitals on each nitrogen atom overlap to give the two π bonds. On each nitrogen, there is a lone pair of electrons in the *sp* hybrid orbital that's not used to form the sigma bond.

10.7 | Molecular Orbital Theory Basics

Molecular orbital theory takes the view that molecules and atoms are alike in one important respect. Both have energy levels that correspond to various orbitals that can be populated by electrons. In atoms, these orbitals are called atomic orbitals; in molecules, they are called **molecular orbitals.** (We shall frequently call them MOs.)

In most cases, the actual shapes and energies of molecular orbitals cannot be determined exactly. Nevertheless, reasonably good estimates of their shapes and energies can be obtained by combining the electron waves corresponding to the atomic orbitals of the atoms that make up the molecule. In forming molecular orbitals, these waves interact by constructive and destructive interference just like other waves we've seen. Their intensities are either added or subtracted when the atomic orbitals overlap.

Formation of Molecular Orbitals from Atomic Orbitals

In Chapter 8 you learned that an atomic orbital is represented mathematically by a wave function, ψ, and that the square of the wave function, ψ^2, describes the distribution of electron density around the nucleus. In MO theory, molecular orbitals are also represented by wave functions, ψ_{MO}, that when squared describe the distribution of electron density around the entire set of nuclei that make up the molecule.

■ When the wave function is squared, it allows us to calculate the probability of finding the electron at different points in an atom or molecule. By squaring the wave function, a positive probability is obtained regardless of the algebraic sign of the original function.

■ The number of MOs formed is always equal to the number of atomic orbitals that are combined.

1s orbital   2p orbital

Figure 10.37 | **Algebraic signs of the wave functions for 1s and 2p atomic orbitals.** The wave function for a 1s orbital is positive everywhere. The wave funcion for a 2p orbital is positive for one lobe and negative for the other.

One of the properties of wave functions in general is they can have positive or negative algebraic signs in different regions of space. Let's look at two examples: the wave functions for a 1s orbital and for a 2p orbital. The 1s orbital has a positive sign in all regions, and we can indicate this as shown in Figure 10.37. The wave function for a 2p orbital, on the other hand, has a positive sign for one of its two lobes and a negative sign for the other (Figure 10.37). The signs of the wave functions become important when the orbitals combine to form molecular orbitals.

Theoreticians have found that they can obtain reasonable estimates of MO wave functions by mathematically adding and subtracting the wave functions for a pair of overlapping atomic orbitals. Adding the atomic orbitals gives one ψ_{MO}, and subtracting them gives another ψ_{MO}. This gives *two* molecular orbitals with special properties, as illustrated in Figure 10.38 for two overlapping 1s orbitals centered on different nuclei. (For subtraction, the sign of one of the orbitals is changed before being added to the other, which is equivalent to subtracting one from the other.) The vertical scale in Figure 10.38 is energy and illustrates that when the atomic orbitals are combined by addition, the resulting MO has a lower energy than the two 1s atomic orbitals. This is because by adding the atomic orbitals, ψ_{MO} (and ψ_{MO}^2) becomes large in regions between the nuclei where the atomic orbitals overlap. Stated another way, adding atomic orbitals produces a molecular orbital that concentrates electron density between the nuclei and leads to a lowering of the energy. This type of molecular orbital helps to stabilize a molecule when occupied by electrons and is called a **bonding molecular orbital**.

In Figure 10.38 we also see what happens when one 1s orbital is subtracted from the other 1s orbital. This also yields a molecular orbital, but the magnitude of ψ_{MO} becomes smaller between the nuclei where the atomic orbitals overlap. In fact, halfway between the nuclei the atomic orbital wave functions have the same magnitude but opposite sign, so when they are combined the resulting ψ_{MO} has a value of zero. As a result, between the two nuclei there is a nodal plane on which ψ_{MO} is equal to zero. On this plane ψ_{MO}^2 is zero and the electron density drops to zero. Notice that this MO, which is called an **antibonding molecular orbital**, has a higher energy than either of the two 1s atomic orbitals. This is because the electron density is reduced between the nuclei, causing the internuclear repulsions to outweigh their attractions for the electron density that remains between the nuclei. Antibonding molecular orbitals tend to destabilize a molecule when occupied by electrons.

Another thing to notice in Figure 10.38 is that both MOs have their maximum electron density on an imaginary line that passes through the two nuclei, giving them properties of sigma bonds. MOs like this are also designated as sigma (σ), with a subscript showing which atomic orbitals make up the MO and an asterisk indicating which is anti-

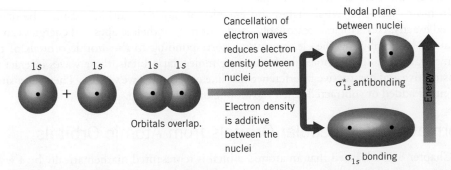

Figure 10.38 | **Combining 1s atomic orbitals to produce bonding and antibonding molecular orbitals.** These are σ-type orbitals because the electron density is concentrated along the imaginary line that passes through both nuclei. The antibonding orbital has a nodal plane between the nuclei where ψ_{MO}, ψ_{MO}^2, and the electron density drop to zero.

bonding. Thus, the bonding and antibonding MOs formed by overlap of $1s$ orbitals are symbolized as σ_{1s} and σ_{1s}^*, respectively.

It is always true that bonding MOs are lower in energy than antibonding MOs formed from the same atomic orbitals, as shown in Figure 10.38. When electrons populate molecular orbitals, they fill the lower energy, bonding MOs first. The rules that apply to filling MOs are the same as those for filling atomic orbitals: *Electrons spread out over molecular orbitals of equal energy (Hund's rule) and two electrons can only occupy the same orbital if their spins are paired.* When filling the MOs, we also have to be sure we've accounted for all of the valence electrons of the separate atoms.

Why H₂ Exists but He₂ Does Not

Figure 10.39*a* is an MO energy level diagram for H_2. The energies of the separate $1s$ atomic orbitals are indicated at the left and right; those of the molecular orbitals are shown in the center. The H_2 molecule has two electrons, and both can be placed in the σ_{1s} orbital. The shape of this bonding orbital, shown in Figure 10.38, should be familiar. It's the same as the shape of the electron cloud that we described using the valence bond theory.

Next, let's consider what happens when two helium atoms come together. Why can't a stable molecule of He_2 be formed? Figure 10.39*b* is the energy diagram for He_2. Notice that both bonding and antibonding orbitals are filled. In situations such as this there is a net destabilization because the antibonding MO is raised in energy more than the bonding MO is lowered, relative to the orbitals of the separated atoms. This means the total energy of He_2 is larger than that of two separate He atoms, so the "molecule" is unstable and immediately comes apart.

In general, the effects of **antibonding electrons** (those in antibonding MOs) cancel the effects of an equal number of **bonding electrons**, and molecules with equal numbers of bonding and antibonding electrons are unstable. If we remove an antibonding electron from He_2 to give He_2^+, there is a net excess of bonding electrons, and the ion should be capable of existence. In fact, the emission spectrum of He_2^+ can be observed when an electric discharge is passed through a helium-filled tube, which shows that He_2^+ is present during the electric discharge. However, the ion is not very stable and cannot be isolated.

Bond Order

The concept of bond order was introduced in Section 9.8 where it was defined as the number of pairs of electrons shared between two atoms. To translate the MO description into these terms, we compute the bond order as follows:

$$\text{Bond order} = \frac{(\text{number of bonding } e^-) - (\text{number of antibonding } e^-)}{2 \text{ electrons/bond}}$$

TOOLS

MO bond order

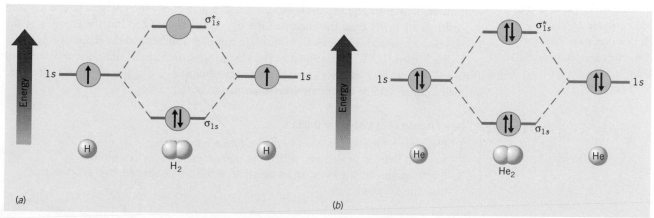

(a)   (b)

Figure 10.39 | **Molecular orbital descriptions of H₂ and He₂.** (*a*) Molecular orbital energy-level diagram for H_2. (*b*) Molecular orbital energy-level diagram for He_2.

For the H_2 molecule, we have

$$\text{Bond order} = \frac{2 - 0}{2} = 1$$

A bond order of 1 corresponds to a single bond. For He_2 we have

$$\text{Bond order} = \frac{2 - 2}{2} = 0$$

A bond order of zero means there is no bond, so the He_2 molecule is unable to exist. For the He_2^+ ion, which *is* able to form, the calculated bond order is

$$\text{Bond order} = \frac{2 - 1}{2} = 0.5$$

Notice that the bond order does not have to be a whole number. In this case, it indicates a bond character equivalent to about half a bond.

MO Description of Homonuclear Diatomic Molecules of Period 2

A **homonuclear diatomic molecule** is one in which both atoms are of the same element. Examples are N_2 and O_2, in which both elements are found in Period 2. As you have learned, the outer shell of a Period 2 element consists of $2s$ and $2p$ subshells. When atoms of this period bond to each other, the atomic orbitals of these subshells interact strongly to produce molecular orbitals. The $2s$ orbitals, for example, overlap to form σ_{2s} and σ_{2s}^* molecular orbitals having essentially the same shapes as the σ_{1s} and σ_{1s}^* MOs, respectively. Figure 10.40 shows the shapes of the bonding and antibonding MOs produced when the $2p$ orbitals overlap. If we label those that point toward each other as $2p_z$, a set of bonding and antibonding MOs are formed that we can label as σ_{2p_z} and $\sigma_{2p_z}^*$. The $2p_x$ and $2p_y$ orbitals, which are perpendicular to the $2p_z$ orbitals, overlap sideways to give π-type molecular orbitals. They are labeled π_{2p_x} and $\pi_{2p_x}^*$, and π_{2p_y} and $\pi_{2p_y}^*$, respectively. Notice in Figure 10.40 that we have indicated the algebraic signs of the $2p$ orbital wave functions. When the $2p$ orbitals overlap with the same sign, bonding MOs are formed, and when the signs are reversed, antibonding MOs are formed. In the bonding MOs, electron density is increased in the region between the two nuclei, whereas in antibonding MOs, electron density is reduced between the nuclei.

The approximate relative energies of the MOs formed from the second shell atomic orbitals are shown in Figure 10.41. Notice that from Li to N, the energies of the π_{2p_x} and π_{2p_y} orbitals are lower than the energy of the σ_{2p_z}. Then from O to Ne, the energies of the two levels are reversed. The reasons for this are complex and beyond the scope of this book.

Using Figure 10.41, we can predict the electronic structures of diatomic molecules of Period 2. These *MO electron configurations* are obtained using the same rules that are applied to the filling of atomic orbitals in atoms, as noted earlier.

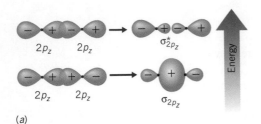

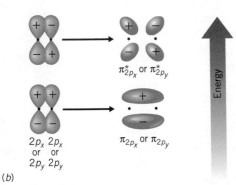

Figure 10.40 | Formation of molecular orbitals by the overlap of *p* orbitals. Where overlapping parts of the $2p$ orbitals have the same algebraic sign, a bonding MO is formed; where the signs are opposite, an antibonding MO is formed. (*a*) Two $2p_z$ orbitals that point at each other combine to give bonding and antibonding σ-type MOs. (*b*) Perpendicular to the $2p_z$ orbitals are $2p_x$ and $2p_y$ orbitals that overlap to give two sets of bonding and antibonding π-type MOs.

TOOLS

How electrons fill MOs

How Electrons Fill Molecular Orbitals

1. Electrons fill the lowest energy orbitals that are available.
2. No more than two electrons, with spins paired, can occupy any orbital.
3. Electrons spread out as much as possible, with spins unpaired, over orbitals that have the same energy.

Applying these rules to the valence electrons of Period 2 atoms gives the MO electron configurations shown in Table 10.1. Let's see how well MO theory performs by examining data that are available for these molecules.

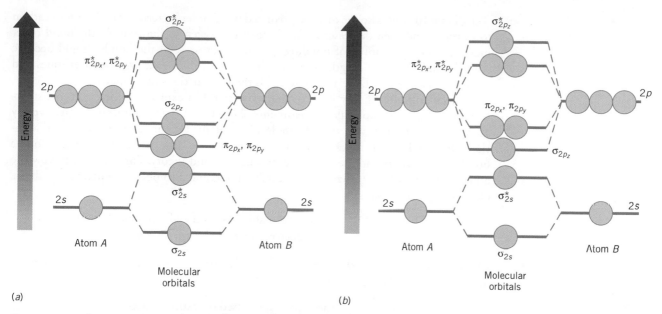

Figure 10.41 | Approximate relative energies of molecular orbitals in Period 2 diatomic molecules. (a) Li_2 through N_2. (b) O_2 through Ne_2.

According to Table 10.1, MO theory predicts that molecules of Be_2 and Ne_2 should not exist at all because they have bond orders of zero. In beryllium vapor and in gaseous neon, no evidence of Be_2 or Ne_2 has ever been found. MO theory also predicts that diatomic molecules of the other Period 2 elements should exist because they all have bond orders greater than zero. These molecules have, in fact, been observed. Although lithium, boron, and carbon are complex solids under ordinary conditions, they can be vaporized. In the vapor, molecules of Li_2, B_2, and C_2 can be detected. Nitrogen, oxygen, and fluorine, as you know, are gaseous elements that exist as N_2, O_2, and F_2.

| Table 10.1 | Molecular Orbital Populations and Bond Orders for Period 2 Diatomic Molecules[a] |

		Li_2	Be_2	B_2	C_2	N_2			O_2	F_2	Ne_2
	$\sigma^*_{2p_z}$	◯	◯	◯	◯	◯		$\sigma^*_{2p_z}$	◯	◯	(⇅)
	$\pi^*_{2p_x}, \pi^*_{2p_y}$	◯◯	◯◯	◯◯	◯◯	◯◯		$\pi^*_{2p_x}, \pi^*_{2p_y}$	(↑)(↑)	(⇅)(⇅)	(⇅)(⇅)
	σ_{2p_z}	◯	◯	◯	◯	(⇅)		π_{2p_x}, π_{2p_y}	(⇅)(⇅)	(⇅)(⇅)	(⇅)(⇅)
Energy	π_{2p_x}, π_{2p_y}	◯◯	◯◯	(↑)(↑)	(⇅)(⇅)	(⇅)(⇅)	Energy	σ_{2p_z}	(⇅)	(⇅)	(⇅)
	σ^*_{2s}	◯	(⇅)	(⇅)	(⇅)	(⇅)		σ^*_{2s}	(⇅)	(⇅)	(⇅)
	σ_{2s}	(⇅)	(⇅)	(⇅)	(⇅)	(⇅)		σ_{2s}	(⇅)	(⇅)	(⇅)
Number of Bonding Electrons		2	2	4	6	8			8	8	8
Number of Antibonding Electrons		0	2	2	2	2			4	6	8
Bond Order		1	0	1	2	3			2	1	0
Bond Energy (kJ/mol)		110	—	300	612	953			501	129	—
Bond Length (pm)		267	—	158	124	109			121	144	—

[a]Although the order of the energy levels corresponding to the σ_{2p_z}, and the π bonding MOs become reversed at oxygen, either sequence would yield the same result—a triple bond for N_2, a double bond for O_2, and a single bond for F_2.

In Table 10.1, we also see that the predicted bond order increases from boron to carbon to nitrogen and then decreases from nitrogen to oxygen to fluorine. As the bond order increases, the *net* number of bonding electrons increases, so the bonds should become stronger and the bond lengths shorter. The *experimentally measured* bond energies and bond lengths given in Table 10.1 agree with these predictions quite nicely.

Molecular orbital theory is particularly successful in explaining the electronic structure of the oxygen molecule. Experiments show that O_2 is paramagnetic (it's weakly attracted to a magnet) and that the molecule contains two unpaired electrons. In addition, the bond length in O_2 is about what is expected for an oxygen–oxygen double bond. These data cannot be explained by valence bond theory. For example, if we write a Lewis structure for O_2 that shows a double bond and also obeys the octet rule, all the electrons appear in pairs.

$$:\ddot{O}::\ddot{O}:$$ (not acceptable based on experimental evidence because all electrons are paired)

On the other hand, if we show the unpaired electrons, the structure has only a single bond and doesn't obey the octet rule.

$$:\ddot{O}\cdot\ddot{O}:$$ (not acceptable based on experimental evidence because of the O—O single bond)

> ■ Although MO theory easily handles the bonding situations that VB theory has trouble with, MO theory loses the simplicity of VB theory. For even quite simple molecules, MO theory is too complicated to make predictions without extensive calculations.

With MO theory, we don't have any of these difficulties. By applying Hund's rule, the two electrons in the π^* orbitals of O_2 spread out over these orbitals with their spins unpaired because both orbitals have the same energy (see Table 10.1). The electrons in the two antibonding π^* orbitals cancel the effects of two electrons in the two bonding π orbitals, so the net bond order is 2 and the bond is effectively a double bond.

Some Simple Heteronuclear Diatomic Molecules

As molecules become more complex, the simple application of MO theory becomes much more difficult. This is because it is necessary to consider the relative energies of the individual atomic orbitals as well as the orientations of the orbitals relative to those on other atoms. Nevertheless, we can take a brief look at the MO descriptions of a couple of diatomic molecules to see what happens when both atoms in the molecule are not the same. Such molecules are said to be **heteronuclear**.

Hydrogen Fluoride

When we consider the possible interaction of the orbitals of different atoms to form molecular orbitals, the first factor we have to consider is the relative energies of the orbitals. This is because orbitals interact most effectively when they are of about equal energy; the greater the difference in energy between the orbitals, the less the orbitals interact, and the more the orbitals behave like simple atomic orbitals.

In HF, the $1s$ orbital of hydrogen is higher in energy than either the $2s$ or $2p$ subshell of fluorine, but it is closest in energy to the $2p$ subshell (Figure 10.42). Taking the z axis as the internuclear axis, the hydrogen $1s$ orbital overlaps with the $2p_z$ orbital of fluorine to give bonding and antibonding σ-type orbitals, as illustrated in Figure 10.43. The $2p_x$ and $2p_y$ orbitals of fluorine, however, have no orbitals on hydrogen with which to interact, so they are unchanged when the molecule is formed. These two orbitals are said to be **nonbonding orbitals** because they are neither bonding nor antibonding; they have no effect on the stability of the molecule.

In the MO description of HF, we have a pair of electrons in the bonding MO formed by the overlap of the hydrogen $1s$ orbital with the fluorine $2p_z$ orbital. Earlier we saw that

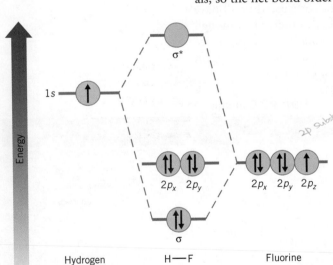

Figure 10.42 | Molecular orbital energy diagram for HF. Only the $1s$ orbital of hydrogen and the $2p$ orbitals of fluorine are shown.

> ■ The $2s$ orbital of fluorine is so much lower in energy than the $2p$ subshell that we don't need to consider its interaction with the hydrogen $1s$ orbital. That's why it isn't shown in the energy diagram.

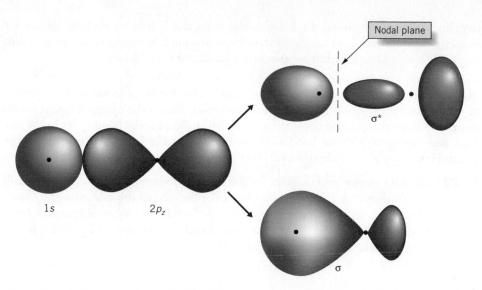

Figure 10.43 | **Formation of** σ **and** σ^* **orbitals in HF.** Once again, where overlapping atomic orbitals have the same sign, a bonding MO is formed; where the signs are opposite, an antibonding MO is formed. Notice that the antibonding σ^* orbital has a nodal plane between the nuclei, which effectively removes electron density from the region between the nuclei and, if occupied, leads to destabilization of the molecule.

valence bond theory explains the bond in HF in the same way—as a pair of electrons shared between the hydrogen $1s$ orbital and a fluorine $2p$ orbital.

Carbon Monoxide

Carbon monoxide is a heteronuclear molecule in which both atoms are from Period 2, so we expect the orbitals of the second shell to be the ones used to form the MOs. The orbital overlaps are similar to those of the homonuclear diatomics of Period 2, so the energy diagram resembles the one shown in Figure 10.41a.

Because the outer shell electrons of oxygen experience a larger effective nuclear charge than those of carbon, the oxygen orbitals will be somewhat lower in energy. This is shown in Figure 10.44. There are a total of 10 valence electrons (4 from carbon and 6 from

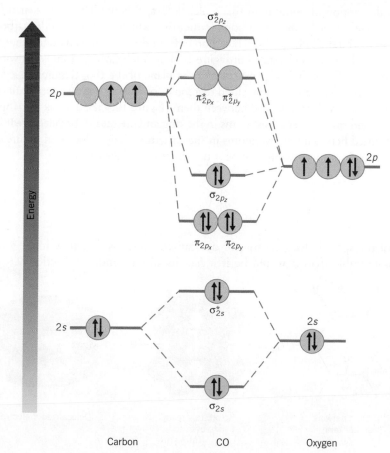

Figure 10.44 | **Molecular orbital energy diagram for carbon monoxide.** The oxygen orbitals are lower in energy than the corresponding carbon orbitals. The net bond order is 3.

oxygen) to distribute among the MOs of the molecule. When we do this, there are 8 bonding electrons and 2 antibonding electrons, so the net bond order is 3, corresponding to a triple bond. As expected, it consists of a σ bond and two π bonds.

Practice Exercises

10.22 | The molecular orbital energy level diagram for the cyanide ion, CN^-, is similar to that of the earlier Period 2 homonuclear diatomics. Sketch the energy diagram for the ion and indicate the electron population of the MOs. What is the bond order in the ion? How does this agree with the bond order predicted from the Lewis structure of the ion? (*Hint:* How many valence electrons are there in the ion?)

10.23 | The MO energy level diagram for the nitrogen monoxide molecule is essentially the same as that shown in Table 10.1 for O_2, except the oxygen orbitals are slightly lower in energy than the corresponding nitrogen orbitals. Sketch the energy diagram for nitrogen monoxide and indicate which MOs are populated. Calculate the bond order for the molecule. (*Hint:* Make adjustments to Figure 10.41*b*.)

10.8 | Delocalized Molecular Orbitals

One of the least satisfying aspects of the way valence bond theory explains chemical bonding is the need to write resonance structures for certain molecules and ions. For example, consider benzene, C_6H_6. As you learned earlier, this molecule has the shape of a ring whose resonance structures can be written as

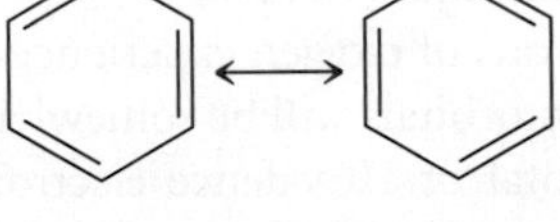

The MO description of bonding in this molecule is as follows: The basic structure of the molecule is determined by the sigma-bond framework, which requires that the carbon atoms use sp^2 hybrid orbitals. This allows each carbon to form three σ bonds (two to other C atoms and one to an H atom) as illustrated in Figure 10.45*a*. Each carbon atom is left with a half-filled unhybridized p orbital perpendicular to the plane of the ring (Figure 10.45*b*). These p orbitals overlap to give a π-electron cloud that looks something like two doughnuts with the sigma-bond framework sandwiched between them (Figure 10.45*c*). The six electrons in this π-electron cloud spread over all six atoms in the ring and are said to be **delocalized** (i.e., they are not localized between any two atoms in the structure). The delocalized nature of the pi electrons is the reason we usually represent the structure of benzene as

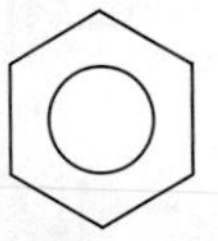

One of the special characteristics of delocalized bonds is that they make a molecule or ion more stable than it would be if it had localized bonds. In Section 9.9 this was

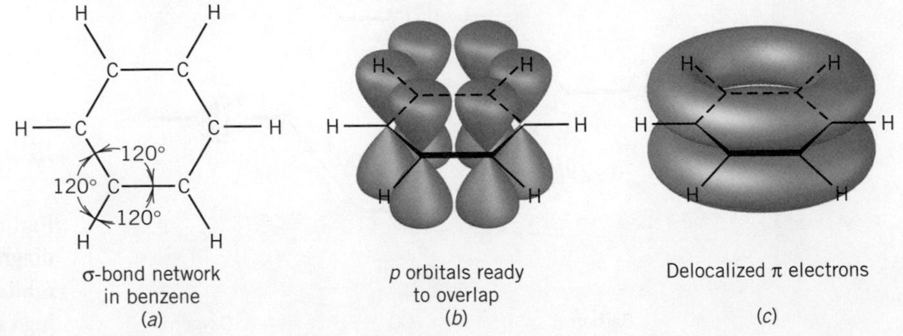

Figure 10.45 | **Benzene.**
(*a*) The σ-bond framework. All atoms lie in the same plane.
(*b*) The unhybridized p orbitals at each carbon prior to side-to-side overlap. (*c*) The double doughnut-shaped electron cloud formed by the delocalized π electrons.

σ-bond network in benzene
(*a*)

p orbitals ready to overlap
(*b*)

Delocalized π electrons
(*c*)

described in terms of *resonance energy*. In the molecular orbital theory, we no longer speak of resonance; instead, we refer to the electrons as being delocalized. The extra stability that is associated with this delocalization is therefore described, in the language of MO theory, as the **delocalization energy**.

■ Functionally, the terms *resonance energy* and *delocalization energy* are the same; they just come from different approaches to bonding theory.

10.9 | Bonding in Solids

Solids have some unique electrical properties that are familiar to everyone. For example, metals are good conductors of electricity, whereas nonmetallic substances are insulators; they are extremely poor electrical conductors. Between these extremes we find metalloids such as silicon and germanium, which are semiconductors; they are weak conductors of electricity. The theory developed to explain these widely differing properties is an extension of the principles of bonding discussed above and is called **band theory.**

According to band theory, an **energy band** in a solid is composed of a very large number of closely spaced energy levels that are formed by combining atomic orbitals of similar energy from each of the atoms within the substance. For example, in sodium the 1*s* atomic orbitals, one from each atom, combine to form a single 1*s* band. The number of energy levels in the band equals the number of 1*s* orbitals supplied by the entire collection of sodium atoms. The same thing occurs with the 2*s*, 2*p*, etc., orbitals, so that we also have 2*s*, 2*p*, etc., bands within the solid.

Figure 10.46 illustrates the energy bands in solid sodium. Notice that the electron density in the 1*s*, 2*s*, and 2*p* bands does not extend far from each individual nucleus, so these bands produce effectively localized energy levels in the solid. However, the 3*s* band (which is formed by overlap of the valence shell orbitals of the sodium atoms) is delocalized and extends continuously through the solid. The same applies to energy bands formed by higher-energy orbitals.

Sodium atoms have filled 1*s*, 2*s*, and 2*p* orbitals, so the corresponding bands in the solid are also filled. The 3*s* orbital of sodium, however, is only half-filled, which leads to a half-filled 3*s* band. The 3*p* and higher-energy bands in sodium are completely empty. When a voltage is applied across a piece of solid sodium, electrons in the half-filled 3*s* band can hop from atom to atom with ease, and this allows sodium to conduct electricity well. However, electrons in the lower-energy filled bands are unable to move through the solid because orbitals on neighboring atoms are already filled and cannot accept an additional electron. Such electrons do not contribute to the conductivity of the solid.

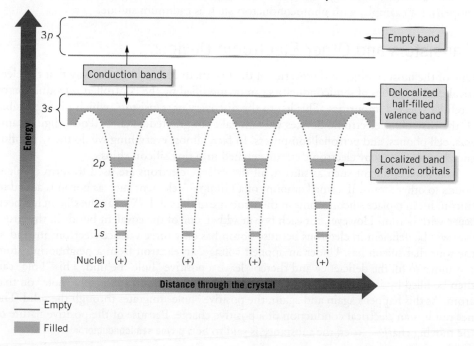

Figure 10.46 | **Energy bands in solid sodium.** The 1*s*, 2*s*, and 2*p* bands do not extend far in either direction from the nucleus, so the electrons in them are localized around each nucleus and can't move through the crystal. The delocalized 3*s* valence band extends throughout the entire solid, as do bands such as the 3*p* band formed from higher-energy orbitals of the sodium atoms.

Figure 10.47 | **Energy bands in different types of solids.** (*a*) In magnesium, a good electrical conductor, the empty 3*p* conduction band overlaps the filled 3*s* valence band and provides a way for this metal to conduct electricity. (*b*) In an insulator, the energy gap between the filled valence band and the empty conduction band prevents electrons from populating the conduction band. (*c*) In a semiconductor, there is a small band gap, and thermal energy can promote some electrons from the filled valence band to the empty conduction band. This enables the solid to conduct electricity weakly.

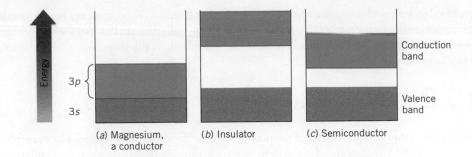

(*a*) Magnesium, a conductor   (*b*) Insulator   (*c*) Semiconductor

■ Recall that at any given temperature there is a distribution of kinetic energies among the particles of the substance. *Thermal energy* is kinetic energy a particle possesses because of its temperature. The higher the temperature, the higher the thermal energy.

We refer to the band containing the outer shell (valence shell) electrons as the **valence band.** Any band that is either vacant or partially filled and uninterrupted throughout the solid is called a **conduction band,** because electrons in it are able to move through the solid and thereby serve to carry electricity.

In metallic sodium the valence band and conduction band are the same, so sodium is a good conductor. In magnesium the 3*s* valence band is filled and therefore cannot be used to transport electrons. However, the vacant 3*p* conduction band actually overlaps the valence band and can easily be populated by electrons when voltage is applied (Figure 10.47*a*). This permits magnesium to be a conductor.

In an insulator such as glass, diamond, or rubber, all the valence electrons are used to form covalent bonds, so all the orbitals of the valence band are filled and cannot contribute to electrical conductivity. In addition, the energy separation, or **band gap,** between the filled valence band and the nearest conduction band (empty band) is large. As a result, electrons cannot populate the conduction band, so these substances are unable to conduct electricity (Figure 10.47*b*).

In a semiconductor such as silicon or germanium, the valence band is also filled, but the band gap between the filled valence band and the nearest conduction band is small (Figure 10.47*c*). At room temperature, *thermal energy* (kinetic energy associated with the temperature of the substance) possessed by the electrons is sufficient to promote some electrons to the conduction band and a small degree of electrical conductivity is observed. One of the interesting properties of semiconductors is that their electrical conductivity increases with increasing temperature. This is because as the temperature rises, the number of electrons with enough energy to populate the conduction band also increases. Photons can also provide the energy needed to promote electrons to the conduction band. This happens, for example, with photoconductors such as cadmium sulfide.

Transistors and Other Electronic Devices

One of the most significant discoveries of the twentieth century was the way that the electrical characteristics of semiconductors can be modified by the controlled introduction of carefully selected impurities. This led to the discovery of transistors, which made possible all the marvelous electronic devices we now take for granted, such as iPods, digital cameras, cell phones, and personal computers. In fact, almost everything we do today is influenced in some way by electronic circuits etched into tiny silicon chips.

In a semiconductor such as silicon, all the valence electrons are used to form covalent bonds to other atoms. If a small amount of a Group 3A element such as boron is added to silicon, it can replace silicon atoms in the structure of the solid. (We say the silicon has been **doped** with boron.) However, for each boron added, one of the covalent bonds in the structure will be deficient in electrons because boron has only three valence electrons instead of the four that silicon has. Under an applied voltage, an electron from a neighboring atom can move to fill the deficiency and thereby leave a positive "hole" behind. This "hole" can then be filled by an electron from a neighboring atom, which creates a new "hole" on that atom. As this happens again and again, the positive "hole" migrates through the solid. The net result is an electrical conduction of a positive charge. Because of the positive nature of the moving charge carrier, the substance is said to be a **p-type semiconductor.**

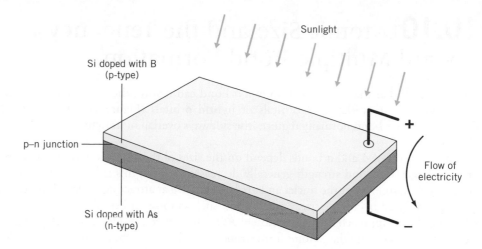

Sunlight

Si doped with B
(p-type)

p–n junction

Si doped with As
(n-type)

+

Flow of
electricity

–

Figure 10.48 | **Construction of
a silicon solar battery.**

If the impurity added to the silicon is a Group 5A element such as arsenic, it has one more electron in its valence shell than silicon. When the bonds are formed in the solid, there will be an electron left over that's not used in bonding. The extra electrons supplied by the impurity can enter the conduction band and move through the solid under an applied voltage, and because the moving charge now consists of electrons, which are negatively charged, the solid is said to be an **n-type semiconductor.**

Transistors are made from n- and p-type semiconductors and can be formed directly on the surface of a silicon chip, which has made possible the microcircuits in devices that seem to be everywhere around us.

Solar Cells

Another interesting application of semiconductors is in **solar cells** (also called **solar batteries**). These devices offer the potential of large scale harnessing of solar energy and are becoming more competitive with traditional forms of energy production as the price of solar cells drops.

A typical silicon solar cell is composed of a silicon wafer doped with arsenic (giving an n-type semiconductor) over which is placed a thin layer of silicon doped with boron (a p-type semiconductor). This is illustrated in Figure 10.48. In the dark there is an equilibrium between electrons and holes at the interface between the two layers, which is called a **p-n junction.** Some electrons from the n-type layer diffuse into the holes in the p-layer and are trapped. This leaves some positive holes in the n-layer. Equilibrium is achieved when the positive holes in the n-layer prevent further movement of electrons into the p-layer.

When light falls on the surface of the cell, the equilibrium is upset. Energy is absorbed, which permits electrons that were trapped in the p-layer to return to the n-layer. As these electrons move across the p-n junction into the n-layer, other electrons leave the n-layer through the wire, pass through the electrical circuit, and enter the p-layer. Thus an electric current flows when light falls on the cell and the external circuit is completed. This electric current can be used to run a motor, power a handheld calculator, or perform whatever other task we wish.

Light-Emitting Diodes (LEDs)

A solar cell absorbs light energy and produces an electric current. If the process is reversed and an electric current is forced through the p-n junction in the opposite direction, light is emitted. A device using this process is called a **light-emitting diode (LED).** By an appropriate choice of materials, the color of the light can range across the visible spectrum. LEDs are used in a variety of applications, ranging from traffic lights to jumbo TV screens in sports stadiums.

A large array of solar cells such as this can produce substantial amounts of electricity. *(Waltraud Grubitzsch/epa/© Corbis)*

The jumbo TV screen in this sports stadium is made up of many light-emitting diodes. *(Juan Ó Campo/NBAEvia/Getty Images, Inc.)*

10.10 | Atomic Size and the Tendency toward Multiple Bond Formation

You learned earlier that the formation of a σ bond can involve the overlap of s orbitals, or an end-to-end overlap of p orbitals or hybrid orbitals (Figure 10.30, page 439). Formation of a π bond normally requires the sideways overlap of unhybridized p orbitals (Figure 10.31).[5]

The strengths of σ and π bonds depend on the sizes of the atoms involved—as atoms become larger, the bond strength generally decreases. In part, this is because the shared electrons are farther from the nuclei and are less effective at attracting them. Pi bonds are especially affected by atomic size. Small atoms, such as those in Period 2 of the periodic table, are able to approach each other closely. As a result, effective sideways overlap of their p orbitals can occur, and these atoms form strong π bonds. Atoms from Periods 3 through 6 are much larger and π-type overlap between their p orbitals is relatively ineffective, so π bonds formed by large atoms are relatively weak compared to σ bonds.

The effect of atomic size on the relative strengths of σ and π bonds leads to the following generalization: *Elements in Period 2 are able to form multiple bonds fairly readily, while elements below them in Periods 3, 4, 5, and 6 have a tendency to prefer single bonds.* The consequences of this generalization are particularly evident when we examine the complexity of the structures that occur for the elemental nonmetals.

Among the nonmetals, only the noble gases exist in nature as single atoms. All the others are found in more complex forms in their free states—some as diatomic molecules and the rest in more complex molecular structures.

TOOLS

Tendency toward multiple bond formation

Nonmetals in Period 2

Fluorine (as well as the other halogens in Group 7A) has seven electrons in its outer shell and needs just one more electron to complete its valence shell. Fluorine is able to form the simple diatomic molecule F_2 with a single σ bond. The other halogens have similar formulas in their elemental states (Cl_2, Br_2, and I_2). Because only single bonds are involved, atomic size doesn't affect the complexity of the molecular structures of the halogens.

Moving to the left in the periodic table, the situation becomes more interesting for the elements in Groups 6A, 5A, and 4A. Oxygen and nitrogen have six and five electrons, respectively, in their valence shells. This means that an oxygen atom needs two electrons to complete its valence shell, and a nitrogen atom needs three. Oxygen and nitrogen, because of their small size, are capable of multiple bonding because they are able to form strong π bonds. This allows them to form a sufficient number of bonds with just a single neighbor to complete their valence shells, so they are able to form diatomic molecules.

The nitrogen molecule, which we discussed earlier, is able to complete its valence shell by forming a triple bond. Although a perfectly satisfactory Lewis structure for O_2 can't be drawn, experimental evidence suggests that the oxygen molecule does possess a double bond. Molecular orbital theory, which provides an excellent explanation of the bonding in O_2, also tells us that there is a double bond in the O_2 molecule.

Oxygen, in addition to forming the stable species O_2 (properly named *dioxygen*), also can exist in another very reactive molecular form called **ozone**, which has the formula O_3. The structure of ozone can be represented as a resonance hybrid,

$$:\ddot{O} \diagdown^{\displaystyle \ddot{O}} \diagup \ddot{O}: \quad \longleftrightarrow \quad :\ddot{O} \diagup^{\displaystyle \ddot{O}} \diagdown \ddot{O}:$$

This unstable molecule can be generated by the passage of an electric discharge through ordinary O_2, and the pungent odor of ozone can often be detected in the vicinity of high-voltage electrical equipment. It is also formed in limited amounts in the upper atmosphere

---

[5]Pi bonds can also be formed by d orbitals, but we do not discuss them in this book.

by the action of ultraviolet radiation from the sun on O_2. The presence of ozone in the upper atmosphere shields earth and its life-forms from exposure to intense and harmful ultraviolet light from the sun.

The existence of an element in more than one form, either as the result of differences in molecular structure as with O_2 and O_3, or as the result of differences in the packing of molecules in the solid, is a phenomenon called **allotropy**. The different forms of the element are called **allotropes**. Thus, O_2 is one allotrope of oxygen and O_3 is another. Allotropy is not limited to oxygen, as you will soon see.

■ Ozone is also a component of photochemical smog formed by the interaction of sunlight with nitrogen oxides released in the exhaust of motor vehicles.

Allotropes of Carbon

An atom of carbon, also a Period 2 element, has four electrons in its valence shell, so it must share four electrons to complete its octet. There is no way for carbon to form a quadruple bond, so a simple C_2 species is not stable under ordinary conditions. Instead, carbon completes its octet in other ways, leading to four allotropic forms of the element. One of these is **diamond**, in which each carbon atom uses sp^3 hybrid orbitals to form covalent bonds to four other carbon atoms at the corners of a tetrahedron (Figure 10.49*a*).

In its other allotropes, carbon employs sp^2 hybrid orbitals to form ring structures with delocalized π systems covering their surfaces. The most stable form of carbon is **graphite**, which consists of layers of carbon atoms, each composed of many hexagonal "benzene-like" rings fused together in a structure reminiscent of chicken wire. A single such layer is called **graphene** (see On the Cutting Edge 10.1). In graphene, a $2p$ orbital on each carbon atom forms a π-type of interaction with identical $2p$ orbitals on its neighbors.

■ The 2010 Nobel Prize in Physics was awarded to Andre Geim and Konstantin Novoselov, both of the University of Manchester, England, for their discovery that individual layers of graphene could be isolated from graphite. Their discovery opened the door to an explosive growth in research on this very unusual material.

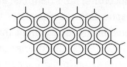

A fragment of a graphene layer in graphite.

In graphite, graphene layers are stacked one on top of another, as shown in Figure 10.49*b*. Graphite is an electrical conductor because of the delocalized π electron system that

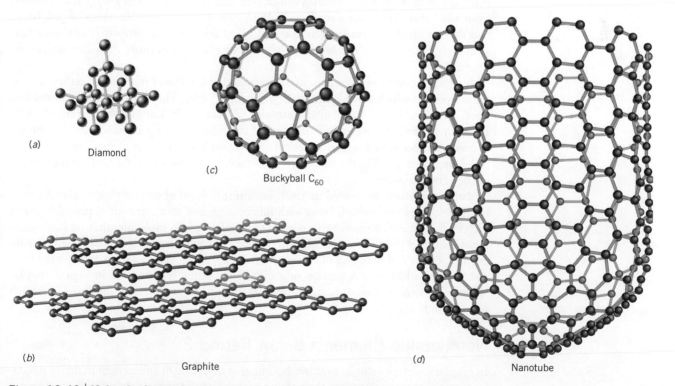

(a) Diamond

(c) Buckyball C_{60}

(b) Graphite

(d) Nanotube

Figure 10.49 | **Molecular forms of carbon.** (*a*) Diamond. (*b*) Graphite. (*c*) Buckminsterfullerene, or "buckyball," C_{60}. (*d*) A portion of a carbon nanotube showing one closed end.

ON THE CUTTING EDGE | 10.1

Graphene and the Future of Electronics

It has long been suspected that single layers of graphite, given the name *graphene* (Figure 1), would have surprising and potentially useful properties. However, difficulties in preparing graphene sheets by peeling them off crystals of graphite have prevented scientists from obtaining useful samples of the material, making accurate measurements impossible. These techniques yielded only small fragments of graphene.

Recently, scientists at IBM have developed a low-cost method of growing high-quality graphene on the surface of commercially available silicon carbide (SiC) wafers. Heating the wafers causes silicon to evaporate from the surface, and the carbon atoms left behind combine to form a graphene sheet.

Single sheets of graphene can transport electrons more quickly than other semiconductors, a property called *electron mobility*. The electron mobility of graphene, for example, is about 100 times greater than that of silicon, the semiconductor used in most currently available devices. For this reason, graphene is ideally suited for high-speed atomic scale operation. Furthermore, graphene's electrical properties can be controlled by switching it among conducting, nonconducting, and semiconducting states. This makes graphene a potential candidate for a variety of electronic devices.

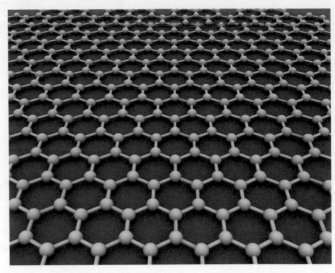

Figure 1. An illustration depicting a single graphene layer.

According to scientists at IBM, they have already created a graphene-based transistor with the capability of operating at speeds of 100 GHz, about three times as fast as a silicon-based processor. Such discoveries suggest that graphene may someday replace silicon in high-speed electronic circuits.

---

extends across the layers. Electrons can be pumped in at one end of a layer and removed from the other. Scientists have been able to isolate separate single layers of graphene, and there is much current interest in the physical and electrical properties of this carbon structure. For example, the breaking strength of graphene is more than 200 times that of steel!

In 1985, a new form of carbon was discovered that consists of tiny balls of carbon atoms, the simplest of which has the formula C_{60} (Figure 10.49c). They were named **fullerenes** and the C_{60} molecule itself was named **buckminsterfullerene** (nickname **buckyball**) in honor of R. Buckminster Fuller, the designer of a type of structure called a geodesic dome. The bonds between carbon atoms in the buckyball are arranged in a pattern of five- and six-membered rings arranged like the seams in a classic soccer ball, as well as the structural elements of the geodesic dome.

Carbon nanotubes, discovered in 1991, are another form of carbon that is related to the fullerenes. They are formed, along with fullerenes, when an electric arc is passed between carbon electrodes. The nanotubes consist of tubular carbon molecules that we can visualize as rolled-up sheets of graphene (with hexagonal rings of carbon atoms). The tubes are capped at each end with half of a spherical fullerene molecule, so a short tube would have a shape like a hot dog. A portion of a carbon nanotube is illustrated in Figure 10.49d. Carbon nanotubes have unusual properties that have made them the focus of much research in recent years.

■ Weight for weight, carbon nanotubes are about 100 times stronger than stainless steel and about 40 times stronger than the carbon fibers used to make tennis rackets and shafts for golf clubs.

Nonmetallic Elements below Period 2

In graphite, carbon exhibits multiple bonding, as do nitrogen and oxygen in their molecular forms. As we noted earlier, their ability to do this reflects their ability to form strong π bonds—a requirement for the formation of a double or triple bond. When we move to the third and successive periods, a different state of affairs exists. There, we have much larger atoms that are able to form relatively strong σ bonds but much weaker π bonds. Because their π bonds are so weak, these elements prefer single bonds (σ bonds), and the molecular structures of the free elements reflect this.

Elements of Group 6A
Below oxygen in Group 6A is sulfur, which has the Lewis symbol

$$: \overset{\displaystyle \cdot}{\underset{\displaystyle \cdot\cdot}{S}} \cdot$$

A sulfur atom requires two electrons to complete its valence shell, so it must form two covalent bonds. However, sulfur doesn't form π bonds well to other sulfur atoms; instead, it prefers to form two stronger single bonds to *different* sulfur atoms. Each of these also prefers to bond to two different sulfur atoms, and this gives rise to a

$$-\overset{\cdot\cdot}{\underset{\cdot\cdot}{S}}-\overset{\cdot\cdot}{\underset{\cdot\cdot}{S}}-\overset{\cdot\cdot}{\underset{\cdot\cdot}{S}}-\overset{\cdot\cdot}{\underset{\cdot\cdot}{S}}-\overset{\cdot\cdot}{\underset{\cdot\cdot}{S}}-$$

sequence. Actually, in sulfur's most stable form, called **orthorhombic sulfur**, the sulfur atoms are arranged in an eight-member ring to give a molecule with the formula S_8 (properly named *cyclooctasulfur*). The S_8 ring has a puckered crown-like shape, which is illustrated in Figure 10.50. Another allotrope is **monoclinic sulfur**, which also contains S_8 rings that are arranged in a slightly different crystal structure.

When solid sulfur is heated, it undergoes some interesting changes (Figure 10.51). When the solid first melts, the liquid that forms consists of S_8 molecules. As the liquid is heated further, the rings begin to open into chains of sulfur atoms that join to form long strands. The strands of sulfur atoms become intertwined, causing the liquid to become very viscous. Further heating causes the strands of sulfur to break into smaller fragments, and when the liquid boils it is no longer viscous.

Selenium, below sulfur in Group 6A, also forms Se_8 rings in one of its allotropic forms. Both selenium and tellurium also can exist in a gray form in which there are long Se_x and Te_x chains (where the subscript x is a large number).

Elements of Group 5A
Like nitrogen, the other elements in Group 5A all have five valence electrons. Phosphorus is an example:

$$: \overset{\displaystyle \cdot}{\underset{\displaystyle \cdot}{P}} \cdot$$

To achieve a noble gas structure, the phosphorus atom must acquire three more electrons. Because there is little tendency for phosphorus to form multiple bonds, as nitrogen does when it forms N_2, the octet is completed by the formation of three single bonds to three *different* phosphorus atoms.

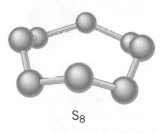

S_8

Figure 10.50 | **The structure of the puckered S_8 ring.**

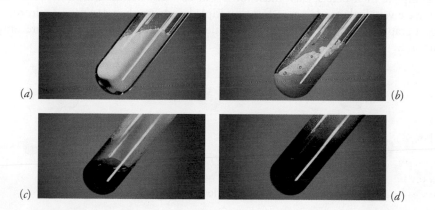

(*a*)

(*b*)

(*c*)

(*d*)

Figure 10.51 | **Changes in sulfur as it is heated.**
(*a*) Crystalline sulfur. (*b*) Molten sulfur just above its melting point. (*c*) Molten sulfur, just below 200 °C, is dark and viscous. (*d*) Boiling sulfur is dark red and no longer viscous. (*Michael Watson*)

Figure 10.52 | **The two main allotropes of phosphorus.** (*a*) White phosphorus. (*b*) Red phosphorus. (*Richard Megna/ Fundamental Photographs*)

■ The preferred angle between bonds formed by *p* orbitals is 90°. Each face of the P_4 tetrahedron is a triangle, however, with 60° angles between edges. This produces less than optimum overlap between the *p* orbitals in the bonds.

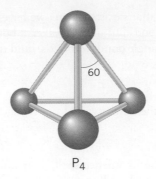

P_4

Figure 10.53 | **The molecular structure of white phosphorus, P_4.** The bond angles of 60° makes the phosphorus–phosphorus bonds quite weak and causes the molecule to be very reactive.

The simplest elemental form of phosphorus is a waxy solid called **white phosphorus** because of its appearance (Figure 10.52). It consists of P_4 molecules in which each phosphorus atom lies at a corner of a tetrahedron, as illustrated in Figure 10.53. Notice that in this structure each phosphorus is bound to three others. This allotrope of phosphorus is very reactive, partly because of the very small P—P—P bond angle of 60°. At this small angle, the *p* orbitals of the phosphorus atoms don't overlap very well, so the bonds are weak. As a result, breaking a P—P bond occurs easily. When a P_4 molecule reacts, this bond breaking is the first step, so P_4 molecules are readily attacked by other chemicals, especially oxygen. White phosphorus is so reactive toward oxygen that it ignites and burns spontaneously in air. For this reason, white phosphorus is used in military incendiary devices, and you've probably seen movies in which exploding phosphorus shells produce arching showers of smoking particles.

A second allotrope of phosphorus that is much less reactive is called **red phosphorus**. At the present time, its structure is unknown, although it has been suggested that it contains P_4 tetrahedra joined at the corners as shown in Figure 10.54. Red phosphorus is also used in explosives and fireworks, and it is mixed with fine sand and used on the striking surfaces of matchbooks. As a match is drawn across the surface, friction ignites the phosphorus, which then ignites the ingredients in the tip of the match.

A third allotrope of phosphorus is called **black phosphorus**, which is formed by heating white phosphorus at very high pressures. This variety has a layered structure in which each phosphorus atom in a layer is covalently bonded to three others in the same layer. As in graphite, these layers are stacked one atop another, with only weak forces between the layers. As you might expect, black phosphorus has many similarities to graphite.

The elements arsenic and antimony, which are just below phosphorus in Group 5A, are also able to form somewhat unstable yellow allotropic forms containing As_4 and Sb_4 molecules, but their most stable forms have a metallic appearance with structures similar to black phosphorus.

Elements of Group 4A

Finally, we look at silicon and germanium, the heavier nonmetallic elements in Group 4A. To complete their octets, each must form four covalent bonds. Unlike carbon, however, they have very little tendency to form multiple bonds, so they don't form allotropes that have a graphite structure. Instead, each of them forms a solid with a structure similar to diamond.

Figure 10.54 | **Proposed molecular structure of red phosphorus.** Red phosphorus is believed to be composed of long chains of P_4 tetrahedra connected at their corners.

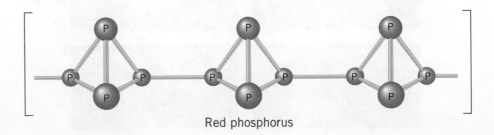

Red phosphorus

Summary

Molecular Shapes and the VSEPR Model. The structures of most molecules can be described in terms of one or another of five basic geometries: **linear, planar triangular, tetrahedral, trigonal bipyramidal,** and **octahedral**. The **VSEPR theory** predicts molecular geometry by assuming that **electron domains**—regions of space that contain bonding electrons, unpaired valence electrons, or lone pairs—stay as far apart as possible from each other, while staying as close as possible to the central atom. Figures 10.4, 10.5, 10.7, and 10.10 illustrate the structures obtained with different numbers of groups of electrons in the valence shell of the central atom in a molecule or ion and with different numbers of lone pairs and attached atoms. The correct shape of a molecule or polyatomic ion can usually be predicted from the Lewis structure.

Molecular Shape and Molecular Polarity. A molecule that contains identical atoms attached to a central atom will be nonpolar if there are no lone pairs of electrons in the central atom's valence shell. It will be polar if lone pairs are present, except in two cases: (1) when there are three lone pairs and two attached atoms, and (2) when there are two lone pairs and four attached atoms. If all the atoms attached to the central atom are not alike, the molecule will usually be polar.

Valence Bond (VB) Theory. According to VB theory, a covalent bond is formed between two atoms when an atomic orbital on one atom **overlaps** with an atomic orbital on the other and a pair of electrons with paired spins is shared between the overlapping orbitals. In general, the better the overlap of the orbitals, the stronger the bond. A given atomic orbital can overlap only with one other orbital on a different atom, so a given atomic orbital can only form one bond with an orbital on one other atom.

Hybrid Atomic Orbitals. **Hybrid orbitals** are formed by mixing pure s, p, and d orbitals. Hybrid orbitals overlap better with other orbitals than the pure atomic orbitals from which they are formed, so bonds formed by hybrid orbitals are stronger than those formed by ordinary atomic orbitals. **Sigma bonds** (σ bonds) are formed by the following kinds of orbital overlap: s–s, s–p, end-to-end p–p, and overlap of hybrid orbitals. Sigma bonds allow free rotation around the bond axis. The side-by-side overlap of p orbitals produces a **pi bond** (π bond). Pi bonds do not permit free rotation around the bond axis because such a rotation involves bond breaking. In complex molecules, the basic molecular framework is built with σ bonds. A double bond consists of one σ bond and one π bond. A triple bond consists of one σ bond and two π bonds.

Molecular Orbital (MO) Theory. MO theory begins with the supposition that molecules are similar to atoms, except that they have more than one positive center. They are treated as collections of nuclei and electrons, with the electrons of the molecule distributed among **molecular orbitals** of different energies. Molecular orbitals can spread over two or more nuclei, and can be considered to be formed by the constructive and destructive interference of the overlapping electron waves corresponding to the atomic orbitals of the atoms in the molecule. **Bonding MOs** concentrate electron density between nuclei; **antibonding MOs** remove electron density from between nuclei. **Nonbonding MOs** do not affect the energy of the molecule. The rules for the filling of MOs are the same as those for atomic orbitals. The ability of MO theory to describe **delocalized orbitals** avoids the need for resonance theory. Delocalization of bonds leads to a lowering of the energy by an amount called the **delocalization energy** and produces more stable molecular structures.

Band Theory of Solids. In solids, atomic orbitals of the atoms combine to yield **energy bands** that consist of many energy levels. The **valence band** is formed by orbitals of the valence shells of the atoms. A **conduction band** is a partially filled or empty band. In an **electrical conductor** the conduction band is either partially filled or is empty and overlaps a filled band. In an **insulator**, the **band gap** between the filled valence band and the empty conduction band is large, so no electrons populate the conduction band. In a **semiconductor**, the band gap between the filled valence band and the conduction band is small and thermal energy can promote some electrons to the conduction band. Silicon becomes a **p-type semiconductor**, in which the charge is carried by positive **"holes,"** if it is **doped** with a Group 3A element such as boron. It becomes an **n-type semiconductor**, in which the charge is carried by electrons, if it is doped with a Group 5A element such as arsenic.

Tendency toward Multiple Bond Formation. Elements of Period 2, because of their small size, form strong π bonds. As a result, these elements easily participate in multiple bonding between like atoms, which accounts for diatomic molecules of O_2 and N_2, and the π-bonded structure of **graphene**. Elements of Periods 3, 4, and 5 are large and their p orbitals do not overlap well to form strong π bonds, so these elements prefer single σ bonds between like atoms, which leads to more complex molecular structures.

Different forms of the same element are called **allotropes**. Oxygen exists in two allotropic forms: dioxygen (O_2) and **ozone** (O_3). Carbon forms several allotropes, including **diamond, graphite** (composed of layers of graphene), C_{60} molecules called **buckminsterfullerene** (one member of the **fullerene** family of structures), and **carbon nanotubes**. Sulfur forms S_8 molecules that can be arranged in two different allotropic forms. Phosphorus occurs as **white phosphorus** (P_4), **red phosphorus**, and **black phosphorus**. Silicon only forms a diamond-like structure.

T O O L S

Tools for Problem Solving   The following tools were introduced in this chapter. Study them carefully so that you can select the appropriate tool when needed.

Basic molecular shapes (pages 409)

You need an understanding of the five basic geometries discussed. Practice drawing them and be sure you know their names.

VSEPR model (page 411)

Electron groups repel each other and arrange themselves in the valence shell of an atom to yield minimum repulsions, which is what determines the shape of the molecule. This tool serves as the foundation for understanding the VSEPR model.

Applying the VSEPR model (page 417)

To obtain a molecular structure, follow these steps: (1) draw the Lewis structure, (2) count electron domains, (3) select the basic geometry, (4) add atoms to bonding domains, and (5) ignore nonbonding domains to describe the shape.

Molecular shape and molecular polarity (page 422)

We can use molecular shape to determine whether a molecule will be polar or nonpolar. Refer to the summary on page 422.

Criteria for bond formation according to VB theory (page 424)

A bond requires overlap of two orbitals sharing two electrons with paired spins. Both orbitals can be half-filled, or one can be filled and the other empty. We use these criteria to establish which orbitals atoms use when bonds are formed.

Hybrid orbitals formed by *s* and *p* atomic orbitals (page 430)

The orientations of these hybrids are the same as those predicted for two, three, and four electron domains.

The VSEPR model and hybrid orbitals involving *s* and *p* electrons (page 432)

These tools are interrelated. Lewis structures permit us to use the VSEPR model to predict molecular shape, which then allows us to select the correct hybrid orbitals for the valence bond description of bonding. After forming the Lewis structure, we determine the number of domains, from which we derive the structure of the molecule or ion. A convenient way of doing this is to describe the VSEPR structure symbolically. In doing this we represent the central atom by M, the atoms attached to the central atom by X, and lone pairs by E. We can then signify the number of bonding and nonbonding domains around M as a formula MX_nE_m, where n is the number of bonding domains and m is the number of nonbonding domains. The resulting formula is related to the structure of the molecule or ion, and to the hybrid orbitals used by the central atom, as shown below. Practice sketching the structures, associating them with the appropriate generalized formula MX_nE_m, and using the structures to select the appropriate set of hybrid orbitals. The following structures are obtained for two, three, and four domains.

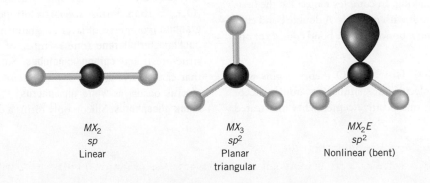

MX_2
sp
Linear

MX_3
sp^2
Planar
triangular

MX_2E
sp^2
Nonlinear (bent)

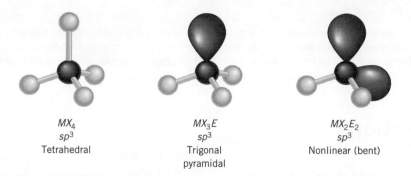

MX_4
sp^3
Tetrahedral

MX_3E
sp^3
Trigonal
pyramidal

MX_2E_2
sp^3
Nonlinear (bent)

The VSEPR model and hybrid orbitals involving *d* electrons (page 434)

As with the preceding tool, we form the Lewis structure, count bonding and nonbonding domains and select the structure. The following structures are obtained for five and six domains using the generalized formula MX_nE_m.

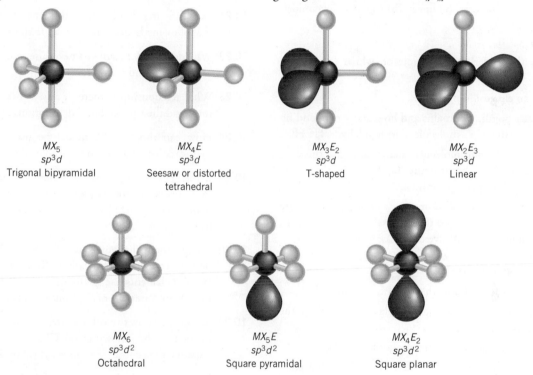

MX_5
sp^3d
Trigonal bipyramidal

MX_4E
sp^3d
Seesaw or distorted
tetrahedral

MX_3E_2
sp^3d
T-shaped

MX_2E_3
sp^3d
Linear

MX_6
sp^3d^2
Octahedral

MX_5E
sp^3d^2
Square pyramidal

MX_4E_2
sp^3d^2
Square planar

σ and π bonds and hybridization (page 433)

The Lewis structure for a polyatomic molecule lets us apply these criteria to determine how many σ and π bonds are between atoms and the kind of hybrid orbitals each atom uses. Remember that the shape of the molecule is determined by the framework of σ bonds, with π bonds used in double and triple bonds.

Calculating bond order in MO theory (page 447)

$$\text{Bond order} = \frac{(\text{number of bonding } e^-) - (\text{number of antibonding } e^-)}{2 \text{ electrons/bond}}$$

How electrons fill molecular orbitals (page 448)

Electrons populate MOs following the same rules that apply to atomic orbitals in an atom. Use this tool to obtain the correct distribution of electrons over the MOs of a molecule or ion.

Tendency toward multiple bond formation (page 456)

Atoms of Period 2 have a stronger tendency to form multiple bonds with each other than do those in Periods 3 and below.

| Review Questions

Shapes of Molecules

10.1 Sketch the following molecular shapes and give the various bond angles in the structures: **(a)** planar triangular, **(b)** tetrahedral, **(c)** octahedral.

10.2 Sketch the following molecular shapes and give the bond angles in the structures: **(a)** linear, **(b)** trigonal bipyramidal.

VSEPR Theory

10.3 What is the underlying principle on which the VSEPR model is based?

10.4 What is an electron domain?

10.5 How many bonding domains and how many nonbonding domains are there in a molecule of formaldehyde, HCHO?

10.6 Sketch the following molecular shapes and give the various bond angles in the structure: **(a)** T-shaped, **(b)** seesaw shaped, and **(c)** square pyramidal.

10.7 What arrangements of domains around an atom are expected when there are **(a)** three domains, **(b)** six domains, **(c)** four domains, or **(d)** five domains?

Predicting Molecular Polarity

10.8 Why is it useful to know the polarities of molecules?

10.9 How do we indicate a bond dipole when we draw the structure of a molecule?

10.10 Under what conditions will a molecule be polar?

10.11 What condition must be met if a molecule having polar bonds is to be nonpolar?

10.12 Use a drawing to show why the SO_2 molecule is polar.

Modern Bonding Theories

10.13 What is the theoretical basis of both valence bond (VB) theory and molecular orbital (MO) theory?

10.14 What shortcomings of Lewis structures and VSEPR theory do VB and MO theories attempt to overcome?

10.15 What is the main difference in the way VB and MO theories view the bonds in a molecule?

Valence Bond Theory

10.16 What is meant by orbital overlap?

10.17 How is orbital overlap related to bond energy?

10.18 Use sketches of orbitals to describe how VB theory would explain the formation of the H—Br bond in hydrogen bromide.

Hybrid Orbitals

10.19 Why do atoms usually use hybrid orbitals for bonding rather than pure atomic orbitals?

10.20 Sketch figures that illustrate the directional properties of the following hybrid orbitals: **(a)** *sp*, **(b)** *sp²*, **(c)** *sp³*.

10.21 Sketch figures that illustrate the directional properties of the following hybrid orbitals: **(a)** *sp³d*, **(b)** *sp³d²*.

10.22 Why do Period 2 elements never use *sp³d* or *sp³d²* hybrid orbitals for bond formation?

10.23 What relationship is there, if any, between Lewis structures and the valence bond descriptions of molecules?

10.24 How can the VSEPR model be used to predict the hybridization of an atom in a molecule?

10.25 If the central oxygen in the water molecule did not use *sp³* hybridized orbitals (or orbitals of any other kind of hybridization), what would be the expected bond angle in H_2O?

10.26 Using orbital diagrams, describe how *sp³* hybridization occurs in each atom: **(a)** carbon, **(b)** nitrogen, **(c)** oxygen. If these elements use *sp³* hybrid orbitals to form bonds, how many lone pairs of electrons would be found on each?

10.27 Sketch the way the orbitals overlap to form the bonds in each of the following: **(a)** CH_4, **(b)** NH_3, **(c)** H_2O. (Assume the central atom uses hybrid orbitals.)

10.28 We explained the bond angles of 107° in NH_3 by using *sp³* hybridization of the central nitrogen atom. If unhybridized *p* orbitals of nitrogen were used to overlap with 1*s* orbitals of each hydrogen, what would the H—N—H bond angles be? Explain.

10.29 Using sketches of orbitals and orbital diagrams, describe *sp²* hybridization of **(a)** boron and **(b)** carbon.

10.30 What two basic shapes have hybridizations that include *d* orbitals?

Coordinate Covalent Bonds and VB Theory

10.31 The ammonia molecule, NH_3, can combine with a hydrogen ion, H^+ (which has an empty 1*s* orbital), to form the ammonium ion, NH_4^+. (This is how ammonia can neutralize acid and therefore function as a base.) Sketch the geometry of the ammonium ion, indicating the bond angles.

10.32 How does the geometry around B and O change in the following reaction? How does the hybridization of each atom change?

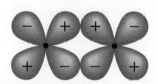

Multiple Bonds and Hybrid Orbitals

10.33 How do σ and π bonds differ?

10.34 Why can free rotation occur easily around a σ-bond axis but not around a π-bond axis?

10.35 Using sketches, describe the bonds and bond angles in ethene, C_2H_4.

10.36 Sketch the way the bonds form in acetylene, C_2H_2.

10.37 How does VB theory treat the benzene molecule? (Draw sketches describing the orbital overlaps and the bond angles.)

Molecular Orbital Theory

10.38 Why is the higher-energy MO in H_2 called an *antibonding orbital*? Make a sketch of the bonding and antibonding orbitals in H_2.

10.39 Below is an illustration showing two $3d$ orbitals about to overlap. The drawings also show the algebraic signs of the wave functions for both orbitals in this combination. Will this combination of orbitals produce a bonding or an antibonding MO? Sketch the shape of the MO.

10.40 Will the combination of $3d$ orbitals in Question 10.39 yield a σ- or π-type of MO? Explain.

10.41 Explain why He_2 does not exist but H_2 does.

10.42 How does MO theory account for the paramagnetism of O_2?

10.43 On the basis of MO theory, explain why Li_2 molecules can exist but Be_2 molecules cannot. Could the ion $Be_2{}^+$ exist?

10.44 What are the bond orders in **(a)** $O_2{}^+$, **(b)** $O_2{}^-$, and **(c)** $C_2{}^+$?

10.45 What relationship is there between bond order and bond energy?

10.46 Sketch the shapes of the π_{2p_y} and $\pi_{2p_y}^*$ MOs.

10.47 What is a delocalized MO? Explain, in terms of orbital overlap, why delocalized MOs are able to form in the benzene molecule.

10.48 What effect does delocalization have on the stability of the electronic structure of a molecule?

10.49 What is delocalization energy? How is it related to resonance energy?

Band Theory of Solids

10.50 On the basis of the band theory of solids, how do conductors, insulators, and semiconductors differ?

10.51 Define the terms **(a)** *valence band* and **(b)** *conduction band*.

10.52 Why does the electrical conductivity of a semiconductor increase with increasing temperature?

10.53 In calcium, why can't electrical conduction take place by movement of electrons through the $2s$ energy band? How does calcium conduct electricity?

10.54 What is a p-type semiconductor? What is an n-type semiconductor?

10.55 Name two elements that would make germanium a p-type semiconductor when added in small amounts. Name two elements that would make silicon an n-type semiconductor when added in small amounts.

10.56 How does a solar cell work? How does that differ from the operation of a light-emitting diode?

Tendency toward Multiple Bond Formation

10.57 Which of the nonmetals occur in nature in the form of isolated atoms?

10.58 Why are the Period 2 elements able to form much stronger π bonds than the nonmetals of Period 3? Why does a Period 3 nonmetal prefer to form all σ bonds instead of one σ bond and several π bonds?

10.59 Even though the nonmetals of Periods 3, 4, and 5 do not tend to form π bonds between like atoms, each of the halogens is able to form diatomic molecules (Cl_2, Br_2, I_2). Why?

10.60 What are *allotropes*? How do they differ from *isotopes*?

10.61 What are the two allotropes of oxygen?

10.62 Construct the molecular orbital diagram for O_2. What is the net bond order in O_2?

10.63 Draw the Lewis structure for O_3. Is the molecule linear, based on the VSEPR model? Assign formal charges to the atoms in the Lewis structure. Does this suggest the molecule is polar or nonpolar?

10.64 What beneficial function does ozone serve in earth's upper atmosphere?

10.65 Describe the structure of diamond. What kind of hybrid orbitals does carbon use to form bonds in diamond? What is the geometry around carbon in this structure?

10.66 Describe the structure of graphene. What kind of hybrid orbitals does carbon use in the formation of the molecular framework of graphene?

10.67 How is the structure of graphite related to the structure of graphene?

10.68 Describe the C_{60} molecule. What is it called? What name is given to the series of similar substances?

10.69 How is the structure of a carbon nanotube related to the structure of graphene?

10.70 What is the molecular structure of sulfur in its most stable allotropic form?

10.71 Make a sketch that describes the molecular structure of white phosphorus.

10.72 What are the P—P—P bond angles in the P_4 molecule? If phosphorus uses p orbitals to form the phosphorus–phosphorus bonds, what bond angle would give the best orbital overlap? On the basis of your answers to these two questions, explain why P_4 is so chemically reactive.

10.73 What structure has been proposed for red phosphorus? How do the reactivities of red and white phosphorus compare?

10.74 What is the molecular structure of black phosphorus? In what way does the structure of black phosphorus resemble that of graphite?

10.75 What is the molecular structure of silicon? Suggest a reason why silicon doesn't form an allotrope that's similar in structure to graphite.

Review Problems

The VSEPR model

10.76 Predict the shapes of (a) NH_2^-, (b) CO_3^{2-}, (c) IF_3, (d) Br_3^-, and (e) GaH_3.

10.77 Predict the shapes of (a) SF_3^+, (b) GeF_4, (c) SO_4^{2-}, (d) O_3, and (e) N_2O.

ILW 10.78 Predict the shapes of (a) FCl_2^+, (b) AsF_5, (c) AsF_3, (d) SbH_3, and (e) SeO_2.

10.79 Predict the shapes of (a) TeF_4, (b) $SbCl_6^-$, (c) NO_2^-, (d) PCl_4^+, and (e) PO_4^{3-}.

10.80 Predict the shapes of (a) IO_4^-, (b) IF_4^-, (c) TeF_6, (d) SiO_4^{4-}, and (e) ICl_2^-.

10.81 Predict the shapes of (a) CS_2, (b) BrF_4^-, (c) ICl_3, (d) ClO_3^-, and (e) SeO_3.

10.82 Which of the following has a shape described by the figure below: (a) IO_4^-, (b) ICl_4^-, (c) $SnCl_4$, or (d) BrF_4^+?

10.83 Which of the following has a shape described by the figure below: (a) BrF_3, (b) PF_3, (c) NO_3^-, or (d) SCl_3^-?

10.84 Ethyne, more commonly called acetylene, is a gas used in welding torches. It has the Lewis structure H—C≡C—H. What would you expect the H—C—C bond angle to be in this molecule?

OH 10.85 Ethene, also called ethylene, is a gas used to ripen tomatoes artificially. It has the Lewis structure

$$H-\underset{\underset{H}{|}}{C}=\underset{\underset{H}{|}}{C}-H$$

What would you expect the H—C—H and H—C≡C bond angles to be in this molecule? (*Caution:* Don't be fooled by the way the structure is drawn here.)

10.86 Predict the bond angle for each of the following molecules: (a) Cl_2O, (b) H_2O, (c) SO_2, (d) I_3^-, (e) NH_2^-.

10.87 Predict the bond angle for each of the following molecules: (a) HOCl, (b) PH_2^-, (c) OCN^-, (d) O_3, (e) SnF_2.

Predicting Molecular Polarity

ILW 10.88 Which of the following molecules would be expected to be polar? (a) HBr, (b) $POCl_3$, (c) CH_2O, (d) $SnCl_4$, (e) $SbCl_5$

10.89 Which of the following molecules would be expected to be polar? (a) PBr_3, (b) SO_3, (c) $AsCl_3$, (d) ClF_3, (e) BCl_3

10.90 Which of the following molecules or ions would be expected to have a net dipole moment? (a) ClNO, (b) XeF_3^+, (c) $SeBr_4$, (d) NO, (e) NO_2

10.91 Which of the following molecules or ions would be expected to have a net dipole moment? (a) H_2S, (b) BeH_2, (c) SCN^-, (d) CN^-, (e) $BrCl_3$

OH 10.92 Explain why SF_6 is nonpolar, but SF_5Br is polar.

10.93 Explain why CH_3Cl is polar, but CCl_4 is not.

Valence Bond Theory

10.94 Hydrogen selenide is one of nature's most foul-smelling substances. Molecules of H_2Se have H—Se—H bond angles very close to 90°. How would VB theory explain the bonding in H_2Se? Use sketches of orbitals to show how the bonds are formed. Illustrate with appropriate orbital diagrams as well.

OH 10.95 Use sketches of orbitals to show how VB theory explains the bonding in the Cl_2 molecule. Illustrate with appropriate orbital diagrams as well.

Hybrid Orbitals

10.96 Use orbital diagrams to explain how the beryllium chloride molecule is formed. What kind of hybrid orbitals does beryllium use in this molecule?

10.97 Use orbital diagrams to describe the bonding in (a) tin tetrachloride and (b) antimony pentachloride. Be sure to indicate hybrid orbital formation.

OH **10.98** Draw Lewis structures for the following and use the geometry predicted by the VSEPR model to determine what kind of hybrid orbitals the central atom uses in bond formation: (a) ClO_3^-, (b) SO_3, and (c) OF_2.

10.99 Draw Lewis structures for the following and use the geometry predicted by the VSEPR model to determine what kind of hybrid orbitals the central atom uses in bond formation: (a) $SbCl_6^-$, (b) PF_3, and (c) XeF_4.

10.100 Use the VSEPR model to help you describe the bonding in the following molecules according to VB theory: (a) arsenic trichloride and (b) chlorine trifluoride. Use orbital diagrams for the central atom to show how hybridization occurs.

10.101 Use the VSEPR model to help you describe the bonding in the following molecules according to VB theory: (a) antimony trichloride and (b) selenium dichloride. Use orbital diagrams for the central atom to show how hybridization occurs.

Coordinate Covalent Bonds and VB Theory

10.102 Use orbital diagrams to show that the bonding in SbF_6^- involves the formation of a coordinate covalent bond.

10.103 What kind of hybrid orbitals are used by tin in $SnCl_6^{2-}$? Draw the orbital diagram for Sn in $SnCl_6^{2-}$. What is the geometry of $SnCl_6^{2-}$?

Multiple Bonding and Valence Bond Theory

10.104 A nitrogen atom can undergo sp^2 hybridization when it becomes part of a carbon–nitrogen double bond, as in $H_2C\!\!=\!\!NH$.

(a) Using a sketch, show the electron configuration of sp^2 hybridized nitrogen just before the overlapping occurs to make this double bond.

(b) Using sketches (and the analogy to the double bond in C_2H_4), describe the two bonds of the carbon–nitrogen double bond.

(c) Describe the geometry of $H_2C\!\!=\!\!NH$ (using a sketch that shows all expected bond angles).

10.105 A nitrogen atom can undergo sp hybridization and then become joined to carbon by a triple bond to give the structural unit $-\!\!C\!\!\equiv\!\!N\!:$. This triple bond consists of one σ bond and two π bonds.

(a) Write the orbital diagram for sp hybridized nitrogen as it would look before any bonds form.

(b) Using the carbon–carbon triple bond as the analogy and drawing pictures to show which atomic orbitals overlap with which, show how the three bonds of the triple bond in $-\!\!C\!\!\equiv\!\!N\!:$ form.

(c) Again using sketches, describe all the bonds in hydrogen cyanide, $H\!\!-\!\!C\!\!\equiv\!\!N\!:$.

(d) What is the likeliest $H\!\!-\!\!C\!\!-\!\!N$ bond angle in HCN?

10.106 Tetrachloroethylene, a common dry-cleaning solvent, has the formula C_2Cl_4. Its structure is

Use the VSEPR and VB theories to describe the bonding in this molecule. What are the expected bond angles in the molecule?

10.107 Phosgene, $COCl_2$, was used as a war gas during World War I. It reacts with moisture in the lungs of its victims to form CO_2 and gaseous HCl, which cause the lungs to fill with fluid. Phosgene is a simple molecule having the structure

Describe the bonding in this molecule using VB theory.

10.108 What kind of hybrid orbitals do the numbered atoms use in the following molecule?

OH **10.109** What kinds of bonds (σ, π) are found in the numbered bonds in the following molecule?

Molecular Orbital Theory

OH **10.110** Use the MO energy diagram to predict which in each
ILW pair has the greater bond energy: (a) O_2 or O_2^+, (b) O_2 or O_2^-, (c) N_2 or N_2^+.

10.111 Assume that in the NO molecule the molecular orbital energy level sequence is similar to that for O_2. What happens to the NO bond length when an electron is removed from NO to give NO^+? How would the bond energy of NO compare to that of NO^+?

10.112 In each of the following pairs, which substance has the longer bond length? (a) N_2 or N_2^+, (b) NO or NO^+, (c) O_2 or O_2^-

10.113 Which of the following molecules or ions are paramagnetic? **(a)** O_2^+, **(b)** O_2, **(c)** O_2^-, **(d)** NO, **(e)** N_2

10.114 Construct the MO energy level diagram for the OH molecule assuming it is similar to that for HF. How many electrons are in **(a)** bonding MOs and **(b)** nonbonding MOs? What is the net bond order in the molecule?

| Additional Exercises

OH **10.116** Formaldehyde has the Lewis structure

$$H-\overset{\overset{\displaystyle H}{\displaystyle |}}{C}=\ddot{\ddot{O}}$$

What would you predict its shape to be?

10.117 The molecule XCl_3 is pyramidal. In which group in the periodic table is element X found? If the molecule were planar triangular, in which group would X be found? If the molecule were T-shaped, in which group would X be found? Why is it unlikely that element X is in Group 6A?

10.118 Antimony forms a compound with hydrogen that is called stibine. Its formula is SbH_3 and the H—Sb—H bond angles are 91.3°. Which kinds of orbitals does Sb most likely use to form the Sb—H bonds: pure p orbitals or hybrid orbitals? Explain your reasoning.

10.119 Describe the changes in molecular geometry and hybridization that take place during the following reactions:
(a) $BF_3 + F^- \longrightarrow BF_4^-$
(b) $PCl_5 + Cl^- \longrightarrow PCl_6^-$
(c) $ICl_3 + Cl^- \longrightarrow ICl_4^-$
(d) $2PCl_3 + Cl_2 \longrightarrow PCl_5$
(e) $C_2H_2 + H_2 \longrightarrow C_2H_4$

10.120 Which one of the following five diagrams best represents the structure of $BrCl_4^+$?

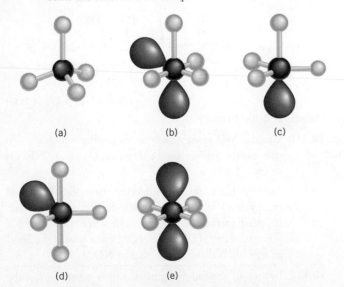

(a)   (b)   (c)

(d)   (e)

OH **10.121** Cyclopropane is a triangular molecule with C—C—C bond angles of 60°. Explain why the σ bonds joining

10.115 If boron and nitrogen were to form a molecule with the formula BN, what would its MO energy level diagram look like, given that the energies of the $2p$ orbitals of nitrogen are lower than those of boron. If Figure 10.44 applies, would the molecule be paramagnetic or diamagnetic? What is the net bond order in the molecule?

carbon atoms in cyclopropane are weaker than the carbon–carbon σ bonds in the noncyclic propane.

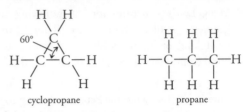

cyclopropane   propane

10.122 Phosphorus trifluoride, PF_3, has F—P—F bond angles of 97.8°.
(a) How would VB theory use hybrid orbitals to explain these data?
(b) How would VB theory use unhybridized orbitals to account for these data?
(c) Do either of these models work very well?

10.123 A six-membered ring of carbons can hold a double bond but not a triple bond. Explain.

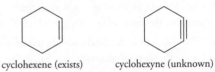

cyclohexene (exists)   cyclohexyne (unknown)

*****10.124** *The more electronegative are the atoms bonded to the central atom, the less are the repulsions between the electron pairs in the bonds. On the basis of this statement, predict the most probable structure for the molecule PCl_3F_2. Do we expect the molecule to be polar or nonpolar?*

*****10.125** *A lone pair of electrons in the valence shell of an atom has a larger effective volume than a bonding electron pair. Lone pairs therefore repel other electron pairs more strongly than do bonding pairs. On the basis of these statements, describe how the bond angles in TeF_4 and BrF_5 deviate from those found in a trigonal bipyramid and an octahedron, respectively. Sketch the molecular shapes of TeF_4 and BrF_5 and indicate these deviations on your drawing.*

*****10.126** *The two electron pairs in a double bond repel other electron pairs more than the single pair of electrons in a single bond. On the basis of this statement, which bond angles should be larger in SO_2Cl_2, the O—S—O bond angles or the Cl—S—Cl bond angles? In the molecule, sulfur is bonded to two oxygen atoms and two chlorine atoms. (Hint: Assign formal charges and work with the best Lewis structure for the molecule.)*

10.127 In a certain molecule, a *p* orbital overlaps with a *d* orbital as shown at the right. The algebraic signs of the lobes of the *d*-orbital wave function are also indicated in the drawing. Which kind of bond is formed, σ or π? Explain your choice. Repeat the drawing twice on a separate sheet of paper. In one of them, indicate the signs of the lobes of the *p*-orbital wave function that would lead to a bonding MO. In the other, indicate the signs of the lobes of the *p*-orbital wave function that would lead to an antibonding MO.

Multi-Concept Problems

*10.129 The peroxynitrite ion, $OONO^-$, is a potent toxin formed in cells affected by diseases such as diabetes and atherosclerosis. Peroxynitrite ion can oxidize and destroy biomolecules crucial for the survival of the cell.

(a) Give the O—O—N and O—N—O bond angles in the peroxynitrite ion.

(b) What is the hybridization of the N atom in the peroxynitrite ion?

(c) Suggest why the peroxynitrite ion is expected to be much less stable than the nitrate ion, NO_3^-.

*10.130 An ammonia molecule, NH_3, is very polar, whereas NF_3 is almost nonpolar. Use this observation along with the valence bond description of bonding in these molecules to justify the following statement: *Lone pairs in hybrid orbitals contribute to the overall dipole moment of a molecule.*

*10.131 There exists a hydrocarbon called butadiene, which has the molecular formula C_4H_6 and the structure

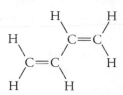

Exercises in Critical Thinking

10.133 Five basic molecular shapes were described for simple molecular structures containing a central atom bonded to various numbers of surrounding atoms. Can you suggest additional possible structures? Provide arguments about the likelihood that these other structures might actually exist.

10.134 Compare and contrast the concepts of delocalization and resonance.

10.135 Why doesn't a carbon–carbon quadruple bond exist?

10.136 What might the structure of the iodine heptafluoride molecule be? If you can think of more than one possible structure, which is likely to be of lowest energy based on the VSEPR model?

10.137 The F—F bond in F_2 is weaker than the Cl—Cl bond in Cl_2. How might the lone pairs on the atoms in the molecules be responsible for this?

10.128 If we assign the internuclear axis in a diatomic molecule to be the *z* axis, what kind of *p* orbital (p_x, p_y, or p_z) on one atom would have to overlap with a d_{xz} orbital on the other atom to give a pi bond?

The C=C bond lengths are 134 pm (about what is expected for a carbon–carbon double bond), but the C—C bond length in this molecule is 147 pm, which is shorter than a normal C—C single bond. The molecule is planar (i.e., all the atoms lie in the same plane).

(a) What kind of hybrid orbitals do the carbon atoms use in this molecule to form the C—C bonds?

(b) Between which pairs of carbon atoms do we expect to find sideways overlap of *p* orbitals (i.e., π-type *p-p* overlap)?

(c) Based on your answer to parts (a) and (b), explain why the center carbon–carbon bond is shorter than a carbon–carbon single bond.

*10.132 A 0.244 g sample of a compound of phosphorus and bromine, when dissolved in water, reacted to give a solution containing phosphorous acid and bromide ion. Addition of excess $AgNO_3$ solution to the mixture led to precipitation of AgBr. When the precipitate of AgBr was collected and dried, it weighed 0.508 g. Determine the chemical formula of the phosphorus–bromine compound and predict whether its molecules are polar or nonpolar.

10.138 Molecular orbital theory predicts the existence of antibonding molecular orbitals. How do antibonding electrons affect the stability in a molecule?

10.139 The structure of the diborane molecule, B_2H_6, is sometimes drawn as

There are not enough valence electrons in the molecule to form eight single bonds, which is what the structure implies. Assuming that the boron atoms use sp^3 hybrid orbitals, suggest a way that hydrogen 1*s* orbitals can be involved in forming delocalized molecular orbitals that bridge the two boron atoms. Use diagrams to illustrate your answer. What would be the average bond order in the bridging bonds?

Chapters 8–10

[Bringing It Together] Once again we pause to provide an opportunity for you to see how well you have grasped the concepts, how familiar you are with important terms, and how able you are at working chemistry problems. Keep in mind that many of the problems require tools developed in more than one chapter, including tools from Chapters 1–7. As you proceed, we encourage you to follow the approach taken by the worked examples you've studied.

1. A beam of green light has a wavelength of 500 nm. What is the frequency of this light? What is the energy, in joules, of one photon of this light? What is the energy, in joules, of one mole of photons of this light? Would blue light have more or less energy per photon than this light?

2. Write the abbreviated electron configuration and construct the orbital diagram for the chromium(III) ion. Is the ion paramagnetic or diamagnetic?

3. Ozone, O_3, consists of a chain of three oxygen atoms.
   (a) Draw the two resonance structures for ozone that obey the octet rule.
   (b) Based on your answer to (a), is the molecule linear or nonlinear?
   (c) Assign formal charges to the atoms in the resonance structures you have drawn in part (a).
   (d) On the basis of your answers to (b) and (c), explain why ozone is a polar molecule even though it is composed of three atoms that have identical electronegativities.

4. Which of the following processes are endothermic?
   (a) $P^-(g) + e^- \longrightarrow P^{2-}(g)$
   (b) $Fe^{3+}(g) + e^- \longrightarrow Fe^{2+}(g)$
   (c) $Cl(g) + e^- \longrightarrow Cl^-(g)$
   (d) $S(g) + 2e^- \longrightarrow S^{2-}(g)$

5. For each of the following, select the particle that has the specified property.
   (a) The atom with the larger radius: Rb or Sr
   (b) The particle with the larger radius: Mn^{2+} or Mn^{3+}
   (c) The atom with the larger radius: P or As
   (d) The atom with the more endothermic ionization energy: O or F
   (e) The atom with the more endothermic ionization energy: Be or B
   (f) The atom with the more exothermic electron affinity: O or S

6. Give the electron configurations of the ions (a) Pb^{2+}, (b) Pb^{4+}, (c) S^{2-}, (d) Fe^{3+}, and (e) Zn^{2+}. Which of the ions are paramagnetic and which are diamagnetic?

7. Why is the change in atomic size, going from one element to the next across a period, smaller among the transition elements than among the representative elements?

8. Some resonance structures that can be drawn for carbon dioxide are shown below.

$$:\ddot{O}=C=\ddot{O}: \quad :O\equiv C-\ddot{\underset{..}{O}}: \quad :\ddot{\underset{..}{O}}-C\equiv O:$$
$$\text{I} \qquad\qquad \text{II} \qquad\qquad \text{III}$$

Explain why Structure I is the preferred structure.

9. Predict the shapes of the following molecules and ions: (a) SbH_3, (b) IF_3, (c) $HClO_2$, (d) C_2^{2-}, (e) AsF_5, (f) O_2^{2-}, (g) HCO_3^-, (h) TeF_6, (i) HNO_3.

10. Why, on the basis of formal charges and relative electronegativities, is it more reasonable to expect the structure of $POCl_3$ to be the one on the left rather than the one on the right?

$$\underset{\underset{:\ddot{Cl}:}{|}}{:\ddot{Cl}-\overset{\overset{:\ddot{Cl}:}{|}}{P}-\ddot{\underset{..}{O}}:} \qquad \underset{\underset{:\ddot{Cl}:}{|}}{:\ddot{Cl}-\overset{\overset{:\ddot{Cl}:}{|}}{O}-\ddot{P}:}$$

Is either of these the "best" Lewis structure that can be drawn for this molecule?

11. The melting point of Al_2O_3 is much higher than the melting point of NaCl. On the basis of lattice energies, explain why this is so.

12. A certain element X was found to form three compounds with chlorine having the formulas XCl_2, XCl_4, and XCl_6. One of its oxides has the formula XO_3, and X reacts with sodium to form the compound Na_2X.
   (a) Is X a metal or a nonmetal?
   (b) In which group in the periodic table is X located?
   (c) In which periods in the periodic table could X possibly be located?
   (d) Draw Lewis structures for XCl_2, XCl_4, XCl_6, and XO_3. (Where possible, follow the octet rule.) Which has multiple bonding?
   (e) What do we expect the molecular structures of XCl_2, XCl_4, XCl_6, and XO_3 to be? Which are polar molecules?
   (f) The element X also forms the oxide XO_2. Draw a Lewis structure for XO_2 that obeys the octet rule.
   (g) Assign formal charges to the atoms in the Lewis structures for XO_2 and XO_3 drawn for parts (d) and (f).
   (h) What kinds of hybrid orbitals would X use for bonding in XCl_4 and XCl_6?
   (i) If X were to form a compound with aluminum, what would be its formula?
   (j) Which compound of X would have the more ionic bonds, Na_2X or MgX?
   (k) If X were in Period 5, what would be the electron configuration of its valence shell?

13. Construct a Born–Haber cycle for the formation of RbBr from its elements that includes the lattice energy as an energy term along one of the paths from $Rb(s)$ and $Br_2(l)$ to $RbBr(s)$. Identify the various energy terms involved and indicate which are endothermic and which are exothermic.

14. The heat of formation of $CaCl_2$ is -795 kJ/mol. The energy needed to change one mole of $Ca(s)$ into one mole of $Ca(g)$ is $+192$ kJ/mol. The first and second ionization energies of Ca are $+590$ kJ/mol and $+1146$ kJ/mol, respectively. The bond energy of Cl_2 is 238 kJ per mole of Cl—Cl bonds. The electron affinity of Cl is -348 kJ/mol. Set up a Born–Haber cycle and calculate the lattice energy of $CaCl_2$. Report the lattice energy in units of kJ/mol.

15. For each of the following pairs of compounds, which has the larger lattice energy: (a) MgO or NaCl, (b) MgO or BeO, (c) NaI or NaF, (d) MgO or CaS? Explain your choices.

16. The oxalate ion has the following arrangement of atoms.

Draw all of its resonance structures.

17. According to the VSEPR model, which of the following best illustrates the structure of the $AsCl_3^{2-}$ ion?

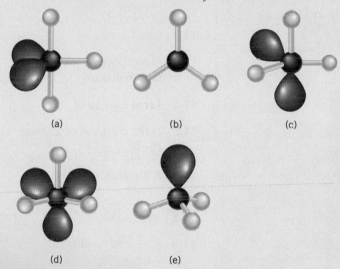

18. The VSEPR model predicts the structure below for a certain molecule. Which kind of hybrid orbitals does the central atom in the molecule use to form its covalent bonds?

19. Which kind of bond, σ or π, is produced by the overlap of d orbitals pictured below?

20. For the orbital interactions in the preceding problem, sketch the shapes you would expect for the bonding and antibonding orbitals created by the orbital overlap shown.

21. Which of the following molecules would be nonpolar: SbH_3, IF_3, AsF_5, $SbCl_3$, OF_2? Which has the most polar bonds?

22. The following is the chemical structure of acetaminophen, the pain killer in Tylenol®.

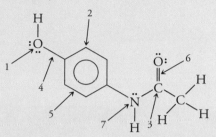

What kind of hybrid orbitals are used by atoms 1, 2, 3, and 7? How many sigma and pi bonds are in bonds 4 and 6? What is the average bond order in bond 5?

23. Construct the MO energy level diagram for the cyanide ion, keeping in mind that the more electronegative element has orbitals lower in energy than the less electronegative element. What is the bond order in this ion? Compare the valence bond and molecular orbital descriptions of bonding in this ion.

24. The simple hydrogen compound of arsenic is called arsine and has the formula AsH_3. The bond angles in the compound are 91.8°. Give a valence bond description of the bonding in this molecule that is consistent with the bond angles.

25. Predict the shapes of the following molecules and ions: (a) PF_3 (b) PF_6^-, (c) PF_4^+, and (d) PF_5. What kinds of hybrid orbitals does phosphorus use in each of them to form the bonds to fluorine atoms? Do any of these molecules contain what might be called a coordinate covalent bond?

26. Consider the following statements: (1) Fe^{2+} is easily oxidized to Fe^{3+}, and (2) Mn^{2+} is difficult to oxidize to Mn^{3+}. On the basis of the electron configurations of the ions, explain the difference in ease of oxidation.

27. The bond energy of O_2 is 501 kJ/mol. What is the wavelength of a photon needed to rupture the bond of a single oxygen molecule?

28. How would you expect the carbon–oxygen bond lengths to change relative to each other when an acetic acid molecule is neutralized by hydroxide ion?

11 Properties of Gases

Understanding the properties of gases saves lives. Molecular oxygen in the air is the essential gas that supports life and also combustion. Other gases, such as molecular nitrogen, will not support life nor fire, but, neither are they inherently toxic. However, many of the gases produced in the fire depicted here are toxic and need to be avoided as the firefighters in the accompanying photo are doing. While the fire department tells us what to do in a fire, this chapter will help us *understand why* we should do it. The properties of gases we study now also explain many other common phenomena we see and use in our daily lives. © Radius Images/ Corbis

⌈ This Chapter in Context

In the preceding chapters we've discussed the chemical properties of a variety of different substances. We've also studied the kinds of forces (chemical bonds) that hold molecular and ionic substances together. In fact, it is the nature of the chemical bonds that dictates chemical properties. With this chapter we begin a systematic study of the *physical properties* of materials, including the factors that govern the behavior of gases, liquids, and solids. We study gases first because they are the easiest to understand and their behavior will help explain some of the properties of liquids and solids in Chapter 12.

We live in a mixture of gases called the earth's atmosphere. Through everyday experience, you have become familiar with many of the properties that gases have. Our goal in this chapter is to refine this understanding in terms of the physical laws that govern the way gases behave. You will also learn how this behavior is interpreted in terms of the way we view gases at a molecular level. In our discussions we will describe how the energy concepts, first introduced to you in Chapter 7, provide an explanation of the gas laws. Finally, you will learn how a close examination of gas properties furnishes clues about molecular size and the attractions that exist between molecules.

11.1 | A Molecular Look at Gases

To early observers the mass loss of a rotting apple or the mass gain of a rusting nail was inexplicable. For a long time, these early scientists didn't recognize the existence of gases as examples of matter and the answer to their perplexing observations. Of course, we now understand that gases are composed of chemical substances that exist in one of the three common states of matter. The reason for the early confusion is that the physical properties of gases differ so much from those of liquids and solids. Consider water, for example. We can see and feel it as a liquid, but it seems to disappear when it evaporates and surrounds us as water vapor. With this in mind, let's examine some of the properties of gaseous substances to look for clues that suggest the nature of gases when viewed at a molecular level.

Because air has so little weight for a given volume, it makes things filled with air float, much to the pleasure of these balloonists at a hot-air balloon festival. *(Raymond Watt/Albuquerque International Balloon Fiesta, Inc.)*

Familiar Properties of Gases

The most common gas, familiar to everyone, is air. Because you've grown up surrounded by this gas, you already are aware of many properties that gases have. Let's look at two of them.

- You can wave your hand through air with little resistance. (Compare that with waving your hand through a tub filled with water.)
- The air in a bottle has little weight to it, so if a bottle of air is submerged under water and released, it quickly bobs to the surface.

Both of these observations suggest that a given volume of air doesn't have much matter in it. (We can express this by saying that air has a low density.) What else do you know about gases?

- Gases can be compressed. Inflating a tire involves pushing more and more air into the same container (the tire). This behavior is a lot different from that of liquids; you can't squeeze more water into an already filled bottle.
- Gases exert a pressure. Whenever you inflate a balloon you have an experience with gas pressure, and the "feel" of a balloon suggests that the pressure acts equally in all directions.

■ Dry air is roughly 21% O_2 and 78% N_2, but it has traces of several other gases.

Aerosol cans carry a warning about subjecting them to high temperatures because the internal pressure can become large enough to cause them to explode. *(Andy Washnik)*

- The pressure of a gas depends on *how much* gas is confined. The *more air* you pump into a tire, the greater the pressure.
- Gases fill completely any container into which they're placed—you've never heard of half a bottle of air. If you put air in a container, it expands and fills the container's entire volume. (This is certainly a lot different from the behavior of liquids and solids.)
- Gases mix freely and quickly with each other. You've experienced this when you've smelled the perfume of someone passing by. The vapors of the person's perfume mix with and spread through the air.
- The pressure of a gas rises when its temperature is increased. That's why there's the warning "Do Not Incinerate" printed on aerosol cans. A sealed can, if made too hot, is in danger of exploding from the increased pressure.

Molecular Model of Gases

The simple qualitative observations about gases described above suggest what gases must be like when viewed at the molecular level (Figure 11.1). The fact that there's so little matter in a given volume suggests that there is a lot of space between the individual molecules, especially when compared to liquids or solids. This would also explain why gases can be so easily compressed—squeezing a gas simply removes some of the empty space.

It also seems reasonable to believe that the molecules of a gas are moving around fairly rapidly. How else could we explain how molecules of a perfume move so quickly through the air? Furthermore, if gas molecules didn't move, gravity would cause them to settle to the bottom of a container (which they don't do). And if gas molecules are moving, some must be colliding with the walls of the container, and the force of these tiny collisions would explain the pressure a gas exerts. It also explains why adding more gas increases the pressure; the more gas in the container, the more collisions with the walls, and the higher the pressure.

Finally, the fact that gas pressure rises with increasing temperature suggests that the molecules move faster with increasing temperature, because faster molecules would exert greater forces when they collide with the walls.

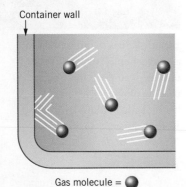

Gas molecule = ●

Figure 11.1 | **A gas viewed at the molecular level.** Simple qualitative observations of the properties of gases lead us to conclude that a gas is composed of widely spaced molecules that are in constant motion. Collisions of molecules with the walls produce tiny forces that, when taken all together, are responsible for the gas pressure.

11.2 | Measurement of Pressure

As we discussed in Chapter 7, **pressure** *is force per unit area*, calculated by dividing the force by the area over which the force acts.

$$\text{Pressure} = \frac{\text{force}}{\text{area}}$$

Earth exerts a gravitational force on everything with mass that is on it or near it. What we call the *weight* of an object, like this book, is simply our measure of the force it exerts because gravity acts on it.

The Barometer

Earth's gravity pulls on the air mass of the atmosphere, causing it to cover the Earth's surface like an invisible blanket. The molecules in the air collide with every object the air contacts, and by doing so, produce a pressure we call the *atmospheric pressure.*

At any particular location on Earth, the atmospheric pressure acts equally in all directions—up, down, and sideways. In fact, it presses against our bodies with a surprising amount of force, but we don't really feel it because the fluids in our bodies push back with equal pressure. We can observe atmospheric pressure, however, if we pump the air from

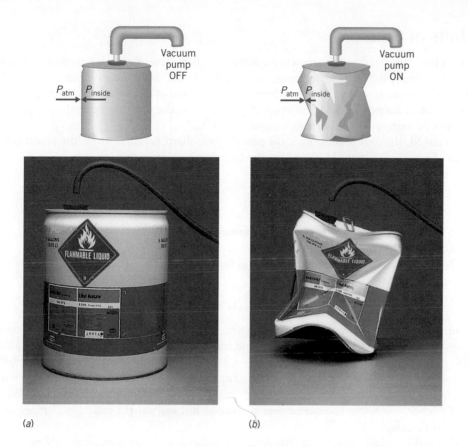

(a)   (b)

Figure 11.2 | **The effect of an unbalanced pressure.** (*a*) The pressure inside the can, P_{inside}, is the same as the atmospheric pressure outside, P_{atm}. The pressures are balanced; $P_{inside} = P_{atm}$. (*b*) When a vacuum pump reduces the pressure inside the can, P_{inside} becomes less than P_{atm}, and the unbalanced outside pressure quickly and violently makes the can collapse. (*OPC, Inc*)

a collapsible container such as the can in Figure 11.2. Before air is removed, the walls of the can experience atmospheric pressure equally inside and out. When some air is pumped out, however, the pressure inside decreases, making the atmospheric pressure outside of the can greater than the pressure inside. The net inward pressure is sufficiently great to make the can crumple.

To measure atmospheric pressure we use a device called a **barometer**. The simplest type is the *Torricelli barometer*[1] (Figure 11.3), which consists of a glass tube sealed at one end, 80 cm or more in length. To set up the apparatus, the tube is filled with mercury, capped, inverted, and then its capped end is immersed in a dish of mercury. When the cap is removed, some, but not all, of the mercury runs out.[2] When, due to its pressure, mercury flows from the tube, the level of the mercury in the dish must rise. Atmospheric pressure, pushing on the surface of the mercury in the dish, opposes this rise in mercury level. Rapidly, the two pressures become equal, and no more mercury can run out. However, a space inside the tube above the mercury level has been created having essentially no atmosphere; it's a *vacuum*.

The height of the mercury column, measured from the surface of the mercury in the dish, is directly proportional to atmospheric pressure. On days when the atmospheric pressure is high, more mercury is forced from the dish into the tube and the height of the column increases. When the atmospheric pressure drops—during an approaching storm, for example—some mercury flows out of the tube and the height of the column decreases. Most people live where this height fluctuates between 730 and 760 mm.

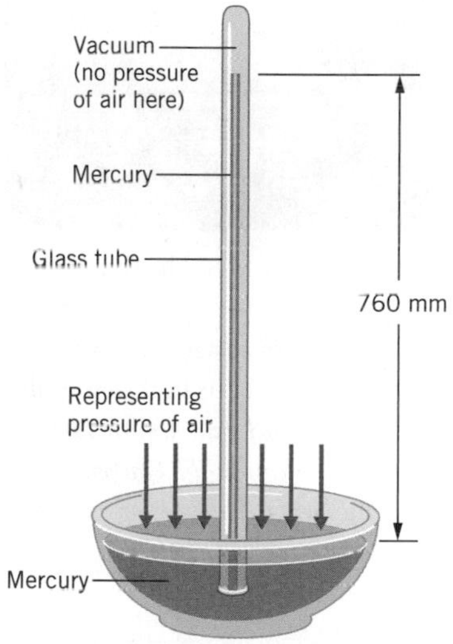

Figure 11.3 | **A Torricelli barometer.** The apparatus is also called a mercury barometer. The height of the mercury column inside the tube is directly proportional to the atmospheric pressure. In the United States, weather reports often give the height of the mercury column in inches.

Vacuum (no pressure of air here)

Mercury

Glass tube

760 mm

Representing pressure of air

Mercury

---

[1]In 1643 Evangelista Torricelli, an Italian mathematician, suggested an experiment, later performed by a colleague, that demonstrated that atmospheric pressure determines the height to which a fluid will rise in a tube inverted over the same liquid. This concept led to the development of the Torricelli barometer, which is named in his honor.

[2]Today, mercury is kept as much as possible in closed containers. Although atoms of mercury do not readily escape into the gaseous state, mercury vapor is a dangerous poison.

Units of Pressure

■ In English units, one atmosphere of pressure is 14.7 lb/in². This means that at sea level, each square inch of your body is experiencing a force of nearly 15 pounds.

At sea level, the height of the mercury column in a barometer fluctuates around a value of 760 mm. Some days it's a little higher, some a little lower, depending on the weather. The average pressure at sea level has long been used by scientists as a standard unit of pressure. The **standard atmosphere (atm)** was originally defined as the pressure needed to support a column of mercury 760 mm high measured at 0 °C.[3]

In the SI, the unit of pressure is the **pascal**, symbolized **Pa**. In SI units, the pascal is the ratio of force in *newtons* (N, the SI unit of force) to area in meters squared,

$$1 \text{ Pa} = \frac{1 \text{ N}}{1 \text{ m}^2} = 1 \text{ N m}^{-2}$$

It's a very small pressure; 1 Pa is approximately the pressure exerted by the weight of a lemon spread over an area of 1 m².

To bring the standard atmosphere unit in line with other SI units, it has been redefined in terms of the pascal as follows.

$$1 \text{ atm} = 101,325 \text{ Pa (exactly)}$$

A unit of pressure related to the pascal is the **bar**, which is defined as 100 kPa. Consequently, one bar is slightly smaller than one standard atmosphere (1 bar = 0.9868 atm). You may have heard the **millibar** unit (1 mb = 10^{-3} bar) used in weather reports describing pressures inside storms such as hurricanes. For example, the lowest atmospheric pressure at sea level ever observed in the Atlantic basin was 882 mb during Hurricane Wilma on October 19, 2005. The storm later weakened but still caused extensive damage as it crossed Florida.

For ordinary laboratory work, the pascal (or kilopascal) is not a conveniently measured unit. Usually we use a unit of pressure called the **torr** (named after Torricelli). The torr is defined as 1/760th of 1 atm.

$$1 \text{ torr} = \frac{1}{760} \text{ atm}$$

$$1 \text{ atm} = 760 \text{ torr (exactly)}$$

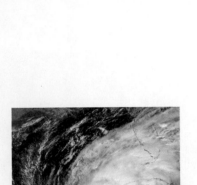

A satellite photo of Hurricane Wilma when it reached Category 5 strength, with sustained winds of 175 miles per hour in the eye wall. *(Terra MODIS data acquired by direct broadcast at the University of South Florida; Judd Taylor. Image processed at the University of Wisconsin-Madison)*

The torr is very close to the pressure that is able to support a column of mercury 1 mm high. In fact, the *millimeter of mercury* (abbreviated *mm Hg*) is often itself used as a pressure unit. Except when the most exacting measurements are being made, it is safe to use the relationship

$$1 \text{ torr} = 1 \text{ mm Hg}$$

Below are values of the standard atmosphere (atm) expressed in different pressure units. Studying the table will give you a feel for the sizes of the different units.

760 torr
101,325 Pa
101.325 kPa
1.013 bar   1.01325 bar
1013 mb
14.7 lb in.$^{-2}$ psi
1.034 kg cm^{-2}

[handwritten: $F = ma$
$= 10^4 \text{ kg} \times 9.8 \text{ m/s}^2 = 1 \times 10^5 \text{ N}$ *]*

---

[3]Because any metal, including mercury, expands or contracts as the temperature increases or decreases, the height of the mercury column varies with temperature (just as in a thermometer). Therefore, the definition of the standard atmosphere required that the temperature at which the mercury height is measured be specified.

11.1 | Using the table on page 476 determine the atmospheric pressure in pounds per square inch and inches of mercury when the barometer reads 730 mm Hg. (*Hint:* Recall your tools for converting units.)

11.2 | The second lowest barometric pressure ever recorded at sea level in the Western Hemisphere was 888 mb during Hurricane Gilbert in 1988. What was the pressure in pascals and torr?

Manometers

Gases used as reactants or formed as products in chemical reactions are kept from escaping by using closed glassware. To measure pressures inside such vessels, a **manometer** is used. Two types are common: open-end and closed-end manometers.

Open-End Manometers

An **open-end manometer** consists of a U-tube partly filled with a liquid, usually mercury (see Figure 11.4). One arm of the U-tube is open to the atmosphere; the other is exposed to a container of some trapped gas. In part (*a*) of this diagram, the mercury levels are equal and the pressure inside the flask is equal to the atmospheric pressure. The second part of the figure, 11.4*b*, shows the mercury level as being higher in the arm exposed to the atmosphere. We conclude that the pressure in the flask is greater than atmospheric pressure. In Figure 11.4*c*, the Hg is higher in the arm connected to the container of gas, indicating that the pressure of the atmosphere must be *higher* than the gas pressure. With mercury in the tube, the difference in the heights in the two arms, represented here as P_{Hg}, is equal to the difference between the pressure of the gas and the pressure of the atmosphere. By measuring P_{Hg} in millimeters, the value equals the pressure difference in torr. For the situation shown in Figure 11.4*b*, we would calculate the pressure of the trapped gas as

$$P_{gas} = P_{atm} + P_{Hg} \quad (\text{when } P_{gas} > P_{atm})$$

In Figure 11.4*c* the calculation of the pressure is

$$P_{gas} = P_{atm} - P_{Hg} \quad (\text{when } P_{gas} < P_{atm})$$

Example 11.1 illustrates how the open-end manometer is used.

■ Advantages of mercury over other liquids are its low reactivity, its low melting point, and particularly its very high density, which permits short manometer tubes.

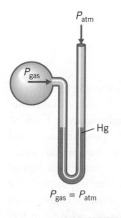

(a)

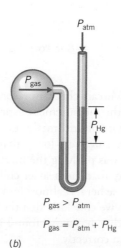

(b)

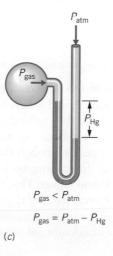

(c)

Figure 11.4 | **An open-end manometer.** The difference in the heights of the mercury in the two arms equals the pressure difference, in torr, between the atmospheric pressure, P_{atm}, and the pressure of the trapped gas, P_{gas}.

Example 11.1
Measuring the Pressure of a Gas Using a Manometer

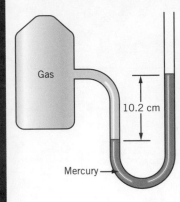

Gas

10.2 cm

Mercury

A student collected a gas in an apparatus connected to an open-end manometer, as illustrated in the figure in the margin. The difference in the heights of the mercury in the two columns was 10.2 cm and the atmospheric pressure was measured to be 756 torr. What was the pressure of the gas in the apparatus?

■ **Analysis:** From the preceding discussion, we know that when using an open-end manometer we will use the atmospheric pressure and either add to it or subtract from it— but which should we do? In a problem of this type, it is best to use some common sense (something that will help a lot in working problems involving gases).

When we look at the diagram of the apparatus, we see that the mercury is pushed up into the arm of the manometer that's open to the air. Common sense tells us that the pressure of the gas inside must be larger than the pressure of the air outside. Therefore, we will add the pressure difference to the atmospheric pressure.

Finally, before we can do the arithmetic, we must be sure the pressure difference is calculated in torr.

■ **Assembling the Tools:** We need the equation for determining the pressure in an open-end manometer,

$$P_{gas} = P_{atm} \pm P_{Hg}$$

where we add or subtract P_{Hg} depending on which side of the manometer has the higher mercury level. We use the usual conversion factors for SI prefixes from Table 2.4 on page 35 to perform the conversion needed.

$$10^{-2} \text{ m} = 1 \text{ cm} \quad \text{and} \quad 10^{-3} \text{ m} = 1 \text{ mm}$$

The other conversion we need is the equality between 1 mm Hg and 1 torr.

■ **Solution:** We first need to convert cm Hg to mm Hg, so we use our conversion factors to write

$$10.2 \text{ cm Hg} \times \frac{10^{-2} \text{ m}}{1 \text{ cm}} \times \frac{1 \text{ mm}}{10^{-3} \text{ m}} = 102 \text{ mm Hg} = 102 \text{ torr}$$

$$102 \text{ mm Hg} = 102 \text{ torr}$$

Based on our analysis, to find the gas pressure, we add 102 torr to the atmospheric pressure.

$$P_{gas} = P_{atm} + P_{Hg}$$
$$= 756 \text{ torr} + 102 \text{ torr}$$
$$= 858 \text{ torr}$$

The gas pressure is 858 torr.

■ **Is the Answer Reasonable?** We can check our conversions because the number of mm should always be larger than the measurement expressed in cm. We can also double-check that we've done the right *kind* of arithmetic (i.e., adding or subtracting). Look at the apparatus again. If the gas pressure were lower than atmospheric pressure, it would appear as though the atmosphere was pushing the mercury higher on the apparatus side of the manometer in the same way that the heavier child on a see-saw pushes his lighter friend higher. That's not what we see here. It almost looks like the gas is trying to push the mercury out of the manometer, so we conclude that the gas pressure must be higher than atmospheric pressure. That's exactly what we've found in our calculation, so we can feel confident we've solved the problem correctly.

11.3 | An open-end manometer is filled with mercury so that each side has a height equal to 25 cm. If the atmospheric pressure is 770 torr on a given day, what are the approximate maximum and minimum pressures that this manometer can measure? (*Hint:* What is the maximum difference in mercury height for this manometer?)

11.4 | In another experiment that same day, it was found that the mercury level in the arm of the manometer attached to the container of gas was 11.7 cm higher than in the arm open to the air. What was the pressure of the gas?

Closed-End Manometers

A **closed-end manometer** (Figure 11.5) is made by sealing the arm that will be farthest from the gas sample and then filling the closed arm completely with mercury. When the gas pressures to be measured are expected to be small, the filled arm can be made short, making the entire apparatus compact. In this design, the mercury is pushed to the top of the closed arm when the open arm of the manometer is exposed to the atmosphere. When connected to a gas at a low pressure, however, the mercury level in the sealed arm will drop, leaving a vacuum above it. The pressure of the gas can then be measured just by reading the difference in heights of the mercury in the two arms, P_{Hg}. No separate measurement of the atmospheric pressure is required.

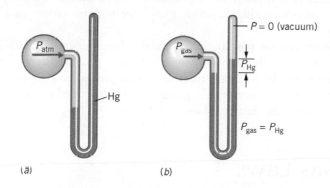

(a)   (b)

Figure 11.5 | **A closed-end manometer for measuring gas pressures less than 1 atm or 760 torr.** (*a*) When constructed, the tube is fully evacuated and then mercury is allowed to enter the tube to completely fill the closed arm. (*b*) When the tube is connected to a bulb containing a gas at low pressure, the difference in the mercury heights (P_{Hg}) equals the pressure, in torr, of the trapped gas P_{gas}.

Manometers with Liquids Other than Mercury

Scientists often use manometers with liquids other than mercury. One compelling reason is to reduce the possibility of a hazardous mercury spill. Another reason is that more precise measurements may be made using other liquids and then converting to the equivalent in mercury. Water, ethyl alcohol, mineral oil, and many other liquids may be used in place of mercury.

In order to convert the difference in heights of a liquid to the equivalent height in mercury, we need to know the density of the substitute liquid. We can reason that the height of different liquids, measuring the same pressure, should be inversely proportional to their densities.

$$\frac{\text{height liquid 1}}{\text{height liquid 2}} = \frac{\text{density liquid 2}}{\text{density liquid 1}}$$

If liquid 1 is mercury, we can rearrange the equation to read

$$\text{mm Hg} = \text{mm liquid} \times \frac{\text{density of liquid}}{\text{density Hg}}$$

This will allow us to use any liquid with a known density in a manometer and then convert the readings to the equivalent in mm Hg.

■ Ten meters is about 33 foot or the height of a three-story building.

Let's consider what will happen if we use water instead of mercury in a manometer. Because of the low density of water compared to the high density of mercury, we will observe a height of water that is 13.6 times the height of mercury. The practical result of using a water manometer is that measurements will be 13.6 times more precise than those using a mercury manometer. The drawback is that a water manometer used to measure barometric pressure would have to be more than 10 meters high.

Modern Pressure Sensors

Digital tire gauge. *(David J. Green/ Alamy)*

Membrane pressure sensor with blue-colored membrane exposed. *(Photo courtesy of Pressure Systems)*

Manometers are obvious in the way readings are related to gas pressures. However, there are a large number of different, and often more convenient, devices in use today.

Almost everyone is familiar with a tire gauge to make sure the pressure in a car tire is correct. The mechanical version is based on the pressure in the tire pushing against a plunger (with the scale on it) attached to a spring. When the force exerted by the tire pressure and the force of the compressed spring are equal, the plunger stops moving and the pressure can be read from the scale. Another device, called a Bourdon tube, relies on gas pressure expanding a coil of tubing. As the coil expands it rotates. A pointer and calibrated scale are attached to measure this rotation as a pressure reading.

Automatic electronic pressure sensors, such as the digital tire pressure gauge, are based on electrical or mechanical properties of thin metallic or plastic membranes that change when pressure is applied. These properties can be monitored continuously, and this type of pressure-measuring device is useful for remote sensors such as deep-sea measurements.

Measurement of very low pressures uses specialized equipment. One device, called an ionization gauge, measures the number of ions that can be produced at charged electrodes. The lower the pressure, the fewer the number of ions produced. Pressures from 10^{-2} to 10^{-11} torr can be measured; however, the gauge must be calibrated because the type of gas molecule present affects the number of ions produced.

11.3 | Gas Laws

Earlier, we examined some properties of gases that are familiar to you. Our discussion was only qualitative, however, and now that we've discussed pressure and its units, we are ready to examine gas behavior quantitatively.

There are four variables that affect the properties of a gas—pressure, volume, temperature, and the amount of gas. In this section, we will study situations in which the amount of gas (measured either by grams or moles) remains constant and observe how gas samples respond to changes in pressure, volume, and temperature.

Pressure–Volume Law

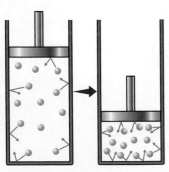

Figure 11.6 | **Compressing a gas increases its pressure.** A molecular view of what happens when a gas is squeezed into a smaller volume. By crowding the molecules together, the number of collisions with a given area of the walls increases, which causes the pressure to rise.

When you inflate a bicycle tire with a hand pump, you squeeze air into a smaller volume and increase its pressure. Packing molecules into a smaller space causes an increased number of collisions with the walls, and because these collisions are responsible for the pressure, the pressure increases (Figure 11.6).

Robert Boyle, an Irish scientist (1627–1691), performed experiments to determine quantitatively how the volume of a fixed amount of gas varies with pressure. Because the volume is also affected by the temperature, he held that variable constant. A graph of typical data collected in his experiments is shown in Figure 11.7*a* and demonstrates that *the volume of a given amount of gas held at constant temperature varies inversely with the applied pressure.* Mathematically, this can be expressed as

$$V \propto \frac{1}{P} \qquad \text{(temperature and amount of gas held constant)}$$

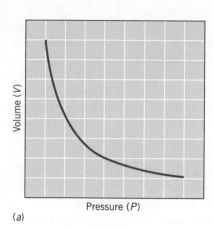 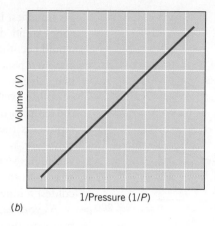

Figure 11.7 | **The variation of volume with pressure at constant temperature for a fixed amount of gas.** (*a*) A typical graph of volume versus pressure, showing that as the pressure increases, the volume decreases. (*b*) A straight line is obtained when volume is plotted against $1/P$, which shows that $V \propto 1/P$.

where V is the volume and P is the pressure. This relationship between pressure and volume is now called **Boyle's law** or the **pressure–volume law**.

In the expression above, the proportionality sign, $\propto$, can be removed by introducing a proportionality constant, C.

$$V = \frac{1}{P} \times C$$

Rearranging gives

$$PV = C = nRT$$

This equation tells us, for example, that if at constant temperature the gas pressure is doubled, the gas volume must be cut in half so that the product of $P \times V$ doesn't change.

What is remarkable about Boyle's discovery is that *this relationship is essentially the same for all gases at temperatures and pressures usually found in the laboratory.*

Ideal Gases

When very precise measurements are made, it's found that Boyle's law doesn't quite work. This is especially a problem when the pressure of the gas is very high or when the gas is at a low temperature where it's on the verge of changing to a liquid. Although real gases do not *exactly* obey Boyle's law or any of the other gas laws that we'll study, it is often useful to imagine a hypothetical gas that would. We call such a hypothetical gas an *ideal gas*. An **ideal gas** *would obey the gas laws exactly over all temperatures and pressures*. A real gas behaves more and more like an ideal gas as its pressure decreases and its temperature increases. Most gases we work with in the lab can be treated as ideal gases unless we're dealing with extremely precise measurements.

Temperature–Volume Law

In 1787 a French chemist and mathematician named Jacques Alexander Charles became interested in hot-air ballooning, which at the time was becoming popular in France. His new interest led him to study what happens to the volume of a sample of gas when the temperature is varied, keeping the pressure constant.

When data from experiments such as his are plotted, a graph like that shown in Figure 11.8 is obtained. Here the volume of the gas is plotted against the temperature in degrees Celsius. The colored points correspond to typical data, and the lines are drawn to most closely fit the data. Each line represents data collected for a different sample. Because all gases eventually become liquids if cooled sufficiently, the solid portions of the lines correspond to temperatures at which measurements are possible; at lower temperatures the

■ Jacques Alexandre César Charles (1746–1823), a French scientist, had a keen interest in hot-air balloons. He was the first to inflate a balloon with hydrogen.

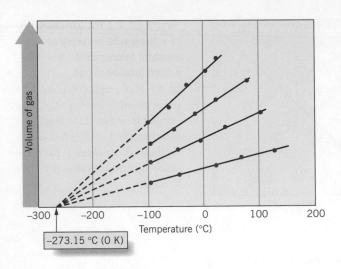

Volume of gas

Temperature (°C)

−273.15 °C (0 K)

Figure 11.8 | **Charles' law plots.** Each line shows how the gas volume changes with temperature for a different-size sample of the same gas.

■ The value of C' depends on the size and pressure of the gas sample.

■ Joseph Louis Gay-Lussac (1778–1850), a French scientist, was a co-discoverer of the element boron.

■ We're using different symbols for the various gas law constants because they are different for each law.

gas liquefies. However, if the lines are extrapolated (i.e., reasonably extended) back to a point where the volume of the gas would become zero if it didn't condense, all the lines meet at the same temperature, −273.15 °C. Especially significant is the fact that this exact same behavior is exhibited by all gases; when plots of volume versus temperature are extrapolated to zero volume, the temperature axis is always crossed at −273.15 °C. This point represents the temperature at which all gases, if they did not condense, would have a volume of zero, and below which they would have a negative volume. Negative volumes are impossible, of course, so it was reasoned that −273.15 °C must be nature's coldest temperature, and it was called **absolute zero.**

As you learned earlier, absolute zero corresponds to the zero point on the Kelvin temperature scale, and to obtain a Kelvin temperature, we add 273.15 °C to the Celsius temperature.[4]

$$T_K = t_C + 273.15$$

For most purposes, we will need only three significant figures, so we can use the following approximate relationship.

$$T_K = t_C + 273$$

The straight lines in Figure 11.8 suggest that at constant pressure, the volume of a gas is directly proportional to its temperature, provided the temperature is expressed in kelvins. This became known as **Charles' law** (or the **temperature–volume law**) and is expressed mathematically as

$$V \propto T \qquad \text{(pressure and amount of gas held constant)}$$

Using a different proportionality constant, C', we can write

$$V = C' T \qquad \text{(pressure and amount of gas held constant)}$$

Pressure–Temperature Law

The French scientist Joseph Louis Gay-Lussac studied how the pressure and temperature of a fixed amount of gas at constant volume are related. (Such conditions exist, for example, when a gas is confined in a vessel with rigid walls, like an aerosol can.) The relationship that he established, called **Gay-Lussac's law** or the **pressure–temperature law**, states that *the pressure of a fixed amount of gas held at constant volume is directly proportional to the Kelvin temperature.* Thus,

$$P \propto T \qquad \text{(volume and amount of gas held constant)}$$

Using still another constant of proportionality, Gay-Lussac's law becomes

$$P = C'' T \qquad \text{(volume and amount of gas held constant)}$$

Combined Gas Law

The three gas laws we've just examined can be brought together into a single equation known as the **combined gas law**, which states that *the ratio PV/T is a constant for a fixed amount of gas.*

$$\frac{PV}{T} = \text{constant} \qquad \text{(for a fixed amount of gas)}$$

---

[4]In Chapter 1 we presented this equation as $T_K = (t_C + 273.15 \text{ °C}) \left(\frac{1 \text{ K}}{1 \text{ °C}} \right)$ to emphasize unit cancellation.

Operationally, however, we just add 273.15 to the Celsius temperature to obtain the Kelvin temperature (or we just add 273 if three significant figures are sufficient).

Usually, we use the combined gas law in problems where we know some given set of conditions of temperature, pressure, and volume (for a fixed amount of gas), and wish to find out how one of these variables will change when the others are changed. If we label the initial conditions of P, V, and T with the subscript 1 and the final conditions with the subscript 2, the combined gas law can be written in the following useful form.

$$\frac{P_1 V_1}{T_1} = \frac{P_2 V_2}{T_2}$$

(11.1)

Combined gas law

In applying this equation, T must always be in kelvins. The pressure and volume can have any units, but whatever the units are on one side of the equation, they must be the same on the other side.

It is simple to show that Equation 11.1 contains each of the other gas laws as special cases. Boyle's law, for example, applies when the temperature is constant. Under these conditions, T_1 equals T_2 and the temperature cancels from the equation. This leaves us with

$$P_1 V_1 = P_2 V_2 \qquad \text{(when } T_1 \text{ equals } T_2\text{)}$$

which is one way to write Boyle's law. Similarly, under conditions of constant pressure, P_1 equals P_2 and the pressure cancels, so Equation 11.1 reduces to

$$V_1/T_1 = V_2/T_2 \qquad \text{(when } P_1 \text{ equals } P_2\text{)}$$

This, of course, is another way of writing Charles' law. Under the constant volume conditions required by Gay-Lussac's law, V_1 equals V_2, and Equation 11.1 reduces to

$$P_1/T_1 = P_2/T_2 \qquad \text{(when } V_1 \text{ equals } V_2\text{)}$$

CHEMISTRY OUTSIDE THE CLASSROOM | 11.1

Whipped Cream

The dessert in Figure 1 looks tempting, but up until 1934 everyone had to whip their own cream by hand. Food scientists at the time were in the midst of using chemistry to produce a wide array of "convenience foods," foods that needed little or no preparation or cooking time.

Many foods can be canned—just look at the rows of vegetables, meats, and fruits lined up in the supermarket. Not only are these handy, but they also have exceptional shelf life compared to fresh vegetables, meats, and fruits. Fresh foods could be kept longer in refrigerators, which became commonly available in the 1930s. Freezers for frozen foods and ice cream came shortly thereafter. Now the consumer could have ice cream at home, but that wonderful sundae still needed the whipped cream.

Around 1934, Charles Getz was a graduate student in chemistry at the University of Illinois when he developed and sought a patent for producing a fluffy aerosol of gas bubbles entrained in cream. The concept was simple. Put some cream in a can, pressurize it with a gas, and when the gas is released along with the cream, it should foam up into whipped cream. Hundreds of gases were tried as propellants and they were all failures. Getz found

that carbon dioxide did create a foam with milk, but it also gave the food a bad taste because of the sour taste of the acidic CO_2. He switched to nitrous oxide because it had no taste and provided a good product. It is now believed that the nonpolar CO_2 and N_2O work by dissolving in the nonpolar fats in liquid cream. When the pressure is released the gas expands to form tiny, relatively uniform bubbles to whip the cream. In 1935 Charles Getz applied for a process patent for his method of preparing whipped cream with nitrous oxide. He was issued Patent 2,294,172 in 1942. Aaron "Bunny" Lapin, an inventor from St. Louis, created Reddi-wip® real whipped cream in 1948.

Figure 1 Whipped cream dispensed from an aerosol container. *Envision/© Corbis*

Example 11.2
Using the Combined Gas Law

© *Tony Lilley Ci/Alamy*

An ordinary incandescent light bulb contains a tungsten filament, which becomes white hot (about 2500 °C) when electricity is passed through it. To prevent the filament from rapidly oxidizing, the bulb is filled to a low pressure with the inert (unreactive) gas argon. Suppose a 12.0 L cylinder containing compressed argon at a pressure of 57.8 atm measured at 24 °C is to be used to fill electric light bulbs, each with a volume of 158 mL, to a pressure of 3.00 torr at 21 °C. How many of these light bulbs could be filled by the argon in the cylinder?

■ **Analysis:** What do we need to know to figure out how many light bulbs can be filled? If we knew the total volume of gas with a pressure of 3.00 torr at 21 °C, we could just divide by the volume of one light bulb; the result is the number of light bulbs that can be filled. So our main problem is determining what volume the argon in the cylinder will occupy when its pressure is reduced to 3.00 torr and its temperature is lowered to 21 °C.

■ **Assembling the Tools:** Because the total amount of argon isn't changing, we can use the combined gas law for the calculation.

$$\frac{P_1V_1}{T_1} = \frac{P_2V_2}{T_2}$$

■ **Solution:** First, we will also make sure that the temperature is expressed in kelvins and that the values for P and V have the same units so that they cancel. To do this we need to convert 57.8 atm to torr,

$$57.8 \ \cancel{atm} \times \frac{760 \text{ torr}}{1 \ \cancel{atm}} = 4.39 \times 10^4 \text{ torr}$$

To use the combined gas law, let's construct a table of data being sure to assign the proper values to either the initial or final conditions.

	Initial (1)		Final (2)
P_1	4.39×10^4 torr	P_2	3.00 torr
V_1	12.0 L	V_2	?
T_1	297 K (24 + 273)	T_2	294 K (21 + 273)

To obtain the final volume, we solve for V_2. To do this we'll rearrange the equation so that V_2 is on one side of the equals sign and the remaining variables are on the other side.

Ratio of temperatures

$$V_2 = V_1 \times \frac{P_1}{P_2} \times \frac{T_2}{T_1}$$

Ratio of pressures

Notice that for V_2 to have the same units as V_1, the units in the numerator and denominator of both ratios must cancel. That's the reason we had to convert atmospheres to torr for P_1. Let's now substitute values from our table of data.

$$V_2 = 12.0 \text{ L} \times \frac{4.39 \times 10^4 \ \cancel{torr}}{3.00 \ \cancel{torr}} \times \frac{294 \ \cancel{K}}{297 \ \cancel{K}}$$

$$= 1.74 \times 10^5 \text{ L}$$

Before we can divide by the volume of one light bulb (158 mL), we have to convert the total volume to milliliters.

$$1.74 \times 10^5 \; \cancel{L} \times \frac{1000 \text{ mL}}{1 \; \cancel{L}} = 1.74 \times 10^8 \text{ mL}$$

The volume per light bulb gives us the relationship

$$1 \text{ light bulb} \Leftrightarrow 158 \text{ mL argon}$$

which we can use to construct a conversion factor to find the number of light bulbs that can be filled.

$$1.74 \times 10^8 \; \cancel{\text{mL argon}} \times \frac{1 \text{ light bulb}}{158 \; \cancel{\text{mL argon}}} = 1.10 \times 10^6 \text{ light bulbs}$$

That's 1.10 million light bulbs! As you can see, there's not much argon in each one.

■ **Is the Answer Reasonable?** To determine whether we've set up the combined gas law properly, we check to see if the pressure and temperature ratios move the volume in the correct direction. Going from the initial to final conditions, the pressure *decreases* from 4.39×10^4 torr to 3.00 torr, so the volume should *increase* a lot. The pressure ratio we used is much larger than 1, so multiplying by it should increase the volume, which agrees with what we expect. Next, look at the temperature change; a *drop in temperature* should tend to *decrease* the volume, so we should be multiplying by a ratio that's less than 1. The ratio 293/298 is less than 1, so that ratio is correct, too.

Now that our setup is okay, we check the math by rounding our numbers. One way we can round the numbers to estimate the answer is:

$$V_2 = 12.0 \text{ L} \times \frac{4.5 \times 10^4 \; \cancel{\text{torr}}}{3 \; \cancel{\text{torr}}} \times \frac{300 \; \cancel{\text{K}}}{300 \; \cancel{\text{K}}}$$

The estimated answer for $V_2 = 18 \times 10^4$ L, which is very close to our calculator answer. We can multiply the liters by 10^3 to get 18×10^7 mL and then we will "round" the 158 mL/bulb to 18×10^1 mL/bulb. Dividing the two gives us 1×10^6 bulbs. This again agrees quite well with the calculated answer.

(An observant student might note that in the end 12 L of argon must remain in the cylinder. However, we can divide 12,000 mL by 158 to get an answer of approximately 75 bulbs. Subtracting 75 from 1.09×10^6 still leaves us with 1.09×10^6 light bulbs.)

■ Notice that we use our knowledge of how gases behave to determine whether we've done the correct arithmetic. If you learn to do this, you can catch your mistakes.

Practice Exercises

11.5 | Use the combined gas law to determine by what factor the pressure of an ideal gas must change if the Kelvin temperature is doubled and the volume is tripled. (*Hint:* Sometimes it is easier to assume a starting set of temperature, volume, and pressure readings and then apply the conditions of the problem.)

11.6 | A sample of nitrogen has a volume of 880 mL and a pressure of 740 torr. What pressure will change the volume to 870 mL at the same temperature?

11.7 | What will be the final pressure of a sample of nitrogen with a volume of 950 m³ at 745 torr and 25.0 °C if it is heated to 60.0 °C and given a final volume of 1150 m³?

11.4 | Stoichiometry Using Gas Volumes

Reactions at Constant *T* and *P*

When scientists studied reactions between gases quantitatively, they made an interesting discovery. If the volumes of the reacting gases, as well as the volumes of gaseous products, are measured under the same conditions of temperature and pressure, the volumes are in simple whole-number ratios. For example, hydrogen gas reacts with chlorine gas to give gaseous hydrogen chloride. Beneath the names in the following equation are the relative volumes with which these gases interact (at the same *T* and *P*).

$$\text{hydrogen} + \text{chlorine} \longrightarrow \text{hydrogen chloride}$$
$$\text{1 volume} \qquad \text{1 volume} \qquad \text{2 volumes}$$

What this means is that if we were to use 1.0 L of hydrogen, it would react with 1.0 L of chlorine and produce 2.0 L of hydrogen chloride. If we were to use 10.0 L of hydrogen, all the other volumes would be multiplied by 10 as well.

Similar simple, whole-number ratios by volume are observed when hydrogen combines with oxygen to give water, which is a gas above 100 °C.

$$\text{hydrogen} + \text{oxygen} \longrightarrow \text{water (gaseous)}$$
$$\text{2 volumes} \qquad \text{1 volume} \qquad \text{2 volumes}$$

Notice that the reacting volumes, *measured under identical temperatures and pressures,* are in ratios of simple, whole numbers.[5]

Observations such as those above led Gay-Lussac to formulate his **law of combining volumes**, which states that *when gases react at the same temperature and pressure, their combining volumes are in ratios of simple whole numbers.* Much later, it was learned that these "simple whole numbers" are the coefficients of the equations for the reactions.

Avogadro's Principle

■ Amedeo Avogadro (1776–1856), an Italian scientist, helped to put chemistry on a quantitative basis.

The observation that the gases react in whole-number volume ratios led Amedeo Avogadro to conclude that, at the same *T* and *P*, equal volumes of gases must have identical numbers of molecules. Today, we know that "equal numbers of *molecules*" is the same as "equal numbers of *moles*," so Avogadro's insight, now called **Avogadro's principle**, is expressed as follows: *When measured at the same temperature and pressure, equal volumes of gases contain equal numbers of moles.* A corollary to Avogadro's principle is that *the volume of a gas is directly proportional to its number of moles, n.*

$$V \propto n \qquad \text{(at constant } T \text{ and } P\text{)}$$

Standard Molar Volume

Avogadro's principle implies that the volume occupied by one mole of *any* gas—its *molar volume*—must be identical for all gases under the same conditions of pressure and temperature. To compare the molar volumes of different gases, scientists agreed to use 1 atm

---

[5]The great French chemist Antoine Laurent Lavoisier (1743–1794) was the first to observe the volume relationships of this particular reaction. In his 1789 textbook, *Elements of Chemistry,* he wrote that the formation of water from hydrogen and oxygen requires that two volumes of hydrogen be used for every volume of oxygen. Lavoisier was unable to extend the study of this behavior of hydrogen and oxygen to other gas reactions because he was beheaded during the French Revolution. (See Michael Laing, *The Journal of Chemical Education,* February 1998, page 177.)

Table 11.1	Molar Volumes of Some Gases at STP	
Gas	**Formula**	**Molar Volume (L)**
Helium	He	22.398
Argon	Ar	22.401
Hydrogen	H_2	22.410
Nitrogen	N_2	22.413
Oxygen	O_2	22.414
Carbon dioxide	CO_2	22.414

and 273.15 K (0 °C) as the **standard conditions of temperature and pressure**,[6] or **STP**, for short. If we measure the molar volumes for a variety of gases at STP, we find that the values fluctuate somewhat because the gases are not "ideal." Some typical values are listed in Table 11.1, and if we were to examine the data for many gases we would find an average of around 22.4 L per mole. This value is taken to be the molar volume of an *ideal gas* at STP and is now called the **standard molar volume** of a gas.

For an ideal gas at STP:

$$\left(1 \text{ mol gas} \Leftrightarrow 22.4 \text{ L gas} \right)$$ → for any gas

1 mol CO_2 = 44.0g = 22.4 L gas
1 mol O_2 = 32.0g = 22.4 L gas
↓↓
different density

Avogadro's principle was a remarkable advance in our understanding of gases. His insight enabled chemists for the first time to determine the formulas of gaseous elements.[7]

Stoichiometry Problems

For reactions involving gases, Avogadro's principle lets us use a new kind of stoichiometric equivalency, one between *volumes* of gases. Earlier, for example, we noted the following reaction and its gas volume relationships.

$$2H_2(g) + O_2(g) \longrightarrow 2H_2O(g)$$

2 volumes   1 volume   2 volumes

Provided we are dealing with gas volumes measured at the same temperature and pressure, we can write the following stoichiometric equivalencies.

2 volumes $H_2(g) \Leftrightarrow$ 1 volume $O_2(g)$	just as	2 mol $H_2 \Leftrightarrow$ 1 mol O_2
2 volumes $H_2(g) \Leftrightarrow$ 2 volumes $H_2O(g)$	just as	2 mol $H_2 \Leftrightarrow$ 2 mol H_2O
1 volume $O_2(g) \Leftrightarrow$ 2 volumes $H_2O(g)$	just as	1 mol $O_2 \Leftrightarrow$ 2 mol H_2O

Relationships such as these can greatly simplify stoichiometry problems, as we see in Example 11.3.

■ The recognition that equivalencies in gas *volumes* are numerically the same as those for numbers of moles of gas in reactions involving gases simplifies many calculations.

---

[6]Today there are more than a dozen definitions of "standard temperature and pressure." Our selection of STP is predicated on tradition and the fact that pressure, commonly measured in mm Hg from a manometer, is easily converted to atmospheres.

[7]Suppose that hydrogen chloride, for example, is correctly formulated as HCl, not as H_2Cl_2 or H_3Cl_3 or higher, and certainly not as $H_{0.5}Cl_{0.5}$. Then the only way that *two* volumes of hydrogen chloride could come from just *one* volume of hydrogen and *one* of chlorine is if each particle of hydrogen and each of chlorine were to consist of *two* atoms of H and Cl, respectively, H_2 and Cl_2. If these particles were single-atom particles, H and Cl, then one volume of H and one volume of Cl could give only *one* volume of HCl, not two. Of course, if the initial assumption were incorrect so that hydrogen chloride is, say, H_2Cl_2 instead of HCl, then hydrogen would be H_4 and chlorine would be Cl_4. The extension to larger subscripts works in the same way.

Example 11.3
Stoichiometry of Reactions of Gases

How many liters of hydrogen, $H_2(g)$, measured at STP, are needed to combine exactly with 1.50 L of nitrogen, also measured at STP, to form ammonia?

■ **Analysis:** The problem states that the reactants are at STP, standard temperature (273 K) and pressure (760 torr). Therefore all the gases in this example are at the same temperature and pressure. That makes the ratios by volume the same as the ratio by moles, which means that the ratios by volume are the same as the ratios of the coefficients of the balanced equation. So we can then substitute the volume ratio for the mole ratio in our calculations.

■ **Assembling the Tools:** We're dealing with a chemical reaction, so we need the balanced chemical equation we learned to construct in Chapter 3.

$$3H_2(g) + N_2(g) \longrightarrow 2NH_3(g)$$

Avogadro's principle then gives us the equivalency we need to perform the calculation.

$$3 \text{ volumes } H_2 \Leftrightarrow 1 \text{ volume } N_2$$

The stoichiometric procedures learned in Chapter 4 can be used to solve the problem.

■ **Solution:** We now restate the problem as

$$1.50 \text{ L } N_2 \Leftrightarrow ? \text{ L } H_2$$

We use the volume ratio, now in L units, to express the equivalence

$$3 \text{ L } H_2 \Leftrightarrow 1 \text{ L } N_2$$

This volume equivalence is used to construct the conversion factor, and our solution is

$$1.50 \text{ L } N_2 \times \frac{3 \text{ L } H_2}{1 \text{ L } N_2} = 4.50 \text{ L } H_2$$

■ **Is the Answer Reasonable?** The volume of H_2 needed is three times the volume of N_2, and 3×1.5 equals 4.5, so the answer is correct. Remember, however, that the simplicity of this problem arises because the volumes are at the same temperature and pressure.

Example 11.4
Stoichiometry Calculations when Gases Are Not at the Same T and P

Nitrogen monoxide, a pollutant released by automobile engines, is oxidized by molecular oxygen to give the reddish-brown gas nitrogen dioxide, which gives smog its characteristic color. The equation is

$$2NO(g) + O_2(g) \longrightarrow 2NO_2(g)$$

How many milliliters of O_2, measured at 22 °C and 755 torr, are needed to react with 184 mL of NO, measured at 45 °C and 723 torr?

■ **Analysis:** Once again, we have a stoichiometry problem involving gas volumes, but this one is more complicated than the one in Example 11.3 because the gases are not at the same temperature and pressure. The way to resolve this difficulty is to make the temperature and pressure the same for both gases. Since we are asked for the volume of O_2 at 22 °C and 755 torr, it will be easiest if we determine the volume of the NO under those conditions. Once we do that, we can use the gas volumes for our stoichiometry calculation as diagrammed below.

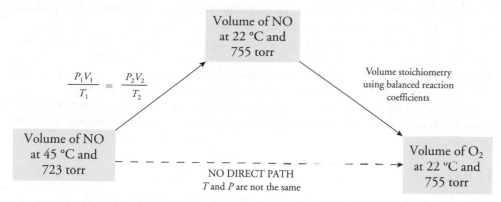

With that analysis, this problem is seen to contain two concepts: the *combined gas law* and a *stoichiometry calculation* using gas volumes.

■ **Assembling the Tools:** We can use the combined gas law to find what volume the NO would occupy if it were at the same temperature and pressure as the O_2. Then we can use the coefficients of the equation to find the volume of O_2.

$$\frac{P_1 V_1}{T_1} = \frac{P_2 V_2}{T_2}$$

We will again use Avogadro's principle once the volumes at the same temperature and pressure are determined.

■ **Solution:** We use the combined gas law applied to the given volume of NO, so let's set up the data as usual.

	Initial (1)		Final (2)
P_1	723 torr	P_2	755 torr
V_1	184 mL	V_2	?
T_1	318 K (45 °C + 273)	T_2	295 K (22 °C + 273)

Solving the combined gas law for V_2 gives

$$V_2 = V_1 \times \left(\frac{P_1}{P_2}\right) \times \left(\frac{T_2}{T_1}\right)$$

Next we substitute values:

$$V_2 = 184 \text{ mL} \times \left(\frac{723 \text{ torr}}{755 \text{ torr}}\right) \times \left(\frac{295 \text{ K}}{318 \text{ K}}\right)$$
$$= 163.5 \text{ mL NO}$$

We can now use the coefficients of the equation to establish the equivalency

$$2 \text{ mL NO} \Leftrightarrow 1 \text{ mL } O_2$$

and apply it to find the volume of O_2 required for the reaction.

$$163.5 \text{ mL NO} \times \frac{1 \text{ mL } O_2}{2 \text{ mL NO}} = 81.7 \text{ mL } O_2$$

Note how we kept an extra significant figure in V_2 until we calculated the final volume of O_2.

■ **Is the Answer Reasonable?** For the first calculation, we can check to see whether the pressure and temperature ratios move the volume in the right direction. The pressure is increasing (723 torr ⟶ 755 torr), so that should decrease the volume. The pressure ratio is smaller than 1, so it is having the proper effect. The temperature is dropping (318 K ⟶ 295 K), so this change should also reduce the volume. The temperature ratio is smaller than 1, so it is also having the correct effect. The volume of NO at 22 °C and 755 torr is probably correct. We can also observe that the two ratios are only slightly less than 1.0 and we expect the answer to be close to the given volume, which it is.

The check of the calculation is simple. According to the equation, the volume of O_2 required should be half the volume of NO, which it is, so the final answer seems to be okay.

Practice Exercises

11.8 | Methane burns according to the following equation.

$$CH_4(g) + 2O_2(g) \longrightarrow CO_2(g) + 2H_2O(g)$$

The combustion of 4.50 L of CH_4 consumes how many liters of O_2, both volumes measured at 25 °C and 740 torr? (*Hint:* Recall Avogadro's principle concerning the number of molecules in a fixed volume of gas at a given temperature and pressure.)

11.9 | How many liters of air (air is 20.9% oxygen) are required for the combustion of 6.75 L of CH_4?

11.10 | The multi-step problem in Example 11.4 can be solved by calculating the volume of oxygen at the initial T and P of the NO and then using the combined gas law to calculate the volume of oxygen at the desired T and P (i.e., we can switch the sequence of the steps). Verify that you get the same answer using this method.

11.5 | Ideal Gas Law

In our discussion of the combined gas law, we noted that the ratio PV/T equals a constant for a fixed amount of gas. However, the value of this "constant" is actually proportional to the number of moles of gas, n, in the sample.[8]

To create an equation even more general than the combined gas law, therefore, we can write

$$\frac{PV}{T} \propto n$$

We can replace the proportionality symbol with an equals sign by including another proportionality constant.

$$\frac{PV}{T} = n \times \text{constant}$$

(handwritten: moles)

This new constant is given the symbol **R** and is called the **universal gas constant**. We can now write the combined gas law in a still more general form called the **ideal gas law**.

$$\frac{PV}{T} = nR$$

■ Sometimes this equation is called the *universal gas law*.

---

[8]In the problems we worked earlier, we were able to use the combined gas law expressed as

$$\frac{P_1V_1}{T_1} = \frac{P_2V_2}{T_2}$$

because the amount of gas remained fixed.

An ideal gas would obey this law exactly over all ranges of the gas variables. The equation, sometimes called the **equation of state for an ideal gas**, is usually rearranged and written as follows.

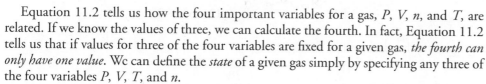

Ideal Gas Law (Equation of State for an Ideal Gas)

$$PV = nRT \qquad\qquad (11.2)$$

Equation 11.2 tells us how the four important variables for a gas, *P*, *V*, *n*, and *T*, are related. If we know the values of three, we can calculate the fourth. In fact, Equation 11.2 tells us that if values for three of the four variables are fixed for a given gas, *the fourth can only have one value*. We can define the *state* of a given gas simply by specifying any three of the four variables *P*, *V*, *T*, and *n*.

■ If *n*, *P*, and *T* in Equation 11.2 are known, for example, then *V* can have *only one value*.

To use the ideal gas law, we have to know the value of the universal gas constant, *R*, which is equal to *PV/nT*. The value of *R* will depend on the values and units we choose for *P*, *V*, *T*, and *n*. We will use units of liters for volume, kelvins for temperature, atmospheres for temperature, and moles for *n*. Earlier, on page 487 we defined the standard temperature and pressure, STP, as 273 K and one atmosphere of pressure. We also noted that one mole of an ideal gas has a volume of 22.4 liters. Using these values we can calculate *R* as follows.

■ More precise measurements give *R* = 0.082057 L atm mol⁻¹ K⁻¹. If we use the bar as the standard pressure, then *R* = 0.083144 L bar mol⁻¹ K⁻¹.

$$R = \frac{PV}{nT} = \frac{(1.00 \text{ atm})(22.4 \text{ L})}{(1.00 \text{ mol})(273 \text{ K})}$$

$$= 0.0821 \ \frac{\text{atm L}}{\text{mol K}}$$

or, arranging the units in a commonly used order,   *for any gas*

$$R = 0.0821 \text{ L atm mol}^{-1} \text{ K}^{-1}$$

To use this value of *R* in working problems, we have to be sure to express volumes in liters, temperatures in kelvins, and pressures in atmospheres. In later chapters we will find *R* defined using different units, and, of course, it will have a different numerical value.

Example 11.5
Using the Ideal Gas Law

In Example 11.2, we described filling a 158 mL light bulb with argon at a temperature of 21 °C and a pressure of 3.00 torr. How many grams of argon are in the light bulb under these conditions?

■ **Analysis:** The question asks for the grams of Ar, and our stoichiometry experience (see Figure 4.6 on page 142) tells us that the only way to calculate the mass of Ar is first to know the moles of Ar (or some way to calculate the moles of Ar). The first step will be to determine the moles of Ar in the light bulb; then we will convert moles to mass.

■ **Assembling the Tools:** The only equation that allows us to calculate the moles of a gas is the ideal gas law equation, *PV = nRT*. We will solve it for *n* by substituting values for *P*, *V*, *R*, and *T*. Once we have the number of moles of Ar, the tool to use is the relationship of atomic mass to moles. For Ar we write

$$1 \text{ mol Ar} = 39.95 \text{ g Ar}$$

A conversion factor $\dfrac{39.95 \text{ g Ar}}{1 \text{ mol Ar}}$ made from this relationship lets us convert moles to grams.

■ **Solution:** When using the ideal gas law we need to be sure that *P*, *V*, and *T* have the correct units. One helpful clue is that the units for *R* must cancel and therefore they prescribe the units we need for our variables. When using $R = 0.0821$ L atm mol^{-1} K^{-1}, we must have V in liters, P in atmospheres, and T in kelvins. Gathering the data and making the necessary unit conversions as we go, we have

$P = 3.95 \times 10^{-3}$ atm   from 3.00 torr $\times \dfrac{1 \text{ atm}}{760 \text{ torr}}$

$V = 0.158$ L   from 158 mL

$T = 294$ K   from (21 °C + 273)

Rearranging the ideal gas law for n gives us

$$n = \frac{PV}{RT}$$

Substituting the proper values of P, V, R, and T into this equation gives

$$n = \frac{(3.95 \times 10^{-3} \text{ atm})(0.158 \text{ L})}{(0.0821 \text{ L atm mol}^{-1} \text{ K}^{-1})(294 \text{ K})}$$
$$= 2.59 \times 10^{-5} \text{ mol of Ar}$$

Now we convert moles of Ar to grams of Ar. Let's set up the question as an equation:

$$2.59 \times 10^{-5} \text{ mol of Ar} = ? \text{ g Ar}$$

Then we use the conversion factor above to complete the calculation.

$$2.59 \times 10^{-5} \text{ mol Ar} \times \frac{39.95 \text{ g Ar}}{1 \text{ mol Ar}} = 1.04 \times 10^{-3} \text{ g Ar}$$

Thus, the light bulb contains only about one milligram of argon.

■ **Is the Answer Reasonable?** As in other problems we approximate the answer by rounding all values to one significant figure to get:

$$n = \frac{(4 \times 10^{-3} \text{ atm})(0.2 \text{ L})}{(0.1 \text{ L atm mol}^{-1} \text{ K}^{-1})(300 \text{ K})} = \frac{(0.8 \times 10^{-3} \text{ mol})}{(30)} \approx 3 \times 10^{-5} \text{ mol}$$

This is close to our answer for the moles of argon.

We multiply the estimate above by 40 g Ar/mol Ar to get 1×10^{-3} grams. The result is very close to our calculated value. (Whenever you're working a problem where there is unit cancellation, be sure to check to be sure that the units do cancel as they are supposed to by adding your own cancellations here.)

Practice Exercises

11.11 | Dry ice, solid $CO_2(s)$, can be made by allowing pressurized $CO_2(g)$ to expand rapidly. If 35% of the expanding $CO_2(g)$ ends up as $CO_2(s)$, how many grams of dry ice can be made from a tank of $CO_2(g)$ that has a volume of 6.0 cubic feet with a gauge pressure of 2.00×10^3 pounds per square inch (PSIG) at 22 °C? (*Hint:* The information in the table on page 476 will help set up the conversions needed. *Note:* PSIG is the pressure above the prevailing atmospheric pressure that we can assume is 1.00 atm.)

11.12 | How many grams of argon were in the 12.0 L cylinder of argon used to fill the light bulbs described in Example 11.2? The pressure of the argon was 57.8 atm and the temperature was 25 °C.

Calculating Molar Mass

When a chemist makes a new compound, its molar mass is usually determined to help establish its chemical identity. In general, *to determine the molar mass of a compound experimentally, we need to find two pieces of information about a given sample—the mass of the sample and the number of moles of the substance in the sample.* Once we have mass and moles for the same sample, we simply divide the number of grams by the number of moles to find the molar mass. For instance, if we had a sample weighing 6.40 g and found that it also contained 0.100 mol of the substance, the molar mass would be

$$\frac{6.40 \text{ g}}{0.100 \text{ mol}} = 64.0 \text{ g mol}^{-1}$$

If the compound is a gas, its molar mass can be found using experimental values of pressure, volume, temperature, and sample mass. The P, V, T data allow us to calculate the number of moles using the ideal gas law (as in Example 11.5). Once we know the number of moles of gas and the mass of the gas sample, the molar mass is obtained by taking the ratio of *grams to moles.*

TOOLS

Determination of molar mass from the ideal gas law

■ Recall that when the molecular mass of a substance is expressed in units of grams per mole, the quantity is called the *molar mass.*

Example 11.6
Determining the Molar Mass of a Gas

As part of a rock analysis, a student added hydrochloric acid to a rock sample and observed a fizzing action, indicating that a gas was being evolved (see the figure in the margin). The student collected a sample of the gas in a 0.220 L gas bulb until its pressure reached 0.757 atm at a temperature of 25.0 °C. The sample weighed 0.299 g. What is the molar mass of the gas? What kind of compound was the likely source of the gas?

■ **Analysis:** The strategy for finding the molar mass was described previously. We use the P, V, T data to calculate the number of moles of gas in the sample. Then we divide the mass by the number of moles to find the molar mass.

■ **Assembling the Tools:** The first tool is the ideal gas law that we use to solve for n,

$$n = \frac{PV}{RT}$$

The next tool is the definition of the molar mass,

$$\text{molar mass} = \frac{\text{mass of sample}}{\text{moles in sample}}$$

■ **Solution:** Any use of the ideal gas law requires the correct units. The pressure given is already in atmospheres and the volume is in liters, but we must convert degrees Celsius into kelvins. Gathering our data, we have

$$P = 0.757 \text{ atm} \qquad V = 0.220 \text{ L} \qquad T = 298 \text{ K} \quad (25.0 \text{ °C} + 273)$$

Now we can substitute the data for P, V, and T, along with the value of R. This gives

$$n = \frac{(0.757 \text{ atm})(0.220 \text{ L})}{(0.0821 \text{ L atm mol}^{-1} \text{ K}^{-1})(298 \text{ K})}$$

$$= 6.81 \times 10^{-3} \text{ mol}$$

The molar mass is obtained from the ratio of grams to moles:

$$\text{molar mass} = \frac{0.299 \text{ g}}{6.81 \times 10^{-3} \text{ mol}} = 43.9 \text{ g mol}^{-1}$$

Hydrochloric acid reacting with a rock sample. *(Andy Washnik)*

We now know the measured molar mass is 43.9, but what gas could this be? Looking back on our discussions in Chapter 5, what gases do we know are given off when a substance reacts with acids? On page 181 we find some options; the gas might be H_2S, HCN, CO_2, or SO_2. Using atomic masses to calculate their molar masses, we get

H_2S	34 g mol^{-1}	CO_2	44 g mol^{-1}
HCN	27 g mol^{-1}	SO_2	64 g mol^{-1}

The only gas with a molar mass close to 43.9 is CO_2, and that gas would be evolved if we treat a carbonate with an acid. The rock probably contains a carbonate compound. (Limestone and marble are examples of such minerals.)

■ **Are the Answers Reasonable?** We don't have to do much mental arithmetic to gain some confidence in our answer. The volume of the gas sample (0.220 L) is a bit less than 1/100 of 22.4 L, the volume of one mole at STP. If the gas were at STP, then 0.299 g would be 1/100 of a mole, so an entire mole would weigh about 30 g (rounded from 29.9 g). Although 30 g per mole is not very close to 43.9 g per mole, we do appear to have the decimal in the right place. We can refine our estimate a bit. We see that the temperature is within 10% of the standard temperature and has a minor effect, but the pressure is only 75% of atmospheric pressure and is the major reason why our first estimate was off. Dividing the estimated molar mass by 0.75 (or multiplying by 1.33) gives an estimated answer of 40, very close to the one we calculated. In addition, the fact that the answer (43.9 g mol^{-1}) agrees so well with the molar mass of one of the gases formed when substances react with acids makes all the puzzle pieces fit. Viewed in total, therefore, we can feel confident in our answers.

Practice Exercises

11.13 | A glass bulb is found to have a volume of 544.23 mL. The mass of the glass bulb filled with argon is 735.6898 g. The bulb is then flushed with a gaseous organic compound. The bulb, now filled with the organic gas, weighs 736.1310 g. The measurements were made at STP. What is the molar mass of the organic gas? (*Hint:* Calculate the difference in molar masses.)

11.14 | The label on a cylinder of a noble gas became illegible, so a student allowed some of the gas to flow into an evacuated gas bulb with a volume of 300.0 mL until the pressure was 685 torr. The mass of the glass bulb increased by 1.45 g; its temperature was 27.0 °C. What is the molar mass of this gas? Which of the Group 8A gases was it?

Gas Densities

■ Recall from Chapter 2 that density is the ratio of mass to volume. For liquids and solids, we usually use units of g mL^{-1} (or g cm^{-3}), but because gases have such low densities, units of g L^{-1} give numbers that are easier to comprehend.

Because one mole of any gas occupies the same volume at a particular pressure and temperature, the mass contained in that volume depends on the molar mass of the gas. Consider, for example, one-mole samples of O_2 and CO_2 at STP (Figure 11.9). Each sample occupies a volume of 22.4 L. The oxygen sample has a mass of 32.0 g while the carbon dioxide sample has a mass of 44.0 g. If we calculate the densities of the gases, we find the density of CO_2 is larger than that of O_2.

$$d_{O_2} = \frac{32.0 \text{ g}}{22.4 \text{ L}} = 1.43 \text{ g L}^{-1} \qquad d_{CO_2} = \frac{44.0 \text{ g}}{22.4 \text{ L}} = 1.96 \text{ g L}^{-1}$$

mole mass ↑ density ↑

Because the volume of a gas is affected by temperature and pressure, the density of a gas changes as these variables change. Gases become less dense as their temperatures rise, which is why hot-air balloons are able to float; the less dense hot air inside the balloon floats in the more dense cool air that surrounds it. Gases also become more dense as their pressures increase because increasing the pressure packs more molecules into the same space. To calculate the density of a gas at conditions other than STP, we use the ideal gas law, as illustrated in Example 11.7.

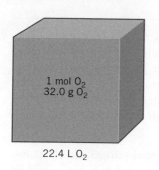
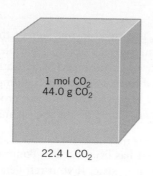

22.4 L O_2 22.4 L CO_2

Figure 11.9 | **One-mole samples of O_2 and CO_2 at STP.** Each sample occupies 22.4 L, but the O_2 weighs 32.0 g whereas the CO_2 weighs 44.0 g. The CO_2 has more mass per unit volume than the O_2 and has the higher density.

Example 11.7
Calculating the Density of a Gas

One procedure used to separate the isotopes of uranium to obtain material to construct a nuclear weapon employs a uranium compound with the formula UF_6. The compound boils at about 56 °C, so at 95 °C it is a gas. What is the density of UF_6 at 95 °C if the pressure of the gas is 746 torr? (Assume the gas contains the mix of uranium isotopes commonly found in nature.)

■ **Analysis:** The ideal gas law has all of the information needed to calculate the density of a gas. We will need to combine two concepts, the ideal gas law and the density of materials. Sometimes it is easier to combine equations before doing any calculations, as we will do here.

■ **Assembling the Tools:** We will need the ideal gas law and the equations for calculating the number of moles, n, and the density, d. Those equations are

$$n = \frac{\text{mass}}{\text{molar mass}} \quad \text{and} \quad d = \frac{\text{mass}}{\text{volume}}$$

760 tor = 1 atm

In many instances we need to convert units, so we should be prepared to convert between torr and atmospheres as well as from °C to K.

■ **Solution:** To combine the two concepts we will substitute the equation for n above into the ideal gas law (Equation 11.2) to get

$$PV = \underset{n}{\frac{\text{mass}}{\text{molar mass}}} \times RT$$

Now we rearrange the equation to the form for density

$$\frac{P \times \text{molar mass}}{RT} - \frac{\text{mass}}{V} = d$$

The right side of this equation is the density. After converting 746 torr to 0.9816 atm and 95 °C to 368 K we enter the data into the equation along with the molar mass of 352.0 g/mol for UF_6 as

$$\frac{(0.9816 \text{ atm})(352.0 \text{ g } UF_6 / \text{mol } UF_6)}{(0.0821 \text{ L atm mol}^{-1} \text{ K}^{-1})(368 \text{ K})} = d = 11.3 \text{ g/L}$$

The density of gaseous UF_6 is 11.3 g/L.

■ **Is the Answer Reasonable?** At STP, the density would be equal to 352 g ÷ 22.4 L = 15.7 g L^{-1}. The given pressure is almost 1 atm, but the temperature is quite a bit higher than 273 K. Gases expand when heated, so a liter of the gas at the higher temperature will have less UF_6 in it. That means the density will be lower at the higher temperature, and our answer agrees with this analysis. Our answer is reasonable.

Practice Exercises

11.15 | Radon, a radioactive gas, is formed in one step of the natural radioactive decay sequence of U-235 to Pb-207. Radon usually escapes harmlessly through the soil to the atmosphere. When the soil is frozen or saturated with water the only escape route is through cracks in the basements of houses and other buildings. In order to detect radon in a residence, would you place the sensor in the attic, the ground floor living area, or the basement? Justify your answer. (*Hint:* Compare the approximate density of air, 1.3 g L^{-1}, to the density of radon.)

11.16 | Sulfur dioxide is a gas that has been used in commercial refrigeration, but not in residential refrigeration because it is toxic. If your refrigerator used SO_2, you could be injured if it developed a leak. What is the density of SO_2 gas measured at −5 °C and a pressure of 96.5 kPa?

Calculating Molar Mass from Gas Density

One of the ways we can use the density of a gas is to determine the molar mass. To do this, we also need to know the temperature and pressure at which the density was measured. Example 11.8 illustrates the reasoning and calculation involved.[9]

Example 11.8
Calculating the Molecular Mass from Gas Density

A liquid sold under the trade name Perclene is used as a dry cleaning solvent. It has an empirical formula CCl_2 and a boiling point of 121 °C. When vaporized, the gaseous compound has a density of 4.93 g L^{-1} at 785 torr and 155 °C. What is the molar mass of the compound and what is its molecular formula?

■ **Analysis:** In Example 11.7 we saw how the density could be calculated using the ideal gas law if we knew P, T, and the molar mass. Knowing the density suggests we can calculate the molar mass. When we know the empirical formula and the molar mass we can determine the molecular formula.

■ **Assembling the Tools:** Again, we need to combine two concepts, the ideal gas law and the density. We can use the information in Example 11.7 to write

$$d = \frac{P \times \text{molar mass}}{RT}$$

---

[9]From the ideal gas law we can derive an equation from which we could calculate the molar mass directly from the density. If we let the mass of gas equal g, we could calculate the number of moles, n, by the ratio

$$n = \frac{g}{\text{molar mass}}$$

Substituting into the ideal gas law gives

$$PV = nRT = \frac{gRT}{\text{molar mass}}$$

Solving for molar mass, we have

$$\text{molar mass} = \frac{gRT}{PV} = \left(\frac{g}{V}\right) \times \frac{RT}{P}$$

The quantity g/V is the ratio of mass to volume, which is the density d, so making this substitution gives

$$\text{molar mass} = \frac{dRT}{P}$$

This equation could also be used to solve the problem in Example 11.8 by substituting values for d, R, T, and P.

As usual, we will be prepared to convert torr to atmospheres and °C to K temperature units. Finally, we add in the third concept involved in this question, the determination of molecular formulas. For this we use the tool found in Section 4.3.

■ **Solution:** Rearranging the equation above to solve for molar mass gives us

$$\text{molar mass} = \frac{dRT}{P}$$

To perform this calculation and cancel the units of R correctly we need to have the pressure in atmosphere units and the temperature in kelvins.

$$T = 428 \text{ K} \qquad \text{from } (155 \text{ °C} + 273)$$

$$P = 1.03 \text{ atm} \qquad \text{from } 785 \text{ torr} \times \frac{1 \text{ atm}}{760 \text{ torr}}$$

$$V = 1.00 \text{ L}$$

Then

$$\text{molar mass} = \frac{(4.93 \text{ g L}^{-1})(0.0821 \text{ L atm mol}^{-1}\text{K}^{-1})(428 \text{ K})}{(1.03 \text{ atm})}$$

$$\text{molar mass} = 168 \text{ g mol}^{-1}$$

To calculate the molecular formula, we divide the empirical formula mass into the molecular mass to see how many times CCl_2 occurs in the molecular formula. The empirical formula mass of CCl_2 is 82.9. We now divide the molar mass by this value:

$$\frac{168}{82.9} = 2.03$$

The result is close enough to 2.00, so to find the molecular formula, we multiply all of the subscripts of the empirical formula by 2:

$$\text{molecular formula} = C_{1 \times 2}Cl_{2 \times 2} = C_2Cl_4$$

(This is the formula for a compound commonly called tetrachloroethylene, which is indeed used as a dry cleaning fluid.)

■ **Is the Answer Reasonable?** Sometimes we don't have to do any arithmetic to see that an answer is almost surely correct. The fact that the molar mass we calculated from the gas density is evenly divisible by the empirical formula mass suggests we've worked the problem correctly.

Practice Exercises

11.17 | A gaseous compound of phosphorus and fluorine with an empirical formula of PF_2 has a density of 5.60 g L^{-1} at 23.0 °C and 750 torr. Determine the molecular formula of this compound. (*Hint:* Calculate the molar mass from the density.)

11.18 | A compound composed of only carbon and hydrogen has a density of 5.55 g/L at 40.0 °C and 1.25 atm. What is the molar mass of the compound? What are the possible combinations of C and H that add up to that molar mass? Using the information in Section 2.6, determine which of your formulas is most likely the correct one.

Stoichiometry Using the Ideal Gas Law

Many chemical reactions either consume or give off gases. The ideal gas law can be used to relate the volumes of such gases to the amounts of other substances involved in the reaction, as illustrated by the following example.

Example 11.9
Calculating the Volume of a Gaseous Product Using the Ideal Gas Law

An important chemical reaction in the manufacture of Portland cement is the high temperature decomposition of calcium carbonate to give calcium oxide and carbon dioxide.

$$CaCO_3(s) \longrightarrow CO_2(g) + CaO(s)$$

Suppose a 1.25 g sample of $CaCO_3$ is decomposed by heating. How many milliliters of CO_2 gas will be evolved if the volume will be measured at 745 torr and 25 °C?

■ **Analysis:** This appears to be a stoichiometry problem where we must to convert the mass of one substance into the volume of a gas that would be expected from the reaction.

■ **Assembling the Tools:** We need to assemble all of the techniques we used for stoichiometry calculations in Section 4.4. In addition we will need the ideal gas law to convert the moles of gaseous product into the expected volume of gas. The specific relationships we need are

$$1 \text{ mol } CaCO_3 \Leftrightarrow 1 \text{ mol } CO_2$$
$$1 \text{ mol } CaCO_3 = 100.1 \text{ g } CaCO_3$$

Our sequence of conversions will be

$$g\ CaCO_3 \longrightarrow mol\ CaCO_3 \longrightarrow mol\ CO_2 \longrightarrow mL\ CO_2$$

■ **Solution:** First, we will convert the 1.25 g of $CaCO_3$ to moles of $CaCO_3$, which is then converted to the number of moles of CO_2. We will use this value for n in the ideal gas law equation to find the volume of CO_2.

The formula mass of $CaCO_3$ is 100.1, so

$$\text{moles of } CaCO_3 = 1.25 \text{ g } CaCO_3 \times \frac{1 \text{ mol } CaCO_3}{100.1 \text{ g } CaCO_3}$$

$$= 1.25 \times 10^{-2} \text{ mol } CaCO_3$$

Because 1 mol $CaCO_3 \Leftrightarrow$ 1 mol CO_2 we must have 1.25×10^{-2} mol CO_2, which we will use for n in the ideal gas law.

Before we use n in the ideal gas law equation, we must convert the given pressure and temperature into the units required by R.

$$P = 745 \text{ torr} \times \frac{1 \text{ atm}}{760 \text{ torr}} = 0.980 \text{ atm} \qquad T = (25.0 \text{ °C} + 273) = 298 \text{ K}$$

By rearranging the ideal gas law equation we obtain

$$V = \frac{nRT}{P}$$

$$= \frac{(1.25 \times 10^{-2} \text{ mol})(0.0821 \text{ L atm mol}^{-1} \text{ K}^{-1})(298 \text{ K})}{0.980 \text{ atm}}$$

$$= 0.312 \text{ L} = 312 \text{ mL}$$

The reaction will yield 312 mL of CO_2 at the conditions specified.

■ **Is the Answer Reasonable?** We round all of the numbers in our calculation to one significant figure to get (cancel the units in the setup below)

$$V = \frac{(1 \times 10^{-2} \text{ mol})(0.1 \text{ L atm mol}^{-1} \text{ K}^{-1})(300 \text{ K})}{1 \text{ atm}} = 0.3 \text{ L} \text{ or } 300 \text{ mL}$$

This answer is close to what we calculated above, and we may assume the calculation is correct. We also note that all units cancel to leave the desired liter units for volume.

11.19 | Carbon disulfide is an extremely flammable liquid. It can be ignited by any small spark or even a very hot surface such as a steam pipe. The combustion reaction is

$$CS_2 + 3O_2 \longrightarrow CO_2 + 2SO_2$$

When 11.0 g of CS_2 are burned in excess oxygen, how many liters of CO_2 and SO_2 are formed at 28 °C and 883 torr? (*Hint:* Treat this as an ordinary stoichiometry problem.)

11.20 | In one lab, the gas-collecting apparatus used a gas bulb with a volume of 257 mL. How many grams of $CaCO_3(s)$ need to be heated to prepare enough $CO_2(g)$ to fill this bulb to a pressure of 738 torr at a temperature of 23 °C? The equation is

$$CaCO_3(s) \longrightarrow CaO(s) + CO_2(g)$$

11.6 | Dalton's Law of Partial Pressures

So far in our discussions we've dealt with only pure gases. However, gas mixtures, such as the air we breathe, are quite common. In general, gas mixtures obey the same laws as pure gases, so Boyle's law applies equally to both pure oxygen and to air. There are times, though, when we must be concerned with the composition of a gas mixture, such as when we are studying a pollutant in the atmosphere. In these cases, the variables affected by the composition of a gas mixture are the numbers of moles of each component and the contribution each component makes to the total observed pressure. Because gases mix completely, all the components of the mixture occupy the same volume—that of the container holding them. Furthermore, the temperature of each gaseous component is the same as the temperature of the entire mixture. Therefore, in a gas mixture, each of the components has the same volume and the same temperature.

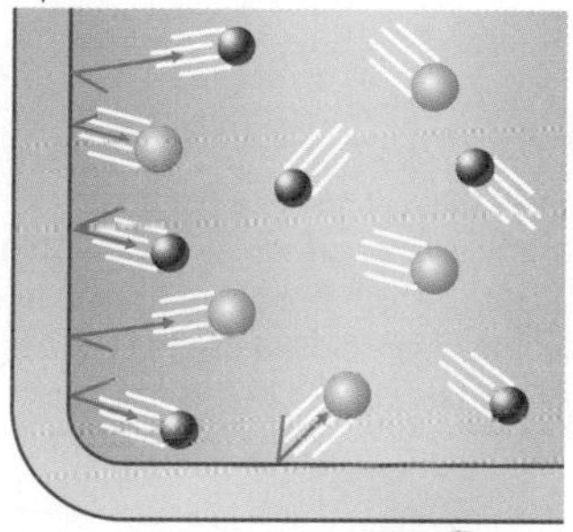

Container wall

Gas *A* ● Gas *B* ○

Figure 11.10 | **Partial pressures viewed at the molecular level.** In a mixture of two gases, *A* and *B*, both collide with the walls of the container and thereby contribute their partial pressures to the total pressure.

■ Under ordinary temperatures and pressures, nitrogen and oxygen in air do not react.

Partial Pressures

In a mixture of nonreacting gases such as air, each gas contributes to the total pressure in proportion to the fraction (by moles) in which it is present (see Figure 11.10). This contribution to the total pressure is called the **partial pressure** of the gas. It is the pressure the gas would exert if it were the only gas in a container of the same size at the same temperature.

The general symbol we will use for the partial pressure of a gas *A* is P_A. For a particular gas, the formula of the gas may be put into the subscript, as in P_{O_2}. What John Dalton discovered about partial pressures is now called **Dalton's law of partial pressures:** *The total pressure of a mixture of gases is the sum of their individual partial pressures.* In equation form, the law is

$$P_{total} = P_A + P_B + P_C + \cdots \tag{11.3}$$

In dry CO_2-free air at STP, for example, P_{O_2} is 159.12 torr, P_{N_2} is 593.44 torr, and P_{Ar} is 7.10 torr. These partial pressures add up to 759.66 torr, just 0.34 torr less than 760 torr or 1.00 atm. The remaining 0.34 torr is contributed by several trace gases, including other noble gases.

TOOLS

Dalton's law of partial pressures

11.21 | At 28 °C a 1.00 liter flask is filled with 11.0 g of Ar, 10.6 g of N_2, and 14.3 g of O_2. What are the partial pressures of each gas, and what is the total pressure in the flask? (*Hint:* Start by calculating the moles of each gas present.)

11.22 | Suppose a tank of oxygen-enriched air prepared for scuba diving has a volume of 17.00 L and a pressure of 237.0 atm at 25 °C. How many grams of oxygen are present if all the other gases in the tank exert a partial pressure of 115.0 atm?

Figure 11.11 | **Collecting a gas over water.** As the gas bubbles through the water, water vapor goes into the gas, so the total pressure inside the bottle includes the partial pressure of the water vapor at the temperature of the water.

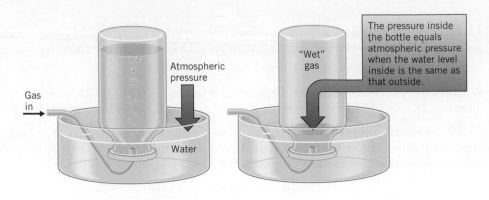

■ Even the mercury in a barometer has a tiny vapor pressure—0.0012 torr at 20 °C—which is much too small to affect readings of barometers and the manometers studied in this chapter.

Collecting Gases over Water

When gases that do not react with water are prepared in the laboratory, they can be trapped over water by an apparatus like that shown in Figure 11.11. Because of the way the gas is collected, it is saturated with water vapor. (We say the gas is "wet.") Water vapor in a mixture of gases has a partial pressure like that of any other gas.

The vapor present in the space above *any* liquid always contains some of the liquid's vapor, which exerts its own pressure called the liquid's **vapor pressure**. Its value for any given substance depends only on the temperature. The vapor pressures of water at different temperatures, for example, are listed in Table 11.2. A more complete table is in Appendix C. 5.

If we have adjusted the height of the collecting jar so the water level inside matches that outside, the total pressure of the trapped gas equals the atmospheric pressure, so the value for P_{total} is obtained from the laboratory barometer. We can now calculate P_{gas}, which is the pressure that the gas would exert if it were dry (i.e., without water vapor in it) and inside the same volume that was used to collect it.[10]

Table 11.2	Vapor Pressure of Water at Various Temperatures[a]		
Temperature (°C)	**Vapor Pressure (torr)**	**Temperature (°C)**	**Vapor Pressure (torr)**
0	4.579	50	92.51
5	6.543	55	118.0
10	2.209	60	149.4
15	12.79	65	187.5
20	17.54	70	233.7
25	23.76	75	289.1
30	31.82	80	355.1
35	42.18	85	433.6
37[b]	47.07	90	527.8
40	55.32	95	633.0
45	71.88	100	760.0

[a]A more complete table is in Appendix C, Table 5. [b]Human body temperature.

[10]If the water levels are not the same inside the flask and outside, a correction has to be calculated and applied to the room pressure to obtain the true pressure in the flask. For example, if the water level is higher inside the flask than outside, the pressure in the flask is lower than atmospheric pressure. The difference in levels is in millimeters of *water*, so this has to be converted to the equivalent in millimeters of mercury using the fact that the pressure exerted by a column of fluid is inversely proportional to the fluid's density.

Example 11.10
Collecting a Gas over Water

A sample of oxygen is collected over water at 15 °C and a pressure of 738 torr. Its volume is 316 mL. (a) What is the partial pressure, in torr, of the oxygen? (b) What would be its volume, in mL, at STP when the water is removed?

■ **Analysis:** There are two parts to this problem. Part (a) concerns the collection of a gas over water, and we will have to separate the partial pressure of oxygen from that of water. Part (b) of the question requires that we perform a gas law calculation to determine the volume at STP.

■ **Assembling the Tools:** For part (a) we will use Dalton's partial pressure equation,

$$P_{total} = P_{water\ vapor} + P_{O_2}$$

For part (b) we see that it will be most convenient to use the combined gas law.

$$\frac{P_1 V_1}{T_1} = \frac{P_2 V_2}{T_2}$$

We might expect that we have to convert units as in previous problems. However, we note that R does not appear in any of our equations and we might not have to convert units; let's see.

■ **Solution:** Part (a): To calculate the partial pressure of the oxygen, we use Dalton's law. We will need the vapor pressure of water at 15 °C, which we find in Table 11.2 to be 12.8 torr. We rearrange the equation above to calculate P_{O_2}.

$$P_{O_2} = P_{total} - P_{water\ vapor}$$
$$= 738\ torr - 12.8\ torr = 725\ torr$$

The answer to part (a) is that the partial pressure of O_2 is 725 torr.

Part (b): We'll begin by making a table of our data.

Initial (1)		Final (2)	
P_1	725 torr (which is P_{O_2})	P_2	760 torr (standard pressure)
V_1	316 mL	V_2	the unknown is V_2
T_1	288 K (15.0 °C + 273)	T_2	273 K (standard temperature)

We use these in the combined gas law equation; solving for V_2 and rearranging the equation a bit we have

$$V_2 = V_1 \times \left(\frac{P_1}{P_2}\right) \times \left(\frac{T_2}{T_1}\right)$$

Now we can substitute values and calculate V_2.

$$V_2 = 316\ mL \times \left(\frac{725\ torr}{760\ torr}\right) \times \left(\frac{273\ K}{288\ K}\right)$$
$$= 286\ mL$$

Thus, when the water vapor is removed from the gas sample, the dry oxygen will occupy a volume of 286 mL at STP.

■ **Are the Answers Reasonable?** We know the pressure of the dry O_2 will be less than that of the wet gas, so the answer to part (a) seems reasonable. To check part (b), we can see if the pressure and temperature ratios move the volume in the correct direction. The pressure is increasing (720 torr ⟶ 760 torr), which should tend to lower the volume. The pressure ratio above will do that. The temperature change (293 K ⟶ 273 K) should also lower the volume, and once again, the temperature ratio above will have that effect. Our answer to part (b) is probably okay.

Practice Exercises

11.23 | A 2.50 L sample of methane was collected over water at 28 °C until the pressure in the flask was 775 torr. A small amount of $CaSO_4(s)$ was then added to the flask to absorb the water vapor (forming $CaSO_4 \cdot 2H_2O(s)$). What is the pressure inside the flask once all the water is absorbed? Assume that the addition of $CaSO_4(s)$ absorbed all the water and did not change the volume of the flask. How many moles of $CH_4(g)$ have been collected? (*Hint:* Find the partial pressure of water at 28 °C.)

11.24 | Suppose you prepared a sample of nitrogen and collected it over water at 15 °C at a total pressure of 745 torr and a volume of 317 mL. Find the partial pressure of the nitrogen, in torr, and the volume, in mL, it would occupy at STP.

Mole Fractions and Mole Percents

■ The concept of mole fraction applies to any uniform mixture in any physical state—gas, liquid, or solid.

One of the useful ways of describing the composition of a mixture is in terms of the *mole fractions* of the components. The **mole fraction** *is the ratio of the number of moles of a given component to the total number of moles of all components.* Expressed mathematically, the mole fraction of substance *A* in a mixture of *A, B, C, . . . , Z* substances is

TOOLS

Mole fractions

$$X_A = \frac{n_A}{n_A + n_B + n_C + n_D + \cdots + n_Z} \tag{11.4}$$

where X_A is the mole fraction of component *A*, and $n_A, n_B, n_C, \ldots, n_Z$ are the numbers of moles of each component, *A, B, C, . . . , Z,* respectively. The sum of all mole fractions for a mixture must always equal 1.

You can see in Equation 11.4 that both numerator and denominator have the same units (moles), so they cancel. As a result, a mole fraction has no units. Nevertheless, always remember the definition: a mole fraction stands for the ratio of *moles* of one component to the total number of *moles* of all components.

Sometimes the mole fraction composition of a mixture is expressed on a percentage basis; we call it a **mole percent** (**mol%**). The mole percent is obtained by multiplying the mole fraction by 100 mol%.

Mole Fractions and Partial Pressures

Partial pressure data can be used to calculate the mole fractions of individual gases in a gas mixture because the number of *moles* of each gas is directly proportional to its partial pressure. We can demonstrate this as follows. The partial pressure, P_A, for any one gas, *A*, in a gas mixture with a total volume *V* at a temperature *T* is found by the ideal gas law equation, $PV = nRT$. So to calculate the number of moles of *A* present, we have

$$n_A = \frac{P_A V}{RT}$$

For any particular gas mixture at a given temperature, the values of *V, R,* and *T* are all constants, making the ratio *V/RT* a constant, too. We can therefore simplify the previous equation by using *C* to stand for *V/RT.* In other words, we can write

$$n_A = P_A C$$

The result is the same as saying that *the number of moles of a gas in a mixture of gases is directly proportional to the partial pressure of the gas.* The constant *C* is the same for all gases in the mixture. So by using different letters to identify individual gases, we can let $P_B C$ stand for n_B, $P_C C$ stand for n_C, and so on in Equation 11.4. Thus,

$$X_A = \frac{P_A C}{P_A C + P_B C + P_C C + \cdots + P_Z C}$$

The constant, C, can be factored out and canceled, so

$$X_A = \frac{P_A}{P_A + P_B + P_C + \cdots + P_Z}$$

The denominator is the sum of the partial pressures of all the gases in the mixture, but this sum equals the total pressure of the mixture (Dalton's law of partial pressures). Therefore, the previous equation simplifies to

$$X_A = \frac{P_A}{P_{\text{total}}}$$ (11.5)

Mole fraction related to partial pressure

Thus, the mole fraction of a gas in a gas mixture is simply the ratio of its partial pressure to the total pressure. Equation 11.5 also gives us a simple way to calculate the partial pressure of a gas in a gas mixture when we know its mole fraction.

Example 11.11
Using Mole Fractions to Calculate Partial Pressures

Suppose a mixture of oxygen and nitrogen is prepared in which there are 0.200 mol O_2 and 0.500 mol N_2. If the total pressure of the mixture is 745 torr, what are the partial pressures of the two gases in the mixture?

■ **Analysis:** This problem asks us to determine the partial pressures of two gases. We have seen a variety of equations so far; let's reason out which to use.

■ **Assembling the Tools:** The combined gas law cannot be used because it deals mainly with changing the P, V, and T conditions of a gas. We cannot solve the ideal gas law since two variables V and T are not given. Aside from the fact that we just discussed partial pressures and mole fractions, it seems that they are the logical choices. For this problem we use

$$X_{O_2} = \frac{\text{moles of } O_2}{\text{moles of } O_2 + \text{moles of } N_2} \quad \text{and} \quad X_{N_2} = \frac{\text{moles of } N_2}{\text{moles of } O_2 + \text{moles of } N_2}$$

and rearranging Equation 11.5 we get

$$P_{O_2} = X_{O_2} P_{\text{total}} \quad \text{and} \quad P_{N_2} = X_{N_2} P_{\text{total}}$$

■ **Solution:** The mole fractions are calculated as follows:

$$X_{O_2} = \frac{\text{moles of } O_2}{\text{moles of } O_2 + \text{moles of } N_2}$$

$$= \frac{0.200 \text{ mol}}{0.200 \text{ mol} + 0.500 \text{ mol}}$$

$$= \frac{0.200 \text{ mol}}{0.700 \text{ mol}} = 0.286$$

Similarly, for N_2 we have[11]

$$X_{N_2} = \frac{0.500 \text{ mol}}{0.200 \text{ mol} + 0.500 \text{ mol}} = 0.714$$

---

[11]Notice that the sum of the mole fractions (0.286 + 0.714) equals 1.00. In fact, we could have obtained the mole fraction of nitrogen with less calculation by subtracting the mole fraction of oxygen from 1.00.

$$X_{O_2} + X_{N_2} = 1.00$$
$$X_{N_2} = 1.00 - X_{O_2}$$
$$= 1.00 - 0.286 = 0.714$$

We can now use Equation 11.5 to calculate the partial pressure. Solving the equation for partial pressure, we have

$$P_{O_2} = X_{O_2} P_{total}$$
$$= 0.286 \times 745 \text{ torr}$$
$$= 213 \text{ torr}$$

$$P_{N_2} = X_{N_2} P_{total}$$
$$= 0.714 \times 745 \text{ torr}$$
$$= 532 \text{ torr}$$

Thus, the partial pressure of O_2 is 213 torr and the partial pressure of N_2 is 532 torr.

■ **Is the Answer Reasonable?** There are three things we can check here. First, the mole fractions add up to 1.000, which they must. Second, the partial pressures add up to 745 torr, which equals the given total pressure. Third, the mole fraction of N_2 is somewhat more than twice that for O_2, so its partial pressure should be somewhat more than twice that of O_2. Examining the answers, we see this is true, so our answers should be correct.

Practice Exercises

11.25 | Sulfur dioxide and oxygen react according to the equation

$$2SO_2(g) + O_2(g) \longrightarrow 2SO_3(g)$$

If 50.0 g of $SO_2(g)$ is added to a flask resulting in a pressure of 0.750 atm, what will be the total pressure in the flask when a stoichiometric amount of oxygen is added? (*Hint:* This problem gives you more information than is needed.)

11.26 | Suppose a mixture containing 2.15 g H_2 and 34.0 g NO has a total pressure of 2.05 atm. What are the partial pressures of both gases in the mixture?

11.27 | What are the mole fraction and the mole percent of oxygen in exhaled air if P_{O_2} is 116 torr and P_{total} is 788 torr?

Graham's Law of Effusion

If you've ever walked past a restaurant and found your mouth watering after smelling the aroma of food, you've learned firsthand about diffusion! **Diffusion** is the spontaneous intermingling of the molecules of one gas, like those of the food aromas, with molecules of another gas, like the air outside the restaurant. (See Figure 11.12*a*). **Effusion**, on the other hand, is the gradual movement of gas molecules through a very tiny hole into a vacuum (Figure 11.12*b*). The rates at which both of these processes occur depends on the speeds of gas molecules; the faster the molecules move, the more rapidly diffusion and effusion occur.

The Scottish chemist Thomas Graham (1805–1869) studied the rates of diffusion and effusion of a variety of gases through porous clay pots and through small apertures. Comparing different gases at the same temperature and pressure, Graham found that their rates of effusion were inversely proportional to the square roots of their densities. This relationship is now called **Graham's law**.

$$\text{Effusion rate} \propto \frac{1}{\sqrt{d}} \qquad \left(\begin{array}{c} \text{when compared at the} \\ \text{same } T \text{ and } P \end{array} \right)$$

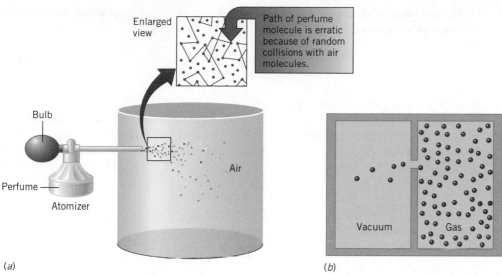

Figure 11.12 | **Spontaneous movements of gases.**
(*a*) Diffusion. (*b*) Effusion.

(*a*)

(*b*)

Graham's law is usually used to compare the rates of effusion of different gases, so the proportionality constant can be eliminated and an equation can be formed by writing the ratio of effusion rates:

■ By taking the ratio, the proportionality constant cancels from numerator and denominator.

$$\frac{\text{effusion rate }(A)}{\text{effusion rate }(B)} = \frac{\sqrt{d_B}}{\sqrt{d_A}} = \sqrt{\frac{d_B}{d_A}} \qquad (11.6)$$

CHEMISTRY AND CURRENT AFFAIRS | **11.2**

Effusion and Nuclear Energy

The fuel used in almost all nuclear reactors is uranium, but only one of its naturally occurring isotopes, ^{235}U, can be easily split to yield energy. Unfortunately, this isotope is present in a very low concentration (about 0.72%) in naturally occurring uranium. Most of the element as it is mined consists of the more abundant isotope ^{238}U. Therefore, before uranium can be fabricated into fuel elements, it must be enriched to a ^{235}U concentration of about 2 to 5 percent. Enrichment requires that the isotopes be separated, at least to some degree.

Separating the uranium isotopes is not feasible by chemical means because the chemical properties of both isotopes are essentially identical. Instead, a method is required that is based on the very small difference in the masses of the isotopes. As it happens, uranium forms a compound with fluorine, UF_6, that is easily vaporized at a relatively low temperature. The UF_6 gas thus formed consists of two kinds of molecules, $^{235}UF_6$ and $^{238}UF_6$, with molecular masses of 349 and 352, respectively. Because of their different masses, their rates of effusion are slightly different; $^{235}UF_6$ effuses 1.0043 times faster than $^{238}UF_6$. Although the difference is small, it is sufficient to enable enrichment, provided the effusion is carried out over and over again enough times. In fact, it takes over 1400 separate effusion chambers arranged one after another to achieve the necessary level of enrichment.

Modern enrichment plants separate the $^{235}UF_6$ and $^{238}UF_6$ in a process using gas centrifuges. Inside the centrifuge the gases rotate at high speeds imparted by an impeller. The heavier $^{238}UF_6$ concentrates slightly toward the outer part of the centrifuge while the lighter $^{235}UF_6$ has slightly higher concentrations toward the center as shown in Figure 1. These are continuously separated, and repeated centrifugation steps lead to the desired purity.

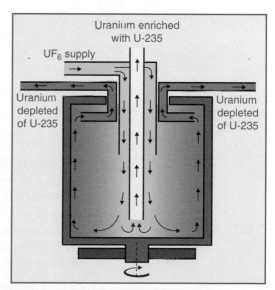

Figure 1 Isotopic Separation by Centrifugation
(*Courtesy of Informationkreis KernEnergie, Berlin*)

Earlier you saw that the density of a gas is directly proportional to its molar mass. Therefore, we can re-express Equation 11.6 as follows:

Graham's law of effusion

$$\frac{\text{effusion rate } (A)}{\text{effusion rate } (B)} = \sqrt{\frac{d_B}{d_A}} = \sqrt{\frac{M_B}{M_A}} \qquad (11.7)$$

where M_A and M_B are the molar masses of gases A and B.

Molecular masses also affect the rates at which gases undergo diffusion. Gases with low molar masses diffuse (and effuse) more rapidly than gases with high molar masses. Thus, hydrogen with a molar mass of 2 will diffuse more rapidly than methane, CH_4, with a molar mass of 16.

Example 11.12
Using Graham's Law

At a given temperature and pressure, which effuses more rapidly and by what factor: ammonia or hydrogen chloride?

■ **Analysis:** This is obviously a gas effusion problem that will require the use of Graham's law. Determining which effuses more rapidly, and obtaining a factor to describe how much more rapidly one effuses compared to the other will require that we set up the correct ratio of effusion rates.

■ **Assembling the Tools:** We are going to need Graham's law of effusion (Equation 11.7), which we can write as

$$\frac{\text{effusion rate } (NH_3)}{\text{effusion rate } (HCl)} = \sqrt{\frac{M_{HCl}}{M_{NH_3}}}$$

We will also recall how to calculate the molar masses of these two molecules.

■ **Solution:** The molar masses are 17.03 g/mol for NH_3 and 36.46 g/mol for HCl, so we immediately know that NH_3, with its smaller molar mass, effuses more rapidly than HCl. The ratio of the effusion rates is given by

$$\frac{\text{effusion rate } (NH_3)}{\text{effusion rate } (HCl)} = \sqrt{\frac{M_{HCl}}{M_{NH_3}}}$$

$$= \sqrt{\frac{36.46}{17.03}} = 1.463$$

We can rearrange the result as

$$\text{effusion rate } (NH_3) = 1.463 \times \text{effusion rate } (HCl)$$

Thus, ammonia effuses 1.463 times more rapidly than HCl under the same conditions.

■ **Is the Answer Reasonable?** The only quick check is to be sure that the arithmetic confirms that ammonia, with its lower molar mass, effuses more rapidly than the HCl, and that's what our result tells us.

Practice Exercises

11.28 | Bromine has two isotopes with masses of 78.9 and 80.9 (to three significant figures), respectively. Bromine boils at 59 °C. At 75 °C, what is the expected ratio of the rate of effusion of Br-81 compared to Br-79? (*Hint:* Recall that bromine is diatomic.)

11.29 | The hydrogen halide gases all have the same general formula, HX, where X can be F, Cl, Br, or I. If HCl(g) effuses 1.88 times more rapidly than one of the others, which hydrogen halide is the other: HF, HBr, or HI?

Analyzing and Solving Multi-Concept Problems

A long time ago, in a poorly equipped lab that had only a balance and an oven, a chemist was asked to determine the formula for a substance that by its crystalline nature appeared to be a single pure substance. The first thing he did was to take a sample of this unknown compound, with a mass of 2.121 g, and heat it at 250 °C for six hours. When cooled, the mass of the substance was now 1.020 g. While waiting for the sample to dry, the chemist tested the substance's solubility and found it was insoluble in water but did dissolve with the release of a gas when a strong acid was added. With that knowledge the chemist set up an apparatus to react the dry sample with acid and collect the gas evolved by bubbling it through water into a 265 mL collection flask. At that time the temperature was 24 °C and the atmospheric pressure was 738 torr and the gas completely filled the flask. Finally, the chemist weighed the flask with the gas and found it to be 182.503 g. The flask weighed 182.346 g when it contained only air. What is the formula for this compound?

■ **Analysis** To write a formula we need the elements that make up the compound and the molar ratio of the elements to each other. We are far from that point. Starting at the beginning, the weight loss on heating could be due to a wet sample or loss of water of hydration. If we knew how many moles of compound were in the remaining 1.020 g of

sample, we could calculate the waters of hydration. The next experiment generated a gas that was carefully collected. It appears that we have all of the information—namely, P, V, and T to calculate the moles of gas. Knowing the masses of the flask with air and then with our compound allows us to calculate the mass of our sample and then its molar mass. In Chapter 5, Table 5.2, we've have a list of gases that can be generated by reaction of a substance with acid. Their molar masses are quite different from each other so we should be able to identify the gas. Once the identity of the gas is known, we can determine the molar mass of the possible cations. Once the cation is identified, we can return to the beginning and determine the number of water molecules in the hydrate.

■ **Strategy** Let's summarize our plan, keeping in mind that we do not have to use the data in the sequence presented. First, determine the moles of gas produced when the dry compound is dissolved in acid. Next, determine the molar mass of the gas and its identity and also the anion that produced it. Then, assuming that the cation could be either M^+, M^{2+}, or M^{3+}, we use the mole ratio with the anion and determine the atomic mass of the cation. We identify the cation if possible. Finally, we determine the number of water molecules in the hydrate and complete the chemical formula.

PART 1

■ **Assembling the Tools** We will need to correct the wet gas pressure for the vapor pressure of water.

$$P_{dry} = P_{total} - P_{water}$$

Next, we need to solve the ideal gas law for the moles of gas.

$$n = \frac{PV}{RT}$$

Finally, the molar mass is

$$\text{molar mass} = \frac{\text{mass of gas}}{\text{moles of gas}}$$

■ **Solution** The tabulated data in Appendix C.5 tell us that the vapor pressure of water at 24 °C is 22.4 torr and therefore our pressure of the dry gas is 738 torr − 24 torr = 714 torr. Converting torr to atmospheres, we get 0.939 atm. We convert the volume to 0.265 L, and the temperature in kelvins is 297 K. Calculating n gives us

$$n = \frac{(0.939 \text{ atm})(0.265 \text{ L})}{(0.0821 \text{ L atm mol}^{-1} \text{ K}^{-1})(297 \text{ K})} = 0.0102 \text{ moles}$$

PART 2

■ **Assembling the Tools** We need to calculate the mass of air inside the flask so we can get a mass with absolutely nothing inside the flask. Then we subtract the mass of the totally empty flask from the flask with our compound in it. The basic equation is the ideal gas law rearranged to calculate mass,

$$\text{mass} = \frac{PV \times \text{molar mass}}{RT}$$

■ **Solution** In Practice Exercise 11.13 it was stated that the average molar mass of air is 28.56 g mol^{-1}. Then the mass of the air in the flask is

$$\text{mass of air} = \frac{(0.939 \text{ atm})(0.265 \text{ L})(28.56 \text{ g mol}^{-1})}{(0.0821 \text{ L atm mol}^{-1} \text{ K}^{-1})(297 \text{ K})} = 0.291 \text{ g air}$$

The mass of the totally empty flask is

$$182.346 \text{ g} - 0.291 \text{ g} = 182.055 \text{ g}$$

The mass of the unknown gas is then

$$182.503 - 182.055 = 0.448 \text{ g}$$

Dividing the mass of the unknown gas by the number of moles from Part 1 yields the molar mass,

$$\text{molar mass} = \frac{0.448 \text{ g gas}}{0.01020 \text{ moles gas}} = 43.9 \text{ g mol}^{-1}$$

Reviewing the gases in Table 5.2, we find that CO_2 is the only gas that has a molar mass close to 43.9 g mol^{-1}. We also know that CO_2 is released when carbonates are treated with acid. Therefore, the anion must be CO_3^{2-}.

PART 3

■ **Assembling the Tools** The tools in Chapter 4 show how to use mole ratios from the formulas M_2CO_3, MCO_3, and $M_2(CO_3)_3$ to calculate the moles of the cation. The same stoichiometry tools let us calculate the mass of the 0.102 moles of CO_3^{2-} in our compound. Subtracting the mass of carbonate from the mass of the sample gives us the mass of the cation. As in Part 2, dividing the mass by the moles will give us the molar mass of the cation.

■ **Solution** The moles of cation in our 0.102-mole sample will depend on the charge of the anion. If the cation is M^+:

$$\text{moles of } M^+ = 0.0102 \text{ mol } CO_3^{2-} \times \frac{2 \text{ mol } M^+}{1 \text{ mol } CO_3^{2-}} = 0.0204 \text{ moles of } M^+$$

If the cation is M^{2+}:

$$\text{moles of } M^{2+} = 0.0102 \text{ mol } CO_3^{2-} \times \frac{1 \text{ mol } M^{2+}}{1 \text{ mol } CO_3^{2-}} = 0.0102 \text{ moles of } M^{2+}$$

If the cation is M^{3+}:

$$\text{moles of } M^{3+} = 0.0102 \text{ mol } CO_3^{2-} \times \frac{2 \text{ mol } M^{3+}}{3 \text{ mol } CO_3^{2-}} = 0.00680 \text{ moles of } M^{3+}$$

We have 0.0102 moles of CO_3^{2-} ions and the mass of carbonate is

$$0.0102 \text{ moles of } CO_3^{2-} \times \frac{60.0 \text{ g } CO_3^{2-}}{1 \text{ mol } CO_3^{2-}} = 0.612 \text{ g } CO_3^{2-}$$

Subtracting this from the 1.020 g sample, we have 0.408 g of cation.

Finally, dividing 0.408 g by the moles of each cation gives us the molar masses of the possible cations. We calculate

$$M^+ = \frac{0.408 \text{ g M}}{0.0204 \text{ mol M}} = 20.0 \text{ g mol}^{-1}$$

$$M^{2+} = \frac{0.408 \text{ g M}}{0.0102 \text{ mol M}} = 40.0 \text{ g mol}^{-1}$$

$$M^{3+} = \frac{0.408 \text{ g M}}{0.0680 \text{ mol M}} = 60.0 \text{ g mol}^{-1}$$

Consulting the periodic table, we find that calcium with an atomic mass of 40 is the closest of all possibilities. Sodium, a +1 ion, has an atomic mass of 23 that is close to the calculated 20. However, our compound is insoluble and we know that sodium compounds are generally soluble, as shown in Table 5.1 on page 176. Therefore, our compound appears to be $CaCO_3$.

PART 4

■ **Assembling the Tools** The last step is to determine the number of water molecules in the hydrate. We have another stoichiometry step in which we calculate the moles of water per mole of compound. We already know the moles of compound, and this step simply involves converting the mass loss, which is water, to moles of water using the stoichiometry concepts in Chapter 4:

$$\text{moles } H_2O = \frac{\text{g } H_2O}{\text{molar mass } H_2O}$$

■ **Solution** The mass of water is the difference between the original mass and the dried mass.

$$\text{moles } H_2O = \frac{(2.121 \text{ g} - 1.020 \text{ g}) \, H_2O}{18.0 \text{ g } H_2O \, \text{mol}^{-1}} = 0.0611 \text{ mol } H_2O$$

$$\text{moles } H_2O \text{ in hydrate} = \frac{\text{mol } H_2O}{\text{mol } CaCO_3} = \frac{0.0611 \text{ mol } H_2O}{0.0102 \text{ mol } CaCO_3} = 5.99 \text{ mol } H_2O$$

This properly rounds to 6 moles of water, and we then write $CaCO_3 \cdot 6H_2O$ as the final answer.

■ **Are the Answers Reasonable?** First, we recheck all of our calculations to be sure that all units cancel and that the math is correctly done. Finally, the fact that all the calculations result so precisely in a formula, $CaCO_3 \cdot 6H_2O$, with a whole number of waters of hydration, is a strong indication that the problem was solved correctly.

11.7 | Kinetic Molecular Theory

Scientists in the nineteenth century, who already knew the gas laws, wondered what had to be true, at the molecular level, about all gases to account for their conformity to a common set of gas laws. The **kinetic molecular theory of gases** provided an answer. We introduced some of its ideas in Chapter 7, and in Section 11.1 we described a number of observations that suggest what gases must be like when viewed at the molecular level. Let's look more closely now at the kinetic molecular theory to see how well it explains the behavior of gases.

The theory, often called simply the kinetic theory of gases, consisted of a set of postulates that describe the makeup of an ideal gas. Then the laws of physics and statistics were applied to see whether the observed gas laws could be predicted from the model. The results were splendidly successful.

■ The particles are assumed to be so small that they have no dimensions at all. They are essentially points in space.

Postulates of the Kinetic Theory of Gases

1. A gas consists of an extremely large number of very tiny particles that are in constant, random motion.
2. The gas particles themselves occupy a net volume so small in relation to the volume of their container that their contribution to the total volume can be ignored.
3. The particles often collide in perfectly elastic collisions[12] with themselves and with the walls of the container, and they move in straight lines between collisions, neither attracting nor repelling each other.

In summary, the model pictures an ideal gas as a collection of very small, constantly moving billiard balls that continually bounce off each other and the walls of their container, and so exert a net pressure on the walls (as described in Figure 11.1, page 474). The gas particles are assumed to be so small that their individual volumes can be ignored, so an ideal gas is effectively all empty space.

Kinetic Theory and the Gas Laws

According to the model, gases are mostly empty space. As we noted earlier, this explains why gases, unlike liquids and solids, can be compressed so much (squeezed to smaller volumes). It also explains why we have gas laws for gases, and *the same laws for all gases*, but not comparable laws for liquids or solids. The chemical identity of the gas does not matter, because gas molecules do not touch each other except when they collide, and there are extremely weak interactions, if any, between them.

We cannot go over the mathematical details, but we can describe some of the ways in which the laws of physics and the model of an ideal gas account for the gas laws and other properties of matter.

Definition of Temperature

The greatest triumph of the kinetic theory came with its explanation of gas temperature, which we discussed in Section 7.2. What the calculations showed was that the product of gas pressure and volume, PV, is proportional to the average kinetic energy of the gas molecules.

$$PV \propto \text{average molecular KE}$$

But from the experimental study of gases, culminating in the equation of state for an ideal gas, we have another term to which PV is proportional—namely, the Kelvin temperature of the gas.

$$PV \propto T$$

(We know what the proportionality constant here is—namely, nR—because by the ideal gas law, PV equals nRT.) With PV proportional *both* to T and to the "average molecular KE," then it must be true that the temperature of a gas is proportional to the average molecular KE.

$$T \propto \text{average molecular KE} \tag{11.8}$$

Boyle's Law

Using the model of an ideal gas, physicists were able to demonstrate that gas pressure is the net effect of innumerable collisions made by gas particles with the walls of the container. Let's imagine that one wall of a gas container is a movable piston that we can push in (or pull

[12]In *perfectly elastic* collisions, no energy is lost by friction as the colliding objects deform momentarily.

out) and so change the volume (see Figure 11.13). If we reduce the volume by one-half, we double the number of molecules per unit volume. This would double the number of collisions per second with each unit area of the wall and therefore double the pressure. Thus, cutting the volume in half forces the pressure to double, which is exactly what Boyle discovered:

$$P \propto \frac{1}{V} \qquad \text{or} \qquad V \propto \frac{1}{P}$$

Gay-Lussac's Law

As you learned earlier, the kinetic theory tells us that increasing the temperature increases the average velocity of gas particles. At higher velocities, the particles strike the container's walls more frequently and with greater force. If we don't change the volume, the *area* being struck remains the same, so the force per unit area (the pressure) must increase. Thus, the kinetic theory explains how the pressure of a fixed amount of gas is proportional to temperature (at constant volume), which is the pressure–temperature law of Gay-Lussac.

Charles' Law

We've just seen that the kinetic theory predicts that increasing the temperature should increase the pressure if the volume doesn't change. But suppose we wanted to keep the pressure constant when we raised the temperature. We could only do this if the volume of the container expanded (and therefore the surface area of the container walls increased) as the temperature increased. Therefore, a gas expands with increasing T in order to keep P constant, which is another way of saying that V is proportional to T at constant P. Thus, the kinetic theory explains Charles' law.

Dalton's Law of Partial Pressures

The law of partial pressures is actually evidence for that part of the third postulate in the kinetic theory that pictures particles of an ideal gas moving in straight lines between collisions, neither attracting nor repelling each other (see Figure 11.14). By not interacting with each other, the molecules act *independently*, so each gas behaves as though it were alone in the container. Only if the particles of each gas do act independently can the partial pressures of the gases add up in a simple way to give the total pressure.

Graham's Law of Effusion

The key conditions of Graham's law are that the rates of effusion of two gases with different molecular masses must be compared at the same pressure and temperature and under conditions where the gas molecules do not hinder each other. When two gases have the same temperature, their particles have identical average molecular kinetic energies. Using subscripts 1 and 2 to identify two gases with molecules having different masses m_1 and m_2, we can write that at a given temperature,

$$\overline{KE_1} = \overline{KE_2}$$

where the bar over KE signifies "average."

For a single molecule, its kinetic energy is $KE = \frac{1}{2}mv^2$. For a large collection of molecules of the same substance, the average kinetic energy is $\overline{KE} = \frac{1}{2}m\overline{v^2}$, where $\overline{v^2}$ is the *average of the velocities squared* (called the *mean square* velocity). We have not extended the "average" notation (the bar) over the mass because all the molecules of a given substance have the same mass (the average of their masses is just the mass).

Once again comparing two gases, 1 and 2, we take $\overline{v_1^2}$ and $\overline{v_2^2}$ to be the average of the velocities squared of their molecules. If both gases are at the same temperature, we have

$$\overline{KE_1} = \frac{1}{2}m_1\overline{v_1^2} = \frac{1}{2}m_2\overline{v_2^2} = \overline{KE_2}$$

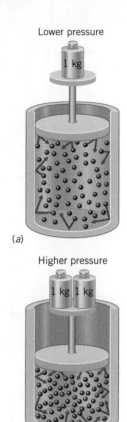

Lower pressure

(a)

Higher pressure

(b)

Figure 11.13 | **The kinetic theory and the pressure–volume law (Boyle's law).** When the gas volume is made smaller in going from (*a*) to (*b*), the number of collisions per second with each unit area of the container's walls increases. Therefore, the pressure increases.

Now let's rearrange the previous equation to get the ratio of $\overline{v^2}$ terms.

$$\frac{\overline{v_1^2}}{\overline{v_2^2}} = \frac{m_2}{m_1}$$

Next, we'll take the square root of both sides. When we do this, we obtain a ratio of quantities called the **root mean square** (abbreviated **rms**) **speeds**, which we will represent as $(\overline{v_1})_{\text{rms}}$ and $(\overline{v_2})_{\text{rms}}$.

$$\frac{(\overline{v_1})_{\text{rms}}}{(\overline{v_2})_{\text{rms}}} = \sqrt{\frac{m_2}{m_1}}$$

The rms speed, $\overline{v}_{\text{rms}}$, is not actually the same as the average speed of the gas molecules, but instead represents the speed of a molecule that would have the average kinetic energy. (The difference is subtle, and the two averages do not differ by much, as noted in the margin.)

For any substance, the mass of an individual molecule is proportional to the molar mass. Representing a molar mass of a gas by M, we can restate this as $m \propto M$. The proportionality constant is the same for all gases. (It's in grams per atomic mass unit when we express m in atomic mass units.) When we take a ratio of two molar masses, the constant cancels anyway, so we can write

$$\frac{(\overline{v_1})_{\text{rms}}}{(\overline{v_2})_{\text{rms}}} = \sqrt{\frac{m_2}{m_1}} = \sqrt{\frac{M_2}{M_1}}$$

According to the preceding equation, the rms speed of the molecules is inversely proportional to the square root of the molecular mass. This means that *at a given temperature, molecules of a gas with a high molecular mass move more slowly, on average, than molecules of a gas with a low molecular mass.*

As you might expect, fast-moving molecules will find an opening in the wall of a container more often than slow-moving molecules, so they will effuse faster. Therefore, the rate of effusion of a gas is proportional to the average speed of its molecules, and therefore, it is also proportional to $1/\sqrt{M}$.

$$\text{Effusion rate} \propto \overline{v}_{\text{rms}} \propto \frac{1}{\sqrt{M}}$$

Let's use k as the proportionality constant. This gives

$$\text{effusion rate} = \frac{k}{\sqrt{M}}$$

Comparing two gases, 1 and 2, and taking a ratio of effusion rates to cause k to cancel, we have

$$\frac{\text{effusion rate (gas 1)}}{\text{effusion rate (gas 2)}} = \sqrt{\frac{M_2}{M_1}}$$

This is the way we expressed Graham's law in Equation 11.7. Thus, still another gas law supports the model of an ideal gas.

Absolute Zero Defined

The kinetic theory found that the temperature is proportional to the average kinetic energy of the molecules.

$$T \propto \text{average molecular } KE \propto \frac{1}{2}m\overline{v^2}$$

If the average molecular KE becomes zero, the temperature must also become zero. However, mass (m) cannot become zero, so the only way that the average molecular KE

■ Suppose we have two molecules with speeds of 6 and 10 m s^{-1}. The average speed is $\frac{1}{2}(6+10) = 8$ m s^{-1}. The rms speed is obtained by squaring each speed, averaging the squared values, and then taking the square root of the result. Thus,

$$\overline{v}_{\text{rms}} = \sqrt{\frac{1}{2}(6^2 + 10^2)} = 8.2 \text{ m s}^{-1}$$

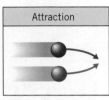
(a)

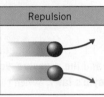
(b)

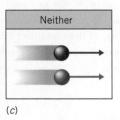
(c)

Figure 11.14 | **Gas molecules act independently when they neither attract nor repel each other.** Gas molecules would not travel in straight lines if they attracted each other as in (a) or repelled each other as in (b). They would have to travel farther between collisions with the walls and, therefore, would collide with the walls less frequently. This would affect the pressure. Only if the molecules traveled in straight lines with no attractions or repulsions, as in (c), would their individual pressures not be influenced by near misses or by collisions between the molecules.

can be zero is if *v* goes to zero. A particle cannot move any slower than it does at a dead standstill, so if the particles stop moving entirely, the substance is as cold as anything can get. It's at absolute zero.[13]

11.8 | Real Gases

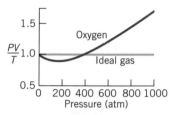

Figure 11.15 | **Deviation from the ideal gas law.** A graph of PV/T versus P for an ideal gas is a straight line, as shown. The same plot for oxygen, a real gas, is not a straight line, showing that O_2 is not "ideal."

According to the ideal gas law, the ratio PV/T for a given gas sample equals a product of two constants, nR. Experimentally, however, for real gases PV/T is actually not quite a constant. When we use experimental values of P, V, and T for a real gas, such as O_2, to plot actual values of PV/T as a function of P, we get the curve shown in Figure 11.15. The *horizontal* line at $PV/T = 1$ in Figure 11.15 is what we should see if PV/T were truly constant over all values of P, as it would be for an ideal gas.

A real gas, like oxygen, deviates from ideal behavior for two important reasons. First, in an ideal gas there would be no attractions between molecules, but in a real gas molecules do experience weak attractions toward each other. Second, the model of an ideal gas assumes that gas molecules are infinitesimally small—that the individual molecules have no volume. But real molecules do take up some space. (If all of the kinetic motions of the gas molecules ceased and the molecules settled, you could imagine the net space that the molecules would occupy in and of themselves.)

At room temperature and atmospheric pressure, most gases behave nearly like an ideal gas, also for two reasons. First, the molecules are moving so rapidly and are so far apart that the attractions between them are hardly felt. As a result, the gas behaves almost as though there are no attractions. Second, the space between the molecules is so large that the volume occupied by the molecules themselves is insignificant. By doubling the pressure, we are able to squeeze the gas into very nearly half the volume.

Let's examine Figure 11.15 more closely. Starting at low pressures, close to $P = 1$, gases often behave as ideal gases. As the pressure is increased along the *x*-axis, the gas particles must be closer together. The first effect noticed as gas particles get closer are attractive forces. These forces between molecules reveal themselves by causing the pressure of a real gas to be slightly lower than that expected for an ideal gas. The attractions cause the paths of the molecules to bend whenever they pass near each other (Figure 11.16). Because the molecules are not traveling in straight lines, as they would in an ideal gas, they have to travel farther between collisions with the walls. As a result, the molecules of a real gas don't strike the walls as frequently as they would if the gas were ideal, and this reduced frequency of collision translates to a reduced pressure. Thus, the ratio PV/T is *less* than that for an ideal gas. The curve for O_2 in Figure 11.15, therefore, dips when we are just starting to increase the pressure.

As we increase the pressure further, the fact that gas molecules must occupy some space becomes more important than the attractive forces. Continued increases in pressure can reduce only the empty space between the molecules, not the volume of the individual particles themselves. So, at very high pressure, the space occupied by the molecules themselves is a significant part of the total volume, and doubling the pressure cannot halve the total volume. As a result, the actual volume of a real gas is larger than expected for an ideal gas, and the ratio PV/T becomes larger as the pressure increases. We see this for O_2 at the right side of the graph in Figure 11.15.

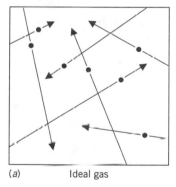

(a)   Ideal gas

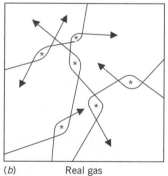

(b)   Real gas

Figure 11.16 | **The effect of attractive forces on the pressure of a real gas.** (*a*) In an ideal gas, the molecules travel in straight lines. (*b*) In a real gas, the paths curve as one molecule passes close to another because the molecules attract each other. Asterisks indicate the points at which molecules come close to each other.

---

[13]Actually, even at 0 K, there must be some slight motion. It's required by the Heisenberg uncertainty principle, which says (in one form) that it's impossible to know precisely both the speed and the location of a particle simultaneously. (If one knows the speed, then there's uncertainty in the location, for example.) If the molecules were actually dead still at absolute zero, there would be no uncertainty in their speed—but then the uncertainty in their *position* would be infinitely great. We would not know where they were! But we do know; they're in this or that container. Thus some uncertainty in speed must exist to have less uncertainty in position and so locate the sample!

The van der Waals Equation

■ J. D. van der Waals (1837–1923), a Dutch scientist, won the 1910 Nobel Prize in physics.

Many attempts have been made to modify the equation of state of an ideal gas to get an equation that better fits the experimental data for individual real gases. One of the more successful efforts was that of J. D. van der Waals. He found ways to correct the measured values of P and V to give better fits of the data to the general gas law equation. The result of his derivation is called the *van der Waals equation of state for a real gas*. Let's take a brief look at how van der Waals made corrections to measured values of P and V to obtain expressions that fit the ideal gas law.

As you know, if a gas were ideal, it would obey the equation

$$P_{\text{ideal}} V_{\text{ideal}} = nRT$$

However, for a real gas, using the measured pressure, P_{meas}, and measured volume, V_{meas},

$$P_{\text{meas}} V_{\text{meas}} \neq nRT$$

The reason is because P_{meas} is smaller than P_{ideal} (as a result of attractive forces between real gas molecules), and because V_{meas} is larger than V_{ideal} (because real molecules do take up some space). Therefore, to get the pressure and volume to obey the ideal gas law, we have to *add* something to the measured pressure and *subtract* something from the measured volume. That's exactly what van der Waals did. Here's his equation.

T⚗OLS

van der Waals equation of state for real gases

The measured pressure   The measured volume

$$\left(P_{\text{meas}} + \frac{n^2 a}{V^2}\right)(V_{\text{meas}} - nb) = nRT \qquad (11.9)$$

Correction to bring measured P up to the pressure an ideal gas would exert   Correction to reduce measured V to the volume an ideal gas would have

The constants a and b are called *van der Waals constants* (see Table 11.3). They are determined for each real gas by carefully measuring P, V, and T under varying conditions.

Table 11.3	van der Waals Constants	
Substance	a (L² atm mol⁻²)	b (L mol⁻¹)
Noble Gases		
Helium, He	0.03421	0.02370
Neon, Ne	0.2107	0.01709
Argon, Ar	1.345	0.03219
Krypton, Kr	2.318	0.03978
Xenon, Xe	4.194	0.05105
Other Gases		
Hydrogen, H_2	0.02444	0.02661
Oxygen, O_2	1.360	0.03183
Nitrogen, N_2	1.390	0.03913
Methane, CH_4	2.253	0.04278
Carbon dioxide, CO_2	3.592	0.04267
Ammonia, NH_3	4.170	0.03707
Water, H_2O	5.464	0.03049
Ethyl alcohol, C_2H_5OH	12.02	0.08407

Then trial calculations are made to figure out what values of the constants give the best matches between the observed data and the van der Waals equation.

Notice that the constant a involves a correction to the pressure term of the ideal gas law, so the size of a would indicate something about attractions between molecules. Larger values of a mean stronger attractive forces between molecules. Thus, the most easily liquefied substances, like water and ethyl alcohol, have the largest values of the van der Waals constant a, suggesting relatively strong attractive forces between their molecules.

The constant b helps to correct for the volume occupied by the molecules themselves, so the size of b indicates something about the sizes of particles in the gas. Larger values of b mean larger molecular sizes. Looking at data for the noble gases in Table 11.3, we see that as the atoms become larger from helium through xenon, the values of b become larger. In the next chapter we'll continue the study of factors that control the physical state of a substance, particularly attractive forces and their origins.

11.9 | Chemistry of the Atmosphere

The atmosphere of the earth is the layer of gases held close to the surface of the planet by gravitational forces. There is no distinct boundary between our atmosphere and outer space, but the concentration of atmospheric gases is greatest at the earth's surface and decreases steadily with altitude. Seventy five percent of the mass of the atmosphere exists below an altitude of 11 km and 99% is found below 30 km, yet spacecraft returning to earth start having frictional heating due to atmospheric molecules at an altitude of 120 km.

Our atmosphere is the only source of the oxygen we, and other animals, breathe and it is the repository for our exhaled carbon dioxide and water vapor. The carbon dioxide in our atmosphere is essential for plants that derive their energy from photosynthesis. Below we consider other chemical and physical properties of our atmosphere that are important to us as chemists and citizens.

Composition of the Atmosphere

Both the chemical composition and physical properties of the atmosphere vary with time and location. Some vary slightly, and others vary significantly from time to time and place to place.

On a dry basis (without water) the gases that surround us are a fairly constant mixture of nitrogen (78.08%), oxygen (20.95%), and argon (0.93%), and traces of other gases (0.04%). Carbon dioxide varies seasonally and by location but comprises almost all of the trace gases at about 0.038%. Water vapor can reach 4% of the atmospheric gases or it can be close to 0% depending on weather conditions. When water is factored in, the percentages of the other elements decrease proportionally. The concentration of ozone, O_3, is very small and varies by location and altitude.

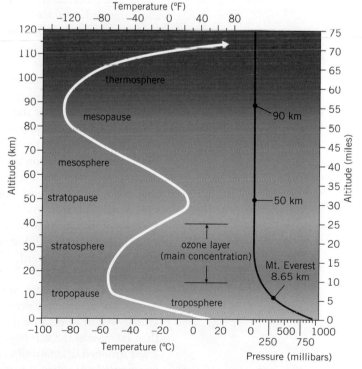

Figure 11.17 | **A representation of the Earth's atmosphere.** The white line represents the temperature and the black line represents the pressure.

In addition to the chemical composition, the physical properties of the atmosphere are important. Figure 11.17 illustrates the pressure and the temperature profile of the atmosphere. Whereas we can see that the pressure of atmospheric gases decreases logarithmically with altitude (a factor of 10 for each 17 km increase in altitude) in a regular manner, the temperature is another matter. Figure 11.17 illustrates that starting from the surface of the Earth, the temperature decreases to the top of the troposphere, then it increases through the stratosphere, approaching the temperature at the surface of the earth. In the mesosphere the temperature decreases again, and yet again it increases in the thermosphere.

We also notice from Figure 11.17 that the "ozone layer" exists at an altitude of approximately 27 km. Also, at higher altitudes, the lighter elements such as H_2 and He dominate the atmospheric composition.

Ozone and the Ozone Layer

Ozone, O_3, forms when molecular oxygen, O_2, is broken apart into oxygen atoms (Equation 11.10), and those atoms combine with O_2 (Equation 11.11).

$$O_2 + energy \longrightarrow 2O \qquad (11.10)$$

$$O + O_2 \longrightarrow O_3 \qquad (11.11)$$

■ Molecular oxygen provides life on earth with some protection from high energy radiation.

The energy for the first reaction comes from high-energy photons (with wavelengths less than 240 nm) from outer space. At the surface of the earth the energy comes from lightning, electrical sparks from motors, and other machinery and some chemical processes. Equation 11.11 shows the combination of atomic oxygen and molecular oxygen to form ozone.

Ozone is a very reactive form of oxygen, acting as an oxidizing agent. Ozone is used to purify water, similar to the way chlorine is used in most municipal water systems. The oxidizing strength of ozone is sufficient to kill most microorganisms. Ozone is also an irritant. Contact with mucus membranes in the eyes or respiratory tract often causes severe reactions that may require medical treatment. Ozone can react with the rubber in automobile tires causing premature failure. Ozone is also an important reactant in the formation of photochemical smog in major cities and the blue haze in wilderness areas. Aside from its use in purifying drinking water, ozone at low altitudes in the atmosphere is usually considered an unwanted pollutant.

On the other hand, the ozone layer that forms at an altitude of approximately 27 km above the earth's surface is considered to be essential and beneficial. The ozone layer is beneficial because ozone absorbs harmful ultraviolet radiation emitted by the sun in the reaction

$$O_3 + h\nu \longrightarrow O_2 + O \qquad (11.12)$$

where $h\nu$ represents electromagnetic radiation in the range of 240–320 nm. As a result, harmful, cancer-causing, ultraviolet radiation is greatly reduced by the ozone layer before it reaches the surface of the earth.

In normal situations, the ozone in the ozone layer is replenished by the formation reactions (Equations 11.10 and 11.11) as fast as it is depleted (Equation 11.12), resulting in a **steady-state** concentration of ozone. This steady state can be altered if other substances also destroy ozone at a significant rate. In the past 50 years many substances that destroy ozone have been identified, and most contain chlorine. Chlorine can enter the atmosphere in a variety of ways, from natural emissions from oceans or volcanoes that release $HCl(g)$ to Freon-type refrigerants containing chlorine, called CFCs. There was concern that the amount of these ozone-destroying molecules would destroy enough ozone to be a serious worldwide health hazard. The *Montreal Protocol*, which bans CFCs, was signed on September 16, 1987.

■ A steady state differs from a dynamic equilibrium in that the formation reaction is different from the decomposition reaction.

■ CFC is an abbreviation for the word "chlorofluorocarbon," indicating organic compounds containing chlorine, fluorine, and carbon.

About the same time, atmospheric scientists were realizing that the ozone layer over Antarctica was severely depleted each October (springtime in the Southern Hemisphere). Usually ozone levels would decrease in the total darkness of winter at the south pole and then increase as the sun began shining again. However, when the sun appeared, the ozone levels dropped dramatically, creating what was popularly called an "**ozone hole.**" The puzzle was figured out when it was demonstrated that clouds of ice crystals containing reactive chlorine compounds melted in the spring, releasing these compounds. The chlorine compounds had been accumulating in the ice crystals all winter at temperatures as low as −80 °C. It is important to note that the ozone hole has no direct relationship to **global climate change**.

Greenhouse Gases and Global Temperature Change

It has been calculated that if the earth's atmosphere did not exist or did not trap heat energy, the average temperature would be $-18\,°C$ ($0\,°F$). With our atmosphere trapping some heat energy, the average temperature is a toasty $14\,°C$. **Greenhouse gases** are those atmospheric gases that absorb energy and keep the Earth warm. We just don't want it to be too warm.

The operation of a greenhouse provides an imperfect, simplistic, but reasonable analogy for describing heat exchange on the Earth. To maintain an optimum temperature in a greenhouse, windows in the ceiling are opened to let excess heat energy escape at a rate that balances the incoming energy of the sun. This is another steady-state situation similar to the ozone layer. If one or more of the windows are closed the steady state will be disturbed and two things will happen. First, the temperature starts to rise and second, as the temperature rises, more heat energy will escape from the remaining open windows. At some point the temperature will rise enough so that the flow of energy into and out of the greenhouse will once again reach a steady state. The greenhouse will then be at a new, higher, temperature that will remain constant until another window is open or closed.

Now we consider the Earth. The major flows of energy are the energy reaching the Earth's surface from unreflected sunlight. Sunlight reflected from clouds, snow, and other surfaces does not appreciably contribute to the greenhouse effect. Sunlight absorbed by the plants, soil, oceans, and so on must be re-emitted to outer space. Figure 8.5 on page 311 illustrates how green plants absorb visible light.

Classical physics tells us that the re-emitted radiation occurs in the infrared region of the spectrum. Some gases, such as water, carbon dioxide, and methane in particular (the main greenhouse gases) absorb infrared radiation. Figure 8.4 on page 311 illustrates how compounds can absorb infrared energy. When a greenhouse gas absorbs infrared radiation it is analogous to closing some windows in our greenhouse. The higher the concentration of the gases, the more the windows, at particular wavelengths, are closed. The windows representing water and carbon dioxide are almost completely closed already. In this analogy the window for methane is still about half open. The result is that doubling the CO_2

■ Most of the energy of sunlight is in the ultraviolet and visible spectral regions.

ON THE CUTTING EDGE | **11.3**

Super Greenhouse Gases

Our common greenhouse gases are water, carbon dioxide, and methane. These are widely held to be responsible for the comfortable temperature of our planet and also the rise in temperature over the last century. A completely different set of gases, the chlorofluorocarbons, CFCs, were used as propellants in consumer sprays and air-conditioning systems. These compounds have been implicated in destroying ozone in the stratosphere. R. S. Mario Molina, Paul Crutzen, and F. Sherwood Rowland were awarded the 1995 Nobel Prize in chemistry[1] for explaining how the chlorine from CFCs finds its way to the South Pole to form the famous "ozone hole."

A new class of compounds, fluorinated hydrocarbons, HFCs, were developed to replace the CFCs that were destroying ozone. They are now commonly used as propellants and in air conditioners. The most common of these is 1,1-difluoroethane, or HFC-134a (Figure 1). It turns out that HFC-134a appears to be a "super greenhouse gas." This means that its effect on global climate may be much greater than water, carbon dioxide, and methane

combined. Apparently one problem has been solved but another may have been created.

Some futurists, when considering that humans will some day overflow our home planet, have been looking for other sites for human habitation. In the early 2000s some asked if we could habitate Mars (Figure 2) if it were just a bit warmer. Since then, researchers have been investigating whether or not it would be feasible to use global warming to heat another globe—Mars. It seems to be possible; however, we are reminded by experience with HFCs that often solutions may cause their own problems.

Figure 1 Space-filling model of 1,1-difluoroethane.

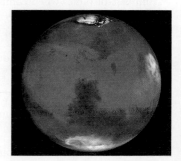

Figure 2 Mars—a candidate for artificial global warming?
NASA/JPL Photo

[1] F. S. Rowland and M. J. Molina, "*Ozone Depletion: 20 Years after the Alarm,*" *Chemical and Engineering News* 72, 8–13, 1994.

in the atmosphere will cause a rise in the temperature, but doubling the concentration of methane will have a much greater effect. This occurs because the amount of open window that is available to be closed by methane is much more than the open window that can be closed by carbon dioxide. Atmospheric scientists call this idea "forcing." Methane has a greater temperature-forcing potential than carbon dioxide.

Overall, gases that absorb infrared radiation can be considered to be greenhouse gases. Global increases in the concentrations of those gases will lead to temperature increases. The physical consequences of global temperature change include crop and species disloca-tion. Weather changes and changes in ocean levels resulting in flooding are also predicted.

Summary

Barometers, Manometers, and Pressure Units. Atmo-spheric pressure is measured with a **barometer**, in which a pres-sure of one **standard atmosphere (1 atm)** will support a column of mercury 760 mm high. This is a pressure of 760 **torr**. By defi-nition, 1 atm = 101,325 **pascals (Pa)** and 1 **bar** = 100 kPa. **Manometers**, both open-end and closed-end, are used to measure the pressure of trapped gases.

Gas Laws. An **ideal gas** is a hypothetical gas that obeys the gas laws exactly over all ranges of pressure and temperature. Real gases exhibit ideal gas behavior most closely at low pressures and high temperatures, which are conditions remote from those that liquefy a gas.

Boyle's Law (Pressure–Volume Law). For a fixed amount of gas at constant temperature, volume varies inversely with pressure. $V \propto 1/P$. A useful form of the equation is $P_1 V_1 = P_2 V_2$.

Charles' Law (Temperature–Volume Law). For a fixed amount of gas at constant pressure, volume varies directly with the Kelvin temperature. $V \propto T$, or $V_1/V_2 = T_1/T_2$.

Gay-Lussac's Law (Temperature–Pressure Law). For a fixed amount of gas at constant volume, pressure varies directly with Kelvin temperature. $P \propto T$, or $P_1/P_2 = T_1/T_2$.

Avogadro's Principle. Equal volumes of gases contain equal numbers of moles when compared at the same temperature and pressure. At **STP**, 273.15 K and 1.00 atm, 1 mol of an ideal gas occupies a volume of 22.4 L.

Combined Gas Law. PV divided by T for a given gas sample is a constant. $PV/T = C$, or $P_1 V_1/T_1 = P_2 V_2/T_2$.

Ideal Gas Law. $PV = nRT$. When P is in atm and V is in L, the value of R is 0.0821 L atm mol^{-1} K^{-1} (T is, as usual, in kelvins).

Gay Lussac's Law of Combining Volumes. When measured at the same temperature and pressure, the volumes of gases consumed and produced in chemical reactions are in the same ratios as their coefficients.

Mole Fraction. The mole fraction X_A of a substance A equals the ratio of the number of moles of A, n_A, to the total number

of moles n_{total} of all the components of a mixture.

$$X_A = \frac{n_A}{n_{\text{total}}}$$

Dalton's Law of Partial Pressures. The total pressure of a mixture of gases is the sum of the partial pressures of the in-dividual gases.

$$P_{\text{total}} = P_A + P_B + P_C + \cdots$$

In terms of mole fractions, $P_A = X_A P_{\text{total}}$ and $X_A = P_A/P_{\text{total}}$.

Graham's Law of Effusion. The rate of effusion of a gas var-ies inversely with the square root of its density (or the square root of its molecular mass) at constant pressure and tempera-ture. Comparing different gases at the same temperature and pressure,

$$\frac{\text{effusion rate } (A)}{\text{effusion rate } (B)} = \sqrt{\frac{d_B}{d_A}} = \sqrt{\frac{M_B}{M_A}}$$

Kinetic Theory of Gases. An ideal gas consists of a large number of particles, each having essentially zero volume, that are in constant, chaotic, random motion, traveling in straight lines with no attractions or repulsions between them. When the laws of physics and statistics are applied to this model and the results compared with the ideal gas law, the Kelvin temperature of a gas is found to be proportional to the average kinetic energy of the gas particles. Pressure is the result of the force and frequency of collisions of the particles with the container's walls.

Real Gases. Because individual gas particles do have real vol-umes and because small forces of attraction do exist between them, real gases do not exactly obey the gas laws. The van der Waals equa-tion of state for a real gas makes corrections for the volume of the gas molecules and for the attractive force between gas molecules. The van der Waals constant a provides a measure of the strengths of the attractive forces between molecules, whereas the constant b gives a measure of the relative size of the gas molecules.

Reaction Stoichiometry: A Summary. With the study in this chapter of the stoichiometry of reactions involving gases, we

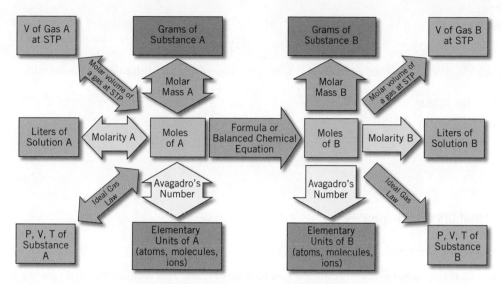

Figure 11.18 | **Pathways for working stoichiometry problems.** This diagram adds two additional ways to convert laboratory units to moles. As in Figures 4.6 and 5.27, the boxed items are given or calculated quantities while the arrows indicate where to find the conversion factors.

now have the tools needed for the calculations of all variations of reaction stoichiometry. The critical link in all such calculations is the set of coefficients given by the balanced chemical equation, which provides the stoichiometric equivalencies needed to convert from the number of moles of one substance into the numbers of moles of any of the others in the reaction. To use the coefficients requires that all the calculations must funnel through *moles.* Whether we start with grams of some compound in a reaction, or the molarity of its solution plus a volume, or *P-V-T* data for a gas in the reaction, *we must get the essential calculation into moles.* After applying the coefficients, we can then move back to any other kind of unit we wish. The flowchart in Figure 11.18 summarizes what we have been doing.

The labels on the arrows of the flowchart suggest the basic tools. Formula masses or molecular masses get us from grams to

moles or from moles to grams. Molarity and volume data move us from concentration to moles or back. With *P-V-T* data we can find moles or, knowing moles of a gas, we can calculate *P, V,* or *T,* as long as the other two are known.

The Atmosphere: A Summary. In this section we have briefly learned about the structure and chemical composition of the atmosphere that gradually becomes less dense with increasing altitude. The **ozone layer** has a steady-state concentration that depends on the continuous formation and destruction of ozone molecules, O_3. Loss of ozone at the poles causes a situation called the "**ozone hole**." **Greenhouse gases**, H_2O, CO_2, and CH_4, naturally cause the earth to be warmer than it would be if they were not present. Excess amounts of CO_2 and CH_4 are of concern because of the potential for significant **global climate changes**.

Tools for Problem Solving

Tools for Problem Solving Below we list the tools you have learned in this chapter. Most of these are mathematical relationships. Review all these tools and refer to them, if necessary, when working on the Review Questions and Problems that follow.

Combined gas law (page 483)

$$\frac{P_1 V_1}{T_1} = \frac{P_2 V_2}{T_2}$$

This law applies when the amount of gas is constant and we are asked how one of the variables (*P, V,* or *T*) changes when we change two of the others. When the amount of gas and one of the variables (*P, V,* or *T*) are constant, the problem reduces to one involving Boyle's, Charles', or Gay-Lussac's law.

Ideal gas law (page 491)

$$PV = nRT$$

This law applies when any three of the four variables P, V, T, or n, are known and we wish to calculate the value of the fourth.

Determination of molar mass:

from the ideal gas law (page 493),

$$\text{molar mass} = \frac{g}{V}\frac{RT}{P} = d\frac{RT}{P}$$

Dalton's law of partial pressures (page 499)

$$P_{\text{total}} = P_A + P_B + P_C + \cdots$$

We use this law to calculate the partial pressure of one gas in a mixture of gases. This requires the total pressure and either the partial pressures of the other gases or their mole fractions. If the partial pressures are known, their sum is the total pressure. When a gas is collected over water, this law is used to obtain the partial pressure of the collected gas in the "wet" gas mixture. $P_{\text{total}} = P_{\text{water}} + P_{\text{gas}}$

Mole fractions (pages 502 and 503)

$$X_A = \frac{n_A}{n_{\text{total}}} = \frac{P_A}{P_{\text{total}}}$$

Given the composition of a gas mixture, we can calculate the mole fraction of a component. The mole fraction can then be used to find the partial pressure of the component given the total pressure. If the total pressure and partial pressure of a component are known, we can calculate the mole fraction of the component.

Graham's law of effusion (page 504)

$$\frac{\text{effusion rate }(A)}{\text{effusion rate }(B)} = \sqrt{\frac{d_B}{d_A}} = \sqrt{\frac{M_B}{M_A}}$$

This law allows us to calculate relative rates of effusion of gases. It also allows us to calculate molecular masses from relative rates of effusion.

van der Walls equation of state for real gases (page 514)

$$\left(P_{\text{meas}} + \frac{n^2 a}{V^2}\right)(V_{\text{meas}} - nb) = nRT$$

This law makes adjustments for the fact that gas molecules may have attractive forces and that gas molecules have a finite volume.

Review Questions

Concept of Pressure; Manometers and Barometers

11.1 If you get jabbed by a pencil, why does it hurt so much more if it's with the sharp point rather than the eraser? Explain in terms of the concepts of force and pressure.

11.2 Write expressions that could be used to form conversion factors to convert between:

(a) kilopascal and atm,

(b) torr and mm Hg,

(c) bar and pascal,

(d) torr and atm,

(e) torr and pascal,

(f) bar and atm

11.3 At 20 °C the density of mercury is 13.6 g mL^{-1} and that of water is 1.00 g mL^{-1}. At 20 °C, the vapor pressure of mercury is 0.0012 torr and that of water is 18 torr. Give and explain two reasons why water would be an inconvenient fluid to use in a Torricelli barometer.

11.4 What is the advantage of using a closed-end manometer, rather than an open-end one, when measuring the pressure of a trapped gas?

Gas Laws

11.5 Express the following gas laws in equation form: (a) temperature–volume law (Charles' law), (b) temperature–pressure law (Gay-Lussac's law), (c) pressure–volume law (Boyle's law), (d) combined gas law

11.6 Which of the four important variables in the study of the physical properties of gases are assumed to be held constant in each of the following laws? (a) Boyle's law, (b) Charles' law, (c) Gay-Lussac's law, (d) combined gas law

11.7 What is meant by an *ideal gas*? Under what conditions does a real gas behave most like an ideal gas? State the ideal gas law in the form of an equation. What is the value of the gas constant in units of L atm mol^{-1} K^{-1}?

11.8 Determine how to plot the two properties of gases listed with each of the following gas laws so that the graph will be a straight line. (a) temperature–volume law (Charles' law), (b) temperature–pressure law (Gay Lussac's law), (c) pressure–volume law (Boyle's law)

11.9 State Dalton's law of partial pressures in the form of an equation.

11.10 Define mole fraction. How is the partial pressure of a gas related to its mole fraction and the total pressure?

11.11 Consider the diagrams below that illustrate three mixtures of gases A and B. If the total pressure of the mixture is 1.00 atm, which of the drawings corresponds to a mixture in which the partial pressure of A equals 0.600 atm? What are the partial pressures of A in the other mixtures? What are the partial pressures of B?

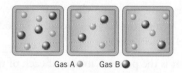

Gas A ●   Gas B ●

11.12 What is the difference between *diffusion* and *effusion*? State Graham's law in the form of an equation.

Kinetic Theory of Gases

11.13 Describe the model of a gas proposed by the kinetic theory of gases?

11.14 If the molecules of a gas at constant volume are somehow given a lower average kinetic energy, what two measurable properties of the gas will change and in what direction?

11.15 Explain *how* raising the temperature of a gas causes it to expand at constant pressure. (*Hint:* Describe how the model of an ideal gas connects the increase in temperature to the gas expansion.)

11.16 Explain in terms of the kinetic theory how raising the temperature of a confined gas makes its pressure increase.

11.17 How does the kinetic theory explain the existence of an absolute zero, 0 K?

11.18 Which of the following gases has the largest value of $\overline{v_{rms}}$ at 25 °C: (a) N_2, (b) CO_2, (c) NH_3, or (d) HBr?

11.19 How would you expect the rate of effusion of a gas to depend on (a) the pressure of the gas, and (b) the temperature of the gas?

Real Gases

11.20 Which postulates of the kinetic theory are not strictly true, and why?

11.21 What does a small value for the van der Waals constant a suggest about the molecules of the gas?

11.22 Which of the molecules below has the larger value of the van der Waals constant b? Explain your choice.

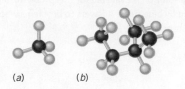

(a)   (b)

11.23 Under the same conditions of T and V, why is the pressure of a real gas less than the pressure the gas would exert if it were ideal? At a given T and P, why is the volume of a real gas larger than it would be if the gas were ideal?

11.24 Suppose we have a mixture of helium and argon. On average, which atoms are moving faster at 25 °C, and why?

| Review Problems

Pressure Unit Conversions

OH **11.25** Carry out the following unit conversions: (a) 1.26 atm to torr, (b) 740 torr to atm, (c) 738 torr to mm Hg, (d) 1.45×10^3 Pa to torr.

11.26 Carry out the following unit conversions: (a) 0.625 atm to torr, (b) 825 torr to atm, (c) 62 mm Hg to torr, (d) 1.22 kPa to bar.

11.27 What is the pressure in torr of each of the following?

(a) 0.329 atm (summit of Mt. Everest, the world's highest mountain)

(b) 0.460 atm (summit of Mt. Denali, the highest mountain in the United States)

11.28 What is the pressure in atm of each of the following? (These are the values of the pressures exerted individually by N_2, O_2, and CO_2, respectively, in typical inhaled air.)

(a) 595 torr   (b) 160 torr   (c) 0.300 torr

Manometers and Barometers

11.29 An open-end manometer containing mercury was connected to a vessel holding a gas at a pressure of 720 torr. The atmospheric pressure was 765 torr. Sketch a diagram of the apparatus showing the relative heights of the mercury in the two arms of the manometer. What is the difference in the heights of the mercury expressed in centimeters?

11.30 An open-end manometer containing mercury was connected to a vessel holding a gas at a pressure of 820 torr. The atmospheric pressure was 750 torr. Sketch a diagram of the apparatus showing the relative heights of the mercury in the two arms of the manometer. What is the difference in the heights of the mercury expressed in centimeters?

11.31 An open-end mercury manometer was connected to a flask containing a gas at an unknown pressure. The mercury in the arm open to the atmosphere was 65 mm higher than the mercury in the arm connected to the flask. The atmospheric pressure was 748 torr. What was the pressure of the gas in the flask (in torr)?

11.32 An open-end mercury manometer was connected to a flask containing a gas at an unknown pressure. The mercury in the arm open to the atmosphere was 82 mm lower than the mercury in the arm connected to the flask. The atmospheric pressure was 752 torr. What was the pressure of the gas in the flask (in torr)?

11.33 Suppose that in a closed-end manometer the mercury in the closed arm was 12.5 cm higher than the mercury in the arm connected to a vessel containing a gas. What is the pressure of the gas expressed in torr?

11.34 Suppose a gas is in a vessel connected to both an open-end and a closed-end manometer. The difference in heights of the mercury in the closed-end manometer was 236 mm, while in the open-end manometer the mercury level in the arm open to the atmosphere was 512 mm below the level in the arm connected to the vessel. Calculate the atmospheric pressure. (It may help to sketch the apparatus.)

Gas Laws for a Fixed Amount of Gas

11.35 A gas has a volume of 255 mL at 725 torr. What volume will the gas occupy at 365 torr if the temperature of the gas doesn't change?

11.36 A bicycle pump has a barrel that is 75.0 cm long (about 30 in.). If air is drawn into the pump at a pressure of 1.00 atm during the upstroke, how long must the downstroke be, in centimeters, to raise the pressure of the air to 5.50 atm (approximately the pressure in the tire of a 10-speed bike)? Assume no change in the temperature of the air.

11.37 A gas has a volume of 3.86 L at 45 °C. What will the volume of the gas be if its temperature is raised to 87 °C while its pressure is kept constant?

OH **11.38** A balloon has a volume of 2.50 L indoors at 22 °C. If the balloon is taken outdoors on a cold day when the air temperature is −15 °C (5 °F), what will its volume be in liters? Assume constant air pressure within the balloon.

11.39 A sample of a gas has a pressure of 854 torr at 285 °C. To what Celsius temperature must the gas be heated to double its pressure if there is no change in the volume of the gas?

11.40 Before taking a trip, you check the air in a tire of your automobile and find it has a pressure of 45 lb in.$^{-2}$ on a day when the air temperature is 12 °C (54 °F). After traveling some distance, you find that the temperature of the air in the tire has risen to 43 °C (approximately 109 °F). What is the air pressure in the tire at this higher temperature, expressed in units of lb in.$^{-2}$?

ILW 11.41 A sample of helium at a pressure of 745 torr and in a volume of 2.58 L was heated from 24.0 to 75.0 °C. The volume of the container expanded to 2.81 L. What was the final pressure (in torr) of the helium?

11.42 When a sample of neon with a volume of 648 mL and a pressure of 0.985 atm was heated from 16.0 to 63.0 °C, its volume became 689 mL. What was its final pressure (in atm)?

11.43 What must be the new volume of a sample of nitrogen (in L) if 2.68 L at 745 torr and 24.0 °C is heated to 375.0 °C under conditions that let the pressure change to 765 torr?

11.44 When 286 mL of oxygen at 741 torr and 18.0 °C was warmed to 33.0 °C, the pressure became 765 torr. What was the final volume (in mL)?

11.45 A sample of argon with a volume of 6.18 L, a pressure of 761 torr, and a temperature of 20.0 °C expanded to a volume of 9.45 L and a pressure of 373 torr. What was its final temperature in °C?

11.46 A sample of a refrigeration gas in a volume of 455 mL, at a pressure of 1.51 atm and at a temperature of 25.0 °C, was compressed into a volume of 222 mL with a pressure of 2.00 atm. To what temperature (in °C) did it have to change?

Ideal Gas Law

11.47 What would be the value of the gas constant R in units of mL torr mol^{-1} K^{-1}?

11.48 The SI generally uses its base units to compute constants involving derived units. The SI unit for volume, for example, is the cubic meter, called the *stere*, because the meter is the base unit of length. We learned about the SI unit of pressure, the pascal, in this chapter. The temperature unit is the kelvin. Calculate the value of the gas constant in the SI units, m^3 Pa mol^{-1} K^{-1}.

11.49 What volume in liters does 0.136 g of O_2 occupy at 20.0 °C and 748 torr?

11.50 What volume in liters does 1.67 g of N_2 occupy at 22.0 °C and 756 torr?

11.51 What pressure (in torr) is exerted by 10.0 g of O_2 in a 2.50 L container at a temperature of 27 °C?

11.52 If 12.0 g of water is converted to steam in a 3.60 L pressure cooker held at a temperature of 108 °C, what pressure will be produced?

11.53 A sample of carbon dioxide has a volume of 26.5 mL at 20.0 °C and 624 torr. How many grams of CO_2 are in the sample?

11.54 Methane is formed in landfills by the action of certain bacteria on buried organic matter. If a sample of methane

collected from a landfill has a volume of 255 mL at 758 torr and 27 °C, how many grams of methane are in the sample?

11.55 To three significant figures, calculate the density in g L^{-1} of the following gases at STP: **(a)** C_2H_6 (ethane), **(b)** N_2, **(c)** Cl_2, **(d)** Ar.

11.56 To three significant figures, calculate the density in g L^{-1} of the following gases at STP: **(a)** Ne, **(b)** O_2, **(c)** CH_4 (methane), **(d)** CF_4.

OH 11.57 What density (in g L^{-1}) does oxygen have at 24.0 °C and 742 torr?

11.58 At 748.0 torr and 20.65 °C, what is the density of argon (in g L^{-1})?

ILW 11.59 A chemist isolated a gas in a glass bulb with a volume of 255 mL at a temperature of 25.0 °C and a pressure (in the bulb) of 10.0 torr. The gas weighed 12.1 mg. What is the molar mass of this gas?

11.60 At 22.0 °C and a pressure of 755 torr, a gas was found to have a density of 1.13 g L^{-1}. Calculate its molar mass.

Stoichiometry of Reactions of Gases

11.61 How many milliliters of oxygen are required to react completely with 175 mL of C_4H_{10} if the volumes of both gases are measured at the same temperature and pressure? The reaction is

$$2C_4H_{10}(g) + 13O_2(g) \longrightarrow 8CO_2(g) + 10H_2O(g)$$

OH 11.62 How many milliliters of O_2 are consumed in the complete combustion of a sample of hexane, C_6H_{14}, if the reaction produces 855 mL of CO_2? Assume all gas volumes are measured at the same temperature and pressure. The reaction is

$$2C_6H_{14}(g) + 19O_2(g) \longrightarrow 12CO_2(g) + 14H_2O(g)$$

ILW 11.63 Propylene, C_3H_6, reacts with hydrogen under pressure to give propane, C_3H_8:

$$C_3H_6(g) + H_2(g) \longrightarrow C_3H_8(g)$$

How many liters of hydrogen (at 740 torr and 24 °C) react with 18.0 g of propylene?

11.64 Nitric acid is formed when NO_2 is dissolved in water.

$$3NO_2(g) + H_2O(l) \longrightarrow 2HNO_3(aq) + NO(g)$$

How many milliliters of NO_2 at 25 °C and 752 torr are needed to form 12.0 g of HNO_3?

11.65 How many milliliters of O_2 measured at 27 °C and 654 torr are needed to react completely with 16.8 mL of CH_4 measured at 35 °C and 725 torr?

11.66 How many milliliters of H_2O vapor, measured at 318 °C and 735 torr, are formed when 33.6 mL of NH_3 at 825 torr and 127 °C react with oxygen according to the following equation?

$$4NH_3(g) + 3O_2(g) \longrightarrow 2N_2(g) + 6H_2O(g)$$

11.67 Calculate the maximum number of milliliters of CO_2, at 745 torr and 27 °C, that could be formed in the combustion of carbon monoxide if 0.300 L of CO at 683 torr and 25 °C is mixed with 155 mL of O_2 at 715 torr and 125 °C.

11.68 A mixture of ammonia and oxygen is prepared by combining 0.300 L of N_2 (measured at 0.750 atm and 28 °C) with 0.220 L of O_2 (measured at 0.780 atm and 50 °C). How many milliliters of N_2 (measured at 0.740 atm and 100.0 °C) could be formed if the following reaction occurs?

$$4NH_3(g) + 3O_2(g) \longrightarrow 2N_2(g) + 6H_2O(g)$$

Dalton's Law of Partial Pressures

*11.69 A 1.00 L container was filled by pumping into it 1.00 L
OH   of N_2 at 20.0 cm Hg, 1.00 L of O_2 at 155 torr, and 1.00 L of He at 0.450 atm. All volumes and pressures were measured at the same temperature. What was the total pressure inside the container after the mixture was made?

11.70 A mixture of N_2, O_2, and CO_2 has a total pressure of 740 torr. In this mixture the partial pressure of N_2 is 12.0 cm Hg and the partial pressure of O_2 is 4.00 dm Hg. What is the partial pressure of the CO_2?

ILW 11.71 A 22.4 L container at 0 °C contains 0.30 mol N_2, 0.20 mol O_2, 0.40 mol He, and 0.10 mol CO_2. What are the partial pressures of each of the gases in torr, atm, and bar?

11.72 A 0.200 mol sample of a mixture of N_2 and CO_2 with a total pressure of 845 torr was exposed to an excess of solid CaO, which reacts with CO_2 according to the equation

$$CaO(s) + CO_2(g) \longrightarrow CaCO_3(s)$$

After the reaction was complete, the pressure of the gas had dropped to 322 torr. How many moles of CO_2 were in the original mixture? (Assume no change in volume or temperature.)

11.73 A sample of carbon monoxide was prepared and collected over water at a temperature of 22 °C and a total pressure of 754 torr. It occupied a volume of 268 mL. Calculate the partial pressure of the CO in torr as well as its dry volume (in mL) under a pressure of 1.00 atm and 25 °C.

11.74 A sample of hydrogen was prepared and collected over water at 25 °C and a total pressure of 742 torr. It occupied a volume of 288 mL. Calculate its partial pressure (in torr) and what its dry volume would be (in mL) under a pressure of 1.00 atm at 25 °C.

11.75 What volume of "wet" methane would you have to collect at 20.0 °C and 742 torr to be sure that the sample contains 244 mL of dry methane (also at 742 torr)?

11.76 What volume of "wet" oxygen would you have to collect if you need the equivalent of 275 mL of dry oxygen at 1.00 atm? (The atmospheric pressure in the lab is 746 torr.) The oxygen is to be collected over water at 15.0 °C.

Graham's Law

11.77 Under conditions in which the density of CO_2 is 1.96 g L^{-1} and that of N_2 is 1.25 g L^{-1}, which gas will effuse more rapidly? What will be the ratio of the rates of effusion of N_2 to CO_2?

11.78 Arrange the following gases in order of increasing rate of diffusion at 25 °C: Cl_2, C_2H_4, SO_2.

11.79 Uranium hexafluoride is a white solid that readily passes directly into the vapor state. (Its vapor pressure at 20.0 °C is 120 torr.) A trace of the uranium in this compound—about 0.7%—is uranium-235, which can be used in a nuclear power plant. The rest of the uranium is essentially uranium-238, and its presence interferes with these applications for uranium-235. Gas effusion of UF_6 can be used to separate the fluoride made from uranium-235 and the fluoride made from uranium-238. Which hexafluoride effuses more rapidly? By how much? (You can check your answer by reading Chemistry and Current Affairs 11.1 on page 505.)

OH **11.80** An unknown gas X effuses 1.65 times faster than C_3H_8. What is the molecular mass of gas X?

| Additional Problems

11.81 One of the oldest units for atmospheric pressure is lb in.$^{-2}$ (pounds per square inch, or psi). Calculate the numerical value of the standard atmosphere in these units to three significant figures. Calculate the mass in pounds of a uniform column of water 33.9 ft high having an area of 1.00 in.^{2} at its base. (Use the following data: density of mercury = 13.6 g mL^{-1}; density of water = 1.00 g mL^{-1}; 1 mL = 1 cm^3; l lb = 454 g; 1 in. = 2.54 cm.)

*11.82 A typical automobile has a weight of approximately 3500 lb. If the vehicle is to be equipped with tires, each of which will contact the pavement with a "footprint" that is 6.0 in. wide by 3.2 in. long, what must the gauge pressure of the air be in each tire? (Gauge pressure is the amount that the gas pressure exceeds atmospheric pressure. Assume that atmospheric pressure is 14.7 lb in.$^{-2}$.)

*11.83 Suppose you were planning to move a house by transporting it on a large trailer. The house has an estimated weight of 45.6 tons (1 ton = 2000 lb). The trailer is expected to weigh 8.3 tons. Each wheel of the trailer will have tires inflated to a gauge pressure of 85 psi (which is actually 85 psi above atmospheric pressure). If the area of contact between a tire and the pavement can be no larger than 100.0 in.^{2} (10.0 in. × 10.0 in.), what is the minimum number of wheels the trailer must have? (Remember, tires are mounted in multiples of two on a trailer. Assume that atmospheric pressure is 14.7 psi.)

*11.84 The motion picture *Titanic* described the tragedy of the collision of the ocean liner of the same name with an iceberg in the North Atlantic. The ship sank soon after the collision on April 14, 1912, and now rests on the sea floor at a depth of 12,468 ft. Recently, the wreck was explored by the research vessel *Nautile*, which has successfully recovered a variety of items from the debris field surrounding the sunken ship. Calculate the pressure in atmospheres and pounds per square inch exerted on the hull of the *Nautile* as it explores the sea bed surrounding the *Titanic*. (*Hint:* The height of a column of liquid required to exert a given pressure is inversely proportional to the liquid's density. Seawater has a density of approximately 1.025 g mL^{-1}; mercury has a density of 13.6 g mL^{-1}; 1 atm = 14.7 lb in.$^{-2}$.)

*11.85 Two flasks (which we will refer to as flask 1 and flask 2) are connected to each other by a U-shaped tube filled with an oil having a density of 0.826 g mL^{-1}. The oil level in the arm connected to flask 2 is 16.24 cm higher than in the arm connected to flask 1. Flask 1 is also connected to an open-end mercury manometer. The mercury level in the arm open to the atmosphere is 12.26 cm higher than the level in the arm connected to flask 1. The atmospheric pressure is 0.827 atm. What is the pressure of the gas in flask 2 expressed in torr? (See the hint given in Problem 11.84.)

*11.86 A bubble of air escaping from a diver's mask rises from
OH a depth of 100 ft to the surface where the pressure is 1.00 atm. Initially, the bubble has a volume of 10.0 mL. Assuming none of the air dissolves in the water, how many times larger is the bubble just as it reaches the surface? Use your answer to explain why scuba divers constantly exhale as they slowly rise from a deep dive. (The density of seawater is approximately 1.025 g mL^{-1}; the density of mercury is 13.6 g mL^{-1}.)

*11.87 In a diesel engine, the fuel is ignited when it is injected into hot compressed air, heated by the compression itself. In a typical high-speed diesel engine, the chamber in the cylinder has a diameter of 10.7 cm and a length of 13.4 cm. On compression, the length of the chamber is shortened by 12.7 cm (a "5-inch stroke"). The compression of the air changes its pressure from 1.00 to 34.0 atm. The temperature of the air before compression is 364 K. As a result of the compression, what will be the final air temperature (in K and °C) just before the fuel injection?

*11.88 Early one cool (60.0 °F) morning you start on a bike ride with the atmospheric pressure at 14.7 lb in.$^{-2}$ and the tire gauge pressure at 50.0 lb in.$^{-2}$. (Gauge pressure is the amount that the pressure exceeds atmospheric pressure.) By late afternoon, the air had warmed up considerably, and this plus the heat generated by tire friction sent the temperature inside the tire to 104 °F. What will the tire gauge now read, assuming that the volume of the air in the tire and the atmospheric pressure have not changed?

OH 11.89 The range of temperatures over which an automobile tire must be able to withstand pressure changes is roughly −50 to 120 °F. If a tire is filled to 35 lb in.$^{-2}$ at −35 °F (on a cold day in Alaska, for example), what will be the pressure in the tire (in the same pressure units) on a hot day in Death Valley when the temperature is 115 °F? (Assume that the volume of the tire does not change.)

OH 11.90 A mixture was prepared in a 0.500 L reaction vessel from 0.300 L of O_2 (measured at 25 °C and 74.0 cm Hg) and 0.400 L of H_2 (measured at 45 °C and 1250 torr). The mixture was ignited and the H_2 and O_2 reacted to form water. What was the final pressure inside the reaction vessel after the reaction was over if the temperature was held at 122 °C?

11.91 A student collected 18.45 mL of H_2 over water at 24 °C. The water level inside the collection apparatus was 8.5 cm higher than the water level outside. The barometric pressure was 746 torr. How many grams of zinc had to react with HCl(*aq*) to produce the H_2 that was collected?

11.92 A mixture of gases is prepared from 87.5 g of O_2 and 12.7 g of H_2. After the reaction of O_2 and H_2 is complete, what is the total pressure of the mixture if its temperature is 162 °C and its volume is 12.0 L? What are the partial pressures of the gases remaining in the mixture?

11.93 A gas was found to have a density of 0.08747 mg mL^{-1} at 17.0 °C and a pressure of 1.00 atm. What is its molecular mass? Can you tell what the gas most likely is?

*11.94 In one analytical procedure for determining the percentage of nitrogen in unknown compounds, weighed samples are made to decompose to N_2, which is collected over water at known temperatures and pressures. The volumes of N_2 are then translated into grams and then into percentages.

(a) Show that the following equation can be used to calculate the percentage of nitrogen in a sample having a mass of *W* grams when the N_2 has a volume of *V* mL and is collected over water at t_c °C at a total pressure of *P* torr. The vapor pressure of water occurs in the equation as $P^\circ_{H_2O}$.

$$\text{Percentage N} = 0.04489 \times \frac{V(P - P^\circ_{H_2O})}{W(273 + t_c)}$$

(b) Use this equation to calculate the percentage of nitrogen in the sample described in Problem 11.97.

| Multi-Concept Problems

*11.95 A common laboratory preparation of hydrogen on a small scale uses the reaction of zinc with hydrochloric acid. Zinc chloride is the other product.

    (a) If 12.0 L of H_2 at 765 torr and 20.0 °C is wanted, how many grams of zinc are needed, in theory?

    (b) If the acid is available as 8.00 M HCl, what is the minimum volume of this solution (in milliliters) required to produce the amount of H_2 described in part (a)?

*11.96 A sample of an unknown gas with a mass of 3.620 g was made to decompose into 2.172 g of O_2 and 1.448 g of S. Before the decomposition, this sample occupied a volume of 1120 mL at 75.0 cm Hg and 25.0 °C. What is the molecular formula of this gas?

*11.97 A sample of a new anti-malarial drug with a mass of 0.2394 g was made to undergo a series of reactions that changed all of the nitrogen in the compound into N_2. This gas had a volume of 18.90 mL when collected over water at 23.80 °C and a pressure of 746.0 torr. At 23.80 °C, the vapor pressure of water is 22.14 torr. When 6.478 mg of the compound was burned in pure oxygen, 17.57 mg of CO_2 and 4.319 mg of H_2O were obtained. What are the percentages of C and H in this compound?

    (a) Assuming that any undetermined element is oxygen, write an empirical formula for the compound.

    (b) The molecular mass of the compound was found to be 324. What is its molecular formula?

11.98 The odor of a rotten egg is caused by hydrogen sulfide, H_2S. Most people can detect it at a concentration of 0.15 ppb (parts per billion), meaning 0.15 L of H_2S in 10^9 L of space. A typical student lab is $42 \times 24 \times 8.6$ ft.

    (a) At STP, how many liters of H_2S could be present in a typical lab to have a concentration of 0.15 ppb?

    (b) How many milliliters of 0.100 M Na_2S would be needed to generate the amount of H_2S in part (a) by the reaction of hydrochloric acid with sodium sulfide? (Assume that all of the H_2S generated enters the atmosphere.)

11.99 Chlorine reacts with sulfite ion to give sulfate ion and chloride ion. How many milliliters of Cl_2 gas measured at 25 °C and 734 torr are required to react with all the SO_3^{2-} in 50.0 mL of 0.200 M Na_2SO_3 solution?

*11.100 In an experiment designed to prepare a small amount of hydrogen by the method described in Problem 11.95, a student was limited to using a gas-collecting bottle with a maximum capacity of 335 mL. The method involved collecting the hydrogen over water. What are the minimum number of grams of Zn and the minimum number of milliliters of 6.00 M HCl needed to produce the *wet* hydrogen that can exactly fit this collecting bottle at 0.932 atm and 25.0 °C?

*11.101 Carbon dioxide can be made in the lab by the reaction of hydrochloric acid with calcium carbonate. How many milliliters of dry CO_2 at 20.0 °C and 745 torr can be prepared from a mixture of 12.3 g of $CaCO_3$ and 185 mL of 0.250 M HCl?

11.102 Boron forms a variety of unusual compounds with hydrogen. A chemist isolated 6.3 mg of one of the boron hydrides in a glass bulb with a volume of 385 mL at 25.0 °C and a bulb pressure of 11 torr. Which of the following is likely to be its molecular formula: BH_3, B_2H_6, or B_4H_{10}?

| Exercises in Critical Thinking

11.103 Firefighters advise that you get out of a burning building by keeping close to the floor. We learned that carbon dioxide and most other hazardous compounds are more dense than air and they should settle to the floor. What other facts do we know that make the firefighter's advice correct?

11.104 Carbon dioxide is implicated in global warming. Propose ways to control or perhaps decrease the carbon dioxide content in our air. Rank each proposal based on its feasibility.

11.105 Methane is another gas implicated in the global warming problem. It has been proposed that much of the methane in the atmosphere is from ruminating cows. Evaluate that suggestion and come up with other possible sources of methane.

*11.106 One of the CFCs that is implicated in decreasing the ozone layer and formation of the ozone hole over Antarctica is Freon-12 or CCl_2F_2. Calculate the density of Freon-12 at STP and compare it to the average density of air. Suggest how Freon-12 can get into the stratosphere to threaten the ozone layer.

Review of Mathematics

The purpose of this Appendix is to provide a brief review of math topics you will use in solving various chemistry problems in this book. We recommend that you refer to the topics discussed here when you find you are having difficulty in following the math in worked examples, when you are unsure as to how to proceed with solving the math in an exercise or homework problem, or when answers you obtain do not match those in Appendix B.

A.1 | Exponential and Scientific Notation

Very large and very small numbers are generally expressed as powers of ten. This is often called **exponential notation.** When the quantity is expressed as *a number between 1 and 10* multiplied by 10 raised to a power (e.g., 3.2×10^5), we also call it **standard scientific notation** (or simply **scientific notation**). Some examples are given in Table A.1. If you have a scientific calculator, it is able to express numbers in scientific notation and it permits you to perform arithmetic on numbers expressed this way. Some tips on using scientific calculators are described later in Appendix A.5.

Even though you have a calculator at your disposal, it is important that you understand how to write these numbers and how to perform arithmetic with them. Such an ability provides a way to quickly check an answer to a problem to be sure you've used the calculator correctly.

Table A.1	
Number	**Exponential Form**
1	1×10^0
10	1×10^1
100	1×10^2
1000	1×10^3
10,000	1×10^4
100,000	1×10^5
1,000,000	1×10^6
0.1	1×10^{-1}
0.01	1×10^{-2}
0.001	1×10^{-3}
0.000 1	1×10^{-4}
0.000 01	1×10^{-5}
0.000 001	1×10^{-6}
0.000 000 1	1×10^{-7}

The Meaning of Positive and Negative Exponents

Positive Exponents

Suppose you come across a number such as 6.4×10^4. This is just an alternative way of writing 64,000. In other words, the number 6.4 is multiplied by 10 four times.

$$6.4 \times 10^4 = 6.4 \times 10 \times 10 \times 10 \times 10 = 64,000$$

Instead of actually writing out all of these 10s, notice that the decimal point is simply moved four places to the right in going from 6.4×10^4 to 64,000. Here are a few other examples. Study them to see how the decimal point changes.

$$53.476 \times 10^2 = 5347.6$$
$$0.0016 \times 10^5 = 160$$
$$0.000056 \times 10^3 = 0.056$$

Here is another example that more forcefully shows the value of expressing a number in scientific notation.

602,000,000,000,000,000,000,000

$$= 6.02 \times 10 \times 10 \times 10 \times 10 \times 10 \times 10 \times 10 \times 10 \times 10 \times 10 \times 10 \times 10 \times$$
$$10 \times 10 \times 10 \times 10 \times 10 \times 10 \times 10 \times 10 \times 10 \times 10 \times 10$$
$$= 6.02 \times 10^{23}$$

(This is Avogadro's number, which is the number of atoms in 12.0 g of carbon.)

In some calculations it is helpful to rewrite large numbers in scientific notation format. To do this, count the number of places you would have to move the decimal point to the left to put it just after the first digit in the number. For example, you would have to move the decimal point four places to the left in the following number.

$$6 \underset{4}{\underbrace{0}} \underset{3}{\underbrace{5}} \underset{2}{\underbrace{3}} \underset{1}{\underbrace{0}}$$

Therefore, we can rewrite 60530 as 6.0530×10^4. Thus the number of moves equals the exponent.

Sometimes it is necessary to change a number from one exponential form to another. For example, suppose we wish to re-express the number 6.0530×10^4 as something times 10^2.

$$6.0530 \times 10^4 = \boxed{} \times 10^2$$

What number goes in the box? Although there are rules that you could learn, it is better to think it through as follows. The number 6.0530×10^4 is a product of two parts, 6.0530 and 10^4. Together they equal 60530. We want to change the exponential part to 10^2, which means the exponential part of the product is becoming *smaller*. The only way the product can remain equal to 60530 is if the decimal part becomes *larger*. Since we are decreasing the exponential part by a factor of 100 (i.e., 10^2), we must increase the decimal part by a factor of 100, which means we change it from 6.0530 to 605.30. Therefore,

$$6.0530 \times 10^4 = \boxed{605.30} \times 10^2$$

Negative Exponents

A negative exponent tells us to take the reciprocal of the quantity and raise it to the power expressed in the exponent. Thus, x^{-1} means $1/x$, and x^{-5} means $1/x^5$.

$$x^{-1} = \frac{1}{x} \qquad x^{-5} = \frac{1}{x^5}$$

Now, imagine you have just encountered a number such as 1.4×10^{-4}. This is an alternative way of writing

$$\frac{1.4}{10 \times 10 \times 10 \times 10}$$

Thus, a negative exponent tells us how many times to divide by ten. Dividing by ten, of course, can be done by simply moving the decimal point. Thus, 1.4×10^{-4} can be re-expressed as 0.00014. Notice that the decimal point is four places to the *left* of the 1. Here are some examples of numbers expressed as negative exponentials and their equivalents.

$$3567.9 \times 10^{-3} = 3.5679$$
$$0.01456 \times 10^{-2} = 0.0001456$$
$$45691 \times 10^{-3} = 45.691$$

To express a number smaller than 1 in scientific notation, we count the number of places the decimal has to be moved to put it to the right of the first nonzero digit. The number that we count equals the negative exponent. For example, you would have to move the decimal point five places to the right to put it to the right of the first nonzero digit in

$$0.0000\overset{\frown}{6}8901$$
5 places

This number can be re-expressed as 6.8901×10^{-5}.

Multiplying Numbers Written in Exponential and Scientific Notation

The real value of exponential forms of numbers comes in carrying out multiplications and divisions of large and small numbers. Suppose we want to multiply 1000 by 10000. Doing this by a long process fills the page with zeros (and some ones). But notice the following relationships.

Numbers	1000	×	10000		
	$[10 \times 10 \times 10]$	×	$[10 \times 10 \times 10 \times 10]$	=	10,000,000
Exponential form	10^3	×	10^4	=	10^7
Exponents	3	+	4	=	7

If we *add* 3 and 4, the exponents of the exponential forms of 1000 and 10000, we get the exponent for the answer. Suppose we want to multiply 4160 by 20000. If we re-express each number in scientific notation we have

Multiply these parts.

$$(4.16 \times 10^3) \times (2.00 \times 10^4)$$

Multiply these parts.

This now simplifies to

$$(4.16 \times 2.00) \times [10^3 \times 10^4]$$

The answer can be easily worked without losing the location of the decimal point. The exponents are added to give the exponent on 10 in the answer, and the numbers 4.16 and 2.00 are multiplied. The product is 8.32×10^7. Thus there are two steps in multiplying numbers that are written in scientific notation.

1. Multiply the decimal parts of the numbers (the parts that precede the 10s).
2. Add the exponents of the 10s algebraically to obtain the exponent on the 10 in the answer.

Dividing Numbers Written in Exponential or Scientific Notation

Suppose we want to divide 10,000,000 by 1000. Doing this by long division would be primitive to say the least. It is much easier using exponential notation, where $10,000,000 = 10^7$ and $1000 = 10^3$. Notice the following relationships.

$$\frac{10,000,000}{1000} = 10,000 \qquad \frac{10^7}{10^3} = 10^4 = 10,000$$

The exponent in the result is $(7 - 3)$. So, to divide numbers in exponential form, we subtract the exponent on 10 in the denominator from the exponent on 10 in the numerator.

To extend this operation one step, let's divide 0.00468 by 0.0000400. The answer can be obtained as follows, expressing the numbers in scientific notation.

$$\frac{4.68 \times 10^{-3}}{4.00 \times 10^{-5}} = \frac{4.68}{4.00} \times 10^{[(-3)-(-5)]}$$
$$= 1.17 \times 10^2$$

Notice that the division proceeds in two steps.

1. Carry out the division of the numbers standing before the 10s.
2. Algebraically subtract the exponent in the denominator from the exponent in the numerator.

Estimating Answers by Mental Arithmetic

Often, in working out chemistry problems, we find it necessary to perform a series of multiplications and divisions. These calculations are most easily handled using a calculator, but to check the answer quickly, we can do some simple mental arithmetic. For example, suppose that in solving a problem we performed the following arithmetic.

$$\frac{(1.908 \times 10^3) \times (4.56 \times 10^{-3}) \times (4.52 \times 10^7)}{(1.664 \times 10^{-1}) \times (2.34 \times 10^9) \times (3.02 \times 10^2)} = 3.34 \times 10^{-3} \text{ (rounded)}$$

To perform a check on the arithmetic to see whether the answer is "in the right ball park," we first separate the powers of ten from the other numbers. (You don't actually have to rewrite the problem setup; we're doing so here to make the procedure clearer.)

$$\frac{(1.908) \times (4.56) \times (4.52)}{(1.664) \times (2.34) \times (3.02)} \times \frac{(10^3) \times (10^{-3}) \times (10^7)}{(10^{-1}) \times (10^9) \times (10^2)}$$

Next, let's check the exponential part of the calculation by combining the powers of 10.

$$\text{exponential part} = 10^{[(3-3+7)-(-1+9+2)]}$$
$$= 10^{-3}$$

This agrees with the results obtained with the calculator, so we know our answer is not unreasonable. If we want to check the rest of the math, we need to estimate the results of the arithmetic involving the pre-exponential parts of the numbers

$$\frac{(1.908) \times (4.56) \times (4.52)}{(1.664) \times (2.34) \times (3.02)}$$

We do this by rounding off the numbers so we can do the arithmetic in our heads. Let's round 1.908 to 2. The next two numbers are both close to 4.5, so we will round one of them down and the other up, hoping to cancel rounding errors: 4.56 becomes 4 and 4.52 becomes 5. Similar rounding applied to the numbers in the denominator gives us the following:

$$\frac{(1.908) \times (4.56) \times (4.52)}{(1.664) \times (2.34) \times (3.02)} \approx \frac{2 \times 4 \times 5}{2 \times 2 \times 3} = \frac{40}{12} = \frac{10}{3} \approx 3.3$$

So, our rough arithmetic gives us an answer of 3.3×10^{-3}, which is almost exactly the answer we obtained using the calculator.

Adding or Subtracting Numbers in Scientific Notation

The important thing to remember here is that to perform the arithmetic, both numbers must have the same power of 10. If they're not given that way, then you have to convert one to have the same exponent on 10 as the other. For example, suppose we had to add the two measured distances, 2.36×10^5 cm and 5.08×10^3 cm. We could change 5.08×10^3 cm to have the exponential part equal 10^5, or we could change 2.36×10^5 cm to have the exponential part equal 10^3.

$$\begin{array}{rr}
2.36 \times 10^5 & 236 \times 10^3 \\
0.0508 \times 10^5 & 5.08 \times 10^3 \\
\hline
2.41 \times 10^5 & 241 \times 10^3
\end{array}$$

Notice that in both cases, we have applied the rules for significant figures as they apply to addition and subtraction, given on page 44.

A.2 | Logarithms

A **logarithm** is simply an exponent. For example, if we have an expression

$$N = a^b$$

we see that to obtain N we must raise a to the b power. The exponent b is said to be the logarithm of N; it is the exponent to which we must raise a, which we call the *base*, to obtain the number N.

$$\log_a N = b$$

We can define a logarithm system for any base we want. For example, if we choose the base 2, then

$$\log_2 8 = 3$$

which means that to obtain the number 8, we must raise the base (2) to the third power.

$$8 = 2^3$$

The most frequently encountered logarithm systems in the sciences are *common logarithms* and *natural logarithms*, which are discussed separately below. However, for any system of logarithms there are some useful relationships that evolve from the behavior of exponents in arithmetic operations. We encounter these at various times throughout the sciences, so it is important that you are familiar with them.

For Multiplication:

> If $\quad N = A \times B$
> then $\log N = \log A + \log B$

For Division:

> If $\quad N = \dfrac{A}{B}$
> then $\log N = \log A - \log B$

For Exponentials:

> If $\quad N = A^b$
> then $\log N = b \log A$

Common Logarithms

The **common logarithm** or **log₁₀** of a number N is the exponent to which 10 must be raised to equal the number N. Thus, if

$$N = 10^x$$

then the common logarithm of N, or **log₁₀ N**, is simply x.

$$\log_{10} N = \log N = x$$

As mentioned earlier, there is another kind of logarithm called a **natural logarithm** that we'll take up later. However, when we use the terms "logarithm" or "log N" without specifying the base, we always mean common logarithms related to the base 10, as indicated above.

If N is just 10 raised to a power, finding the logarithm is simple. For example, suppose we want to find the logarithm of 10^{18}.

$$\log 10^{18} = ?$$

This expression is asking, "To what power do we raise 10 to obtain 10^{18}?" The answer, of course, is 18. (We have to raise 10 to the power 18 to obtain 10^{18}.)

$$\log 10^{18} = 18$$

Here are a few more examples.

$$
\begin{aligned}
N = 10 &= 10^1 & \log N &= 1 \\
= 100 &= 10^2 & &= 2 \\
= 0.1 &= 10^{-1} & &= -1 \\
= 0.0001 &= 10^{-4} & &= -4
\end{aligned}
$$

The logarithms of these numbers were easy to figure out by just using the definition of logarithms, but usually it isn't this simple. For example, what is the value of x in the following equations?

$$4.23 = 10^x$$
$$\log 4.23 = x$$

In other words, to what power of x must we raise 10 to obtain 4.23? Obviously, the exponent is not a whole number. Therefore, to determine the value of x we use a scientific calculator. We will have more to say about this in Section A.5.

Natural Logarithms

In the sciences there are many phenomena in which observed quantities are related to each other logarithmically, which means that there is an exponential relationship between them. However, this exponential relationship does not involve 10 raised to a power. Instead it involves powers of a number symbolized by the letter e, which is said to be the base of the system of natural logarithms.

The quantity e is derived from calculus and is an irrational number, just like another quantity you are familiar with, π. This means that e is a nonrepeating decimal. To eight significant figures its value is

$$e = 2.7182818\ldots$$

To truly appreciate the significance of this number and the system of logarithms based on it, you must have a good foundation in calculus. A discussion of calculus is beyond the scope of this text, so we will not attempt to explain the origin of the value of e further. Nevertheless, we can still use the results and discuss the system of **natural logarithms** that has the number e as its base.

Natural logarithms use the symbol ln instead of log. Thus, if the number N equals e^x,

$$N = e^x$$

then

$$\log_e N = \ln N = x$$

Scientific calculators have the ability to calculate natural logarithms and their corresponding *antilogarithms*. This is discussed in Section A.5 of this appendix. There is a simple relationship between common and natural logarithms. To four significant figures,

$$\ln N = 2.303 \log N$$

In other words, to find $\ln N$, simply find the common log of N and multiply it by 2.303.

A.3 | Graphing

One of the most useful ways of describing the relationship between two quantities is by means of a graph. It allows us to obtain an overall view of how one quantity changes when the other changes. Constructing graphs from experimental data, or from data calculated from an equation, is therefore a common operation in the sciences, so it is important that you understand how to present data graphically. Let's look at an example.

Suppose that we wanted to know how the volume of a given amount of gas varies as we change its pressure. In Chapter 11 we find an equation that gives the pressure–volume relationship for a fixed amount of gas at a constant temperature,

$$PV = \text{constant} \hspace{4cm} \text{(A.1)}$$

where P = pressure and V = volume. For calculations, this equation can be used in two ways. If we solve for the volume, we get

$$V = \frac{\text{constant}}{P} \qquad \text{(A.2)}$$

Knowing the value of the constant for a given gas sample at a given temperature allows us to calculate the volume that the gas occupies at any particular pressure. Simply substitute in the values for the constant and the pressure and compute the volume.

Equation A.1 can also be solved for the pressure.

$$P = \frac{\text{constant}}{V} \qquad \text{(A.3)}$$

From this equation the pressure corresponding to any particular volume can be calculated.

Now, suppose, that we want to see graphically how the pressure and volume of a gas are related as the pressure is raised from 1.0 to 10.0 atm in steps of 1.0 atm. Let's also suppose that for this sample of gas the value of the constant in our equation is 0.25 L atm. To construct the graph we first must decide how to label and number the axes.

Usually, the horizontal axis, called the **abscissa**, is chosen to correspond to the **independent variable**—the variable whose values are chosen first and from which the values of the **dependent variable** are determined. In our example, we are choosing values of pressure (1.0 atm, 2.0 atm, etc.), so we will label the abscissa "pressure." We will also mark off the axis evenly from 1.0 to 10.0 atm, as shown in Figure A.1. Next we put the label "volume" on the vertical axis (the ordinate). Before we can number this axis, however, we need to know over what range the volume will vary. Using Equation A.2 we can calculate the data in Table A.2, and we see that the volume ranges from a low of 0.025 L to a high of 0.25 L. We can therefore mark off the ordinate evenly in increments of 0.025 L, starting at the bottom with 0.025 L. Notice that in labeling the axes we have indicated the units of P and V in parentheses.

Next we plot the data as shown in Figure A.2. To clearly show each plotted point, we use a small circle that has its center located at the coordinates of the point. Then we draw a *smooth* curve through the points.

Sometimes, when plotting experimentally measured data, the points do not fall exactly on a smooth line (Figure A.3). However, nature generally is not irregular even though that's what the data appear to suggest. The fluctuations are usually due to experimental error of some sort. Therefore, rather that draw an irregular line connecting all the data points (the dashed line), we draw a smooth curve that passes as close as possible to all of the points, even though it may not actually pass through any of them.

Table A.2	
Pressure (atm)	Volume (L)
1.0	0.25
2.0	0.125
3.0	0.083
4.0	0.062
5.0	0.050
6.0	0.042
7.0	0.036
8.0	0.031
9.0	0.028
10.0	0.025

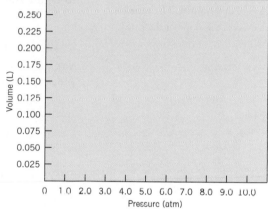

Figure A.1 | Choosing and labeling the axes of a graph.

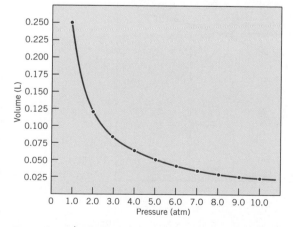

Figure A.2 | Plotting points and drawing the curve.

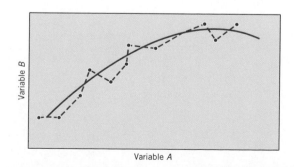

Figure A.3 | Experimental data do not all fall on a smooth curve when they are plotted because they contain experimental error. A smooth curve is drawn as close to all of the data points as possible, rather than the jerky dashed line.

Slope

One of the properties of curves and lines on a graph is their *slope* or steepness. Consider Figure A.4, which is a straight line drawn on a set of xy coordinate axes. The slope of the line is defined as the change in y, Δy, divided by the change in x, Δx.

$$\text{slope} = \frac{\Delta y}{\Delta x} = \frac{y_2 - y_1}{x_2 - x_1}$$

Curved lines have slopes too, but the slope changes from point to point on the curve. To obtain the slope graphically, we can draw a line that is tangent to the curve at the point where we want to know the slope. The slope of this tangent is the same as the slope of the curve at this point. In Figure A.5 we see a curve for which the slope is determined at two different points. At point M the curve is rising steeply and $\Delta y/\Delta x$ for the tangent is large. At point N the curve is rising less steeply, and $\Delta y/\Delta x$ for the tangent at N is small. Therefore, the slope at M is larger than the slope at N.

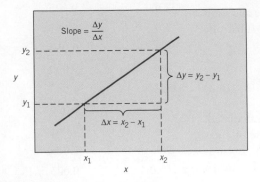

Figure A.4 | Determining the slope of a straight line. Two points are chosen on the line and Δx and Δy are determined. The ratio $\Delta x/\Delta y$ is the slope of the line.

Straight Line Graphs

A type of graph that scientists find especially useful is a straight line graph—one similar to Figure A.4. A straight line is obtained when we plot an equation with the general form

$$y = mx + b$$

where m is the slope of the line and b is the intercept of the line with the y axis (where $x = 0$). Usually, the experimental data correspond to the x and y values. When the data are plotted, the slope and intercept can be obtained from the graph. Let's look at an example.

In Figure A.2 we plotted the P-V data in Table A.2. Pressure and volume for a gas are related by the following equation, obtained by solving Equation A.1 for P.

$$P = \frac{\text{constant}}{V} \qquad\qquad \textbf{(A.4)}$$

Let's rewrite this equation as follows, noting it's similarity of the equation for a straight line.

$$P = (\text{constant})\frac{1}{V} + 0$$

$$\downarrow \qquad\quad \downarrow \quad\ \downarrow \quad \downarrow$$

$$y = \qquad m \quad x \ + \ b$$

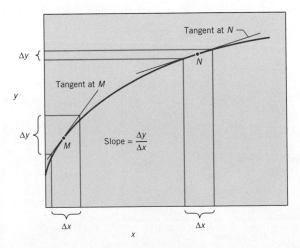

Figure A.5 | For a given Δx, Δy is much larger at M than it is at N. Therefore, the slope at M is larger than at N.

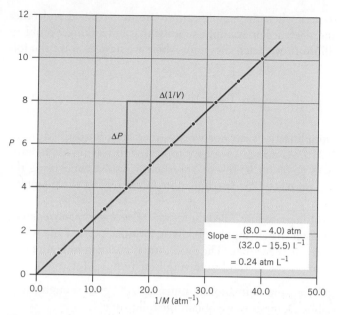

Table A.3	Data for a graph of P versus 1/V using values from Table A.2
P (atm)	**1/V (L^{-1})**
1	4.0
2	8.0
3	12.0
4	16.1
5	20.0
6	23.8
7	27.8
8	32.3
9	35.7
10	40.0

Figure A.6 | A graph of P versus $1/V$.

This tells us that if we plot P versus $1/V$, we should obtain a straight line with a slope that's equal to the constant in Equation A.4, and with an intercept of zero (i.e., the line should pass through zero). Table A.3 contains P and $1/V$ data obtained from the data in Table A.2. These data are plotted in Figure A.6. The slope of the line is obtained as described in Figure A.4 by choosing two points on the graph, estimating x and y values, and calculating the slope. The results are also shown in Figure A.6.

Sometimes the relationship between x and y is as follows,

$$y = A\, e^{Bx}$$

where e is the base of the natural logarithm system. In such situations, we take the natural logarithm of both sides of the equation,

$$\ln y = \ln A + B x$$

which we can rearrange as

$$\ln y = B x + \ln A$$
$$\downarrow \quad \downarrow\downarrow \quad \downarrow$$
$$y \;\; = m x + b$$

Notice how we have once again obtained an equation that follows the form of a straight line, so by plotting $\ln y$ versus x, we should obtain a straight line with a slope equal to B and an intercept of $\ln A$.

A.4 | Method of Successive Approximations

This section of the appendix applies primarily to problems associated with Chapters 15 and 17 where we discuss problems involved with chemical equilibria.

In nearly all of the examples described in Chapter 17, simplifications in the algebra are possible because K_a or K_b are very small and the concentration of the solute is relatively large. However, there are instances when the simplifications are not justified and other methods are needed to solve the algebra. For example, suppose that in working a problem dealing with a weak acid equilibrium we reach the point where we have to solve the following equation for x.

$$\frac{x^2}{(0.010 - x)} = 1.4 \times 10^{-3} \qquad \text{(A.5)}$$

For this problem, the usual simplifications do not work, so we are not justified in assuming that $(0.010 - x) \approx 0.010$. As a result, we have to deal with solving a quadratic equation. There are two ways to go about it. In one approach, we solve for x using the quadratic formula, as described on page 725. For Equation A.5, applying the quadratic formula yields $x = 3.1 \times 10^{-3}$.

The second approach is to apply a procedure called the *method of successive approximations.* This method is not only much faster than using the quadratic formula, particularly with a scientific calculator, but it is also just as accurate. The procedure is outlined in Figure A.7, which you should follow as we apply the method to solving Equation A.5 for x.

Step 1 We apply the simplifying approximation to Equation A.5, even though we know it is not really applicable. Doing this, we obtain the following:

$$\frac{x^2}{(0.010 - x)} \approx \frac{x^2}{0.010} = 1.4 \times 10^{-3}$$

for which we obtain the solution $x = 3.7 \times 10^{-3}$. We call this quantity, $x = 3.7 \times 10^{-2}$, our *first approximation.*

Step 2 We substitute $x = 3.7 \times 10^{-3}$ (our first approximation) into the term in the denominator, $(0.100 - x)$, and then recompute x. This gives us

$$\frac{x^2}{(0.010 - 0.0037)} = 1.4 \times 10^{-3}$$

or

$$x^2 = (0.006) \times 1.4 \times 10^{-3}$$

Taking only the positive root,

$$x = 2.9 \times 10^{-3} \; (\textit{second approximation})$$

We call $x = 2.9 \times 10^{-3}$ our *second approximation.*

Step 3 We compare the second approximation to the first and we see they are not the same, so we repeat Step 2.

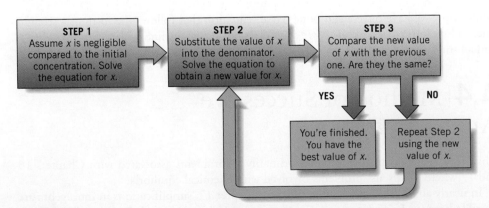

Figure A.7 | Steps in the method of successive approximations.

Step 2 again We substitute $x = 2.9 \times 10^{-3}$ (our second approximation) into the term in the denominator, $(0.100 - x)$, and then recompute x. This gives us a *third approximation*,

$$\frac{x^2}{(0.010 - 0.0029)} = 1.4 \times 10^{-3}$$

$$x^2 = (0.007) \times 1.4 \times 10^{-3}$$

$$x = 3.1 \times 10^{-3} \quad (third\ approximation)$$

Step 3 again The third approximation is not the same as the second approximation, so we repeat Step 2 again.

Step 2 again We substitute $x = 3.1 \times 10^{-3}$ (our third approximation) into the term in the denominator, $(0.100 - x)$, and then recompute x. This gives us

$$\frac{x^2}{(0.010 - 0.0031)} = 1.4 \times 10^{-3}$$

$$x^2 = (0.007) \times 1.4 \times 10^{-3}$$

$$x = 3.1 \times 10^{-3} \quad (fourth\ approximation)$$

Step 3 again When we compare the third and fourth approximations, we see that they are identical, so we are finished. The method of successive approximations tells us that $x = 3.1 \times 10^{-3}$.

First, you might notice that the answer obtained by the method of successive approximations is identical to that obtained using the quadratic formula (which also gave $x = 3.1 \times 10^{-3}$). Also notice that the second pass through Step 2 gave a smaller correction than the first. Each succeeding approximation differs from the preceding one by a smaller and smaller amount. We stop the calculation when the difference between two approximations is insignificant. Try this approach by working Problem 17.131 on page 827.

A.5 | Tips on Using Scientific Calculators

Scientific Calculators and Scientific Notation

Scientific calculators give you the ability to easily perform arithmetic of all kinds, and they are especially useful when you have to deal with large or small numbers expressed as exponentials. As you would expect, addition, subtraction, multiplication, and division are performed with the keys $+$, $-$, $\times$, and $\div$, respectively.[1] However, students often have difficulty in properly entering numbers in scientific notation, so let's take a detailed look at this.

To deal with numbers in scientific notation, such as 2.3×10^5 or 6.7×10^{-12}, calculators have a special key often labeled EXP or EE. If we read the number 2.3×10^5 as "two point three times ten to the fifth," the EXP (or EE) key should be read as ". . . times ten to the . . ." Thus the sequence of keys that enter the number 2.3×10^5 is

"two" "point" "three" "fifth"

$\boxed{2}\ \boxed{.}\ \boxed{3}\ \boxed{\text{EXP}}\ \boxed{5}$

"times ten to the"

---

[1] You're probably familiar with the old adage: "When all else fails, read the instructions!" We strongly encourage you to read the *Instruction Manual* that came with your calculator.

Try this on your own calculator and check to be sure that the number is correctly displayed after you've entered it.[2] If not, check the instruction booklet that came with the calculator or ask your instructor for help.

When entering a number such as 6.7×10^{-12}, be sure to press the "change sign" or "$+/-$" key after pressing the EXP key. Calculators will not give the correct entry if the "minus" key is pressed instead of the "$+/-$" key. For example, clear the display and then try the following sequence of keystrokes on your calculator.

$$\boxed{6}\ \boxed{.}\ \boxed{7}\ \boxed{\text{EXP}}\ \boxed{+/-}\ \boxed{1}\ \boxed{2}$$

If you wish to multiply these two numbers together, enter the first one, press the $\boxed{\times}$ key, then enter the second number, and finally press the $\boxed{=}$ key. The answer displayed on the calculator should be 1.541×10^{-6}.

$$(2.3 \times 10^5) \times (6.7 \times 10^{-12}) = 1.541 \times 10^{-6}$$

Chain Calculations

It is not uncommon to have to calculate the value of a fraction in which there is a string of numbers that must be multiplied together in the numerator and another string of numbers to be multiplied together in the denominator. For example,

$$\frac{5.0 \times 7.3 \times 8.5}{6.2 \times 2.5 \times 3.9}$$

Many students will compute the value of the numerator and write down the answer, then compute the value of the denominator and write it down, and finally divide the value of the numerator by the value of the denominator (whew!). Although this gives the correct answer, there is a simpler way to do the arithmetic that doesn't require writing down any intermediate values. The procedure is as follows:

1. Enter the first value from the numerator (5.0).
2. Any of the other values from the numerator are entered by *multiplication* and any of the values from the denominator are entered by *division*.

The following is one sequence that gives the answer.

$$5.0 \times 7.3 \times 8.5 \div 6.2 \div 2.5 \div 3.9 = 5.13234 \ldots$$

Notice that each value from the denominator is entered by division. It also doesn't matter in what sequence the numbers are entered. The following gives the same answer.

$$5.0 \div 6.2 \times 7.3 \div 2.5 \div 3.9 \times 8.5 = 5.13234 \ldots$$

Logarithms and Antilogarithms

Your scientific calculator works with both common logarithms and natural logarithms. To find the common log of a number, enter the number in the calculator and press the $\boxed{\text{log}}$ or $\boxed{\text{LOG}}$ button. Try this for the following and check your results. (The values here are rounded so they have the same number of digits after the decimal point as there are significant figures in the number. This is the rule for significant figures in logarithms as described below):

$$\log 12.35 = 1.0917 \text{ (rounded)}$$

$$\log (3.70 \times 10^{-4}) = -3.432 \text{ (rounded)}$$

---

[2]Sometimes students make the mistake of trying to enter a number such as 2.3×10^5 as follows: $\boxed{2}\ \boxed{.}\ \boxed{3}$ $\boxed{\times}\ \boxed{1}\ \boxed{0}\ \boxed{\text{EXP}}\ \boxed{5}$. What this series of operations accomplishes is to multiply 2.3 by 10, giving 23, and then entering the exponential notation 10^5.

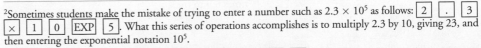

$$\boxed{2}\ \boxed{.}\ \boxed{3}\ \boxed{\times}\ \boxed{1}\ \boxed{0}\ \boxed{\text{EXP}}\ \boxed{5} = 23 \times 10^5$$

This is certainly not what was intended. If you are doing arithmetic and your answers are off by powers of 10, check to be sure you're entering the numbers correctly into the calculator.

Obtaining the antilogarithm is equally easy. For the first number above, 12.35 is the anti-log of 1.0917, which means that

$$12.35 = 10^{1.0917}$$

Some calculators have a key labeled $\boxed{10^x}$; others use a combination of an inverse function key, usually labeled $\boxed{INV}$, and the key used to obtain the logarithm. Thus, entering the value 1.0917 and pressing either $\boxed{10^x}$ or the sequence $\boxed{INV}$ $\boxed{log}$ yields the value 12.35. Try it.

To obtain natural logarithms of a number we use key labeled either $\boxed{\ln x}$ or $\boxed{LN}$ or sometimes $\boxed{\ln}$. Thus the natural logarithm of 12.35 is obtained by entering the number and pressing the $\boxed{\ln x}$ key. Try it.

$$\ln 12.35 = 2.5137 \text{ (rounded)}$$

The value 12.35 is the antinatural logarithm (antiln) of 2.5137, which means

$$12.35 = e^{2.5137}$$

Therefore, to obtain the antilogarithm of 2.5137, we enter the number into the calculator and press either the key labeled $\boxed{e^x}$ or the sequence $\boxed{INV}$ $\boxed{\ln x}$. Try it.

$$\text{antiln } 2.5137 = 12.35$$

Significant Figures and Logarithms

The logarithm of a number is composed of two parts. There is a part that comes before the decimal point (which is called the *characteristic*) and a part that comes after the decimal point (which is called the *mantissa*). Let's look at an example, for the moment keeping all the digits shown on the calculator.

$$\log (4.23 \times 10^5) = 5.\underbrace{626340367}_{\text{mantissa}}$$

(characteristic indicated above the 5)

The characteristic comes from the exponent on the 10 ($\log 10^5 = 5$) and is an exact number, so it need not be considered for the purposes of significant figures. The mantissa, on the other hand, is the logarithm of the number that precedes the power of ten [$\log (4.23) = 0.626340367$]. The 4.23 has three significant figures, so the mantissa should also have three significant figures. Therefore, rounded correctly,

$$\log (4.23 \times 10^5) = 5.626 \text{ (rounded)}$$

This leads to the rule that *when we take the logarithm of a quantity, the number of decimal places shown in the logarithm should equal the number of significant figures in the quantity.* Here is another example.

$$\log (5.246 \times 10^{-7}) = -6.280171714$$
$$= -6.2802 \text{ (rounded correctly)}$$

The quantity 5.246×10^{-7} has four significant figures, so we round off the logarithm to the fourth decimal place.

When taking an antilogarithm, the same relationship applies. If we take the antilog of 6.557, the answer will have three significant figures because the logarithm has three digits after the decimal.

$$\text{antilog } (6.557) = 3.61 \times 10^6 \text{ (rounded correctly)}$$

The same rules for significant figures apply for both common and natural logarithms.

Powers and Roots

Squares and square roots are handled easily with keys labeled $\boxed{x^2}$ and $\boxed{\sqrt{x}}$. For higher powers and higher roots (e.g., cube roots or fourth roots) we use the key that on most scientific calculators is labeled $\boxed{x^y}$. To use this function, we must enter two values—the number and its exponent. For example, to raise the number 2.6 to the 5th power,

$$(2.6)^5$$

we enter the number 2.6, press the $\boxed{x^y}$ key enter the value of the exponent (5), and then press either the "equals" key or the next function key desired if we are performing a chain calculation. Thus, the sequence

$$\boxed{2}\ \boxed{.}\ \boxed{6}\ \boxed{x^y}\ \boxed{5}\ \boxed{=}$$

produces the result 118.81376 on the display of the calculator. Therefore,

$$(2.6)^5 = 118.81376$$

To take a root, the procedure is quite similar, because we make use of the relationship

$$\sqrt[n]{(\text{number}} = (\text{number})^{1/n}$$

Thus, the cube root of a number such as 56.4 is obtained as

$$\sqrt[3]{56.4} = (56.4)^{1/3} = (56.4)^{0.333333\ldots}$$

In other words, we raise 56.4 to the one-third power, for which the decimal equivalent is $0.3333333\ldots$ (with as many threes as will fit on the display). Let's try it. Clear the display and enter the number 56.4. Next, press the $\boxed{x^y}$ key. Then enter 0.33333 with as many threes after the decimal point as you can. Finally, press the "equals" key. The answer should be $3.834949\ldots$. If we had wanted to take the 5th root of 56.4, we would raise the number to the 1/5 power, or 0.20. Try it. You should get $2.24004\ldots$ as the answer.

Some calculators have a key labeled $\boxed{x^{1/y}}$, which makes taking a root even easier. Thus, to take the 5th root of 56.4, we would enter the number 56.4, then press the $\boxed{x^{1/y}}$ key, and then press 5. Once again, the answer displayed should be 2.24004.

Appendix B

Answers to Practice Exercises and Selected Review Problems

Chapter 1

Practice Exercises

1.1 (a) 1 S, 6 F **(b)** 4 C, 12 H, 2 N **(c)** 3 Ca, 2 P, 8 O
(d) 1 Co, 2 N, 12 O, 12 H. **1.2 (a)** 2 N nitrogen, 4 H hydrogen,
3 O oxygen. **(b)** 1 Fe iron, 1 N nitrogen, 4 H hydrogen, 2 S sulfur,
8 O oxygen. **(c)** 1 Mo molybdenum, 2 N nitrogen, 11 O oxygen,
10 H hydrogen. **(d)** 6 C carbon, 4 H hydrogen, 1 Cl chlorine,
1 N nitrogen, 2 O oxygen. **1.3** C_2H_7N, CH_3NHCH_3.
1.4 Reactants: 4 N, 12 H, and 6 O; Products: 4 N, 12 H, and 6 O.
1.5 Reactants: 6 N, 42 H, 2 P, 20 O, 3 Ba, 12 C; Products: 3 Ba,
2 P, 20 O, 6 N, 42 H, 12 C; Reaction is balanced.
1.6

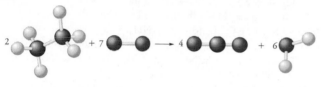

Review Problems

1.30 1 Cr, 6 C, 9 H, 6 O. **1.32** $MgSO_4$. **1.34** CH_3COOH or
$C_2H_4O_2$. **1.36** NH_3. **1.38 (b)** $\overset{H}{\underset{H}{\overset{|}{N}}}\diagdown H$. **1.40 (a)** 2 K potassium,
2 C carbon, 4 O oxygen. **(b)** 2 H hydrogen, 1 S sulfur, 3 O oxygen.
(c) 12 C carbon, 26 H hydrogen. **(d)** 4 H hydrogen, 2 C carbon,
2 O oxygen. **(e)** 9 H hydrogen, 2 N nitrogen, 1 P phosphorus,
4 O oxygen. **1.42 (a)** 1 Ni nickel, 2 Cl chlorine, 8 O oxygen.
(b) 1 C carbon, 1 O oxygen, 2 Cl chlorine **(c)** 2 K potassium,
2 Cr chromium, 7 O oxygen. **(d)** 2 C carbon, 4 H hydrogen,
2 O oxygen. **(e)** 2 N nitrogen, 9 H hydrogen, 1 P phosphorus,
4 O oxygen. **1.44 (a)** 6 N, 3 O **(b)** 8 C, 24 H, 4 S **(c)** 2 Cu, 2 S,
18 O, 20 H **1.46** $C_2H_6O_2$, C_3H_6O These two compounds illustrate
that different masses of carbon combine with the same mass of
hydrogen and those masses are in small, whole-number ratios. It is
also true for the ratio of oxygen to a fixed mass of hydrogen.
1.48 (a) 6. **(b)** 3 **(c)** 27 **(d)** 2
1.50 $2S(CH_3)_2$, 9 O_2, 2 SO_2, 4 CO_2, 6 H_2O
$2S(CH_3)_2(g) + 9\ O_2(g) \longrightarrow 2\ SO_2(g) + 4\ CO_2(g) + 6\ H_2O(l)$.
1.52 Reaction is not balanced as written, $2C_8H_{18}(l) + 25O_2(g) \longrightarrow$
$16CO_2(g) + 18H_2O(l)$.

Chapter 2

Practice Exercises

2.1 meters^3 or m^3. **2.2** kg$\frac{m}{s^2}$ or kg m s^{-2}. **2.3** 187 °F.
2.4 10 °C, 293 K.
2.5 (a) 42.0 g, **(b)** 0.857 g/mL, **(c)** 149 cm. **2.6 (a)** 30.0 mL,
(b) 54.155 g, **(c)** 11.3 g, **(d)** 3.62 ft, **(e)** 0.48 m^2. **2.7** 11.5 m^2.
2.8 (a) 108 in., **(b)** 1.25×10^5 cm, **(c)** 0.0107 ft, **(d)** 8.59 km L^{-1}.

2.9 $d = 16.5$ g cm^{-3}. The object is not composed of pure gold.
2.10 647 lb. **2.11** 0.899 g/cm^3. **2.12** 0.0639 cm^3

Review Problems

2.26 (a) 0.01 m, **(b)** 1000 m, **(c)** 10^{12} pm, **(d)** 0.1 m, **(e)** 0.001 kg,
(f) 0.01 g **2.28 (a)** 135 °F, **(b)** 61 °F, **(c)** –3.61 °C, **(d)** 9.4 °C,
(e) 335 K, **(f)** 242 K. **2.30** 39.7 °C This dog has a fever; the
temperature is out of normal canine range. **2.32** Range in Celsius:
1.0×10^7 °C to 2.5×10^7 °C, Range in Fahrenheit: 1.8×10^7 °F to
4.5×10^7 °F. **2.34** –269 °C **2.36 (a)** 4 significant figures,
(b) 5 significant figures, **(c)** 4 significant figures, **(d)** 2 significant
figures **(e)** 4 significant figures, **(f)** 2 significant figures
2.38 (a) 0.72 m^2, **(b)** 84.24 kg, **(c)** 4.19 g/cm^3, **(d)** 19.42 g/mL,
(e) 858.0 cm^2 **2.40 (a)** 11.5 km/h, **(b)** 8.2×10^6 μg/L,
(c) 7.53×10^{-5} kg, **(d)** 0.1375 L, **(e)** 25 mL, **(f)** 3.42×10^{-20} dm^2
2.42 (a) 91 cm, **(b)** 2.3 kg, **(c)** 2800 mL, **(d)** 200 mL, **(e)** 88 km.hr,
(f) 80.4 km **2.44 (a)** 7,800 cm^2, **(b)** 577 km^2 **(c)** 6.54×10^6 cm^3
2.46 4,000 pistachios (don't try this at home). **2.48** 90 m/s.
2.50 1520 mi/hr **2.52** 5.1×10^{13} mi **2.54** 11,034 m
2.56 0.798 g/mL **2.58** 31.6 mL **2.60** 276 g **2.62** 11 g/cm^3
2.64 Density = 0.591 lb/gal; 0.0709 g/mL,; specific gravity =
0.0708

Chapter 3

Practice Exercises

3.1 $^{240}_{94}$Pu, 94 electrons **3.2** 17 protons, 17 electrons, and
18 neutrons. **3.3** We can discard the 17 since the 17 tells the number
of protons, which is information that the symbol "Cl" also provides.
In addition, the number of protons equals the number of electrons in
a neutral atom, so the symbol "Cl" also indicates the number of
electrons. The 35 is necessary to state which isotope of chlorine is
in question and therefore the number of neutrons in the atom.
3.4 26.9814 u **3.5** 5.2955 times as heavy as carbon **3.6** 10.8 u
3.7 20.2 u **3.8 (a)** 26 protons, 26 electrons **(b)** 26 protons,
23 electrons **(c)** 7 protons, 10 electrons **(d)** 7 protons, 7 electrons
3.9 (a) 8 protons, 8 electrons **(b)** 8 protons, 10 electrons
(c) 13 protons, 10 electrons **(d)** 13 protons, 13 electrons
3.10 (a) NaF **(b)** Na_2O **(c)** MgF_2 **(d)** Al_4C_3 **3.11 (a)** Ca_3N_2
(b) $AlBr_3$ **(c)** K_2S **(d)** CsCl **3.12 (a)** $CrCl_3$ and $CrCl_2$, Cr_2O_3 and
CrO **(b)** CuCl, $CuCl_2$, Cu_2O and CuO **3.13 (a)** Au_2S and Au_2S_3,
Au_3N and AuN **(b)** TiS and TiS_2, Ti_3N_2 and Ti_3N_4 **3.14 (a)** $KC_2H_3O_2$
(b) $Sr(NO_3)_2$ **(c)** $Fe(C_2H_3O_2)_3$ **3.15 (a)** Na_2CO_3 **(b)** $(NH_4)_2SO_4$
3.16 (a) K_2S **(b)** $BaBr_2$ **(c)** NaCN **(d)** $Al(OH)_3$ **(e)** Ca_3P_2
3.17 (a) aluminum chloride **(b)** barium hydroxide **(c)** sodium bromide
(d) calcium fluoride **(e)** potassium phosphide **3.18** lithium sulfide,
magnesium phosphide, nickel(II) chloride, titanium(II) chloride,
iron(III) oxide **3.19 (a)** Al_2S_3 **(b)** SrF_2 **(c)** TiO_2 **(d)** CoO
(e) Au_2O_3 **3.20 (a)** lithium carbonate **(b)** potassium permanganate
(c) iron(III) hydroxide **3.21 (a)** $KClO_3$ **(b)** NaOCl

(c) $Ni_3(PO_4)_2$ **3.22** C_8H_{18}, $CH_3CH_2CH_2CH_2CH_2CH_2CH_2CH_3$,
3.23 $C_{10}H_{22}$, $CH_3CH_2CH_2CH_2CH_2CH_2CH_2CH_2CH_2CH_3$.
3.24 (a) Propanol: C_3H_8O, $CH_3CH_2CH_2OH$ (b) Butanol:
$C_4H_{10}O$, $CH_3CH_2CH_2CH_2OH$ **3.25** (a) Phosphorus trichloride
(b) sulfur dioxide (c) dichlorine heptoxide (d) hydrogen sulfide
3.26 (a) $AsCl_5$ (b) SCl_6 (c) S_2Cl_2 (d) H_2Te **3.27** Diiodine pentoxide
3.28 Chromium(III) acetate **3.29** Potassium perchlorate

Review Problems

3.69 1.008 u **3.71** The element is Al **3.73** The ratio would not
change. **3.75** 63.55 u **3.77** (a) 88 protons, 88 electrons, 138
neutrons (b) 82 protons, 82 electrons, 124 neutrons (c) 6 protons,
6 electrons, 8 neutrons (d) 11 protons, 11 electrons, 12 neutrons
3.79 53 protons, 53 electrons, 78 neutrons **3.81** (a) K^+ (b) Br^-
(c) Mg^{2+} (d) S^{2-} (e) Al^{3+} **3.83** (a) NaBr (b) KI (c) BaO (d) $MgBr_2$
(e) BaF_2 **3.85** (a) KNO_3 (b) $Ca(C_2H_3O_2)_2$ (c) NH_4Cl (d) $Fe_2(CO_3)_3$
(e) $Mg_3(PO_4)_2$ **3.87** (a) PbO and PbO_2 (b) SnO and SnO_2
(c) MnO and Mn_2O_3 (d) FeO and Fe_2O_3 (e) Cu_2O and CuO
3.89 (a) calcium sulfide (b) aluminum bromide (c) sodium phosphide
(d) barium arsenide (e) rubidium sulfide **3.91** (a) silicon dioxide
(b) xenon tetrafluoride (c) tetraphosphorus decoxide (d) dichlorine
heptoxide **3.93** (a) Iron(II) sulfide (b) copper(II) oxide (c) tin(IV)
oxide (d) cobalt(II) chloride hexahydrate **3.95** (a) sodium nitrite
(b) potassium permanganate (c) magnesium sulfate heptahydrate
(d) potassium thiocyanate **3.97** (a) ionic, chromium(II) chloride
(b) molecular, disulfur dichloride (c) ionic, ammonium acetate
(d) molecular, sulfur trioxide (e) ionic, potassium iodate (f) molecular,
tetraphosphorus hexoxide (g) ionic, calcium sulfite (h) ionic, silver
cyanide (i) ionic, zinc(II) bromide (j) molecular, hydrogen selenide
3.99 (a) Na_2HPO_4 (b) Li_2Se (c) $Cr(C_2H_3O_2)_3$ (d) S_2F_{10} (e) $Ni(CN)_2$
(f) Fe_2O_3 (g) SbF_5 **3.101** (a) $(NH_4)_2S$ (b) $Cr_2(SO_4)_3 \cdot 6H_2O$ (c)
SiF_4 (d) MoS_2 (e) $SnCl_4$ (f) H_2Se (g) P_4S_7 **3.103** Diselenium
hexasulfide and diselenium tetrasulfide

Chapter 4

Practice Exercise

4.1 0.129 mol Al **4.2** $\pm 1.15 \times 10^{-5}$ mol K_2SO_4 **4.3** 0.00238 g
4.4 3.5×10^{18} molecules of sucrose **4.5** 0.0516 mol Al^{3+}
4.6 3.44 mol N atoms **4.7** 59.6 g Fe **4.8** 10.5 g Fe **4.9** 18.0 g Ti
4.10 % H = 13.04%, % C = 52.17; It is likely that the compound
contains another element since the percentages do not add up to
100%. **4.11** % N = 36.84, % O = 63.16; Since these two values
constitute 100%, there are no other elements present.
4.12 % N = 30.45, % O = 69.55
4.13 N_2O: % N = 63.65, % O = 36.34
   NO: % N = 46.68, % O = 53.32
   NO_2: % N = 30.45, % O = 69.55
   N_2O_3: % N = 36.86, % O = 63.14
   N_2O_4: % N = 30.45, % O = 69.55
   N_2O_5: % N = 25.94, % O = 74.06
The compound N_2O_3 corresponds to the data in Practice Exercise 4.11.
4.14 NO **4.15** SO_2 **4.16** Al_2O_3 **4.17** N_2O_5 **4.18** Na_2SO_4
4.19 C_9H_8O **4.20** CS_2 **4.21** CH_2O **4.22** $C_2H_4Cl_2$ and $C_6H_6Cl_6$
4.23 N_2H_4
4.24 $3CaCl_2(aq) + 2K_3PO_4(aq) \longrightarrow Ca_3(PO_4)_2(s) + 6KCl(aq)$
4.25 $2Ca(NO_3)_2(aq) + 2\,(NH_4)_3PO_4(aq) \longrightarrow$
$\qquad Ca_3(PO_4)_2(s) + 6NH_4NO_3(aq)$
4.26 3.38 mol O_2 **4.27** 0.183 mol H_2SO_4 **4.28** 78.5 g Al_2O_3
4.29 1.18×10^2 g CO_2 **4.30** 55.0 g CO_2, 34 g HCl remaining
4.31 30.01 g NO **4.32** 36.78 g $HOOCC_6H_4O_2C_2H_3$, 83.5%

4.33 30.9 g $HC_2H_3O_2$, 86.1% **4.34** The two-step process is the
preferred process.

Review Problems

4.27 1:2, 1 mol N to 2 mol O **4.29** 2.59×10^{-3} mole Ta
4.31 (a) 6 atom C:11 atom H (b) 12 mole C:11 mole O
   (c) 2 atom H:1 atom O (d) 2 mole H:1 mole O
4.33 1.05 mol Bi **4.35** 4.32 mol Cr
4.37 (a) $\left(\dfrac{2\ \text{mol Al}}{3\ \text{mol S}}\right)$ or $\left(\dfrac{3\ \text{mol S}}{2\ \text{mol Al}}\right)$
   (b) $\left(\dfrac{3\ \text{mol S}}{1\ \text{mol Al}_2(\text{SO}_4)_3}\right)$ or $\left(\dfrac{1\ \text{mol Al}_2(\text{SO}_4)_3}{3\ \text{mol S}}\right)$
   (c) 0.600 mol Al
   (d) 3.48 mol S
4.39 0.0725 mol N_2, 0.218 mol H_2 **4.41** 0.833 mol UF_6
4.43 9.33×10^{23} atoms C **4.45** 3.76×10^{24} atoms
4.47 3.01×10^{23} atoms C–12 **4.49** (a) 75.4 g Fe (b) 392 g O
(c) 35.1 g Ca **4.51** 1.30×10^{-10} g K **4.53** 0.302 mol Ni
4.55 Note: all masses are in g/mole
   (a) $NaHCO_3$ 84.0066 g/mol
   (b) $(NH_4)_2CO_3$ 96.0858 g/mol
   (c) $CuSO_4 \cdot 5H_2O$ 249.685 g/mole
   (d) $K_2Cr_2O_7$ 294.1846 g/mole
   (e) $Al_2(SO_4)_3$ 342.151 g/mol
4.57 (a) 388 g $Ca_3(PO_4)_2$ (b) 0.151 g $Fe(NO_3)_3$
(c) 3.49×10^{-5} g C_4H_{10} (d) 139 g $(NH_4)_2CO_3$
4.59 (a) 0.215 moles $CaCO_3$ (b) 9.16×10^{-11} moles NH_3
(c) 7.94×10^{-2} moles $Sr(NO_3)_2$ (d) 4.31×10^{-8} moles Na_2CrO_4
4.61 0.0750 moles of Ca, 3.01 g Ca
4.63 1.30 mol N, 62.5 g $(NH_4)_2CO_3$ **4.65** 3.43 kg fertilizer
4.67 Assume one mole total for each of the following.
   (a) 19.2% Na, 1.68% H, 25.8% P, 53.3% O
   (b) 12.2% N, 5.26% H, 25.9% P, 55.6% O
   (c) 62.0% C, 10.4% H, 27.6% O
   (d) 23.3% Ca, 18.6% S, 55.7% O, 2.34% H
   (e) 23.2% Ca, 18.6% S, 55.7% O, 2.34% H
4.69 Heroin has a higher percentage oxygen **4.71** Freon 141b has a
higher percentage chlorine **4.73** 22.9% P, 77.1% Cl **4.75** These
data are consistent with the experimental values cited in the
problem. **4.77** 0.474 g O **4.79** (a) SCl (b) CH_2O (c) NH_3
(d) AsO_3 (e) HO **4.81** $NaTcO_4$ **4.83** CCl_2 **4.85** $C_9H_8O_2$
4.87 C_2H_6O **4.89** $C_{19}H_{30}O_2$ **4.91** (a) $Na_2S_4O_6$ (b) $C_6H_4Cl_2$
(c) $C_6H_3Cl_3$ **4.93** $C_{19}H_{30}O_2$ **4.95** HgBr, Hg_2Br_2
4.97 CHNO, $C_3H_3N_3O_3$
4.99 (a) 2 atoms of Ba, 20 atoms of O, and 36 atoms of H
   (b) 2 moles of Ba, 20 moles of O, and 36 moles of H
4.101 $4Fe(s) + 3O_2(g) \longrightarrow 2Fe_2O_3(s)$
4.103 (a) $Ca(OH)_2 + 2HCl \longrightarrow CaCl_2 + 2H_2O$
   (b) $2AgNO_3 + CaCl_2 \longrightarrow Ca(NO_3)_2 + 2AgCl$
   (c) $Pb(NO_3)_2 + Na_2SO_4 \longrightarrow PbSO_4 + 2NaNO_3$
   (d) $2Fe_2O_3 + 3C \longrightarrow 4Fe + 3CO_2$
   (e) $2C_4H_{10} + 13O_2 \longrightarrow 8CO_2 + 10H_2O$
4.105 (a) $Mg(OH)_2 + 2HBr \longrightarrow MgBr_2 + 2H_2O$
   (b) $2HCl + Ca(OH)_2 \longrightarrow CaCl_2 + 2H_2O$
   (c) $Al_2O_3 + 3H_2SO_4 \longrightarrow Al_2(SO_4)_3 + 3H_2O$
   (d) $2KHCO_3 + H_3PO_4 \longrightarrow K_2HPO_4 + 2H_2O + 2CO_2$
   (e) $C_9H_{20} + 14O_2 \longrightarrow 9CO_2 + 10H_2O$
4.107 $4NH_2CHO + 5O_2 \longrightarrow 4CO_2 + 6H_2O + 2N_2$
4.109 (a) 0.030 mol Cl_2 (b) 0.24 mol HCl (c) 0.15 mol H_2O
(d) 0.15 mol H_2O **4.111** (a) 3.6 g Zn (b) 22 g Au
(c) 55 g $Au(CN)_2^-$ **4.113** (a) $4P + 5O_2 \longrightarrow P_4O_{10}$ (b) 8.85 g O_2

(c) 14.2 g P_4O_{10} (d) 3.26 g P **4.115** 30.28 g HNO_3
4.117 0.47 kg O_2 **4.119** 2 molecules of SO_2 **4.121** (a) Fe_2O_3 is the
limiting reactant (b) 195 g Fe **4.123** 26.7 g $FeCl_3$
4.125 0.913 mg HNO_3 **4.127** 66.98 g $BaSO_4$, 96.22%
4.129 88.72% **4.131** 9.2 g C_7H_8

Chapter 5

Practice Exercises

5.1 (a) $FeCl_3(s) \longrightarrow Fe^{3+}(aq) + 3Cl^-(aq)$
  (b) $K_3PO_4(s) \longrightarrow 3K^+(aq) + PO_4^{3-}(aq)$
5.2 (a) $MgCl_2(s) \longrightarrow Mg^{2+}(aq) + 2Cl^-(aq)$
  (b) $Al(NO_3)_3(s) \longrightarrow Al^{3+}(aq) + 3NO_3^-(aq)$
  (c) $Na_2CO_3(s) \longrightarrow 2Na^+(aq) + CO_3^{2-}(aq)$
5.3 Molecular: $(NH_4)_2SO_4(aq) + Ba(NO_3)_2(aq) \longrightarrow$
$$BaSO_4(s) + 2NH_4NO_3(aq)$$
Ionic: $2NH_4^+(aq) + SO_4^{2-}(aq) + Ba^{2+}(aq) + 2NO_3^-(aq) \longrightarrow$
$$BaSO_4(s) + 2NH_4^+(aq) + 2NO_3^-(aq)$$
Net ionic: $Ba^{2+}(aq) + SO_4^{2-}(aq) \longrightarrow BaSO_4(s)$
5.4 Molecular: $CdCl_2(aq) + Na_2S(aq) \longrightarrow CdS(s) + 2NaCl(aq)$
Ionic: $Cd^{2+}(aq) + 2Cl^-(aq) + 2Na^+(aq) + S^{2-}(aq) \longrightarrow$
$$CdS(s) + 2Na^+(aq) + 2Cl^-(aq)$$
Net ionic: $Cd^{2+}(aq) + S^{2-}(aq) \longrightarrow CdS(s)$
5.5 $HCHO_2(aq) + H_2O \longrightarrow H_3O^+(aq) + CHO_2^-(aq)$
5.6

$CH_3CH_2CH_2CHOOH(l) + H_2O \longrightarrow$
$$CH_3CH_2CH_2COO^-(aq) + H_3O^+(aq)$$

5.7 $H_3C_6H_5O_7(s) + H_2O \longrightarrow H_3O^+(aq) + H_2C_6H_5O_7^-(aq)$
$H_2C_6H_5O_7^-(aq) + H_2O \longrightarrow H_3O^+(aq) + HC_6H_5O_7^{2-}(aq)$
$HC_6H_5O_7^{2-}(aq) + H_2O \longrightarrow H_3O^+(aq) + C_6H_5O_7^{3-}(aq)$
5.8 $(C_2H_5)_3N(aq) + H_2O \longrightarrow (C_2H_5)_3NH^+(aq) + OH^-(aq)$
5.9 $HONH_2(aq) + H_2O \longrightarrow HONH_3^+(aq) + OH^-(aq)$
5.10

$CH_3CH_2NH_2(aq) + H_2O \longrightarrow CH_3CH_2NH_3^+(aq) + OH^-(aq)$
5.11 $CH_3NH_2(aq) + H_2O \longrightarrow CH_3NH_3^+(aq) + OH^-(aq)$
5.12 $HNO_2(aq) + H_2O \longrightarrow H_3O^+(aq) + NO_2^-(aq)$
5.13 sodium arsenate **5.14** calcium formate, calcium methanoate
5.15 hydrofluoric acid, sodium fluoride; hydrobromic acid, sodium
bromide **5.16** Iodic acid **5.17** $NaHSO_3$, sodium hydrogen sulfite
5.18 $H_3PO_4(aq) + NaOH(aq) \longrightarrow NaH_2PO_4(aq) + H_2O$
                                    sodium dihydrogen phosphate
$NaH_2PO_4(aq) + NaOH(aq) \longrightarrow Na_2HPO_4(aq) + H_2O$
                                    sodium hydrogen phosphate
$Na_2HPO_4(aq) + NaOH(aq) \longrightarrow Na_3PO_4(aq) + H_2O$
                                    sodium phosphate

5.19 Molecular: $Zn(NO_3)_2(aq) + Ca(C_2H_3O_2)_2(aq) \longrightarrow$
$$Zn(C_2H_3O_2)_2(aq) + Ca(NO_3)_2(aq)$$
Ionic: $Zn^{2+}(aq) + 2NO_3^-(aq) + Ca^{2+}(aq) + 2C_2H_3O_2^-(aq) \longrightarrow$
$$Zn^{2+}(aq) + 2C_2H_3O_2^-(aq) + Ca^{2+}(aq) + 2NO_3^-(aq)$$
Net ionic: No reaction
5.20 (a) Molecular: $AgNO_3(aq) + NH_4Cl(aq) \longrightarrow$
$$AgCl(s) + NH_4NO_3(aq)$$
Ionic: $Ag^+(aq) + NO_3^-(aq) + NH_4^+(aq) + Cl^-(aq) \longrightarrow$
$$AgCl(s) + NH_4^+(aq) + NO_3^-(aq)$$
Net ionic: $Ag^+(aq) + Cl^-(aq) \longrightarrow AgCl(s)$
  (b) Molecular: $Na_2S(aq) + Pb(C_2H_3O_2)_2(aq) \longrightarrow$
$$2NaC_2H_3O_2(aq) + PbS(s)$$
Ionic: $2Na^+(aq) + S^{2-}(aq) + Pb^{2+}(aq) + 2C_2H_3O_2^-(aq) \longrightarrow$
$$2Na^+(aq) + 2C_2H_3O_2^-(aq) + PbS(s)$$
Net ionic: $S^{2-}(aq) + Pb^{2+}(aq) \longrightarrow PbS(s)$
5.21 Molecular: $2HNO_3(aq) + Ca(OH)_2(aq) \longrightarrow$
$$Ca(NO_3)_2(aq) + 2H_2O$$
Ionic: $2H^+(aq) + 2NO_3^-(aq) + Ca^{2+}(aq) + 2OH^-(aq) \longrightarrow$
$$Ca^{2+}(aq) + 2NO_3^-(aq) + 2H_2O$$
Net ionic: $H^+(aq) + OH^-(aq) \longrightarrow H_2O$
5.22 (a) Molecular: $HCl(aq) + KOH(aq) \longrightarrow H_2O + KCl(aq)$
Ionic: $H^+(aq) + Cl^-(aq) + K^+(aq) + OH^-(aq) \longrightarrow$
$$H_2O + K^+(aq) + Cl^-(aq)$$
Net ionic: $H^+(aq) + OH^-(aq) \longrightarrow H_2O$
  (b) Molecular: $HCHO_2(aq) + LiOH(aq) \longrightarrow H_2O + LiCHO_2(aq)$
Ionic: $HCHO_2(aq) + Li^+(aq) + OH^-(aq) \longrightarrow$
$$H_2O + Li^+(aq) + CHO_2^-(aq)$$
Net ionic: $HCHO_2(aq) + OH^-(aq) \longrightarrow H_2O + CHO_2^-(aq)$
  (c) Molecular: $N_2H_4(aq) + HCl(aq) \longrightarrow N_2H_5Cl(aq)$
Ionic: $N_2H_4(aq) + H^+(aq) + Cl^-(aq) \longrightarrow N_2H_5^+(aq) + Cl^-(aq)$
Net ionic: $N_2H_4(aq) + H^+(aq) \longrightarrow N_2H_5^+(aq)$
5.23 Molecular: $CH_3NH_2(aq) + HCHO_2(aq) \longrightarrow$
$$CH_3NH_3CHO_2(aq)$$
Ionic: $CH_3NH_2(aq) + HCHO_2(aq) \longrightarrow$
$$CH_3NH_3^+(aq) + CHO_2^-(aq)$$
Net ionic: $CH_3NH_2(aq) + HCHO_2(aq) \longrightarrow$
$$CH_3NH_3^+(aq) + CHO_2^-(aq)$$
5.24 Molecular: $2HCHO_2(aq) + Co(OH)_2(s) \longrightarrow$
$$Co(CHO_2)_2(aq) + 2H_2O$$
Ionic: $2HCHO_2(aq) + Co(OH)_2(s) \longrightarrow$
$$2CHO_2^-(aq) + Co^{2+}(aq) + 2H_2O$$
Net ionic: $2HCHO_2(aq) + Co(OH)_2(s) \longrightarrow$
$$2CHO_2^-(aq) + Co^{2+}(aq) + 2H_2O$$
5.25 (a) Formic acid, a weak acid will form.
Molecular: $KCHO_2(aq) + HCl(aq) \longrightarrow KCl(aq) + HCHO_2(aq)$
Ionic: $K^+(aq) + CHO_2^-(aq) + H^+(aq) + Cl^-(aq) \longrightarrow$
$$K^+(aq) + Cl^-(aq) + HCHO_2(aq)$$
Net ionic: $CHO_2^-(aq) + H^+(aq) \longrightarrow HCHO_2(aq)$
  (b) Carbonic acid will form and it will further dissociate to water
and carbon dioxide:
$CuCO_3(s) + 2H^+(aq) \longrightarrow CO_2(g) + H_2O + Cu^{2+}(aq)$
Molecular: $CuCO_3(s) + 2HC_2H_3O_2(aq) \longrightarrow$
$$CO_2(g) + H_2O + Cu(C_2H_3O_2)_2(aq)$$
Ionic: $CuCO_3(s) + 2HC_2H_3O_2(aq) \longrightarrow$
$$CO_2(g) + H_2O + Cu^{2+} + 2C_2H_3O_2^-(aq)$$
Net ionic: $CuCO_3(s) + 2HC_2H_3O_2(aq) \longrightarrow$
$$CO_2(g) + H_2O + Cu^{2+} + 2C_2H_3O_2^-(aq)$$
  (c) No reaction will occur. All acetate salts and nitrate salts are
soluble
  (d) Insoluble nickel hydroxide will precipitate.
$Ni^{2+}(aq) + 2OH^-(aq) \longrightarrow Ni(OH)_2(s)$

Molecular: $NiCl_2(aq) + 2NaOH(aq) \longrightarrow Ni(OH)_2(s) + 2NaCl(aq)$
Ionic: $Ni^{2+}(aq) + 2Cl^-(aq) + 2Na^+(aq) + 2OH^-(aq) \longrightarrow$
$$Ni(OH)_2(s) + 2Na^+(aq) + 2Cl^-(aq)$$
Net ionic: $Ni^{2+}(aq) + 2OH^-(aq) \longrightarrow Ni(OH)_2(s)$

5.26 $CuO(s) + 2HNO_3(aq) \longrightarrow Cu(NO_3)_2(aq) + H_2O(l)$
Or
$Cu(OH)_2(s) + 2HNO_3(aq) \longrightarrow Cu(NO_3)_2(aq) + 2H_2O(l)$

5.27 You want to use a metathesis reaction that produces CoS, which is insoluble, and a second product that is soluble. You may want the reactants to be soluble.
$CoCl_2(aq) + Na_2S(aq) \longrightarrow CoS(s) + 2NaCl(aq)$

5.28 1.53 M HNO_3 **5.29** 0.1837 M **5.30** 0.0438 mol HCl
5.31 143 mL of HCl **5.32** 2.11 g $Sr(NO_3)_2$ **5.33** 0.531 g $AgNO_3$
5.34 250.0 mL **5.35** 600 mL of water. **5.36** 31.6 mL H_3PO_4
5.37 26.8 mL NaOH **5.38** 0.40 M Fe^{3+}, 1.2 M Cl^-
5.39 0.750 M Na^+ **5.40** 0.0449 M $CaCl_2$ **5.41** 60.0 mL KOH
5.42 0.605 g Na_2SO_4
5.43 (a) 5.41×10^{-3} mol Ca^{2+}
    (b) 5.41×10^{-3} mol Ca^{2+}
    (c) 5.41×10^{-3} mol $CaCl_2$
    (d) 0.600 g $CaCl_2$
    (e) 30.0% $CaCl_2$
    (f) 70.0 % $MgCl_2$
5.44 0.178 M H_2SO_4 **5.45** 0.0220 M HCl, 0.0803%

Review Problems

5.53 $HClO_4(l) + H_2O \longrightarrow H_3O^+(aq) + ClO_4^-(aq)$
5.55 $N_2H_4(aq) + H_2O \longrightarrow N_2H_5^+(aq) + OH^-(aq)$
5.57 $HNO_2(aq) + H_2O \longrightarrow H_3O^+(aq) + NO_2^-(aq)$
5.59 $H_2CO_3(aq) + H_2O \longrightarrow H_3O^+(aq) + HCO_3^-(aq)$
$HCO_3^-(aq) + H_2O \longrightarrow H_3O^+(aq) + CO_3^{2-}(aq)$
5.61 Molecular: $Na_2S(aq) + Cu(NO_3)_2(aq) \longrightarrow$
$$CuS(s) + 2NaNO_3(aq)$$
Ionic: $2Na^+(aq) + S^{2-}(aq) + Cu^{2+}(aq) + 2NO_3^-(aq) \longrightarrow$
$$CuS(s) + 2Na^+(aq) + 2NO_3^-(aq)$$
Net: $Cu^{2+}(aq) + S^{2-}(aq) \longrightarrow CuS(s)$
5.63 (a), **(b)**, and **(d)**.
5.65
(a) Ionic: $3Fe^{2+}(aq) + 3SO_4^{2-}(aq) + 6K^+(aq) + 2PO_4^{3-}(aq) \longrightarrow$
$$Fe_3(PO_4)_2(s) + 6K^+(aq) + 3SO_4^{2-}(aq)$$
Net: $3Fe^{2+}(aq) + 2PO_4^{3-}(aq) \longrightarrow Fe_3(PO_4)_2(s)$
(b) Ionic: $3Ag^+(aq) + 3C_2H_3O_2^-(aq) + Al^{3+}(aq) + 3Cl^-(aq) \longrightarrow$
$$3AgCl(s) + Al^{3+}(aq) + 3C_2H_3O_2^-(aq)$$
Net: $Ag^+(aq) + Cl^-(aq) \longrightarrow AgCl(s)$
(c) Ionic: $2Cr^{3+}(aq) + 6Cl^-(aq) + 3Ba^{2+}(aq) + 6OH^-(aq) \longrightarrow$
$$2Cr(OH)_3(s) + 3Ba^{2+}(aq) + 6Cl^-(aq)$$
Net: $Cr^{3+}(aq) + 3OH^-(aq) \longrightarrow Cr(OH)_3(s)$
5.67 (a) Molecular: $Ca(OH)_2(aq) + 2HNO_3(aq) \longrightarrow$
$$Ca(NO_3)_2(aq) + 2H_2O$$
Ionic: $Ca^{2+}(aq) + 2OH^-(aq) + 2H^+(aq) + 2NO_3^-(aq) \longrightarrow$
$$Ca^{2+}(aq) + 2NO_3^-(aq) + 2H_2O$$
Net: $H^+(aq) + OH^-(aq) \longrightarrow H_2O$
(b) Molecular: $Al_2O_3(s) + 6HCl(aq) \longrightarrow 2AlCl_3(aq) + 3H_2O$
Ionic: $Al_2O_3(s) + 6H^+(aq) + 6Cl^-(aq) \longrightarrow$
$$2Al^{3+}(aq) + 6Cl^-(aq) + 3H_2O$$
Net: $Al_2O_3(s) + 6H^+(aq) \longrightarrow 2Al^{3+}(aq) + 3H_2O$
(c) Molecular: $Zn(OH)_2(s) + H_2SO_4(aq) \longrightarrow ZnSO_4(aq) + 2H_2O$
Ionic: $Zn(OH)_2(s) + 2H^+(aq) + SO_4^{2-}(aq) \longrightarrow$
$$Zn^{2+}(aq) + SO_4^{2-}(aq) + 2H_2O$$
Net: $Zn(OH)_2(s) + 2H^+(aq) \longrightarrow Zn^{2+}(aq) + 2H_2O$

5.69 The electrical conductivity would decrease regularly, until one solution had neutralized the other, forming a non-electrolyte:
$Ba^{2+}(aq) + 2OH^-(aq) + 2H^+(aq) + SO_4^{2-}(aq) \longrightarrow$
$$BaSO_4(s) + 2H_2O$$
Once the point of neutralization had been reached, the addition of excess sulfuric acid would cause the conductivity to increase, because sulfuric acid is a strong electrolyte itself.
5.71 (a) $2H^+(aq) + CO_3^{2-}(aq) \longrightarrow H_2O + CO_2(g)$
    (b) $NH_4^+(aq) + OH^-(aq) \longrightarrow NH_3(g) + H_2O$
5.73 These reactions have the following "driving forces":
    (a) Formation of insoluble $Cr(OH)_3$
    (b) Formation of water, a weak electrolyte
5.75 (a) Molecular: $3HNO_3(aq) + Cr(OH)_3(s) \longrightarrow$
$$Cr(NO_3)_3(aq) + 3H_2O$$
Ionic: $3H^+(aq) + 3NO_3^-(aq) + Cr(OH)_3(s) \longrightarrow$
$$Cr^{3+}(aq) + 3NO_3^-(aq) + 3H_2O$$
Net: $3H^+(aq) + Cr(OH)_3(s) \longrightarrow Cr^{3+}(aq) + 3H_2O$
(b) Molecular: $HClO_4(aq) + NaOH(aq) \longrightarrow NaClO_4(aq) + H_2O$
Ionic: $H^+(aq) + ClO_4^-(aq) + Na^+(aq) + OH^-(aq) \longrightarrow$
$$Na^+(aq) + ClO_4^-(aq) + H_2O$$
Net: $H^+(aq) + OH^-(aq) \longrightarrow H_2O$
(c) Molecular: $Cu(OH)_2(s) + 2HC_2H_3O_2(aq) \longrightarrow$
$$Cu(C_2H_3O_2)_2(aq) + 2H_2O$$
Ionic: $Cu(OH)_2(s) + 2H^+(aq) + 2C_2H_3O_2^-(aq) \longrightarrow$
$$Cu^{2+}(aq) + 2C_2H_3O_2^-(aq) + 2H_2O$$
Net: $Cu(OH)_2(s) + 2H^+(aq) \longrightarrow Cu^{2+}(aq) + 2H_2O$
(d) Molecular: $ZnO(s) + H_2SO_4(aq) \longrightarrow ZnSO_4(aq) + H_2O$
Ionic: $ZnO(s) + 2H^+(aq) + SO_4^{2-}(aq) \longrightarrow$
$$Zn^{2+}(aq) + SO_4^{2-}(aq) + H_2O$$
Net: $ZnO(s) + 2H^+(aq) \longrightarrow Zn^{2+}(aq) + H_2O$
5.77 (a) Molecular: $Na_2SO_3(aq) + Ba(NO_3)_2(aq) \longrightarrow$
$$BaSO_3(s) + 2NaNO_3(aq)$$
Ionic: $2Na^+(aq) + SO_3^{2-}(aq) + Ba^{2+}(aq) + 2NO_3^-(aq) \longrightarrow$
$$BaSO_3(s) + 2Na^+(aq) + 2NO_3^-(aq)$$
Net: $Ba^{2+}(aq) + SO_3^{2-}(aq) \longrightarrow BaSO_3(s)$
(b) Molecular: $2HCHO_2(aq) + K_2CO_3(aq) \longrightarrow$
$$CO_2(g) + H_2O + 2KCHO_2(aq)$$
Ionic: $2H^+(aq) + 2CHO_2^-(aq) + 2K^+(aq) + CO_3^{2-}(aq) \longrightarrow$
$$CO_2(g) + H_2O + 2K^+(aq) + 2CHO_2^-(aq)$$
Net: $2H^+(aq) + CO_3^{2-}(aq) \longrightarrow CO_2(g) + H_2O$
(c) Molecular: $2NH_4Br(aq) + Pb(C_2H_3O_2)_2(aq) \longrightarrow$
$$2NH_4C_2H_3O_2(aq) + PbBr_2(s)$$
Ionic: $2NH_4^+(aq) + 2Br^-(aq) + Pb^{2+}(aq) + 2C_2H_3O_2^-(aq) \longrightarrow$
$$2NH_4^+(aq) + 2C_2H_3O_2^-(aq) + PbBr_2(s)$$
Net: $Pb^{2+}(aq) + 2Br^-(aq) \longrightarrow PbBr_2(s)$
(d) Molecular: $2NH_4ClO_4(aq) + Cu(NO_3)_2(aq) \longrightarrow$
$$Cu(ClO_4)_2(aq) + 2NH_4NO_3(aq)$$
Ionic: $2NH_4^+(aq) + 2ClO_4^-(aq) + Cu^{2+}(aq) + 2NO_3^-(aq) \longrightarrow$
$$Cu^{2+}(aq) + 2ClO_4^-(aq) + 2NO_3^-(aq) + 2NH_4^+(aq)$$
Net: N.R.
5.79 There are numerous possible answers. One of many possible sets of answers would be:
(a) $NaHCO_3(aq) + HCl(aq) \longrightarrow NaCl(aq) + CO_2(g) + H_2O$
(b) $FeCl_2(aq) + 2NaOH(aq) \longrightarrow Fe(OH)_2(s) + 2NaCl(aq)$
(c) $Ba(NO_3)_2(aq) + K_2SO_3(aq) \longrightarrow BaSO_3(s) + 2KNO_3(aq)$
(d) $2AgNO_3(aq) + Na_2S(aq) \longrightarrow Ag_2S(s) + 2NaNO_3(aq)$
(e) $ZnO(s) + 2HCl(aq) \longrightarrow ZnCl_2(aq) + H_2O$
5.81 (a) 1.00 M NaOH **(b)** 0.577 M $CaCl_2$
5.83 658 mL $NaC_2H_3O_2$
5.85 (a) 1.46 g NaCl **(b)** 16.2 g $C_6H_{12}O_6$ **(c)** 6.13 g H_2SO_4
5.87 0.11 M H_2SO_4 **5.89** 300 mL. **5.91** 225 mL water

5.93 (a) 0.0147 mol Ca^{2+}, 0.0294 mol Cl^-
(b) 0.0204 mol Al^{3+}, 0.061 mol Cl^-
5.95 (a) 0.25 M Cr^{2+}, 0.50 M NO_3^-
(b) 0.10 M Cu^{2+}, 0.10 M SO_4^{2-}
(c) 0.48 M Na^+, 0.16 M PO_4^{3-}
(d) 0.15 M Al^{3+}, 0.22 M SO_4^{2-}
5.97 1.07 g $Al_2(SO_4)_3$ **5.99** 11.9 mL $NiCl_2$ soln, 0.36 g $NiCO_3$
5.101 0.113 M KOH
$KOH(aq) + HCl(aq) \longrightarrow KCl(aq) + H_2O$
5.103 0.485 g $Al_2(SO_4)_3$ **5.105** 2.00 mL $FeCl_3$ soln, 0.129 g AgCl
5.107 13.3 mL $AlCl_3$ **5.109** 0.167 M Fe^{3+}, 3.67 g Fe_2O_3
5.111 0.114 M HCl   **5.113 (a)** 2.67×10^{-3} mol $HC_3H_5O_3$
(b) 0.240 g
5.115 (a) 3.56×10^{-3} mol Pb, 0.7386 g Pb, 48.40 % Pb

| Chapter 6

Practice Exercises

6.1 Oxygen is reduced since it gains electrons. Sodium is oxidized since it loses electrons.
6.2 Aluminum is oxidized and is, therefore, the reducing agent. Chlorine is reduced and is, therefore, the oxidizing agent.
6.3 Fe_2O_3 is reduced and is, therefore, the oxiding agent. Al is oxidized and is, therefore, the reducing agent.
6.4 +3
6.5 (a) Ni +2; Cl –1
(b) Mg +2; Ti +4; O –2
(c) K +1; Cr +6; O –2
(d) H +1; P +5, O –2
(e) V +3; C 0; H +1; O –2
(f) N –3; H +1
6.6 +8/3.
6.7 (a) Mo +3; Cl –1
(b) Mo +4; S –2
(c) Mo +6; O –2; Cl –1
(d) Mo +6; P –3
6.8 $KClO_3 + 3HNO_2 \longrightarrow KCl + 3HNO_3$
$KClO_3$ is reduced and HNO_2 is oxidized.
6.9 There is no simple way to tell which chlorines are reduced and which are oxidized in this reaction. One analysis would have the Cl in Cl_2 end up as the Cl in NaCl, while the Cl in $NaClO_2$ ends up as the Cl in ClO_2. In this case Cl_2 is reduced and is the oxidizing agent, while $NaClO_2$ is oxidized and is the reducing agent.
6.10 The product is water, because the oxygen is reduced.
6.11 CH_4 undergoes oxidation and O_2 undergoes reduction. This means that CH_4 is the reducing agent and O_2 is the oxidizing agent.
6.12 The charges are not balanced.
$2Al(s) + 3Cu^{2+}(aq) \longrightarrow 2Al^{3+}(aq) + 3Cu(s)$
6.13 $3Sn^{2+} + 16H^+ + 2TcO_4^- \longrightarrow 2Tc^{4+} + 8H_2O + 3Sn^{4+}$
6.14 $4Cu + 2NO_3^- + 10H^+ \longrightarrow 4Cu^{2+} + N_2O + 5H_2O$
6.15 $4C_5H_5N + 29O_2 \longrightarrow 4NO_2 + 20CO_2 + 10H_2O$
6.16 $4OH^- + SO_2 \longrightarrow SO_4^{2-} + 2e^- + 2H_2O$
6.17 $2MnO_4^- + 3C_2O_4^{2-} + 4OH^- \longrightarrow$
$2MnO_2 + 6CO_3^{2-} + 2H_2O$
6.18 $6Br_2 + 12OH^- \longrightarrow 10Br^- + 2BrO_3^- + 6H_2O$
6.19 $Zn + 2MnO_2 \longrightarrow ZnO + Mn_2O_3$
6.20 $Zn \longrightarrow Zn^{2+} + 2e^-$ $2H^+ + 2e^- \longrightarrow H_2$
6.21 (a) Molecular: $Mg(s) + 2HCl(aq) \longrightarrow MgCl_2(aq) + H_2(g)$
Ionic: $Mg(s) + 2H^+(aq) + 2Cl^-(aq) \longrightarrow$
$Mg^{2+}(aq) + 2Cl^-(aq) + H_2(g)$

Net ionic: $Mg(s) + 2H^+(aq) \longrightarrow Mg^{2+}(aq) + H_2(g)$
(b) Molecular: $2Al(s) + 6HCl(aq) \longrightarrow 2AlCl_3(aq) + 3H_2(g)$
Ionic: $2Al(s) + 6H^+(aq) + 6Cl^-(aq) \longrightarrow$
$2Al^{3+}(aq) + 6Cl^-(aq) + 3H_2(g)$
Net ionic: $2Al(s) + 6H^+(aq) \longrightarrow 2Al^{3+}(aq) + 3H_2(g)$
6.22 $H_2SO_4 + 8HI \longrightarrow H_2S + 4I_2 + 4H_2O$
6.23 $Cu^{2+}(aq) + Mg(s) \longrightarrow Cu(s) + Mg^{2+}(aq)$
6.24 (a) $2Al(s) + 3Cu^{2+}(aq) \longrightarrow 2Al^{3+}(aq) + 3Cu(s)$
(b) $Ag(s) + Mg^{2+}(aq) \longrightarrow$ No reaction
6.25 $2C_{20}H_{42}(s) + 21O_2(g) \longrightarrow 40C(s) + 42H_2O(g)$
6.26 $2C_5H_8(g) + 9O_2(g) \longrightarrow 10CO_2(g) + 8H_2O(g)$
6.27 $C_2H_5OH(l) + 3O_2(g) \longrightarrow 2CO_2(g) + 3H_2O(g)$
6.28 $2Sr(s) + O_2(g) \longrightarrow 2SrO(s)$
6.29 $4Fe(s) + 3O_2(g) \longrightarrow 2Fe_2O_3(s)$

Review Problems

6.23 The sum of the oxidation numbers should be equal to the total charge:
(a) S^{2-}: –2
(b) SO_2: S +4, O –2
(c) P_4: P 0
(d) PH_3: P –3, H +1
6.25 The sum of the oxidation numbers should be equal to the total charge:

(a) O: –2	**(c)** O: –2
Na: +1	Na: +1
Cl: +1	Cl: +5
(b) O: –2	**(d)** O: –2
Na: +1	Na: +1
Cl: +3	Cl: +7

6.27 The sum of the oxidation numbers should be zero:
(a) S: –2   **(c)** Cs +1
Pb: +2   O –1/2 (The Cs can only have an oxidation number of +1 or 0.)
(b) Cl: –1   **(d)** F –1
Ti: +4   O +1
6.29 Ti +3; N –3   **6.31** O_3; oxidation number of O is 0
6.33 In the forward direction: **Cl_2 is reduced**. However, in HOCl, chlorine has an oxidation number of +1, so **Cl_2 also is oxidized!** (One atom is reduced, the other is oxidized.) In the reverse direction: Cl^- ion is oxidized: This means **Cl^- is the reducing agent. HOCl is the oxidizing agent**.
6.35 (a) Substance reduced (and oxidizing agent): HNO_3
Substance oxidized (and reducing agent): H_3AsO_3
(b) Substance reduced (and oxidizing agent): HOCl
Substance oxidized (and reducing agent): NaI
(c) Substance reduced (and oxidizing agent): $KMnO_4$
Substance oxidized (and reducing agent): $H_2C_2O_4$
(d) Substance reduced (and oxidizing agent): H_2SO_4
Substance oxidized (and reducing agent): Al
6.37 (a) $OCl^- + 2S_2O_3^{2-} + 2H^+ \longrightarrow S_4O_6^{2-} + Cl^- + H_2O$
(b) $2NO_3^- + Cu + 4H^+ \longrightarrow 2NO_2 + Cu^{2+} + 2H_2O$
(c) $3H_3AsO_3 + IO_3^- \longrightarrow I^- + 3H_3AsO_4$
(d) $Zn + SO_4^{2-} + 4H^+ \longrightarrow Zn^{2+} + SO_2 + 2H_2O$
(e) $NO_3^- + 4Zn + 10H^+ \longrightarrow 4Zn^{2+} + NH_4^+ + 3H_2O$
(f) $2Cr^{3+} + 3BiO_3^- + 4H^+ \longrightarrow Cr_2O_7^{2-} + 3Bi^{3+} + 2H_2O$
(g) $I_2 + 5OCl^- + H_2O \longrightarrow 2IO_3^- + 5Cl^- + 2H^+$
(h) $2Mn^{2+} + 5BiO_3^- + 14H^+ \longrightarrow 2MnO_4^- + 5Bi^{3+} + 7H_2O$
(i) $3H_3AsO_3 + Cr_2O_7^{2-} + 8H^+ \longrightarrow$
$3H_3AsO_4 + 2Cr^{3+} + 4H_2O$

6.39 (a) $2CrO_4^{2-} + 3S^{2-} + 4H_2O \longrightarrow 2CrO_2^- + 3S + 8OH^-$
(b) $3C_2O_4^{2-} + 2MnO_4^- + 4H_2O \longrightarrow$
$$6CO_2 + 2MnO_2 + 8OH^-$$
(c) $4ClO_3^- + 3N_2H_4 \longrightarrow 4Cl^- + 6NO + 6H_2O$
(d) $NiO_2 + 2Mn(OH)_2 \longrightarrow Ni(OH)_2 + Mn_2O_3 + H_2O$
(e) $3SO_3^{2-} + 2MnO_4^- + H_2O \longrightarrow$
$$3SO_4^{2-} + 2MnO_2 + 2OH^-$$
6.41 $10H^+(aq) + NO_3^-(aq) + 4Mg(s) \longrightarrow$
$$NH_4^+(aq) + 4Mg^{2+}(aq) + 3H_2O$$
6.43 $4OCl^- + S_2O_3^{2-} + H_2O \longrightarrow 4Cl^- + 2SO_4^{2-} + 2H^+$
6.45 $O_3 + Br^- \longrightarrow BrO_3^-$
6.47 (a) M: $Mn(s) + 2HCl(aq) \longrightarrow MnCl_2(aq) + H_2(g)$
I: $Mn(s) + 2H^+(aq) + 2Cl^-(aq) \longrightarrow$
$$Mn^{2+}(aq) + 2Cl^-(aq) + H_2(g)$$
NI: $Mn(s) + 2H^+(aq) \longrightarrow Mn^{2+}(aq) + H_2(g)$
(b) M: $Cd(s) + 2HCl(aq) \longrightarrow CdCl_2(aq) + H_2(g)$
I: $Cd(s) + 2H^+(aq) + 2Cl^-(aq) \longrightarrow$
$$Cd^{2+}(aq) + 2Cl^-(aq) + H_2(g)$$
NI: $Cd(s) + 2H^+(aq) \longrightarrow Cd^{2+}(aq) + H_2(g)$
(c) M: $Sn(s) + 2HCl(aq) \longrightarrow SnCl_2(aq) + H_2(g)$
I: $Sn(s) + 2H^+(aq) + 2Cl^-(aq) \longrightarrow$
$$Sn^{2+}(aq) + 2Cl^-(aq) + H_2(g)$$
NI: $Sn(s) + 2H^+(aq) \longrightarrow Sn^{2+}(aq) + H_2(g)$
6.49 (a) $3Ag(s) + 4HNO_3(aq) \longrightarrow$
$$3AgNO_3(aq) + 2H_2O + NO(g)$$
(b) $Ag(s) + 2HNO_3(aq) \longrightarrow AgNO_3(aq) + H_2O + NO_2(aq)$
6.51 (a) N.R.
(b) $2Cr(s) + 3Pb^{2+}(aq) \longrightarrow 2Cr^{3+}(aq) + 3Pb(s)$
(c) $2Ag^+(aq) + Fe(s) \longrightarrow 2Ag(s) + Fe^{2+}(aq)$
(d) $3Ag(s) + Au^{3+}(aq) \longrightarrow Au(s) + 3Ag^+(aq)$
6.53 Increasing ease of oxidation: Pt, Ru, Tl, Pu
6.55 $Cd(s) + PtCl_2(aq) \longrightarrow CdCl_2(aq) + Pt(s)$
6.57 $5Mg(s) + 5Zn^{2+}(aq) + 10Cl^-(aq) \longrightarrow$
$$5Mg^{2+}(aq) + 10Cl^-(aq) + 5Zn(s)$$
6.59 $10Li(s) + 10H_2O(l) \longrightarrow 5H_2(g) + 10OH^-(aq)$
6.61 (a) $2C_6H_6(l) + 15O_2(g) \longrightarrow 12CO_2(g) + 6H_2O(g)$
(b) $2C_4H_{10}(g) + 13O_2(g) \longrightarrow 8CO_2(g) + 10H_2O(g)$
(c) $C_{21}H_{44}(s) + 32O_2(g) \longrightarrow 21CO_2(g) + 22H_2O(g)$
6.63 (a) $2C_6H_6(l) + 9O_2(g) \longrightarrow 12CO(g) + 6H_2O(g)$
$2C_4H_{10}(g) + 9O_2(g) \longrightarrow 8CO(g) + 10H_2O(g)$
$2C_{21}H_{44}(s) + 43O_2(g) \longrightarrow 42CO(g) + 44H_2O(g)$
(b) $2C_6H_6(l) + 3O_2(g) \longrightarrow 12C(s) + 6H_2O(g)$
$2C_4H_{10}(g) + 5O_2(g) \longrightarrow 8C(s) + 10H_2O(g)$
$C_{21}H_{44}(s) + 11O_2(g) \longrightarrow 21C(s) + 22H_2O(g)$
6.65 $2CH_3OH(l) + 3O_2(g) \longrightarrow 2CO_2(g) + 4H_2O(g)$
6.67 $2(CH_3)_2S(g) + 9O_2(g) \longrightarrow 4CO_2(g) + 6H_2O(g) + 2SO_2(g)$
6.69 (a) $2Zn(s) + O_2(g) \longrightarrow 2ZnO(s)$
(b) $4Al(s) + 3O_2(g) \longrightarrow 2Al_2O_3(s)$
(c) $2Mg(s) + O_2(g) \longrightarrow 2MgO(s)$
(d) $4Fe(s) + 3O_2(g) \longrightarrow 2Fe_2O_3(s)$
6.71 (a) $IO_3^- + 3SO_3^{2-} \longrightarrow I^- + 3SO_4^{2-}$
(b) 9.55 g Na_2SO_3
6.73 3.53 g Cu
6.75 (a) $2MnO_4^- + 5Sn^{2+} + 16H^+ \longrightarrow 2Mn^{2+} + 5Sn^{4+} + 8H_2O$
(b) 17.4 mL $KMnO_4$
6.77 (a) 6.38×10^{-3} M I_3^-
(b) 1.01×10^{-3} g SO_2
(c) $2.10 \times 10^{-3}\%$
(d) 21 ppm
6.79 (a) 9.463% **(b)** 18.40%
6.81 (a) 0.02994 g H_2O_2 **(b)** 2.994% H_2O_2

6.83 (a) $2CrO_4^{2-} + 3SO_3^{2-} + H_2O \longrightarrow$
$$2CrO_7^- + 3SO_4^{2-} + 2OH^-$$
(b) 0.875 g Cr in the original alloy
(c) 25.4% Cr
6.85 (a) 5.405×10^{-3} mol $C_2O_4^{2-}$ **(b)** 0.5999 g $CaCl_2$
(c) 24.35% $CaCl_2$

| Chapter 7

Practice Exercises
7.1 55.1 J/°C **7.2** 5335 J, 5.34 kJ, 1275 cal, 1.28 kcal
7.3 127. 3 °C
7.4 12.4 kJ °C^{-1} **7.5** 394 kJ/mol carbon **7.6** -58 kJ mol^{-1} NaOH
7.7 3.7 kJ, 74 kJ/mole **7.8** 24.3 kJ/mole
7.9 $\frac{1}{4}CH_4(g) + \frac{1}{2}O_2(g) \longrightarrow \frac{1}{4}CO_2(g) + \frac{1}{2}H_2O(l)$
$$\Delta H = -222.6 \text{ kJ}$$
7.10 $5H_2(g) + 2.5O_2(g) \longrightarrow 5H_2O(l)$ $\Delta H = -1429.5$ kJ
7.11

$2Cu(s) + O_2(g)$

-310 kJ	-169 kJ
	$Cu_2O(s) + 1/2\ O_2(g)$
$2CuO(s)$	-141 kJ

7.12

$NO(g) + 1/2\ O_2(g)$

$+90.4$ kJ	-56.6 kJ
	$NO_2(g)$
$1/2\ N_2(g) + O_2(g)$	$+33.8$ kJ

7.13 $+857.7$ kJ **7.14** $+99.2$ kJ **7.15** -44.0 kJ **7.16** 385 kJ
7.17 2.62×10^6 kJ
7.18 $\frac{1}{2}N_2(g) + 2H_2(g) + \frac{1}{2}Cl_2(g) \longrightarrow NH_4Cl(s)$
7.19 $Na(s) + \frac{1}{2}H_2(g) + C(s) + \frac{3}{2}O_2(g) \longrightarrow NaHCO_3(s)$
7.20 -10.98 kJ
7.21 $S(s) + \frac{3}{2}O_2(g) \longrightarrow SO_3(g)$ $\Delta H_f^\circ = -395.2$ kJ/mol
$S(s) + O_2(g) \longrightarrow SO_2(g)$ $\Delta H_f^\circ = -296.9$ kJ/mol
Reverse the first reaction and add the two reactions together to get
$SO_3(g) \longrightarrow SO_2(g) + \frac{1}{2}O_2(g)$ $\Delta H_f^\circ = +98.3$ kJ
The answers for the enthalpy of reaction are the same using either method.
7.22 (a) -113.1 kJ **(b)** -177.8 kJ

Review Problems
7.40 -17 J **7.42** $+100$ J **7.44** 250 J **7.46** -1320 J, -315 cal
7.48 45.7 g H_2O **7.50 (a)** 1.67×10^3 J **(b)** 1.67×10^3 J
(c) 23.2 J °C^{-1} **(d)** 4.64 J g^{-1} °C^{-1} **7.52** 25.12 J mol^{-1} °C^{-1}
7.54 -30.4 kJ **7.56** $HNO_3(aq) + KOH(aq) \longrightarrow$
$KNO_3(aq) + H_2O$, 3800 J, -53 kJ mol^{-1}
7.58 (a) $C_3H_8(g) + 5O_2(g) \longrightarrow 3CO_2(g) + 4H_2O$
(b) 2.22×10^5 J, **(c)** -222 kJ/mol
7.60 (a) $2CO(g) + O_2(g) \longrightarrow 2CO_2(g)$ $\Delta H^\circ = -566$ kJ,
(b) -283 kJ/mol
7.62 162 kJ of heat are evolved
7.64 8.64 g
7.66

$Ge(s) + O_2(g)$

-534.7 kJ	-255 kJ
	$GeO(s) + 1/2\ O_2(g)$
$GeO_2(s)$	-280 kJ

7.68 $2NO_2(g) \longrightarrow N_2O_4(g)$ $\Delta H° = -57.93$ kJ
$2NO(g) + O_2(g) \longrightarrow 2NO_2(g)$ $\Delta H° = -113.14$ kJ
$2NO(g) + O_2(g) \longrightarrow N_2O_4(g)$ $\Delta H° = -171.07$ kJ

7.70 $\frac{1}{2} Na_2O(s) + HCl(g) \longrightarrow \frac{1}{2} H_2O(l) + NaCl(s)$
$\Delta H° = -253.66$ kJ
$NaNO_2(s) \longrightarrow \frac{1}{2} Na_2O(s) + \frac{1}{2} NO_2(g) + \frac{1}{2} NO(g)$
$\Delta H° = +213.57$ kJ
$\frac{1}{2} NO(g) + \frac{1}{2} NO_2(g) \longrightarrow \frac{1}{2} N_2O(g) + \frac{1}{2} O_2(g)$
$\Delta H° = -21.34$ kJ
$\frac{1}{2} H_2O(l) + \frac{1}{2} O_2(g) + \frac{1}{2} N_2O(g) \longrightarrow HNO_2(l)$
$\Delta H° = -17.18$ kJ
$HCl(g) + NaNO_2(s) \longrightarrow HNO_2(l) + NaCl(s)$
$\Delta H° = -78.61$ kJ

7.72 $\frac{1}{2} CaO(s) + \frac{1}{2} Cl_2(g) \longrightarrow \frac{1}{2} CaOCl_2(s)$ $\Delta H° = \frac{1}{2}(-110.9 \text{ kJ})$
$\frac{1}{2} H_2O(l) + \frac{1}{2} CaOCl_2(s) + NaBr(s) \longrightarrow$
$NaCl(s) + \frac{1}{2} Ca(OH)_2(s) + \frac{1}{2} Br_2(l)$ $\Delta H° = \frac{1}{2}(-60.2 \text{ kJ})$
$\frac{1}{2} Ca(OH)_2(s) \longrightarrow \frac{1}{2} CaO(s) + \frac{1}{2} H_2O(l)$ $\Delta H° = \frac{1}{2}(+65.1 \text{ kJ})$
$\frac{1}{2} Cl_2(g) + NaBr(s) \longrightarrow NaCl(s) + \frac{1}{2} Br_2(l)$
$\Delta H° = \frac{1}{2}(-106 \text{ kJ}) = -53$ kJ

7.74 $12NH_3(g) + 21O_2(g) \longrightarrow 12NO_2(g) + 18H_2O(g)$
$\Delta H° = 3(-1132 \text{ kJ})$
$12NO_2(g) + 16NH_3(g) \longrightarrow 14N_2(g) + 24H_2O(g)$
$\Delta H° = 2(-2740 \text{ kJ})$
$28NH_3(g) + 21O_2(g) \longrightarrow 14N_2(g) + 42H_2O(g)$
$\Delta H° = -8876$ kJ
$4NH_3(g) + 3O_2(g) \longrightarrow 2N_2(g) + 6H_2O(g)$
$\Delta H° = 1/7(-8876 \text{ kJ}) = -1268$ kJ

7.76 Only (c) satisfies this requirement

7.78 (a) $2C(s, \text{graphite}) + 2H_2(g) + O_2(g) \longrightarrow HC_2H_3O_2(l)$
$\Delta H_f° = -487.0$ kJ
(b) $2C(s, \text{graphite}) + \frac{1}{2}O_2(g) + 3H_2(g) \longrightarrow C_2H_5OH(l)$
$\Delta H_f° = -277.63$ kJ
(c) $Ca(s) + \frac{1}{8}S_8(s) + 3O_2(g) + 2H_2(g) \longrightarrow CaSO_4 \cdot 2H_2O(s)$
$\Delta H_f° = -2021.1$ kJ
(d) $2Na(s) + \frac{1}{8}S_8(s) + 2O_2(g) \longrightarrow Na_2SO_4(s)$
$\Delta H_f° = -1384.5$ kJ

7.80 (a) -196.6 kJ (b) -177.8 kJ

7.82 $C_{12}H_{22}O_{11}(s) + 12O_2(g) \longrightarrow 12CO_2(g) + 11H_2O(l)$
$\Delta H_f° = -2.21 \times 10^3$ kJ

| Chapter 8

Practice Exercises

8.1 5.10×10^{14} Hz **8.2** 2.75×10^{13} Hz **8.3** 3.25 m
8.4 2.63 μm
8.5 656 nm, which is red
8.6 (a) 4, 2
(b) 5, 3
(c) 7, 0
Each value of ℓ has a corresponding letter.

8.7 When $n = 2$, ℓ can be 0, or 1. Thus we have s, and p subshells. When $n = 5$, ℓ can be 0, 1, 2, 3, or 4. Thus we have s, p, d, f, and g subshells.
Shell 1: 1 subshell
Shell 2: 2 subshells
Shell 3: 3 subshells
Shell 4: 4 subshells
Shell 5: 5 subshells
Shell 6: 6 subshells

8.8 (a) Mg: $1s^2 2s^2 2p^6 3s^2$
(b) Ge: $1s^2 2s^2 2p^6 3s^2 3p^6 3d^{10} 4s^2 4p^2$

(c) Cd: $1s^2 2s^2 2p^6 3s^2 3p^6 3d^{10} 4s^2 4p^6 4d^{10} 5s^2$
(d) Gd: $1s^2 2s^2 2p^6 3s^2 3p^6 3d^{10} 4s^2 4p^6 4d^{10} 4f^7 5s^2 5p^6 5d^1 6s^2$

8.9 The electron configuration of an element follows the periodic table. The electrons are filled in the order of the periodic table and the energy levels are determined by the row the element is in and the subshell is given by the column, the first two columns are the s-block, the last six columns are the p-block, the d-block has ten columns, and the f-block has 14 columns.

8.10 (a) O: $1s^2 2s^2 2p^4$
S: $1s^2 2s^2 2p^6 3s^2 3p^4$
Se: $1s^2 2s^2 2p^6 3s^2 3p^6 3d^{10} 4s^2 4p^4$
(b) P: $1s^2 2s^2 2p^6 3s^2 3p^3$
N: $1s^2 2s^2 2p^3$
Sb: $1s^2 2s^2 2p^6 3s^2 3p^6 3d^{10} 4s^2 4p^6 4d^{10} 5s^2 5p^3$
The elements have the same number of electrons in the valence shell, and the only differences between the valence shells are the energy levels.

8.11 (a)
Na: (↑↓) (↑↓) (↑↓)(↑↓)(↑↓) (↑)
  $1s$ $2s$ $2p$ $3s$

(b)
S: (↑↓) (↑↓) (↑↓)(↑↓)(↑↓) (↑↓) (↑↓)(↑)(↑)
  $1s$ $2s$ $2p$ $3s$ $3p$

(c)
Fe: (↑↓) (↑↓) (↑↓)(↑↓)(↑↓) (↑↓) (↑↓)(↑↓)(↑↓) (↑↓) (↑↓)(↑)(↑)(↑)(↑)
  $1s$ $2s$ $2p$ $3s$ $3p$ $4s$ $3d$

8.12 (a) 0 unpaired electrons (b) 2 unpaired electrons (c) 0 unpaired electrons (d) 8 unpaired electrons

8.13 Yes

8.14 (a)
P: $[Ne]3s^2 3p^3$
$[Ne]$ (↑↓) (↑)(↑)(↑)
       $3s$ $3p$
(3 unpaired electrons)

(b)
Sn: $[Kr]4d^{10}5s^2 5p^2$
$[Kr]$ (↑↓)(↑↓)(↑↓)(↑↓)(↑↓) (↑↓) (↑)(↑)( )
        $4d$ $5s$ $5p$
(2 unpaired electrons)

8.15 Based on the definition of valence, there are no examples where more than 8 electrons would occupy the valence shell. For representative elements the valence shell is defined as the occupied shell with the highest value of n. In the ground state atom, only s and p electrons fit this definition. The transition elements have outer electron configurations: $(n-1)d^n\ ns^m$ so the valence shell is the ns subshell.

8.16 (a) Se: $4s^2 4p^4$ (b) Sn: $5s^2 5p^2$ (c) I: $5s^2 5p^5$
8.17 (a) Sn (b) Ga (c) Cr (d) S^{2-}
8.18 (a) P (b) Fe^{3+} (c) Fe (d) Cl^-
8.19 (a) Be (b) C **8.20** (a) C^{2+} (b) Mg^{2+}

Review Problems

8.73 6.88×10^{14} Hz
8.75 4.38×10^{13} Hz
8.77 1.02×10^{15} Hz
8.79 2.965 m
8.81 5.00×10^6 m, 5.00×10^3 km
8.83 2.7×10^{-19} J photon^{-1}, 1.6×10^5 J mol^{-1}
8.85 (a) Violet (see Figure 8.7) (b) 7.307×10^{14} s^{-1}
(c) 4.842×10^{-19} J

8.87 1094 nm We would not expect to see the light since it is not in the visible region **8.89** 1.737×10^{-6} m, We would not expect to see the light since it is not in the visible region.

8.91 (a) p (b) f

8.93 (a) $n = 3$, $\ell = 0$ (b) $n = 5$, $\ell = 2$

8.95 0, 1, 2, 3, 4, 5

8.97 (a) $m_\ell = 1$, 0, or -1 (b) $m_\ell = 3$, 2, 1, 0, -1, -2, or -3

8.99 When $m_\ell = -4$ the minimum value of ℓ is 4 and the minimum value of n is 5.

8.101

n	ℓ	m_ℓ	m_s
2	1	-1	$+1/2$
2	1	-1	$-1/2$
2	1	0	$+1/2$
2	1	0	$-1/2$
2	1	$+1$	$+1/2$
2	1	$+1$	$-1/2$

8.103 21 electrons have $\ell = 1$, 20 electrons have $\ell = 2$

8.105 (a) S $\quad 1s^2 2s^2 2p^6 3s^2 3p^4$

(b) K $\quad 1s^2 2s^2 2p^6 3s^2 3p^6 4s^1$

(c) Ti $\quad 1s^2 2s^2 2p^6 3s^2 3p^6 3d^2 4s^2$

(d) Sn $\quad 1s^2 2s^2 2p^6 3s^2 3p^6 3d^{10} 4s^2 4p^6 4d^{10} 5s^2 5p^2$

8.107 (a) Mn is paramagnetic (b) As is paramagnetic (c) S is paramagnetic (d) Sr is not paramagnetic (e) Ar is not paramagnetic

8.109 (a) Mg, zero unpaired electrons (b) P, three unpaired electrons (c) V, three unpaired electrons

8.111 (a) Ni [Ar]$3d^8 4s^2$ (b) Cs [Xe]$6s^1$ (c) Ge [Ar] $3d^{10} 4s^2 4p^2$ (d) Br [Ar] $3d^{10} 4s^2 4p^5$ (e) Bi [Xe] $4f^{14} 5d^{10} 6s^2 6p^3$

8.113 (a)

Mg:
1s 2s 2p   3s

(b)

Ti:
1s 2s 2p   3s 3p   4s 3d

8.115 (a)

Ni: [Ar]
4s 3d

(b)

Cs: [Xe]
6s

(c)

Ge: [Ar]
4s 3d   4p

(d)

Br: [Ar]
4s 3d   4p

8.117 (a) 5 (b) 4 (c) 4 (d) 6

8.119 (a) Na $3s^1$ (b) Al $3s^2 3p^1$ (c) Ge $4s^2 4p^2$ (d) P $3s^2 3p^3$

8.121 (a)

Na:
3s

(b)

Al:
3s 3p

(c)

Ge:
4s 4p

(d)

P:
3s 3p

8.123 (a) 1 (b) 6 (c) 7 **8.125** (a) Mg (b) Bi **8.127** Sb **8.129** (a) Na (b) Co^{2+} (c) Cl^- **8.131** (a) N (b) S (c) Cl **8.133** (a) Br (b) As

8.135 Mg

Chapter 9

Practice Exercises

9.1 There is one electron missing, and it should go into the $5s$ orbital, and the $5p$ orbital should be empty.

$$1s^1 2s^2 2p^6 3s^2 3p^6 3d^{10} 4s^2 4p^6 4d^{10} 5s^2$$

9.2 (a) Cr^{2+}: [Ar]$3d^4$ The $4s$ electron and one $3d$ electron are lost.

(b) Cr^{3+}: [Ar]$3d^3$ The $4s$ electron and two $3d$ electrons are lost.

(c) Cr^{6+}: [Ar] The $4s$ electron and all of the $3d$ electrons are lost.

9.3 The electron configurations are identical

9.4

9.5

9.6

aldedyde

amine

acid

ketone

alcohol

9.7 (a) CH_3NHCH_3

(b) HCOOH

(c)

9.8 1.24 D

9.9 0.795 e^-

9.10 The bond is polar and the Cl carries the negative charge.

9.11 (a) Br (b) Cl (c) Cl

9.12

$$\text{H} \quad \text{O} \quad \overset{\displaystyle \text{O}}{\underset{\displaystyle \text{O}}{\text{P}}} \quad \text{O} \quad \text{H}$$

32 valence electrons

9.13 SO_2

$$\text{O} \quad \text{S} \quad \text{O}$$

NO_3^-

$$\text{O} \quad \overset{\displaystyle \text{O}}{\text{N}} \quad \text{O}$$

$HClO_3$

$$\text{O} \quad \overset{\displaystyle \text{O}}{\text{Cl}} \quad \text{O} \quad \text{H}$$

H_3AsO_4

$$\text{H} \quad \text{O} \quad \overset{\displaystyle \text{H}}{\underset{\displaystyle \text{O}}{\text{As}}} \quad \text{O} \quad \text{H}$$

9.14 SO_2 has 18 valence electrons
$SeO_4{}^{2-}$ has 32 valence electrons
NO^+ has 10 valence electrons

9.15

$$:\!\ddot{\text{F}}\!-\!\ddot{\text{O}}\!-\!\ddot{\text{F}}\!:$$

$$\left[\text{H}-\overset{\displaystyle \text{H}}{\underset{\displaystyle \text{H}}{\text{N}}}-\text{H} \right]^{+}$$

$$\ddot{\text{O}}\!=\!\text{S}\!-\!\ddot{\text{O}}\!:$$

$$\left[:\!\ddot{\text{O}}\!-\!\overset{\displaystyle :\!\ddot{\text{O}}:}{\text{N}}\!=\!\ddot{\text{O}} \right]^{-}$$

$$:\!\ddot{\text{F}}\!-\!\overset{\displaystyle :\!\ddot{\text{F}}:}{\text{Cl}}\!-\!\ddot{\text{F}}\!:$$

$$\text{H}\!-\!\ddot{\text{O}}\!-\!\overset{\displaystyle :\!\ddot{\text{O}}:}{\underset{\displaystyle :\!\ddot{\text{O}}:}{\text{Cl}}}\!-\!\ddot{\text{O}}\!:$$

9.16 The negative sign should be on the oxygen atoms.

$$\left[:\!\ddot{\text{O}}\!\underset{\displaystyle :\!\ddot{\text{O}}}{\overset{\displaystyle \ddot{\text{O}}}{\text{S}}}\!\ddot{\text{O}}\!: \right]^{2-}$$

9.17

(a) $\overset{\displaystyle \circleddash 2}{:\!\ddot{\text{N}}}\!\underset{\displaystyle \oplus 1}{-}\!\underset{\displaystyle \oplus 1}{\text{N}}\!\equiv\!\text{O}\!:$

(b) $\left[\underset{\displaystyle \circledcirc}{\ddot{\text{S}}}\!=\!\underset{\displaystyle \circledcirc}{\text{C}}\!=\!\underset{\displaystyle \circleddash 1}{\ddot{\text{N}}} \right]^{-}$

9.18

(a) $\ddot{\text{O}}\!=\!\ddot{\text{S}}\!=\!\ddot{\text{O}}$

(b) $\text{H}\!-\!\ddot{\text{O}}\!-\!\overset{\displaystyle :\!\ddot{\text{O}}}{\text{Cl}}\!=\!\ddot{\text{O}}\!:$

(c) $\text{H}\!-\!\ddot{\text{O}}\!-\!\overset{\displaystyle :\!\ddot{\text{O}}\!-\!\text{H}}{\underset{\displaystyle :\!\ddot{\text{O}}:}{\text{P}}}\!-\!\ddot{\text{O}}\!-\!\text{H}$

9.19

$$\text{H}\!-\!\overset{\displaystyle \text{H}}{\underset{\displaystyle \text{H}}{\ddot{\text{N}}}} \; + \; \text{H}^+ \longrightarrow \left[\text{H}\!-\!\overset{\displaystyle \text{H}}{\underset{\displaystyle \text{H}}{\text{N}}}\!-\!\text{H} \right]^{+}$$

There is no difference between the coordinate covalent bond and the other covalent bonds.

9.20

$$\text{H}\!-\!\ddot{\text{O}}\!: \; + \; \text{H}^+ \longrightarrow \text{H}\!-\!\overset{\displaystyle \uparrow}{\ddot{\text{O}}}\!-\!\text{H}$$

9.21

$$\left[:\!\ddot{\text{O}}\!-\!\overset{\displaystyle :\!\ddot{\text{O}}:}{\underset{\displaystyle :\!\ddot{\text{O}}:}{\text{P}}}\!-\!\ddot{\text{O}}\!: \right]^{3-} \longleftrightarrow \left[\ddot{\text{O}}\!=\!\overset{\displaystyle :\!\ddot{\text{O}}:}{\underset{\displaystyle :\!\ddot{\text{O}}:}{\text{P}}}\!-\!\ddot{\text{O}}\!: \right]^{3-} \longleftrightarrow$$

$$\left[:\!\ddot{\text{O}}\!-\!\overset{\displaystyle :\!\text{O}:}{\underset{\displaystyle :\!\ddot{\text{O}}:}{\text{P}}}\!-\!\ddot{\text{O}}\!: \right]^{3-} \longleftrightarrow \left[:\!\ddot{\text{O}}\!-\!\overset{\displaystyle :\!\ddot{\text{O}}:}{\underset{\displaystyle :\!\ddot{\text{O}}:}{\text{P}}}\!=\!\ddot{\text{O}} \right]^{3-}$$

9.22

$$\left[\ddot{\text{O}}\!=\!\text{C}\!-\!\overset{\displaystyle :\!\ddot{\text{O}}:}{\underset{\displaystyle \text{H}}{}}\ddot{\text{O}}\!: \right]^{-} \longleftrightarrow \left[:\!\ddot{\text{O}}\!-\!\text{C}\!=\!\ddot{\text{O}} \right]^{-}$$

9.23

$$\left[\ddot{\text{O}}\!=\!\overset{\displaystyle :\!\ddot{\text{O}}:}{\text{Br}}\!-\!\ddot{\text{O}}\!: \right]^{-} \longleftrightarrow \left[:\!\ddot{\text{O}}\!=\!\overset{\displaystyle :\!\ddot{\text{O}}:}{\text{Br}}\!=\!\ddot{\text{O}} \right]^{-} \longleftrightarrow \left[:\!\ddot{\text{O}}\!-\!\overset{\displaystyle :\!\text{O}:}{\text{Br}}\!=\!\ddot{\text{O}} \right]^{-}$$

Review Problems

9.60 In order for $NaCl_2$ to be more stable than NaCl, the lattice energy should be almost 30 times larger. 4.36×10^3 kJ/148 kJ = 29.5

9.62 Magnesium loses two electrons and bromine gains an electron. To keep the overall change of the formula unit neutral, two Br^- ions combine with one Mg^{2+} ion to form $MgBr_2$.

9.64 [Xe] $4f^{14}5d^{10}6s^2$, [Xe]$4f^{14}5d^{10}$

9.66 [Ar]$3d^4$ 4 unpaired electrons

9.68 (a) $\cdot\dot{\text{Si}}\cdot$

(b) $:\dot{\text{Sb}}\cdot$

(c) $\cdot\text{Ba}\cdot$

(d) $\cdot\dot{\text{Al}}\cdot$

(e) $:\dot{\text{S}}:$

9.70

(a) $:\dot{\text{Br}}\,\curvearrowleft\,\cdot\text{Ca}\cdot\,\curvearrowright\,\dot{\text{Br}}: \longrightarrow \text{Ca}^{2+} + 2\left[:\!\ddot{\text{Br}}\!: \right]^{-}$

(b) $\cdot\dot{\ddot{\text{O}}}\,\curvearrowright\,\text{Al}\,\curvearrowright\,\dot{\ddot{\text{O}}}\,\curvearrowright\,\text{Al}\,\curvearrowright\,\dot{\ddot{\text{O}}}\cdot \longrightarrow 2\,\text{Al}^{3+} + 3\left[:\!\ddot{\text{O}}\!: \right]^{2-}$

(c) $\text{K}\,\curvearrowright\,\dot{\ddot{\text{S}}}\,\curvearrowleft\,\text{K} \longrightarrow 2\,\text{K}^+ + \left[:\!\ddot{\text{S}}\!: \right]^{2-}$

9.72 0.029 e^-, The nitrogen atom is positive.

9.74 $0.42\ e^-$

9.76 4.029×10^{-19} J/molecule

9.78 344 nm, ultraviolet region

9.80 (a) $: \ddot{B}r\cdot + \cdot \ddot{B}r : \longrightarrow : \ddot{B}r — \ddot{B}r :$

(b) $2H\cdot + \cdot\ddot{O}\cdot \longrightarrow H—\ddot{O}—H$

(c) $3H\cdot + \cdot\ddot{N}\cdot \longrightarrow H—\underset{\underset{H}{|}}{\overset{}{N}}—H$

9.82 (a) H_2Se **(b)** H_3As **(c)** SiH_4

9.84 (a) S **(b)** Si **(c)** Br **(d)** C

9.86 N—S

9.88

(a) $\left[\begin{array}{c} :\ddot{C}l: \\ | \\ :\ddot{C}l—As—\ddot{C}l: \\ | \\ :\ddot{C}l: \end{array}\right]^+$

(b) $\left[:\ddot{O}—\ddot{C}l—\ddot{O}:\right]^-$

(c) $H—\ddot{O}—N=\ddot{O}$

(d) $:\ddot{F}—\ddot{X}e—\ddot{F}:$

9.90 (a)
$$:\ddot{C}l:$$
$$| $$
$$:\ddot{C}l—Si—\ddot{C}l:$$
$$| $$
$$:\ddot{C}l:$$

(b)
$$:\ddot{F}:$$
$$| $$
$$:\ddot{F}—P—\ddot{F}:$$

(c)
$$H$$
$$| $$
$$H—P—H$$

(d) $:\ddot{C}l—\ddot{S}—\ddot{C}l:$

9.92 (a) $\ddot{S}=C=\ddot{S}$

(b) $[:C\equiv N:]^-$

9.94 (a)
$$H$$
$$| $$
$$H—\underset{\cdot\cdot}{As}—H$$

(b) $H—\ddot{O}—\ddot{C}l—\ddot{O}:$

(c)
$$:\ddot{O}:$$
$$| $$
$$H—\ddot{O}—Se—\ddot{O}—H$$

(d)
$$H$$
$$| $$
$$:O:$$
$$| $$
$$H—\ddot{O}—As—\ddot{O}—H$$
$$| $$
$$:O:$$

9.96 (a)
$$:O:$$
$$\| $$
$$H—C—H$$

(b)
$$:O:$$
$$\| $$
$$:\ddot{C}l—S—\ddot{C}l:$$

9.98 (a) $\overset{0}{H}—\overset{0}{\ddot{O}}—\overset{+1}{\ddot{C}l}—\overset{-1}{\ddot{O}}:$

(b)
$$:\overset{1-}{\ddot{O}}:$$
$$| $$
$$\overset{0}{\ddot{O}}=\underset{2+}{S}—\overset{1-}{\ddot{O}}:$$

(c) $\overset{0}{\ddot{O}}=\underset{1+}{S}—\overset{1-}{\ddot{O}}:$

9.100

$$\begin{array}{c} :\ddot{O}:^{(1-)} \\ | \\ {}^{(1-)}:\ddot{O}—\underset{(3+)}{Cl}—\overset{}{\underset{(0)}{\ddot{O}}}—H^{(0)} \\ | \\ :\ddot{O}:^{(1-)} \end{array} \qquad \begin{array}{c} :O: \\ \| \\ :\ddot{O}—Cl—\ddot{O}—H \\ \| \\ :O: \end{array}$$

9.102 The formal charges on all of the atoms of the left structure are zero, therefore, the potential energy of this molecule is lower and it is more stable. Group 2 atoms normally have only two bonds.

9.104

$$H—\ddot{O}—H \quad H^+ \longrightarrow \left[H—\underset{\underset{H}{|}}{\overset{}{\ddot{O}}}—H\right]^+$$

9.106 The average bond order is 4/3

$$\left[\begin{array}{c} :\ddot{O}: \\ \| \\ \ddot{O}=C—\ddot{O}: \end{array}\right]^{2-} \longleftrightarrow \left[\begin{array}{c} :O: \\ \| \\ :\ddot{O}—C—\ddot{O}: \end{array}\right]^{2-} \longleftrightarrow \left[\begin{array}{c} :\ddot{O}: \\ \| \\ :\ddot{O}—C=\ddot{O} \end{array}\right]^{2-}$$

9.108

$$\left[\ddot{O}=N—\ddot{O}:\right]^- \longleftrightarrow \left[:\ddot{O}—N=\ddot{O}\right]^-$$

N—O bonds in NO_2^- should be shorter than that in NO_3^-.

9.110

$$:O\equiv C—\ddot{O}: \longleftrightarrow :\ddot{O}—C\equiv O:$$

These are not preferred structures, because in each Lewis diagram, one oxygen bears a formal charge of +1 whereas the other bears a formal charge of –1.

| Chapter 10

Practice Exercises

10.1 Octahedral

10.2 Trigonal bipyramidal

10.3 Linear

10.4 Linear

10.5 Square planar

10.6 In SO_3^{2-} trigonal pyramidal
   $PbCl_4$ tetrahedral
   XeO_4 tetrahedral
   OF_2 bent

10.7 Polar

10.8 (a) Non-polar. **(b)** polar. **(c)** polar. **(d)** polar. **(e)** polar.

10.9 The H–Cl bond is formed by the overlap of the half-filled $1s$ atomic orbital of a H atom with the half-filled $3p$ valence orbital of a Cl atom:

Cl atom in HCl (x = H electron):

$$\textcircled{\text{N}} \quad \textcircled{\text{N}}\textcircled{\text{N}}\textcircled{\text{1x}}$$
$$3s \qquad 3p$$

The overlap that gives rise to the H–Cl bond is that of a $1s$ orbital of H with a $3p$ orbital of Cl:

10.10 The half-filled $1s$ atomic orbital of each H atom overlaps with a half-filled $3p$ atomic orbital of the P atom, to give three P–H

bonds. This should give a bond angle of 90°.
P atom in PH_3 (x = H electron):

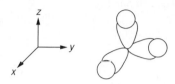
$3s$ $3p$

The orbital overlap that forms the P–H bond combines a $1s$ orbital of hydrogen with a $3p$ orbital of phosphorus. (Note: only half of each p orbital is shown):

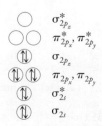

10.11 sp^2 hybrid orbitals on the B, x = Cl electron

sp^2 $2p$

10.12 sp hybrid orbitals on the Be; x = F electron

sp $2p$

10.13 sp^3

sp^3

10.14 Since there are five bonding pairs of electrons on the central phosphorous atom, we choose sp^3d hybridization for the P atom. Each of phosphorous's five sp^3d hybrid orbitals overlaps with a $3p$ atomic orbital of a chlorine atom to form a total of five P–Cl single bonds. Four of the $3d$ atomic orbitals of P remain unhybridized.

10.15 Trigonal bipyramidal, sp^3d—p bonds
10.16 sp^3d^2
10.17 (a) sp^3 (b) sp^3d
10.18 NH_3 is sp^3 hybridized. Three of the electron pairs are used for bonding with the three hydrogens. The fourth pair of electrons is a lone pair of electrons. This pair of electrons is used for the formation of the bond between the nitrogen of NH_3 and the hydrogen ion, H^+.
10.19 Octahdderal, sp^3d^2
P atom in PCl_6^- (x = Cl electron):

sp^3d^2 $3d$

10.20 Atom 1: sp^2 atom 2: sp^3 atom 3: sp^2
There are 10 σ bonds and 2 π bonds in the molecule.
10.21 Atom 1: sp atom 2: sp^2 atom 3: sp^3
There are 9 σ bonds and 3 π bonds in the molecule.
10.22 The bond order is 3 and this does agree with the Lewis structure.

$\sigma^*_{2p_z}$
$\pi^*_{2p_x}, \pi^*_{2p_y}$
σ_{2p_z}
π_{2p_x}, π_{2p_y}
σ^*_{2s}
σ_{2s}

10.23

$\sigma^*_{2p_z}$
$\pi^*_{2p_x}, \pi^*_{2sp_y}$
π_{2p_x}, π_{2p_y}
σ_{2p_z}
σ^*_{2s}
σ_{2s}

The bond order is 5/2

Review Problems

10.76 (a) Bent
  (b) Planar triangular
  (c) T-shaped
  (d) Linear
  (e) Planar triangular
10.78 (a) Nonlinear
  (b) Trigonal bipyramidal
  (c) Trigonal pyramidal
  (d) Trigonal pyramidal
  (e) Nonlinear
10.80 (a) Tetrahedral
  (b) Square planar
  (c) Octahedral
  (d) Tetrahedral
  (e) Linear
10.82 BrF_4^+
10.84 180°
10.86 (a) 109.5° (b) 109.5°
  (c) 120° (d) 180°
  (e) 109.5°
10.88 (a), (b), and (c)
10.90 All are polar
10.92 In SF_6, although the individual bonds in this substance are polar bonds, the geometry of the bonds is symmetrical which serves to cause the individual dipole moments of the various bonds to cancel one another. In SF_5Br, one of the six bonds has a different polarity so the individual dipole moments of the various bonds do not cancel one another.
10.94 The $1s$ atomic orbitals of the hydrogen atoms overlap with the mutually perpendicular p atomic orbitals of the selenium atom. Se atom in H_2Se (x = H electrons):

$4s$ $4p$

10.96 Atomic Be:

$2s$ $2p$

Hybridized Be: (x = a Cl electron)

sp $2p$

10.98 (a) sp^3

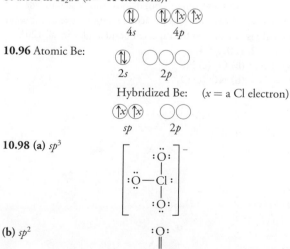

(b) sp^2

(c) sp^3

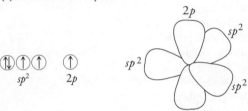

10.100 (a) sp^3

The hybrid orbital diagram for As: (x = a Cl electron)

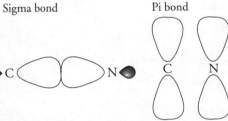
sp^3

(b) sp^3d

The hybrid orbital diagram for Cl: (x = a F electron)

sp^3d $3d$

10.102 Sb in SbF_6^-: (xx = an electron pair from the donor F^-)

sp^3d^2

10.104 (a) N in the C≡N system:

sp^2 $2p$

$2p$

sp^2

sp^2

sp^2

sp^2

(b) Sigma bond   Pi bond

C   N   C   N

(c)

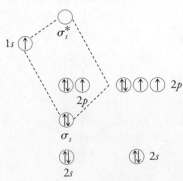

10.106 Each carbon atom is sp^2 hybridized, and each C—Cl bond is formed by the overlap of an sp^2 hybrid of carbon with a p atomic orbital of a chlorine atom. The C=C double bond consists first of a C—C σ bond formed by "head on" overlap of sp^2 hybrids from each C atom. Second, the C=C double bond consists of a side-to-side overlap of unhybridized p orbitals of each C atom, to give one π bond. The molecule is planar, and the expected bond angles are all 120°.

10.108 1. sp^3 **2.** sp **3.** sp^2 **4.** sp^2

10.110 (a) O_2^+ **(b)** O_2 **(c)** N_2

10.112 (a) N_2^+ **(b)** NO **(c)** O_2^-

10.114

σ_s^*

$1s$

$2p$

$2p$

σ_s

$2s$ $2s$

Hydrogen   Oxygen

There are two electrons in bonding MOs and three electrons in nonbonding MOs.
The bond order is 1.

Chapter 11

Practice Exercises

11.1 14.1 psi, 28.7 in. Hg

11.2 88,800 pascal, 666 torr

11.3 1270 mm Hg, 270 mm Hg

11.4 653 mm Hg

11.5 2/3

11.6 750 torr

11.7 688 torr

11.8 9.00 L O_2

11.9 64.6 L air

11.10

$$V_{O_2} = \left(\frac{1 \text{ volume } O_2}{2 \text{ volume NO}}\right) \times 184 \text{ ml NO} = 92 \text{ mL } O_2$$

$$V_2 = \frac{(723 \text{ torr})(92.0 \text{ mL})(295 \text{ K})}{(755 \text{ torr})(318 \text{ K})} = 81.7 \text{ mL } O_2$$

11.11 15,000 g solid CO_2

11.12 1,130 g Ar

11.13 58.1 g/mol

11.14 132 g mol^{-1}, Xe

11.15 Since radon is almost eight times denser than air, the sensor should be in the lowest point in the house: the basement.

11.16 2.77 g/L

11.17 P_2F_4

11.18 114 g mol^{-1}

     9 C and 6 H
     8 C and 18 H
     7 C and 30 H
     6 C and 42 H
     5 C and 54 H
     4 C and 66 H
     3 C and 78 H
     2 C and 90 H
     1 C and 102 H

The most probable compound is C_8H_{18}

11.19 3.07 L CO_2, 6.14 L SO_2, total volume = 9.21 L

11.20 1.03 g $CaCO_3$

11.21 P_{Ar} = 6.80 atm, P_{N_2} = 9.34 atm, P_{O_2} = 11.04 atm, P_{total} = 27.18 atm

11.22 2713 g O_2

11.23 746 torr, 0.0994 mol CH_4

11.24 732 torr, 289 mL

11.25 1.125 atm

11.26 P_{H_2} = 0.996 atm

     P_{NO} = 1.05 atm

11.27 0.147, 14.7%

11.28 0.988

11.29 HI

Review Problems

11.25 (a) 958 torr **(b)** 0.974 atm **(c)** 738 mm Hg
(d) 10.9 torr

11.27 (a) 250 torr **(b)** 350 torr

11.29 4.5 cm Hg

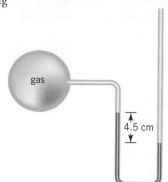

11.31 813 torr
11.33 125 torr
11.35 507 mL
11.37 4.37 L
11.39 843 °C
11.41 801 torr
11.43 5.69 L
11.45 −53 °C
11.47 $6.24 \times 10^4 \dfrac{\text{mL torr}}{\text{mol K}}$
11.49 0.104 L
11.51 2340 torr
11.53 0.0398 g
11.55 (a) 1.34 g L^{-1} (b) 1.25 g L^{-1} (c) 3.17 g L^{-1} (d) 1.78 g L^{-1}
11.57 1.28 g/L
11.59 88.2 g/mol
11.61 1.14×10^3 mL
11.63 10.7 L H$_2$
11.65 36.3 mL O$_2$
11.67 224 mL
11.69 697 torr
11.71
P_{N_2} = 0.30 atm, P_{O_2} = 0.20 atm, P_{He} = 0.40 atm, P_{CO_2} = 0.10 atm
P_{N_2} = 228 torr, P_{O_2} = 152 torr, P_{He} = 304 torr, P_{CO_2} = 76 torr
P_{N_2} = 0.304 bar, P_{O_2} = 0.203 bar, P_{He} = 0.405 bar, P_{CO_2} = 0.101 bar
11.73 734 torr, 262 mL
11.75 250 mL
11.77 N$_2$, 1.25
11.79 ^{235}UF$_6$, 1.0043

| Chapter 12

Practice Exercises

12.1 (a) CH$_3$CH$_2$CH$_2$CH$_2$CH$_3$ < CH$_3$CH$_2$OH < KBr
(b) CH$_3$CH$_2$OCH$_2$CH$_3$ < CH$_3$CH$_2$NH$_2$ <
HOCH$_2$CH$_2$CH$_2$CH$_2$OH
12.2 Propylamine, because of its ability to form hydrogen bonds
12.3 The piston should be pushed in.
12.4 The number of molecules in the vapor will decrease, and the number of molecules in the liquid will increase, but the sum of the molecules in the vapor and the liquid remains the same.
12.5 Decreasing the temperature will decrease the vapor pressure and, therefore, decrease the number of molecules in the vapor state. The volume will remain constant as long as the external pressure on the piston is also decreased by the same amount as the product of nT.
12.6 The boiling point is most likely (a) less than 10 °C above 100 °C.

12.7 Approximately 75 °C
12.8 3.0×10^4 J
12.9 The heat released when 10 g of water vapor condenses is 2.7×10^4 J.
The heat content of 10 g of water at 100 °C cooling to 37 °C is 2.6×10^3 J.
12.10 530 mm Hg
12.11 350.5 K
12.12 Adding heat will shift the equilibrium to the right, producing more vapor.
12.13
Boiling	Endothermic
Melting	Endothermic
Condensing	Exothermic
Subliming	Endothermic
Freezing	Exothermic

No, each physical change is always exothermic or always endothermic as shown.
12.14 Vapor pressure curve. See Figure 12.23
12.15 Solid to gas
12.16 Liquid
12.17 2 Cr atoms
12.18 The ratio is 1 to 1.
12.19 A molecular crystal
12.20 A covalent or network solid.
12.21 A molecular solid

Review Problems

12.83 Diethyl ether
12.85 (a) London forces, dipole–dipole and hydrogen bonding
(b) London forces, dipole–dipole
(c) London forces
(d) London forces, dipole–dipole
12.87 Chloroform would be expected to display larger dipole-dipole attractions because it has a larger dipole moment than bromoform. On the other hand, bromoform would be expected to show stronger London forces due to having larger electron clouds, which are more polarizable than those of chlorine.

Since bromoform in fact has a higher boiling point that chloroform, we must conclude that it experiences stronger intermolecular attractions than chloroform, which can only be due to London forces. Therefore, London forces are more important in determining the boiling points of these two compounds.

12.89 London forces are higher in chains than in branched isomers. Therefore, octane has higher London forces between molecules than 2,2,3,3-tetramethylbutane so octane would be more viscous.
12.91 Ethanol
12.93 Ether < acetone < benzene < water < acetic acid
12.95

Compound	Intermolecular forces broken
CH$_3$CH$_2$OH	London, dipole, hydrogen bonding
H$_3$CCN	London, dipole
NaCl	London, Ionic

12.97 305 kJ
12.99 (a) The final temperature will be 0 °C.
(b) 47.9 g of water must melt.
12.101 3.46×10^{-6} atm
12.103 31,400 J mol^{-1}

12.105

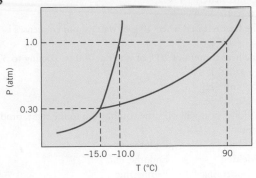

12.107 (a) Solid (b) gas (c) liquid (d) solid, liquid, and gas
12.109 4 Zn^{2+}, 4 S^{2-}
12.111 3.51 Å, 351 pm
12.113 656 pm
12.115 (a) 6.57° (b) 27.3°
12.117 176 pm
12.119 Molecular solid
12.121 Metallic solid
12.123 (a) molecular   (d) metallic   (g) ionic
     (b) ionic   (e) covalent
     (c) ionic   (f) molecular

Chapter 13

Practice Exercises

13.1 3.7 g L^{-1}, Hydrogen sulfide is more soluble in water than nitrogen and oxygen. Hydrogen sulfide reacts with the water to form hydronium ions and HS^-.
13.2 1.12 mg O_2, 1.85 mg N_2 mL
13.3 405.7 mL water
13.4 0.250 g of NaBr, 24.75 g H_2O, 25.0 mL H_2O
13.5 2.0×10^1 g
13.6 1.239 m, smaller
13.7 g CH_3OH for 0.050 m = 0.320 g
     g CH_3OH for 0.100 m = 0.640 g
     g CH_3OH for 0.150 m = 0.960 g
     g CH_3OH for 0.200 m = 1.28 g
     g CH_3OH for 0.250 m = 1.60 g
13.8 (a) 28.3 g (b) 70.7 g (c) 1.41 g
13.9 27 m
13.10 16.1 m
13.11 6.82 M
13.12 0.00469 M, $Al(NO_3)_3$, 0.00470 m $Al(NO_3)_3$
13.13 4.90×10^2 torr
13.14 34.5 g stearic acid
13.15 55.4 torr
13.16 45.1 torr
13.17 89.5% to 91.2%
13.18 213 g glucose
13.19 157 g mol^{-1}
13.20 125 g mol^{-1}
13.21 3.68 mm Hg, 50.0 mm H_2O
13.22 222 torr, B. P. = 100.006 °C, M. P. = −0.021 °C note that the significant figure rules were not used for the boiling points
13.23 5.00×10^3 g mol^{-1}
13.24 5.38×10^2 g mol^{-1}
13.25 −0.882 °C, −0.441 °C
13.26 (a) −0.372 °C (b) −0.0372 °C (c) −0.00372 °C

The first freezing point depression, solution (a), could be estimated using a laboratory thermometer that can measure 1 °C increments.

Review Problems

13.42 $KCl(s) \longrightarrow K^+(g) + Cl^-(g)$, $\Delta H° = +715$ kJ mol^{-1}
$K^+(g) + Cl^-(g) \longrightarrow K^+(aq) + Cl^-(aq)$, $\Delta H° = -686$ kJ mol^{-1}
$KCl(s) \longrightarrow K^+(aq) + Cl^-(aq)$, $\Delta H° = +29$ kJ mol^{-1}
13.44 0.038 g/L
13.46 0.020 g L^{-1}
13.48 3.35 m
13.50 0.133 m, 2.39×10^{-3}, 2.34%
13.52 5.45%
13.54 7.89%, 4.76 m
13.56 0.359 M $NaNO_3$, 3.00 %, 6.49×10^{-3}
13.58 22.8 torr
13.60 52.7 torr
13.62 70 mol% toluene and 30 mol% benzene
13.64 (a) 0.029 (b) 2.99×10^{-2} moles (c) 278 g/mol
13.66 68.9 g
13.68 240 g/mol
13.70 127 g/mol, $C_8H_4N_2$.
13.72 (a) If the equation is correct, the units on both sides of the equation should be g/mol. The units on the right side of this equation are:

$$\frac{(g) \times (\cancel{L} \text{ atm mol}^{-1} \cancel{K^{-1}}) \times (\cancel{K})}{\cancel{L} \times \cancel{atm}} = g/mol$$

which is correct.
(b) 1.8×10^6 g/mol
13.74 15.3 torr
13.76 1.3×10^4 torr
13.78 −1.1 °C
13.80 2
13.82 1.89

Chapter 14

Practice Exercises

14.1 Rate of production of I^- = 8.0×10^{-5} mol L^{-1} s^{-1}. Rate of production of SO_4^{2-} = 2.4×10^{-4} mol L^{-1} s^{-1}.
14.2 Rate of disappearance of O_2 = 0.45 mol L^{-1} s^{-1}. Rate of disappearance of H_2S = 0.30 mol L^{-1} s^{-1}.
14.3 -2.1×10^{-4} mol L^{-1} s^{-1}
14.4 A value near 1×10^{-4} mol L^{-1} s^{-1} is correct.
14.5 (a) 9.8×10^{14} L^2 mol^{-2} s^{-1} (b) L^2 mol^{-2} s^{-1}
14.6 (a) 8.0×10^{-2} L mol^{-1} s^{-1} (b) L mol^{-1} s^{-1}
14.7 Order of the reaction with respect to $[BrO_3^-]$ = 1
     Order of the reaction with respect to $[SO_3^{2-}]$ = 1
     Overall order of the reaction = 1 + 1 = 2
14.8 Rate = $k[Cl_2]^2[NO]$
14.9 The order with respect to Br_2 is 1, the order with respect to HCO_2H is zero. The overall order of the reaction is 1.
14.10 2.0×10^2 L^2 mol^{-2} s^{-1}. Each of the other data sets also gives the same value.
14.11 (a) The rate will increase nine-fold.
     (b) The rate will increase three-fold.
     (c) The rate will decrease by three fourths.
14.12 (a) Rate = $k[NO]^2[H_2]^1$
     (b) 2.1×10^5 L^2 mol^{-2} s^{-1}
     (c) L^2 mol^{-2} s^{-1}

14.13 (a) First order with respect to sucrose
(b) $6.17 \times 10^{-4}\,s^{-1}$
14.14 (a) Rate $= k[A]^2[B]^2$ **(b)** $6.9 \times 10^{-3}\,L^3\,mol^{-3}\,s^{-1}$
(c) $L^3\,mol^{-3}\,s^{-1}$ **(d)** 4
14.15 $2.56 \times 10^{-2}\,yr^{-1}$
14.16 (a) $4.71 \times 10^{-3}\,M$ **(b)** 7.8 min
14.17 18.7 min, 37.4 min
14.18 27.1 yr
14.19 5.41%
14.20 1.90×10^4 yrs
14.21 The upper limit of dates is 24,800 years and the lower limit of dates is 424 years.
14.22 63 min
14.23 $4.0 \times 10^{-4}\,M$
14.24 $k = 1.03\,L\,mol^{-1}\,s^{-1}$ $t_{1/2} = 1.48 \times 10^3\,s$
14.25 The reaction is first-order
14.26 322 K or 49 °C
14.27 (a) $1.4 \times 10^2\,kJ/mol$ **(b)** $0.40\,L\,mol^{-1}\,s^{-1}$
14.28 684 K
14.29 (a), **(b)**, and **(e)** may be elementary processes.
Equations **(c)**, **(d)**, and **(f)** are not elementary processes because they have more than two molecules colliding at one time, and this is very unlikely.
14.30 Rate $= k[NO][O_3]$
14.31 Rate $= \dfrac{k[NO_2Cl]^2}{[NO_2]}$

Review Problems

14.46

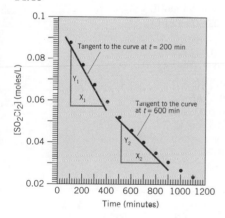

At 200 min: $1 \times 10^{-4}\,M/min$. At 600 min: $7 \times 10^{-5}\,M/min$.
14.48 The rate of disappearance of hydrogen is three times the rate of disappearance of nitrogen. NH_3 appears twice as fast as N_2 disappears.
14.50 (a) Rate for $O_2 = 11.4\,mol\,L^{-1}\,s^{-1}$
(b) Rate for $CO_2 = 7.20\,mol\,L^{-1}\,s^{-1}$
(c) Rate for $H_2O = 8.40\,mol\,L^{-1}\,s^{-1}$
14.52 (a) $-\dfrac{d}{dt}[CH_3Cl] = -\dfrac{1}{3}\dfrac{d}{dt}[Cl_2] = \dfrac{d}{dt}[CCl_4] = \dfrac{1}{3}\dfrac{d}{dt}[HCl]$
(b) $9.7 \times 10^{-3}\,M\,s^{-1}$
14.54 $8.0 \times 10^{-11}\,mol\,L^{-1}\,s^{-1}$
14.56 $2.4 \times 10^2\,mol\,L^{-1}\,s^{-1}$
14.58 $6.4 \times 10^2\,M\,s^{-1}$
14.60 Rate $= k[M][N]^2$, $2.5 \times 10^3\,L^2\,mol^{-2}\,s^{-1}$
14.62 Rate $= k[OCl^-][I^-]$, $6.8 \times 10^9\,L\,mol^{-1}\,s^{-1}$
14.64 Rate $= k[ICl][H_2]$, $1.04 \times 10^{-1}\,L\,mol^{-1}\,s^{-1}$

14.66

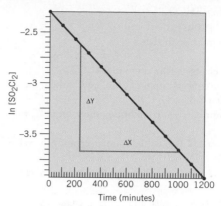

$1.32 \times 10^{-3}\,min^{-1}$
14.68 (a) $3.7 \times 10^{-3}\,M$ **(b)** $6.0 \times 10^{-4}\,M$
14.70 $1.85 \times 10^{-2}\,min^{-1}$
14.72 $4.26 \times 10^{-3}\,min^{-1}$
14.74 1.3×10^4 min
14.76 11 mg/kg
14.78 1/256
14.80 Approximately 500 min. The reaction is first-order in SO_2Cl_2.
14.82 33.2 hr
14.84 1.3×10^9 years old
14.86 4.0×10^{-13}
14.88 The slope is: $-9.5 \times 10^3\,K$, $E_a = 79\,kJ/mol$
Using the equation $E_a = 79.3\,kJ/mol$
14.90 $E_a = 99\,kJ/mol$, $A = 6.6 \times 10^9\,mol^{-1}\,s^{-1}$,
$k = 7.9 \times 10^{-2}\,L\,mol^{-1}\,s^{-1}$
14.92 (a) $3.8 \times 10^{-5}\,s^{-1}$ **(b)** $1.6 \times 10^1\,s^{-1}$
14.94 Rate $= k\,[AB][C]$
14.96 The intermediate in this reaction is N_2O_2
The overall reaction is:
$2NO(g) + O_2(g) \rightleftharpoons 2NO_2(g)$
Rate $= k[NO]^2[O_2]$

| Chapter 15
Practice Exercises
15.1 $2N_2O_3 + O_2 \rightleftharpoons 4NO_2$
15.2

(a) $\dfrac{[H_2O]^2}{[H_2]^2[O_2]} = K_c$ **(b)** $\dfrac{[CO_2][H_2O]^2}{[CH_4][O_2]^2} = K_c$

15.3 1.2×10^{-13}
15.4 1.9×10^5
15.5 $K_P = \dfrac{(P_{N_2O})^2}{(P_{N_2})^2(P_{O_2})}$

15.6 $K_P = \dfrac{(P_{HI})^2}{(P_{H_2})^2(P_{I_2})}$

15.7 1.8×10^{36}
15.8 K_P is smaller than K_c. $K_c = 57$
15.9 $K_c = \dfrac{1}{[NH_3(g)][HCl(g)]}$

15.10

(a) $K_c = \dfrac{1}{[Cl_2(g)]}$

(b) $K_c = [Na^+(aq)][OH^-(aq)][H_2(g)]$

(c) $K_c = [Ag^+]^2[CrO_4^{2-}]$

(d) $K_c = \dfrac{[Ca^{+2}(aq)][HCO_3^-(aq)]^2}{[CO_2(aq)]}$

15.11 The reaction will move to the left.

15.12 (a), (c), (b)

15.13 There will be no change in the amount of H_3PO_4.

15.14 (a) Decreasing the concentration of Cl_2 at equilibrium, the value of K_p will be unchanged.
(b) Increasing the amount of Cl_2 at equilibrium, the value of K_p will be unchanged.
(c) Increasing the amount of Cl_2 at equilibrium, decreasing the value of K_p.
(d) Decreasing the concentration of Cl_2 at equilibrium, the value of K_p will be unchanged.

15.15 [CO] decreases by 0.060 mol/L and [CO$_2$] increases by 0.060 mol/L

15.16 $K_c = 4.06$

15.17 (a) $[PCl_3] = 0.200\ M$
    $[Cl_2] = 0.100\ M$
    $[PCl_5] = 0.000\ M$
(b) The change in concentration of PCl_3 was $(0.200 - 0.120)$ $M = 0.080$ mol/L. The Cl_2 has decreased by 0.080 M and PCl_5 has increased by 0.080 M.
(c) $[PCl_3] = 0.120\ M$, $[PCl_5] = 0.080\ M$, $[Cl_2] = 0.020\ M$.
(d) $K_c = 33$

15.18 $[NO_2] = 1.04 \times 10^{-2}\ M$

15.19 $[C_2H_5OH] = 8.98 \times 10^{-3}\ M$

15.20 $[H_2] = [I_2] = 0.044\ M$, $[HI] = 0.312\ M$.

15.21 $[H_2] = 0.107\ M$
    $[I_2] = 0.0066\ M$
    $[HI] = 0.1868\ M$.

15.22 $[N_2] = 6.2 \times 10^{-4}$
    $[H_2] = 1.9 \times 10^{-3}$

15.23 $[NO] = 1.1 \times 10^{-17}\ M$

Review Problems

15.19 (a) $K_c = \dfrac{[POCl_3]^2}{[PCl_3]^2[O_2]}$ (d) $K_c = \dfrac{[NO_2]^2[H_2O]^8}{[N_2H_4][H_2O_2]^6}$

(b) $K_c = \dfrac{[SO_2]^2[O_2]}{[SO_3]^2}$ **(e)** $K_c = \dfrac{[SO_2][HCl]^2}{[SOCl_2][H_2O]}$

(c) $K_c = \dfrac{[NO]^2[H_2O]^2}{[N_2H_4][O_2]^2}$

15.21 (a) $K_p = \dfrac{(P_{POCl_3})^2}{(P_{PCl_3})^2(P_{O_2})}$ (d) $K_p = \dfrac{(P_{NO_2})^2(P_{H_2O})^8}{(P_{N_2H_4})(P_{H_2O_2})^6}$

(b) $K_p = \dfrac{(P_{SO_2})^2(P_{O_2})}{(P_{SO_3})^2}$ **(e)** $K_p = \dfrac{(P_{SO_2})(P_{HCl})^2}{(P_{SOCl_2})(P_{H_2O})}$

(c) $K_p = \dfrac{(P_{NO})^2(P_{H_2O})^2}{(P_{N_2H_4})(P_{O_2})^2}$

15.23 (a) $K_c = \dfrac{[Ag(NH_3)_2^+]}{[Ag^+][NH_3]^2}$ (b) $K_c = \dfrac{[Cd(SCN)_4^{2-}]}{[Cd^{2+}][SCN^-]^4}$

15.25 1×10^{85}

15.27

(a) $K_c = \dfrac{[HCl]^2}{[H_2][Cl_2]}$ **(b)** $K_c = \dfrac{[HCl]}{[H_2]^{1/2}[Cl_2]^{1/2}}$

K_c for reaction (b) is the square root of K_c for reaction (a).

15.29 $0.0375\ M$

15.31 b

15.33 $K_c = 11$

15.35 $K_p = 2.7 \times 10^{-2}$

15.37 $K_p = 5.4 \times 10^{-5}$

15.39 (a) 55.5 M (b) 55.5 M (c) 55.5 M

15.41

(a) $K_c = \dfrac{[CO]^2}{[O_2]}$ **(d)** $K_c = \dfrac{[H_2O][CO_2]}{[HF]^2}$

(b) $K_c = [H_2O][SO_2]$ **(e)** $K_c = [H_2O]^5$

(c) $K_c = \dfrac{[CH_4][CO_2]}{[H_2O]^2}$

15.43

$[HI] = 1.47 \times 10^{-12}\ M$
$[Cl_2] = 7.37 \times 10^{-13}\ M$

15.45 (a) The system shifts to the right to consume some of the added methane.
(b) The system shifts to the left to consume some of the added hydrogen.
(c) The system shifts to the right to make some more carbon disulfide.
(d) The system shifts to the left to decrease the amount of gaseous moles.
(e) The system shifts to the right to absorb some of the added heat.

15.47 (a) Right (b) left (c) left (d) right (e) no effect (f) left

15.49 (a) No (b) To the left

15.51 $[CH_3OH] = 4.36 \times 10^{-3}\ M$.

15.53 $K_c = 0.398$

15.55 $K_c = 0.0955$

15.57 $K_c = 0.915$

15.59 $[Br_2] = [Cl_2] = 0.011\ M$

15.61 $[NO_2] = [SO_2] = 0.0497$ mol/L
    $[NO] = [SO_3] = 0.0703$ mol/L

15.63 $[H_2] = [CO_2] = 7.7 \times 10^{-3}\ M$
    $[CO] = [H_2O] = 0.0123\ M$

15.65 $[H_2] = [Cl_2] = 8.9 \times 10^{-19}\ M$

15.67 $[CO] = 5.0 \times 10^{-4}\ M$

15.69 $[PCl_5] = 3.0 \times 10^{-5}\ M$.

15.71 $[NO_2] = [SO_2] = 0.0281\ M$

15.73 $[CO] = [H_2O] = 0.200\ M$

Chapter 16

Practice Exercises

16.1 Conjugate acid base pairs (a), (c), and (f)
(b) The conjugate base of HI is I^-
(d) The conjugate base of HNO_2 is NO_2^- and the conjugate base of NH_4^+ is NH_3
(e) The conjugate acid of CO_3^{2-} is HCO_3^- and the conjugate acid of CN^- is HCN

16.2 In each case the conjugate base is obtained by removing a proton from the acid:
(a) OH^- **(b)** I^- **(c)** NO_2^- **(d)** $H_2PO_4^-$
(e) HPO_4^{2-} **(f)** PO_4^{3-} **(g)** HS^- **(h)** NH_3

16.3 In each case the conjugate acid is obtained by adding a proton to the base:
(a) H_2O_2 **(b)** HSO_4^- **(c)** HCO_3^- **(d)** HCN
(e) NH_3 **(f)** NH_4^+ **(g)** H_3PO_4 **(h)** $H_2PO_4^-$

16.4 HCN and CN^- HCl and Cl^-

16.5 The Brønsted acids: $H_2PO_4^-(aq)$ and $H_2CO_3(aq)$
The Brønsted bases: $HCO_3^-(aq)$ and $HPO_4^{2-}(aq)$

16.6

$$PO_4^{3-}(aq) + HC_2H_3O_2(aq) \rightleftharpoons HPO_4^{2-}(aq) + C_2H_3O_2^-(aq)$$

base $\quad$ acid $\qquad\qquad$ acid $\qquad$ base

16.7 (a) $H_2PO_4^-$ amphoteric, since it can both accept and donate a proton **(b)** HPO_4^{2-} amphoteric, since it can both accept and donate a proton **(c)** H_2S amphoteric, since it can both accept and donate a proton **(d)** H_3PO_4 not amphoteric: it can only donate protons **(e)** NH_4^+ not amphoteric: it can only donate protons **(f)** H_2O amphoteric, since it can both accept and donate a proton **(g)** HI not amphoteric: it can only donate protons **(h)** HNO_2 not amphoteric: it can only donate protons

16.8 $HPO_4^{2-}(aq) + OH^-(aq) \longrightarrow PO_4^{3-}(aq) + H_2O$;
$\qquad\qquad\qquad\qquad HPO_4^{2-}$ acting as an acid

$HPO_4^{2-}(aq) + H_3O^+(aq) \longrightarrow H_2PO_4^- + H_2O$;
$\qquad\qquad\qquad\qquad HPO_4^{2-}$ acting as a base

16.9 $HSO_4^-(aq) + HPO_4^{2-}(aq) \longrightarrow SO_4^{2-}(aq) + H_2PO_4^-(aq)$

16.10 The substances on the right because they are the weaker acid and base.

16.11 (a) HF < HBr < HI
(b) PH_3 < H_2S < HCl
(c) H_2O < H_2Se < H_2Te
(d) AsH_3 < H_2Se < HBr
(e) PH_3 < H_2Se < HI

16.12 (a) HBr **(b)** H_2Te **(c)** H_2S
16.13 (a) $HClO_3$ **(b)** H_2SO_4
16.14 (a) H_3AsO_4 **(b)** H_2TeO_4
16.15 (a) HIO_4 **(b)** H_2TeO_4 **(c)** H_3AsO_4
16.16 (a) H_2SO_4 **(b)** H_3AsO_4
16.17 The acid strength decreases as follows:
FCH_2COOH > $ClCH_2COOH$ > $BrCH_2COOH$

16.18 (a) NH_3, Lewis base
$\qquad$ H^+, Lewis acid
(b) O^{2-}, Lewis base
$\qquad$ SeO_3, Lewis acid
(c) Ag^+, Lewis acid
$\qquad$ NH_3, Lewis base

16.19 (a) Fluoride ions have a filled octet of electrons and are likely to behave as Lewis bases, i.e., electron pair donors.
(b) $BeCl_2$ is a likely Lewis acid since it has an incomplete shell. The Be atom has only two valence electrons and it can easily accept a pair of electrons.
(c) It could reasonably be considered a potential Lewis base since it contains three oxygens, each with lone pairs and partial negative charges. However, it is more effective as a Lewis acid, since the central sulfur bears a significant positive charge.

Review Problems

16.38

(a) $HNO_3 + N_2H_4 \rightleftharpoons N_2H_5^+ + NO_3^-$

acid $\quad$ base $\qquad$ acid $\qquad$ base

(b)

$NH_3 + N_2H_5^+ \rightleftharpoons NH_4^+ + N_2H_4$

base $\quad$ acid $\qquad$ acid $\quad$ base

(c)

$H_2PO_4^- + CO_3^{2-} \rightleftharpoons HCO_3^- + HPO_4^{2-}$

acid $\qquad$ base $\qquad$ acid $\qquad$ base

(d)

$HIO_3 + HC_2O_4^- \rightleftharpoons H_2C_2O_4 + IO_3^-$

acid $\qquad$ base $\qquad$ acid $\qquad$ base

16.40 (a) HBr **(b)** HF **(c)** HBr
16.42 (a) $HClO_2$ **(b)** H_2SeO_4
16.44 (a) $HClO_3$ **(b)** $HClO_3$ **(c)** $HBrO_4$
16.46 $Cr(H_2O)_6^{3+}(aq) + H_2O \longrightarrow$
$\qquad\qquad\qquad Cr(H_2O)_5OH^{2+}(aq) + H_3O^+(aq)$

16.48

Lewis bases: NH_2^- $\quad$ Lewis acid: H^+

16.50

16.52

16.54

Lewis bases: NH_2^- and OH^- $\quad$ Lewis acid: H^+

Chapter 17

Practice Exercises

17.1 $[OH^-] = 8.3 \times 10^{-16}\ M$
17.2 $[H_3O^+] = 1.3 \times 10^{-9}$ The solution is basic

17.3 $pOH = 9.75$
$[H^+] = 5.6 \times 10^{-5}\ M$
$[OH^-] = 1.8 \times 10^{-10}\ M$

17.4 $pH = 4.49$
$pOH = 9.51$

17.5 (a) $[H^+] = 1.3 \times 10^{-3}\ M$
$[OH^-] = 7.7 \times 10^{-12}\ M$
The solution is acidic.
(b) $[H^+] = 1.4 \times 10^{-4}\ M$
$[OH^-] = 7.1 \times 10^{-11}\ M$
The solution is acidic.
(c) $[H^+] = 1.6 \times 10^{-11}\ M$
$[OH^-] = 6.5 \times 10^{-4}\ M$
The solution is basic.
(d) $[H^+] = 7.8 \times 10^{-5}\ M$
$[OH^-] = 1.3 \times 10^{-10}\ M$
The solution is acidic.
(e) $[H^+] = 2.5 \times 10^{-12}\ M$
$[OH^-] = 4.1 \times 10^{-3}\ M$
The solution is basic.

17.6 $[H^+] = 0.0050\ M$
$pH = 2.30$
$pOH = 11.70$

17.7 $pOH = 1.07$
$pH = 12.93$
$[H^+] = 1.2 \times 10^{-13}\ M$

17.8 $[H^+] = 3.2 \times 10^{-6}\ M$

17.9 (a) $HC_2H_3O_2 + H_2O \rightleftharpoons H_3O^+ + C_2H_3O_2^-$
$$K_a = \frac{[H_3O^+][C_2H_3O_2^-]}{[HC_2H_3O_2]}$$
(b) $(CH_3)_3NH^+ + H_2O \rightleftharpoons H_3O^+ + (CH_3)_3N$
$$K_a = \frac{[H_3O^+][(CH_3)_3N]}{[(CH_3)_3NH^+]}$$
(c) $H_3PO_4 + H_2O \rightleftharpoons H_3O^+ + H_2PO_4^-$
$$K_a = \frac{[H_3O^+][H_2PO_4^-]}{[H_3PO_4]}$$

17.10 (a) $HCHO_2 + H_2O \rightleftharpoons H_3O^+ + CHO_2^-$
$$K_a = \frac{[H_3O^+][CHO_2^-]}{[HCHO_2]}$$
(b) $(CH_3)_2NH_2^+ + H_2O \rightleftharpoons H_3O^+ + (CH_3)_2NH$
$$K_a = \frac{[H_3O^+][(CH_3)_2NH]}{[(CH_3)_2NH_2^+]}$$
(c) $H_2PO_4^- + H_2O \rightleftharpoons H_3O^+ + HPO_4^{2-}$
$$K_a = \frac{[H_3O^+][HPO_4^{2-}]}{[H_2PO_4^-]}$$

17.11 Barbituric acid and hydrazoic acid.

17.12 HA is the strongest acid. $K_a(HA) = 6.9 \times 10^{-4}$
$K_a(HB) = 7.2 \times 10^{-5}$

17.13 (a) $(CH_3)_3N + H_2O \rightleftharpoons (CH_3)_3NH^+ + OH^-$
$$K_b = \frac{[(CH_3)_3NH^+][OH^-]}{[(CH_3)_3N]}$$
(b) $SO_3^{2-} + H_2O \rightleftharpoons HSO_3^- + OH^-$
$$K_b = \frac{[HSO_3^-][OH^-]}{[SO_3^{2-}]}$$
(c) $NH_2OH + H_2O \rightleftharpoons NH_3OH^+ + OH^-$
$$K_b = \frac{[NH_3OH^+][OH^-]}{[NH_2OH]}$$

17.14 (a) $HS^- + H_2O \rightleftharpoons H_2S + OH^-$
$$K_b = \frac{[H_2S][OH^-]}{[HS^-]}$$
(b) $H_2PO_4^- + H_2O \rightleftharpoons H_3PO_4 + OH^-$
$$K_b = \frac{[H_3PO_4][OH^-]}{[H_2PO_4^-]}$$
(c) $HPO_4^{2-} + H_2O \rightleftharpoons H_2PO_4^- + OH^-$
$$K_b = \frac{[H_2PO_4^-][OH^-]}{[HPO_4^{2-}]}$$
(d) $HCO_3^- + H_2O \rightleftharpoons H_2CO_3 + OH^-$
$$K_b = \frac{[H_2CO_3][OH^-]}{[HCO_3^-]}$$
(e) $HSO_3^- + H_2O \rightleftharpoons H_2SO_3 + OH^-$
$$K_b = \frac{[H_2SO_3][OH^-]}{[HSO_3^-]}$$

17.15 $K_b = 4.3 \times 10^{-4}$
17.16 $K_a = 1.8 \times 10^{-4}$
17.17 $K_a = 1.2 \times 10^{-3}$
$pK_a = 2.93$
17.18 $K_a = 1.7 \times 10^{-5}$
$pK_a = 4.78$
17.19 $K_b = 1.6 \times 10^{-6}$
$pK_b = 5.79$
17.20 $[H^+] = 1.2 \times 10^{-3}\ M$
$pH = 2.91$
17.21 $[H^+] = 8.4 \times 10^{-4}\ M$
$pH = 3.08$
17.22 $pOH = 5.51$
17.23 $pH = 8.62$
17.24 $pH = 5.35$
17.25 (a) Basic **(b)** neutral **(c)** acidic
17.26 (a) Neutral **(b)** basic **(c)** acidic
17.27 5.39
17.28 8.17
17.29 5.13
17.30 Acidic
17.31 Acidic
17.32 Upon addition of a strong acid, the concentration of $HC_2H_3O_2$ will increase. When a strong base is added, it reacts with the acid to form more of the acetate ion; therefore the concentration of the acetic acid will decrease.
17.33 (a) $H^+ + NH_3 \longrightarrow NH_4^+$
(b) $OH^- + NH_4^+ \longrightarrow H_2O + NH_3$
17.34 4.83, the difference is due to rounding errors
17.35 4.61
17.36 Acetic acid buffer, 26.2 g $NaC_2H_3O_2$
Hydrazoic acid buffer, 29.0 NaN_3
Butanoic acid buffer, 29.6 g $NaC_4H_7O_2$
Propanoic acid, 22.3 g $NaC_3H_5O_2$
17.37 Yes, 0.70, 9.66 g $NaCHO_2$
17.38 0.14 pH units
17.39 $pH = 9.76$, $pH = 9.67$
17.40

$H_3PO_4 + H_2O \rightleftharpoons H_3O^+ + H_2PO_4^-$ $\quad K_a = \dfrac{[H_3O^+][H_2PO_4^-]}{[H_3PO_4]}$

$H_2PO_4^- + H_2O \rightleftharpoons H_3O^+ + HPO_4^{2-}$ $\quad K_a = \dfrac{[H_3O^+][HPO_4^{2-}]}{[H_2PO_4^-]}$

$HPO_4^{2-} + H_2O \rightleftharpoons H_3O^+ + PO_4^{3-}$ $\quad K_a = \dfrac{[H_3O^+][PO_4^{3-}]}{[HPO_4^{2-}]}$

17.41 $[H^+] = 2.8 \times 10^{-3}\ M$, pH = 2.55, $[C_6H_6O_6^{2-}] = 1.6 \times 10^{-12}$

17.42 pH = 11.66, It is not a substitute for $NaHCO_3$

17.43 pH = 10.25

17.44 $[H_2SO_3] = K_{b2}$ for SO_3^{2-}

17.45

(a) H_2O, K^+, $HC_2H_3O_2$, H^+, $C_2H_3O_2^-$, and OH^-
$[H_2O] > [K^+] > [C_2H_3O_2^-] > [OH^-] > [HC_2H_3O_2] > [H^+]$

(b) H_2O, $HC_2H_3O_2$, H^+, $C_2H_3O_2^-$, and OH^-
$[H_2O] > [HC_2H_3O_2] > [H^+] = [C_2H_3O_2^-] > [OH^-]$

(c) H_2O, K^+, $HC_2H_3O_2$, H^+, $C_2H_3O_2^-$, and OH^-
$[H_2O] > [K^+] > [OH^-] > [C_2H_3O_2^-] > [HC_2H_3O_2] > [H^+]$

(d) H_2O, K^+, $HC_2H_3O_2$, H^+, $C_2H_3O_2^-$, and OH^-
$[H_2O] > [K^+] > [HC_2H_3O_2] > [H^+] > [C_2H_3O_2^-] > [OH^-]$

17.46 (a) 2.37 (b) 3.74 (c) 4.22 (d) 8.22

17.47 pH = 3.66

Review Problems

17.40 $[D^+] = 3.0 \times 10^{-8}\ M = [OD^-]$
pD = 7.52
pOD = 7.52

17.42 (a) $[H^+] = 1.5 \times 10^{-12}\ M$, pH = 11.83, pOH = 2.17
(b) $[H^+] = 1.6 \times 10^{-10}\ M$, pH = 9.81, pOH = 4.19
(c) $[H^+] = 6.3 \times 10^{-7}\ M$, pH = 6.20, pOH = 7.80
(d) $[H^+] = 1.2 \times 10^{-3}\ M$, pH = 2.91, pOH = 11.09

17.44 4.72

17.46 (a) $[H^+] = 7.2 \times 10^{-9}\ M$
$[OH^-] = 1.4 \times 10^{-6}\ M$
(b) $[H^+] = 2.7 \times 10^{-3}\ M$
$[OH^-] = 3.6 \times 10^{-12}\ M$
(c) $[H^+] = 5.6 \times 10^{-12}\ M$
$[OH^-] = 1.8 \times 10^{-3}\ M$
(d) $[H^+] = 5.3 \times 10^{-14}\ M$
$[OH^-] = 1.9 \times 10^{-1}\ M$
(e) $[H^+] = 2.0 \times 10^{-7}\ M$
$[OH^-] = 5.0 \times 10^{-8}\ M$

17.48 $[H^+] = 2 \times 10^{-6}\ M$
$[OH^-] = 5 \times 10^{-9}\ M$

17.50 $[H^+] = 0.00065\ M$
pH = 3.19
$[OH^-] = 1.55 \times 10^{-11}\ M$

17.52 $[OH^-] = 0.15\ M$, pOH = 0.82
pH = 13.18
$[H^+] = 6.67 \times 10^{-14}\ M$

17.54 $2.0 \times 10^{-3}\ M$

17.56 The molarity of OH^- from the ionization water is $5.0 \times 10^{-12}\ M$.

17.58 6.49, 3.2×10^{-7}

17.60 0.43 %

17.62 $K_b = 1.5 \times 10^{-11}$

17.64 (a) $K_b = 7.1 \times 10^{-11}$ (b) Lactate ion is a weaker base

17.66 0.30 % ionized, $K_a = 1.8 \times 10^{-6}$

17.68 $K_a = 2.3 \times 10^{-2}$, $pK_a = 1.64$

17.70 $K_b = 5.5 \times 10^{-4}$, $pK_b = 3.23$

17.72 $[HC_3H_5O_2] = 0.145$
$[H^+] = 4.6 \times 10^{-3}$
$[C_3H_5O_2^-] = 4.6 \times 10^{-3}$
pH = 2.34

17.74 10.25

17.76 0.47 M

17.78 10.49

17.80 $[H^+] = 6.0 \times 10^{-4}\ M$, pH = 3.22

17.82 pH = 11.30
$[HCN] = 2.0 \times 10^{-3}\ M$

17.84 pH = 5.72

17.86 $K_a = 1.4 \times 10^{-5}$

17.88 pH = 10.67

17.90 pH = 4.97

17.92 pH = 9.00

17.94 The concentration of NH_3 will decrease by $2.5 \times 10^{-2}\ M$ and the NH_4^+ will increase by the same amount.

17.96 The pH of the solution changes –0.12 pH.

17.98 Initial pH = 9.36, final pH = 9.26, pH change = −0.1

17.100 2.2 g

17.102 Initial pH = 4.79, the final pH = 4.76, pH = 1.71

17.104 $[H_2C_6H_6O_6] \cong 0.15\ M$
$[H_3O^+] = [HC_6H_6O_6^-] = 3.5 \times 10^{-3}\ M$
$[C_6H_6O_6^{2-}] = 1.6 \times 10^{-12}\ M$
pH = 2.50

17.106 $[H_3PO_4] = 2.0 - 0.12 = 1.9\ M$
$[H^+] = [H_2PO_3^-] = 0.12\ M$
$[HPO_4^{2-}] = 6.2 \times 10^{-8}$
$[PO_4^{3-}] = 2.2 \times 10^{-19}$
pH = $-\log(0.12) = 0.92$

17.108 $0.20\ M = [H^+] = [H_2PO_3^-]$
$[HPO_3^{2-}] = 2.0 \times 10^{-7}\ M$
pH = 0.70

17.110 pH = 10.28
$[H_2SO_3] = 8.3 \times 10^{-13}$
$[HSO_3^-] = [OH^-] = 1.9 \times 10^{-4}\ M$
$[SO_3^{2-}] = 0.24\ M$ $[Na^+] = 0.24\ M$
$[H_3O^+] = 5.3 \times 10^{-11}$

17.112 pH = 9.70

17.114 pH = 12.99
$[H_3PO_4] = 2.1 \times 10^{-18}\ M$
$[H_2PO_4^-] = 1.6 \times 10^{-7}$
$[HPO_4^{2-}] = 9.8 \times 10^{-2}\ M$

17.116 pH = 8.07

17.118 pH = 12.93

17.120 (a) 2.87 (b) 4.44 (c) 4.74 (d) 8.72

Chapter 18

Practice Exercises

18.1 $Ba_3(PO_4)_2(s) \rightleftharpoons 3Ba^{2+}(aq) + 2PO_4^{3+}(aq)$
$K_{sp} = [Ba^{2+}]^3[PO_4^{3+}]^2$

18.2 (a) $K_{sp} = [Ca^{2+}][C_2O_4^{2-}]$ (b) $K_{sp} = [Ag^+]^2[SO_4^{2-}]$

18.3 3.2×10^{-10}

18.4 3.98×10^{-8}

18.5 2.78×10^{-18}

18.6 (a) $7.3 \times 10^{-7}\ M$ (b) $1.3 \times 10^{-4}\ M$

18.7 $4.5 \times 10^{-5}\ M$

18.8 $2.1 \times 10^{-16}\ M$ in $0.2\ M$ CaI_2, $9.2 \times 10^{-9}\ M$ in pure water

18.9 $2.24 \times 10^{-35}\ M$

18.10 7.5×10^{-5}, a precipitate will form

18.11 7.8×10^{-13}, no precipitate will form

18.12 $PbSO_4$, precipitate will form

18.13 $PbCl_2$, no precipitate will form

18.14 $[SO_4^{2-}] > 2.2 \times 10^{-9}\ M$ and $[SO_4^{2-}] < 2.0 \times 10^{-4}\ M$

18.15 $7.4 \times 10^{-6}\ M < [OH^-] < 5.0 \times 10^{-3}\ M$

18.16 CoS would precipitate

18.17 pH = 2.9
18.18 $[H^+] = 1.54 \times 10^{-1}$
18.19 Between pH = 5.34 and pH = 6.14
18.20 $4.9 \times 10^{-3} M$, $1.3 \times 10^{-5} M$
18.21 4.1 mol

Review Problems

18.18 (a) $K_{sp} = [Ca^{2+}][F^-]^2$ **(d)** $K_{sp} = [Fe^{3+}][OH^-]^3$
(b) $K_{sp} = [Ag^+]^2[CO_3^{2-}]$ **(e)** $K_{sp} = [Pb^{2+}][I^-]^2$
(c) $K_{sp} = [Pb^{2+}][SO_4^{2-}]$ **(f)** $K_{sp} = [Cu^{2+}][OH^-]^2$
18.20 $K_{sp} = (0.016)(0.032)^2 = 1.6 \times 10^{-5}$
18.22 $1.05 \times 10^{-5} M$, $K_{sp} = 1.10 \times 10^{-10}$
18.24 $K_{sp} = 1.7 \times 10^{-6}$
18.26 $K_{sp} = 2.8 \times 10^{-18}$
18.28 $MgCO_3$
18.30 $1.2 \times 10^{-2} M$
18.32 $4.2 \times 10^{-6} M$
18.34 LiF
$4.1 \times 10^{-2} M$ = molar solubility of LiF
$7.5 \times 10^{-3} M$ = molar solubility of BaF_2
18.36 2.8×10^{-18}
18.38 7.0×10^{-3} moles/L
18.40 8.0×10^{-7}
18.42 (a) $4.1 \times 10^{-4} M$ **(b)** $8.5 \times 10^{-6} M$ **(c)** $8.5 \times 10^{-7} M$
(d) $5.7 \times 10^{-7} M$
18.44 $5.6 \times 10^{-9} M$
18.46 $[Pb^{2+}] = 1.7 \times 10^{-3} M$
18.48 (a) 3.0×10^{-11} moles/L **(b)** 1.2×10^{-6} moles/L
18.50 2.2 g $Fe(OH)_2$, $[Fe^{2+}] = 2.0 \times 10^{-12} M$
18.52 $4.9 \times 10^{-8} M$
18.54 No precipitate will form.
18.56 (a) No precipitate will form. **(b)** A precipitate will form.
18.58 A precipitate will not form.
18.60 $2.3 \times 10^{-8} M$
18.62 $[H^+] = 0.045 M$, pH = 1.35
18.64 pH range = 4.8–8.1 $Mn(OH)_2$ will be soluble, but some $Cu(OH)_2$ will precipitate out of solution
18.66 pH range = 4.54–6.13
18.68
(a) $Cu^{2+}(aq) + 4Cl^-(aq) \rightleftharpoons CuCl_4^{2-}(aq)$

$$K_{form} = \frac{[CuCl_4^{2-}]}{[Cu^{2+}][Cl^-]^4}$$

(b) $Ag^+(aq) + 2I^-(aq) \rightleftharpoons AgI_2^-(aq)$ $K_{form} = \frac{[AgI_2^-]}{[Ag^+][I^-]^2}$

(c) $Cr^{3+}(aq) + 6NH_3(aq) \rightleftharpoons Cr(NH_3)_6^{3+}(aq)$

$$K_{form} = \frac{[Cr(NH_3)_6^{3+}]}{[Cr^{3+}][NH_3]^6}$$

18.70
(a) $Co^{3+}(aq) + 6NH_3(aq) \rightleftharpoons Co(NH_3)_6^{3+}(aq)$

$$K_{form} = \frac{[Co(NH_3)_6^{3+}]}{[Co^{3+}][NH_3]^6}$$

(b) $Hg^{2+}(aq) + 4I^-(aq) \rightleftharpoons HgI_4^{2-}(aq)$ $K_{form} = \frac{[HgI_4^{2-}]}{[Hg^{2+}][I^-]^4}$

(c) $Fe^{2+}(aq) + 6CN^-(aq) \rightleftharpoons Fe(CN)_6^{4-}(aq)$

$$K_{form} = \frac{[Fe(CN)_6^{4-}]}{[Fe^{2+}][CN^-]^6}$$

18.72 (a) $Co(NH_3)_6^{3+}(aq) \rightleftharpoons Co^{3+}(aq) + 6NH_3(aq)$
(b) $HgI_4^{2-}(aq) \rightleftharpoons Hg^{2+}(aq) + 4I^-(aq)$
(c) $Fe(CN)_6^{4-}(aq) \rightleftharpoons Fe^{2+}(aq) + 6CN^-(aq)$
18.74 4.3×10^{-4}
18.76 412 g NaCN
18.78 2.0×10^{-4} g AgI
18.80 $4.9 \times 10^{-3} M$
18.82 3.7×10^{-11}

Chapter 19

Practice Exercises

19.1 +154 L atm
19.2 Energy is added to the system in the form of work.
19.3 -2.64 kJ ΔE is more exothermic
19.4 -214.6 kJ, 1%
19.5 Negative
19.6 (a) Negative **(b)** positive
19.7 (a) Negative **(b)** negative
19.8 (a) Negative **(b)** negative **(c)** positive
19.9 -99.1 J K^{-1}
19.10 (a) -229 J/K **(b)** -120.9 J/K
19.11 98.3 kJ mol^{-1}
19.12 -1482 kJ
19.13 -30.3 kJ
19.14 (a) -69.7 kJ/mol **(b)** -120.1 kJ/mol
19.15 3596 kJ work for $C_2H_5OH(l)$, 5803 kJ for $C_8H_{18}(l)$, C_8H_{18} is a better fuel on a gram basis.
19.16 788 kJ
19.17 +90.5 J K^{-1}
19.18 614 K (341 °C)
19.19 The reaction should be spontaneous
19.20 We do not expect to see products formed from reactants.
19.21 -4.3 kJ
19.22 +32.8 kJ, -34.7 kJ, the equilibrium shifts to products
19.23 $\Delta G = 0$ the system is at equilibrium
19.24 The reaction will proceed to the right
19.25 -33 kJ
19.26 0.26
19.27 -260.5 kJ for 1-propanol, -88 kJ for 2-bromobutane
19.28 -117 kJ for C_6H_{12}, +255.6 kJ for C_6H_6

Review Problems

19.46 +1.000 kJ, endothermic
19.48 81 J
19.50 (a) $\Delta H° = +24.58$ kJ $\Delta E = 19.6$ kJ
(b) $\Delta H° = -178$ kJ $\Delta E = -175$ kJ
(c) $\Delta H° = 847.6$ kJ $\Delta E = \Delta H°$
(d) $\Delta H° = 65.029$ kJ $\Delta E = \Delta H°$
19.52 $\Delta E = -350$ kJ $\Delta E_{217\,°C} = -354$ kJ
19.54 (a) $\Delta H° = -178$ kJ, spontaneous **(b)** $\Delta H° = -311$ kJ, spontaneous **(c)** $\Delta H° = +1084.3$ kJ, not spontaneous
19.56 (1) The number of moles of products and reactants
(2) The state of the products versus reactants
(3) The complexity of the molecules
19.58 (a) Negative **(b)** negative **(c)** negative **(d)** positive
19.60 (a) -198.3 J/K, not spontaneous **(b)** -332.3 J/K, not spontaneous **(c)** +92.6 J/K, spontaneous **(d)** +14 J/K, spontaneous
(e) +159 J/K, spontaneous

19.62 (a) -52.8 J mol^{-1} K^{-1} **(b)** -868.9 J mol^{-1} K^{-1}
(c) -318 J mol^{-1} K^{-1}
19.64 -269.7 J/K
19.66 -209 kJ/mol
19.68 (a) -82.3 kJ **(b)** -8.8 kJ **(c)** $+70.7$ kJ
19.70 $+0.16$ kJ
19.72 -1299.8 kJ
19.74 333 K
19.76 101 J mol^{-1} K^{-1}
19.78 Spontaneous
19.80 (a) $K_p = 3.63 \times 10^{43}$ **(b)** $K_p = 5.37 \times 10^{-13}$
19.82 The system is not at equilibrium and must shift to the right to reach equilibrium.
19.84 $K_p = 8.000 \times 10^8$
This is a favorable reaction, since the equilibrium lies far to the side favoring products and is worth studying as a method for methane production.
19.86 If $\Delta G° = 0$, $K_c = 1$. If we start with pure products, the value of Q will be infinite (there are zero reactants) and, since $Q > K_c$, the equilibrium will shift toward the reactants, i.e., the pure products will decompose to their reactants.
19.88 1.16×10^3 kJ/mol
19.90 354 kJ/mol
19.92 577.7 kJ/mol
19.94 308.0 kJ/mol
19.96 85 kJ/mol
19.98 The heat of formation of CF$_4$ should be more exothermic than that of CCl$_4$ because more energy is released on formation of a C—F bond than on formation of a C—Cl bond. Also, less energy is needed to form gaseous F atoms than to form gaseous Cl atoms.

Chapter 20

Practice Exercises

20.1 Anode: $Mg(s) \longrightarrow Mg^{2+}(aq) + 2e^-$
Cathode: $Fe^{2+}(aq) + 2e^- \longrightarrow Fe(s)$
Cell notation: $Mg(s) \mid Mg^{2+}(aq) \parallel Fe^{2+}(aq) \mid Fe(s)$

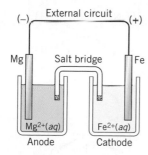

20.2 Anode: $Al(s) \longrightarrow Al^{3+}(aq) + 3e^-$
Cathode: $Ni^{2+}(aq) + 2e^- \longrightarrow Ni(s)$
Overall: $3Ni^{2+}(aq) + 2Al(s) \longrightarrow 2Al^{3+}(aq) + 3Ni(s)$
20.3 Zinc
20.4 -0.44 V
20.5 (a) $2I^-(aq) + 2Fe^{3+}(aq) \longrightarrow I_2(aq) + 2Fe^{2+}(aq)$
(b) $3Mg(s) + 2Cr^{3+}(aq) \longrightarrow 3Mg^{2+}(aq) + 2Cr(s)$
(c) $SO_4^{2-}(aq) + 4H^+(aq) + Co(s) \longrightarrow$
$\qquad\qquad\qquad H_2SO_3(aq) + H_2O + Co^{2+}(aq)$
20.6 $Br_2(aq) + H_2SO_3(aq) + H_2O \longrightarrow$
$\qquad\qquad 2Br^-(aq) + SO_4^{2-}(aq) + 4H^+(aq)$

20.7 Non-spontaneous
$Ni(s) + 2Fe^{3+}(aq) \longrightarrow Ni^{2+}(aq) + 2Fe^{2+}(aq)$
20.8 $NiO_2(s) + Fe(s) + 2H_2O \longrightarrow Ni(OH)_2(s) + Fe(OH)_2(s)$
$\qquad\qquad\qquad\qquad\qquad\qquad E°_{cell} = 1.37$ V
20.9 $5Cr(s) + 3MnO_4^-(aq) + 24H^+(aq) \longrightarrow$
$\qquad 3Mn^{2+}(aq) + 12H_2O(l) + 5Cr^{3+}(aq)$
$\qquad\qquad\qquad\qquad\qquad\qquad E°_{cell} = 2.25$ V
20.10 $3Cu^{2+}(aq) + 2Cr(s) \longrightarrow 3Cu(s) + 2Cr^{3+}(aq)$
$\qquad\qquad\qquad\qquad\qquad\qquad E°_{cell} = 1.08$ V
20.11 (a) Spontaneous **(b)** spontaneous
20.12 (a) Non-spontaneous **(b)** spontaneous
20.13 3 electrons
20.14 For 20.11 **(a)** -102 kJ **(b)** -343 kJ
$\qquad$ For 20.12 **(a)** 108 kJ **(b)** -11.6 kJ
20.15 $K_c = 2.7 \times 10^{-16}$, K $= 3.7 \times 10^{15}$
20.16 $K = \dfrac{1}{[Ag^+][Br^-]}$
$\qquad 2.23 \times 10^{12}$
20.17 $Cu^{2+}(aq) + Mg(s) \longrightarrow Cu(s) + Mg^{2+}(aq)$ 2.82 V
20.18 pH $= 2.37$
20.19 1.04 V
20.20 $[Mg^{2+}] = 2.95 \times 10^{-5}$ M
20.21 Sample 1 (0.57 V): $[Cu^{2+}] = 9.6 \times 10^{-6}$ M,
$\qquad$ sample 2 (0.82 V): $[Cu^{2+}] = 3.4 \times 10^{-14}$ M
20.22 $[Cr^{3+}] = 6.6 \times 10^{-4}$ M
20.23 I_2 will be produced at the anode
20.24 Sn(s) will be produced at the cathode
20.25 7.46×10^{-3} mol OH$^-$
20.26 7.33 min
20.27 3.67 A
20.28 0.0187 M

Review Problems

20.50 (a) $Cd(s) \longrightarrow Cd^{2+}(aq) + 2e^-$
$\qquad Au^{3+}(aq) + 3e^- \longrightarrow Au(s)$
$\qquad 3Cd(s) + 2Au^{3+}(aq) \longrightarrow 3Cd^{2+}(aq) + 2Au(s)$
(b) $Fe(s) \longrightarrow Fe^{2+}(aq) + 2e^-$
$\qquad Br_2(aq) + 2e^- \longrightarrow 2Br^-(aq)$
$\qquad Fe(s) + Br_2(aq) \longrightarrow Fe^{2+}(aq) + 2Br^-(aq)$
(c) $Cr(s) \longrightarrow Cr^{3+}(aq) + 3e^-$
$\qquad Cu^{2+}(aq) + 2e^- \longrightarrow Cu(s)$
$\qquad 2Cr(s) + 3Cu^{2+}(aq) \longrightarrow 2Cr^{3+}(aq) + 3Cu(s)$
20.52 (a) $Pt(s) \mid Fe^{2+}(aq), Fe^{3+}(aq) \parallel NO_3^-(aq), H^+(aq) \mid NO(g) \mid Pt(s)$
(b) $Pt(s) \mid Br_2(aq), Br^-(aq) \parallel Cl^-(aq), Cl_2(g) \mid Pt(s)$
(c) $Ag(s) \mid Ag^+(aq) \parallel Au^{3+}(aq) \mid Au(s)$
20.54 (a) Sn(s) **(b)** Br$^-(aq)$ **(c)** Zn(s) **(d)** I$^-(aq)$
20.56 (a) $E°_{cell} = 0.19$ V **(b)** $E°_{cell} = -0.29$ V **(c)** $E°_{cell} = 0.62$ V
20.58 (a) Spontaneous **(b)** spontaneous **(c)** spontaneous
20.60 $BrO_3^-(aq) + 6I^-(aq) + 6H^+(aq) \longrightarrow$
$\qquad 3I_2(s) + Br^-(aq) + 3H_2O, \qquad F_c = 0.90$ V
20.62 $4HOCl(aq) + 2H^+(aq) + S_2O_3^{2-}(aq) \longrightarrow$
$\qquad\qquad 2Cl_2(g) + H_2O + 2H_2SO_3(aq)$
20.64 Non-spontaneous
20.66 1.0×10^2 kJ
20.68 (a) $E°_{cell} = 0.54$ V **(b)** -5.2×10^2 kJ **(c)** 2.1×10^{91}
20.70 0.31
20.72 2.38 V
20.74 $[Cd^{2+}] = 2.86 \times 10^{-15}$ M
20.76 $K_{sp} = 8.66 \times 10^{-14}$

20.78 $E^\circ_{cell} = 0.090$ V $E^{348\,K}_{cell} = 0.105$ V
20.80 (a) 0.40 mol e^- (b) 0.70 mol e^- (c) 4.50 mol e^-
(d) 5.0×10^{-2} mol e^-
20.82 2.68 g $Fe(OH)_2$
20.84 51.5 hr
20.86 66.2 amp
20.88 0.0996 M
20.90 H_2 and O_2, $2H_2O \longrightarrow 2H_2(g) + O_2(g)$
20.92 Cu and Br_2, $Cu^{2+} + 2Br^- \longrightarrow Br_2 + Cu(s)$
20.94 Al^{3+}, Mg^{2+}, Na^+, Ca^{2+}, K^+, and Li^+

Chapter 21

Practice Exercises

21.1 45.9 g
21.2 46.5 g
21.3 0.166974 u
21.4 9.965×10^{-12} J/nucleon
21.5 $^{226}_{88}Ra \longrightarrow {}^{222}_{86}Rn + {}^{4}_{2}He + {}^{0}_{0}\gamma$ An alpha particle is emitted.
21.6 $^{90}_{38}Sr \longrightarrow {}^{90}_{39}Y + {}^{0}_{-1}e$
21.7 $^{11}_{6}C \longrightarrow {}^{11}_{5}B + {}^{0}_{1}e + \nu$
21.8 $^{13}_{4}Be \longrightarrow {}^{12}_{4}Be + {}^{1}_{0}n$
21.9 $^{72}_{34}Se + {}^{0}_{-1}e \longrightarrow {}^{72}_{33}As + X\ ray + \nu$
21.10 $^{242}_{96}Cm \longrightarrow {}^{238}_{94}Pu + {}^{4}_{2}He$
21.11 $^{56}_{26}Fe \longrightarrow {}^{59}_{27}Co + {}^{0}_{-1}e$
21.12 50.4% Pu
21.13 7.36×10^4 atoms ^{222}Rn
21.14 20 m
21.15 100 units

Review Problems

21.48 (a) 1.01 kg (b) 3.91 kg (c) 12.3 kg
21.50 1.11×10^{-11} g
21.52 3.18 ng, $1.77 \times 10^{-8}\%$
21.54 1.8×10^{-13} J per nucleon
21.56 0.5526646 u, 8.2485×10^{-11} J
21.58 (a) $^{211}_{83}Bi$ (b) $^{177}_{72}Hf$ (c) $^{216}_{84}Po$ (d) $^{19}_{9}F$
21.60 (a) $^{242}_{94}Pu \longrightarrow {}^{4}_{2}He + {}^{238}_{92}U$
(b) $^{28}_{12}Mg \longrightarrow {}^{0}_{-1}e + {}^{28}_{13}Al$
(c) $^{26}_{14}Si \longrightarrow {}^{0}_{1}e + {}^{26}_{13}Al$
(d) $^{37}_{18}Ar \longrightarrow {}^{0}_{-1}e + {}^{37}_{17}Cl$
21.62 (a) $^{261}_{102}No$ (b) $^{211}_{82}Pb$ (c) $^{141}_{61}Pm$ (d) $^{179}_{74}W$
21.64 $^{87}_{36}Kr \longrightarrow {}^{86}_{36}Kr + {}^{1}_{0}n$
21.66 The more likely process is positron emission, because this produces a product having a higher neutron-to-proton ratio:
$^{38}_{19}K \longrightarrow {}^{0}_{1}e + {}^{38}_{18}Ar$
21.68 $^{209}_{84}Po \longrightarrow {}^{205}_{82}Pb + {}^{4}_{2}He$
21.70 0.0469 mg
21.72 $^{53}_{24}Cr^*$ forms. The reaction is:
$^{51}_{23}V + {}^{2}_{1}H \longrightarrow {}^{53}_{24}Cr^* \longrightarrow {}^{1}_{1}p + {}^{52}_{23}V$
21.74 $^{80}_{35}Br$
21.76 $^{55}_{26}Fe$; $^{55}_{25}Mn + {}^{1}_{1}p \longrightarrow {}^{1}_{0}n + {}^{55}_{26}Fe$
21.78 $^{70}_{30}Zn + {}^{208}_{82}Pb \longrightarrow {}^{278}_{112}Uub \longrightarrow {}^{1}_{0}n + {}^{277}_{112}Uub$
21.80 6.3 m
21.82 6.6 m
21.84 This is one curie. It is also 3.7×10^{10} Bq
21.86 2.4×10^7 Bq, 650 μCi
21.88 6.9×10^5 s
21.90 3.2%
21.92 2.84×10^{-3} Ci/g

21.94 1.3×10^9 years old
21.96 2.7×10^4 yr
21.98 $^{235}_{92}U + {}^{1}_{0}n \longrightarrow {}^{94}_{38}Sr + {}^{140}_{54}Xe + 2{}^{1}_{0}n$

Chapter 22

Practice Exercises

22.1 $[Ag(S_2O_3)_2]^{3-}$ $(NH_4)_3Ag(S_2O_3)_2$
22.2 $AlCl_3 \cdot 6H_2O$ $[Al(H_2O)_6]^{3+}$
22.3 $[CrCl_2(H_2O)_4]^+$ The counter ion would be a halide
22.4 (a) $[SnCl_6]^{2-}$
(b) $(NH_4)_2[Fe(CN)_4(H_2O)_2]$
(c) $OsBr_2(H_2NCH_2CH_2NH_2)_2$ or $OsBr_2(en)_2$
22.5 (a) potassium hexacyanoferrate(III)
(b) dichlorobis(ethylenediamine)chromium(III) sulfate
(c) hexaaquacobalt(II) hexafluorochromate(II)
22.6 Six
22.7 (a) six (b) six (c) six
22.8 (a) four, square planar (b) two, linear

Review Problems

22.40 The net charge is –3, and the formula is $[Fe(CN)_6]^{3-}$, hexacyanoferrate(III) ion
22.42 $[CoCl_2(en)_2]^+$
22.44 (a) $C_2O_4^{2-}$ oxalato (b) S^{2-} sulfido or thio (c) Cl^- chloro
(d) $(CH_3)_2NH$ dimethylamine
22.46 (a) hexaamminenickel(II) chloride
(b) triamminetrichlorochromate(II) ion
(c) hexanitrocobaltate(III) ion
(d) diamminetetracyanomanganate(II) ion
(e) potassium trioxalatoferrate(III) or potassium trisoxalatoferrate(III)
22.48 (a) $[Fe(CN)_2(H_2O)_4]^+$
(b) $[Ni(C_2O_4)(NH_3)_4]$
(c) $[Al(OH)(H_2O)_5]Cl_2$
(d) $K_3[Mn(SCN)_6]$
(e) $[CuCl_4]^{2-}$
22.50 Coordination number is six, oxidation number is +2.
22.52 (a)

(b)

The curved lines represent the backbone of the oxalate ion.
22.54

The curved lines represent $-CH_2-C(=O)-$ groups.

22.56 Since both are the *cis* isomer, they are identical.

22.58

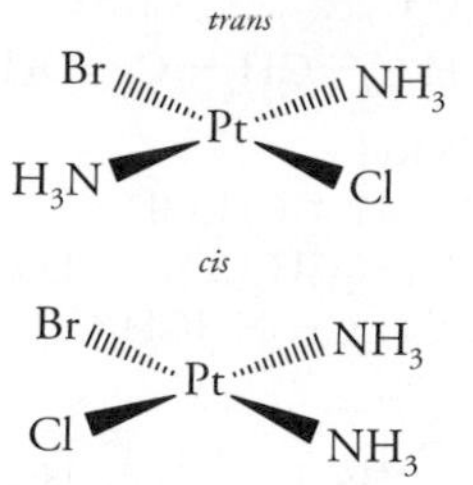

trans / cis Pt complex structures

22.60

Co complex structures

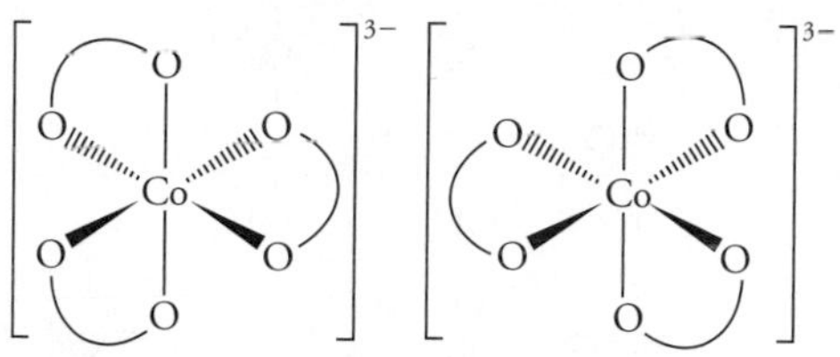

22.62 (a) $[Cr(H_2O)_6]^{3+}$ **(b)** $[Cr(en)_3]^{3+}$
22.64 $[Cr(CN)_6]^{3-}$
22.66 (a) $[RuCl(NH_3)_5]^{3+}$
  (b) $[Ru(NH_3)_6]^{3+}$
22.68 CoA_6^{2+}, Λ produces a larger crystal filed splitting than B, so you are removing a higher energy electron in CoA_6^{2+} than in CoB_6^{2+}.
22.70 High-spin d^7; it cannot be diamagnetic.

| Chapter 23

Practice Exercises

23.1 2,2-dimethylpropane
23.2 (a) 3-methylhexane
  (b) 4-ethyl-2,3-dimethylheptane
  (c) 5-ethyl-2,4,6-trimethyloctane
23.3

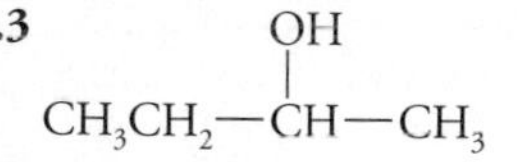

$CH_3CH_2-CH-CH_3$ with OH

23.4 (a)

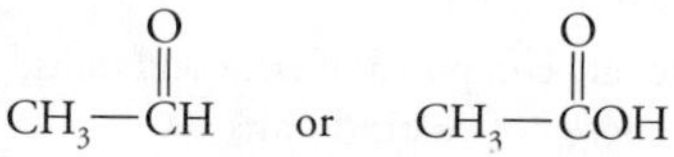

CH_3-CH or CH_3-COH

  (b)

$CH_3CH_2CCH_2CH_3$

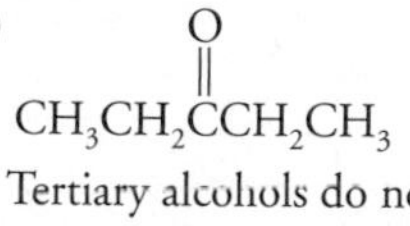

  (c) Tertiary alcohols do not undergo oxidation in the same manner as primary and secondary alcohols.

23.5 (a)

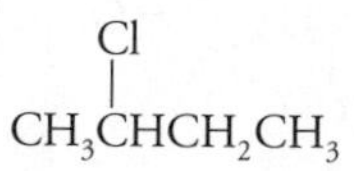

$CH_3CHCH_2CH_3$ with Cl

  (b) $CH_3CH=CH_2$

23.6

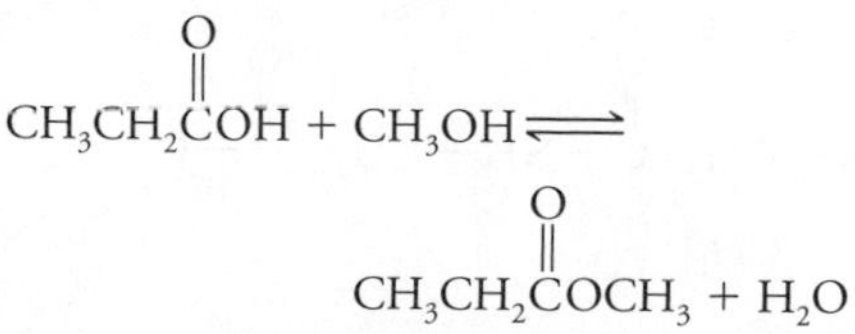

$CH_3CH_2COH + CH_3OH \rightleftharpoons$
$CH_3CH_2COCH_3 + H_2O$
methylpropanoate

23.7 (a)

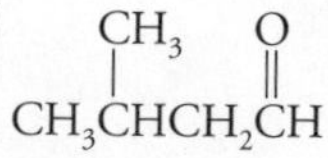

CH_3CHCH_2CH with CH_3

  (b)

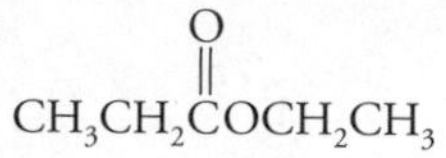

$CH_3CH_2COCH_2CH_3$

  (c)

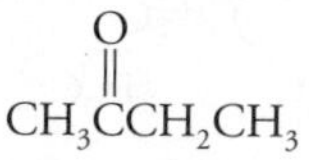

$CH_3CCH_2CH_3$

23.8

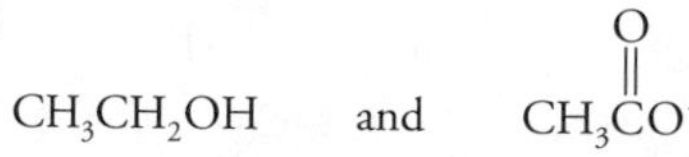

CH_3CH_2OH and CH_3CO^-

23.9

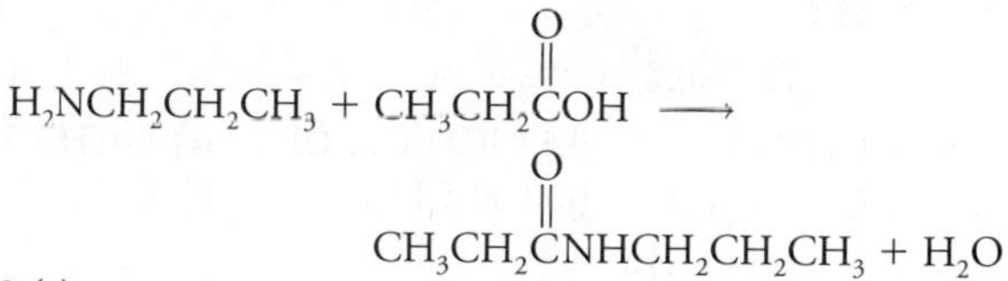

$H_2NCH_2CH_2CH_3 + CH_3CH_2COH \longrightarrow$
$CH_3CH_2CNHCH_2CH_2CH_3 + H_2O$

23.10 (a)

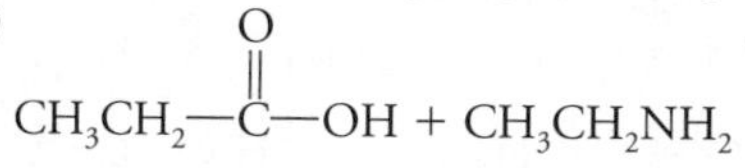

$CH_3CH_2-C-OH + CH_3CH_2NH_2$

  (b)

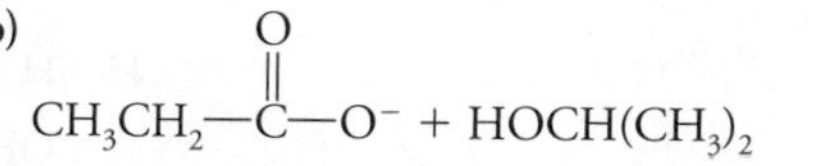

$CH_3CH_2-C-O^- + HOCH(CH_3)_2$

  (c) $CH_3CH_2CH=CH_2$

23.11

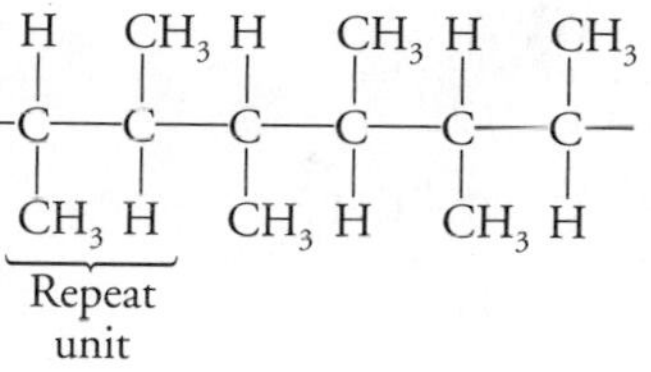

Polymer repeat unit structure

23.12

Fluorinated polymer repeat unit structure

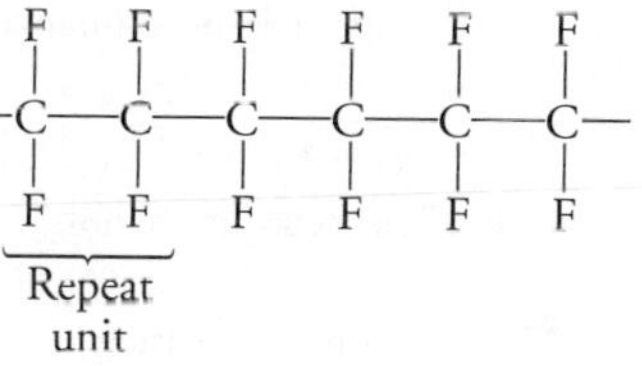

Review Problems

23.91 (a)

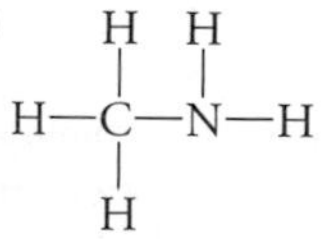

  (b)

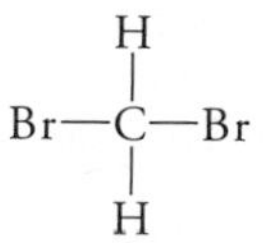

  (c)

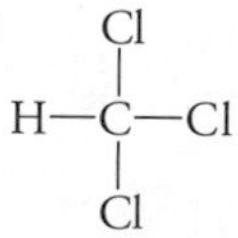

  (d)

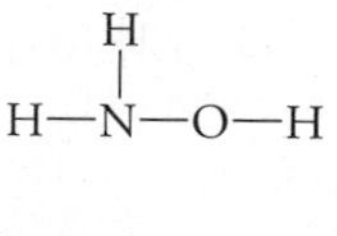

  (e) $H-C\equiv C-H$ **(f)**

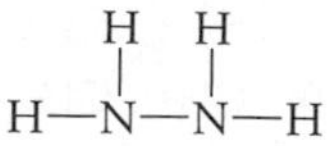

23.93 (a) alkene **(d)** carboxylic acid
  (b) alcohol **(e)** amine
  (c) ester **(f)** alcohol
23.95 b, e, and f
23.97 (a) amine **(b)** amine **(c)** amide **(d)** amine, ketone
23.99 (a) Identical **(b)** identical **(c)** unrelated
  (d) isomers **(e)** identical **(f)** identical
  (g) isomers
23.101 (a) pentane **(b)** 2-methylpentane **(c)** 2,4-dimethylhexane

23.103 (a) No isomers

(b)

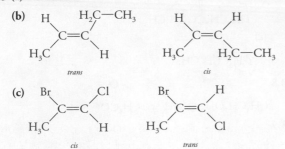

trans *cis*

(c)

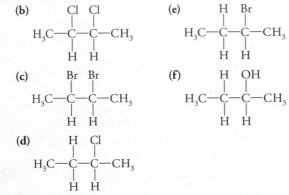

cis *trans*

23.105 (a) CH_3CH_3 **(b)** $ClCH_2CH_2Cl$ **(c)** $BrCH_2CH_2Br$
(d) CH_3CH_2Cl **(e)** CH_3CH_2Br **(f)** CH_3CH_2OH

23.107 (a) $CH_3CH_2CH_2CH_3$

(b)

$$H_3C-\overset{\overset{Cl}{|}}{\underset{\underset{H}{|}}{C}}-\overset{\overset{Cl}{|}}{\underset{\underset{H}{|}}{C}}-CH_3$$

(c)

$$H_3C-\overset{\overset{Br}{|}}{\underset{\underset{H}{|}}{C}}-\overset{\overset{Br}{|}}{\underset{\underset{H}{|}}{C}}-CH_3$$

(d)

$$H_3C-\overset{\overset{H}{|}}{\underset{\underset{H}{|}}{C}}-\overset{\overset{Cl}{|}}{\underset{\underset{H}{|}}{C}}-CH_3$$

(e)

$$H_3C-\overset{\overset{H}{|}}{\underset{\underset{H}{|}}{C}}-\overset{\overset{Br}{|}}{\underset{\underset{H}{|}}{C}}-CH_3$$

(f)

$$H_3C-\overset{\overset{H}{|}}{\underset{\underset{H}{|}}{C}}-\overset{\overset{OH}{|}}{\underset{\underset{H}{|}}{C}}-CH_3$$

23.109 This sort of reaction would disrupt the π delocalization of the benzene ring. The subsequent loss of resonance energy would not be favorable.

23.111

CH_3OH	IUPAC name = methanol;	common name = methyl alcohol
CH_3CH_2OH	IUPAC name = ethanol;	common name = ethyl alcohol
$CH_3CH_2CH_2OH$	IUPAC name = 1-propanol;	common name = propyl alcohol

$(CH_3)_2COH$ or as shown below

$$H_3C-\overset{\overset{CH_3}{|}}{C}H-OH \quad \text{IUPAC name = 2-propanol;} \quad \text{common name = isopropyl alcohol}$$

23.113 $CH_3CH_2CH_2-O-CH_3$ methyl propyl ether
$CH_3CH_2-O-CH_2CH_3$ diethyl ether
$(CH_3)_2CH-O-CH_3$ methyl 2-propyl ether

23.115 (a) (cyclopentene)   **(b)** (phenyl) $-CH=CH_2$

(c) (phenyl) $-CH=CH_2$

23.117 (a) (cyclopentanone with O)   **(b)** (phenyl) $\overset{\overset{O}{\|}}{C}-CH_3$ **(c)** (phenyl) $-CH_2-\overset{\overset{O}{\|}}{C}H$

23.119 The elimination of water can result in a C=C double bond in two locations:

$CH_2=CHCH_2CH_3$ $CH_3CH=CHCH_3$
1-butene   2-butene

23.121 The aldehyde is more easily oxidized. The product is:

$$H_3C-CH_2-\overset{\overset{O}{\|}}{C}-OH$$

23.123 (a) $CH_3CH_2CO_2H$
(b) $CH_3CH_2CO_2H + CH_3OH$
(c) $Na^+ + CH_3CH_2CH_2CO_2^- + H_2O$

23.125 $CH_3CO_2H + CH_3CH_2NHCH_2CH_3$

23.127

$$\overset{H}{\underset{}{C}}\overset{CH_2}{}\overset{H}{\underset{}{C}}\overset{CH_2}{}\overset{H}{\underset{}{C}}\overset{CH_2}{}$$
$$O \qquad O \qquad O$$
$$C=O \quad C=O \quad C=O$$
$$CH_3 \quad CH_3 \quad CH_3$$

23.129

$$-O-\overset{\overset{O}{\|}}{C}-\text{(benzene ring)}-\overset{\overset{O}{\|}}{C}-O-CH_2-\text{(cyclohexane ring)}-CH_2-$$

23.131

$$H_2C-O-\overset{\overset{O}{\|}}{C}-(CH_2)_7-CH=CH(CH_2)_7CH_3$$
$$|$$
$$HC-O-\overset{\overset{O}{\|}}{C}-(CH_2)_7-CH=CH-CH_2-CH=CH(CH_2)_4CH_3$$
$$|$$
$$H_2C-O-\overset{\overset{O}{\|}}{C}-(CH_2)_{14}CH_3$$

23.133

$$H_2C-O-\overset{\overset{O}{\|}}{C}-(CH_2)_{16}CH_3$$
$$|$$
$$HC-O-\overset{\overset{O}{\|}}{C}-(CH_2)_{12}CH_3$$
$$|$$
$$H_2C-O-\overset{\overset{O}{\|}}{C}-(CH_2)_{16}CH_3$$

23.135 Hydrophobic sites are composed of fatty acid units. Hydrophilic sites are composed of charged units.

23.137

$$^+H_3N-CH_2-\overset{\overset{O}{\|}}{C}-NH-CH_2-\overset{\overset{O}{\|}}{C}-O^-$$

23.139

$$^+H_3N-CH_2-\overset{\overset{O}{\|}}{C}-NH-\overset{\underset{\underset{CH_2}{|}}{|}}{C}H-\overset{\overset{O}{\|}}{C}-O^-$$
(phenyl)

$$^+H_3N-\overset{\underset{\underset{CH_2}{|}}{|}}{C}H-\overset{\overset{O}{\|}}{C}-NH-CH_2-\overset{\overset{O}{\|}}{C}-O^-$$
(phenyl)

Tables of Selected Data

Table C.1	Electron Configurations of the Elements

Atomic Number			Atomic Number			Atomic Number		
1	H	$1s^1$	41	Nb	[Kr] $5s^1 4d^4$	81	Tl	[Xe] $6s^2 4f^{14} 5d^{10} 6p^1$
2	He	$1s^2$	42	Mo	[Kr] $5s^1 4d^5$	82	Pb	[Xe] $6s^2 4f^{14} 5d^{10} 6p^2$
3	Li	[He] $2s^1$	43	Tc	[Kr] $5s^2 4d^5$	83	Bi	[Xe] $6s^2 4f^{14} 5d^{10} 6p^3$
4	Be	[He] $2s^2$	44	Ru	[Kr] $5s^1 4d^7$	84	Po	[Xe] $6s^2 4f^{14} 5d^{10} 6p^4$
5	B	[He] $2s^2 2p^1$	45	Rh	[Kr] $5s^1 4d^8$	85	At	[Xe] $6s^2 4f^{14} 5d^{10} 6p^5$
6	C	[He] $2s^2 2p^2$	46	Pd	[Kr] $4d^{10}$	86	Rn	[Xe] $6s^2 4f^{14} 5d^{10} 6p^6$
7	N	[He] $2s^2 2p^3$	47	Ag	[Kr] $5s^1 4d^{10}$	87	Fr	[Rn] $7s^1$
8	O	[He] $2s^2 2p^4$	48	Cd	[Kr] $5s^2 4d^{10}$	88	Ra	[Rn] $7s^2$
9	F	[He] $2s^2 2p^5$	49	In	[Kr] $5s^2 4d^{10} 5p^1$	89	Ac	[Rn] $7s^2 6d^1$
10	Ne	[He] $2s^2 2p^6$	50	Sn	[Kr] $5s^2 4d^{10} 5p^2$	90	Th	[Rn] $7s^2 6d^2$
11	Na	[Ne] $3s^1$	51	Sb	[Kr] $5s^2 4d^{10} 5p^3$	91	Pa	[Rn] $7s^2 5f^2 6d^1$
12	Mg	[Ne] $3s^2$	52	Te	[Kr] $5s^2 4d^{10} 5p^4$	92	U	[Rn] $7s^2 5f^3 6d^1$
13	Al	[Ne] $3s^2 3p^1$	53	I	[Kr] $5s^2 4d^{10} 5p^5$	93	Np	[Rn] $7s^2 5f^4 6d^1$
14	Si	[Ne] $3s^2 3p^2$	54	Xe	[Kr] $5s^2 4d^{10} 5p^6$	94	Pu	[Rn] $7s^2 5f^6$
15	P	[Ne] $3s^2 3p^3$	55	Cs	[Xe] $6s^1$	95	Am	[Rn] $7s^2 5f^7$
16	S	[Ne] $3s^2 3p^4$	56	Ba	[Xe] $6s^2$	96	Cm	[Rn] $7s^2 5f^7 6d^1$
17	Cl	[Ne] $3s^2 3p^5$	57	La	[Xe] $6s^2 5d^1$	97	Bk	[Rn] $7s^2 5f^9$
18	Ar	[Ne] $3s^2 3p^6$	58	Ce	[Xe] $6s^2 4f^1 5d^1$	98	Cf	[Rn] $7s^2 5f^{10}$
19	K	[Ar] $4s^1$	59	Pr	[Xe] $6s^2 4f^3$	99	Es	[Rn] $7s^2 5f^{11}$
20	Ca	[Ar] $4s^2$	60	Nd	[Xe] $6s^2 4f^4$	100	Fm	[Rn] $7s^2 5f^{12}$
21	Sc	[Ar] $4s^2 3d^1$	61	Pm	[Xe] $6s^2 4f^5$	101	Md	[Rn] $7s^2 5f^{13}$
22	Ti	[Ar] $4s^2 3d^2$	62	Sm	[Xe] $6s^2 4f^6$	102	No	[Rn] $7s^2 5f^{14}$
23	V	[Ar] $4s^2 3d^3$	63	Eu	[Xe] $6s^2 4f^7$	103	Lr	[Rn] $7s^2 5f^{14} 6d^1$
24	Cr	[Ar] $4s^1 3d^5$	64	Gd	[Xe] $6s^2 4f^7 5d^1$	104	Rf	[Rn] $7s^2 5f^{14} 6d^2$
25	Mn	[Ar] $4s^2 3d^5$	65	Tb	[Xe] $6s^2 4f^9$	105	Db	[Rn] $7s^2 5f^{14} 6d^3$
26	Fe	[Ar] $4s^2 3d^6$	66	Dy	[Xe] $6s^2 4f^{10}$	106	Sg	[Rn] $7s^2 5f^{14} 6d^4$
27	Co	[Ar] $4s^2 3d^7$	67	Ho	[Xe] $6s^2 4f^{11}$	107	Bh	[Rn] $7s^2 5f^{14} 6d^5$
28	Ni	[Ar] $4s^2 3d^8$	68	Er	[Xe] $6s^2 4f^{12}$	108	Hs	[Rn] $7s^2 5f^{14} 6d^6$
29	Cu	[Ar] $4s^1 3d^{10}$	69	Tm	[Xe] $6s^2 4f^{13}$	109	Mt	[Rn] $7s^2 5f^{14} 6d^7$
30	Zn	[Ar] $4s^2 3d^{10}$	70	Yb	[Xe] $6s^2 4f^{14}$	110	Ds	[Rn] $7s^2 5f^{14} 6d^8$
31	Ga	[Ar] $4s^2 3d^{10} 4p^1$	71	Lu	[Xe] $6s^2 4f^{14} 5d^1$	111	Rg	[Rn] $7s^2 5f^{14} 6d^9$
32	Ge	[Ar] $4s^2 3d^{10} 4p^2$	72	Hf	[Xe] $6s^2 4f^{14} 5d^2$	112	Cn	[Rn] $7s^2 5f^{14} 6d^{10}$
33	As	[Ar] $4s^2 3d^{10} 4p^3$	73	Ta	[Xe] $6s^2 4f^{14} 5d^3$	113	Uut	[Rn] $7s^2 5f^{14} 6d^{10} 7p^1$
34	Se	[Ar] $4s^2 3d^{10} 4p^4$	74	W	[Xe] $6s^2 4f^{14} 5d^4$	114	Uuq	[Rn] $7s^2 5f^{14} 6d^{10} 7p^2$
35	Br	[Ar] $4s^2 3d^{10} 4p^5$	75	Re	[Xe] $6s^2 4f^{14} 5d^5$	115	Uup	[Rn] $7s^2 5f^{14} 6d^{10} 7p^3$
36	Kr	[Ar] $4s^2 3d^{10} 4p^6$	76	Os	[Xe] $6s^2 4f^{14} 5d^6$	116	Uuh	[Rn] $7s^2 5f^{14} 6d^{10} 7p^4$
37	Rb	[Kr] $5s^1$	77	Ir	[Xe] $6s^2 4f^{14} 5d^7$	117	Uus	[Rn] $7s^2 5f^{14} 6d^{10} 7p^5$
38	Sr	[Kr] $5s^2$	78	Pt	[Xe] $6s^1 4f^{14} 5d^9$	118	Uuo	[Rn] $7s^2 5f^{14} 6d^{10} 7p^6$
39	Y	[Kr] $5s^2 4d^1$	79	Au	[Xe] $6s^1 4f^{14} 5d^{10}$			
40	Zr	[Kr] $5s^2 4d^2$	80	Hg	[Xe] $6s^2 4f^{14} 5d^{10}$			

Table C.2 — Thermodynamic Data for Selected Elements, Compounds, and Ions (25 °C)

Substance	ΔH_f° (kJ mol^{-1})	S° (J mol^{-1} K^{-1})	ΔG_f° (kJ mol^{-1})	Substance	ΔH_f° (kJ mol^{-1})	S° (J mol^{-1} K^{-1})	ΔG_f° (kJ mol^{-1})
Aluminum				$CdCl_2(s)$	−392	115	−344
$Al(s)$	0	28.3	0	$CdO(s)$	−258.2	54.8	−228.4
$Al^{3+}(aq)$	−524.7		−481.2	$CdS(s)$	−162	64.9	−156
$AlCl_3(s)$	−704	110.7	−629	$CdSO_4(s)$	−933.5	123	−822.6
$Al_2O_3(s)$	−1669.8	51.0	−1576.4	**Calcium**			
$Al_2(SO_4)_3(s)$	−3441	239	−3100	$Ca(s)$	0	41.4	0
Arsenic				$Ca^{2+}(aq)$	−542.83	−53.1	−553.58
$As(s)$	0	35.1	0	$CaCO_3(s)$	−1207	92.9	−1128.8
$AsH_3(g)$	+66.4	223	+68.9	$CaF_2(s)$	−741	80.3	−1166
$As_4O_6(s)$	−1314	214	−1153	$CaCl_2(s)$	−795.0	114	−750.2
$As_2O_5(s)$	−925	105	−782	$CaBr_2(s)$	−682.8	130	−663.6
$H_3AsO_3(aq)$	−742.2			$CaI_2(s)$	−535.9	143	
$H_3AsO_4(aq)$	−902.5			$CaO(s)$	−635.5	40	−604.2
Barium				$Ca(OH)_2(s)$	−986.59	76.1	−896.76
$Ba(s)$	0	66.9	0	$Ca_3(PO_4)_2(s)$	−4119	241	−3852
$Ba^{2+}(aq)$	−537.6	9.6	−560.8	$CaSO_3(s)$	−1156		
$BaCO_3(s)$	−1219	112	−1139	$CaSO_4(s)$	−1433	107	−1320.3
$BaCrO_4(s)$	−1428.0			$CaSO_4 \cdot \frac{1}{2}H_2O(s)$	−1575.2	131	−1435.2
$BaCl_2(s)$	−860.2	125	−810.8	$CaSO_4 \cdot 2H_2O(s)$	−2021.1	194.0	−1795.7
$BaO(s)$	−553.5	70.4	−525.1	**Carbon**			
$Ba(OH)_2(s)$	−998.22	−8	−875.3	$C(s, \text{graphite})$	0	5.69	0
$Ba(NO_3)_2(s)$	−992	214	−795	$C(s, \text{diamond})$	+1.88	2.4	+2.9
$BaSO_4(s)$	−1465	132	−1353	$CCl_4(l)$	−134	214.4	−65.3
Beryllium				$CO(g)$	−110.5	197.9	−137.3
$Be(s)$	0	9.50	0	$CO_2(g)$	−393.5	213.6	−394.4
$BeCl_2(s)$	−468.6	89.9	−426.3	$CO_2(aq)$	−413.8	117.6	−385.98
$BeO(s)$	−611	14	−582	$H_2CO_3(aq)$	−699.65	187.4	−623.08
Bismuth				$HCO_3^-(aq)$	−691.99	91.2	−586.77
$Bi(s)$	0	56.9	0	$CO_3^{2-}(aq)$	−677.14	−56.9	−527.81
$BiCl_3(s)$	−379	177	−315	$CS_2(l)$	+89.5	151.3	+65.3
$Bi_2O_3(s)$	−576	151	−497	$CS_2(g)$	+117	237.7	+67.2
Boron				$HCN(g)$	+135.1	201.7	+124.7
$B(s)$	0	5.87	0	$CN^-(aq)$	+150.6	94.1	+172.4
$BCl_3(g)$	−404	290	−389	$CH_4(g)$	−74.848	186.2	−50.79
$B_2H_6(g)$	+36	232	+87	$C_2H_2(g)$	+226.75	200.8	+209
$B_2O_3(s)$	−1273	53.8	−1194	$C_2H_4(g)$	+52.284	219.8	+68.12
$B(OH)_3(s)$	−1094	88.8	−969	$C_2H_6(g)$	−84.667	229.5	−32.9
Bromine				$C_3H_8(g)$	−104	269.9	−23
$Br_2(l)$	0	152.2	0	$C_4H_{10}(g)$	−126	310.2	−17.0
$Br_2(g)$	+30.9	245.4	+3.11	$C_6H_6(l)$	+49.0	173.3	+124.3
$HBr(g)$	−36	198.5	+53.1	$CH_3OH(l)$	−238.6	126.8	−166.2
$Br^-(aq)$	−121.55	82.4	−103.96	$C_2H_5OH(l)$	−277.63	161	−174.8
Cadmium				$HCHO_2(g)$	−363	251	+335
$Cd(s)$	0	51.8	0	$HC_2H_3O_2(l)$	−487.0	160	−392.5
$Cd^{2+}(aq)$	−75.90	−73.2	−77.61	$HCHO(g)$	−108.6	218.8	−102.5
				$CH_3CHO(g)$	−167	250	−129

(Continued)

Table C.2 — Thermodynamic Data for Selected Elements, Compounds, and Ions (25 °C) (Continued)

Substance	ΔH_f° (kJ mol^{-1})	S° (J mol^{-1} K^{-1})	ΔG_f° (kJ mol^{-1})	Substance	ΔH_f° (kJ mol^{-1})	S° (J mol^{-1} K^{-1})	ΔG_f° (kJ mol^{-1})
$(CH_3)_2CO(l)$	−248.1	200.4	−155.4	**Hydrogen**			
$C_6H_5CO_2H(s)$	−385.1	167.6	−245.3	$H_2(g)$	0	130.6	0
$CO(NH_2)_2(s)$	−333.19	104.6	−197.2	$H_2O(l)$	−285.9	69.96	−237.2
$CO(NH_2)_2(aq)$	−391.2	173.8	−203.8	$H_2O(g)$	−241.8	188.7	−228.6
$CH_2(NH_2)CO_2H(s)$	−532.9	103.5	−373.4	$H_2O_2(l)$	−187.6	109.6	−120.3
				$H_2Se(g)$	+76	219	+62.3
Chlorine				$H_2Tc(g)$	+154	234	+138
$Cl_2(g)$	0	223.0	0				
$Cl^-(aq)$	−167.2	56.5	−131.2	**Iodine**			
$HCl(g)$	−92.30	186.7	−95.27	$I_2(s)$	0	116.1	0
$HCl(aq)$	−167.2	56.5	−131.2	$I_2(g)$	+62.4	260.7	+19.3
$HClO(aq)$	−131.3	106.8	−80.21	$HI(g)$	+26.6	206	+1.30
Chromium				**Iron**			
$Cr(s)$	0	23.8	0	$Fe(s)$	0	27	0
$Cr^{3+}(aq)$	−232			$Fe^{2+}(aq)$	−89.1	−137.7	−78.9
$CrCl_2(s)$	−326	115	−282	$Fe^{3+}(aq)$	−48.5	−315.9	−4.7
$CrCl_3(s)$	−563.2	126	−493.7	$Fe_2O_3(s)$	−822.2	90.0	−741.0
$Cr_2O_3(s)$	−1141	81.2	−1059	$Fe_3O_4(s)$	−1118.4	146.4	−1015.4
$CrO_3(s)$	−585.8	72.0	−506.2	$FeS(s)$	−100.0	60.3	−100.4
$(NH_4)_2Cr_2O_7(s)$	−1807			$FeS_2(s)$	−178.2	52.9	−166.9
$K_2Cr_2O_7(s)$	−2033.01						
				Lead			
Cobalt				$Pb(s)$	0	64.8	0
$Co(s)$	0	30.0	0	$Pb^{2+}(aq)$	−1.7	10.5	−24.4
$Co^{2+}(aq)$	−59.4	−110	−53.6	$PbCl_2(s)$	−359.4	136	−314.1
$CoCl_2(s)$	−325.5	106	−282.4	$PbO(s)$	−219.2	67.8	−189.3
$Co(NO_3)_2(s)$	−422.2	192	−230.5	$PbO_2(s)$	−277	68.6	−219
$CoO(s)$	−237.9	53.0	−214.2	$Pb(OH)_2(s)$	−515.9	88	−420.9
$CoS(s)$	−80.8	67.4	−82.8	$PbS(s)$	−100	91.2	−98.7
				$PbSO_4(s)$	−920.1	149	−811.3
Copper							
$Cu(s)$	0	33.15	0	**Lithium**			
$Cu^{2+}(aq)$	+64.77	−99.6	+65.49	$Li(s)$	0	28.4	0
$CuCl(s)$	−137.2	86.2	−119.87	$Li^+(aq)$	−278.6	10.3	
$CuCl_2(s)$	−172	119	−131	$LiF(s)$	−611.7	35.7	−583.3
$Cu_2O(s)$	−168.6	93.1	−146.0	$LiCl(s)$	−408	59.29	−383.7
$CuO(s)$	−155	42.6	−127	$LiBr(s)$	−350.3	66.9	−338.87
$Cu_2S(s)$	−79.5	121	−86.2	$Li_2O(s)$	−596.5	37.9	−560.5
$CuS(s)$	−53.1	66.5	−53.6	$Li_3N(s)$	−199	37.7	−155.4
$CuSO_4(s)$	−771.4	109	−661.8				
$CuSO_4 \cdot 5H_2O(s)$	−2279.7	300.4	−1879.7	**Magnesium**			
				$Mg(s)$	0	32.5	0
Fluorine				$Mg^{2+}(aq)$	−466.9	−138.1	−454.8
$F_2(g)$	0	202.7	0	$MgCO_3(s)$	−1113	65.7	−1029
$F^-(aq)$	−332.6	−13.8	−278.8	$MgF_2(s)$	−1124	79.9	−1056
$HF(g)$	−271	173.5	−273	$MgCl_2(s)$	−641.8	89.5	−592.5
				$MgCl_2 \cdot 2H_2O(s)$	−1280	180	−1118
Gold				$Mg_3N_2(s)$	−463.2	87.9	−411
$Au(s)$	0	47.7	0	$MgO(s)$	−601.7	26.9	−569.4
$Au_2O_3(s)$	+80.8	125	+163	$Mg(OH)_2(s)$	−924.7	63.1	−833.9
$AuCl_3(s)$	−118	148	−48.5				

(Continued)

Table C.2   Thermodynamic Data for Selected Elements, Compounds, and Ions (25 °C) *(Continued)*

Substance	ΔH_f° (kJ mol^{-1})	S° (J mol^{-1} K^{-1})	ΔG_f° (kJ mol^{-1})	Substance	ΔH_f° (kJ mol^{-1})	S° (J mol^{-1} K^{-1})	ΔG_f° (kJ mol^{-1})
Manganese				$PCl_3(g)$	−287.0	311.8	−267.8
$Mn(s)$	0	32.0	0	$PCl_5(g)$	−374.9	364.6	−305.0
$Mn^{2+}(aq)$	−223	−74.9	−228	$PH_3(g)$	+5.4	210.2	+12.9
$MnO_4^-(aq)$	−542.7	191	−449.4	$P_4O_6(s)$	−1640		
$KMnO_4(s)$	−813.4	171.71	−713.8	$POCl_3(g)$	−558.5	325.5	−512.9
$MnO(s)$	−385	60.2	−363	$POCl_3(l)$	−597.1	222.5	−520.8
$Mn_2O_3(s)$	−959.8	110	−882.0	$P_4O_{10}(s)$	−2984	228.9	−2698
$MnO_2(s)$	−520.9	53.1	−466.1	$H_3PO_4(s)$	−1279	110.5	−1119
$Mn_3O_4(s)$	−1387	149	−1280				
$MnSO_4(s)$	−1064	112	−956	**Potassium**			
				$K(s)$	0	64.18	0
Mercury				$K^+(aq)$	−252.4	102.5	−283.3
$Hg(l)$	0	76.1	0	$KF(s)$	−567.3	66.6	−537.8
$Hg(g)$	+61.32	175	+31.8	$KCl(s)$	−435.89	82.59	−408.3
$Hg_2Cl_2(s)$	−265.2	192.5	−210.8	$KBr(s)$	−393.8	95.9	−380.7
$HgCl_2(s)$	−224.3	146.0	−178.6	$KI(s)$	−327.9	106.3	−324.9
$HgO(s)$	−90.83	70.3	−58.54	$KOH(s)$	−424.8	78.9	−379.1
$HgS(s, \text{red})$	−58.2	82.4	−50.6	$K_2O(s)$	−361	98.3	−322
				$K_2SO_4(s)$	−1433.7	176	−1316.4
Nickel							
$Ni(s)$	0	30	0	**Silicon**			
$NiCl_2(s)$	−305	97.5	−259	$Si(s)$	0	19	0
$NiO(s)$	−244	38	−216	$SiH_4(g)$	+33	205	+52.3
$NiO_2(s)$			−199	$SiO_2(s, \text{alpha})$	−910.0	41.8	−856
$NiSO_4(s)$	−891.2	77.8	−773.6				
$NiCO_3(s)$	−664.0	91.6	−615.0	**Silver**			
$Ni(CO)_4(g)$	−220	399	−567.4	$Ag(s)$	0	42.55	0
				$Ag^+(aq)$	+105.58	72.68	+77.11
Nitrogen				$AgCl(s)$	−127.0	96.2	−109.7
$N_2(g)$	0	191.5	0	$AgBr(s)$	−100.4	107.1	−96.9
$NH_3(g)$	−46.19	192.5	−16.7	$AgNO_3(s)$	−124	141	−32
$NH_4^+(aq)$	−132.5	113	−79.37	$Ag_2O(s)$	−31.1	121.3	−11.2
$N_2H_4(g)$	+95.40	238.4	+159.3				
$N_2H_4(l)$	+50.6	121.2	+149.4	**Sodium**			
$NH_4Cl(s)$	−315.4	94.6	−203.9	$Na(s)$	0	51.0	0
$NO(g)$	+90.37	210.6	+86.69	$Na^+(aq)$	−240.12	59.0	−261.91
$NO_2(g)$	+33.8	240.5	+51.84	$NaF(s)$	−571	51.5	−545
$N_2O(g)$	+81.57	220.0	+103.6	$NaCl(s)$	−411.0	72.38	−384.0
$N_2O_4(g)$	+9.67	304	+98.28	$NaBr(s)$	−360	83.7	−349
$N_2O_5(g)$	+11	356	+115	$NaI(s)$	−288	91.2	−286
$HNO_3(l)$	−173.2	155.6	−79.91	$NaHCO_3(s)$	−947.7	102	−851.9
$NO_3^-(aq)$	−205.0	146.4	−108.74	$Na_2CO_3(s)$	−1131	136	−1048
				$Na_2O_2(s)$	−510.9	94.6	−447.7
Oxygen				$Na_2O(s)$	−510	72.8	−376
$O_2(g)$	0	205.0	0	$NaOH(s)$	−426.8	64.18	−382
$O_3(g)$	+143	238.8	+163	$Na_2SO_4(s)$	−1384.49	149.49	−1266.83
$OH^-(aq)$	−230.0	−10.75	−157.24				
				Sulfur			
Phosphorus				$S(s, \text{rhombic})$	0	31.9	0
$P(s, \text{white})$	0	41.09	0	$SO_2(g)$	−296.9	248.5	−300.4
$P_4(g)$	+314.6	163.2	+278.3	$SO_3(g)$	−395.2	256.2	−370.4

(Continued)

Table C.2	Thermodynamic Data for Selected Elements, Compounds, and Ions (25 °C) *(Continued)*						
Substance	ΔH_f° (kJ mol^{-1})	S° (J mol^{-1} K^{-1})	ΔG_f° (kJ mol^{-1})	Substance	ΔH_f° (kJ mol^{-1})	S° (J mol^{-1} K^{-1})	ΔG_f° (kJ mol^{-1})
$H_2S(g)$	−20.6	206	−33.6	**Zinc**			
$H_2SO_4(l)$	−811.32	157	−689.9	$Zn(s)$	0	41.6	0
$H_2SO_4(aq)$	−909.3	20.1	−744.5	$Zn^{2+}(aq)$	−153.9	−112.1	−147.06
$SF_6(g)$	−1209	292	−1105	$ZnCl_2(s)$	−415.1	111	−369.4
				$ZnO(s)$	−348.3	43.6	−318.3
Tin				$ZnS(s)$	−205.6	57.7	−201.3
$Sn(s, white)$	0	51.6	0	$ZnSO_4(s)$	−982.8	120	−874.5
$Sn^{2+}(aq)$	−8.8	−17	−27.2				
$SnCl_4(l)$	−511.3	258.6	−440.2				
$SnO(s)$	−285.8	56.5	−256.9				
$SnO_2(s)$	−580.7	52.3	−519.6				

Table C.3	Heats of Formation of Gaseous Atoms from Elements In Their Standard States		
Element	ΔH_f° (kJ mol^{-1})[a]	Element	ΔH_f° (kJ mol^{-1})[a]
Group 1A		**Group 4A**	
H	217.89	C	716.67
Li	161.5	Si	450
Na	107.8		
K	89.62	**Group 5A**	
Rb	82.0	N	472.68
Cs	78.2	P	332.2
Group 2A		**Group 6A**	
Be	324.3	O	249.17
Mg	146.4	S	276.98
Ca	178.2		
Sr	163.6	**Group 7A**	
Ba	177.8	F	79.14
		Cl	121.47
Group 3A		Br	112.38
B	560	I	107.48
Al	329.7		

[a]All values in this table are positive because forming the gaseous atoms from the elements is endothermic: it involves bond breaking.

Table C.4   Average Bond Energies

Bond	Bond Energy (kJ mol^{-1})	Bond	Bond Energy (kJ mol^{-1})
C—C	348	C—Br	276
C=C	612	C—I	238
C≡C	960	H—H	436
C—H	412	H—F	565
C—N	305	H—Cl	431
C=N	613	H—Br	366
C≡N	890	H—I	299
C—O	360	H—N	388
C=O	743	H—O	463
C—F	484	H—S	338
C—Cl	338	H—Si	376

Table C.5   Vapor Pressure of Water as a Function of Temperature

Temp (°C)	Vapor Pressure (torr)	Temp (°C)	Vapor Pressure (torr)	Temp (°C)	Vapor Pressure (torr)	Temp (°C)	Vapor Pressure (torr)
0	4.58	26	25.2	52	102.1	78	327.3
1	4.93	27	26.7	53	107.2	79	341.0
2	5.29	28	28.3	54	112.5	80	355.1
3	5.68	29	30.0	55	118.0	81	369.7
4	6.10	30	31.8	56	123.8	82	384.9
5	6.54	31	33.7	57	129.8	83	400.6
6	7.01	32	35.7	58	136.1	84	416.8
7	7.51	33	37.7	59	142.6	85	433.6
8	8.04	34	39.9	60	149.4	86	450.9
9	8.61	35	41.2	61	156.4	87	468.7
10	9.21	36	44.6	62	163.8	88	487.1
11	9.84	37	47.1	63	171.4	89	506.1
12	10.5	38	49.7	64	179.3	90	525.8
13	11.2	39	52.4	65	187.5	91	546.0
14	12.0	40	55.3	66	196.1	92	567.0
15	12.8	41	58.3	67	205.0	93	588.6
16	13.6	42	61.5	68	214.2	94	610.9
17	14.5	43	64.8	69	223.7	95	633.9
18	15.5	44	68.3	70	233.7	96	657.6
19	16.5	45	71.9	71	243.9	97	682.1
20	17.5	46	75.6	72	254.6	98	707.3
21	18.7	47	79.6	73	265.7	99	733.2
22	19.8	48	83.7	74	277.2	100	760.0
23	21.1	49	88.0	75	289.1		
24	22.4	50	92.5	76	301.4		
25	23.8	51	97.2	77	314.1		

Table C.6   Solubility Product Constants

Salt	K_{sp}	Salt	K_{sp}	Salt	K_{sp}
Fluorides		$Co(OH)_3$	3×10^{-45}	**Carbonates**	
MgF_2	5.2×10^{-11}	$Ni(OH)_2$	5.5×10^{-16}	$MgCO_3$	6.8×10^{-8}
CaF_2	3.4×10^{-11}	$Cu(OH)_2$	4.8×10^{-20}	$CaCO_3$	3.4×10^{-9}
SrF_2	4.3×10^{-9}	$V(OH)_3$	4×10^{-35}	$SrCO_3$	5.6×10^{-10}
BaF_2	1.8×10^{-7}	$Cr(OH)_3$	2×10^{-30}	$BaCO_3$	2.6×10^{-9}
LiF	1.8×10^{-3}	Ag_2O	1.9×10^{-8}	$MnCO_3$	2.2×10^{-11}
PbF_2	3.3×10^{-8}	$Zn(OH)_2$	3×10^{-17}	$FeCO_3$	3.1×10^{-11}
		$Cd(OH)_2$	7.2×10^{-15}	$CoCO_3$	1.0×10^{-10}
Chlorides		$Al(OH)_3$ (alpha form)	3×10^{-34}	$NiCO_3$	1.4×10^{-7}
$CuCl$	1.7×10^{-7}			$CuCO_3$	2.5×10^{-10}
$AgCl$	1.8×10^{-10}	**Cyanides**		Ag_2CO_3	8.5×10^{-12}
Hg_2Cl_2	1.4×10^{-18}	$AgCN$	6.0×10^{-17}	Hg_2CO_3	3.6×10^{-17}
$TlCl$	1.9×10^{-4}	$Zn(CN)_2$	3×10^{-16}	$ZnCO_3$	1.5×10^{-10}
$PbCl_2$	1.7×10^{-5}			$CdCO_3$	1.0×10^{-12}
$AuCl_3$	3.2×10^{-25}	**Sulfites**		$PbCO_3$	7.4×10^{-14}
		$CaSO_3 \cdot \frac{1}{2}H_2O$	3.1×10^{-7}		
Bromides		Ag_2SO_3	1.5×10^{-14}	**Phosphates**	
$CuBr$	6.3×10^{-9}	$BaSO_3$	5.0×10^{-10}	$Ca_3(PO_4)_2$	2.1×10^{-33}
$AgBr$	5.4×10^{-13}			$Mg_3(PO_4)_2$	1.0×10^{-24}
Hg_2Br_2	6.4×10^{-23}	**Sulfates**		$SrHPO_4$	1.2×10^{-7}
$HgBr_2$	6.2×10^{-20}	$CaSO_4$	4.9×10^{-5}	$BaHPO_4$	4.0×10^{-8}
$PbBr_2$	6.6×10^{-6}	$SrSO_4$	3.4×10^{-7}	$LaPO_4$	3.7×10^{-23}
		$BaSO_4$	1.1×10^{-10}	$Fe_3(PO_4)_2$	1×10^{-36}
Iodides		$RaSO_4$	3.7×10^{-11}	Ag_3PO_4	8.9×10^{-17}
CuI	1.3×10^{-12}	Ag_2SO_4	1.2×10^{-5}	$FePO_4$	9.9×10^{-16}
AgI	8.5×10^{-17}	Hg_2SO_4	6.5×10^{-7}	$Zn_3(PO_4)_2$	5×10^{-36}
Hg_2I_2	5.2×10^{-29}	$PbSO_4$	2.5×10^{-8}	$Pb_3(PO_4)_2$	3.0×10^{-44}
HgI_2	2.9×10^{-29}			$Ba_3(PO_4)_2$	5.8×10^{-38}
PbI_2	9.8×10^{-9}	**Chromates**			
		$BaCrO_4$	1.2×10^{-10}	**Ferrocyanides**	
Hydroxides		$CuCrO_4$	3.6×10^{-6}	$Zn_2[Fe(CN)_6]$	2.1×10^{-16}
$Mg(OH)_2$	5.6×10^{-12}	Ag_2CrO_4	1.1×10^{-12}	$Cd_2[Fe(CN)_6]$	4.2×10^{-18}
$Ca(OH)_2$	5.0×10^{-6}	Hg_2CrO_4	2.0×10^{-9}	$Pb_2[Fe(CN)_6]$	9.5×10^{-19}
$Mn(OH)_2$	1.6×10^{-13}	$CaCrO_4$	7.1×10^{-4}		
$Fe(OH)_2$	4.9×10^{-17}	$PbCrO_4$	1.8×10^{-14}		
$Fe(OH)_3$	2.8×10^{-39}				
$Co(OH)_2$	5.9×10^{-15}				

Table C.7 Formation Constants of Complexes (25 °C)

Complex Ion Equilibrium	K_{form}	Complex Ion Equilibrium	K_{form}
Halide Complexes		**Complexes with Other Monodentate Ligands**	
$Al^{3+} + 6F^- \rightleftharpoons [AlF_6]^{3-}$	1×10^{20}	**Methylamine (CH_3NH_2)**	
$Al^{3+} + 4F^- \rightleftharpoons [AlF_4]^-$	2.0×10^8	$Ag^+ + 2CH_3NH_2 \rightleftharpoons [Ag(CH_3NH_2)_2]^+$	7.8×10^6
$Be^{2+} + 4F^- \rightleftharpoons [BeF_4]^{2-}$	1.3×10^{13}	**Thiocyanate Ion (SCN^-)**	
$Sn^{4+} + 6F^- \rightleftharpoons [SnF_6]^{2-}$	1×10^{25}	$Cd^{2+} + 4SCN^- \rightleftharpoons [Cd(SCN)_4]^{2-}$	1×10^3
$Cu^+ + 2Cl^- \rightleftharpoons [CuCl_2]^-$	3×10^5	$Cu^{2+} + 2SCN^- \rightleftharpoons [Cu(SCN)_2]$	5.6×10^3
$Ag^+ + 2Cl^- \rightleftharpoons [AgCl_2]^-$	1.8×10^5	$Fe^{3+} + 3SCN^- \rightleftharpoons [Fe(SCN)_3]$	2×10^6
$Pb^{2+} + 4Cl^- \rightleftharpoons [PbCl_4]^{2-}$	2.5×10^{15}	$Hg^{2+} + 4SCN^- \rightleftharpoons [Hg(SCN)_4]^{2-}$	5.0×10^{21}
$Zn^{2+} + 4Cl^- \rightleftharpoons [ZnCl_4]^{2-}$	1.6	**Hydroxide Ion (OH^-)**	
$Hg^{2+} + 4Cl^- \rightleftharpoons [HgCl_4]^{2-}$	5.0×10^{15}	$Cu^{2+} + 4OH^- \rightleftharpoons [Cu(OH)_4]^{2-}$	1.3×10^{16}
$Cu^+ + 2Br^- \rightleftharpoons [CuBr_2]^-$	8×10^5	$Zn^{2+} + 4OH^- \rightleftharpoons [Zn(OH)_4]^{2-}$	2×10^{20}
$Ag^+ + 2Br^- \rightleftharpoons [AgBr_2]^-$	1.7×10^7	**Complexes with Bidentate Ligands***	
$Hg^{2+} + 4Br^- \rightleftharpoons [HgBr_4]^{2-}$	1×10^{21}	$Mn^{2+} + 3\ en \rightleftharpoons [Mn(en)_3]^{2+}$	6.5×10^5
$Cu^+ + 2I^- \rightleftharpoons [CuI_2]^-$	8×10^8	$Fe^{2+} + 3\ en \rightleftharpoons [Fe(en)_3]^{2+}$	5.2×10^9
$Ag^+ + 2I^- \rightleftharpoons [AgI_2]^-$	1×10^{11}	$Co^{2+} + 3\ en \rightleftharpoons [Co(en)_3]^{2+}$	1.3×10^{14}
$Pb^{2+} + 4I^- \rightleftharpoons [PbI_4]^{2-}$	3×10^4	$Co^{3+} + 3\ en \rightleftharpoons [Co(en)_3]^{3+}$	4.8×10^{48}
$Hg^{2+} + 4I^- \rightleftharpoons [HgI_4]^{2-}$	1.9×10^{30}	$Ni^{2+} + 3\ en \rightleftharpoons [Ni(en)_3]^{2+}$	4.1×10^{17}
Ammonia Complexes		$Cu^{2+} + 2\ en \rightleftharpoons [Cu(en)_2]^{2+}$	3.5×10^{19}
$Ag^+ + 2NH_3 \rightleftharpoons [Ag(NH_3)_2]^+$	1.6×10^7	$Mn^{2+} + 3\ bipy \rightleftharpoons [Mn(bipy)_3]^{2+}$	1×10^6
$Zn^{2+} + 4NH_3 \rightleftharpoons [Zn(NH_3)_4]^{2+}$	7.8×10^8	$Fe^{2+} + 3\ bipy \rightleftharpoons [Fe(bipy)_3]^{2+}$	1.6×10^{17}
$Cu^{2+} + 4NH_3 \rightleftharpoons [Cu(NH_3)_4]^{2+}$	1.1×10^{13}	$Ni^{2+} + 3\ bipy \rightleftharpoons [Ni(bipy)_3]^{2+}$	3.0×10^{20}
$Hg^{2+} + 4NH_3 \rightleftharpoons [Hg(NH_3)_4]^{2+}$	1.8×10^{19}	$Co^{2+} + 3\ bipy \rightleftharpoons [Co(bipy)_3]^{2+}$	8×10^{15}
$Co^{2+} + 6NH_3 \rightleftharpoons [Co(NH_3)_6]^{2+}$	5.0×10^4	$Mn^{2+} + 3\ phen \rightleftharpoons [Mn(phen)_3]^{2+}$	2×10^{10}
$Co^{3+} + 6NH_3 \rightleftharpoons [Co(NH_3)_6]^{3+}$	4.6×10^{33}	$Fe^{2+} + 3\ phen \rightleftharpoons [Fe(phen)_3]^{2+}$	1×10^{21}
$Cd^{2+} + 6NH_3 \rightleftharpoons [Cd(NH_3)_6]^{2+}$	2.6×10^5	$Co^{2+} + 3\ phen \rightleftharpoons [Co(phen)_3]^{2+}$	6×10^{19}
$Ni^{2+} + 6NH_3 \rightleftharpoons [Ni(NH_3)_6]^{2+}$	2.0×10^8	$Ni^{2+} + 3\ phen \rightleftharpoons [Ni(phen)_3]^{2+}$	2×10^{24}
Cyanide Complexes		$Co^{2+} + 3C_2O_4^{2-} \rightleftharpoons [Co(C_2O_4)_3]^{4-}$	4.5×10^6
$Fe^{2+} + 6CN^- \rightleftharpoons [Fe(CN)_6]^{4-}$	1.0×10^{24}	$Fe^{3+} + 3C_2O_4^{2-} \rightleftharpoons [Fe(C_2O_4)_3]^{3-}$	3.3×10^{20}
$Fe^{3+} + 6CN^- \rightleftharpoons [Fe(CN)_6]^{3-}$	1.0×10^{31}	**Complexes of Other Polydentate Ligands***	
$Ag^+ + 2CN^- \rightleftharpoons [Ag(CN)_2]^-$	5.3×10^{18}	$Zn^{2+} + EDTA^{4-} \rightleftharpoons [Zn(EDTA)]^{2-}$	3.8×10^{16}
$Cu^+ + 2CN^- \rightleftharpoons [Cu(CN)_2]^-$	1.0×10^{16}	$Mg^{2+} + 2NTA^{3-} \rightleftharpoons [Mg(NTA)_2]^{4-}$	1.6×10^{10}
$Cd^{2+} + 4CN^- \rightleftharpoons [Cd(CN)_4]^{2-}$	7.7×10^{16}	$Ca^{2+} + 2NTA^{3-} \rightleftharpoons [Ca(NTA)_2]^{4-}$	3.2×10^{11}
$Au^+ + 2CN^- \rightleftharpoons [Au(CN)_2]^-$	2×10^{38}		

*en = ethylenediamine

bipy = bipyridyl

bipyridyl

phen = 1,10-phenanthroline

1,10-phenanthroline

$EDTA^{4-}$ = ethylenediaminetetraacetate ion

NTA^{3-} = nitrilotriacetate ion

| Table C.8 | Ionization Constants of Weak Acids and Bases (Alternative Formulas in Parentheses) |

Monoprotic Acid	Name	K_a
$HC_2O_2Cl_3$ (Cl_3CCO_2H)	trichloroacetic acid	2.2×10^{-1}
HIO_3	iodic acid	1.7×10^{-1}
$HC_2HO_2Cl_2$ (Cl_2CHCO_2H)	dichloroacetic acid	5.0×10^{-2}
$HC_2H_2O_2Cl$ (ClH_2CCO_2H)	chloroacetic acid	1.4×10^{-3}
HNO_2	nitrous acid	4.6×10^{-4}
HF	hydrofluoric acid	3.5×10^{-4}
$HOCN$	cyanic acid	2×10^{-4}
$HCHO_2$ (HCO_2H)	formic acid	1.8×10^{-4}
$HC_3H_5O_3$ [$CH_3CH(OH)CO_2H$]	lactic acid	1.4×10^{-4}
$HC_4H_3N_2O_3$	barbituric acid	9.8×10^{-5}
$HC_7H_5O_2$ ($C_6H_5CO_2H$)	benzoic acid	6.3×10^{-5}
$HC_4H_7O_2$ ($CH_3CH_2CH_2CO_2H$)	butanoic acid	1.5×10^{-5}
HN_3	hydrazoic acid	2.5×10^{-5}
$HC_2H_3O_2$ (CH_3CO_2H)	acetic acid	1.8×10^{-5}
$HC_3H_5O_2$ ($CH_3CH_2CO_2H$)	propanoic acid	1.3×10^{-5}
$HC_6H_4NO_2$	nicotinic acid (niacin)	1.4×10^{-5}
$HOCl$	hypochlorous acid	3.0×10^{-8}
$HOBr$	hypobromous acid	2.1×10^{-9}
HCN	hydrocyanic acid	4.9×10^{-10}
HC_6H_5O	phenol	1.3×10^{-10}
HOI	hypoiodous acid	2.3×10^{-11}
H_2O_2	hydrogen peroxide	2.4×10^{-12}

Polyprotic Acid	Name	K_{a_1}	K_{a_2}	K_{a_3}
H_2SO_4	sulfuric acid	large	1.2×10^{-2}	
H_2CrO_4	chromic acid	5.0	1.5×10^{-6}	
$H_2C_2O_4$	oxalic acid	6.0×10^{-2}	6.1×10^{-5}	
H_3PO_3	phosphorous acid	5.0×10^{-2}	2.0×10^{-7}	
$H_2S(aq)$	hydrosulfuric acid	8.9×10^{-8}	1×10^{-19}	
H_2SO_3	sulfurous acid	1.2×10^{-2}	6.6×10^{-8}	
H_2SeO_4	selenic acid	large	1.2×10^{-2}	
H_2SeO_3	selenous acid	4.5×10^{-3}	1.1×10^{-8}	
H_6TcO_6	telluric acid	2×10^{-8}	1×10^{-11}	
H_2TeO_3	tellurous acid	3.3×10^{-3}	2.0×10^{-8}	
$H_2C_3H_2O_4$ ($HO_2CCH_2CO_2H$)	malonic acid	1.4×10^{-3}	2.0×10^{-6}	
$H_2C_8H_4O_4$	phthalic acid	1.1×10^{-3}	3.9×10^{-6}	
$H_2C_4H_4O_6$	tartaric acid	9.2×10^{-4}	4.3×10^{-5}	
$H_2C_6H_6O_6$	ascorbic acid	8.0×10^{-5}	1.6×10^{-12}	
H_2CO_3	carbonic acid	4.3×10^{-7}	5.6×10^{-11}	
H_3PO_4	phosphoric acid	7.5×10^{-3}	6.2×10^{-8}	4.2×10^{-13}
H_3AsO_4	arsenic acid	5.5×10^{-3}	1.7×10^{-7}	5.1×10^{-12}
$H_3C_6H_5O_7$	citric acid	7.1×10^{-4}	1.7×10^{-5}	6.3×10^{-6}

(*Continued*)

Table C.8	Ionization Constants of Weak Acids and Bases (Alternative Formulas in Parentheses) *(Continued)*	
Weak Base	**Name**	K_b
$(CH_3)_2NH$	dimethylamine	9.6×10^{-4}
$C_4H_9NH_2$	butylamine	5.9×10^{-4}
CH_3NH_2	methylamine	4.4×10^{-4}
$CH_3CH_2NH_2$	ethylamine	4.3×10^{-4}
$(CH_3)_3N$	trimethylamine	7.4×10^{-5}
NH_3	ammonia	1.8×10^{-5}
$C_{21}H_{22}N_2O_2$	strychnine	1.8×10^{-6}
N_2H_4	hydrazine	1.3×10^{-6}
$C_{17}H_{19}NO_3$	morphine	1.6×10^{-6}
NH_2OH	hydroxylamine	1.1×10^{-8}
C_5H_5N	pyridine	1.7×10^{-9}
$C_6H_5NH_2$	aniline	3.9×10^{-10}
PH_3	phosphine	10^{-28}

Table C.9	Standard Reduction Potentials (25 °C)
$E°$ (Volts)	**Half-Cell Reaction**
+2.87	$F_2(g) + 2e^- \rightleftharpoons 2F^-(aq)$
+2.08	$O_3(g) + 2H^+(aq) + 2e^- \rightleftharpoons O_2(g) + H_2O$
+2.01	$S_2O_8^{2-}(aq) + 2e^- \rightleftharpoons 2SO_4^{2-}(aq)$
+1.82	$Co^{3+}(aq) + e^- \rightleftharpoons Co^{2+}(aq)$
+1.77	$H_2O_2(aq) + 2H^+(aq) + 2e^- \rightleftharpoons 2H_2O$
+1.695	$MnO_4^-(aq) + 4H^+(aq) + 3e^- \rightleftharpoons MnO_2(s) + 2H_2O$
+1.69	$PbO_2(s) + HSO_4^-(aq) + 3H^+(aq) + 2e^- \rightleftharpoons PbSO_4(s) + 2H_2O$
+1.63	$2HOCl(aq) + 2H^+(aq) + 2e^- \rightleftharpoons Cl_2(g) + 2H_2O$
+1.51	$Mn^{3+}(aq) + e^- \rightleftharpoons Mn^{2+}(aq)$
+1.51	$MnO_4^-(aq) + 8H^+(aq) + 5e^- \rightleftharpoons Mn^{2+}(aq) + 4H_2O$
+1.46	$PbO_2(s) + 4H^+(aq) + 2e^- \rightleftharpoons Pb^{2+}(aq) + 2H_2O$
+1.44	$BrO_3^-(aq) + 6H^+(aq) + 6e^- \rightleftharpoons Br^-(aq) + 3H_2O$
+1.42	$Au^{3+}(aq) + 3e^- \rightleftharpoons Au(s)$
+1.36	$Cl_2(g) + 2e^- \rightleftharpoons 2Cl^-(aq)$
+1.33	$Cr_2O_7^{2-}(aq) + 14H^+(aq) + 6e^- \rightleftharpoons 2Cr^{3+}(aq) + 7H_2O$
+1.24	$O_3(g) + H_2O + 2e^- \rightleftharpoons O_2(g) + 2OH^-(aq)$
+1.23	$MnO_2(s) + 4H^+(aq) + 2e^- \rightleftharpoons Mn^{2+}(aq) + 2H_2O$
+1.23	$O_2(g) + 4H^+(aq) + 4e^- \rightleftharpoons 2H_2O$
+1.20	$Pt^{2+}(aq) + 2e^- \rightleftharpoons Pt(s)$
+1.07	$Br_2(aq) + 2e^- \rightleftharpoons 2Br^-(aq)$
+0.96	$NO_3^-(aq) + 4H^+(aq) + 3e^- \rightleftharpoons NO(g) + 2H_2O$
+0.94	$NO_3^-(aq) + 3H^+(aq) + 2e^- \rightleftharpoons HNO_2(aq) + H_2O$
+0.91	$2Hg^{2+}(aq) + 2e^- \rightleftharpoons Hg_2^{2+}(aq)$
+0.87	$HO_2^-(aq) + H_2O + 2e^- \rightleftharpoons 3OH^-(aq)$
+0.80	$NO_3^-(aq) + 4H^+(aq) + 2e^- \rightleftharpoons 2NO_2(g) + 2H_2O$
+0.80	$Ag^+(aq) + e^- \rightleftharpoons Ag(s)$
+0.77	$Fe^{3+}(aq) + e^- \rightleftharpoons Fe^{2+}(aq)$
+0.69	$O_2(g) + 2H^+(aq) + 2e^- \rightleftharpoons H_2O_2(aq)$
+0.54	$I_2(s) + 2e^- \rightleftharpoons 2I^-(aq)$
+0.49	$NiO_2(s) + 2H_2O + 2e^- \rightleftharpoons Ni(OH)_2(s) + 2OH^-(aq)$
+0.45	$SO_2(aq) + 4H^+(aq) + 4e^- \rightleftharpoons S(s) + 2H_2O$
+0.401	$O_2(g) + 2H_2O + 4e^- \rightleftharpoons 4OH^-(aq)$
+0.34	$Cu^{2+}(aq) + 2e^- \rightleftharpoons Cu(s)$
+0.27	$Hg_2Cl_2(s) + 2e^- \rightleftharpoons 2Hg(l) + 2Cl^-(aq)$
+0.25	$PbO_2(s) + H_2O + 2e^- \rightleftharpoons PbO(s) + 2OH^-(aq)$
+0.2223	$AgCl(s) + e^- \rightleftharpoons Ag(s) + Cl^-(aq)$
+0.172	$SO_4^{2-}(aq) + 4H^+(aq) + 2e^- \rightleftharpoons H_2SO_3(aq) + H_2O$
+0.169	$S_4O_6^{2-}(aq) + 2e^- \rightleftharpoons 2S_2O_3^{2-}(aq)$
+0.16	$Cu^{2+}(aq) + e^- \rightleftharpoons Cu^+(aq)$
+0.15	$Sn^{4+}(aq) + 2e^- \rightleftharpoons Sn^{2+}(aq)$
+0.14	$S(s) + 2H^+(aq) + 2e^- \rightleftharpoons H_2S(g)$
+0.07	$AgBr(s) + e^- \rightleftharpoons Ag(s) + Br^-(aq)$
0 (exactly)	$2H^+(aq) + 2e^- \rightleftharpoons H_2(g)$
−0.13	$Pb^{2+}(aq) + 2e^- \rightleftharpoons Pb(s)$

(Continued)

Table C.9 Standard Reduction Potentials (25 °C) (Continued)

$E°$ (Volts)	Half-Cell Reaction
−0.14	$Sn^{2+}(aq) + 2e^- \rightleftharpoons Sn(s)$
−0.15	$AgI(s) + e^- \rightleftharpoons Ag(s) + I^-(aq)$
−0.25	$Ni^{2+}(aq) + 2e^- \rightleftharpoons Ni(s)$
−0.28	$Co^{2+}(aq) + 2e^- \rightleftharpoons Co(s)$
−0.34	$In^{3+}(aq) + 3e^- \rightleftharpoons In(s)$
−0.34	$Tl^+(aq) + e^- \rightleftharpoons Tl(s)$
−0.36	$PbSO_4(s) + H^+(aq) + 2e^- \rightleftharpoons Pb(s) + HSO_4^-(aq)$
−0.40	$Cd^{2+}(aq) + 2e^- \rightleftharpoons Cd(s)$
−0.44	$Fe^{2+}(aq) + 2e^- \rightleftharpoons Fe(s)$
−0.56	$Ga^{3+}(aq) + 3e^- \rightleftharpoons Ga(s)$
−0.58	$PbO(s) + H_2O + 2e^- \rightleftharpoons Pb(s) + 2OH^-(aq)$
−0.74	$Cr^{3+}(aq) + 3e^- \rightleftharpoons Cr(s)$
−0.76	$Zn^{2+}(aq) + 2e^- \rightleftharpoons Zn(s)$
−0.81	$Cd(OH)_2(s) + 2e^- \rightleftharpoons Cd(s) + 2OH^-(aq)$
−0.83	$2H_2O + 2e^- \rightleftharpoons H_2(g) + 2OH^-(aq)$
−0.88	$Fe(OH)_2(s) + 2e^- \rightleftharpoons Fe(s) + 2OH^-(aq)$
−0.91	$Cr^{2+}(aq) + 2e^- \rightleftharpoons Cr(s)$
−1.16	$N_2(g) + 4H_2O + 4e^- \rightleftharpoons N_2O_4(aq) + 4OH^-(aq)$
−1.18	$V^{2+}(aq) + 2e^- \rightleftharpoons V(s)$
−1.216	$ZnO_2^-(aq) + 2H_2O + 2e^- \rightleftharpoons Zn(s) + 4OH^-(aq)$
−1.63	$Ti^{2+}(aq) + 2e^- \rightleftharpoons Ti(s)$
−1.66	$Al^{3+}(aq) + 3e^- \rightleftharpoons Al(s)$
−1.79	$U^{3+}(aq) + 3e^- \rightleftharpoons U(s)$
−2.02	$Sc^{3+}(aq) + 3e^- \rightleftharpoons Sc(s)$
−2.36	$La^{3+}(aq) + 3e^- \rightleftharpoons La(s)$
−2.37	$Y^{3+}(aq) + 3e^- \rightleftharpoons Y(s)$
−2.37	$Mg^{2+}(aq) + 2e^- \rightleftharpoons Mg(s)$
−2.71	$Na^+(aq) + e^- \rightleftharpoons Na(s)$
−2.76	$Ca^{2+}(aq) + 2e^- \rightleftharpoons Ca(s)$
−2.89	$Sr^{2+}(aq) + 2e^- \rightleftharpoons Sr(s)$
−2.90	$Ba^{2+}(aq) + 2e^- \rightleftharpoons Ba(s)$
−2.92	$Cs^+(aq) + e^- \rightleftharpoons Cs(s)$
−2.92	$K^+(aq) + e^- \rightleftharpoons K(s)$
−2.93	$Rb^+(aq) + e^- \rightleftharpoons Rb(s)$
−3.05	$Li^+(aq) + e^- \rightleftharpoons Li(s)$

Glossary

This glossary has the definitions of the key terms that were marked in boldface throughout the chapters plus a few additional terms. The numbers in parentheses that follow the definitions are the numbers of the sections in which the glossary entries received their principal discussions.

A

Abbreviated Electron Configurations: A shorthand method to write electron configurations using the preceding noble gas to represent core electrons. (8.8)

Absolute Zero: 0 K, -273.15 °C. Nature's lowest temperature. (2.2, 11.3)

Acceptor: A Lewis acid; the central metal ion in a complex ion. (18.4, 22.1)

Accuracy: The closeness of a measurement to the true value. (2.3)

Acid: *Arrhenius definition:* A substance that produces hydronium ions (hydrogen ions) in water. (5.3)
Brønsted definition: A proton donor. (16.1)
Lewis definition: An electron-pair acceptor. (16.4)

Acid Anhydride: Generally, an oxide of a nonmetal. (5.3)

Acid–Base Indicator: A dye with one color in acid and another color in base. (5.3, 5.8)

Acid–Base Neutralization: The reaction of an acid with a base. (5.3, 16.4)

Acid Ionization Constant (K_a):

$$K_a = \frac{[H^+][A^-]}{[HA]} \text{ for the equilibrium,}$$

$$HA \rightleftharpoons H^+ + A^- \qquad (17.3)$$

Acid Rain: Rain made acidic by dissolving sulfur and nitrogen oxides from the atmosphere.

Acid Salt: A salt of a partially neutralized polyprotic acid, for example, $NaHSO_4$ or $NaHCO_3$. (5.4)

Acid Solubility Product: The special solubility product expression for metal sulfides in dilute acid and related to the equation for their dissolving. For a divalent metal sulfide, MS,

$$MS(s) + 2H^+(aq) \rightleftharpoons$$

$$M^{2+}(aq) + H_2S(aq)$$

$$K_{spa} = \frac{[M^{2+}][H_2S]}{[H^+]^2} \qquad (18.2)$$

Acidic Anhydride: An oxide that reacts with water to make the solution acidic. (5.3)

Acidic Solution: An aqueous solution in which $[H^+] > [OH^-]$. (7.1)

Actinide Elements (Actinide Series): Elements 90–103. (3.2)

Activated Complex: The chemical species that exists with partly broken and partly formed bonds in the transition state. (14.6)

Activation Energy (E_a): The minimum kinetic energy that must be possessed by the reactants in order to result in an effective collision (one that produces products). (14.5)

Activities: Effective concentrations which properly should be substituted into a mass action expression to satisfy the equilibrium law. The activity of a solid is defined as having a value of 1. (15.4)

Activity: For a radioactive material, the number of disintegrations per second. (21.6)

Activity Series: A list of metals in order of their reactivity as reducing agents. (6.4)

Actual Yield: See *Yield, Actual.*

Addition Compound: A molecule formed by the joining of two simpler molecules through formation of a covalent bond (usually a coordinate covalent bond). (9.8)

Addition Polymer: A polymer formed by the simple addition of one monomer unit to another, a process that continues over and over until a very long chain of monomer units is produced. (23.5)

Addition Reaction: The addition of a molecule to a double or triple bond. (23.2)

Adiabatic Change: A change within a system during which no energy enters or leaves the system. (7.3, 19.1)

Aerogel: A modern ceramic that is extremely porous and has a low density (16.6)

Alcohol: An organic compound whose molecules have the —OH group attached to tetrahedral carbon. (3.6, 9.6, 22.3)

Aldehyde: An organic compound whose molecules have the —OH group. (9.6)

Alkali Metals: The Group 1A elements (except hydrogen)—lithium, sodium, potassium, rubidium, cesium, and francium. (3.2)

Alkaline Battery (Alkaline Dry Cell): A zinc–manganese dioxide galvanic cell of 1.54 V used commonly in flashlight batteries. (20.6)

Alkaline Earth Metals: The Group 2A elements—beryllium, magnesium, calcium, strontium, barium, and radium. (3.2)

Alkane: A hydrocarbon whose molecules have only single bonds. (3.6, 23.2)

Alkene: A hydrocarbon whose molecules have one or more double bonds. (23.2)

Alkyl Group: An organic group of carbon and hydrogen atoms related to an alkane but with one less hydrogen atom (e.g., CH_3—, methyl; CH_3CH_2—, ethyl). (16.6, 23.2)

Alkyne: A hydrocarbon whose molecules have one or more triple bonds. (23.2)

Allotrope: One of two or more forms of an element. (10.10)

Allotropy: The existence of an element in two or more molecular or crystalline forms called allotropes. (10.10)

Alpha Particle: The nucleus of a helium atom. (22.3)

Alpha Radiation: A high-velocity stream of alpha particles produced by radioactive decay. (21.3)

Alum: A double salt with the general formula $M^+M^{3+}(SO_4)_2 \cdot 12H_2O$, such as potassium alum: $KAl(SO_4)_2 \cdot 12H_2O$.

Amalgam: A solution of a metal in mercury.

Amide: An organic compound whose molecules have any one of the following groups: (23.4)

$$\underset{\text{—CNH}_2}{\overset{\displaystyle O \atop \|}{}} \quad \underset{\text{—CNHR}}{\overset{\displaystyle O \atop \|}{}} \quad \underset{\text{—CNR}_2}{\overset{\displaystyle O \atop \|}{}}$$

α-Amino Acid: One of about 20 monomers of polypeptides. (23.6)

Amine: An organic compound whose molecules contain the group NH_2, NHR, or NR_2. (9.6, 23.4)

Amorphous Solid: A noncrystalline solid. A glass. (12.11)

Ampere (A): The SI unit for electric current; one coulomb per second. (20.8)

Amphiprotic Compound: A compound that can act either as a proton donor or as a proton acceptor; an amphoteric compound. (16.1)

Amphoteric Compound: A compound that can react as either an acid or a base. (16.1)

Amplitude: The height of a wave, which is a measure of the wave's intensity. (8.1)

amu: See *Atomic Mass Unit.*

Angstrom (Å): $1 \text{ Å} = 10^{-10} \text{ m} = 100 \text{ pm} = 0.1 \text{ nm}$. (8.10)

Anhydrous: Without water. (1.5)

Anion: A negatively charged ion. (3.4)

Anode: The positive electrode in a gas discharge tube. The electrode at which oxidation occurs during an electrochemical change. (3.1, 20.1)

Antibonding Electrons: Electrons that occupy antibonding molecular orbitals. (10.7)

Antibonding Molecular Orbital: A molecular orbital that denies electron density to the space between nuclei and destabilizes a molecule when occupied by electrons. (10.7)

Antimatter: Any particle annihilated by a particle of ordinary matter. (22.3)

Aqua Regia: One part concentrated nitric acid and three parts concentrated hydrochloric acid (by volume).

Aqueous Solution: A solution that has water as the solvent.

Aromatic Compound: An organic compound whose molecules have the benzene ring system. (23.2)

Aromatic Hydrocarbon: Hydrocarbons that contain a benzene ring or similar ring systems with alternating single and double bonds. (23.2)

Arrhenius Acid: See *Acid*.

Arrhenius Base: See *Base*.

Arrhenius Equation: An equation that relates the rate constant of a reaction to the reaction's activation energy. (14.7)

Association: The joining together of molecules by hydrogen bonds. (13.7)

Asymmetric Carbon Atom: A carbon atom that is bonded to four different groups and which is a chiral center. (23.1)

Atmosphere, Standard (atm): 101,325 Pa. The pressure that supports a column of mercury 760 mm high at 0 °C; 760 torr. (7.5, 11.2)

Atmospheric Pressure: The pressure exerted by the mixture of gases in our atmosphere. (7.5, 11.2)

Atom: A neutral particle having one nucleus; the smallest representative sample of an element. (1.2)

Atomic force microscope: A modern instrument that determines the topology of materials with a resolution on the order of atomic dimensions. Orientations of atoms and structures of molecular assemblies on these surfaces can be deduced from these measurements. (1.6)

Atomic Mass: The average mass (in u) of the atoms of the isotopes of a given element as they occur naturally. (3.1)

Atomic Mass Unit (u): $1.6605402 \times 10^{-24}$ g; 1/12th the mass of one atom of carbon-12. Sometimes given the symbol amu. (3.1)

Atomic Number: The number of protons in a nucleus. (3.1)

Atomic Radiation: Radiation consisting of particles or electromagnetic radiation given off by radioactive elements. (21.3)

Atomic Spectrum: The line spectrum produced when energized or excited atoms emit electromagnetic radiation. (8.2)

Atomic Weight: See *Atomic Mass*.

Atomization Energy (ΔH_{atom}): The energy needed to rupture all of the bonds in one mole of a substance in the gas state and produce its atoms, also in the gas state. (19.10)

Aufbau Principle: A set of rules enabling the construction of an electron structure of an atom from its atomic number. (8.7)

Average: See *Mean*.

Average Bond Order: The bond order of two or more equivalent bonds, determined by dividing the total number of sigma and pi bonds by the number of bonding electron domains. (9.9)

Avogadro's Number (Avogadro's Constant): 6.022×10^{23}; the number of particles or formula units in one mole. (4.1)

Avogadro's Principle: Equal volumes of gases contain equal numbers of molecules when they are at identical temperatures and pressures. (11.4)

Axial Bonds: Covalent bonds oriented parallel to the vertical axis in a trigonal bipyramidal molecule. (10.1)

Azimuthal Quantum Number: The quantum number. (8.5) (See also *Secondary Quantum Number*.)

B

Backbone (Polymer): The long chain of atoms in a polymer to which other groups are attached. (23.5)

Background Radiation: The atomic radiation from the natural radionuclides in the environment and from cosmic radiation. (21.6)

Balance: An apparatus for measuring mass. (2.2)

Balanced Equation: A chemical equation that has on opposites sides of the arrow the same number of each atom and the same net charge. (1.6, 4.4)

Ball and Stick Model: The representation of molecules using colored balls for atoms and sticks representing bonds. (1.5)

Band Gap: The energy difference between the valence band and the conduction band. (10.9)

Band Theory: A theory used to explain electron conduction in metals, semiconductors and insulators. (10.9)

Band of Stability: The envelope that encloses just the stable nuclides in a plot

of all nuclides constructed according to their numbers of neutrons versus their numbers of protons. (21.4)

Bar: The standard pressure for thermodynamic quantities; 1 bar = 105 pascals, 1 atm = 101,325 Pa. (7.5, 11.2, 19.5)

Barometer: An apparatus for measuring atmospheric pressure. (11.2)

Base: *Arrhenius theory:* A substance that releases OH^- ions in water. (5.3) *Brønsted theory:* A proton acceptor. (16.1) *Lewis theory:* An electron-pair acceptor. (16.3)

Base Anhydride: Oxides of metals that when dissolved in water produce a basic solution (5.3)

Base Ionization Constant, K_b:

$$K_b = \frac{[BH^+][OH^-]}{[B]} \text{ for the equilibrium,}$$

$$B + H_2O \rightleftharpoons BH^+ + OH^- \qquad (17.3)$$

Base Units: The units of the fundamental measurements of the SI. (2.2)

Basic Anhydride: An oxide that can neutralize acid or that reacts with water to give OH^-. (5.3)

Basic Solution: An aqueous solution in which $[H^+] < [OH^-]$. (17.1)

Battery: One or more galvanic cells arranged to serve as a practical source of electricity. (20.6)

Becquerel (Bq): 1 disintegration s^{-1}. The SI unit for the activity of a radioactive source. (21.6)

Bent Molecule (V-Shaped Molecule): A molecule that is nonlinear. (10.2)

Beta Particle: An electron emitted by radioactive decay. (22.3)

Beta Radiation: A stream of electrons produced by radioactive decay. (22.3)

Bidentate Ligand: A ligand that has two atoms that can become simultaneously attached to the same metal ion. (22.1)

Bimolecular Collision: A collision of two molecules. (14.8)

Binary Acid: An acid with the general formula H_nX, where X is a nonmetal. (5.4, 16.3)

Binary Compound: A compound composed of two different elements. (3.4)

Binding Energy, Nuclear: The energy equivalent of the difference in mass between an atomic nucleus and the sum of the masses of its nucleons. (21.2)

Biochemistry: The study of the organic substances in organisms. (3.6, 23.6)

Biological Catalyst: Biological molecule such as an enzyme that catalyzes a chemical reaction.

Black Phosphorus: An allotrope of phosphorus that has a layered structure. (10.10)

Body-Centered Cubic (bcc) Unit Cell: A unit cell having identical atoms, molecules, or ions at the corners of a cube plus one more particle in the center of the cube. (12.11)

Boiling Point: The temperature at which the vapor pressure of the liquid equals the atmospheric pressure. (12.6)

Boiling Point Elevation: A colligative property of a solution by which the solution's boiling point is higher than that of the pure solvent. (13.7)

Bond Angle: The angle formed by two bonds that extend from the same atom. (10.1)

Bond Dipole: A dipole within a molecule associated with a specific bond. (10.3)

Bond Dissociation Energy: See *Bond Energy.*

Bond Distance: See *Bond Length.*

Bond Energy: The energy needed to break one mole of a particular bond to give electrically neutral fragments. (9.5, 19.10)

Bond Length: The distance between two nuclei that are held together by a chemical bond. (9.5)

Bond Order: The number of electron pairs shared between two atoms. The *net* number of pairs of bonding electrons. (9.8)

Bond order = $1/2 \times$ (no. of bonding e^- − no. of antibonding e^-)

Bonding Domain: A region between two atoms that contains one or more electron pairs in bonds and that influences molecular shape. (10.2)

Bonding Electrons: Electrons that occupy bonding molecular orbitals. (10.7)

Bonding Molecular Orbital: A molecular orbital that introduces a buildup of electron density between nuclei and stabilizes a molecule when occupied by electrons. (10.7)

Born-Haber Cycle: A method for visualizing energy contributions to a physical or chemical change such as the dissolution of a compound in a solvent or the formation of a compound. (9.2)

Boundary: The interface between a system and its surroundings across which energy or matter might pass. (7.3)

Boyle's Law: See *Pressure–Volume Law.*

Bragg Equation: $n\lambda = 2d \sin \theta$. The equation used to convert X-ray diffraction data into a crystal structure. (12.12)

Branched-Chain Compound: An organic compound in whose molecules the carbon atoms do not all occur one after another in a continuous sequence. (23.1)

Branching (Polymer): The formation of side chains (branches) along the main backbone of a polymer. (23.5)

Branching Step: A step in a chain reaction that produces more chain-propagating species than it consumes. (Chemistry Outside the Classroom 14.1)

Brine: An aqueous solution of sodium chloride, often with other salts. (20.9)

Brønsted Acid: See *Acid.*

Brønsted Base: See *Base.*

Brownian Motion: The random, erratic motions of colloidally dispersed particles in a fluid. (3.6)

Buckminsterfullerene: The C-60 molecule. Also called buckyball. (10.10)

Buckyball: See *Buckminsterfullerene.*

Buffer: (a) A pair of solutes, a conjugate weak acid–weak base pair, that can keep the pH of a solution almost constant if either acid or base is added. (b) A solution containing such a pair of solutes. (17.7)

Buffer Capacity: A measure of how much strong acid or strong base is needed to change the pH of a buffer by some specified amount. (17.7)

Buret: A long tube of glass usually marked in mL and 0.1 mL units and equipped with a stopcock for the controlled addition of a liquid to a receiving flask. (5.8)

By-product: The substances formed by side reactions. (4.6)

C

Calorie (cal): 4.184 J. The energy that will raise the temperature of 1.00 g of water from 14.5 to 15.5 °C. (The nutritional *Calorie*, with a capital C, means 1000 cal or 1 kcal.) (7.1)

Calorimeter: An apparatus used in the determination of the heat of a reaction. (7.5)

Calorimetry: The science of measuring the quantities of heat that are involved in a chemical or physical change. (7.5)

Carbohydrates: Polyhydroxyaldehydes or polyhydroxyketones or substances that yield these by hydrolysis and that are obtained from plants or animals. (23.6)

Carbon Nanotube: Tubular carbon molecules that can be visualized as rolled up sheets of graphite (with hexagonal rings of carbon atoms) capped at each end by half of a spherical fullerene molecule. (10.10)

Carbon Ring: A series of carbon atoms arranged in a ring. (23.1)

Carbonyl Group: An organic functional group consisting of a carbon atom joined to an oxygen atom by a double bond; C=O. (9.6, 23.3)

Carboxyl Group: The organic functional group of an acid consisting of a carbon joined to an oxygen atom with a double bond and an OH group; —CO$_2$H or —COOH. (9.6, 23.3)

Carboxylic Acid: An organic compound whose molecules have the carboxyl group (9.6, 23.3)

Catalysis: Rate enhancement caused by a catalyst. (14.9)

Catalyst: A substance that in relatively small proportion accelerates the rate of a reaction without being permanently chemically changed. (14.9)

Catenation: The linking together of atoms of the same element to form chains.

Cathode: The negative electrode in a gas discharge tube. The electrode at which reduction occurs during an electrochemical change. (3.1, 20.1)

Cathode Ray: A stream of electrons ejected from a hot metal and accelerated toward a positively charged site in a vacuum tube. (3.1)

Cation: A positively charged ion. (3.4)

Cell Potential, E_{cell}: The potential (voltage) of a galvanic cell when no current is drawn from the cell. (20.2)

Cell Reaction: The overall chemical change that takes place in an electrolytic cell or a galvanic cell. (20.1)

Celsius Scale: A temperature scale on which water freezes at 0 °C and boils at 100 °C (at 1 atm) and that has 100 divisions called Celsius degrees between those two points. (2.2)

Centimeter (cm): 0.01 m. (2.2)

Chain-Growth Polymer: See *Addition Polymer.*

Chain Reaction: A self-sustaining change in which the products of one event cause one or more new events. (Chemistry Outside the Classroom 14.1)

Change of State: Transformation of matter from one physical state to another. In thermochemistry, any change in a variable used to define the state of a particular system—a change in composition, pressure, volume, or temperature. (12.4)

Charles' Law: See *Temperature–Volume Law.*

Chelate: A complex ion containing rings formed by polydentate ligands. (22.1)

Chelate Effect: The extra stability found in complexes that contain chelate rings. (22.1)

Chemical Bond: The force of electrical attraction that holds atoms together in compounds. (3.6, 9 Introduction)

Chemical Change: A change that converts substances into other substances; a chemical reaction. (1.3)

Chemical Energy: The potential energy of chemicals that is transferred during chemical reactions. (7.1)

Chemical Equation: A before-and-after description that uses formulas and coefficients to represent a chemical reaction. (1.6)

Chemical Equilibrium: Dynamic equilibrium in a chemical system. (5.3, 15.1)

Chemical Formula: A formula written using chemical symbols and subscripts that describes the composition of a chemical compound or element. (1.5)

Chemical Kinetics: The study of rates of reaction. (14 Introduction)

Chemical Property: The ability of a substance, either by itself or with other substances, to undergo a change into new substances. (2.1)

Chemical Reaction: A change in which new substances (products) form from starting materials (reactants). (1.3)

Chemical Symbol: A formula for an element. (1.3)

Chemical Thermodynamics: See *Thermodynamics.*

Chemistry: The study of the compositions of substances and the ways by which their properties are related to their compositions. (1.1)

Chirality: The "handedness" of an object; the property of an object (like a molecule) that makes it unable to be superimposed onto a model of its own mirror image. (22.4)

Cis Isomer: A stereoisomer whose uniqueness is in having two groups on the same side of some reference plane. (22.4)

Clausius–Clapeyron Equation: The relationship between the vapor pressure, the temperature, and the molar heat of vaporization of a substance (where C is a constant). (12.8)

$$\ln P = \frac{\Delta H_{vap}}{RT} + C$$

Closed-End Manometer: See *Manometer.*

Closed System: A system that can absorb or release energy but not mass across the boundary between the system and its surroundings. (7.3)

Closest-Packed Structure: A crystal structure in which atoms or molecules are packed as efficiently as possible. (12.11)

Codon: An individual unit of hereditary instruction that consists of three, side by side, side chains on a molecule of mRNA. (23.7)

Coefficients: Numbers in front of formulas in chemical equations. (1.6)

Coinage Metals: Copper, silver, and gold.

Collapsing Atom Paradox: The paradox faced by classical physics that predicts a moving electron in an atom should emit energy and spiral into the nucleus. (8 Introduction)

Colligative Property: A property such as vapor pressure lowering, boiling point elevation, freezing point depression, and osmotic pressure whose physical value depends only on the ratio of the numbers of moles of solute and solvent particles and not on their chemical identities. (13.7)

Collision Theory: The rate of a reaction is proportional to the number of effective collisions that occur each second between the reactants. (14.5)

Colloid: Particles with at least one dimension between 1 and 100 nm suspended in a solvent. (13.8)

Combined Gas Law: See *Gas Law, Combined.*

Combustion: A rapid reaction with oxygen accompanied by a flame and the evolution of heat and light. (6.5)

Combustion Analysis: A method for obtaining percentage composition data for organic compounds. (4.3)

Common Ion: The ion in a mixture of ionic substances that is common to the formulas of at least two. (17.7)

Common Ion Effect: The solubility of one salt is reduced by the presence of another having a common ion. (17.7)

Competing Reaction: A reaction that reduces the yield of the main product by forming by-products. (4.6)

Complementary Colors: Two colors, when mixed, result in a neutral color such as gray, black or white. (22.5)

Complex Ion (Complex): The combination of one or more anions or neutral molecules (ligands) with a metal ion. (15.6, 18.4, 22.1)

Compound: A substance consisting of chemically combined atoms from two or more elements and present in a definite ratio. (1.3)

Compound Nucleus: An atomic nucleus carrying excess energy following its capture of some bombarding particle. (21.5)

Compressibility: Capable of undergoing a reduction in volume under increasing pressure. (11.1, 12.3)

Concentrated Solution: A solution that has a large ratio of the amounts of solute to solvent. (5.1)

Concentration: The ratio of the quantity of solute to the quantity of solution (or the quantity of solvent). (5.1) (See *Molal Concentration, Molar Concentra-*

tion, Mole Fraction, Percentage Concentration.)

Concentration Table: A part of the strategy for organizing data needed to make certain calculations, particularly any involving equilibria. (15.7)

Conclusion: A statement that is based on what we think about a series of observations. (1.2)

Condensation: The change of a vapor to its liquid or solid state. (12.4)

Condensation Polymer (Step-Growth Polymer): A polymer formed from monomers by splitting out a small molecule such as H_2O or CH_3OH. (23.5)

Condensation Polymerization: The process of forming a condensation polymer. (23.5)

Condensed Formula: Generally a formula of an organic compound written to show the sequence of carbon atoms and functional groups without individual bonds. (9.6, 23.1)

Condensed Structural Formulas (Condensed Structures): See *Condensed Formula.*

Conduction Band: In band theory, this consists of any band of atomic energy levels that is continuous throughout the solid and empty or partially filled with electrons. (10.9)

Conformation: A particular relative orientation or geometric form of a flexible molecule. (10.5)

Conjugate Acid: The species in a conjugate acid–base pair that has the greater number of H-units. (16.1)

Conjugate Acid–Base Pair: Two substances (ions or molecules) whose formulas differ by only one H-unit. (16.1)

Conjugate Base: The species in a conjugate acid–base pair that has the fewer number of H-units. (16.1)

Conservation of Energy, Law of: See *Law of Conservation of Energy.*

Conservation of Mass–Energy, Law of: See *Law of Conservation of Mass–Energy.*

Continuous Spectrum: The electromagnetic spectrum corresponding to the mixture of frequencies present in white light. (8.2)

Contributing Structure: One of a set of two or more Lewis structures used in applying the theory of resonance to the structure of a compound. A resonance structure. (9.9)

Conversion Factor: A ratio constructed from the relationship between two units such as 2.54 cm/1 in., from 1 in. = 2.54 cm. (2.4)

Cooling Curve: A graph showing how the temperature of a substance changes as heat is removed from it at a constant rate as the substance undergoes changes in its physical state. (12.7)

Coordinate Covalent Bond: A covalent bond in which both electrons originated from one of the joined atoms, but otherwise like a covalent bond in all respects. (9.8)

Coordination Compound (Coordination Complex): A complex or its salt. (19.4, 22.1)

Coordination Number: The number of donor atoms that surround a metal ion. (22.3)

Copolymer: A polymer made from two or more different monomers. (22.6)

Core Electrons: The inner electrons of an atom that are not exposed to the electrons of other atoms when chemical bonds form. (8.10)

Corrosion: The slow oxidation of metals exposed to air or water. (6.5)

Coulomb (C): The SI unit of electrical charge; the charge on 6.25×10^{18} electrons; the amount of charge that passes a fixed point of a wire conductor when a current of 1 A flows for 1 s. (20.2)

Coulomb's Law: This is the mathematical equation that describes the attractive and repulsive forces between charged particles. (9.2)

Counter Ions: Ions present in a system to assure that the overall charge is zero. (22.1)

Covalent Bond: A chemical bond that results when atoms share electron pairs. (9.5)

Covalent Crystal (Network Solid): A crystal in which the lattice positions are occupied by atoms that are covalently bonded to the atoms at adjacent lattice sites. (12.13)

Critical Mass: The mass of a fissile isotope above which a self-sustaining chain reaction occurs. (21.8)

Critical Point: The point at the end of a vapor pressure versus temperature curve for a liquid and that corresponds to the critical pressure and the critical temperature. (12.10)

Critical Pressure (P_c): The vapor pressure of a substance at its critical temperature. (12.10)

Critical Temperature (T_c): The temperature above which a substance cannot exist as a liquid regardless of the pressure. (12.10)

Crystal Field Splitting (Δ): The difference in energy between sets of d orbitals in a complex ion. (22.5)

Crystal Field Theory: A theory that considers the effects of the polarities or the charges of the ligands in a complex ion on the energies of the d orbitals of the central metal ion. (22.5)

Crystal Lattice: The repeating symmetrical pattern of atoms, molecules, or ions that occurs in a crystal. (12.11)

Cubic Closest Packing (ccp): Efficient packing of spheres with an A-B-C-A-B-C … alternating stacking of layers of spheres. (12.11)

Cubic Meter (m³): The SI derived unit of volume. (2.2)

Curie (Ci): A unit of activity for radioactive samples, equal to 3.7×10^{10} disintegrations per second. (21.6)

D

Dalton: One atomic mass unit, u.

Dalton's Atomic Theory: Matter consists of tiny, indestructible particles called atoms. All atoms of one element are identical. The atoms of different elements have different masses. Atoms combine in definite ratios by atoms when they form compounds. (1.4)

Dalton's Law of Partial Pressures: See *Partial Pressures, Law of.*

Data: The information (often in the form of physical quantities) obtained in an experiment or other experience or from references. (1.2)

Debye: Unit used to express dipole moments. $1 D \times 3.34 \times 10^{-30}$ C m (coulomb meter). (9.7)

Decay Constant: The first-order rate constant for radioactive decay. (21.6)

Decimal Multipliers: Factors—exponentials of 10 or decimals—that are used to define larger or smaller SI units. (2.2)

Decomposition: A chemical reaction that changes one substance into two or more simpler substances. (1.3)

Dehydration: Removal of water from a substance. (23.3)

Dehydration Reaction: Formation of a carbon–carbon double bond by removal of the components of water from an alcohol. (23.3)

Deliquescent Compound: A compound able to absorb enough water from humid air to form a concentrated solution.

Delocalization Energy: The difference between the energy a substance would have if its molecules had no delocalized molecular orbitals and the energy it has because of such orbitals. (10.8)

Delocalized Molecular Orbital: A molecular orbital that spreads over more than two nuclei. (10.8)

ΔH_{fusion}: See *Molar Heat of Fusion*
$\Delta H_{sublimation}$: See *Molar Heat of Sublimation*
$\Delta H_{vaporization}$: See *Molar Heat of Vaporization*

Density: The ratio of an object's mass to its volume. (2.5)

Dependent Variable: The experimental variable of a pair of variables whose value is determined by the other, the independent variable.

Deposition: The term describing the opposite of sublimation. (12.4)

Derived Unit: Any unit defined solely in terms of base units. (2.2)

Deuterium: The isotope of hydrogen with a mass number of 2. (21.8)

Diagonal Trend: Physical or chemical properties that generally vary diagonally from one corner to the other in the periodic table (e.g., ionization energy, electron affinity, and electronegativity). (8.10)

Dialysis: The passage of small molecules and ions, but not species of a colloidal size, through a semipermeable membrane. (13.7)

Dialyzing membrane: A membrane that allows the passage of solvent and small solutes through its pores, but large molecules cannot pass through the pores. (13.7)

Diamagnetism: The property experienced by a substance that contains no unpaired electrons whereby the substance is repelled weakly by a magnet. (8.6)

Diamond: A crystalline form of carbon in which each carbon atom is bonded in a tetrahedral structure to four other carbon atoms. (10.10)

Diaphragm Cell: An electrolytic cell used to manufacture sodium hydroxide by the electrolysis of aqueous sodium chloride. (20.9)

Diatomic Substance (Diatomic Molecule): A molecular substance made from two atoms. (1.5)

Diffraction: Constructive and destructive interference by waves. (8.4)

Diffraction Pattern: The image formed on a screen or a photographic film caused by the diffraction of electromagnetic radiation such as visible light or X rays. (12.12)

Diffusion: The spontaneous intermingling of one substance with another. (11.6)

Dilute Solution: A solution in which the ratio of the quantities of solute to solvent is small. (5.1)

Dilution: The process whereby a concentrated solution is made more dilute. (4.6)

Dimensional Analysis: A method for converting one set of units to another that relies on a logical sequence of steps and unit cancellation. (2.4)

Dimer: Two monomer units joined by chemical bonds or intramolecular forces. (13.7)

Dipole (Electric): Partial positive and partial negative charges separated by a distance. (9.7, 12.2)

Dipole–Dipole Attraction: Attraction between molecules that are dipoles. (12.2)

Dipole Moment (μ): The product of the sizes of the partial charges in a dipole multiplied by the distance between them; a measure of the polarity of a molecule. (9.7)

Diprotic Acid: An acid that can furnish two H^+ per molecule. (5.3)

Disaccharide: A carbohydrate whose molecules can be hydrolyzed to two monosaccharides. (23.6)

Dispersions: Mixtures of very small particles of immiscible substances that do not readily separate into different phases. Often used when describing emulsions. (13.8)

Dispersion Forces: Another term for London forces. (12.2)

Disproportionation: A redox reaction in which a portion of a substance is oxidized at the expense of the rest, which is reduced.

Dissociation: The separation of preexisting ions when an ionic compound dissolves or melts. (5.2)

Dissymmetric: Lacking or deficient in symmetry. In a dissymmetric molecule the effects of the individual bond dipoles do not cancel, causing the molecule as a whole to be polar. (10.3)

Distorted Tetrahedron: A description of a molecule in which the central atom is surrounded by five electron pairs, one of which is a lone pair of electrons. The central atom is bonded to four other atoms. The structure is also said to have a seesaw shape. (10.2)

DNA: Deoxyribonucleic acid; a nucleic acid that hydrolyzes to deoxyribose, phosphate ion, adenine, thymine, guanine, and cytosine, and that is the carrier of genes. (23.7)

DNA Double Helix: Two oppositely running strands of DNA held in a helical configuration by inter strand hydrogen bonds. (23.7)

Donor Atom: The atom on a ligand that makes an electron pair available in the formation of a complex. (18.4, 22.1)

Doped: A semiconductor material such as Si or Ge that has small amounts of electron rich (e.g., P) or electron deficient (e.g., B) atoms added. (10.9)

Double Bond: (a) A covalent bond formed by sharing two pairs of electrons. (9.5) (b) A covalent bond consisting of one sigma bond and one pi bond. (10.6)

Double Replacement Reaction (Metathesis Reaction): A reaction of two salts in which cations and anions exchange partners

$$(\text{e.g., } AgNO_3 + NaCl \longrightarrow$$
$$AgCl + NaNO_3). \text{ (5.5)}$$

Downs Cell: An electrolytic cell for the industrial production of sodium. (20.9)

Ductility: A metal's ability to be drawn (or stretched) into wire. (3.3)

Dynamic Equilibrium: A condition in which two opposing processes are occurring at equal rates. (5.3, 14.1)

E

ΔE: See *Internal Energy Change*.

Effective Collision: A collision between molecules that is capable of leading to a net chemical change. (14.5)

Effective Nuclear Charge: The net positive charge an outer electron experiences as a result of the partial screening of the full nuclear charge by core electrons. (8.10)

Effusion: The movement of a gas through a very tiny opening into a region of lower pressure. (11.6)

Effusion, Law of (Graham's Law): The rates of effusion of gases are inversely proportional to the square roots of their densities when compared at identical pressures and temperatures.

$$\text{Effusion rate} \propto \frac{1}{\sqrt{d}} \text{ (constant } P \text{ and } T)$$

where d is the gas density. (11.6)

Einstein Equation: $\Delta E = m_0 c^2$ where ΔE is the energy obtained when a quantity of rest mass, Δm_0, is destroyed, or the energy lost when this quantity of mass is created. (21.1)

Electric Dipole: Two poles of electric charge separated by a distance. (9.7)

Electrochemical Change: A chemical change that is caused by or that produces electricity. (20 Introduction)

Electrochemistry: The study of electrochemical changes. (20 Introduction)

Electrolysis: The production of a chemical change by the passage of electricity through a solution that contains ions or through a molten ionic compound. (20.7)

Electrolysis Cell: An apparatus for electrolysis. (20.7)

Electrolyte: A compound that conducts electricity either in solution or in the molten state. (5.2)

Electrolytic Cell: See *Electrolysis Cell*.

Electrolytic Conduction: The transport of electrical charge by ions. (20.1)

Electromagnetic Radiation: (See *Electromagnetic Wave*)

Electromagnetic Spectrum: The distribution of frequencies of electromagnetic radiation among various types of such radiation—microwave, infrared, visible, ultraviolet, X rays, and gamma rays. (8.1)

Electromagnetic Wave (Electromagnetic Radiation): The successive series of oscillations in the strengths of electrical and magnetic fields associated with light, microwaves, gamma rays, ultraviolet rays, infrared rays, and the like. (8.1)

Electron (e^- or $_{-1}^0e$): (a) A subatomic particle with a charge of 1− and mass of 0.0005486 u (9.109383×10^{-28} g) that occurs outside an atomic nucleus. The particle that moves when an electric current flows. (3.1) (b) A beta particle. (21.3)

Electron Affinity (EA): The energy change (usually expressed in kJ mol^{-1}) that occurs when an electron adds to an isolated gaseous atom or ion. (8.10)

Electron Capture: The capture by a nucleus of an orbital electron and that changes a proton into a neutron in the nucleus. (21.3)

Electron Cloud: Because of its wave properties, an electron's influence spreads out like a cloud around the nucleus. (8.9)

Electron Configuration: The distribution of electrons in an atom's orbitals. (8.7)

Electron Density: The concentration of the electron's charge within a given volume. (8.9)

Electron Domain: A region around an atom where one or more electron pairs are concentrated and which influences the shape of a molecule. (10.2)

Electron Domain Model: See *Valence Shell Electron Pair Repulsion Model*.

Electron Pair Bond: A covalent bond. (9.5)

Electron Spin: The spinning of an electron about its axis that is believed to occur because the electron behaves as a tiny magnet. (8.6)

Electron Volt (eV): The energy an electron receives when it is accelerated under the influence of 1 V and equal to 1.6×10^{-19} J. (29.3)

Electronegativity: The relative ability of an atom to attract electron density toward itself when joined to another atom by a covalent bond. (9.7)

Electronic Structure: The distribution of electrons in an atom's orbitals. (8.7)

Electroplating: Depositing a thin metallic coating on an object by electrolysis. (20.9)

Element: A substance in which all of the atoms have the same atomic number.

A substance that cannot be broken down by chemical reactions into anything that is both stable and simpler. (1.3, 3.1)

Elementary Process: One of the individual steps in the mechanism of a reaction. (14.8)

Elimination Reaction: The loss of a small molecule from a larger molecule as in the elimination of water from an alcohol. (23.3)

Emission Spectrum: See *Atomic Spectrum*.

Empirical Formula: A chemical formula that uses the smallest whole-number subscripts to give the proportions by atoms of the different elements present. (4.3)

Emulsion: A mixture of small globules of one immiscible liquid in another. (13.8)

Enantiomers: Stereoisomers whose molecular structures are related as an object to its mirror image but that cannot be superimposed. (22.4)

End Point: The moment in a titration when the indicator changes color and the titration is ended. (5.8, 17.9)

Endergonic: Descriptive of a change accompanied by an increase in free energy. (19.4)

Endothermic: Descriptive of a change in which a system's internal energy increases. (7.4)

Energy: Something that matter possesses by virtue of an ability to do work. (7.1)

Energy Band: Closely spaced energy levels in materials that can be described as a band of energy (10.9)

Energy Density: For a galvanic cell, the ratio of the energy available to the volume of the cell. (20.6)

Energy Level: A particular energy an electron can have in an atom or a molecule. (8.3)

English System: Old system of weights and measures that includes such units as pounds, ounces, gallons and miles. (2.2)

Enthalpy (H): The heat content of a system. (7.6, 19.1)

Enthalpy Change (ΔH): The difference in enthalpy between the initial state and the final state for some change. (7.6, 19.1)

Enthalpy Diagram: A graphical depiction of enthalpy changes following different paths from reactants to products. (7.8)

Enthalpy of Solution: See *Heat of Solution*.

Entropy (S): A thermodynamic quantity related to the number of equivalent ways the energy of a system can be distributed. The greater this number, the more probable is the state and the higher is the entropy. (19.3)

Entropy Change (ΔS): The difference in entropy between the initial state and the final state for some change. (19.4)

Enzyme: A catalyst in a living system and that consists of a protein. (23.6)

Equation of State of an Ideal Gas: See *Gas Law, Ideal*.

Equatorial Bond: A covalent bond located in the plane perpendicular to the long axis of a trigonal bipyramidal molecule. (10.1)

Equilibrium: See *Dynamic Equilibrium*.

Equilibrium Constant, K: The value that the mass action expression has when the system is at equilibrium. (15.2)

Equilibrium Law: The mathematical equation for a particular equilibrium system that sets the mass action expression equal to the equilibrium constant. (15.2)

Equilibrium Vapor Pressure of a Liquid: The pressure exerted by a vapor in equilibrium with its liquid state. (12.5)

Equilibrium Vapor Pressure of a Solid: The pressure exerted by a vapor in equilibrium with its solid state. (12.5)

Equivalence: A relationship between two quantities expressed in different units. (2.4)

Equivalence Point: The moment in a titration when the number of equivalents of the reactant added from a buret equals the number of equivalents of another reactant in the receiving flask. (17.9)

Error in a Measurement: The difference between a measurement and the "true" value we are trying to measure. (2.3)

Ester: An organic compound whose molecules have the ester group. (23.3)

$$-\overset{\displaystyle O}{\underset{}{\overset{\|}{C}}}-O-C$$
ester group

Ether: An organic compound in whose molecules two hydrocarbon groups are joined to an oxygen. (23.3)

Ethyl Group: Alkyl group derived from ethane, $-CH_2CH_3$ (23.2)

Evaporation: Change of state from a liquid to a vapor. (12.3)

Exact Number: A number obtained by a direct count or that results by a definition; and that is considered to have an infinite number of significant figures. (2.3)

Excess Reactant: The reactant left over once the limiting reactant is used up. (4.5)

Excited State: A term describing an atom or molecule where all of the electrons are not in their lowest possible energy levels. (8.2)

Exergonic: Descriptive of a change accompanied by a decrease in free energy. (19.4)

Exothermic: Descriptive of a change in which energy leaves a system and enters the surroundings. (7.4)

Expansion Work: See *Pressure–Volume Work*.

Exponential Notation: See *Scientific Notation*.

Extensive Property: A property of an object that is described by a physical quantity whose magnitude is proportional to the size or amount of the object (e.g., mass or volume). (2.1)

F

Face-Centered Cubic (fcc) Unit Cell: A unit cell having identical atoms, molecules, or ions at the corners of a cube and also in the center of each face of the cube. (12.11)

Factor-Label Method: See *Dimensional Analysis*

Fahrenheit Scale: A temperature scale on which water freezes at 32 °F and boils at 212 °F (at 1 atm) and between which points there are 180 degree divisions called Fahrenheit degrees. (2.2)

Family of Elements: See *Group*.

Faraday ($\mathscr{F}$): One mole of electrons; 9.65×10^4 coulombs. (20.4)

Faraday Constant ($\mathscr{F}$): 9.65×10^4 coulombs/mol e^-. (20.4)

Fatty Acid: One of several long-chain carboxylic acids produced by the hydrolysis (digestion) of a lipid. (23.6)

Film Dosimeter: A device used by people working with radioactive isotopes that records doses of atomic radiation by the darkening of photographic film. (21.6)

First Law of Thermodynamics: A formal statement of the law of conservation of energy, $\Delta E = q + w$. (7.5, 19.1)

First-Order Reaction: A reaction with a rate law in which rate = $k[A]^1$, where A is a reactant. (14.4)

Fissile Isotope: An isotope capable of undergoing fission following neutron capture. (21.8)

Fission: The breaking apart of atomic nuclei into smaller nuclei accompanied by the release of energy, and the source of energy in nuclear reactors. (21.2, 21.8)

Force: Anything that can cause an object to change its motion or direction.

Formal Charge: The apparent charge on an atom in a molecule or polyatomic ion as calculated by a set of rules. (9.8)

Formation Constant (K_{form}): The equilibrium constant for an equilibrium involving the formation of a complex ion. Also called the stability constant. (18.4)

Formula: See *Chemical Formula*.

Formula Mass: The sum of the atomic masses (in u) of all of the atoms represented in a chemical formula. Often used with units of g mol^{-1} to represent masses of ionic substances. (4.1) See also *Molar Mass*.

Formula Unit: A particle that has the composition given by the chemical formula. (3.4)

Forward Reaction: In a chemical equation, the reaction as read from left to right. (5.3, 15.1)

Fossil Fuels: Coal, oil, and natural gas.

Free Element: An element that is not combined with another element in a compound. (1.5)

Free Energy: See *Gibbs Free Energy* or *Standard Free Energy Change*

Free Energy Diagram: A plot of the changes in free energy for a multicomponent system versus the composition. (19.8)

Free Radical: An atom, molecule, or ion that has one or more unpaired electrons. (Chemistry Outside the Classroom 14.1, 21.6)

Freezing Point Depression: A colligative property of a liquid solution by which the freezing point of the solution is lower than that of the pure solvent. (13.7)

Frequency (ν): The number of cycles per second of electromagnetic radiation. (8.1)

Frequency Factor: The proportionality constant, A, in the Arrhenius equation. (14.7)

Fuel: Commonly one component of a combustion reaction; specifically the reducing agent. (7.9)

Fuel Cell: An electrochemical cell in which electricity is generated from the redox reactions of common fuels. (20.6)

Fullerene: An allotrope of carbon made of an extended joining together of five- and six-membered rings of carbon atoms. (10.10)

Functional Group: The group of atoms of an organic molecule that enters into a characteristic set of reactions that are independent of the rest of the molecule. (9.6)

Fusion: (a) Melting. (12.4) (b) The formation of atomic nuclei by the joining together of the nuclei of lighter atoms. (21.2, 21.8)

G

G: See *Gibbs Free Energy*.

ΔG: See *Gibbs Free Energy Change*.

$\Delta G°$: See *Standard Free Energy Change*.

$\Delta G_f°$: See *Standard Free Energy of Formation*.

Galvanic Cell: An electrochemical cell in which a spontaneous redox reaction produces electricity. (20.1)

Gamma Radiation: Electromagnetic radiation with wavelengths in the range of 1 Å or less (the shortest wavelengths of the spectrum). (20.3)

Gas: One of the states of matter. A gas consists of rapidly moving widely spaced atomic or molecular sized particles. (2.1)

Gas Constant, Universal (R):
$R = 0.0821$ liter atm mol^{-1} K^{-1} or $R = 8.314$ J mol^{-1} K^{-1} (11.5)

Gas Law, Combined: For a given mass of gas, the product of its pressure and volume divided by its Kelvin temperature is a constant. (11.3)

$$PV/T = \text{a constant}$$

Gas Law, Ideal: $PV = nRT$. (11.5)

Gay-Lussac's Law: See *Pressure–Temperature Law*.

Geiger Counter: A device that detects beta and gamma radiation. (21.6)

Genetic Code: The correlation of codons with amino acids. (23.7)

Geometric Isomer: One of a set of isomers that differ only in geometry. (22.4, 23.2)

Geometric Isomerism: The existence of isomers whose molecules have identical atomic organizations but different geometries; cis-trans isomers. (22.4, 23.2)

Gibbs Free Energy (G): A thermodynamic quantity that relates enthalpy (H), entropy (S), and temperature (T) by the equation: (19.4)

$$G = H - TS$$

Gibbs Free Energy Change (ΔG): The difference given by: (19.4)

$$\Delta G = \Delta H - T\Delta S$$

Glass: Any amorphous solid. (12.11)

Global climate change: A term used to describe the overall effect of man-made and natural substances in the atmosphere that may cause heating or cooling of the Earth. (11.9)

Glycogen: A polysaccharide that animals use to store glucose units for energy. (23.6)

Graham's Law: See *Effusion, Law of*.

Gram (g): 0.001 kg. (2.2)

Graphene: A sheet of graphite, one atom thick. (10.10)

Graphite: The most stable allotrope of carbon, consisting of layers of joined six-membered rings of carbon atoms. (10.10)

Gray (Gy): The SI unit of radiation absorbed dose. (21.6)

$$1\ \text{Gy} = 1\ \text{J kg}^{-1}$$

Greenhouse Effect: The retention of solar energy made possible by the ability of the greenhouse gases (e.g., CO_2, CH_4, H_2O, and the chlorofluorocarbons) to absorb outgoing radiation and reradiate some of it back to earth. (11.9)

Ground State: The lowest energy state of an atom or molecule. (8.3)

Group: A vertical column of elements in the periodic table. (3.2)

H

ΔH: See *Enthalpy Change*.

ΔH_{atom}: See *Atomization Energy*.

ΔH_c: See *Heat of Combustion*.

$\Delta H°$: See *Standard Heat of Reaction*.

$\Delta H_f°$: See *Standard Heat of Formation*.

ΔH_{fusion}: See *Molar Heat of Fusion*.

ΔH_{soln}: See *Heat of Solution*.

$\Delta H_{sublimation}$: See *Molar Heat of Sublimation*.

$\Delta H_{vaporization}$: See *Molar Heat of Vaporization*.

Half-Cell: That part of a galvanic cell in which either oxidation or reduction takes place. (20.1)

Half-Life ($t_{1/2}$): The time required for a reactant concentration or the mass of a radionuclide to be reduced by half. (14.4)

Half-Reaction: A hypothetical reaction that constitutes exclusively either the oxidation or the reduction half of a redox reaction and all species taking part in the change are given together with enough electrons to give the correct electrical balance. (6.2)

Hall–Héroult Process: A method for manufacturing aluminum by the electrolysis of aluminum oxide in molten cryolite. (20.8)

Halogen Family: Group 7A in the periodic table—fluorine, chlorine, bromine, iodine, and astatine. (3.2)

Hard Water: Water with dissolved Mg^{2+}, Ca^{2+}, Fe^{2+}, or Fe^{3+} ions at a concentration high enough (above 25 mg L^{-1}) to interfere with the use of soap. (Chemistry Outside the Classroom 5.2)

Heat: Energy that flows from a hot object to a cold object as a result of their difference in temperature. (7.1)

Heat Capacity: The quantity of heat needed to raise the temperature of an object by 1 °C. (7.3)

Heat of Combustion (ΔH_c): The heat evolved in the combustion of a substance. (7.6)

Heat of Formation, Standard: See *Standard Heat of Formation*.

Heat of Reaction: The heat exchanged between a system and its surroundings when a chemical change occurs in the system. (7.5)

Heat of Reaction at Constant Pressure (q_p): The heat of a reaction in an open system, ΔH. (7.5, 19.1)

Heat of Reaction at Constant Volume (q_v): The heat of a reaction in a sealed vessel, like a bomb calorimeter, ΔE. (7.6)

Heat of Reaction, Standard: See *Standard Heat of Reaction*.

Heat of Solution (ΔH_{soln}): The energy exchanged between the system and its surroundings when one mole of a solute dissolves in a solvent to make a dilute solution. (13.2)

Heating Curve: A graph showing how the temperature of a substance changes as heat is added to it at a constant rate as the substance undergoes changes in its physical state. (12.7)

Henderson–Hasselbalch Equation:

$$pH = pK_a + \log\frac{[A^-]_{initial}}{[HA]_{initial}} \text{ or }$$

$$pH = pK_a + \log\frac{[salt]}{[acid]} \quad (16.5)$$

$$(17.7)$$

Henry's Law: See *Pressure–Solubility Law.*

Hertz (Hz): 1 cycle s^{-1}; the SI unit of frequency. (8.1)

Hess's Law: For any reaction that can be written in steps, the standard heat of reaction is the same as the sum of the standard heats of reaction for the steps. (7.8)

Hess's Law Equation: For the change,

$$aA + bB + \cdots \longrightarrow nN + mM + \cdots \quad (6.8)$$

$$\Delta H° = \left(\begin{array}{c}\text{sum of } \Delta H_f° \text{ of all} \\ \text{of the products}\end{array}\right) - \left(\begin{array}{c}\text{sum of } \Delta H_f° \text{ of all} \\ \text{of the reactants}\end{array}\right)$$

$$(7.9)$$

Heterocyclic Rings: Molecular rings that include one or more multivalent atoms other than carbon. (23.1)

Heterogeneous Catalyst: A catalyst that is in a different phase than the reactants and onto whose surface the reactant molecules are adsorbed and where they react. (14.9)

Heterogeneous Equilibrium: An equilibrium involving more than one phase. (15.4)

Heterogeneous Mixture: A mixture that has two or more phases with different properties. (1.3)

Heterogeneous Reaction: A reaction in which not all of the chemical species are in the same phase. (14.1, 15.4)

Heteronuclear Molecule: A molecule in which not all atoms are of the same element. (10.7)

Hexagonal Closest Packing (hcp): Efficient packing of spheres with an A-B-A-B-. . . alternating stacking of layers of spheres. (12.11)

High-Spin Complex: A complex ion or coordination compound in which there is the maximum number of unpaired electrons. (22.5)

Hole: An electron deficient site in a semiconductor. A positive charge carrier. (20.6)

Homogeneous Catalyst: A catalyst that is in the same phase as the reactants. (14.9)

Homogeneous Equilibrium: An equilibrium system in which all components are in the same phase. (15.2)

Homogeneous Mixture: A mixture that has only one phase and that has uniform properties throughout; a solution. (1.3)

Homogeneous Reaction: A reaction in which all of the chemical species are in the same phase. (14.1, 15.2)

Homonuclear Diatomic Molecule: A diatomic molecule in which both atoms are of the same element. (10.7)

Hund's Rule: Electrons that occupy orbitals of equal energy are distributed with unpaired spins as much as possible among all such orbitals. (8.7)

Hybrid Atomic Orbitals: Orbitals formed by mixing two or more of the basic atomic orbitals of an atom and that make possible more effective overlaps with the orbitals of adjacent atoms than do ordinary atomic orbitals. (10.5)

Hydrate: A compound that contains molecules of water in a definite ratio to other components. (1.5)

Hydrated Ion: An ion surrounded by a cage of water molecules that are attracted by the charge on the ion. (5.2)

Hydration: The development in an aqueous solution of a cage of water molecules about ions or polar molecules of the solute. (13.1)

Hydration Energy: The enthalpy change associated with the hydration of gaseous ions or molecules as they dissolve in water. (13.2)

Hydride: (a) A binary compound of hydrogen. (3.6) (b) A compound containing the hydride ion (H$^-$).

Hydrocarbon: An organic compound whose molecules consist entirely of carbon and hydrogen atoms. (3.6, 23.2)

Hydrogen Bonding: An extra strong dipole–dipole attraction between a hydrogen bound covalently to nitrogen, oxygen, or fluorine and another nitrogen, oxygen, or fluorine atom. (12.2)

Hydrogen Electrode: The standard of comparison for reduction potentials and for which $E°_{H^+}$ has a value of 0.00 V at 25 °C, when $P_{H_2} = 1$ atm and $[H^+] = 1\ M$ in the reversible half-cell reaction: $2H^+(aq) + 2e^- \rightleftharpoons H_2(g)$. (20.2)

Hydrolysis: A reaction with water (16.6, 17.6)

Hydrometer: A device for measuring specific gravity. (20.6)

Hydronium Ion: H_3O^+. (5.3)

Hydrophilic: Miscible with water, literally, "water loving." (13.8, 23.6)

Hydrophilic Group: A polar molecular unit capable of having dipole–dipole attractions or hydrogen bonds with water molecules. (23.6)

Hydrophobic. Not miscible with water, literally, "afraid of water." (13.8, 23.6)

Hydrophobic Group: A nonpolar molecular unit with no affinity for water. (22.7)

Hypertonic Solution: A solution that has a higher osmotic pressure than cellular fluids. (13.7)

Hypothesis: A tentative explanation of the results of experiments. (1.2)

Hypotonic Solution: A solution that has a lower osmotic pressure than cellular fluids. (13.7)

Hypoxia: Condition of natural water where there is not dissolved oxygen to support aquatic life. (13.3)

I

Ideal Gas: A hypothetical gas that obeys the gas laws exactly. (11.3)

Ideal Gas Law: $PV = nRT$. (11.5)

Ideal Solution: A hypothetical solution that would obey the vapor pressure–concentration law (Raoult's law) exactly. (13.2)

Immiscible: Mutually insoluble. Usually used to describe liquids that are insoluble in each other. (13.1)

Incompressible: Incapable of losing volume under increasing pressure. (12.3)

Independent Variable: The experimental variable of a pair of variables whose value is first selected and from which the value of the dependent variable then results.

Indicator: A chemical put in a solution being titrated and whose change in color signals the end point. (5.8, 17.9)

Induced Dipole: A dipole created when the electron cloud of an atom or a molecule is distorted by a neighboring dipole or by an ion. (12.2)

Inert Gas: See *Noble Gases*

Initiation Step: The step in a chain reaction that produces reactive species that can start chain propagation steps. (Chemistry Outside the Classroom 14.1)

Inner Transition Elements: Members of the two long rows of elements below the main body of the periodic table—elements 58–71 and elements 90–103. (3.2)

Inorganic Compound: A compound made from any elements except those compounds of carbon classified as organic compounds. (3.5)

Instability Constant (K_{inst}): The reciprocal of the formation constant for an equilibrium in which a complex ion forms. (18.4)

Instantaneous Dipole: A momentary dipole in an atom, ion, or molecule caused by the erratic movement of electrons. (12.2)

Instantaneous Rate: The rate of reaction at any particular moment during a reaction. (14.2)

Integrated Rate Law: A rate law that relates concentration versus time. (14.4)

Intensive Property: A property whose physical magnitude is independent of the size of the sample, such as density or temperature. (2.1)

Intercalation: The insertion of small atoms or ions between layers in a crystal such as graphite. (20.6)

Interference Fringes: Pattern of light produced by waves that undergo diffraction. (8.4)

Intermolecular Forces (Intermolecular Attractions): Attractions *between* neighboring molecules. (12.2)

Internal Energy (E): The sum of all of the kinetic energies and potential energies of the particles within a system. (7.2, 19.1)

Internal Energy Change (ΔE): The difference in internal energy between the initial state and the final state for some change. (7.2)

International System of Units (SI): The successor to the metric system of measurements that retains most of the units of the metric system and their decimal relationships but employs new reference standards. (2.2)

Intramolecular Forces: Forces of attraction within molecules; chemical bonds. (11.2)

Inverse Square Law: The intensity of a radiation is inversely proportional to the square of the distance from its source. (21.6)

Ion: An electrically charged particle on the atomic or molecular scale of size. (3.4)

Ion–Dipole Attraction: The attraction between an ion and the charged end of a polar molecule. (12.2)

Ion–Electron Method: A method for balancing redox reactions that uses half-reactions. (6.2)

Ion–Induced Dipole Attraction: Attraction between an ion and a dipole induced in a neighboring molecule. (12.2)

Ion Pair: A more or less loosely associated pair of ions in a solution. (13.7)

Ion Product: The mass action expression for the solubility equilibrium involving the ions of a salt and equal to the product of the molar concentrations of the ions, each concentration raised to a power that equals the number of ions obtained from one formula unit of the salt. (18.1)

Ion Product Constant of Water (K_w): $K_w = [H^+][OH^-]$ (17.1)

Ionic Bond: The attractions between ions that hold them together in ionic compounds. (9.2)

Ionic Character: The extent to which a covalent bond has a dipole moment and is polarized. (9.7)

Ionic Compound: A compound consisting of positive and negative ions. (3.4)

Ionic Crystal: A crystal that has ions located at the lattice points. (12.13)

Ionic Equation: A chemical equation in which soluble strong electrolytes are written in dissociated or ionized form. (5.2)

Ionic Reaction: A chemical reaction in which ions are involved. (5.2)

Ionization Energy (IE): The energy needed to remove an electron from an isolated, gaseous atom, ion, or molecule (usually given in units of kJ mol^{-1}). (8.10)

Ionization Reaction: A reaction of chemical particles that produces ions. (5.3)

Ionizing Radiation: Any high-energy radiation—X rays, gamma rays, or radiations from radionuclides—that generates ions as it passes through matter. (22.6)

Isolated System: A system that cannot exchange matter or energy with its surroundings. (7.3)

Isomer: One of a set of compounds that have identical molecular formulas but different structures. (22.4)

Isomerism: The existence of sets of isomers. (9.6, 22.4)

Isopropyl Group: Alkyl group derived from propane, $-CH(CH_3)_2$ (23.2)

Isothermal: A system where the temperature remains unchanged. (19.1)

Isotonic Solution: A solution that has the same osmotic pressure as cellular fluids. (12.8)

Isotopes: Atoms of the same element with different atomic masses. Atoms of the same element with different numbers of neutrons in their nuclei. (3.1)

IUPAC Rules: The formal rules for naming substances as developed by the International Union of Pure and Applied Chemistry. (3.5, 23.2)

J

Joule (J): The SI unit of energy. (7.1)
$1\ J = 1\ kg\ m^2\ s^{-2}$
$4.184\ J = 1\ cal$ (exactly)

K

K: See *Kelvin.*

K_a: See *Acid Ionization Constant.*

K_b: See *Base Ionization Constant.*

K_{form}: See *Formation Constant.*

K_{inst}: See *Instability Constant.*

K_{sp}: See *Solubility Product Constant.*

K_{spa}: See *Acid Solubility Product.*

K_w: See *Ion Product Constant of Water.*

K-Capture: See *Electron Capture.*

Kelvin (K): One degree on the Kelvin scale of temperature and identical in size to the Celsius degree. (2.2)

Kelvin Scale: The temperature scale on which water freezes at 273.15 K and boils at 373.15 K and that has 100 degree divisions called kelvins between these points. K = °C + 273.15. (2.2)

Ketone: An organic compound whose molecules have the carbonyl group ($C=O$) flanked by hydrocarbon groups. (9.6)

Kilocalorie (kcal): 1000 cal. (7.1)

Kilogram (kg): The base unit for mass in the SI and equal to the mass of a cylinder of platinum–iridium alloy kept by the International Bureau of Weights and Measures at Sevres, France. 1 kg = 1000 g. (2.2)

Kilojoule (kJ): 1000 J. (7.1)

Kinetic Energy (KE): Energy of motion. KE = $(1/2)mv^2$. (7.1)

Kinetic Molecular Theory: Molecules of a substance are in constant motion with a distribution of kinetic energies at a given temperature. The average kinetic energy of the molecules is proportional to the Kelvin temperature. (7.2)

Kinetic Molecular Theory of Gases: A set of postulates used to explain the gas laws. A gas consists of an extremely large number of very tiny, very hard particles in constant, random motion. They have negligible volume and, between collisions, experience no forces between themselves. (11.7)

L

Lanthanide Elements: Elements 58–71. (3.2)

Lattice: A symmetrical pattern of points arranged with constant repeat distances along lines oriented at constant angles. (12.11)

Lattice Energy: Energy released by the imaginary process in which isolated ions come together to form a crystal of an ionic compound. (9.2)

Law: A description of behavior (and not an *explanation* of behavior) based on the results of many experiments. (1.2)

Law of Combining Volumes: When gases react at the same temperature and pressure, their combining volumes are in ratios of simple whole numbers. (11.4)

Law of Conservation of Energy: The energy of the universe is constant; it can be neither created nor destroyed but only transferred and transformed. (7.1)

Law of Conservation of Mass: No detectable gain or loss in mass occurs in chemical reactions. Mass is conserved. (1.4)

Law of Conservation of Mass–Energy: The sum of all the mass in the universe and of all of the energy, expressed as an equivalent in mass (calculated by the Einstein equation), is a constant. (22.1)

Law of Definite Proportions: In a given chemical compound, the elements are always combined in the same proportion by mass. (1.4)

Law of Gas Effusion: See *Effusion, Law of.*

Law of Multiple Proportions: Whenever two elements form more than one compound, the different masses of one element that combine with the same mass of the other are in a ratio of small whole numbers. (2.4)

Law of Partial Pressures: See *Partial Pressures, Dalton's Law of.*

Law of Radioactive Decay:

$$\text{Activity} = -\frac{\Delta N}{\Delta t} = kN,$$

where ΔN is the change in the number of radioactive nuclei during the time span Δt, and k is the decay constant. (21.6)

Le Châtelier's Principle: When a system that is in dynamic equilibrium is subjected to a disturbance that upsets the equilibrium, the system undergoes a change that counteracts the disturbance and, if possible, restores the equilibrium. (15.6)

Lead Storage Battery: A galvanic cell of about 2 V involving lead and lead(IV) oxide in sulfuric acid. (20.6)

Leclanché Cell: See *Zinc–Manganese Dioxide Cell.*

Lewis Acid: An electron-pair acceptor. (16.4)

Lewis Base: An electron-pair donor. (16.4)

Lewis Structure (Lewis Formula): A structural formula drawn with Lewis symbols and that uses dots and dashes to show the valence electrons and shared pairs of electrons. (9.5)

Lewis Symbol: The symbol of an element that includes dots to represent the valence electrons of an atom of the element. (9.4)

Ligand: A molecule or an anion that can bind to a metal ion to form a complex. (18.4, 22.1)

Light-Emitting Diode (LED): A semiconductor device where a small applied voltage will eject visible photons. (10.9)

Like Dissolves Like Rule: Strongly polar and ionic solutes tend to dissolve in polar solvents and nonpolar solutes tend to dissolve in nonpolar solvents. (13.1)

Limiting Reactant: The reactant that determines how much product can form when nonstoichiometric amounts of reactants are used. (4.5)

Line Spectrum: An atomic spectrum. So named because the light emitted by an atom and focused through a narrow slit yields a series of lines when projected on a screen. (8.1)

Linear Molecule: A molecule all of whose atoms lie on a straight line. (10.1, 10.2)

Lipid: Any substance found in plants or animals that can be dissolved in nonpolar solvents. (23.6)

Liquid: One of the states of matter. A liquid consists of tightly packed atomic or molecular sized particles that can move past each other. (2.1)

Liter (L): 1 dm³. 1 L = 1000 mL = 1000 cm³. (2.2)

Lithium Ion Cell: A cell in which lithium ions are transferred between the electrodes through an electrolyte, while electrons travel through the external circuit. (20.6)

Lithium–Manganese Dioxide Battery: A battery that uses metallic lithium as the anode and manganese dioxide as the cathode. (20.6)

Localized Bond: A covalent bond in which the bonding pair of electrons is localized between two nuclei. (10.2)

London Forces (Dispersion Forces): Weak attractive forces caused by instantaneous dipole–induced dipole attractions. (12.2)

Lone Pair: A pair of electrons in the valence shell of an atom that is not shared with another atom. An unshared pair of electrons. (10.2)

Low-Spin Complex: A coordination compound or a complex ion with electrons paired as much as possible in the lower energy set of *d* orbitals. (22.5)

M

Macromolecule: A molecule whose molecular mass is very large. (23.5)

Macroscopic: A scale that includes masses in the range of 1 to 1000 g or the equivalent. Also considered the laboratory scale. (1.2)

Magic Numbers: The numbers 2, 8, 20, 28, 50, 82, and 126, numbers whose significance in nuclear science is that a nuclide in which the number of protons or neutrons equals a magic number has nuclei that are relatively more stable than those of other nuclides nearby in the band of stability. (21.4)

Magnetic Quantum Number (m_ℓ): A quantum number that can have values from zero to $N - 1$. (8.5)

Main Group Elements: Elements in any of the A groups in the periodic table. (3.2)

Main Reaction: The desired reaction between the reactants as opposed to competing reactions that give by-products. (4.6)

Malleability: A metal's ability to be hammered or rolled into thin sheets. (3.3)

Manometer: A device for measuring the pressure within a closed system. The two types—*closed end* and *open end*—differ according to whether the operating fluid (e.g., mercury) is exposed at one end to the atmosphere. (11.2)

Mass: A measure of the amount of matter that there is in a given sample. (1.3)

Mass Action Expression: A fraction in which the numerator is the product of the molar concentrations of the products, each raised to a power equal to its coefficient in the equilibrium equation, and the denominator is the product of the molar concentrations of the reactants, each also raised to the power that equals its coefficient in the equation. (For gaseous reactions, partial pressures can be used in place of molar concentrations.) (15.2)

Mass Defect: For a given isotope, it is the mass that changed into energy as the nucleons gathered to form the nucleus, this energy being released from the system. (21.2)

Mass Fraction: The ratio of the mass of one component of a mixture to the total mass of that same mixture. (13.5)

Mass Number: The numerical sum of the protons and neutrons in an atom of a given isotope. (3.1)

Matter: Anything that has mass and occupies space. (1.3)

Mean: The sum of N numerical values divided by N; the average. (2.3)

Measurement: A numerical observation. (2.2)

Mechanism of a Reaction: The series of individual steps (called elementary processes) in a chemical reaction that gives the net, overall change. (14.8)

Melting Point: The temperature at which a substance melts; the temperature at which a solid is in equilibrium with its liquid state. (12.4)

Meniscus: The interface between a liquid and a gas.

Metal: An element or an alloy that is a good conductor of electricity, that has a shiny surface, and that is malleable and ductile; an element that normally forms positive ions and has an oxide that is basic. (3.3)

Metallic Conduction: Conduction of electrical charge by the movement of electrons. (20.1)

Metallic Crystal: A solid having positive ions at the lattice positions that are attracted to a "sea of electrons" that extends throughout the entire crystal. (12.13)

Metalloids: Elements with properties that lie between those of metals and nonmetals, and that are found in the periodic table around the diagonal line running from boron (B) to astatine (At). (3.3)

Metathesis Reaction: See *Double Replacement Reaction*.

Meter (m): The SI base unit for length. (2.2)

Methyl Group: Alkyl group derived from methane, —CH₃

Metric Units: A decimal system of units for physical quantities taken over by the SI. (2.2) See also *International System of Units*.

Micelle: A structure formed from molecules that have a hydrophobic and hydrophilic end. The result is a circular or spherical structure with the molecules forming a rudimentary membrane. (13.8)

Millibar: 1 mb = 10^{-3} bar. (11.2)

Milliliter (mL): 0.001 L. 1000 mL = 1 L. (2.2)

Millimeter (mm): 0.001 m. 1000 mm = 1 m. (2.2)

Millimeter of Mercury (mm Hg): A unit of measurement that is proportional to pressure; equal to 1/760 atm. 760 mm Hg = 1 atm. 1 mm Hg = 1 torr. (11.2)

Miscible: Mutually soluble. (13.1)

Mixture: Any matter consisting of two or more substances physically combined in no particular proportion by mass. (1.3)

MO Theory: See *Molecular Orbital Theory*.

Model, Theoretical: A picture or a mental construction derived from a set of ideas and assumptions that are imagined to be true because they can be used to explain certain observations and measurements (e.g., the model of an ideal gas). (1.2)

Mol L⁻¹ s⁻¹: See *Rate of Reaction*

Molal Boiling Point Elevation Constant (K_b): The number of degrees (°C) per unit of molal concentration that a boiling point of a solution is higher than that of the pure solvent. (13.7)

Molal Concentration (*m*): The number of moles of solute in 1000 g of solvent. (13.5)

Molal Freezing Point Depression Constant (K_f): The number of degrees (°C) per unit of molal concentration that a freezing point of a solution is lower than that of the pure solvent. (13.7)

Molality: The molal concentration. (13.5)

Molar Concentration (*M*): The number of moles of solute per liter of solution. The molarity of a solution. (5.6)

Molar Enthalpy of Solution: See *Heat of Solution*.

Molar Heat Capacity: The heat that can raise the temperature of 1 mol of a substance by 1 °C; the heat capacity per mole. (7.3)

Molar Heat of Fusion, ΔH_{fusion}: The heat absorbed when 1 mol of a solid melts to give 1 mol of the liquid at constant temperature and pressure. (12.7)

Molar Heat of Sublimation, $\Delta H_{sublimation}$: The heat absorbed when 1 mol of a solid sublimes to give 1 mol of its vapor at constant temperature and pressure. (12.7)

Molar Heat of Vaporization, $\Delta H_{vaporization}$: The heat absorbed when 1 mol of a liquid changes to 1 mol of its vapor at constant-temperature and pressure. (12.7)

Molar Mass: The mass of one mole of a substance; the mass in grams equal to the sum of the atomic masses of the atoms in a substance, with units of g mol⁻¹. (4.1)

Molar Solubility: The number of moles of solute required to give 1 L of a saturated solution of the solute. (18.1)

Molar Volume, Standard: The volume of 1 mol of a gas at STP; 22.4 L mol⁻¹. (11.4)

Molarity: See *Molar Concentration*.

Mole (mol): The SI unit for amount of substance; the formula mass in grams of an element or compound; an amount of a chemical substance that contains 6.022×10^{23} formula units. (4.1)

Mole Fraction: The ratio of the number of moles of one component of a mixture to the total number of moles of all components. (11.6)

Mole Percent (mol%): The mole fraction of a component expressed as a percent; mole fraction × 100%. (11.6, 13.5)

Molecular Compound: A compound consisting of electrically neutral molecules. (2.6)

Molecular Crystal: A crystal that has molecules or individual atoms at the lattice points. (12.13)

Molecular Equation: A chemical equation that gives the full formulas of all of the reactants and products and that is used to plan an actual experiment. (5.2)

Molecular Formula: A chemical formula that gives the actual composition of one molecule. (3.6, 4.3)

Molecular Kinetic Energy: The energy associated with the motions of and within molecules as they fly about, spinning and vibrating. (7.2)

Molecular Mass: The sum of the atomic masses (in u) of all of the atoms represented in a molecular chemical substance; also called the *molecular weight*.

May be used with units of g mol⁻¹. (4.1) See also *Molar Mass*.

Molecular Orbital (MO): An orbital that extends over two or more atomic nuclei. (10.7)

Molecular Orbital Theory (MO Theory): A theory about covalent bonds that views a molecule as a collection of positive nuclei surrounded by electrons distributed among a set of bonding, antibonding, and nonbonding orbitals of different energies. (10.4)

Molecular Weight: See *Molecular Mass*.

Molecule: A neutral particle composed of two or more atoms combined in a definite ratio of whole numbers. (1.5, 3.6)

Monatomic: A particle consisting of just one atom. (3.5)

Monoclinic Sulfur: An allotrope of sulfur. (10.10)

Monodentate Ligand: A ligand that can attach itself to a metal ion by only one atom. (22.1)

Monomer: A substance of relatively low formula mass that is used to make a polymer. (23.5)

Monoprotic Acid: An acid that can furnish one H⁺ per molecule. (5.3)

Monosaccharide: A carbohydrate that cannot be hydrolyzed. (23.6)

N

n-type Semiconductor: A semiconductor that carries electrical charge by means of electron movement. (10.9)

Nanotechnology: The study and use of unique properties of matter that has dimensions measured in nanometers. (1.6)

Negative Charge: A type of electrical charge possessed by certain particles such as the electron. A negative charge is attracted by a positive charge and is repelled by another negative charge. (3.1)

Negative Charge Carrier: In a semiconductor, the electrons are considered to be negative charge carriers. (20.6)

Nernst Equation: An equation relating cell potential and concentration. (20.5)

$$E_{cell} = E^{\circ}_{cell} - \frac{RT}{n\mathscr{F}} \ln Q$$

Net Ionic Equation: A chemical equation that shows only the reacting ions and from which spectator ions have been omitted. It is balanced when both atoms and electrical charge balance. (5.2)

Network Solid: See *Covalent Crystal*.

Neutral Solution: A solution in which [H⁺] = [OH⁻]. (17.1)

Neutralization, Acid–Base: See *Acid–Base Neutralization*.

Neutron: A subatomic particle with a charge of zero, a mass of 1.0086649 u $(1.674927 \times 10^{-24}$ g) and that exists in all atomic nuclei except those of the hydrogen-1 isotope. (3.1)

Neutron Activation Analysis: A technique to analyze for trace impurities in a sample by studying the frequencies and intensities of the gamma radiations they emit after they have been rendered radioactive by neutron bombardment of the sample. (21.7)

Neutron Emission: A nuclear reaction in which a neutron is ejected. (21.3)

Nicad Battery: A nickel–cadmium cell. (20.6)

Nickel–Cadmium Storage Cell: A galvanic cell of about 1.4 V involving the reaction of cadmium with nickel(IV) oxide. (20.6)

Nitrogen Family: Group 5A in the periodic table—nitrogen, phosphorus, arsenic, antimony, and bismuth. (3.2)

Noble Gases: Group 8A in the periodic table—helium, neon, argon, krypton, xenon, and radon. (3.2)

Noble Metals: The group of transition metals, including gold, silver and platinum, that have relatively low chemical reactivity. (9.7)

Nodal Plane: A plane that can be drawn to separate opposing lobes of p, d, and f orbitals. (8.9)

Node: A place where the amplitude or intensity of a wave is zero. (8.4)

Nomenclature: The names of substances and the rules for devising names. (3.5)

Nonbonding Domain: A region in the valence shell of an atom that holds an unshared pair of electrons and that influences the shape of a molecule. (10.2)

Nonbonding Molecular Orbital: A molecular orbital that has no net effect on the stability of a molecule when populated with electrons and that is localized on one atom in the molecule. (10.7)

Nonelectrolyte: A compound that in its molten state or in solution cannot conduct electricity. (5.2)

Nonlinear Molecule: A molecule in which the atoms do not lie in a straight line. (10.2)

Nonmetal: A nonductile, nonmalleable, nonconducting element that tends to form negative ions (if it forms them at all) far more readily than positive ions and whose oxide is likely to show acidic properties. (3.3)

Nonmetal Hydrides: Usually binary compounds that contain hydrogen and a nonmetal. (3.6)

Nonmetallic Element: See *Nonmetals*

Nonoxidizing Acid: An acid in which the anion is a poorer oxidizing agent than the hydrogen ion (e.g., HCl, H_2SO_4, H_3PO_4). (6.3)

Nonpolar Covalent Bond: A covalent bond in which the electron pair(s) are shared equally by the two atoms. (9.7)

Nonpolar Molecule: A molecule that has no net dipole moment. (9.3)

Nonvolatile: Descriptive of a substance with a high boiling point, a low vapor pressure. and that does not evaporate. (12.6)

Normal Boiling Point: The temperature at which the vapor pressure of a liquid equals 1 atm. (12.6)

Nuclear Binding Energy: See *Binding Energy, Nuclear.*

Nuclear Chain Reaction: A self-sustaining nuclear reaction. (21.8)

Nuclear Equation: A description of a nuclear reaction that uses the special symbols of isotopes, that describes some kind of nuclear transformation or disintegration, and that is balanced when the sums of the atomic numbers on either side of the arrow are equal and the sums of the mass numbers are also equal. (21.3)

Nuclear Fission: See *Fission.*

Nuclear Fusion: See *Fusion.*

Nuclear Radiation: Alpha, beta, or gamma radiation emitted by radioactive nuclei. (21.3)

Nuclear Reaction: A change in the composition or energy of the nuclei of isotopes accompanied by one or more events such as the radiation of nuclear particles or electromagnetic energy, transmutation, fission, or fusion. (13.4, 20.3)

Nucleic Acids: Polymers in living cells that store and translate genetic information and whose molecules hydrolyze to give a sugar unit (ribose from ribonucleic acid, RNA, or deoxyribose from deoxyribonucleic acid, DNA), a phosphate, and a set of four of the five nitrogen-containing, heterocyclic bases (adenine, thymine, guanine, cytosine, and uracil). (23.7)

Nucleon: A proton or a neutron. (3.1, 21.2)

Nucleus: The hard, dense core of an atom that holds the atom's protons and neutrons. (3.1)

Nylon 6,6: A polymer of a six-carbon dicarboxylic acid and a six-carbon diamine. (23.5)

O

Observation: A statement that accurately describes something we see, hear, taste, feel, or smell. (1.2)

Octahedral Molecule: A molecule in which a central atom is surrounded by six atoms located at the vertices of an imaginary octahedron. (10.1)

Octahedron: An eight-sided figure that can be envisioned as two square pyramids sharing the common square base. (10.1)

Octet (of Electrons): Eight electrons in the valence shell of an atom. (9.3)

Octet Rule: An atom tends to gain or lose electrons until its outer shell has eight electrons. (9.3, 9.5)

Odd–Even Rule: When the numbers of protons and neutrons in an atomic nucleus are both even, the isotope is more likely to be stable than when both numbers are odd. (21.4)

Open System: A system that can exchange both matter and energy with its surroundings. (7.3)

Open-End Manometer: See *Manometer.*

Optical Isomers: Stereoisomers other than geometric (cis–trans) isomers and that include substances that can rotate the plane of plane-polarized light. (22.4)

Orbital: An electron waveform with a particular energy and a unique set of values for the quantum numbers n, ℓ, and m_ℓ. (8.5)

Orbital Diagram: A diagram in which the electrons in an atom's orbitals are represented by arrows to indicate paired and unpaired spins. (8.7)

Order (of a Reaction): The sum of the exponents in the rate law is the *overall* order. Each exponent gives the order of the reaction with respect to a specific reactant. (14.3)

Organic Acid: An acid that contains the

carboxyl group, $-\overset{\overset{\displaystyle O}{\|}}{C}-OH$ (8.3, 9.6, 22.6)

Organic Chemistry: The study of the compounds of carbon that are not classified as inorganic. (3.6, 23.1)

Organic Compound: Any compound of carbon other than a carbonate, bicarbonate, cyanide, cyanate, carbide, or gaseous oxide. (3.5, 9.6)

Orthorhombic Sulfur: The most stable allotrope of sulfur, composed of S_8 rings. (10.10)

Osmosis: The passage of solvent molecules, but not those of solutes, through a semipermeable membrane; the limiting case of dialysis. (13.7)

Osmotic Membrane: A membrane that allows passage of solvent, but not solute particles. (13.7)

Osmotic Pressure: The back pressure that would have to be applied to prevent osmosis; one of the colligative properties. (13.7)

Outer Electrons: The electrons in the occupied shell with the largest principal quantum number. An atom's electrons in its valence shell. (8.8)

Outer Shell: The occupied shell in an atom having the highest principal quantum number (n). (8.8)

Overall Order of Reaction: The sum of the exponents on the concentration terms in a rate law. (14.3)

Overlap of Orbitals: A portion of two orbitals from different atoms that share the same space in a molecule. (10.4)

Oxidation: A change in which an oxidation number increases (becomes more positive). A loss of electrons. (6.1)

Oxidation Number: The charge that an atom in a molecule or ion would have if all of the electrons in its bonds belonged entirely to the more electronegative atoms; the oxidation state of an atom. (6.1)

Oxidation State: See *Oxidation Number*.

Oxidation–Reduction Reaction: A chemical reaction in which changes in oxidation numbers occur. (6.1)

Oxidizing Acid: An acid in which the anion is a stronger oxidizing agent than H^+ (e.g., $HClO_4$, HNO_3). (6.3)

Oxidizing Agent: The substance that causes oxidation and that is itself reduced. (6.1)

Oxoacid: An acid that contains oxygen besides hydrogen and another element (e.g., HNO_3, H_3PO_4, H_2SO_4). (5.4, 16.3)

Oxoanion: The anion of an oxoacid (e.g., ClO_4^-, SO_4^{2-}). (16.3)

Oxygen Family: Group 6A in the periodic table—oxygen, sulfur, selenium, tellurium, and polonium.

Ozone: A very reactive allotrope of oxygen with the formula O_3. (11.9)

Ozone Hole: The large decrease of stratospheric ozone at the Earth's poles at the end of winter each year; ascribed to the effect of chlorine compounds. (11.9)

P

p-n Junction: The surface where a p-type semiconductor and an n-type semiconductor meet. (10.9)

p-type Semiconductor: A semiconductor material with a deficit of electrons causing charge to be carried by positive charge carriers or "holes." (10.9)

Pairing Energy: The energy required to force two electrons to become paired and occupy the same orbital. (22.5)

Paramagnetism: The weak magnetism of a substance whose atoms, molecules, or ions have one or more unpaired electrons. (8.6)

Partial Charge: Charges at opposite ends of a dipole that are fractions of full 1+ or 1– charges. (9.7)

Partial Pressure: The pressure contributed by an individual gas to the total pressure of a gas mixture. (11.6)

Partial Pressure, Law of (Dalton's Law of Partial Pressures): The total pressure of a mixture of gases equals the sum of their partial pressures. (11.6)

Pascal (Pa): The SI unit of pressure equal to 1 newton m^{-2}; 1 atm = 101,325 Pa. (11.2)

Pauli Exclusion Principle: No two electrons in an atom can have the same values for all four of their quantum numbers. (8.6)

Peptide Bond: The amide linkage in molecules of polypeptides. (23.6)

Percentage Composition: A list of the percentages by weight of the elements in a compound. (4.2)

Percentage Concentration: A ratio of the amount of solute to the amount of solution expressed as a percent. (5.1)
Weight/weight: Grams of solute in 100 g of solution.
Weight/volume: Grams of solute in 100 mL of solution.
Volume/volume: Volumes of solute in 100 volumes of solution.

Percentage Ionization: An equation that quantifies the ionization of a substance in solution. (17.4)

Percentage ionization
$$= \frac{\text{amount of substance ionized}}{\text{initial amount of substance}} \times 100\%$$

Percentage by Mass (Percentage by Weight): (a) The number of grams of an element combined in 100 g of a compound. (4.2) (b) The number of grams of a substance in 100 g of a mixture or solution. (13.5)

Percentage Yield: The ratio (taken as a percent) of the mass of product obtained to the mass calculated from the reaction's stoichiometry. (4.6)

Period: A horizontal row of elements in the periodic table. (3.2)

Periodic Table: A table in which symbols for the elements are displayed in order of increasing atomic number and arranged so that elements with similar properties lie in the same column (group). (Inside front cover, 3.2)

pH: $-\log [H^+]$. (17.1)

Phase: A homogeneous region within a sample. (1.3)

Phase Diagram: A pressure–temperature graph on which are plotted the temperatures and the pressures at which equilibrium exists between the states of a substance. It defines regions of T and P in which the solid, liquid, and gaseous states of the substance can exist. (12.10)

Photoelectric Effect: The phenomenon whereby energetic photons can eject electrons from certain materials. (8.1)

Photon: A unit of energy in electromagnetic radiation equal to $h\nu$, where ν is the frequency of the radiation and h is Planck's constant. (8.1)

Photosynthesis: The use of solar energy by a plant to make high-energy molecules from carbon dioxide, water, and minerals. (8.1)

Physical Change: A change that is not accompanied by a change in chemical makeup. (1.3)

Physical Law: A relationship between two or more physical properties of a system, usually expressed as a mathematical equation, that describes how a change in one property affects the others.

Physical Property: A property that can be specified without reference to another substance and that can be measured without causing a chemical change. (2.1)

Physical State: The condition of aggregation of a substance's formula units, whether as a solid, a liquid, or a gas. (1.4)

Pi Bond (π Bond): A bond formed by the sideways overlap of a pair of p orbitals and that concentrates electron density into two separate regions that lie on opposite sides of a plane that contains an imaginary line joining the nuclei. (10.6)

pK_a: $-\log K_a$. (17.3)

pK_b: $-\log K_b$. (17.3)

pK_w: $-\log K_w$. (17.1)

Planar Triangular Molecule: A molecule in which a central atom holds three other atoms located at the corners of an equilateral triangle and that includes the central atom at its center. (10.1)

Plane-Polarized Light: Light in which all the oscillations occur in one plane. (22.4)

Planck's Constant (h): The ratio of the energy of a photon to its frequency; $6.6260755 \times 10^{-34}$ J Hz^{-1}. (8.1)

Plasma: An electrically neutral, very hot gaseous mixture of nuclei and unattached electrons. (21.8)

pOH: $-\log [OH^-]$. (17.1)

Polar Covalent Bond (Polar Bond): A covalent bond in which more than half of the bond's negative charge is concentrated around one of the two atoms. (9.7)

Polar Molecule: A molecule in which individual bond polarities do not cancel and in which, therefore, the centers of density of negative and positive charges do not coincide. (9.7)

Polarizability: A term that describes the ease with which the electron cloud of a molecule or ion is distorted. (12.2)

Polyatomic Ion: An ion composed of two or more atoms. (3.4)

Polydentate Ligand: A ligand that has two or more atoms that can become simultaneously attached to a metal ion. (22.1)

Polymer: A substance consisting of macromolecules that have repeating structural units. (23.5)

Polymerization: A chemical reaction that converts a monomer into a polymer. (23.5)

Polypeptide: A polymer of α-amino acids that makes up all or most of a protein. (23.6)

Polyprotic Acid: An acid that can furnish more than one H^+ per molecule. (5.3)

Polysaccharide: A carbohydrate whose molecules can be hydrolyzed to hundreds of monosaccharide molecules. (23.6)

Polystyrene: An addition polymer of styrene with the following structure.

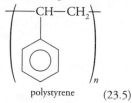

polystyrene　　(23.5)

Position of Equilibrium: The relative amounts of the substances on both sides of the double arrows in the equation for an equilibrium. (5.3, 12.9, 15.5)

Positive Charge: A type of electrical charge possessed by certain particles such as the proton. A positive charge is attracted by a negative charge and is repelled by another positive charge. (3.1)

Positive Charge Carrier: In a semiconductor material doped with an electron deficient element, the holes carry the charge. (20.6)

Positron ($_{0}^{1}p$): A positively charged particle with the mass of an electron. (21.3)

Post-transition Metal: A metal that occurs in the periodic table immediately to the right of a row of transition elements. (3.4)

Potential: See *Volt*.

Potential Energy (PE): Stored energy. (7.1)

Potential Energy Diagram: A diagram indicating the conversion of kinetic energy to potential energy and back again as atoms or molecules collide and then recoil in a chemical reaction. (13.5)

Precipitate: A solid that separates from a solution usually as the result of a chemical reaction. (5.1)

Precipitation Reaction: A reaction in which a precipitate forms. (5.1, 5.5)

Precision: How reproducible measurements are; the fineness of a measurement as indicated by the number of significant figures reported in the physical quantity. (2.3)

Pre-exponential Factor: A number or variable that precedes the exponential part of a number. (14.7)

Pressure: Force per unit area. (7.5, 11.2)

Pressure–Concentration Law: See *Vapor Pressure–Concentration Law*.

Pressure–Solubility Law (Henry's Law): The concentration of a gas dissolved in a liquid at any given temperature is directly proportional to the partial pressure of the gas above the solution. $C_{gas} = k_H P_{gas}$. (13.4)

Pressure–Temperature Law (Gay-Lussac's Law): The pressure of a given mass of gas is directly proportional to its Kelvin temperature if the volume is kept constant. $P \propto T$. (11.3)

Pressure–Volume Law (Boyle's Law): The volume of a given mass of a gas is inversely proportional to its pressure if the temperature is kept constant. $V \propto 1/P$. (11.3)

Pressure–Volume Work (P–V Work): The energy transferred as work when a system expands or contracts against the pressure exerted by the surroundings. At constant pressure, $w = -P \Delta V$. (7.5)

Primary Cell: A galvanic cell (battery) not designed to be recharged; it is discarded after its energy is depleted. (20.6)

Primitive Cubic Unit Cell: See *Simple Cubic Unit Cell*.

Principal Quantum Number (n): The quantum number that defines the principal energy levels and that can have values of 1, 2, 3, . . . , ∞. (8.5)

Products: The substances produced by a chemical reaction and whose formulas follow the arrows in chemical equations. (1.6, 15.1)

Propagation Step: A step in a chain reaction for which one product must serve in a succeeding propagation step as a reactant and for which another (final) product accumulates with each repetition of the step. (Chemistry Outside the Classroom 14.1)

Property: A characteristic of matter. (2.1)

Propyl Group: Alkyl group derived from propane, $-CH_2CH_2CH_3$.

Protein: A macromolecular substance found in cells that consists wholly or mostly of one or more polypeptides that often are combined with an organic molecule or a metal ion. (23.6)

Proton ($_{1}^{1}p$ or $_{1}^{1}H^+$): (a) A subatomic particle, with a charge of 1+ and a mass of 1.0072765 u ($1.6726217 \times 10^{-24}$ g)

and that is found in atomic nuclei. (3.1) (b) The name often used for the hydrogen ion and symbolized as H^+.

Proton Acceptor: A Brønsted base. (16.1)

Proton Donor: A Brønsted acid. (16.1)

Pure Substance: An element or a compound. (1.3)

Q

Qualitative Analysis: The use of experimental procedures to determine what elements are present in a substance. (5.8)

Qualitative Observation: Observations that do not involve numerical information. (2.2)

Quanta: Packets of electromagnetic radiation now commonly called photons. (8.1)

Quantitative Analysis: The use of experimental procedures to determine the percentage composition of a compound or the percentage of a component of a mixture. (5.8)

Quantitative Observation: An observation involving a measurement and numerical information. (2.2)

Quantized: Descriptive of a discrete, definite amount as of *quantized energy*. (8.3)

Quantum: The energy of one photon. (8.1)

Quantum Mechanics: See *Wave Mechanics*.

Quantum Number: A number related to the energy, shape, or orientation of an orbital, or to the spin of an electron. (8.3)

Quantum Theory: The physics of objects that exhibit wave/particle duality. (8 Introduction)

R

R: See *Gas Constant, Universal*.

Rad (rd): A unit of radiation-absorbed dose and equal to 10^{-5} J g^{-1} or 10^{-2} Gy. (21.6)

Radioactive Decay: The change of a nucleus into another nucleus (or into a more stable form of the same nucleus) by the loss of a small particle or a gamma ray photon. (21.3)

Radioactive Disintegration Series: A sequence of nuclear reactions beginning with a very long-lived radionuclide and ending with a stable isotope of lower atomic number. (21.3)

Radioactivity: The emission of one or more kinds of radiation from an isotope with unstable nuclei. (21.3)

Radiological Dating: A technique for measuring the age of a geologic formation or an ancient artifact by determining the ratio of the concentrations of two isotopes, one radioactive and the other a stable decay product. (13.4, 21.7)

Radionuclide: A radioactive isotope. (21.3)

Raoult's Law: See *Vapor Pressure–Concentration Law*.

Rare Earth Metals: The lanthanides.

Rate: A ratio in which a unit of time appears in the denominator, for example, 40 miles hr^{-1} or 3.0 mol L^{-1} s^{-1}. (14.2)

Rate Constant (k): The proportionality constant in the rate law; the rate of reaction when all reactant concentrations are 1 M. (14.3)

Rate Law: An equation that relates the rate of a reaction to the molar concentrations of the reactants raised to powers. (14.3)

Rate of Reaction: How quickly the reactants disappear and the products form and usually expressed in units of mol L^{-1} s^{-1}. (14.1, 14.2)

Rate-Determining Step (Rate-Limiting Step): The slowest step in a reaction mechanism. (14.8)

Reactant, Limiting: See *Limiting Reactant*.

Reactants: The substances brought together to react and whose formulas appear before the arrow in a chemical equation. (1.6, 15.1)

Reaction Coordinate: The horizontal axis of a potential energy diagram of a reaction. (14.6)

Reaction Mechanism: A sequence of elementary processes that sum to the overall reaction and possess one process that can derive the experimental rate law. (14.8)

Reaction Quotient (Q): The numerical value of the mass action expression. (15.2) See *Mass Action Expression*.

Reactivity: A description of the tendency for a substance to undergo reaction. For a metal, it is the tendency to undergo oxidation. (9.7)

Red Phosphorus: A relatively unreactive allotrope of phosphorus. (10.10)

Redox Reaction: An oxidation–reduction reaction. (6.1)

Reducing Agent: A substance that causes reduction and is itself oxidized. (6.1)

Reduction: A change in which an oxidation number decrease (becomes less positive and more negative). A gain of electrons. (6.1)

Reduction Potential: A measure of the tendency of a given half-reaction to occur as a reduction. (20.2)

Rem: A dose in rads multiplied by a factor that takes into account the variations that different radiations have in their damage-causing abilities in tissue. (20.6)

Replication: In nucleic acid chemistry, the reproductive duplication of DNA double helices prior to cell division. (23.7)

Representative Element: An element in one of the A groups in the periodic table. (3.2)

Resonance: A concept in which the actual structure of a molecule or polyatomic ion is represented as a composite or average of two or more Lewis structures, which are called the resonance or contributing structures (and none of which has real existence). (9.9)

Resonance Energy: The difference in energy between a substance and its principal resonance (contributing) structure. (9.9)

Resonance Hybrid: The actual structure of a molecule or polyatomic ion taken as a composite or average of the resonance or contributing structures. (9.9)

Resonance Structure: A Lewis structure that contributes to the hybrid structure in resonance-stabilized systems; a contributing structure. (9.9)

Reverse Osmosis: The procedure where a pressure, exceeding the osmotic pressure, is applied to an osmotic membrane to force pure solvent from a mixture. (13.7)

Reverse Reaction: In a chemical equation, the reaction as read from right to left. (5.3, 15.1)

Reversible Reaction: A reaction capable of proceeding in either the forward or reverse direction. (13.5, 14.7, 19.7)

Ring, Carbon: A closed-chain sequence of carbon atoms. (23.1)

RNA: Ribonucleic acid; a nucleic acid that gives ribose, phosphate ion, adenine, uracil, guanine, and cytosine when hydrolyzed. It occurs in several varieties. (23.7)

Rock Salt Structure: The face-centered cubic structure observed for sodium chloride, which is also possessed by crystals of many other compounds. (12.11)

Root Mean Square Speed (rms Speed): The square root of the average of the speeds-squared of the molecules in a substance. (11.7)

Rydberg Equation: An equation used to calculate the wavelengths of all the spectral lines of hydrogen. (8.2)

S

Salt: An ionic compound in which the anion is not OH^- or O^{2-} and the cation is not H^+. (5.2, 5.3)

Salt Bridge: A tube that contains an electrolyte that connects the two half-cells of a galvanic cell. (20.1)

Saponification: The reaction of an organic ester with a strong base to give an alcohol and the salt of the organic acid. (23.3)

Saturated Organic Compound: A compound whose molecules have only single bonds. (23.2)

Saturated Solution: A solution that holds as much solute as it can at a given temperature. A solution in which there is an equilibrium between the dissolved and the undissolved states of the solute. (5.1, 18.1)

Scanning Tunneling Microscope (STM): An instrument that enables the imaging of individual atoms on the surface of an electrically conducting specimen. (1.4)

Scientific Law: See *Law*.

Scientific Method: The observation, explanation, and testing of an explanation by additional experiments. (1.2)

Scientific Notation: The representation of a quantity as a decimal number between 1 and 10 multiplied by 10 raised to a power (e.g., 6.02×10^{23}). (2.3)

Scintillation Counter: A device for measuring nuclear radiation that contains a sensor composed of a substance called a *phosphor* that emits a tiny flash of light when struck by a particle of ionizing radiation. These flashes can be magnified electronically and automatically counted. (21.6)

Second Law of Thermodynamics: Whenever a spontaneous event takes place, it is accompanied by an increase in the entropy of the universe. (19.4)

Second-Order Reaction: A reaction with a rate law of the type: rate $= k[A]^2$ or rate $= k[A][B]$, where A and B are reactants. (14.4)

Secondary Cell: A galvanic cell (battery) designed for repeated use; it is able to be recharged. (20.6)

Secondary Quantum Number (ℓ): The quantum number whose values can be 0, 1, 2, ..., $(n-1)$, where n is the principal quantum number. (8.5)

Seesaw Shaped Molecule: A description given to a molecule in which the central atom has five electron pairs in its valence shell, one of which is a lone pair and the others are used in bonds to other atoms. (10.2) See also *Distorted Tetrahedron*.

Selective Precipitation: A technique that uses differences in the solubilities of specific salts to separate ions from each other. (18.3)

Semiconductor: A substance that conducts electricity weakly. (3.3)

Shell: All of the orbitals associated with a given value of n (the principal quantum number). (8.5)

SI (International System of Units): The modified metric system adopted in 1960 by the General Conference on Weights and Measures. (2.2)

Side Reaction: A reaction that occurs simultaneously with another reaction (the main reaction) in the same mixture to produce by-products.

Sievert (Sv): The SI unit for dose equivalent. The dose equivalent H is calculated from D (the dose in grays), Q (a measure of the effectiveness of the radiation at causing harm), and N (a variable that accounts for other modifying factors). $H = DQN$. (21.6)

Sigma Bond (σ Bond): A bond formed by the head-to-head overlap of two atomic orbitals and in which electron density becomes concentrated along and around the imaginary line joining the two nuclei. (10.6)

Significant Figures (Significant Digits): The digits in a physical measurement that are known to be certain plus the first digit that contains uncertainty. (2.3)

Simple Cubic Unit Cell: A cubic unit cell that has atoms only at the corners of the cell. (12.11)

Simplest Formula: See *Empirical Formula*.

Single Bond: A covalent bond in which a single pair of electrons is shared. (9.5)

Single Replacement Reaction: A reaction in which one element replaces another in a compound; usually a redox reaction. (6.4)

Skeletal Structure: A diagram of the arrangement of atoms in a molecule, which is the first step in constructing the Lewis structure. (9.8)

Skeleton Equation: An unbalanced equation showing only the formulas of reactants and products. (6.2)

Solar Battery: A battery that is charged by electrical current from photovoltaic cells. (10.9)

Solar Cell: A semiconductor device that produces electrical current and voltage in the presence of sunlight. (10.9)

Sol-Gel Process: A method for producing sol gels, very porous materials. (16.6)

Solid: One of the states of matter. A solid consists of tightly packed atomic or molecular sized particles held rigidly in place. (2.1)

Solubility: The ratio of the quantity of solute to the quantity of solvent in a saturated solution and that is usually expressed in units of (g solute)/(100 g solvent) at a specified temperature. (5.1)

Solubility Product Constant (K_{sp}): The equilibrium constant for the solubility of a salt and that, for a saturated solution, is equal to the product of the molar concentrations of the ions, each raised to a power equal to the number of its ions in one formula unit of the salt. (18.1) See also *Acid Solubility Product*.

Solubility Rules: A set of rules describing salts that are soluble and those that are insoluble. They enable the prediction of the formation of a precipitate in a metathesis reaction. (5.5)

Solute: Something dissolved in a solvent to make a solution. (5.1)

Solution: A homogeneous mixture in which all particles are of the size of atoms, small molecules, or small ions. (1.3, 5.1)

Solvation: The development of a cagelike network of a solution's solvent molecules about a molecule or ion of the solute. (13.1)

Solvation Energy: The enthalpy of the interaction of gaseous molecules or ions of solute with solvent molecules during the formation of a solution. (13.2)

Solvent: A medium, usually a liquid, into which something (a solute) is dissolved to make a solution. (5.1)

Space Filling Model: A method of depicting molecules by the shape and volume that the molecule actually occupies. (1.5)

sp Hybrid Orbital: A hybrid orbital formed by mixing one s and one p atomic orbital. The angle between a pair of sp hybrid orbitals is 180°. (10.5)

sp^2 Hybrid Orbital: A hybrid orbital formed by mixing one s and two p atomic orbitals. sp^2 hybrids are planar triangular with the angle between two sp^2 hybrid orbitals being 120°. (10.5)

sp^3 Hybrid Orbital: A hybrid orbital formed by mixing one s and three p atomic orbitals. sp^3 hybrids point to the corners of a tetrahedron; the angle between two sp^3 hybrid orbitals is 109.5°. (10.5)

sp^3d Hybrid Orbital: A hybrid orbital formed by mixing one s, three p, and one d atomic orbital. sp^3d hybrids point to the corners of a trigonal bipyramid. (10.5)

sp^3d^2 Hybrid Orbital: A hybrid orbital formed by mixing one s, three p, and two d atomic orbitals. sp^3d^2 hybrids point to the corners of an octahedron. (10.5)

Specific Gravity: A dimensionless property of matter. Its value is determined by dividing the density by the density of water under the same conditions. (2.5)

Specific Heat (Specific Heat Capacity): The quantity of heat that will raise the temperature of 1 g of a substance by 1 °C, usually in units of cal g^{-1} °C^{-1} or J g^{-1} °C^{-1}. (7.3)

Spectator Ion: An ion whose formula appears in an ionic equation identically on both sides of the arrow, that does not participate in the reaction, and that is excluded from the net ionic equation. (5.2)

Spectrochemical Series: A listing of ligands in order of their ability to produce a large crystal field splitting. (22.5)

Speed of Light (c): The speed at which light travels in a vacuum; 3.00×10^8 m s^{-1}. (7.1)

Spin Quantum Number (m_s): The quantum number associated with the spin of a subatomic particle and for the electron can have a value of $+\frac{1}{2}$ or $-\frac{1}{2}$. (8.6)

Spontaneous Change: A change that occurs by itself without outside assistance. (19.2)

Square Planar Molecule: A molecule with a central atom having four bonds that point to the corners of a square. (10.2)

Square Pyramid: A pyramid with four triangular sides and a square base. (10.2)

Stability Constant: See *Formation Constant*.

Stabilization Energy: See *Resonance Energy*.

Standard Atmosphere: See *Atmosphere, Standard*

Standard Cell Notation: A way of describing the anode and cathode half-cells in a galvanic cell. The anode half-cell is specified on the left, with the electrode material of the anode given first and a vertical bar representing the phase boundary between the electrode and the solution. Double bars represent the salt bridge between the half-cells. The cathode halfcell is specified on the right, with the material of the cathode given last. Once again, a single vertical bar represents the phase boundary between the solution and the electrode. (20.1)

Standard Cell Potential ($E°_{cell}$): The potential of a galvanic cell at 25 °C and when all ionic concentrations are exactly 1 M and the partial pressures of all gases are 1 atm. (20.2)

Standard Conditions of Temperature and Pressure (STP): Standard reference conditions for gases. 273 K (0 °C) and 1 atm (760 torr). (11.4)

Standard Electrode Potential: The electrode potential measured versus the standard hydrogen electrode at standard state conditions. (20.2)

Standard Enthalpy Change ($\Delta H°$): See *Standard Heat of Reaction*.

Standard Enthalpy of Formation ($\Delta H°_f$): See *Standard Heat of Formation*.

Standard Entropy ($S°$): The entropy of 1 mol of a substance at 25 °C and 1 atm. (19.5)

Standard Entropy Change ($\Delta S°$): The entropy change of a reaction when determined with reactants and products at 25 °C and 1 atm and on the scale of the mole quantities given by the coefficients of the balanced equation. (19.5)

Standard Entropy of Formation (ΔS_f°): The value of ΔS° for the formation of one mole of a substance from its elements in their standard states. (19.5)

Standard Free Energy Change (ΔG°): $\Delta G^\circ = \Delta H^\circ - T\Delta S^\circ$. (19.6)

Standard Free Energy of Formation (ΔG_f°): The value of ΔG° for the formation of *one* mole of a compound from its elements in their standard states. (19.6)

Standard Heat of Combustion: The enthalpy change for the combustion of one mole of a compound under standard conditions. (7.9)

Standard Heat of Formation (ΔH_f°): The amount of heat absorbed or evolved when one mole of the compound is formed from its elements in their standard states. (7.9)

Standard Heat of Reaction (ΔH°): The enthalpy change of a reaction when determined with reactants and products at 25 °C and 1 atm and on the scale of the mole quantities given by the coefficients of the balanced equation. (7.7)

Standard Hydrogen Electrode: See *Hydrogen Electrode.*

Standard Molar Volume: See *Molar Volume, Standard.*

Standard Reduction Potential, E°: The reduction potential of a half-reaction at 25 °C when all ion concentrations are 1 M and the partial pressures of all gases are 1 atm. Also called standard electrode potential. (20.2)

Standard Solution: Any solution whose concentration is accurately known. (5.8)

Standard State: The condition in which a substance is in its most stable form at 25 °C and 1 atm. (7.7, 7.9, 20.2)

Standing Wave: A wave whose peaks and nodes do not change position. (8.4)

Starch: A polymer of glucose used by plants to store energy. (23.6)

State: The set of specific values of the physical properties of a system—its composition, physical form, concentration, temperature, pressure, and volume. (7.2)

State Function: A quantity whose value depends only on the initial and final states of the system and not on the path taken by the system to get from the initial to the final state. ($P, V, T, H, S,$ and G are all state functions.) (7.2)

State of Matter: A physical state of a substance: solid, liquid, or gas. (2.1) See also *Standard State.*

Steady State: A system where material or energy enter and exit at the same rate producing no observable changes in pres-

sure, volume, temperature or amount of material. (11.9)

Step-Growth Polymer: See *Condensation Polymer*

Stereoisomerism: The existence of isomers whose structures differ only in spatial orientations (e.g., geometric isomers and optical isomers). (22.4)

Stock System: A system of nomenclature that uses Roman numerals to specify oxidation states. (3.5)

Stoichiometry: A description of the relative quantities by moles of the reactants and products in a reaction as given by the coefficients in the balanced equation. (4.1)

Stopcock: A valve on a buret that is used to control the flow of titrant. (5.8)

Stored Energy: See *Potential Energy.*

STP: See *Standard Conditions of Temperature and Pressure.*

Straight-Chain Compound: An organic compound in whose molecules the carbon atoms are joined in one continuous open-chain sequence. (23.1)

Strong Acid: An acid that is essentially 100% ionized in water. A good proton donor. An acid with a large value of K_a. (5.3)

Strong Base: Any powerful proton acceptor. A base with a large value of K_b. A metal hydroxide that dissociates essentially 100% in water. (5.3)

Strong Electrolyte: Any substance that ionizes or dissociates in water to essentially 100%. (5.2, 5.3)

Structural Formula (Lewis Structure): A chemical formula that shows how the atoms of a molecule or polyatomic ion are arranged, to which other atoms they are bonded, and the kinds of bonds (single, double, or triple). (9.5)

Subatomic Particles: Electrons, protons, neutrons, and atomic nuclei. (3.1)

Sublimation: The conversion of a solid directly into a gas without passing through the liquid state. (12.3)

Subscript: In a chemical formula, a number after a chemical symbol, written below the line, and indicating the number of the preceding atoms in the formula (e.g., CH_4). Subscripts are also used to differentiate many variables such as the acid ionization constant (K_a) and the base ionization constant (K_b). (1.5)

Subshell: All of the orbitals of a given shell that have the same value of their secondary quantum number, ℓ. (8.5)

Substance: See *Pure Substance.*

Substitution Reaction: The replacement of an atom or group on a molecule by another atom or group. (23.2, 23.3)

Superconductor: A material in a state in which it offers no resistance to the flow of electricity.

Supercooled Liquid: A liquid at a temperature below its freezing point. An amorphous solid. (12.11)

Supercritical Fluid: A substance at a temperature above its critical temperature. (12.10)

Superheated Liquid: The condition of a substance in its liquid state above its boiling point. (12.7)

Superheating: The process where a substance is heated to a temperature above its normal boiling point. (12.7)

Superimposability: A test of structural chirality in which a model of one structure and a model of its mirror image are compared to see if the two could be made to blend perfectly, with every part of one coinciding simultaneously with the parts of the other. (22.4)

Supersaturated Solution: A solution that contains more solute than it would hold if the solution were saturated. Supersaturated solutions are unstable and tend to produce precipitates. (5.1)

Surface Tension: A measure of the amount of energy needed to expand the surface area of a liquid. (12.3)

Surfactant: A substance that lowers the surface tension of a liquid and promotes wetting. (12.3)

Surroundings: That part of the universe other than the system being studied and separated from the system by a real or an imaginary boundary. (7.3)

Suspension: A heterogeneous mixture that will eventually separate into its component parts under the influence of gravity. (13.8)

Symmetric: An object is symmetric if it looks the same when rotated, reflected in a mirror, or reflected through a point. (10.3)

System: That part of the universe under study and separated from the surroundings by a real or an imaginary boundary. (7.3, 7.7)

T

$t_{1/2}$: See *Half-Life.*

T-Shaped Molecule: A molecule having five electron domains in its valence shell, two of which contain lone pairs. The other three are used in bonds to other atoms. The molecule has the shape of the letter T, with the central atom located at the intersection of the two crossing lines. (10.2)

Tarnishing: See *Corrosion*.

Temperature: A measure of the hotness or coldness of something. A property related to the average kinetic energy of the atoms and molecules in a sample. A property that determines the direction of heat flow—from high temperature to low temperature. (2.2, 7.1)

Temperature–Volume Law (Charles' Law): The volume of a given mass of a gas is directly proportional to its Kelvin temperature if the pressure is kept constant. $V \propto T$. (11.3)

Termination Step: A step in a chain reaction in which a reactive species needed for a chain propagation step disappears without helping to generate more of this species. (Chemistry Outside the Classroom 14.1)

Tetrahedral Molecule: A molecule with a central atom bonded to four other atoms located at the corners of an imaginary tetrahedron. (10.1)

Tetrahedron: A four-sided figure with four triangular faces and shaped like a pyramid. (10.1)

Theoretical Model: See *Model, Theoretical*.

Theoretical Yield: See *Yield, Theoretical*

Theory: A tested explanation of the results of many experiments. (1.2)

Thermal Decomposition: The decomposition of a substance caused by heating it. (21.3)

Thermal Energy: The molecular kinetic energy possessed by molecules as a result of the temperature of the sample. Energy that is transferred as heat. (7.1)

Thermal Equilibrium: A condition reached when two or more substances in contact with each other come to the same temperature. (7.2)

Thermal Property: A physical property, like heat capacity or heat of fusion, that concerns a substance's ability to absorb heat without changing chemically.

Thermochemical Equation: A balanced chemical equation accompanied by the value of $\Delta H°$ that corresponds to the mole quantities specified by the coefficients. (7.7)

Thermochemistry: The study of the energy changes of chemical reactions. (7 Introduction)

Thermodynamic Equilibrium Constant (K): The equilibrium constant that is calculated from $\Delta G°$ (the standard free energy change) for a reaction at T K by the equation, $\Delta G° = RT \ln K$. (19.9)

Thermodynamically Reversible: A process that occurs by an infinite number of steps during which the driving force for the change is just barely greater than the force that resists the change. (19.7)

Thermodynamics (Chemical Thermodynamics): The study of the role of energy in chemical change and in determining the behavior of materials. (7 Introduction, 19.1)

Third Law of Thermodynamics: For a pure crystalline substance at 0 K, $S = 0$. (19.5)

Titrant: The solution added from a buret during a titration. (5.8)

Titration: An analytical procedure in which a solution of unknown concentration is combined slowly and carefully with a standard solution until a color change of some indicator or some other signal shows that equivalent quantities have reacted. Either solution can be the titrant in a buret with the other solution being in a receiving flask. (5.8)

Titration Curve: For an acid–base titration, a graph of pH versus the volume of titrant added. (17.9)

Torr: A unit of pressure equal to 1/760 atm. 1 mm Hg. (11.2)

Tracer Analysis: The use of small amounts of a radioisotope to follow (trace) the course of a chemical or biological change. (21.7)

Trans Isomer: A stereoisomer whose uniqueness lies in having two groups that project on opposite sides of a reference plane. (22.4)

Transcription: The synthesis of mRNA at the direction of DNA. (23.7)

Transition Elements: The elements located between Groups 2A and 3A in the periodic table. (3.2)

Transition Metals: The transition elements. (3.2)

Transition State: The structure and energy of the substances in an elementary process of a reaction mechanism when the species involved have acquired the minimum amount of potential energy and geometric configuration needed for a successful reaction. (14.6)

Transition State Theory: A theory about the formation and breakup of activated complexes. (14.6)

Translation: The synthesis of a polypeptide at the direction of a molecule of mRNA. (23.7)

Transmutation: The conversion of one isotope into another. (21.5)

Transuranium Elements: Elements 93 and higher. (21.5)

Traveling Wave: A wave whose peaks and nodes move. (8.4)

Triacylglycerol: An ester of glycerol and three fatty acids. (23.6)

Trigonal Bipyramid: A six-sided figure made of two three-sided pyramids that share a common face. (10.1)

Trigonal Bipyramidal Molecule: A molecule with a central atom holding five other atoms that are located at the corners of a trigonal bipyramid. (10.1, 10.2)

Trigonal Pyramidal Molecule: A molecule that consists of an atom, situated at the top of a three-sided pyramid, that is bonded to three other atoms located at the corners of the base of the pyramid. (10.2)

Triple Bond: A covalent bond comprised of one sigma bond and two pi bonds. Three pairs of electrons are shared between two atoms. (10.6)

Triple Point: The temperature and pressure at which the liquid, solid, and vapor states of a substance can coexist in equilibrium. (12.10)

Triprotic Acid: An acid that can furnish three H^+ ions per molecule. (5.3)

Tyndall Effect: Colloidal dispersions scatter light while true solutions do not scatter light. This light scattering is known as the Tyndall effect. (13.8)

U

u: See *Atomic Mass Unit*.

Ultraviolet Catastrophe: The term given to the fact that classical physics predicts large amounts of ultraviolet radiation should be emitted from heated materials. In fact, very little ultraviolet radiation is produced. (7 Introduction)

Uncertainty: The amount by which a measured quantity deviates from the true or actual value. (2.3)

Uncertainty Principle: There is a limit to our ability to measure a particle's speed and position simultaneously. (8.9)

Unit Cell: The smallest portion of a crystal that can be repeated over and over in all directions to give the crystal lattice. (12.11)

Unit of Measurement: A reference quantity, such as the meter or kilogram, in terms of which the sizes of measurements can be expressed. (2.2)

Universal Gas Constant (R): See *Gas Constant, Universal*.

Universe: The system and surroundings taken together. (7.3)

Unsaturated Compound: A compound whose molecules have one or more double or triple bonds. (23.2)

Unsaturated Solution: Any solution with a concentration less than that of a saturated solution of the same solute and solvent. (5.1)

V

V-Shaped Molecule: See *Bent Molecule.*

Vacuum: An enclosed space containing no matter whatsoever. A *partial vacuum* is an enclosed space containing a gas at a very low pressure.

Valence Band: Very closely spaced energy levels of valence electrons, particularly in metals is called the valence band. (10.9)

Valence Bond Theory (VB Theory): A theory of covalent bonding that views a bond as being formed by the sharing of one pair of electrons between two overlapping atomic or hybrid orbitals. (10.4)

Valence Electrons: The electrons of an atom in its valence shell that participate in the formation of chemical bonds. (8.8)

Valence Shell: The electron shell with the highest principal quantum number, n, that is occupied by electrons. (8.8)

Valence Shell Electron Pair Repulsion Model (VSEPR Model): The bonding and nonbonding (lone pair) electron domains in the valence shell of an atom seek an arrangement that leads to minimum repulsions and thereby determine the geometry of a molecule. (10.2)

Van der Waals' Constants: Empirical constants that make the van der Waals' equation conform to the gas law behavior of a real gas. (11.8)

Van der Waals' Equation: An equation of state for a real gas that corrects V and P for the excluded volume and the effects of intermolecular attractions. (11.8)

Van der Waals' Forces: Attractive forces including dipole–dipole, ion–dipole, and induced dipole forces. (12.2)

Van't Hoff Factor (i): The ratio of the observed freezing point depression to the value calculated on the assumption that the solute dissolves as un-ionized molecules. (13.7)

Vapor Pressure: The pressure exerted by the vapor above a liquid (usually referring to the *equilibrium* vapor pressure when the vapor and liquid are in equilibrium with each other). (11.6, 12.5)

Vapor Pressure–Concentration Law (Raoult's Law): The vapor pressure of one component above a mixture of molecular compounds equals the product of its vapor pressure when pure and its mole fraction. (13.7)

Viscosity: A liquid's resistance to flow. (12.3)

Visible Spectrum: That region of the electromagnetic spectrum whose frequencies can be detected by the human eye. (8.1)

Volatile: Descriptive of a liquid that has a low boiling point, a high vapor pressure at room temperature, and therefore evaporates easily. (12.5, 13.7)

Volt (V): The SI unit of electric potential or emf in joules per coulomb. (20.2)

$$1\ V = 1\ J\ C^{-1}$$

Voltaic Cell: See *Galvanic Cell.*

Volumetric Flask: A piece of glassware calibrated to hold an exact volume of liquid. Volumetric flasks come in a variety of sizes. (5.6)

VSEPR Model: See *Valence Shell Electron Pair Repulsion Model.*

W

Wave: An oscillation that moves outward from a disturbance. (8.1)

Wave Function (ψ): A mathematical function that describes the intensity of an electron wave at a specified location in an atom. The square of the wave function at a particular location specifies the probability of finding an electron there. (8.4)

Wave Mechanics (Quantum Mechanics): A theory of atomic structure based on the wave properties of matter. (8 Introduction)

Wave/Particle Duality: A particle such as the electron behaves like a particle in some experiments and like a wave in others. (8 Introduction)

Wavelength (λ): The distance between crests in the wavelike oscillations of electromagnetic radiations. (8.1)

Weak Acid: An acid with a low percentage ionization in solution; a poor proton donor; an acid with a low value of K_a. (5.3)

Weak Base: A base with a low percentage ionization in solution; a poor proton acceptor; a base with a low value of K_b. (5.3)

Weak Electrolyte: A substance that has a low percentage ionization or dissociation in solution. (5.3)

Weighing: The operation of measuring the mass of something using a balance. (1.5)

Weight: The force with which something is attracted to the earth by gravity. (1.3)

Weight Percent: See *Percentage by Mass.*

Wetting: The spreading of a liquid across a solid surface. (12.3)

White Phosphorus: A very reactive allotrope of phosphorus consisting of tetrahedral P_4 molecules. (10.10)

Work (w): The energy expended in moving an opposing force through some particular distance. Work has units of *force $\times$ distance.* (6.1, 6.5, 18.1)

X

X Ray: A stream of very high-energy photons emitted by substances when they are bombarded by high-energy beams of electrons or are emitted by radionuclides that have undergone K-electron capture. (21.3)

Xerogel: An extremely low density material that, among other things, can serve as a very low weight insulating material. (16.6)

Y

Yield, Actual: The amount of a product obtained in a laboratory experiment. (4.6)

Yield, Percentage: The ratio, given as a percent, of the quantity of product actually obtained in a reaction to the theoretical yield. (4.6)

Yield, Theoretical: The amount of a product calculated by the stoichiometry of the reaction. (4.6)

Z

Zero-Order Reaction: A reaction that occurs at a constant rate regardless of the concentration of the reactant. (14.4)

Zinc–Manganese Dioxide Cell (Leclanché Cell): A galvanic cell of about 1.5 V involving zinc and manganese dioxide under mildly acidic conditions. (20.6)

Index

Porphyrin structure, 1039
Portland cement, 133, 498
Position of equilibrium:
    and catalysts, 714
    and equilibrium constant, 708–709
    and Le Châtelier's principle, 555–556
    and reciprocal acid–base relationships, 749–750
    and standard free energy change, 896–898
    for weak acids, 172
Positive catalysts, 680
Positive charge, 68, 760
Positive charge carriers, 951
Positive charge density, 760
Positive ions, 66, 572
Positive polarity, 922
Positrons, 985
Positron emission, 985–986
Positron emission tomography (PET), 990
Positron emitters, 990
Post-transition metals:
    cations of, 83–84, 363–364
    complex ions of, 855
Potassium-40, 997–1000
Potassium iodate, 251
Potassium iodide:
    heat of solution for, 589–590
    and lead(II) nitrate, 160–162, 175–176
Potassium permanganate, 239–240
Potassium sulfate, 954–956
Potential, of galvanic cells, 924
Potential energy (PE), 254–256
    of covalent bond formation, 369
    and electron affinity, 347
    of electrons in atoms, 316–317
    on heating and cooling curves, 549
    of ions, 361–362
    and surface tension, 538
    and transition state theory, 667–669
Power:
    of microscope, 320
    nuclear, 1002
    wind, 946
Power plants, 946, 1002–1003
Precipitates, 157, 160, 841–843
Precipitation reactions:
    defined, 157
    and hard water, 181
    for metal carbonates, 851n.3
    as metathesis reactions, 175–177
    selective, 847–855
    for silver bromide, 191
Precision, 43, 55
Pre-exponential factor, 670
Pressure:
    atmospheric, 267, 474, 546, 547
    barometers, 474–475
    in calorimetry, 267–269, 272–275
    and chemical equilibrium, 703–706, 712, 714
    critical, 558, 560
    external, 871
    and heat of reaction, 272, 872
    heat of reaction at constant pressure, 272–275, 872
    manometers, 477–480

measuring, 474–480
    and melting point, 556–557
    osmotic, 613–618
    partial, see Partial pressure
    SI units of, 476, 884n.2
    standard temperature and, 487, 494–495, 884n.2
    vapor, see Vapor pressure
Pressure cookers, 673
Pressure sensors, 480
Pressure–temperature law (Gay-Lussac's law), 482, 511
Pressure–volume law (Boyle's law), 480–481, 510–511
Pressure–volume work, 268–269, 871–872
Pressurized water reactors, 1002–1003
Primary cells, 946
Primitive (simple) cubic lattice, 561–562
Principal quantum number (n), 324
Problem solving, tips on, 14
Products:
    of acid and base ionization constants, 783–784
    defined, 20
    of electrolysis reactions, 956–958
    in equilibrium, 697–698, 710–711
    ion, 832–833, 841–843
    by products, 139
Propagation step, of chain reactions, 677
Propanal, 1064
Propane, 297, 640, 641
Properties (term), 30
Propionic acid, 790
Propylene, 1058
Propylene glycol, 536
Propyl group, 1055
Proteins, 533, 1083–1085
Protons, 65–67
    in band of stability, 989
    and Brønsted–Lowry acids and bases, 741
    of isotopes, 69
    repulsions between, 980
    size and charge of, 68
Protonated amines, 1068
Proton–proton cycle, 1005
Proton transfer reactions, 742
p subshells, 339
p-type semiconductors, 454, 951
Pure substances, 7
Pycnometer, 61
Pyridine, 208
Pyrimidine bases, 370

Q

Q, see Reaction quotient
q_p (heat of reaction at constant pressure), 272–275, 872
q_v (heat of reaction at constant volume), 270–271
Qualitative analysis:
    of aqueous solutions, 196
    of metal ions, 854–855
Qualitative observations, 32
Quantitative analysis, for aqueous solutions, 196–197
Quantitative observations, 32

Quantitative reactions, 597
Quantized energies, 316–317, 321–324
Quantum mechanics, 305–350
    atomic orbitals, 337–340
    Bohr theory, 316–318
    defined, 306
    electromagnetic radiation, 306–313
    electron spin, 326–328
    and elements' properties, 340–349
    energy levels, 328–330
    ground state electron configurations, 328–337
    line spectra and Rydberg equation, 314–316
    periodic table, 330–337, 340–349
    and quantum numbers of electrons, 324–325
    wave mechanical model, 318–324
Quantum numbers:
    defined, 317
    of electrons, 324–325
    magnetic, 325
    and Pauli exclusion principle, 327–328
    principal, 324
    secondary, 324–325
    spin, 327
    and standing waves, 321–323
Quantum theory, 306
Quinine, 1068

R

R (universal gas constant), 490, 552
R (symbol), in structural formulas, 1052–1053
Rad (radiation absorbed dose), 996
Radiation, 98, 404
    alpha, 981–982
    annihilation radiation photons, 985
    atomic, 980
    background, 997–998
    beta, 982–983
    electromagnetic, see Electromagnetic radiation
    energy from, 983–984
    gamma, 983–984, 999
    and greenhouse effect, 517, 518
    ionizing, 994, 997
    and living tissue, 997–998
    nuclear, 980
    units of, 994–997
Radiation absorbed dose (rad), 996
Radiation sickness, 997
Radicals, free, 677, 997, 1072
Radioactive decay:
    and alpha rays, 66
    and carbon-14 dating, 659–660
    defined, 981
    law of, 995–996
    modes of, 993
Radioactive disintegration series, 986–987
Radioactive waste, 1003–1004
Radioactivity, 980–987, 994–998
    alpha radiation, 981–982
    beta radiation, 982–983
    gamma radiation, 983–985
    measuring, 994–998
    in nuclear equations, 982

RELATIONSHIPS AMONG UNITS

(Values in boldface are exact.)

Length

1 in. = **2.54** cm

1 ft = **30.48** cm

1 yd = **0.9144** m

1 mi = **5280** ft

1 ft = **12** in.

1 yd = **36** in.

Volume

1 liq. oz = **29.57353** mL

1 qt = **946.352946** mL

1 gallon = **3.785411784** L

1 gallon = **4** qt = **8** pt

1 qt = **2** pt = **32** liq. oz

Mass

1 oz = **28.349523125** g

1 lb = **453.59237** g

1 lb = **16** oz

Pressure

1 atm = **760** torr

1 atm = **101,325** Pa

1 atm = 14.696 psi (lb/in.^{2})

1 atm = 29.921 in. Hg

Energy

1 cal = **4.184** J

1 ev = 1.6022×10^{-19} J

1 ev/molecule = 96.49 kJ/mol

1 ev/molecule = 23.06 kcal/mol

1 J = 1 kg m^2 s^{-2} = 10^7 erg

PHYSICAL CONSTANTS

Rest mass of electron	$m_e = 5.485799094 \times 10^{-4}$ u ($9.1093821 \times 10^{-28}$ g)
Rest mass of proton	$m_p = 1.0072764668$ u ($1.67262164 \times 10^{-24}$ g)
Rest mass of neutron	$m_n = 1.0086649160$ u ($1.67492721 \times 10^{-24}$ g)
Electronic charge	$e = 1.60217649 \times 10^{-19}$ C
Atomic mass unit	u = $1.66053878 \times 10^{-24}$ g
Gas constant	R = 0.0820575 L atm mol^{-1} K^{-1}
	= 8.31447 J mol^{-1} K^{-1}
	= 1.98721 cal mol^{-1} K^{-1}
Molar volume, ideal gas	= 22.4140 L (at STP)
Avogadro's number	= 6.0221418×10^{23} things/mol
Speed of light in a vacuum	c = 2.99792458×10^8 m s^{-1} (Exactly)
Planck's constant	h = $6.6260690 \times 10^{-34}$ J s
Faraday constant	F = 9.6485340×10^4 C mol^{-1}

LABORATORY REAGENTS

(Values are for the average concentrated reagents available commercially.)

Reagent	Percent (w/w)	Mole Solute Liter Solution	Gram Solute 100 mL Solution
NH_3	29	15	26
$HC_2H_3O_2$	99.7	17	105
HCl	37	12	44
HNO_3	71	16	101
H_3PO_4	85	15	144
H_2SO_4	96	18	177